Name	Symbol	At. no.	At. wt.*	Mass no.	% or half-life
				occurring isotopes	
Neodymium	Nd	60	144.28	142	27.13
Neon	Ne	10	20.184	20	90.51
Neptunium	Np	93	(237)	—	—
Nickel	Ni	28	58.71	58	67.8
Niobium	Nb	41	92.91	93	100.00
Nitrogen	N	7	14.009	14	99.64
Nobelium	No	102	(253)	—	—
Osmium	Os	76	190.2	192	41.0
Oxygen	O	8	16.001	16	99.76
Palladium	Pd	46	106.4	106	27.1
Phosphorus	P	15	30.977	31	100.00
Platinum	Pt	78	195.10	195	33.7
Plutonium	Pu	94	242	242	5×10^5 y
Polonium	Po	84	(209)	—	—
Potassium	K	19	39.102	39	93.1
Praseodymium	Pr	59	140.93	141	100.00
Promethium	Pm	61	(147)	—	—
Protoactinium	Pa	91	(231)	—	—
Radium	Ra	88	226	226	1620 y
Radon	Rn	86	222	222	3.825 d
Rhenium	Re	75	186.23	187	62.93
Rhodium	Rh	45	102.92	103	100.00
Rubidium	Rb	37	85.48	85	72.15
Ruthenium	Ru	44	101.1	102	31.34
Samarium	Sm	62	150.36	152	26.90
Scandium	Sc	21	44.96	45	100.00
Selenium	Se	34	78.96	80	49.96
Silicon	Si	14	28.09	28	92.28
Silver	Ag	47	107.885	107	51.35
Sodium	Na	11	22.992	23	100.00
Strontium	Sr	38	87.63	88	82.74
Sulfur	S	16	32.068	32	95.06
Tantalum	Ta	73	180.96	181	100.00
Technetium	Tc	43	(99)	—	—
Tellurium	Te	52	127.62	130	34.27
Terbium	Tb	65	158.94	159	100.00
Thallium	Tl	81	204.40	205	70.48
Thorium	Th	90	232.06	232	100.00
Thulium	Tm	69	168.95	169	100.00
Tin	Sn	50	118.71	120	32.75
Titanium	Ti	22	49.90	48	73.45
Tungsten	W	74	183.87	184	30.64
Uranium	U	92	238.08	238	99.28
Vanadium	V	23	50.95	51	99.75
Xenon	Xe	54	131.31	132	26.93
Ytterbium	Yb	70	173.05	174	31.77
Yttrium	Y	39	88.92	89	100.00
Zinc	Zn	30	65.38	64	48.87
Zirconium	Zr	40	91.22	90	51.46

* Based on mass of C^{12} as 12.000. . . . The ratio of these weights to those on the older chemical scale (in which oxygen of natural isotopic composition was assigned a mass of 16.0000 . . .) is 1.000050.

ADVANCED INORGANIC CHEMISTRY
A Comprehensive Text

ADVANCED INORGANIC CHEMISTRY

A Comprehensive Text

F. ALBERT COTTON
PROFESSOR OF CHEMISTRY
MASSACHUSETTS INSTITUTE OF TECHNOLOGY
CAMBRIDGE, MASSACHUSETTS

and

G. WILKINSON
PROFESSOR OF INORGANIC CHEMISTRY
IMPERIAL COLLEGE OF SCIENCE AND TECHNOLOGY
LONDON, ENGLAND

INTERSCIENCE PUBLISHERS
A DIVISION OF JOHN WILEY & SONS

1962

Preface

It is now a truism that, in recent years, inorganic chemistry has experienced an impressive renaissance. Academic and industrial research in inorganic chemistry is flourishing, and the output of research papers and reviews is growing exponentially.

In spite of this interest, however, there has been no comprehensive textbook on inorganic chemistry at an advanced level incorporating the many new chemical developments, particularly the more recent theoretical advances in the interpretation of bonding and reactivity in inorganic compounds. It is the aim of this book, which is based on courses given by the authors over the past five to ten years, to fill this need. It is our hope that it will provide a sound basis in contemporary inorganic chemistry for the new generation of students and will stimulate their interest in a field in which trained personnel are still exceedingly scarce in both academic and industrial laboratories.

The content of this book, which encompasses the chemistry of all of the chemical elements and their compounds, including interpretative discussion in the light of the latest advances in structural chemistry, general valence theory, and, particularly, ligand field theory, provides a reasonable achievement for students at the B.Sc. honors level in British universities and at the senior year or first year graduate level in American universities. Our experience is that a course of about eighty lectures is desirable as a guide to the study of this material.

We are indebted to several of our colleagues, who have read sections of the manuscript, for their suggestions and criticism. It is, of course, the authors alone who are responsible for any errors or omissions in the final draft. We also thank the various authors and editors who have so kindly given us permission to reproduce diagrams from their papers: specific acknowledgments are made in the text. We sincerely appreciate the secretarial assistance of Miss C. M. Rose and Mrs. A. B. Blake in the preparation of the manuscript.

F. A. COTTON
Cambridge, Massachusetts

G. WILKINSON
London, England

v

Contents

PART THREE

Chemistry of the Transition Elements

PART ONE

General Theory

1

The Electronic Structures of Atoms

INTRODUCTION

1-1. The General Constitution of Atoms

Every atom consists of a nucleus surrounded by electrons. The components of a nucleus are protons, which are positively charged, and neutrons, which are uncharged. The masses of the proton and the neutron are very nearly the same, and the mass of either is very nearly equal to what is called an *atomic mass unit*, abbreviated a.m.u. It is customary to call the total number of *nucleons*—that is, protons and neutrons—the *mass number* of the atom, represented by the symbol A. The number of protons in the nucleus is the *atomic number* (symbol Z), and this determines the nuclear charge, in units of the proton charge. An atom as a whole has no net charge because the nucleus is surrounded by Z electrons, each having a negative charge numerically equal to the charge of the proton. Thus, any atom whose nucleus contains Z protons will have Z extranuclear electrons when un-ionized, and it is this number, Z, which determines its chemical identity.

All elements are found or may be made in various isotopic forms. These isotopic forms of an element are atoms having the same value of Z but different values of A. To put it perhaps less abstractly, they have the same number of protons in the nucleus and hence the same number of extranuclear electrons, but they differ in the number of neutrons in the nucleus. Since the chemical properties of an atom depend mainly on the number of electrons and only to a very slight and usually negligible extent on its mass, all atoms with the same Z are considered to be atoms of the same element. Two or more atoms of an element differing in their mass numbers are called *isotopes* of the element.

It has been known since the work (1913) of Rutherford on the scattering of α particles (helium nuclei) by matter that the nucleus contains nearly all of the mass and all of the positive charge within a very small volume. Present-day estimates of nuclear radii are $\sim 10^{-12}$ cm. However, from various lines of evidence we know that the radii of entire atoms are of the order of 10^{-8} cm., or, let us say, of the order of an *Angstrom unit*, since this unit, abbreviated A. and defined as 10^{-8} cm., is commonly used. Thus we have the general picture of an atom as a group of electrons distributed through a sphere several Angstroms in diameter with a dense positively charged nucleus at the center of the sphere.

The chemical behavior of any given atom depends on the detailed nature of what we may call the arrangement of the electrons in this sphere. The purpose of this chapter is to outline the salient principles governing the arrangement of electrons in atoms. In the following chapters we shall consider how electrons in one atom can interact with those in another atom to produce forces of attraction and repulsion.

1-2. The Bohr Theory of the Hydrogen Atom

Although the Bohr theory is now outmoded, it is worthwhile to consider briefly the sort of physical model involved before proceeding to discuss atomic structure from the standpoint of wave mechanics.

According to Bohr's proposal, with modifications made by Sommerfeld, we may assume that in the hydrogen atom the electron revolves around the nucleus (proton) in one of a series of circular or elliptical paths called, by analogy with the solar system, orbits. Each orbit is characterized by its radius if it is circular or by a mean radius and its ellipticity (ratio of major to minor axes) if elliptical. For simplicity let us consider only the circular orbits.

Bohr showed that if we assume that only certain values of angular momentum are permitted to the electron—specifically, integral multiples of $\mathbf{h}/2\pi$, where $\mathbf{h}$ is Planck's constant—then only orbits of certain radii and certain energies will be possible. He showed that the energies, E_n, of these orbits are given by (see Appendix A-1 for details):

$$E_n = -\frac{2\pi^2\mu e^4}{\mathbf{h}^2}\frac{1}{n^2} = -\frac{R}{n^2} \tag{1-1}$$

where n is the number of units, $\mathbf{h}/2\pi$, of angular momentum for this orbit; μ is the reduced mass of the hydrogen atom (very nearly equal to the mass of the electron); e is the electronic charge; and $\mathbf{h}$ is Planck's constant. The indicated combination of fundamental constants, all of which are measurable in various ways, is called R.*

Thus, Bohr's theory states that the energy of the hydrogen atom cannot have any arbitrary value, but must have only the values permitted by equation 1-1, when n takes the values 1, 2, 3, ... Since R and n^2 are intrinsically positive, all these energies are negative. This is in accordance with the convention that a state of zero energy exists when the proton and the electron are infinitely far apart and thus not interacting in any way and each is at rest. As they move together, energy is released so that the energy of the system becomes negative. Thus bound states are characterized by negative energies, the most stable state having the most negative energy. According to equation 1-1 we may construct an energy level diagram for the hydrogen atom as shown in Figure 1-1.

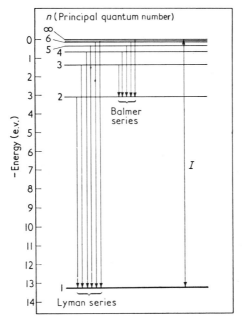

Fig. 1-1. Simplified energy level diagram of the hydrogen atom, showing some of the spectral series.

Bohr's theory was in remarkable agreement with many experimental facts and provided the first satisfactory explanation of the line spectra of

* This constant, which has units of energy, is called Rydberg's constant, since its value had previously been derived by Rydberg from spectral studies.

atoms. For example, one can compute easily from equation 1-1 the energy required to ionize the atom in its ground state, that is, to separate the electron and proton to an infinite separation with each at rest. This energy is simply R and is indicated in Figure 1-1 by the arrow marked I, which is the customary generic symbol for ionization energies. The value so computed is in good agreement with the experimentally measured value. Moreover, by assuming that a hydrogen atom in any given state characterized by an n value n' may make a transition to another state which is characterized by n'', either absorbing energy if $n'' > n'$ or radiating energy if $n'' < n'$, Bohr was able to calculate the frequencies of all of the lines observed in the absorption and emission spectra of the hydrogen atom using equation 1-1 with a value of R calculated from the values of the fundamental constants which compose it. All of these had been measured independently. In Figure 1-1, the arrows indicate a few of the transitions responsible for well-known lines in the hydrogen emission spectrum.

The main physical features of Bohr's model of the atom may be recapitulated as follows:

1. The electron is regarded as a discrete particle of negative charge whose position in space and velocity may be specified exactly at any given time.

2. The electron revolves about the nucleus in one of many orbits of definite size, and for each orbit the atom has a well-defined energy value, all other energy values being forbidden. This is the concept of *quantization*. We may say that, from the assumption that the angular momentum is quantized, in units of $h/2\pi$, it follows mathematically that the energy is quantized. The number, n, which specifies a given quantized state is called a *quantum number*.

3. When the atom goes from one state to another, or makes what is called a *transition*, a definite amount of energy is either emitted or absorbed. In general, the energy involved is in the form of electromagnetic radiation. This radiation has a certain frequency, ν. According to Bohr's model it also has a definite energy, E. Thus the frequency and the energy must be proportional, and it turns out that the proportionality constant is just h, Planck's constant:

$$E = h\nu \qquad\qquad (1\text{-}2)$$

This equation did not originate with the Bohr theory, but was known previously. In a sense it was built into Bohr's theory at the start by quantizing angular momentum in units of $h/2\pi$.

There is a very important physical concept underlying equation 1-2. Although it is well known that light has the properties of wave motion and can for many purposes be regarded purely as waves, in dealing with the atomic processes in which it is generated or absorbed it must be regarded as a stream of energy packets or *quanta*, each having the energy prescribed by equation 1-2 according to the frequency, ν. Thus, when an atom undergoes a transition releasing some energy, E, one quantum of light with frequency $E/\mathbf{h}$ always appears, not, for example, two quanta of different frequencies with energies adding up to the correct total. Conversely, when an atom absorbs radiant energy in order to make a transition involving an increase in energy by the amount E, it will only absorb one quantum of light of frequency $E/\mathbf{h}$ and not two or more quanta with differing frequencies even if the energies of the several quanta total E. These simple facts make it possible for us to infer in a direct way the separations of various energy states of an atom or molecule from the frequencies of light emitted or absorbed (further discussion will be found in Appendix A-2).

Sommerfeld's amendments to the Bohr theory were based upon the use of elliptical as well as circular orbitals. It was found that the energy still depended primarily upon a *principal quantum number*, n, defining the radius, but in addition on another quantum number, k, related to the ellipticity of the orbit.

Remarkable as the success of the Bohr-Sommerfeld theory was in the case of the hydrogen atom and one-electron ions (such as Li^{2+}, Be^{3+}, F^{8+}, etc.), it failed when applied to two- and three-electron, and in general multielectron, atoms. The way out of these difficulties was found by others, mainly Schrödinger and Heisenberg. Schrödinger's theory, known as *wave mechanics*, can, in principle, deal with all cases, while giving the same correct equation as Bohr had derived for the one-electron atom. We must therefore turn attention to wave mechanics and the description of the electronic structure of atoms which it provides.

THE BASIC PRINCIPLES OF WAVE MECHANICS

1-3. General Considerations

The basic idea in wave mechanics is that for so small a body as the electron we cannot say, as Bohr did, precisely where it is and where it is going at a definite moment. We can only state the relative *probability* of its being at a given place and having a certain momentum at a certain time. This may appear at first sight to be a somewhat vague state of affairs, but actually we are able to know quite enough to deal with problems of atomic and molecular structure.

We need consider here only a limited form of wave mechanics, namely, that part of the theory which deals with *stationary states*. A stationary state is one which persists for a long period of time unless subject to outside stimuli. Any of the energy states of the hydrogen atom given by equation 1-1, for example, is a stationary state of that system.

According to wave mechanics any system—an atom, a molecule, an electron in free space, etc.—is described by a *state function* or *wave function*, symbolized by ψ, which is a function of the coordinates of all the particles constituting the system. That is, the magnitude of ψ depends only on the positions in space of all the particles. We shall return later (page 10) to further discussion of the physical meaning of the quantity ψ.

In order to understand why ψ is called a wave function, and why Schrödinger's wave mechanics presupposes that we cannot precisely define the position of an electron, we may consider some developments in physics which occurred just prior to Schrödinger's work. De Broglie had suggested in 1924 that just as light, usually considered to be undulatory in nature, did behave under certain circumstances as if it consisted of particles (the quanta discussed above and in Appendix A-2), so very small particles such as electrons might also have certain wave properties. From certain theoretical considerations he was led to propose that we could associate with a beam of electrons a wavelength, λ, given by

$$\lambda = \frac{\mathbf{h}}{p} \tag{1-3}$$

where $\mathbf{h}$ is again Planck's constant, and p is the momentum of an electron in the beam, that is, its mass times its velocity.

The physical reality of this wave nature of the electron was actually demonstrated in 1927–28 by Davisson and Germer and by Thomson who showed that a beam of electrons could be diffracted by a suitable grating (the atoms in a crystal of gold) in a manner analogous to the diffraction of a beam of light.

The fact that systems of small particles manifest wave properties, at least under certain conditions, suggests the possibility of describing such systems with equations similar to those which are known to describe other kinds of wave motion, for example, the waves which run along a vibrating string or the wave motion attributed to electromagnetic radiation. Indeed, it is possible to begin with the wave equation appropriate to electromagnetic waves and, by certain substitutions, convert it into an equation appropriate to matter. Although these substitutions are dictated by physical reasoning, they are basically arbitrary and acceptable only because they lead to an equation which experience has shown will enable us to get correct answers to physical problems. We therefore prefer simply to state the *wave equation* as a postulate since, as chemists, our prime concern is with the application of the wave equation to atomic and molecular systems rather than with the physical and mathematical background which led Schrödinger to propose it.

1-4. The Wave Equation

The form of the wave equation which applies to stationary states of a system can be written in an exceedingly simple symbolic form:

$$\mathcal{3C}\psi = E\psi \tag{1-4}$$

where $\mathcal{3C}$ represents a certain way of expressing the total energy of the system, and E is the numerical value of that energy. For all systems which will normally concern us as chemists, the total energy is just the sum of the kinetic energy, T, and the potential energy, V, that is,

$$H = T + V \tag{1-5}$$

This relation was first demonstrated by the theoretical physicist, Hamilton, and H is frequently called the Hamiltonian of a system.

As an illustration, let us consider the Bohr model of the hydrogen atom. For simplicity, we shall assume that the heavy nucleus (which is nearly but not quite immobile as the electron goes around it) is fixed. Then, all of the kinetic energy, T, of the system is just the kinetic energy of the electron and is given by

$$T = \tfrac{1}{2} mv^2 \tag{1-6}$$

where m is the mass of the electron, and v is its velocity. The potential energy of the system is just that resulting from the electrostatic interaction (the gravitational forces are $\sim 10^{18}$ times smaller) and can thus be expressed as

$$V = -\frac{e^2}{r} \tag{1-7}$$

where e is the electronic charge, and r is the radius of the orbit; the minus sign arises because one charge is $+e$ and the other is $-e$. Therefore, for the hydrogen atom the Hamiltonian, in classical (i.e., pre-quantum mechanical) physics, is

$$H = \tfrac{1}{2}mv^2 - \frac{e^2}{r} \tag{1-8a}$$

For a reason which will become apparent presently, we prefer to write equation 1-8a in the form

$$H = \frac{p^2}{2m} - \frac{e^2}{r} \tag{1-8b}$$

where we have simply used the definition of the momentum of the electron, $p = mv$.

Now, the way in which we go from the classical description of this or any other system to the description in wave mechanics is to take its classical Hamiltonian (e.g., eqs. 1-8) and make certain substitutions. An exact prescription of these rules would involve mathematics beyond the scope of this book, but we can give a simplified and illustrative account.

The basic rule is that wherever a momentum occurs in the classical Hamiltonian, we replace it with a derivative of the form:

$$\frac{\mathbf{h}}{2\pi i}\left(\frac{\partial}{\partial x} + \frac{\partial}{\partial y} + \frac{\partial}{\partial z}\right) \tag{1-9}$$

Thus, the Hamiltonian for the hydrogen atom in its wave mechanical form, $\mathcal{H}$, is

$$\mathcal{H} = -\frac{\mathbf{h}^2}{8\pi^2 m}\left(\frac{\partial^2}{\partial x^2} + \frac{\partial^2}{\partial y^2} + \frac{\partial^2}{\partial z^2}\right) - \frac{e^2}{r} \tag{1-10}$$

If we now substitute this form of the Hamiltonian into the general form of the wave equation (eq. 1-4), we obtain

$$\mathcal{H}\psi = \left[-\frac{\mathbf{h}^2}{8\pi^2 m}\left(\frac{\partial^2}{\partial x^2} + \frac{\partial^2}{\partial y^2} + \frac{\partial^2}{\partial z^2}\right) - \frac{e^2}{r}\right]\psi = E\psi \tag{1-11}$$

This is the wave equation for the hydrogen atom. We have seen, to a certain extent, how it is obtained, but much remains to be said about what it means and how to solve it.

1-5. The Meaning and Solution of the Wave Equation

Equation 1-11 tells us that we should take the indicated second derivatives of a function, ψ, add them together, and multiply by $-\mathbf{h}^2/8\pi^2 m$. If to this we then add $(-e^2/r)\psi$, we shall have something identical with $E\psi$. When we have found a function, ψ, which permits us to do this, that function is said to be a solution of the wave equation and is called a *wave function*. In general, there will be many different functions, $\psi_1, \psi_2, \ldots \psi_i$, which will be solutions, each giving a value of the energy, $E_1, E_2, \ldots E_i$.

But still, to know what the wave equation "means" we must know what ψ "means." From the fact that we take the second derivatives of ψ with respect to the coordinates x, y, and z of the electron, it follows that ψ must be a function of these coordinates. In fact, $\psi(x, y, z)$ has a particular value for any particular combination of values of x, y, and z; or, to put it another way, at any point in space (where we use the position of the proton as the origin of the coordinate system) specified by the coordinates x, y, and z, ψ has a certain value.

The physical meaning of this value is that *it is related to the probability that the electron will be found at that point*. The exact form of the relation is very simple. The probability, P, of finding the electron at the point (x, y, z) is given by

$$P = \psi(x, y, z)\psi^*(x, y, z) \tag{1-12}$$

ψ^* is the complex conjugate of ψ; since ψ can have imaginary values, we must in general multiply it by its complex conjugate in order that P be real. The probability of finding the electron at any point may be large or small, even zero, but, obviously, it cannot be imaginary. Of course, if ψ is real, $\psi^* = \psi$, and equation 1-12 simply says that the probability equals the square of ψ.

From this definition of the physical significance of ψ, it follows that any such function must satisfy the following requirements:

1. It must have only one value at each and every point because—whatever the values of x, y, and z—there must be only one definite answer to the question "What is the probability that the electron is at the point (x, y, z)?"

2. It must not have the value ∞ at any point.

3. Its absolute values at all points must be such that

$$\int_{-\infty}^{+\infty} \int_{-\infty}^{+\infty} \int_{-\infty}^{+\infty} \psi(x, y, z)\psi^*(x, y, z)\ dx\ dy\ dz = \int \psi\psi^*\ d\tau = 1 \tag{1-13}$$

The left term in equation 1-13 gives us the sum of the probabilities of finding the electron at each point throughout all space. Since there is one electron and it must be somewhere, this total probability must then equal one. The middle term in equation 1-13 is simply a shorthand for the left term where τ is a general symbol for all the coordinates, the integration is understood to be over all coordinates, and ψ is understood to be a function of all coordinates. When a wave function satisfies this condition it is said to be *normalized*. There are still some further properties of wave functions to be mentioned, but before doing this it may help give a sense of reality to the wave-mechanical approach if we examine one of the solutions of the wave equation for the hydrogen atom.

Although equation 1-11 is perfectly correct, it is not very convenient to solve. It can be made far more amenable to solution, although more forbidding in appearance, if we substitute polar coordinates, r, θ, and ϕ, in three dimensions for the cartesian coordinates, x, y, and z. These are illustrated in Figure 1-2. When the coordinate system is thus changed, and a few algebraic manipulations performed, equation 1-11 becomes

$$\frac{1}{r^2}\frac{\partial}{\partial r}\left(r^2\frac{\partial\psi}{\partial r}\right) + \frac{1}{r^2\sin\theta}\frac{\partial}{\partial\theta}\left(\sin\theta\frac{\partial\psi}{\partial\theta}\right) + \frac{1}{r^2\sin\theta}\frac{\partial^2\psi}{\partial\phi^2} + \frac{8\pi^2m}{\mathbf{h}^2}\left(E + \frac{e^2}{r}\right)\psi = 0$$

$$(1\text{-}14)$$

There is a whole series of functions, ψ_i, which are solutions of this equation, and we shall discuss the whole set presently. (The method of solving equation 1-14 is outlined in Appendix A-3.) Let us now consider only the one, ψ_1, which gives the lowest energy, E_1. This has a rather simple form

$$\psi_1 = \frac{1}{\sqrt{\pi}}\frac{\exp(-r/a_0)}{a_0^{3/2}} \tag{1-15}$$

in which a_0 is a unit of length equal to 0.529 A. and called, for reasons we shall soon see, the Bohr radius. In Figure 1-3 is a plot of ψ_1 and ψ_1^2. It

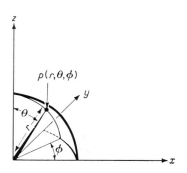

Fig. 1-2.   Polar coordinate system.

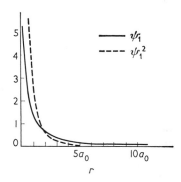

Fig. 1-3.   Plot of ground state wave function ψ_1 and ψ_1^2 for hydrogen atom.

should be recognized that these functions are spherically symmetrical, since their values do not depend on the angles θ and ϕ. It can be seen that ψ_1 satisfies the requirements for an acceptable wave function in that it is (a) single-valued, (b) never infinite, and (c) normalized.

Another way of depicting the function ψ_1 is shown in Figure 1-4. This picture may be interpreted in several ways.

1. We may imagine having a very large number of hydrogen atoms. At a certain time the electrons in each atom will in general each be at a different distance from the nucleus. If we were to superpose pictures of all of these atoms, we would obtain Figure 1-4.

2. We may take only one atom and observe it many times as the electron changes its position with respect to the nucleus. If we shade each small

region of space in proportion to how often we find the electron in it, we obtain Figure 1-4.

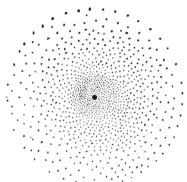

Fig. 1-4.   Another representation of the ground state wave function of the hydrogen atom.

3. We may abandon altogether our picture of the electron as a tiny hard body moving around the proton and regard it instead as a certain amount of negative charge and mass which is distributed, or smeared out, around the nucleus as required by equation 1-15. In this case Figure 1-4 represents roughly what we would "see" if we could look at the atom. This last view may be a little difficult to get used to, but is probably the most useful one to take.

Let us now see how the wave mechanical picture of the ground state of the hydrogen atom—with its smeared-out electron—compares with Bohr's picture. Suppose we consider the space around the nucleus to be divided

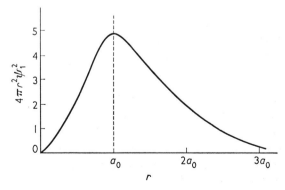

Fig. 1-5.   Probability density function, $4\pi r^2 \psi_1^2$, for the ground state orbital of the hydrogen atom.

into an infinite number of infinitesimally thin concentric spherical shells
and ask what is the probability that the electron will be found in each of
these. The total volume of such a shell, of thickness Δr, is $4\pi r^2 \Delta r$, and the
total probability of finding the electron within it is $(4\pi r^2 \Delta r)\psi_1^2$. In Figure
1-5 we have plotted $4\pi r^2 \psi_1^2$ against r. The maximum lies at a value of r
equal to a_0. Now a_0, as we have said, is called the Bohr radius because it
is the radius of the lowest orbital of the Bohr hydrogen atom. Thus, although Bohr's model of the hydrogen atom led to the conclusion that in
the ground state the electron would *always* be found going around the
proton on a spherical path exactly a_0 in radius, wave mechanics says only
that this is the *most probable* radius.

It will be recalled that Bohr was able to predict the energy of the ground
state of the hydrogen atom. If the wave function ψ_1 is inserted in equation
1-14, the same, correct energy value is calculated.

THE HYDROGEN ATOM

1-6. The Complete Set of Orbitals of the Hydrogen Atom

In the preceding section we have discussed the wave equation for the
hydrogen atom and also the wave function for the ground state. The
mathematical procedures used to obtain general solutions for this equation
are briefly outlined in Appendix A-3. Our purpose here is to discuss the properties of these solutions once they have been worked out. The first fourteen
solutions, in order of increasing energy, are given in Table 1-1. It will be
seen that each function or *orbital* (a word coined to resemble the term orbit
used in the Bohr theory) is identified by three quantum numbers, n, l,
and m, which may have the following values:

$$n = 1, 2, 3, \ldots \infty$$
$$l = n - 1, n - 2, n - 3, \ldots 0$$
$$m = 0, \pm 1, \pm 2, \ldots, \pm(l - 1), \pm l$$

The first, n, is called the principal quantum number and is identical
with the quantum number n in the Bohr theory; l and m are additional
quantum numbers, whose most important property, for the moment, is
that the values they may take are determined by the value of n. Thus, in
the first principal electron shell, where $n = 1$, l and m can only be 0,
and there is only one orbital of principal quantum number 1. When $n = 2$,
l may take the values 1 and 0; when $l = 0$, $m = 0$, and when $l = 1$, m
may be 1, 0, -1. Thus there are four orbitals of principal quantum number
2, as shown in Table 1-1. Extension of these results follows easily.

TABLE 1-1

Orbitals of a Hydrogen-like Atom

Quantum numbers			General symbol	Radial wave function[a]	Angular wave function	Explicit symbol
n	l	m				
1	0	0	$1s$	$2(Z/a_0)^{3/2}e^{-\rho}$	$(2\sqrt{\pi})^{-1}$	$1s$
2	0	0	$2s$	$2^{-3/2}(Z/a_0)^{3/2}(2-\rho)e^{-\rho/2}$	$(2\sqrt{\pi})^{-1}$	$2s$
2	1	0	$2p$	$2^{-1}\cdot6^{-1/2}(Z/a_0)^{3/2}\rho e^{-\rho/2}$	$2^{-1}\cdot3^{1/2}\pi^{-1/2}\cos\theta$	$2p_z$
2	1	1		``	$2^{-1}\cdot3^{1/2}\pi^{-1/2}\sin\theta\cos\phi$	$2p_x$
2	1	-1		``	$2^{-1}\cdot3^{1/2}\pi^{-1/2}\sin\theta\sin\phi$	$2p_y$
3	0	0	$3s$	$2\cdot81^{-1}\cdot3^{-1/2}(Z/a_0)^{3/2}(27-18\rho+2\rho^2)e^{-\rho/3}$	$(2\sqrt{\pi})^{-1}$	$3s$
3	1	0	$3p$	$4\cdot81^{-1}\cdot6^{-1/2}(Z/a_0)^{3/2}(6\rho-\rho^2)e^{-\rho/3}$	$2^{-1}\cdot3^{1/2}\pi^{-1/2}\cos\theta$	$3p_z$
3	1	1		``	$2^{-1}\cdot3^{1/2}\pi^{-1/2}\sin\theta\cos\phi$	$3p_x$
3	1	-1		``	$2^{-1}\cdot3^{1/2}\pi^{-1/2}\sin\theta\sin\phi$	$3p_y$
3	2	0	$3d$	$4\cdot81^{-1}\cdot30^{-1/2}(Z/a_0)^{3/2}\rho^2e^{-\rho/3}$	$4^{-1}\cdot5^{1/2}\pi^{-1/2}(3\cos^2\theta-1)$	$3d_{z^2}$
3	2	1		``	$2^{-3/2}\cdot30^{1/2}\pi^{-1/2}\sin\theta\cos\theta\cos\phi$	$3d_{xz}$
3	2	-1		``	$2^{-3/2}\cdot30^{1/2}\pi^{-1/2}\sin\theta\cos\theta\sin\phi$	$3d_{yz}$
3	2	2		``	$4^{-1}\cdot15^{1/2}\pi^{-1/2}\sin^2\theta\cos2\phi$	$3d_{x^2-y^2}$
3	2	-2		``	$4^{-1}\cdot15^{1/2}\pi^{-1/2}\sin^2\theta\sin2\phi$	$3d_{xy}$

[a] $\rho = Zr/a_0$; Z = nuclear charge.

Table 1-1 also lists the general symbols for these orbitals, each of which consists of a number and a letter. The number is simply the principal quantum number. The letters correspond to the values of l in the following way:

$$l = 0 \quad 1 \quad 2 \quad 3 \quad 4 \quad 5$$
$$\quad s \quad p \quad d \quad f \quad g \quad h$$

The first four letters are arbitrary for historical reasons, but following f they go in alphabetical order. Note that the general symbol does not distinguish between orbitals with the same values of n and l but differing values of m. We shall discuss symbols for indicating the difference between each of the three p orbitals or five d orbitals shortly.

Before closing this section let us re-emphasize that there are an infinite number of orbitals for the hydrogen atom, and Table 1-1 lists only the first fourteen, which have principal quantum numbers of 1, 2, and 3. For principal quantum number 4 there are sixteen orbitals; $4s$, three $4p$, five $4d$, and seven $4f$.

1-7. The Shapes of the Hydrogen Orbitals

Table 1-1 gives explicit expressions for the first fourteen orbitals of the hydrogen atom. If we take the trouble to plot these functions, we can see what these orbitals look like spatially. In so doing, we shall interpret these functions as representing the density of a smeared-out electron.

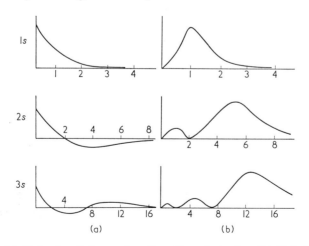

Fig. 1-6.   (a) Plots of radial wave function, R, against r/a_0. (b) Plot of density distribution function, $4\pi r^2 \psi^2$, against r/a_0. Ordinates only relative; note different abscissa scales.

s **Orbitals.** Let us consider first the s orbitals. Note that there is an s orbital in every *principal shell*, that is, in every group of orbitals with the same principal quantum number. It may be inferred from Table 1-1 that all s orbitals are spherically symmetrical since they all have an angular wave function which is independent of the angles θ and ϕ. The radial dependence of the first three s orbitals is plotted in Figure 1-6. The most important features of these plots to be noted are:

1. The number of *nodes*. Nodes are surfaces at which ψ and consequently ψ^2 go to 0. For s orbitals the number of these *radial nodes* is always $(n - 1)$. These nodes are spherical surfaces.

2. The electron density is concentrated farther out as the value of n increases, and, in general, the radial density function has its largest value beyond the last node.

Another simple and commonly used representation of the spatial properties of orbitals is that shown in Figure 1-7. These balloon pictures are constructed so that the skin of the balloon includes within it most (say, $\sim90\%$) of the electron density. The sign of the wave function is also given. The

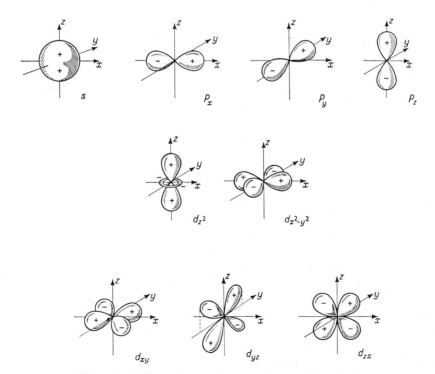

Fig. 1-7.   Balloon pictures of s, p, and d atomic orbitals.

picture of the s orbital is actually only correct in sign for the $1s$ orbital since for all others there will be concentric spherical regions in which the sign alternates, always being positive in the innermost region. However, the main purpose of placing the signs on these diagrams is to show how the sign varies as a function of angle, and for all s orbitals the sign is independent of angle in any given spherical shell.

p Orbitals. Beginning with $n = 2$, each principal shell has three p orbitals. From Table 1-1 we see that these depend upon the angles θ and ϕ and thus are not spherically symmetrical. The three p orbitals in each set are classified as p_x, p_y, and p_z. Let us look first at the $2p_z$ orbital. It is completely symmetric about the z axis, has no radial nodes, and appears roughly as shown in Figure 1-7. Note that the signs of the two *lobes* are different. The p_x and p_y orbitals have exactly the same radial functions as the p_z orbital. They may easily be shown, using the angular wave functions in Table 1-1, to have the shapes indicated in Figure 1-7. The purpose of the brackets in Table 1-1 is to indicate that the p_x and p_y orbitals are *not* identical with $\psi_{2,1,1}$ and $\psi_{2,1,-1}$, respectively. These two ψ's are actually complex, but appropriate sums and differences of them give the real functions called p_x and p_y. Note that the signs of the orbitals are strictly correct only for $2p$ orbitals where there are no radial nodes and an entire lobe has the same sign. For any p orbital, however, it is true that at a given radius the signs of the two lobes are opposite.

d Orbitals. Beginning with $n = 3$, each principal shell will have a set of five d orbitals. All d orbitals of a given set have the same radial dependence, but differ considerably in their angular distribution. The balloon pictures in Figure 1-7 are obtained by plotting the wave functions in Table 1-1. Note the following features of the d orbitals:

1. The d_{z^2} orbital is symmetrical around the z axis.

2. The d_{xy}, d_{yz}, and d_{zx} orbitals are exactly alike except that they lie in the xy, yz, and zx planes, respectively.

3. The $d_{x^2-y^2}$ orbital is exactly like the d_{xy} orbital except that it is rotated by 45° around the z axis so that its lobes are directed along the axes.

Now that we have discussed the complete set of orbitals of the hydrogen atom and examined the lower ones in some detail, we may point out an important property of these orbitals which will be of use later. This is the property of *orthogonality*, which means that the net overlap between any two of these orbitals is exactly zero. This may easily be seen by examining Figure 1-7. For example, if we draw the $1s$ and the $2p_z$ orbitals on the same set of axes (Fig. 1-8), it is clear that the regions of space in which the two lobes of the p orbital overlap the s orbital are exactly equal, but the

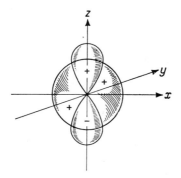

Fig. 1-8.   Diagram indicating the net zero overlap between an *s* and a *p* orbital.

signs of these overlaps are opposite, so that the net overlap is zero. This orthogonality may be expressed mathematically by writing

$$\int \psi_i \psi_j \, d\tau = 0 \qquad (1\text{-}16)$$

ELECTRON SPIN, THE EXCLUSION PRINCIPLE, AND THE PERIODIC TABLE

1-8. Electron Spin

We have seen that the state of an electron in a hydrogen or hydrogen-like atom can be specified by stating which orbital it is in, which means, in effect, assigning it three quantum numbers, n, l, and m. Actually, one further quantum number is necessary because the electron has a property of its own, called *spin*, which is quantized. Here the classical view of the electron as a tiny sphere of negative charge localized at some point in space—not really tenable in wave mechanics—is useful. We thus think of this sphere as spinning about an axis through its center. Now, just as the Bohr theory required the *orbital angular momentum*—that is, the angular momentum due to the motion of the electron around the nucleus—to be quantized in integral units of $\mathbf{h}/2\pi$, so the spin of the electron is quantized in units of $\mathbf{h}/2\pi$. However, experiments have shown that the electron spin is quantized in half-integral multiples of $\mathbf{h}/2\pi$, with the only two values allowed being $+\frac{1}{2}\mathbf{h}/2\pi$ and $-\frac{1}{2}\mathbf{h}/2\pi$. Thus, in order to specify *completely* the state of an electron in a hydrogen or hydrogen-like atom (or indeed in any atom), we must not only give the three quantum numbers characterizing the orbital it occupies but also state whether the value of the *spin quantum number, s,** is $+\frac{1}{2}$ or $-\frac{1}{2}$.

1-9. Magnetism of the Electron

If we carry further the classical picture, we can easily see that because of its spin the electron must have a magnetic moment. Just as electrons traveling around a loop of wire create a magnetic dipole perpendicular to the plane of the loop, so the outer portions of the negative charge constituting the electron, as they revolve, are equivalent to a current, and a magnetic dipole is produced. The magnitude of this magnetic dipole will be discussed more fully later; for the present we shall just call it an electron moment. One way of interpreting the spin quantum number of the electron is to say that it tells us the direction of the spin. If the electron has $s = +\frac{1}{2}$, there is a magnetic moment in a certain direction which we may take as the positive direction of the z axis in our coordinate system. When $s = -\frac{1}{2}$ (the electron is spinning in the opposite direction), there will be a moment of the same magnitude in the opposite direction. Thus any system like the hydrogen atom with only one electron must be magnetic, or, more precisely, paramagnetic. A paramagnetic body is drawn into a magnetic field. If, however, a system contains two electrons, it can either be paramagnetic with a moment resulting from two electron spin moments (but not exactly their sum) or it can have no paramagnetism depending on whether the spins of the electrons are in the same or opposite directions.

1-10. The Exclusion Principle

Having discussed all of the quantum numbers required to specify the state of an electron in a hydrogen atom, we shall now consider the electronic structure of atoms with two or more electrons. First, however, we must introduce one more restriction on the behavior of electrons, known as *Pauli's exclusion principle,* after the physicist Wolfgang Pauli who first recognized and formulated this restriction. It can be stated in several ways, but a statement which is useful for our purposes is: *No two electrons in one atom can have an identical set of quantum numbers.*

1-11. The Aufbau Principle

The aufbau principle (German *Aufbau,* "building up") is used to deduce the electronic structures of multielectron atoms by building them up, that

---

* This symbol is the same as that of an s orbital. Care should be taken not to confuse the two meanings.

is, by adding protons and electrons to the hydrogen atom. In its simplest form the aufbau principle states that we should place the electrons of a multielectron atom in a set of orbitals formally the same as those for hydrogen, filling them in the order of decreasing stability and taking account of the exclusion principle. The order of energies of the orbitals in multielectron atoms is somewhat the same as the order for the hydrogen orbitals, but differences, to be discussed below, do occur. In assuming that the multielectron atom has a set of orbitals corresponding to the hydrogen orbitals, we are really assuming that one electron does not interact with the other electrons, but acts as though it were the only electron there. This is a good assumption except that each electron will tend to modify the effect which the electrostatic field of the nucleus has on each of the other electrons.

The ground state of the hydrogen atom can be specified as $1s$, meaning that the single electron occupies a $1s$ orbital. In this case we need not specify the spin of this electron since it has no effect on the energy, and we need not consider the exclusion principle since there is only one electron. Actually in a large number of hydrogen atoms in free space, half of the spins would be $+\frac{1}{2}$ and half of them $-\frac{1}{2}$. The next element in order of increasing atomic number is helium with two electrons. Its electronic structure is worked out as follows. If we start with the nucleus, He^{2+}, and add one electron we have a hydrogen-like atom, He^+, and the electron will occupy the $1s$ orbital. It can be assigned the quantum numbers $n = 1$, $l = 0$, $m = 0$, $s = \frac{1}{2}$, where the choice of $+\frac{1}{2}$ for s is arbitrary. Now, where will the second electron go in the process $He^+ + e = He$? The $1s$ orbital is still the most stable one so that the electron will prefer to go into it, if this can be done without violating the exclusion principle. Indeed, it can; this second electron can have the quantum numbers $n = 1$, $l = 0$, $m = 0$, $s = -\frac{1}{2}$. This set differs from the first only in the spin, so that both electrons in the helium atom in its ground state are $1s$ electrons. This electron configuration is symbolized $1s^2$, the superscript indicating the number of electrons of the type specified. The spins of the two electrons are said to be *paired*. The atom is not paramagnetic.

It should be clear that with the configuration $1s^2$ the first principal shell is filled. Thus, when we come to lithium with three electrons, the first two go in to give Li^+ the configuration $1s^2$, but the remaining electron will have to enter the next most stable orbital, namely, $2s$. Thus the electronic configuration of Li is $1s^2 2s$. It has already been noted that in the hydrogen atom the energies of the orbitals increase with increasing n. While in hydrogen the energy difference between an ns and an np level is small, with ns slightly more stable, the difference decidedly favors the ns level in all multielectron atoms (see below). That is why the third electron of Li has been assigned as $2s$ rather than $2p$. The beryllium atom, which has four electrons, has the configuration $1s^2 2s^2$, and all electron spins are paired. When we reach boron, which has five electrons, the configuration must be $1s^2 2s^2 2p$, and there is one unpaired spin due to the $2p$ electron.

Hund's First Rule.   When we come next to carbon, which has six electrons, we can easily enough decide that the electron configuration of its ground state must be $1s^2 2s^2 2p^2$, but we have as yet no basis for deciding whether the spins of the two $2p$ electrons will be paired or unpaired. Pairing is not required by the exclusion principle since the two electrons which have $n = 2$, $l = 1$ can have the same spin and differ in their m values. There is a general principle known as Hund's first rule which practically always gives the correct answer in a problem of this kind. It works without exception for light atoms. This rule states that: *So long as the exclusion principle permits, electrons with the same* n *and* l *values will occupy orbitals with different values of* m *and their spins will not pair up.*

There is a simple physical reason for this. Suppose there are two $2p$ electrons and the first is placed in the p_z orbital. If the second electron is also placed in the p_z orbital, both of these electrons will be spending their time in the same region of space, rather close together. However, if the second electron enters the p_x or p_y orbital, it will get as far away, on the average, as it can from the first one and still be a $2p$ electron. Since the two electrons have the same charge, simple electrostatics tells us that the second arrangement will be preferred. Now, if the two electrons differ in their m values, they need not differ in spin to satisfy the exclusion principle, but in fact they do since the energy of spin pairing is unfavorable.

Thus for carbon the particular $1s^2 2s^2 2p^2$ configuration which occurs is that in which the two p orbitals are different, and the atom has paramagnetism corresponding to two unpaired electron spins. Similarly, for nitrogen the configuration is $1s^2 2s^2 2p^3$, and the p electrons are spread out among the three $2p$ orbitals with their spins parallel.

When we come to oxygen we add a fourth $2p$ electron and this must enter a $2p$ orbital already occupied. Its n, l, and m quantum numbers will then be identical with those of the electron already occupying this orbital, so these two electrons must have their spins opposed. Thus in oxygen there is a paramagnetism corresponding to two unpaired spins. In fluorine the configuration is $1s^2 2s^2 2p^5$, and there is only one unpaired electron spin. Neon has the configuration $1s^2 2s^2 2p^6$ and is not paramagnetic. At this point all orbitals in the first and second principal shells are filled.

As in hydrogen, the next most stable orbitals after the $2s$ and $2p$ levels are the $3s$ and $3p$ orbitals. Consequently, beginning with sodium, $Z = 11$, and going through to argon, $Z = 18$, eight electrons are added in a manner quite analogous to the filling of the second shell. Beyond this, however, the pattern of levels does not exactly follow that for hydrogen. If it did, we should expect that potassium, with $Z = 19$, would have the configuration [Ar]$3d$, where [Ar] represents a core with the configuration of argon, that is, $1s^2 2s^2 2p^6 3s^2 3p^6$. Actually the configuration of potassium is [Ar]$4s$. In order to explain in a general way why this deviation from the hydrogen pattern occurs, let us pause to consider in more detail the assumption implicit in the aufbau principle, namely, that a multielectron atom ought to have a set of orbitals formally similar to those for a one-electron atom like hydrogen.

In a hydrogen or hydrogen-like atom the energy of an electron in a particular orbital depends only on the quantity Z/n^2, or, for a particular atom, on the quantum number n (see eq. 1-1). Thus, for example, the $3s$, $3p$, and $3d$ orbitals should all have the same energy. Actually there are slight differences due to higher order effects. An electron in one of these orbitals in hydrogen feels the presence of exactly one positive charge at the nucleus. Now, in the sodium atom an electron in, say, the $3s$ orbital feels a greater nuclear charge. If the $3s$ electron spent all of its time in regions completely outside of that occupied by the electrons of the neon core, then the charge of $+11$ on the nucleus would be shielded by the charge of -10 of the neon core, and the $3s$ electron would feel a net nuclear charge of exactly $+1$. However, this is not the case because the $3s$ wave function has a finite value even at the nucleus (Fig. 1-6) where it is subject to the full nuclear charge. Figure 1-9 illustrates how the $3s$ electron in sodium *penetrates* the neon core. Rather than being perfectly shielded so that the

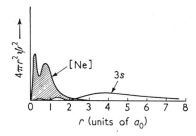

Fig. 1-9.   Penetration of the $3s$ orbital into the neon core, [Ne], in the sodium atom.

TABLE 1-2

The Electronic Configurations of the Atoms of the Elements

Symbol	Atomic number (Z)	Number and distribution of electrons																		
		$1s$	$2s$	$2p$	$3s$	$3p$	$3d$	$4s$	$4p$	$4d$	$4f$	$5s$	$5p$	$5d$	$5f$	$6s$	$6p$	$6d$	$6f$	$7s$
H	1	1																		
He	2	2																		
Li	3	2	1																	
Be	4	2	2																	
B	5	2	2	1																
C	6	2	2	2																
N	7	2	2	3																
O	8	2	2	4																
F	9	2	2	5																
Ne	10	2	2	6																
Na	11	2	2	6	1															
Mg	12	2	2	6	2															
Al	13	2	2	6	2	1														
Si	14	2	2	6	2	2														
P	15	2	2	6	2	3														
S	16	2	2	6	2	4														
Cl	17	2	2	6	2	5														
Ar	18	2	2	6	2	6														
K	19	2	2	6	2	6		1												
Ca	20	2	2	6	2	6		2												
Sc	21	2	2	6	2	6	1	2												
Ti	22	2	2	6	2	6	2	2												
V	23	2	2	6	2	6	3	2												

	Z	1s	2s	2p	3s	3p	3d	4s	4p	4d	5s	5p
Cr	24	2	2	6	2	6	5	1				
Mn	25	2	2	6	2	6	5	2				
Fe	26	2	2	6	2	6	6	2				
Co	27	2	2	6	2	6	7	2				
Ni	28	2	2	6	2	6	8	2				
Cu	29	2	2	6	2	6	10	1				
Zn	30	2	2	6	2	6	10	2				
Ga	31	2	2	6	2	6	10	2	1			
Ge	32	2	2	6	2	6	10	2	2			
As	33	2	2	6	2	6	10	2	3			
Se	34	2	2	6	2	6	10	2	4			
Br	35	2	2	6	2	6	10	2	5			
Kr	36	2	2	6	2	6	10	2	6			
Rb	37	2	2	6	2	6	10	2	6		1	
Sr	38	2	2	6	2	6	10	2	6		2	
Y	39	2	2	6	2	6	10	2	6	1	2	
Zr	40	2	2	6	2	6	10	2	6	2	2	
Nb	41	2	2	6	2	6	10	2	6	4	1	
Mo	42	2	2	6	2	6	10	2	6	5	1	
Tc	43	2	2	6	2	6	10	2	6	6	1	
Ru	44	2	2	6	2	6	10	2	6	7	1	
Rh	45	2	2	6	2	6	10	2	6	8	1	
Pd	46	2	2	6	2	6	10	2	6	10		
Ag	47	2	2	6	2	6	10	2	6	10	1	
Cd	48	2	2	6	2	6	10	2	6	10	2	
In	49	2	2	6	2	6	10	2	6	10	2	1
Sn	50	2	2	6	2	6	10	2	6	10	2	2
Sb	51	2	2	6	2	6	10	2	6	10	2	3
Te	52	2	2	6	2	6	10	2	6	10	2	4
I	53	2	2	6	2	6	10	2	6	10	2	5
Xe	54	2	2	6	2	6	10	2	6	10	2	6

(continued)

25

TABLE 1-2 (continued)

Symbol	Atomic number (Z)	1s	2s	2p	3s	3p	3d	4s	4p	4d	4f	5s	5p	5d	5f	6s	6p	6d	6f	7s
Cs	55	2	2	6	2	6	10	2	6	10		2	6			1				
Ba	56	2	2	6	2	6	10	2	6	10		2	6			2				
La	57	2	2	6	2	6	10	2	6	10		2	6	1		2				
Ce	58	2	2	6	2	6	10	2	6	10	2	2	6			2				
Pr	59	2	2	6	2	6	10	2	6	10	3	2	6			2				
Nd	60	2	2	6	2	6	10	2	6	10	4	2	6			2				
Pm	61	2	2	6	2	6	10	2	6	10	5	2	6			2				
Sm	62	2	2	6	2	6	10	2	6	10	6	2	6			2				
Eu	63	2	2	6	2	6	10	2	6	10	7	2	6			2				
Gd	64	2	2	6	2	6	10	2	6	10	7	2	6	1		2				
Tb	65	2	2	6	2	6	10	2	6	10	9	2	6			2				
Dy	66	2	2	6	2	6	10	2	6	10	10	2	6			2				
Ho	67	2	2	6	2	6	10	2	6	10	11	2	6			2				
Er	68	2	2	6	2	6	10	2	6	10	12	2	6			2				
Tm	69	2	2	6	2	6	10	2	6	10	13	2	6			2				
Yb	70	2	2	6	2	6	10	2	6	10	14	2	6			2				
Lu	71	2	2	6	2	6	10	2	6	10	14	2	6	1		2				
Hf	72	2	2	6	2	6	10	2	6	10	14	2	6	2		2				
Ta	73	2	2	6	2	6	10	2	6	10	14	2	6	3		2				
W	74	2	2	6	2	6	10	2	6	10	14	2	6	4		2				
Re	75	2	2	6	2	6	10	2	6	10	14	2	6	5		2				
Os	76	2	2	6	2	6	10	2	6	10	14	2	6	6		2				
Ir	77	2	2	6	2	6	10	2	6	10	14	2	6	9		2				

Z		1s	2s	2p	3s	3p	3d	4s	4p	4d	4f	5s	5p	5d	5f	6s	6p	6d	7s
78	Pt	2	2	6	2	6	10	2	6	10	14	2	6	9		1			
79	Au	2	2	6	2	6	10	2	6	10	14	2	6	10		1			
80	Hg	2	2	6	2	6	10	2	6	10	14	2	6	10		2			
81	Tl	2	2	6	2	6	10	2	6	10	14	2	6	10		2	1		
82	Pb	2	2	6	2	6	10	2	6	10	14	2	6	10		2	2		
83	Bi	2	2	6	2	6	10	2	6	10	14	2	6	10		2	3		
84	Po	2	2	6	2	6	10	2	6	10	14	2	6	10		2	4		
85	At	2	2	6	2	6	10	2	6	10	14	2	6	10		2	5		
86	Rn	2	2	6	2	6	10	2	6	10	14	2	6	10		2	6		
87	Fr	2	2	6	2	6	10	2	6	10	14	2	6	10		2	6		1
88	Ra	2	2	6	2	6	10	2	6	10	14	2	6	10		2	6		2
89	Ac	2	2	6	2	6	10	2	6	10	14	2	6	10		2	6	1	2
90	Th	2	2	6	2	6	10	2	6	10	14	2	6	10		2	6	2	2
91	Pa	2	2	6	2	6	10	2	6	10	14	2	6	10	2	2	6	1	2
92	U	2	2	6	2	6	10	2	6	10	14	2	6	10	3	2	6	1	2
93	Np	2	2	6	2	6	10	2	6	10	14	2	6	10	5	2	6		2
94	Pu	2	2	6	2	6	10	2	6	10	14	2	6	10	6	2	6		2
95	Am	2	2	6	2	6	10	2	6	10	14	2	6	10	7	2	6		2
96	Cm	2	2	6	2	6	10	2	6	10	14	2	6	10	7	2	6	1	2
97	(Bk	2	2	6	2	6	10	2	6	10	14	2	6	10	8	2	6	1	2)
98	(Cf	2	2	6	2	6	10	2	6	10	14	2	6	10	10	2	6		2)

effective nuclear charge, Z^*, would be 1.0, it is, in fact, imperfectly shielded so that the effective nuclear charge is ~ 2. Now, the $3p$ orbital is also partly penetrating but not as much as the $3s$ orbital; consequently, it feels an effective nuclear charge between 1 and 2. The $3d$ orbital is practically nonpenetrating, and Z^* for it is very nearly 1.0. Thus, when the neon core is complete, there are appreciable differences in the energies of these orbitals such that the order of stability is $3s$, $3p$, $3d$.

In the region of argon and potassium in the sequence of elements, the shielding effects of inner, filled orbitals are such that the $4s$ orbital is less shielded than the $3d$ orbitals and hence more stable, whereas the $4p$ orbitals are not only more shielded than the $4s$, as usual, but also more shielded than the $3d$ orbitals. Thus the order of energies is $3s$, $3p$, $4s$, $3d$, $4p$. Similarly, following $4p$, the $5s$ orbital is more stable than $4d$. Now, in the fourth principal shell we have the first set of f orbitals. These do not, however, follow the $4d$ orbitals. Instead, again mainly because of differences in the degrees of penetration of the core, they are less stable than the $5p$ and $6s$ orbitals. The complete list of the orbitals for neutral atoms, in decreasing order of stability, is: $1s$, $2s$, $2p$, $3s$, $3p$, $4s$, $3d$, $4p$, $5s$, $4d$, $5p$, $6s$, $4f$, $5d$, $6p$, $7s$, $6d \sim 5f$ . . . .

The electronic structures of most of the remaining atoms which are known can be worked out using this order and the principles discussed above. There are certain minor anomalies which will be discussed at appropriate places in the text. Table 1-2 gives a complete list of the known elements and their ground state electron configurations.

1-12. The Periodic Table

The title "*the* periodic table" is perhaps inappropriate since literally hundreds of different forms of a periodic table of the elements have been devised. The first ones date from long before the advent of the modern theory of atomic structure and were based upon comparison of the chemical properties of the elements. It was Mendeleev who first devised tables essentially similar to those used today. One of his tables is shown in Figure 1-10. The formulas for the typical oxides and hydrides in the groups, which are given in the group headings, indicate the type of chemical reasoning behind the groupings given. This table includes the elements known at the time it was formulated and has gaps. For example, there is a gap in the position where germanium is now known to belong. Mendeleev was led to predict the existence of the missing elements. By interpolation between the properties of the neighboring elements and their compounds he was also

Series	Group I R_2O	Group II RO	Group III R_2O_3	Group IV RH_4 RO_2	Group V RH_3 R_2O_5	Group VI RH_2 RO_3	Group VII RH R_2O_7	Group VIII — RO_4
1	H=1							
2	Li=7	Be=9.4	B=11	C=12	N=14	O=16	F=19	
3	Na=23	Mg=24	Al=27.3	Si=28	P=31	S=32	Cl=35.5	
4	K=39	Ca=40	=44	Ti=48	V=51	Cr=52	Mn=55	Fe=56,Co=59, Ni=59,Cu=63
5	(Cu=63)	Zn=65	=68	=72	As=75	Se=78	Br=80	
6	Rb=85	Sr=87	?Yt=88	Zr=90	Nb=94	Mo=96	=100	Ru=104,Rh=104, Pd=106,Ag=108
7	(Ag=108)	Cd=112	In=113	Sn=118	Sb=122	Te=125	I=127	
8	Cs=133	Ba=137	?Dy=138	?Ce=140				
9			?Er=178	?La=180	Ta=182	W=184		Os=195,Ir=197, Pt=198,Au=199
10								
11	(Au=199)	Hg=200	Tl=204	Pb=207	Bi=208			
12				Th=231		U=240		

Fig. 1-10. Mendeleev's periodic table of 1872. The notation used indicates either the atomic weight as known to Mendeleev (e.g., Sb = 122) or the weight of an anticipated but then undiscovered element (e.g., = 72 for the element now known as germanium).

29

Period	Group Ia	Group IIa	Group IIIa	Group IVa	Group Va	Group VIa	Group VIIa	Group VIII			Group Ib	Group IIb	Group IIIb	Group IVb	Group Vb	Group VIb	Group VIIb	Group O
1 1s	1 H																1 H	2 He
2 2s2p	3 Li	4 Be											5 B	6 C	7 N	8 O	9 F	10 Ne
3 3s3p	11 Na	12 Mg											13 Al	14 Si	15 P	16 S	17 Cl	18 Ar
4 4s3d 4p	19 K	20 Ca	21 Sc	22 Ti	23 V	24 Cr	25 Mn	26 Fe	27 Co	28 Ni	29 Cu	30 Zn	31 Ga	32 Ge	33 As	34 Se	35 Br	36 Kr
5 5s4d 5p	37 Rb	38 Sr	39 Y	40 Zr	41 Nb	42 Mo	43 Tc	44 Ru	45 Rh	46 Pd	47 Ag	48 Cd	49 In	50 Sn	51 Sb	52 Te	53 I	54 Xe
6 6s (4f) 5d 6p	55 Cs	56 Ba	57* La	72 Hf	73 Ta	74 W	75 Re	76 Os	77 Ir	78 Pt	79 Au	80 Hg	81 Tl	82 Pb	83 Bi	84 Po	85 At	86 Rn
7 7s (5f) 6d	87 Fr	88 Ra	89** Ac															

*Lanthanide series 4f	58 Ce	59 Pr	60 Nd	61 Pm	62 Sm	63 Eu	64 Gd	65 Tb	66 Dy	67 Ho	68 Er	69 Tm	70 Yb	71 Lu

**Actinide series 5f	90 Th	91 Pa	92 U	93 Np	94 Pu	95 Am	96 Cm	97 Bk	98 Cf	99 Es	100 Fm	101 Md	102 No(?)	103 Lw

Fig. 1-11. A common long form of the periodic table.

able to predict, often with astonishing accuracy, the properties of the missing elements and their compounds.

It can be seen that the basic reason given by Mendeleev for the groupings is the similarity of the valences of the elements in a given group. These similarities can now be explained in terms of the electronic structures of the atoms. We can now also understand why the coinage metals Ag, Cu, and Au, although formally similar to the alkali metals Li, Na, K, Rb, and Cs in having stable +1 oxidation states, are otherwise not very similar to these elements. In the alkali metals there is one valence electron outside of a very stable, rigid inert gas core, whereas in the coinage metals, the outer electron has beneath it a complete d shell which is not particularly resistant to loss of electrons and is rather soft and deformable. We can also see why the formal similarities of the oxidation states of elements with partially filled d shells to those of elements which have only s and p electrons in their outer shells are really only formal. Certainly N and V have no genuine chemical similarities. In contemporary forms of the periodic table, these sequences of elements in which d and f shells are being filled, called *transition series*, are set apart from the *nontransition elements*. A periodic table of this "long form" type is shown in Figure 1-11.

The vertical sequences are called *groups*, and the horizontal sequences are called *periods*. The sequences Li–Ne and Na–Ar are called the first short period and the second short period, respectively. The sequences Sc–Ni, Y–Pd, and La–Pt (excluding the fourteen elements following immediately after La) are called the first, second, and third transition series, respectively. The fourteen elements Ce–Lu, in which the $4f$ orbitals are being filled, are called the *rare earths* or the *lanthanides* (because the $4f$ electrons have little effect on their chemical properties, they all resemble lanthanum chemically). The elements in the sequence Th to element 104 are called the *actinides*, although on the whole their resemblance to actinium is not nearly so close as that of the lanthanides to lanthanum.

Certain of the groups have acquired trivial names which are very commonly used. The group Ia elements (excluding hydrogen) are the *alkali metals.* Group IIa consists of the *alkaline earth metals,* group Ib of the *coinage metals.* The VIIb elements are the *halogens.* The group 0 elements are the *rare gases* or *inert gases.* The group VIb elements are sometimes called the chalcogens, but this term is not as common as the others mentioned.

FURTHER PROPERTIES OF ATOMS

1-13. Energy Units

In discussions of the energy changes which occur in physical and chemical processes, several energy units and conventions are commonly used and will occur throughout this book. The principal ones are the following. The *calorie*, or "small" calorie, is approximately the amount of heat required to raise the temperature of 1 gram of water 1°C., but its exact definition is in terms of electrical units. Chemical energies of a relatively weak nature are frequently expressed in units of calories per mole (cal./mole). Normal chemical bonds and differences in energies of the principal levels of atoms and molecules, however, are usually of the order of thousands of calories per mole. These are usually expressed in terms of the *kilocalorie*, which is, by definition, 1000 calories. For example, the energies required to separate the molecules O_2, I_2, and H_2 into atoms are 119.1, 36.1, and 104.2 kcal./mole, respectively.

An even larger unit is the *electron volt* (e.v.), which is the kinetic energy acquired by an electron when it passes through a potential difference of 1 volt. One electron volt is equal to 23.06 kcal./mole.

As we have noted already, one of the main sources of information about the energy levels in atoms and molecules is their spectra. Usually the wavelengths of spectral lines are measured directly. The most common units for their expression are

$$Angstrom \text{ (A.): } 1 \text{ A.} = 10^{-8} \text{ cm.}$$

$$Micron \text{ } (\mu)\text{: } 1 \text{ } \mu = 10^{-4} \text{ cm.} = 10^{-3} \text{ mm.}$$

$$Millimicron \text{ (m}\mu)\text{: } 1 \text{ m}\mu = 10^{-3} \text{ } \mu$$

Energy cannot conveniently be measured in any wavelength units, but, because of the relation

$$E = h\nu$$

can be expressed in frequency units. In the above equation Planck's constant is in its usual units of erg-second, and the frequency is in cycles per second. For various reasons, cycles per second is not a convenient frequency unit, and the one most commonly used is the *reciprocal centimeter* (cm.$^{-1}$), also called a *wave number* (no abbreviation) or a *Kayser* (K). Since the frequency, f, in cycles per second is related to the wavelength, λ, in centimeters by the relation $f = c/\lambda$ (cm.) where c is the velocity of light, energy in ergs is given by E (ergs) $= c \times$ frequency (in cm.$^{-1}$). Applying suitable conversion factors, the wave number, as a unit of energy, is related to other energy units as follows:

$$1 \text{ kcal./mole} = 350 \text{ cm.}^{-1}$$

$$1 \text{ e.v.} = 8067 \text{ cm.}^{-1}$$

In any description of a change in energy, it is necessary to have a convention regarding the algebraic sign to be given to the energy released or absorbed. We shall follow the so-called American convention which states that the energy of any exothermic process is negative (energy released or lost by the system) and the energy of any endothermic process is positive (energy gained by the system).

1-14. Ionization Potentials

It is always possible to detach one or more electrons from an atom, ion, or molecule if sufficient energy is provided to do the necessary work. The minimum energy required to remove an electron from an atom, ion, or molecule, leaving each without any kinetic energy, is called the *ionization potential*. For a given species, the energy required to remove the first electron is called the first ionization potential, and so on. Note that the first ionization potential of, say, Cl_2^+ is the same as the second ionization potential of Cl_2. Because of the convention mentioned above, the algebraic signs of all ionization potentials are positive. The symbol I is usually used to signify an ionization potential.

The first ionization potentials of the elements vary in relation to the positions of the elements in the periodic table, as shown in Figure 1-12. It

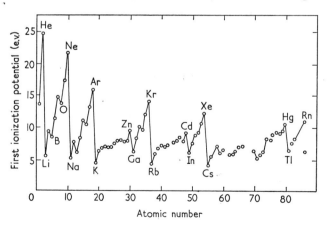

Fig. 1-12. Variation in first ionization potentials with atomic number.

will be seen that with the exception of mercury, the maxima in the curve all occur at inert gases, and the deeper minima all occur with the alkali metals. These facts show that the closed configurations of the inert gases are most difficult to disturb by removal of an electron, whereas the lone electron outside of an inert gas configuration which is the common feature of each alkali metal atom is very easy to remove. Furthermore, although there are irregularities, the potentials rise steeply in going from an alkali metal to the following inert gas. These facts can be accounted for on the basis of the shielding of one electron upon another.

As we go from, say, sodium, with a nuclear charge of 11 to argon with a nuclear charge of 18, the eight electrons which are also added are all in the same principal shell. Because the radial wave functions of all electrons in the same shell are either identical or very similar, no one electron spends much time between the nucleus and any other electron. Thus the extent to which these electrons shield one another from the steadily increasing nuclear charge is slight. For example, the effective nuclear charge for the $3s$ electron in sodium is ~ 2, whereas that for the s or p electron in argon is ~ 6.7. It is this substantially greater restraining force which is responsible for the much tighter binding of the electrons.

1-15. Electron Affinities

In general, it is also possible to attach an additional electron to any atom, ion, or molecule. The energy which is *released* when this takes place is called the *electron affinity* of the species, usually symbolized A. It will be noted that this sign convention is opposite to the general one stated above, but this definition of electron affinity is so well established that we must accept it as it is. Negative electron affinities do exist—that is, when the species concerned does not "want" another electron and must be forced to accept it—but the cases of greatest interest are those in which the electron affinity is positive. As examples we may take the several halogen atoms which have the following electron affinities:

$$F(g) + e = F^-(g) \qquad A = 83.5 \pm 2 \text{ kcal./mole}$$
$$Cl(g) + e = Cl^-(g) \qquad A = 87 \text{ kcal./mole}$$
$$Br(g) + e = Br^-(g) \qquad A = 82 \text{ kcal./mole}$$
$$I(g) + e = I^-(g) \qquad A = 75 \text{ kcal./mole}$$

These relatively high values may be attributed to the fact that the electron acquired completes an inert gas electron configuration. On the other hand, for the alkali metals, which do not bind their outermost electron very strongly to begin with, the electron affinities are very low: ~ 17 kcal./mole for sodium and hydrogen and probably close to zero for the other alkalies.

Beryllium and magnesium both have negative electron affinities in the range of -10 to -20 kcal./mole.

As might be expected, second electron affinities of atoms (e.g., $O^- + e = O^{2-}$) are all negative so far as is known. This is because of the electrostatic repulsion of the second electron by the negative charge on the ion. Finally, it may be noted that the electron affinity of an atom is numerically equal to the ionization potential of the corresponding anion.

References

Herzberg, G., *Atomic Spectra and Atomic Structure*, Dover, New York, 1944. A classic which presents lucidly and succinctly "what every chemist should know" about atomic spectra and the electronic structure of atoms.

Linnett, J. W., *Wave Mechanics and Valency*, Wiley, New York, 1960. A short and lucidly written introduction which can be recommended.

Slater, J. C., *Quantum Theory of Atomic Structure*, Vol. I, McGraw-Hill, New York, 1960. A very fine introduction to the necessary wave mechanics which carries the theory of atomic structure with elegance and clarity through most topics of importance to inorganic chemistry.

2

Ionic Compounds and Electrostatic Bonding

2-1. General Considerations

The reason atoms combine to form chemical compounds is that, when the several atoms approach one another closely, they interact in such a way that the energy of the system is lowered. We can also say that the interactions are such as to produce forces of attraction. In this chapter we consider one of the simplest kinds of attractive force, namely, the electrostatic attraction between ions of opposite charge. There are a vast number of solid compounds which can be considered as very closely approximating aggregates of positive and negative ions interacting in a purely electrostatic manner. We shall first consider the energetics of perfectly ionic materials, assuming the existence of a certain arrangement of the ions in the lattice, and we shall then consider the various kinds of lattices which commonly occur, the factors favoring one or another type of lattice, and the effects of deviations from the idealized concept of an ionic substance.

Most ionic compounds are formed by combination of elements near opposite ends of the periodic table. They are usually oxides, sulfides, or halides of the electropositive metals such as those of groups I, II, and III and the transition series. Tin and lead in their $+2$ oxidation state also form more or less ionic salts, and large oxy anions—ClO_4^-, CO_3^{2-}, NO_3^-, and others—form ionic salts with many metal ions. The main requirements for the formation of ionic compounds, that is, those solids which consist of an array of positive and negative ions held together almost entirely by the coulomb forces between the oppositely charged ions, are that the metal ions have a relatively low ionization potential and that the nonmetal atoms or radicals have a relatively high electron affinity. Even taking extreme values of ionization potentials and electron affinities—for example, those of Cs and F, respectively—the electron affinity is only about one-half of the ionization potential; it is therefore clear that other factors must be involved in the formation of ionic solids. Similarly, in view of the fact that the electron affinity of oxygen (for the acquisition of two electrons to form the oxide ion) is actually negative, it may seem surprising that so many oxides are ionic. An explanation for this and similar facts will be given in this chapter.

2-2. Lattice Energies of Ionic Crystals

As an example of an *idealized* ionic substance let us consider a 1:1 compound of the type $(M^+)(X^-)$. M^+ is a cation, spherical in shape, incompressible, and having a sharply defined surface. Similarly, X^- is a spherical anion, also incompressible and having a definite size. This kind of model is commonly called a hard-sphere electrostatic model. When these cations and anions are brought together in large and equal numbers, they will arrange themselves in a regular array in which they tend to occupy the minimum volume and have the least electrostatic energy (the geometry of the array will depend on the relative sizes of the two ions (see page 44)).

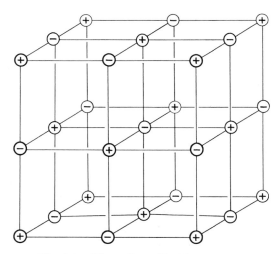

Fig. 2-1. The sodium chloride structure.

Let us assume that the arrangement adopted is that shown in Figure 2-1, the type of lattice arrangement occurring in sodium chloride.

Let us call the M—X distances r. Using Figure 2-1 and simple trigonometry it can be shown that an M^+ ion is surrounded by six X^- ions (nearest neighbors) at a distance r, twelve M^+ ions (second nearest neighbors) at a distance $\sqrt{2}r$, eight more distant X^- ions at $\sqrt{3}r$, six M^+ ions at $2r$, twenty-four more X^- ions at $\sqrt{5}r$, etc. The electrostatic interaction energy of the M^+ ion with each of these surrounding ions is equal to the product of the charge on each ion, Z^+ and Z^-, divided by the distance. Hence the total electrostatic energy of this positive ion can be written

$$E = \frac{6e^2}{r}(Z^+)(Z^-) + \frac{12e^2}{\sqrt{2}r}(Z^+)^2 + \frac{8e^2}{\sqrt{3}r}(Z^+)(Z^-) + \frac{6e^2}{2r}(Z^+)^2 \ldots$$

$$= -\frac{e^2|Z|^2}{r}\left(6 - \frac{12}{\sqrt{2}} + \frac{8}{\sqrt{3}} - \frac{6}{2} + \frac{24}{\sqrt{5}} \ldots\right) \tag{2-1}$$

Actually, it is possible to set up the general formula for the terms in equation 2-1 from geometrical considerations. The sum of all these terms, that is, the sum of an infinite series, is called the *Madelung constant*. It should be clear that the value of the Madelung constant is characteristic of the geometrical arrangement and independent of the particular ions or their charges (i.e., they might both be doubly or triply charged). The above series converges to a value of 1.747558 . . . and can be evaluated to any required degree of accuracy. In many cases the series diverge, and the evaluation of the Madelung constants for such structures requires considerable mathematical manipulation. The Madelung constants for many commonly occurring lattices have been calculated.

If we made a mole (N ion pairs) of the compound MX, then NE would be the energy of the process

$$M^+(g) + X^-(g) = MX(s)$$

This is so because if we wrote out an expression for the electrostatic energy of an X^- ion it would be identical with equation 2-1. If we added the electrostatic energies for a mole of each ion, the result would be twice the true electrostatic energy per mole because we would be counting each pairwise interaction twice. Thus NE is the electrostatic potential energy per mole for a hard-sphere ionic solid with the NaCl structure.

In the hard-sphere model the M^+—X^- distance is fixed by the sum of the radii of M^+ and X^-. We know that real atoms are not rigid spheres, and their equilibrium separation in an ionic solid must therefore be a consequence of some short-range repulsive energy due to overlapping of their electron clouds which comes into play as they approach. Born proposed the simple assumption that the repulsive energy between two ions could be represented by the expression B'/r^n in which B' and n are constants, as yet undetermined, characteristic of the ion pair concerned. We can therefore write, for the repulsive energy of a particular ion in a crystal,

$$E_{\text{rep}} = \frac{B}{r^n} \tag{2-2}$$

where B is related to B' by the crystal geometry. The total energy of the crystal, that is, the lattice energy, U, is then given by

$$U = \frac{A(Z^+)(Z^-)Ne^2}{r} + \frac{NB}{r^n} \tag{2-3}$$

where A is the Madelung constant. This energy, U, is exactly the energy of the process

$$M^+(g) + X^-(g) = M^+X^-(s) \tag{2-4}$$

if these are the only forces involved. There is a relation between B and n which may be determined if we recognize that in the equilibrium state of the crystal ($r = r_0$) the energy is a minimum as a function of r. Thus

$$\left(\frac{dU}{dr}\right)_{r=r_0} = 0 = \frac{-A(Z^+)(Z^-)Ne^2}{r_0^2} - \frac{nNB}{r_0^{n+1}} \tag{2-5}$$

which yields

$$B = -\frac{A(Z^+)(Z^-)e^2}{n} r_0^{n-1} \tag{2-6}$$

Substituting equation 2-6 into equation 2-3, we obtain

$$U = N(Z^+)(Z^-)A \frac{e^2}{r_0}\left(1 - \frac{1}{n}\right) \tag{2-7}$$

The numerical value of n can be derived from measurements of the compressibility of the solid and may also be estimated theoretically. The experimentally derived values and the values calculated by Pauling for inert gas-like ions are given in Table 2-1. It can be seen that the ex-

TABLE 2-1

Sample n Values

Determined by experiment		Estimated from theory	
Compound	n	Inert gas configuration of ion	n
LiF	5.9	He	5
LiCl	8.0	Ne	7
LiBr	8.7	Ar	9
NaCl	9.1	Kr	10
NaBr	9.5	Xe	12

perimental values are reasonably close to the averages of the appropriate theoretical estimates. It can also be seen that even if the n used is off by 1.0, the lattice energy will be in error only by 1–2%.

In very accurate calculations some correction factors are required because equation 2-3 does not take account of other minor forces. There are three main refinements.

1. *Inclusion of van der Waals forces.* Van der Waals forces operate between all atoms, ions, or molecules, but are relatively very weak. They are due to attractions between oscillating dipoles in adjacent atoms and vary approximately as $1/r^6$. They can be calculated from the polarizabilities and ionization potentials of the atoms or ions.

2. *Use of a more rigorous expression for the repulsive energy.* The simple Born expression (eq. 2-2) for the repulsive energy is not strictly correct from quantum mechanical considerations. More refined expressions do not greatly change the results, however.

3. *Consideration of "zero point energy" of the crystal.* The "zero point energy" of the crystal is that energy of vibration of the ions which the crystal possesses even at the absolute zero. This can be calculated from the lattice vibration frequencies.

The data given in Table 2-2 indicate the relative importance of the various contributions to the lattice energy.

TABLE 2-2

Components of Lattice Energy
(In electron volts)

Energy	LiF	NaCl	CsI
Coulomb	-12.4	-8.92	-6.4
Repulsion	$+1.9$	$+1.03$	$+0.63$
Van der Waals	-0.17	-0.13	-0.48
Zero point	$+0.17$	$+0.08$	$+0.3$

The calculation of lattice energies of ionic compounds is very important since in general, there is no *direct* way to measure them experimentally, although they can be obtained from certain experimental data using the Born-Haber cycle (Section 2-3). For example, the heat of vaporization of NaCl does not give the lattice energy because up to the highest temperatures at which accurate measurements can be made the gas phase consists of NaCl molecules (or ion pairs), and it has so far proved impossible to get an accurate estimate of the heat of dissociation of NaCl(g) into Na^+(g) and Cl^-(g) since NaCl(g) normally dissociates into atoms.

2-3. The Born-Haber Cycle

The heats of formation of various ionic compounds show tremendous variations. In a general way, we know that many factors contribute to the over-all heat of formation, namely, the ionization potentials, electron affinities, heats of vaporization and dissociation of the elements, and the lattice energy of the compound. The Born-Haber cycle is a thermodynamic cycle which shows the interrelation of these quantities and enables us to see how variations in heats of formation can be attributed to the variations in these individual quantities. In order to construct the Born-Haber cycle we consider the following thermochemical equations, using NaCl as an example.

$$
\begin{array}{ll}
\text{Na(s)} = \text{Na(g)} & \Delta H_{\text{subl}}(\text{Na}) \\
\text{Na(g)} = \text{Na}^+(\text{g}) + e^- & I_{\text{Na}} \\
\tfrac{1}{2}\text{Cl}_2(\text{g}) = \text{Cl(g)} & \tfrac{1}{2}\Delta H_{\text{diss}}(\text{Cl}_2) \\
\text{Cl(g)} + e^- = \text{Cl}^-(\text{g}) & -A_{\text{Cl}} \\
\text{Na}^+(\text{g}) + \text{Cl}^-(\text{g}) = \text{NaCl(s)} & U \\
\hline
\text{Na(s)} + \tfrac{1}{2}\text{Cl}_2(\text{g}) = \text{NaCl(s)} & \Delta H_f(\text{NaCl})
\end{array}
$$

The net change expressed by the last equation can be achieved by carrying out the preceding five steps successively, as indicated in Figure 2-2, which is an example of the Born-Haber cycle.

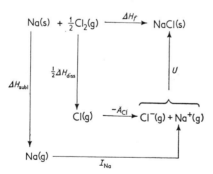

Fig. 2-2.   Born-Haber cycle for NaCl.

The energies are interrelated by the equation

$$\Delta H_f = \Delta H_{\text{subl}} + I + \tfrac{1}{2}\Delta H_{\text{diss}} - A_{\text{Cl}} + U \tag{2-8}$$

The Born-Haber cycle is used to calculate any one of the quantities in equation 2-8 when all of the others are known or to provide a check on the internal consistency of a complete set of these quantities. Normally, ΔH_f, ΔH_{subl}, I, and ΔH_{diss} are known. Direct measurement of electron affinities is usually rather difficult, and only for the halogens have really accurate values been obtained. In these cases the cycle can then be used as a check on the calculated lattice energies, which, when all refinements are included, are found to be quite accurate. For example, the calculated lattice energy of NaCl is 7.94 e.v., and the value obtained from the Born-Haber cycle is 7.86 e.v., a difference of $\sim 1\%$. Since we have such checks to give us confidence in the accuracy of computed lattice energies, the cycle is more commonly used to determine electron affinities. For example, the electron affinity of oxygen is a very important quantity which cannot be measured directly, if for no other reason than that it is highly negative, namely, -7.3 e.v. This value has been obtained by applying the Born-Haber cycle to various ionic oxides.

The Born-Haber cycle is also valuable as a means of analyzing and correlating the variations in stability of various ionic compounds and will be so used at various places in the text. As an example, it enables us to explain why MgO is a stable ionic compound despite the fact that the Mg^{2+} and O^{2-} ions are both formed endothermically, not to mention the considerable energies required to vaporize Mg(s) and to dissociate $O_2(g)$. ΔH_f is highly negative despite these opposing tendencies because the lattice energy of MgO more than balances them out.

2-4. Ionic Radii

It is already apparent from the nature of the wave functions for atoms and ions that they have no definite size. The only way we can assign a radius to an atom or ion is to measure in one way or another how close two atoms or ions can approach one another under the influence of forces of the magnitude encountered in chemical processes. For the ions in a crystal we can do this by considering the distance between the centers of two adjacent ions to be the sum of their ionic radii. Two questions then arise:

1. Are the radii, so defined, truly constant?

2. How do we apportion a given internuclear distance between the radii of the two ions?

The answer to the first question is that the radii are not exactly constant, but nearly enough so as to be useful. For example:

$$r_{K^+} - r_{Na^+} = a_{KF} - a_{NaF} = 0.35 \text{ A.}$$
$$r_{K^+} - r_{Na^+} = a_{KCl} - a_{NaCl} = 0.33 \text{ A.}$$
$$r_{K^+} - r_{Na^+} = a_{KBr} - a_{NaBr} = 0.32 \text{ A.}$$
$$r_{K^+} - r_{Na^+} = a_{KI} - a_{NaI} = 0.30 \text{ A.}$$

where a_{KF} is the K^+—F^- distance in KF, etc. We assume that if $r_{K^+} - r_{Na^+}$ is substantially constant, then r_{K^+} and r_{Na^+} are individually reasonably constant. From X-ray measurements of the interionic distances in a large number of ionic solids, extensive tables of the average sums and differences of ionic radii can be compiled. A table of individual ionic radii can then be prepared if the radius of one or perhaps several of the ions can be determined independently. Goldschmidt and Pauling have independently made such estimates by somewhat different methods. The ionic radii for a number of important ions, obtained by the two procedures, are given in Table 2-3. In general, those obtained by the methods of Goldschmidt are

TABLE 2-3

Goldschmidt (G) and Pauling (P) Ionic Radii
(In Angstroms)

Ion	G	P[a]	Ion	G	P[a]
H^-	1.54	2.08	Pb^{2+}	1.17	1.21
F^-	1.33	1.36			
Cl^-	1.81	1.81	Mn^{2+}	0.80	0.80
Br^-	1.96	1.95	Fe^{2+}	0.76	0.75
I^-	2.19	2.16	Co^{2+}	0.70	0.72
			Ni^{2+}	0.68	0.69
O^{2-}	1.45	1.40	Cu^{2+}	0.92	—
S^{2-}	1.90	1.84			
Se^{2-}	2.02	1.98	B^{3+}	0.2	0.20
Te^{2-}	2.22	2.21	Al^{3+}	0.45	0.50
			Sc^{3+}	0.68	0.81
Li^+	0.68	0.60	Y^{3+}	0.90	0.93
Na^+	0.98	0.95	La^{3+}	1.04	1.15
K^+	1.33	1.33	Ca^{3+}	0.60	0.62
Rb^+	1.48	1.48	In^{3+}	0.81	0.81
Cs^+	1.67	1.69	Tl^{3+}	0.91	0.95
Cu^+	0.95	0.96			
Ag^+	1.13	1.26	Fe^{3+}	0.53	—
Au^+	—	1.37	Cr^{3+}	0.55	—
Tl^+	1.51	1.44			
			C^{4+}	0.15	0.15
Be^{2+}	0.30	0.31	Si^{4+}	0.38	0.41
Mg^{2+}	0.65	0.65	Ti^{4+}	0.60	0.68
Ca^{2+}	0.94	0.99	Zr^{4+}	0.77	0.80
Sr^{2+}	1.10	1.13	Ce^{4+}	0.87	1.01
Ba^{2+}	1.29	1.35	Ge^{4+}	0.54	0.53
Zn^{2+}	0.69	0.74	Sn^{4+}	0.71	0.71
Cd^{2+}	0.92	0.97	Pb^{4+}	0.81	0.84
Hg^{2+}	0.93	1.10			

[a] These radii are obtained using the *rock salt type of structure* as standard (i.e., six coordination); for other structures with different values of the Madelung constant, A, and the Born coefficient, B, small corrections can be made.

more purely empirical. The differences are not large except in a few cases. The large disagreement for H^- is discussed in Chapter 5 (page 116). It must be emphasized that although radii can be *estimated*, some of the ions, for example, C^{4+} or Au^+, are strictly hypothetical.

2-5. Ionic Crystal Lattices

Most ionic compounds of the type M^+X^- occur with one of three structures: the *sodium chloride* (see Fig. 2-1), the *cesium chloride* (Fig. 2-3a), or the *zinc blende* (ZnS) (Fig. 2-3b) structure. In an ionic lattice

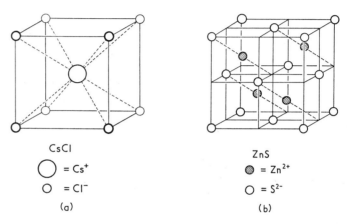

CsCl

◯ = Cs^+

○ = Cl^-

(a)

ZnS

⊘ = Zn^{2+}

○ = S^{2-}

(b)

Fig. 2-3. The cesium chloride and zinc blende structures.

each ion is surrounded by a certain number of ions of the opposite sign; this number is called the *coordination number* of the ion. In the three structures mentioned the cations have the coordination numbers 6, 8, and 4, respectively. The question now arises as to why a particular compound crystallizes with one or another of these structures.

To answer this question, we first recognize that, ignoring the possibility of metastability, which seldom arises, the compound will choose the arrangement providing the greatest stability, that is, the lowest energy. The factors which contribute to the energy are the attractive force between oppositely charged ions, which will increase with increasing coordination number, and the forces of repulsion, which will increase very rapidly if ions of the same charge are "squeezed" together. Thus the optimum arrangement in any crystal should be the one allowing the greatest number of oppositely charged ions to "touch" without requiring any squeezing together of ions with the same charge. The ability of a given compound to meet these requirements will depend on the relative sizes of the ions.

Again using the hard sphere model as a first approximation, let us analyze the situation for the CsCl structure. Let us place eight negative ions of radius r^- around a positive ion with radius r^+ so that the M^+—X^- distance is $r^+ + r^-$ and the adjacent X^- ions are just touching. Then the shortest X^- to X^- distance, a, is given by

$$a = \frac{2}{\sqrt{3}}(r^+ + r^-) = 2r^-$$

or
$$\frac{r^-}{r^+} = 1.37$$

Now, if the ratio r^-/r^+ is greater than 1.37, the only way we can have all eight X^- ions touching the M^+ ion is to squeeze the X^- ions together. Alternatively, if $r^-/r^+ > 1.37$, and we do not squeeze the X^- ions, then they cannot touch the M^+ ion, and a certain amount of electrostatic stabilization energy will be unattainable. Thus when r^-/r^+ becomes equal to 1.37 the competition between attractive and repulsive coulomb forces is balanced, and any increase in the ratio may make the CsCl structure unfavorable relative to a structure with a lower coordination number, such as, the NaCl structure.

In the NaCl structure, in order to have all ions just touching but not squeezed, with radius r^- for X^- and r^+ for M^+ we have

$$2r^- = \sqrt{2}(r^+ + r^-)$$

which gives for the critical radius ratio

$$r^-/r^+ = 2.44$$

If the ratio r^-/r^+ exceeds 2.44, then the NaCl structure becomes disfavored, and the zinc blende structure, for which the critical value of r^-/r^+ is 4.55, may become more favorable. To summarize, packing considerations, in the hard-sphere approximation, would lead us to expect the various structures to have the following ranges of stability in terms of the r^-/r^+ ratio:

CsCl structure:	$1 < r^-/r^+ < 1.37$
NaCl structure:	$1.37 < r^-/r^+ < 2.44$
ZnS structure:	$2.44 < r^-/r^+ < 4.55$

Obviously, similar reasoning may be applied to other structures and other types of ionic compounds. In view of the fact that the hard sphere model is a rather crude approximation, we must not expect these calculations to be more than a rough guide. We can certainly expect that in compounds where $r^- \sim r^+$ the CsCl structure will be found, whereas when $r^- \gg r^+$ the zinc blende structure is expected. Table 2-4 gives some representative data.

TABLE 2-4

Structures and Radius Ratios for Some Ionic Salts

CsCl structure		NaCl structure		Zinc blende structure	
Salt	r^-/r^+	Salt	r^-/r^+	Salt	r^-/r^+
CsCl	1.1	NaCl	1.9	ZnS	2.1
CsBr	1.2	NaI	2.3	ZnSe	2.3
CsI	1.3	KCl	1.4	CuCl	1.9
TlCl	1.2	RbI	1.5	CuBr	2.0
TlBr	1.3	RbF	0.92	CuI	2.3
TlI	1.5			BeS	5.1
				BeSe	5.6

The three structures we have mentioned for compounds of the M^+X^- type are not, of course, the only ones, but they are probably the most common. Ionic compounds with different stoichiometries crystallize in other types of lattice. Many of these will be mentioned at appropriate places in the text, but we shall also describe here two structures which are quite common for compounds of the type $M^{2+}X_2^-$ or $M_2^+X^{2-}$. One of these is the structure of the mineral fluorite, CaF_2, shown in Figure 2-4. When a compound of the type $M^{2+}X_2^-$ crystallizes in this same way, it is said to

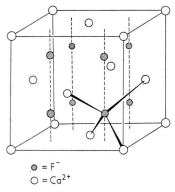

$\odot$ = F$^-$
$\bigcirc$ = Ca^{2+}

Fig. 2-4. The calcium fluoride (fluorite) structure.

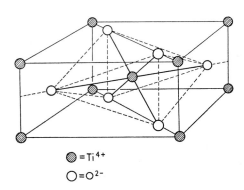

$\oslash$ = Ti^{4+}
$\bigcirc$ = O^{2-}

Fig. 2-5. The rutile structure.

have the *fluorite structure*; when a compound of the type $M_2^+X^{2-}$ crystallizes in the analogous way, with X^{2-} ions at the Ca^{2+} positions and M^+ ions at the F^- positions, it is said to have the *antifluorite structure*. The second structure frequently found for 1:2 compounds is the structure of the mineral rutile, TiO_2, and called the *rutile structure*, shown in Figure 2-5. Some $M_2^+X^{2-}$ also crystallize in an antirutile structure.

In the fluorite structure the cations form a face-centered cube, and there are eight anions occupying the eight tetrahedral interstices in this cube. Note that each cation is surrounded by eight such interstices and therefore attains a coordination number of 8. In the rutile structure the unit cell is not cubic, and the cations have a coordination number of 6. Thus, roughly speaking, packing considerations favor the fluorite structure when the radius ratio r^-/r^+ is less than ~ 1.37, and the rutile structure when it is greater than ~ 1.37.

2-6. Other Electrostatic Interactions

In addition to the electrostatic interactions already discussed, which we may call ion–ion interactions, there are several other kinds, all much weaker but nevertheless often of great importance. These are ion–dipole, dipole–dipole, ion–induced dipole, dipole–induced dipole, and finally, induced dipole–induced dipole interactions. The hydrogen bond, which owes most if not all of its strength to electrostatic forces, is of immense importance, and it will be discussed at length in Chapter 5. It may be thought of as a combination of several of the above types of interactions, principally dipole–induced dipole, ion-induced dipole, and ion–dipole, depending on circumstances.

The induced dipole–induced dipole interaction is the well-known van der Waals attraction (an indication of its magnitude relative to the magnitudes of ion–ion forces is given in Table 2-2). Van der Waals forces will be mentioned in other connections throughout the text, particularly to explain the liquefaction and solidification of the inert gases, for which, owing to their spherical, closed-shell electron distributions, no other forces of attraction are possible. The energies of attraction due to van der Waals forces seldom exceed a few kcal./mole. It should also be noted that they are always present, irrespective of and more or less independent of any other forces; they are inherent in the nature of matter. They are proportional to the polarizabilities and inversely proportional to the ionization potentials of the molecules, atoms, or ions concerned, and they are short range, being proportional to about the sixth power of the distance.

Ion dipole and ion–induced dipole interactions play an important role in solution chemistry, accounting for all or part of the solvation energies of electrolytes in solvents of varying polarities. For example, the interaction of an ion such as the sodium ion with the (presumably six) water molecules surrounding it in aqueous solution is at least partly and very likely largely an electrostatic attraction between the positive sodium ion and the dipole of the water molecule, oriented as shown in Figure 2-6. The dipole of the

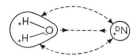

Fig. 2-6. The combined ion–dipole and ion–induced dipole attraction of sodium ion for water molecules in aqueous solution.

water molecule here will be larger than that of the free water molecule because the positive charge on the sodium ion will cause additional polarization. Thus we have a superposition of ion–dipole and ion–induced dipole attractions. In the case of a species containing an ion and a neutral molecule lacking a dipole (e.g., the silver benzene complex, $AgC_6H_6^+$), the force of attraction may be considered as at least partially due to an ion–induced dipole attraction. There is, however, no rigorous way to distinguish between this and a genuine covalence resulting from overlap of orbitals; indeed, the two are to a certain extent merely different ways of looking at the same thing.

Dipole–dipole and dipole–induced dipole interactions are of very common occurrence, for practically all molecules either are polar in their entirety or contain polar bonds. Forces of this kind are probably of major importance in supplying the lattice energy of molecular compounds.

References

Dunitz, J. D., and L. E. Orgel, in H. J. Emeléus and A. G. Sharpe, eds., *Advances in Inorganic Chemistry and Radiochemistry*, Vol. 2, Academic Press, New York, 1960, p. 1. Although concerned mainly with stereochemistry of transition metal with compounds, much useful data and discussion are included and many references given.

Ketelaar, J. A. A., *Chemical Constitution*, Elsevier, New York, 1958.

Pauling, L., *Nature of the Chemical Bond*, 3rd ed., Cornell University Press, Ithaca, N. Y., 1960.

Rice, O. K., *Electronic Structures and Chemical Binding*, McGraw-Hill, New York, 1940. This useful book is concerned only with inorganic compounds and has a good section on ionic compounds.

Stern, K. H., and E. S. Amis, *Chem. Rev.*, **59,** 1 (1959). A comprehensive review of ionic size in crystals and in solution.

van Arkel, A. E., *Molecules and Crystals in Inorganic Chemistry*, 2nd ed., Interscience, New York, 1957. A small, general, readable book on bonding with good sections on ionic compounds.

Waddington, T. C., in H. J. Emeléus and A. G. Sharpe, eds., *Advances in Inorganic Chemistry and Radiochemistry*, Vol. 1, Academic Press, New York, 1959, p. 157. A thorough treatment of the Born-Haber cycle, lattice energies and their significance in inorganic chemistry, with copious data and information.

3

The Nature of Chemical Bonding

THE VALENCE BOND (VB) THEORY OF BONDING

3-1. Introduction; Lewis' Electron Pair Bond

In this chapter we shall make a general survey of the types of forces which hold atoms together in chemical compounds. We have already considered the very simple case of crystalline ionic compounds where, typically, a metal atom having a few loosely bound outer electrons will lose them completely, one or more nonmetallic atoms having configurations just short of an inert gas configuration will accept these electrons, and the ions so formed will fall together into an ionic lattice. In such a case there are no chemical bonds in the usual sense of the word.

Normally, we use the word bond to describe the linkage between a particular pair of atoms as, for example, the H and Cl atoms in HCl or the N and one of the H atoms in NH_3. The student is probably familiar with the Lewis electron dot symbols for atoms and molecules whereby we would represent the HCl and NH_3 molecules by 3-I and 3-II. The basic idea of

$$H : \overset{..}{\underset{..}{Cl}} : \qquad \overset{\textstyle H}{\underset{\textstyle H}{: \overset{..}{N} : H}}$$

$$(3\text{-}I) \qquad\qquad (3\text{-}II)$$

the Lewis theory is that chemical bonds are due to the sharing of one or more pairs of electrons between two atoms. Thus the bond in HCl results from the sharing of one hydrogen electron and one chlorine electron (eq. 3-1).

$$H^{\textstyle \cdot} + . \overset{..}{\underset{..}{Cl}} : \ \rightarrow \ H : \overset{..}{\underset{..}{Cl}} : \qquad\qquad (3\text{-}1)$$

In other cases, though much less commonly, two or three pairs may be shared (eq. 3-2).

$$: \overset{..}{N} \cdot + \cdot \overset{.}{N} : \rightarrow : N : : : N : \qquad (3\text{-}2)$$

Furthermore, it is not necessary that the electrons constituting the bond be contributed equally by the two atoms. For example, there is the *coordinate bond*, illustrated by equation 3-3.

$$
\overset{\displaystyle F}{\underset{\displaystyle F}{F : \overset{..}{\underset{..}{B}}}} + : O \overset{\displaystyle C_2H_5}{\underset{\displaystyle C_2H_5}{\Big\langle}} \quad \rightarrow \quad \overset{\displaystyle F}{\underset{\displaystyle F}{F : \overset{..}{\underset{..}{B}}}} : O \overset{\displaystyle C_2H_5}{\underset{\displaystyle C_2H_5}{\Big\langle}} \qquad (3\text{-}3)
$$

All of these various bonds, whether single or multiple, are called *covalent bonds*. However, it is possible even in this simple approach to recognize the difference between nonpolar covalent bonding and polar covalent bonding. In a homonuclear diatomic molecule, the shared electron pair or pairs must be equally shared and hence there is no polarity in the system nucleus–electrons–nucleus. In a heteronuclear diatomic molecule, however, one of the atoms will, in general, have a greater affinity for the electrons than the other, and the bond will therefore be polar as in 3-III. The

$$\overset{\delta+}{H} \quad \overset{\overset{\delta-}{..}}{: \overset{..}{Cl} :}$$

(3-III)

intrinsic polarity of the bond should not be confused with the polarity that the molecule as a whole may have for other reasons which are discussed in Section 4-4.

These simple ideas were formulated before the advent of wave mechanics. It has been found that quantum theory not only justifies their use but enables us to refine and extend them. The great difficulty with applying wave mechanics to chemical problems is that the equations are far too complicated to be solved in an analytical and exact way. Therefore, the main function of molecular quantum mechanics has been to find approximate solutions to the equations and from these approximate solutions to gain an understanding of the factors which come into play and their relative importance, without attempting quantitative computations.

3-2. The Electron Pair Bond According to Quantum Mechanics

If we have two atoms—for simplicity, two hydrogen atoms—infinitely far apart, the wave function of this system is

$$\psi = \psi_A \psi_B \qquad (3\text{-}4)$$

where ψ_A is the wave function for the first hydrogen atom, ψ_B is the wave function for the second hydrogen atom, and ψ is the joint wave function for the system. Equation 3-4 implies that neither atom disturbs the other, which is, of course, to be expected if they are far apart. We can also see that the total energy of the system ought to be

$$E^0 = E_A + E_B = 2E_H \qquad (3\text{-}5)$$

This result can easily be shown to follow by putting equation 3-4 into the wave equation.

$$\mathcal{3C}\psi = E\psi$$
$$\mathcal{3C}(\psi_A\psi_B) = \psi_A\mathcal{3C}\psi_B + \psi_B\mathcal{3C}\psi_A$$
$$= \psi_A E_B\psi_B + \psi_B E_A\psi_A$$
$$= (E_A + E_B)(\psi_A\psi_B) = E^0\psi \qquad (3\text{-}6)$$

What we have done so far is completely rigorous but also rather useless since we are interested in calculating the energy of the system when the two hydrogen atoms approach one another closely and form a bond. The energy of the system is then E', which is less than E^0 by an amount we call the *bond energy*. However, our first attempt to calculate the bond energy makes use of the above considerations regarding the wave function.

We begin by assuming that the wave function in equation 3-4 remains a reasonably good approximation, even when the atoms approach one another closely. We shall rewrite it in the following more explicit form:

$$\psi_1 = \psi_A(1)\psi_B(2) \qquad (3.7)$$

where we have specifically assigned electron 1 to atom A and electron 2 to atom B. Now in order to calculate the energy of the molecule we must solve the wave equation for small values of the internuclear distance. To do so we first rearrange it in the following way:

$$\mathcal{3C}\psi = E\psi$$
$$\psi^*\mathcal{3C}\psi = \psi^* E\psi = E\psi^*\psi$$
$$\int \psi^*\mathcal{3C}\psi \, d\tau = E \int \psi^*\psi \, d\tau$$

or
$$E = \frac{\int \psi^*\mathcal{3C}\psi \, d\tau}{\int \psi^*\psi \, d\tau} \qquad (3\text{-}8)$$

Note that in these arrangements we have written $\psi^* E\psi = E\psi^*\psi$ because E is simply a numerical factor, whereas $\psi^*\mathcal{3C}\psi$ cannot be so rearranged because $\mathcal{3C}$ is not simply a number but a symbol for an operation to be performed on whatever function follows it.

At close distances our Hamiltonian contains terms involving the reciprocals of the distance of electron 1 from nucleus B, the distance of electron 2 from nucleus A, and r_{12}, the distance between the two electrons. Now when the atoms are far apart these reciprocal distances are so small that these terms are negligible, but as the atoms move together they become progressively more important. Thus the numerator on the right hand side of equation 3-8 is a function of the internuclear distance, r. If we compute the energy as a function of the internuclear distance, which can be done by laboriously solving equation 3-8, we obtain the results shown in curve a of Figure 3-1. Thus we find that the energy of the system does decrease

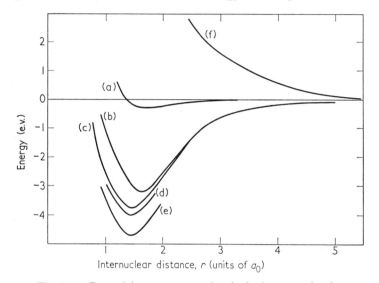

Fig. 3-1.   Potential energy curves for the hydrogen molecule.

(by $\sim 1/4$ e.v. at the minimum) as the atoms approach, giving a minimum at $r = 1.7 a_0$. Curve e is the actual potential energy function for H_2, and it can be seen that our calculated results are qualitatively right but quantitatively rather disappointing.

We can make a dramatic improvement in our results by correcting an error in our wave function. Equation 3-7 states that we know that electron 1 is associated with atom A and electron 2 is associated with atom B. But in fact we do not and cannot know this. The electrons are not labeled so we cannot tell them apart to begin with, and, more important, we cannot attempt to follow any one electron in a system containing several. This is because wave mechanics does not tell us where any particular electron is but only the probability of finding an electron at a given place. Thus we are no more entitled to use ψ_1 as an approximate wave function than to use ψ_2.

$$\psi_2 = \psi_A(2)\psi_B(1) \tag{3-9}$$

Thus if either one is equally likely to be right, we use both, namely,

$$\psi_{cov} = (\psi_1 + \psi_2) \tag{3-10}$$

If now we solve for the energy as a function of r using equation 3-10 we obtain curve b of Figure 3-1, which is obviously a vast improvement and indicates that provided we allow for the indistinguishability of electrons, the basic approach we have taken is not unrealistic.

Further improvement in the results can be made by modifying ψ_{cov} in accord with the dictates of physical intuition. ψ_{cov} is only a combination of the hydrogenic wave functions. Although we are correct in assuming that one electron does not affect the other one at large distances, we may well expect that when they are close together the forms of ψ_A and ψ_B will differ at least quantitatively from that of the unperturbed hydrogen orbital. Just as in a multielectron atom we use hydrogenic wave functions, but recognize that the electrons mutually shield one another to varying degrees from the nuclear charge, so we can allow for the existence of shielding in the H_2 molecule. We can do this again by using a number, Z^*, rather than $Z = 1$ for the effective nuclear charge. When this is done, curve c (Fig. 3-1) is obtained. We now have a binding energy of 3.76 e.v., which is a reasonably good approximation to the experimental value of 4.72 e.v. There is another refinement which can be made fairly straightforwardly, and a consideration of this introduces the concept of *resonance*.

Any wave function of the type 3-10, however we modify the exact forms of ψ_A and ψ_B, still states that we consider only the possibility that one electron is associated with one atom and the other electron is associated with the other atom. But there is, of course, some finite chance that both electrons will occasionally be in the same atomic orbital. Wave functions describing such a state would be $\psi_A(1)\psi_A(2)$ and $\psi_B(1)\psi_B(2)$, and, because ψ_A and ψ_B are identical in form, we have no reason to prefer one over the other. We therefore use both as follows:

$$\psi_{ion} = \psi_A(1)\psi_A(2) + \psi_B(1)\psi_B(2) \tag{3-11}$$

We have called the wave function 3-10 ψ_{cov} because it states that the electrons are shared (in this case shared *exactly equally* because the two atoms are identical); similarly, we call the wave function 3-11 ψ_{ion} since it represents a state to which ionic forms contribute. The way in which we combine equations 3-10 and 3-11 is to write

$$\psi = \psi_{cov} + \lambda\psi_{ion} \tag{3-12}$$

in which λ is a *mixing coefficient*. It tells how much of the ionic wave function is mixed in with the covalent wave function. It is necessary to do a considerable amount of tedious calculation to determine what value of λ gives the best (that is, lowest) value of the energy. It turns out to be $\sim 1/6$, and the new value of the minimum energy is 4.10 e.v. Curve d (Fig. 3-1) shows part of the potential energy function obtained with a wave function of the type 3-12.

The formulation we have described for the bond in H_2 is, in essence, the following. We have selected an orbital on each atom, ψ_A and ψ_B, each containing one electron, and combined the wave functions of these orbitals into a wave function for the two electrons together, namely, $\psi_A(1)\psi_B(2) + \psi_A(2)\psi_B(1)$. This process is called pairing the electrons, and the valence bond (VB) method is sometimes called the method of electron pairs. There is another important feature of the process which we have not as yet mentioned explicitly. The wave function for the bonding electrons can, like a single atomic wave function, be described by a set of quantum numbers. Whatever these quantum numbers may be, it is clear that both electrons in the bond have the same set, since by the nature of equation 3-12 their distributions in space are identical. They must therefore differ in their spins in order to satisfy the exclusion principle. We can in fact state the general rule that only when spin pairing can and does occur does there result an attractive force and hence an electron pair bond. Curve f (Fig. 3-1) shows the potential energy curve when two hydrogen atoms approach in such a way that their spins remain unpaired, that is, with the same quantum number or direction. It is seen that the net force of interaction is strongly repulsive, and this state is called a *repulsive state*.

It is obvious that these principles can be extended to describe many chemical bonds and that they represent a rationalization in terms of wave mechanics of G. N. Lewis' idea of the electron pair bond. Whenever we have two atoms, each with at least one unpaired electron, they may unite to form a bond in which these two electrons are paired. For example, two lithium atoms, each with the configuration $1s^2 2s$, combine to form Li_2 by pairing their $2s$ electrons, and two chlorine atoms, each with the configuration [Ne] $3s^2 3p_x^2 3p_y^2 3p_z$, combine by pairing their odd $3p_z$ electrons.

Multiple bonding may also be treated in this way. For example, two nitrogen atoms, each with the configuration $1s^2 2s^2 2p_x 2p_y 2p_z$, unite and form a triple bond by pairing electrons in corresponding p orbitals. Similarly, we can consider a methylene radical, $H_2C:$, to have two unpaired electrons, so that two of them unite to give ethylene with a double bond. There is one case in which the VB method leads to a qualitatively incorrect prediction concerning multiple bonding, and that is O_2. An oxygen atom has the ground state configuration $1s^2 2s^2 2p_x^2 2p_y 2p_z$, and we should therefore expect two of them to unite forming two electron pair bonds. Actually the O_2 molecule has only a single bond and two unpaired electrons, namely,

$: \overset{..}{O} : \overset{..}{O} :$. This failure is due not to any fundamental error in the VB

method, but to our use of too rough an approximation. However, the molecular orbital (MO) method, even in a very crude approximation, gives the correct result for O_2.

3-3. Resonance

The wave function (eq. 3-12) has an interpretation in terms of simple electron dot pictures. The three *canonical forms*, 3-IVa, b, and c cor-

$$H : H \quad \leftrightarrow \quad H^+ \quad : H^- \quad \leftrightarrow \quad H : ^- \quad H^+$$
$$(3\text{-IVa}) \qquad (3\text{-IVb}) \qquad (3\text{-IVc})$$

respond, respectively, to the wave functions $\psi_A(1)\psi_B(2) + \psi_A(2)\psi_B(1)$, $\psi_A(1)\psi_A(2)$, and $\psi_B(1)\psi_B(2)$. The double-pointed arrows between them indicate that they are in *resonance* with one another, or, to put it another way, that the actual electronic state of the molecule is a *resonance hybrid* of these three structures. This concept of resonance is a useful one provided it is not misinterpreted. H_2 *never has, at any time in its normal ground state life*, any one of the three structures shown. Taken one at a time they are only figments of our imagination, but as shown in the preceding section, we obtain a satisfactory description of the molecule by supposing it to be in a state which is a hybrid of all three in certain proportions.

Before proceeding to consider further examples of resonance, a few remarks about the mathematical justification for the concept should be made. We have already seen that for H_2 when we used the function $\psi_{cov} + \lambda\psi_{ion}$ instead of just ψ_{cov}, we calculated a lower and more nearly correct energy for the system. If we had used ψ_{ion} alone, we would have gotten an extremely high energy. Yet, the *linear combination* of the two gives us an energy which is lower than that for either one separately. The amount by which the energy of the mixed state lies below the energy of the more stable of the two single states is called the *resonance energy*. It would be simpler to see how it comes naturally out of the solution of the wave equation if we take an example in which the two canonical forms are equivalent. We can write for NO_2^-, the nitrite ion, the two canonical forms 3-Va and 3-Vb. Each of these forms can be described by a wave

$$\overset{\displaystyle \cdot\cdot}{N} \qquad \overset{\displaystyle \cdot\cdot}{N}$$

$$\underset{O}{}\diagup \diagdown \underset{O \quad O}{} \overset{\longleftrightarrow}{} \diagup \diagdown \underset{O}{}$$

$$\text{(3-Va)} \qquad \text{(3-Vb)}$$

function, namely, ψ_{Va} and ψ_{Vb}, and each of these wave functions would give the same energy, E^0, if used in the wave equation with the appropriate Hamiltonian, $\mathfrak{IC}$:

$$E^0 = \frac{\int \psi_{Va}{}^{*}\mathfrak{IC}\psi_{Va}\, d\tau}{\int \psi_{Va}{}^{*}\psi_{Va}\, d\tau} = \int \psi_{Va}{}^{*}\mathfrak{IC}\psi_{Va}\, d\tau$$

$$= \int \psi_{Vb}{}^{*}\mathfrak{IC}\psi_{Vb}\, d\tau = \frac{\int \psi_{Vb}{}^{*}\mathfrak{IC}\psi_{Vb}\, d\tau}{\int \psi_{Vb}{}^{*}\psi_{Vb}\, d\tau} \qquad (3\text{-}13)$$

where we have assumed that ψ_{Va} and ψ_{Vb} are each already normalized. If we wish to take account, mathematically, of the resonance depicted above, we must solve the wave equation, using the same Hamiltonian but with a linear combination of ψ_{Va} and ψ_{Vb}. From the symmetry it is obvious that this must be the symmetrical combination $(\psi_{Va} + \psi_{Vb})$ where the two are given equal weights. Let us now see what happens when we solve for the energy, E', using this wave function.

$$E' = \frac{\int (\psi_{Va}{}^{*} + \psi_{Vb}{}^{*})\mathfrak{IC}(\psi_{Va} + \psi_{Vb})\, d\tau}{\int (\psi_{Va}{}^{*} + \psi_{Vb}{}^{*})(\psi_{Va} + \psi_{Vb})\, d\tau}$$

$$= \frac{\int \psi_{Va}{}^{*}\mathfrak{IC}\psi_{Va}\, d\tau + \int \psi_{Va}{}^{*}\mathfrak{IC}\psi_{Vb}\, d\tau + \int \psi_{Vb}{}^{*}\mathfrak{IC}\psi_{Va}\, d\tau + \int \psi_{Vb}{}^{*}\mathfrak{IC}\psi_{Vb}\, d\tau}{\int \psi_{Va}{}^{*}\psi_{Va}\, d\tau + \int \psi_{Va}{}^{*}\psi_{Vb}\, d\tau + \int \psi_{Vb}{}^{*}\psi_{Va}\, d\tau + \int \psi_{Vb}{}^{*}\psi_{Vb}\, d\tau}$$

$$(3\text{-}14)$$

Taking account of the normalization, using the following definitions

$$\int \psi_{Va}{}^{*}\psi_{Vb}\, d\tau = \int \psi_{Vb}{}^{*}\psi_{Va}\, d\tau = S$$

$$\int \psi_{Va}{}^{*}\mathfrak{IC}\psi_{Vb}\, d\tau = \int \psi_{Vb}{}^{*}\mathfrak{IC}\psi_{Va} = E_R$$

and remembering equation 3-13, we can rewrite equation 3-14 as

$$E' = \frac{E^0 + E_R}{1 + S} \approx E^0 + E_R \qquad (3\text{-}15)$$

since S, called the overlap integral, is usually small compared to 1. Thus we see that E' is lower than E^0 by E_R, the resonance energy.*

* It is *lower* because all three are intrinsically negative.

The equality of the two integrals called E_R is only true so long as ψ_{Va} and ψ_{Vb} are wave functions giving the same energy. Moreover, the value of such an integral diminishes rapidly the greater the difference in the energies given by ψ_{Va} and ψ_{Vb} separately in case the two wave functions are not equivalent. Thus stabilization of a molecule by resonance is greatest when the canonical forms contributing to the hybrid are close in energy, and best of all, identical. We might, for example, have taken the trouble to make our calculations using a wave function $(\psi_{Va} + \psi_{Vb} + \lambda\psi_{Vc})$ where ψ_{Vc} describes structure 3-Vc. For various reasons (for example, the

$$\ddot{N}$$
$$\overset{\cdot\cdot}{O}\!\!-\!\!-\!\!-\!\!\overset{\cdot\cdot}{O}$$

(3-Vc)

O—O distance is too great to permit the formation of a strong O—O bond, whereas we are at the same time giving up a rather strong N—O bond), 3-Vc would have a far higher energy than 3-Va or 3-Vb, and this calculation using $(\psi_{Va} + \psi_{Vb} + \psi_{Vc})$ will not give us a significantly lower energy than we can obtain using just $(\psi_{Va} + \psi_{Vb})$.

The hydrogen molecule has provided an example of *covalent-ionic resonance* in a particular bond. Because structures 3-IVb and 3-IVc are of importance in an accurate description of the bond from the VB point of view, we say that the bond has some ionic character. However, the polarity which 3-Vb introduces is exactly balanced by the polarity which 3-Vc introduces so that the bond has no net polarity. It is therefore called a *nonpolar covalent* bond. It is important not to confuse polarity and ionic character, although, unfortunately, the literature contains many instances of such confusion. When we turn to a heteronuclear diatomic molecule, we necessarily have bonds which have both ionic and polar character. Even for the pure covalent canonical structure of HCl (3-I) there is bond polarity

$$H : \overset{\cdot\cdot}{\underset{\cdot\cdot}{Cl}} : \quad \leftrightarrow \quad \overset{+}{H} \;\; : \overset{\cdot\cdot}{\underset{\cdot\cdot}{Cl}} : \quad \leftrightarrow \quad \overset{-}{H} : \quad \overset{\cdot\cdot}{\underset{\cdot\cdot}{Cl}} : \overset{+}{}$$

(3-Ia)   (3-Ib)   (3-Ic)

because the two different atoms necessarily have different affinities for the electron pair. It is thus shared but not equally shared. It is also to be expected that the ionic structures 3-Ib and 3-Ic make some contribution. Owing to the facts that (*a*) hydrogen and chlorine have about equal first ionization potentials, but (*b*) chlorine has a far higher electron affinity than hydrogen, 3-Ic is much less energetically favorable and hence contributes much less to the resonance hybrid than 3-Ib. Since the whole scheme we are using here is essentially qualitative, we normally ignore 3-Ic and consider the ionic-covalent resonance in HCl to be adequately described by 3-Ia ↔ 3-Ib.

Two other examples of the resonance description may be cited to round out the discussion. There is the classic case of benzene (3-VI) for which at least five canonical structures are of some importance. 3-VIa and 3-VIb

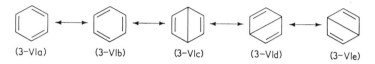

(3-VIa)   (3-VIb)   (3-VIc)   (3-VId)   (3-VIe)

are the well-known Kekulé structures and contribute most to the hybrid, while 3-VIc, d, and e are the Dewar structures, which are much less important. An estimate of the resonance stabilization energy can be made in the following way. From empirical knowledge of the average energies of C=C, C—C, and C—H bonds, the energy of the most stable canonical form, 3-VIa (or 3-VIb), can be estimated. Thermochemical studies show that the actual energy of benzene is some 35–40 kcal./mole lower. Actually, a correction to the resonance energy so computed should be made if we recall that the benzene molecule is a regular hexagon, and hence the hypothetical structures 3-VIa and 3-VIb should be also. When we estimate the energy for 3-VIa or 3-VIb using empirical bond energies, we get a result which applies to a molecule in which the double bonds are ~1.35 A. and the single bonds are ~1.54 A. Thus in order to estimate the energy of a structure such as 3-VIa or 3-VIb with equal bond lengths, we must raise the energy previously estimated by the amount of energy necessary to stretch and contract the various bonds, thus increasing our estimate of the resonance energy.

The CO molecule can be considered as a resonance hybrid of the following canonical structures:

$$:C::\overset{\cdot\cdot}{O}: \quad \leftrightarrow \quad :\overset{+}{C}:\overset{\overset{-}{\cdot\cdot}}{O}: \quad \leftrightarrow \quad :\overset{-}{C}:::\overset{+}{O}: $$

(3-VIIa)   (3-VIIb)   (3-VIIc)

Pauling has estimated that all three are of comparable importance, which is in accord with the low (0.1 D.) dipole moment of the molecule, although the very short bond distance (1.13 A.) would suggest that 3-VIIc is predominant. The low dipole moment can be perhaps explained on the basis of smaller contributions from 3-VIIa and 3-VIIb if polarity due to lone pair moments (see Chapter 4) is taken into account.

One final comment should be made here concerning the error of attributing any physical reality to a particular canonical form. The two or more wave functions we combine to make the total wave function must represent only differences in the distribution of electrons about a *fixed and constant* nuclear framework. Now, if such a molecule as is represented by 3-Va or 3-Vb for NO_2^- really existed, we should expect that the N=O distance would be appreciably shorter than the N—O distance. Thus 3-Vb could not be obtained from 3-Va simply by redistributing electrons. We should also have to shift the nuclear framework, and it is just that which is foreign to the whole concept of resonance. Thus the structures 3-Va and 3-Vb cannot represent real molecules, but only hypothetical ones. In our subsequent discussion of molecular orbital theory we shall develop an alternative, and perhaps to some tastes more realistic, method of getting the same results.

3-4. Promotion Energies and Valence States

The ground state of the carbon atom is $1s^2 2s^2 2p_x 2p_y$, and it thus has only two unpaired electrons. It would therefore seem to follow that its most stable compounds with atoms, X, having a single unpaired electron—H, F, Cl, etc.—would be of the type CX_2. This, of course, is contrary to fact, its most stable compounds with such atoms being of the type CX_4, for example, CH_4 and CCl_4. In order to explain these facts, we must assume that the electronic configuration of carbon is altered so as to give it four unpaired electrons before it combines with four X's. The lowest configuration we can write for such a four-spin state is $1s^2 2s 2p_x 2p_y 2p_z$, and it lies some 97 kcal. above the $1s^2 2s^2 2p^2$ state. In order to understand why the carbon atom makes this initial sacrifice in stability, consider the energy level diagram for methane (Fig. 3-2).

The enthalpy of formation of $CH_4(g)$ from $C(s)$ and $2H_2(g)$ is -18 kcal./mole. The various steps into which we analyze this over-all process are shown on the right side of the figure. First, four hydrogen atoms, each with an unpaired electron, must be formed from $2H_2$. Next, the graphite must be vaporized to carbon atoms in their ground states, which requires the input of energy, L. The gaseous carbon atoms must now be promoted to the state sp^3 (abbreviation for $1s^2 2s 2p_x 2p_y 2p_z$), which requires $E_1 = 97$ kcal., as mentioned already. The carbon atom in this state is not actually ready to form bonds yet, however; it must still be promoted to its tetravalent valence state, denoted V_4. (We shall discuss the reason for this in detail later when we take up the subject of hybridization.) It then forms four bonds to the hydrogen atoms releasing four times the mean C—H

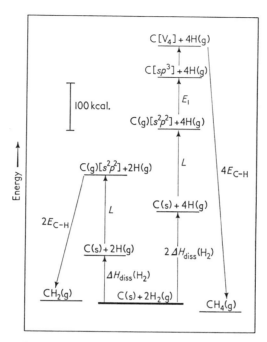

Fig. 3-2. Diagram showing various promotion energies in the formation of CH_4 and CH_2.

bond energy. Despite all of the various energies required to promote $C(s)$ to $C[V_4]$, ~560 kcal., the net energy is favorable since four strong bonds are formed. Now let us consider the formation of the hypothetical CH_2. To do this, one H_2 must be dissociated into $2H$ and the carbon must be vaporized only to ground state atoms, C $(1s^2 2s 2p^2)$, so the total promotion energy is only ~275 kcal. However, even if we assume the energy of a C—H bond in CH_2 to be the same as in CH_4 (and there are good reasons to believe it is weaker), we regain only ~289 kcal. or less on forming the bonds. Thus the reaction $C(s) + H_2(g) = CH_2(g)$ is less favorable than $C(s) + 2H_2(g) = CH_4(g)$ despite the much larger promotion energy required in the latter case.

Before leaving this subject a few more words must be said about the valence state. It is not a true stationary state of the atom which can be located, energywise, by experiment. It is really a hypothetical state whose energy can, however, be calculated from sufficient information on true stationary states. It is a useful concept, however, and its use will be given further justification when we discuss hybridization.

3-5. The Overlap Criterion of Bond Strength

The best theoretical criterion we have for the strength of a given electron pair bond is, of course, the energy we calculate to be released when the bond is formed. We have seen, however, that even in the simple, prototype case of H_2 lengthy and tedious calculations are required to obtain even an approximate value for this energy. Obviously a simpler, if less fundamentally correct criterion is desirable, and such a criterion does exist. Pauling and Mulliken have pointed out that there is a qualitative and, under some well-defined conditions, even a semiquantitative relation between bond energies and the overlap of the atomic orbitals used in forming the bonds. It is not difficult to see qualitatively why good overlap makes for strong bonding. The more the two bonding orbitals overlap, the more the bonding electrons are concentrated between the nuclei where they can minimize the nuclear repulsion and maximize the attractive forces between themselves and both nuclei jointly.

The overlap between a pair of atomic orbitals, S, is given by the equation

$$S = \int \psi_A \psi_B \, d\tau \tag{3-16}$$

and S is called the overlap integral. In the case of the H_2 molecule, this integral can be calculated exactly since we know the exact forms of the wave functions, but normally it must be approximated. The simplest approximation is one due to Pauling and commonly called Pauling's bond strength criterion. Let us consider the overlap of a $3s$ orbital on one atom with the $3s$, $3p$, and $3d$ orbitals of another atom. These are illustrated in a diagrammatic way in Figure 3-3, where the overlapping areas are shaded. It can be seen that we are here considering the best overlap obtainable when the orientation of the orbitals is optimum. If the radial wave functions of the $3s$, $3p$, and $3d$ orbitals were exactly the same, then the relative magnitudes would be in proportion to the values of their respective angular wave functions along the bond directions, namely, the proportions $1 : \sqrt{3} : \sqrt{5}$. The radial functions are not identical, but in the outer regions of the wave functions where the greater part of the overlap occurs, they are not actually very different. Thus Pauling proposes that we assign bond-forming powers to s, p, and d orbitals of 1, $\sqrt{3}$, and $\sqrt{5}$ and calculate the relative strength of bonds by taking the product of the bond-forming strengths of the two orbitals involved. Thus we would expect bonds formed using s–s, s–p, and p–p orbitals to have relative strengths of 1, $\sqrt{3}$, and 3, respectively. This is, of course, a very rough rule and must be used with caution, but it does reflect the fact that orbitals more con-

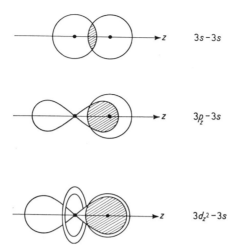

Fig. 3-3. Diagrammatic representation of the overlaps of $3s$, $3p_z$, and $3d_{z^2}$ orbitals with a $3s$ orbital.

centrated along the bond direction overlap better. The main limitation is that it is only applicable when the radial wave functions for orbitals being compared are really similar and it can give results which are not even qualitatively right when the radial dissimilarity is even moderately large.

A better approximation—and indeed the simplest one which is really any good at all when orbitals which differ appreciably in their radial functions are to be compared—is actually to calculate the overlap integrals using some kind of approximate wave functions. Those ordinarily used are the so-called *Slater orbitals* in which the exact hydrogenic angular functions are used together with radial functions of exponential form containing empirically estimated effective nuclear charges.

Our purpose here, however, is not to give a quantitative treatment of overlap but only to emphasize that it is frequently possible to make qualitative guesses about the strengths of bonds by considering qualitatively how well the orbitals involved overlap. There are certain cases in which the *symmetry properties* of the orbitals can determine whether any net overlap at all is possible. It will be recalled (page 19) that the various hydrogen orbitals (on the same atom) have the property of orthogonality, which means simply that the net overlap of any one with another is exactly zero. This was illustrated in Figure 1-8 (page 19) for an s and a p_z orbital. The symmetry of the s orbital, of course, is spherical, but in particular it has exactly the same value at all points (z,x,y) as it has at points $(-z,x,y)$, whereas the value of the p orbital at the point (z,x,y) is equal to but of opposite sign to its value at $(-z,x,y)$. Thus from symmetry considerations alone we can say that any s orbital is orthogonal to any p orbital in the same atom without making any kind of calculation. Similarly, simple symmetry considerations can show that certain pairs of orbitals on two atoms will have no net overlap, and hence that no chemical bond will result from pairing electrons in such orbitals. It should now become obvious to the student why it is important to remember not only the shapes but also the *signs* of the lobes of orbitals.

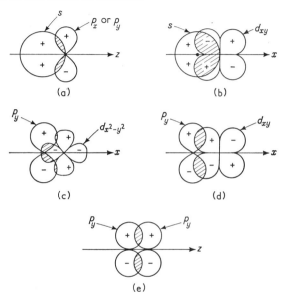

Fig. 3-4. Diagrammatic representation of some overlaps.

Figure 3-4 shows three examples (a, b, and c) in which the net overlap must be zero on symmetry grounds alone and two instances (d and e) in which electron density is not concentrated along the internuclear axis, but where there is some net overlap permitted by symmetry, and hence some bonding interaction can take place between electrons in the two orbitals. Note that in case e the Pauling bond strength criterion would give the bond a strength of zero since the two axes along which the lobes lie are parallel, whereas there is in fact a certain degree of overlap.

3-6. Hybridization

In discussing the promotion energy required to transform the carbon atom from its divalent s^2p^2 ground state to the tetravalent state necessary to form its normal compounds (e.g., CH_4), we mentioned but did not properly explain the energy, E_2 in Figure 3-2, required to promote the atom from the observable, stationary state sp^3, to what we called its valence state, V_4. The sp^3 state referred to is, more specifically, the state $2s2p_x2p_y2p_z$. Now, according to the preceding discussion, if one atom, say A, with an orbital ψ_A containing one electron, is to form the strongest bond with another atom, B, then the A—B axis should be along the direction in which ψ_A has its maximum value. Thus if atom A is to use its p_x orbital, we should expect the A—B axis to be colinear with the x axis. For an s orbital, of course, all directions are equivalent. Thus if the valence state of the carbon atom were really the $2s2p_x2p_y2p_z$ stationary state, we should expect three hydrogen atoms to form bonds to the p_x, p_y, and p_z orbitals, and thus lie along the x, y, and z axes. The fourth hydrogen atom would bond to the s orbital and probably take up a position equidistant from the other three.

This hypothetical state of affairs is depicted in Figure 3-5. It is easily

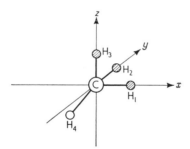

Fig. 3-5. Geometric structure methane would have if the carbon atom used pure hydrogenic orbitals, $2s$, $2p_x$, $2p_y$, and $2p_z$ to form C—H bonds.

seen that the three angles H_1—C—H_2, H_1—C—H_3, and H_2—C—H_3 are 90°, and the three equivalent angles such as H_1—C—H_4 are $\sim$125°. Moreover, since H_1, H_2, and H_3 are bonded to carbon through its p orbitals, all of these bonds should be equivalent and hence of equal length, whereas the C—H_4 bond is formed using a carbon s orbital and would not be expected to have the same length. It is known with complete certainty, however, that methane does not have such a structure. Actually all C—H distances and H—C—H angles are equal, and the molecule is a regular tetrahedron. From this we infer that the valence state of the carbon atom is one in which its four valence electrons are in four equivalent orbitals which have their lobes directed toward the apices of a tetrahedron. It is this valence state which we have denoted as V_4. Our next question, then, is how can we express such a set of equivalent orbitals in terms of the basic set of hydrogenic orbitals $2s$, $2p_x$, $2p_y$, and $2p_z$.

If we are to have four completely equivalent orbitals, they must each have the same fraction of s *character*, namely, one-fourth, and the same fraction of p *character*, namely, three-fourths, and the resulting orbitals must be normalized. We can pick the direction for the first one arbitrarily, so let us put it along the z axis. Neither p_x nor p_y can contribute to this one since they have precisely the value zero along the z axis, so this first one will consist entirely of s and p_z. Its general form must therefore be

$$N(s + kp_z)$$

where k is a mixing coefficient yet to be evaluated, and N is a normalizing factor. k can be shown to be $\sqrt{3}$ since the probability of the electron having p_z character must be three times greater than its having s character, and these probabilities are proportional to the squares of the wave functions, namely,

$$\frac{\int (kp_z)^2 \, d\tau}{\int (s)^2 \, d\tau} = 3$$

and since p_z and s are separately normalized, $k = \sqrt{3}$. The value of N is then easily found by normalizing $(s + \sqrt{3}p_z)$, namely,

$$\int [N(s + \sqrt{3}p_z)]^2 \, d\tau = 1$$
$$N^2 = \left[\int s^2 \, d\tau + 3\int p_z^2 \, d\tau\right]^{-1}$$
$$= [1 + 3]^{-1}$$
$$N = 1/2$$

where we have also made use of the orthogonality of the s and p_z orbitals.

The expressions for the other three orbitals, equivalent to this one and having their lobes lying along directions 109° from the z axis, can be derived by similar reasoning, but trigonometric complications make it impractical to carry out the derivation here. (A complete derivation of all orbitals in a set is given in Appendix C-2 for a simpler case.) This set of four equivalently directed orbitals is one example of a set of *hybrid orbitals*; these four are commonly called sp^3 hybrids to indicate their composition in terms of hydrogenic atomic orbitals. In common—though somewhat loose—parlance it is said that the carbon atom "has sp^3 hybridization."

Before proceeding to further discussion of hybridization, we may complete our explanation of the difference between the valence state V_4 and the sp^3 stationary state. In order to promote the carbon atom from the sp^3 stationary state to the valence state, two things are done: (1) the s and the three p orbitals are hybridized to produce four sp^3 hybrids which are each occupied by one electron, and (2) any preferred orientations of the spins of these electrons due to interactions of their spins with one another or with their orbital motions are destroyed, leaving them completely free, random, and ready to be paired with electron spins of other atoms. Both of these processes require input of energy, the total in this case being ~ 65 kcal./g.-atom. Let us emphasize again that the valence state is in general not identical with any observable stationary state of the atom, and the idea of "promotion to the valence state" is only a mental construction which is useful in thinking about the bonding.

We return now to systematic consideration of hybridization, beginning with the simplest common type, namely, sp hybridization. Beryllium in its ground state has the configuration $1s^2 2s^2$, and without promotion to a higher state could form no electron pair bonds. Normally, it forms compounds such as $BeCl_2$, $BeBr_2$, and $Be(CH_3)_2$, which, as free gaseous molecules, are linear. To explain this we assume that the atom is first promoted to the state $2s2p$ followed by promotion to a valence state involving sp hybridization. The physical reasoning behind the construction of these hybrids can be understood with reference to Figure 3-6; the algebraic

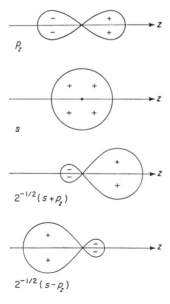

Fig. 3-6. Schematic illustration of the formation of sp digonal hybrid orbitals by combination of an s and a p orbital.

details will be found in Appendix C-1. A wave function—orbital—which is the sum of s and p_z must have the form shown in Figure 3-6 for the orbital designated $2^{-1/2}(s + p_z)$. The factor $2^{-1/2}$ is a normalizing factor. Similarly, it is obvious that a wave function which is the difference of s and p_z will have the form shown in Figure 3-6 for the orbital designated $2^{-1/2}(s - p_z)$. It should not be difficult to see that these two hybrid orbitals are completely equivalent but oppositely directed along the z axis. They are also symmetrical around the z axis.

An atom, X, using a pair of such sp or digonal hybrid orbitals, will form two equivalent bonds to two other atoms or univalent groups, Y, giving a linear YXY molecule. The gaseous halides (though not the solid compounds) of all of the group II elements have linear structures which may be attributed to the sp hybridization of the metal atoms. Of course, a completely ionic molecule $Y^-X^{2+}Y^-$ would tend to be linear for electrostatic reasons, so linearity does not, by itself, demonstrate that the bonds are covalent; in many cases, however, there are various kinds of evidence suggesting appreciable covalent character in the bonds. Mercuric halides and pseudo halides (e.g., $Hg(CN)_2$) are doubtless predominantly covalent. In these linear molecules we postulate that mercury with a configuration $[Xe]5d^{10}6s^2$, uses $6s6p$ hybrid orbitals.

The elements of group III which have ground state configurations ns^2np form many molecules of the type MX_3 where M is B, Al, Ga, In, or Tl, and X is a halogen or an organic radical, CH_3, C_6H_5, etc. In all of these the monomeric molecules (some dimerize; e.g., Al_2Cl_6) are known or presumed to have the shape of a planar equilateral triangle. Thus we assume that the metal atoms, B, for example, must first be excited to the stationary state sp_xp_y and then further promoted to a valence state in which there is

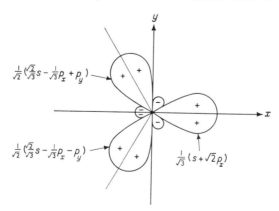

Fig. 3-7. Schematic illustration of sp^2 trigonal hybrid orbitals.

a set of equivalent sp^2 hybrid orbitals. The correct algebraic expressions and schematic "balloon" picture of a set of sp^2 or trigonal hybrids are shown in Figure 3-7. Each one has its maximum along one of a set of three axes, lying in the same plane making angles of 120° with one another. Moreover, the orbitals are equivalent in shape. Each one, if rotated 120°, would be exactly superposed on the orbital already on that axis.

It can be seen from examination of Figures 3-6 and 3-7 that hybrid orbitals provide much greater concentrations of the electron cloud in particular directions than do the simple hydrogenic orbitals of which they are constructed. Thus hybrid orbitals can provide better overlap with orbitals of other atoms along these preferred directions, and they consequently make certain configurations of the molecule preferred. In general, the increased overlap means that the bonds are stronger, and this more than compensates for the promotion energy required to attain the hybridized valence state.

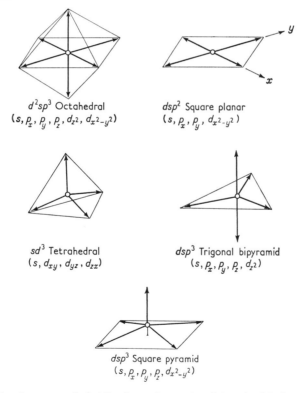

Fig. 3-8. Five important hybridization schemes involving d orbitals. Heavy arrows show the directions in which the lobes point.

Hybridization is not limited to s and p orbitals, but may, in general, involve the mixing of all types of atomic orbitals. Hybrids involving d orbitals occur quite commonly among the heavier elements and are particularly important in complexes of the transition elements. We shall mention five of the most important hybridizations involving one or more d orbitals, each of which is illustrated in Figure 3-8.

1. d^2sp^3, *octahedral hybridization*. When the $d_{x^2-y^2}$ and d_{z^2} orbitals are combined with an s orbital and a set of p_x, p_y, and p_z orbitals, a set of equivalent orbitals with lobes directed to the apices of an octahedron can be formed.

2. dsp^2, *square planar hybridization*. A $d_{x^2-y^2}$ orbital, an s orbital, and p_x and p_y orbitals can be combined to give a set of equivalent hybrid orbitals with lobes directed to the corners of a square in the xy plane.

3. sd^3, *tetrahedral hybridization*. An s orbital and the set d_{xy}, d_{xz}, d_{yz} may be combined to give a tetrahedrally directed set of orbitals.

4. dsp^3, *trigonal bipyramidal hybridization*. The orbitals s, p_x, p_y, p_z, and d_{z^2} may be combined to give a nonequivalent (see below) set of five hybrid orbitals directed to the apices of a trigonal bipyramid.

5. dsp^3, *square pyramidal hybridization*. The orbitals s, p_x, p_y, p_z, and $d_{x^2-y^2}$ may be combined to give a nonequivalent (see below) set of five hybrid orbitals directed to the apices of a square pyramid.

We have now examined some hybridization schemes from the point of view of the kinds of atomic orbitals required to construct them. So long as the required orbitals are available, the existence of a particular set of hybrids is possible from this point of view. However, there are some energy considerations which are also important. If one or more of the orbitals required in the hybridization lie at a much higher energy than the others, it may not be energetically possible for the atom to actually achieve full hybridization. For example, referring again to methane and Figure 3-2, if the promotion energy E_1 were very much higher, say, > 115 kcal./g.-atom, instead of ~ 96 kcal./g.-atom, CH_2 would be more stable than CH_4. As another example, sulfur, though it has six electrons in its valence shell, forms only a few compounds in which six d^2sp^3 hybrid orbitals are used because the energy required to promote the sulfur atom from its $[Ne]3s^23p^4$ ground state to a $[Ne]3s3p^33d^2$ state is too great to be offset by the energy of formation of the six bonds except in a few instances. It is also possible to have a mixture of hybrid states for energetic reasons. The two hybridization schemes giving a set of tetrahedrally directed orbitals, namely, sp^3 and sd^3, are only extremes, and it is possible to have a set of tetrahedral hybrids using one s orbital and portions of each of the two sets $d_{xy}d_{xz}d_{yz}$ and $p_xp_yp_z$. For carbon, the amount of d character is doubtless negligible since the lowest available d orbitals, the $3d$'s, are so far above the $2p$'s that their use could only be a great energetic disadvantage. In the tetrahedral ions MnO_4^-, CrO_4^{2-}, etc., however, the $3d$ orbitals are of about the same energy as the $4s$ orbitals, and the $4p$ orbitals are only slightly higher. The hybridization of the Mn and Cr atoms in these cases is thus probably a mixture of sd^3 and sp^3, and it is virtually impossible to calculate the amount of d and p character.

Sets of hybrid orbitals have been described above as equivalent and nonequivalent. The orbitals in an equivalent set are all identical in every respect except for their direction in space. Their fractions of s, p, d, etc., character are identical. For an atom using sp^3, sd^3, or dsp^2 hybrid orbitals to form bonds to four identical atoms, sp hybrids to bond two identical atoms, sp^2 orbitals to bond three identical atoms, or d^2sp^3 hybrids to bond six identical atoms, all of the orbitals in the set are equivalent. However, in CH_3Cl the four hybrid orbitals used by the carbon atom are not equivalent, for surely the carbon atom will form its best bond to chlorine using a more or less different orbital from the ones it uses to bond the hydrogen atoms. The three orbitals used to bond the hydrogens are equivalent. As evidence of this, it is found that the three H—C—H angles are equal and the three H—C—Cl angles are equal, but the H—C—H angles are not exactly the same as the H—C—Cl angles. All of the angles are, however, very close to the tetrahedral angle, and it is a good approximation to regard the four hybrid orbitals used by carbon as approximately sp^3 hybrids. It should be remembered, however, that in this or any analogous situation all the hybrid orbitals in the set are not *exactly* the same; that is, they are not an equivalent set.

The two dsp^3 sets, giving either trigonal bipyramid or square pyramid arrangements, depending upon the d orbital used, are sets which are intrinsically nonequivalent, even if the five atoms bonded—as in PF_5, for example, which has a trigonal bipyramidal structure—are identical. In the trigonal bipyramid there are two equivalent orbitals called axial orbitals and three equivalent orbitals called equatorial orbitals, but those in different sets are not equivalent. Two p orbitals, p_x and p_y, contribute to the three equatorial hybrid orbitals, whereas only one p orbital, p_z, contributes to the two axial hybrid orbitals, so that an axial orbital could not possibly be identical in composition with an equatorial orbital. Similarly, in the square pyramid, the four basal orbitals form an equivalent set, but no one of these is equivalent to the unique axial orbital.

To conclude this discussion of hybridization, we shall consider the water molecule. The ground state configuration of the oxygen atom is $1s^2 2s^2 2p_x^2 2p_y 2p_z$. Thus no promotion is required in order for oxygen to form electron pair bonds to two hydrogen atoms; it can do so using its $2p_x$ and $2p_y$ electrons. Since, from the overlap criterion, we should expect the hydrogen atoms to approach the oxygen atom in such directions as to give the best $H(1s)$—$O(2p)$ overlaps, we should expect the H—O—H angle in H_2O to be 90°. However, this angle is not 90°; it is about 104°. The first explanation proposed for this was the following. Each O—H bond is somewhat polar so that each hydrogen atom has a partial positive charge. The repulsion between these charges then causes the H—O—H angle to open out. As it does so, of course, the overlaps and hence the O—H bond strengths decrease, and it was to be presumed that at 104° the optimum balance of O—H bond strength and hydrogen–hydrogen repulsion was reached. More recently it has been shown that this very plausible idea cannot be quantitatively correct. There are enough data on the forces required to expand the H—O—H angle so that it can be calculated that the electrostatic repulsion between the hydrogen atoms would open it only to ~97°. Present theoretical ideas indicate that the best explanation of the observed angle is to assume the use of hybrid orbitals by the oxygen atom. In order to see what sort of hybrids these are, let us review some of the s–p hybrid orbitals, which have been developed above. In particular, we are interested in the angle between two orbitals in a set and the fraction of s and p character in each orbital (Table 3-1).

TABLE 3-1

| Hybridization | Character | | Angle, deg. |
	s	p	
sp, digonal	$\frac{1}{2}$	$\frac{1}{2}$	180
sp^2, trigonal	$\frac{1}{3}$	$\frac{2}{3}$	120
sp^3, tetrahedral	$\frac{1}{4}$	$\frac{3}{4}$	109
p^2 (i.e., two pure p orbitals)	0	1	90

It can be seen that as the amount of s character increases, the angle between two orbitals opens out. Thus in the case of H_2O, the bond angle of 104° may be explained by assuming that oxygen forms the two O—H bonds using s–p hybrid orbitals with p character intermediate between 1 and 0.75. Also, if the two orbitals used to bond the hydrogens are hybrids with p character $>3/4$, then the two unshared pairs of electrons must occupy hybrid orbitals with p character $<3/4$.

The purpose of this discussion of H_2O is to emphasize that there is nothing unique about the particular hybridization schemes previously discussed except that they produce highly symmetric arrangements of orbitals. However, hybridization can and does occur in many other cases, and we should, in general, expect it, for it is not likely that pure, unhybridized atomic orbitals will more than occasionally lead to the best compromise between bond strength and promotion energy.

THE MOLECULAR ORBITAL (MO) THEORY OF BONDING

3-7. Introduction

In the preceding section we have discussed the valence bond (VB) or electron pair theory of bonding. The basic qualitative idea in this theory is essentially Lewis' idea that each bonded atom pair in a molecule is held together by an electron pair or perhaps several electron pairs. These electron pairs are *localized* between particular pairs of nuclei. Moreover, it is assumed that the wave functions for these electrons are just the products of atomic wave functions. The MO theory starts with a qualitatively different assumption.

In building up a multielectron atom we started with a nucleus and a set of *one-center orbitals* about that nucleus and fed the required number of electrons into these orbitals in increasing order of orbital energy. We discovered the forms of these orbitals by solving exactly the problem with only one electron and then assumed that when many electrons are present the orbitals have the same form but that their relative energies are affected by the shielding of one electron by another. In other words, we treat each electron as if it moves in the effective field produced by the nucleus and all of the other electrons. In its essentials, the molecular orbital theory treats a molecule in the same way. We start with several nuclei, arranged as they are in the complete molecule. We then determine the various orbitals which *one* electron would have in the field of this set of nuclei. These *multicenter orbitals* are taken as the set to be filled with as many electrons as are required in the molecule under consideration. Again it is understood that the mutual shielding of the electrons and other interactions between them will have an important effect on the relative energies of the various molecular orbitals.

Although this scheme is just as good in principle for molecules as for atoms, it has a severe limitation in practice. As we have seen, we can get our basic set of atomic orbitals readily by exact solution of the wave equation of the hydrogen atom. In general, the problem of an electron moving in the field of several nuclei cannot be solved exactly. Therefore, we must begin by using only an approximate form for our one-electron MO's.

3-8. The Linear Combination of Atomic Orbitals (LCAO) Method

The LCAO method is a simple and qualitatively useful approximation. It is based on the very reasonable idea that as the electron moves around in the nuclear framework it will at any given time be close to one nucleus and relatively far from others, and that when near a given nucleus it will behave more or less as though it were in an atomic orbital belonging to that nucleus. To develop this idea more concretely we shall use the hydrogen molecule ion H_2^+. This is a prototype for homonuclear diatomic molecules just as the hydrogen atom is for atoms in general.

If the electron belonged to either of the hydrogen nuclei A or B alone, its behavior in the ground state would be described by ϕ_A or ϕ_B alone. When it is in some general position with reference to the nuclear framework it can be approximately described by a superposition of both, that is, by $\phi_A \pm \phi_B$. Such an algebraic sum of functions is called a linear combination. If we assume that ϕ_A and ϕ_B are orthogonal to one another, the two normalized LCAO wave functions are

$$\psi_b = 2^{-1/2}(\phi_A + \phi_B)$$
$$\psi_a = 2^{-1/2}(\phi_A - \phi_B)$$

In order to appreciate the meaning of these two LCAO-MO's, let us first

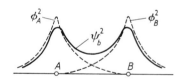

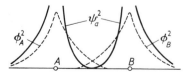

Fig. 3-9.   Plots of the atomic orbitals, ϕ_A^2 and ϕ_B^2, and of the bonding ψ_b^2 and antibonding ψ_a^2 LCAO—MO's of H_2^+.

plot them and then consider their energies (that is, the energy of an electron occupying each of them). They are plotted in Figure 3-9. Turning first to ψ_b we see that an electron in this MO is heavily concentrated between the nuclei where it will do the most good in binding them together. Note that its concentration there is even greater than the simple sum of contributions from two separate atomic orbitals since $(\phi_A + \phi_B)^2 > \phi_A{}^2 + \phi_B{}^2$. On the other hand, ψ_a actually has a nodal plane bisecting the H_A—H_B axis and gives much less electron density between the nuclei than the two separate, noninteracting orbitals, ϕ_A and ϕ_B, alone would give. Thus the repulsion between the nuclei is great, and this state is actually repulsive. This explains why we have designated the first MO as ψ_b meaning *bonding* and the second as ψ_a meaning *antibonding*.

The energies of these two MO's, relative to the energy of an isolated hydrogen atom, are shown in Figure 3-10. (The method of calculation is given in Appendix C-3). In Figure 3-10 the atomic orbitals, ϕ_A and ϕ_B, are shown to have the same energy, whereas the bonding molecular orbital, ψ_b, is more stable by an energy, E_{AB}, and the antibonding MO, ψ_a, is less stable by the same amount, E_{AB}.

This qualitative feature is common to all energy level diagrams showing the energies of MO's formed between two atoms, each supplying one orbital. If the two atomic orbitals do not have the same energy, then ψ_a and ψ_b will be placed approximately equal distances above and below the mean energy of the two atomic orbitals. Figure 3-10 is also a typical energy

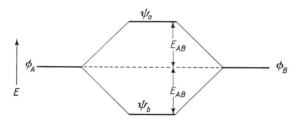

Fig. 3-10. Energy level diagram showing the formation of bonding and antibonding MO's from two equivalent atomic orbitals in a homonuclear diatomic molecule.

level diagram in its arrangement. The atomic orbitals of the constituent atoms are placed on each side, and the resulting MO's are placed in the center.

We can now proceed to build up the electronic structures of some other molecules just as we used the aufbau principle to build up the electron configurations of atoms. If we add an additional electron to $H_2{}^+$ we have, of course, the hydrogen molecule H_2. This second electron will enter ψ_b

along with the first, since ψ_b is the lowest energy orbital with a vacancy in it. In order to satisfy the exclusion principle, the spins of the two electrons must be paired. Thus we can write the electron configuration of H_2, from the MO viewpoint, as $(\psi_b)^2$. The binding energy will be approximately $2E_{AB}$ with some correction for the mutual shielding effect. Thus in this simple case MO theory gives us a physical description of the bond in H_2 which is rather similar to what we obtain from VB theory, namely, that there are two electrons with spins paired which are concentrated between the nuclei. In more complicated cases we shall presently see more clearly how the two theories differ.

Let us continue applying the aufbau principle in the present situation. Suppose we bring together a helium atom and a hydrogen atom, so that again we have a bonding orbital, $\psi_b = \phi_{He} + \phi_H$, and an antibonding orbital, $\psi_a = \phi_{He} - \phi_H$. Again ψ_b will be more stable than the mean energy of the He $1s$ and H $1s$ orbitals, and ψ_a will be less stable, by roughly equal amounts. Because the exclusion principle prevents us from placing more than two electrons in one MO, the three electrons must occupy the two MO's in the following way: $(\psi_b)^2(\psi_a)^1$. Thus the molecule HeH should be stable by about the energy E_{AB}. Such a molecule is known in the vapor phase.

Finally, let us suppose we bring together two helium atoms. Then we have four electrons to be housed in two MO's of the sort shown in Figure 3-10. Clearly, two must be placed in the bonding orbital and two in the antibonding orbital so that, according to the LCAO approximation, the binding energy of He_2 is precisely zero. A similar argument may be framed for all of the inert gases, and this explains why they are all monatomic.

3-9. Homonuclear Diatomic Molecules

So far we have considered only cases in which the only important MO's are formed by overlap of an s orbital on each of the two atoms. MO's of this type are called σ (*sigma*) *MO's* and the property which so classifies them is their cylindrical symmetry about the internuclear axis. That such symmetry must exist should be clear from the fact that each of the two s orbitals composing them is symmetrical about this axis.

We must next consider how p orbitals may combine, in terms of the LCAO approximation, to form MO's in a homonuclear diatomic molecule. Suppose we define the internuclear axis as the z axis. If each atom has available a p_z orbital, they may be combined into a bonding MO, $p_z(1) + p_z(2)$ (Fig. 3-11a), and an antibonding MO, $p_z(1) - p_z(2)$. These MO's are also σ MO's. Note that a p_z orbital on one atom may also combine with an s

orbital on the other to produce bonding (Fig. 3-11b) and nonbonding MO's. In general, any kind of s–p_z hybrid orbitals on the two atoms may combine to give σ MO's. Because of its ability to contribute to a σ MO, a p orbital (in this case, the p_z orbital, since we have chosen to identify the inter-nuclear axis with the z axis of our coordinate system) lying along the molec-ular axis is called a $p\sigma$ orbital. An s orbital is simply understood to be of σ character and is not so denoted.

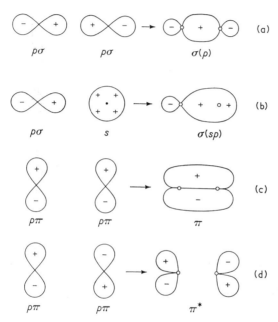

Fig. 3-11. Diagrams illustrating the formation of some simple two-center MO's from atomic orbitals.

If the p_z orbital is a $p\sigma$ orbital, then the p_x and p_y orbitals are not. They are $p\pi$ orbitals. A π type orbital is one whose nodal plane includes the molecular axis. It is not therefore cylindrically symmetric about this axis, but has equal electron density on either side of a plane containing the axis, while the wave function itself is of opposite sign on the two sides. Two such $p\pi$ orbitals can be combined into a bonding π MO, $p\pi(1) + p\pi(2)$ and an antibonding π MO, $p\pi(1) - p\pi(2)$. These two are simply denoted π and π^*, respectively. Their formation is illustrated in Figures 3-11c and 3-11d.

Let us consider an element in the first short period which has $2s$ and $2p$ orbitals in its valence shell. When two such atoms are combined into a homonuclear diatomic molecule, the two sets of atomic orbitals may combine into various MO's. Before we can apply the aufbau principle to determine the electronic structures of the diatomic molecules of these elements, we must know the relative energies of these MO's. The results of theoretical and experimental study have shown that the order is generally as shown in Figure 3-12. This diagram introduces a new concept,

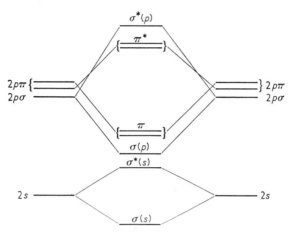

Fig. 3-12. A schematic energy level diagram showing how atomic orbitals of two (identical) atoms of the first short period combine to form molecular orbitals.

that of *degenerate orbitals*. Note that the π and π^* MO's each consist of two levels which have been bracketed together to indicate that they have the same energy. One of the π orbitals is formed from the combination of the two p_y orbitals and the other from a combination of the two p_x orbitals. These π orbitals are completely equivalent to each other except that their spatial orientations differ by 90°. Since, however, the diatomic molecule is symmetrical about its axis, this difference in orientation cannot make any difference in the energies. The concept of degeneracy is quite general. Any set of two or more atomic or molecular orbitals all having the same energy is said to be degenerate. There is one final point which slightly mars the clarity of the picture. Figure 3-12 shows the π levels slightly above the $\sigma(p)$ orbital, which would be expected from simple LCAO theory. However, the separation appears in some cases to be extremely small, and there may even be a slight inversion in some molecules as we shall see.

Let us see now how we can apply these principles to formulate the electron configurations of the diatomic molecules of the first short period.

Li₂. This is perfectly analogous to H₂ except that two 2s atomic orbitals are combined into σ MO's and the bonding MO, $\sigma(2s)$, holds two electrons. The $1s$ electrons on each atom remain essentially unperturbed and can be ignored. Figure 3-13 shows the electron configuration of Li_2.

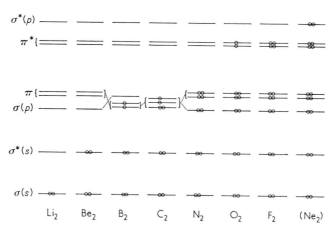

Fig. 3-13.   Electron configurations of the diatomic molecules of the first short period elements according to simple MO theory.

Be_2.   If we combine the two Be^{2+} cores and then drop the four electrons into the MO's, two will go into $\sigma(s)$ and the next two into $\sigma^*(s)$. Thus we have two electrons in a bonding orbital and two in the corresponding antibonding orbital, so the net bond energy is zero. A Be_2 molecule does exist under some conditions; little is known about it, but it appears to be very unstable.

B_2.   Here we have six electrons to occupy the MO's. The first four must fill the $\sigma(s)$ and $\sigma^*(s)$ MO's, and hence their net contribution to the binding energy is approximately zero. The B_2 molecule is found experimentally to have two unpaired electrons. This means that either the π levels must be below $\sigma(p)$ or accidentally degenerate with it. At any rate, the two electrons do occupy the π levels as shown.

C_2.   In this case there is experimental evidence that the π and $\sigma(p)$ levels are of virtually the same energy and are populated as shown in Figure 3-13.

N_2.   Here, the relative order of the π and $\sigma(p)$ levels is not important for our purposes since the ten electrons completely fill $\sigma(s)$, $\sigma^*(s)$, $\sigma(p)$, and π. Thus the molecule has an N—N $\sigma(p)$ bond and two π bonds.

O_2.   The electron configuration is shown in Figure 3-13. It can be seen that if we suppose that the π^* orbitals lie below the $\sigma^*(p)$ orbital we get a natural explanation for the presence of two unpaired electrons in the molecule, whereas this fact cannot readily be explained in simple VB theory.

F_2. On adding two or more electrons to the O_2 configuration we fill the π^* orbitals.

Bond Order. The qualitative concept of bond order can be defined in both VB and MO theories. In the former it is the number of shared electron pairs; in the latter it is the number of bonding electrons minus the number of antibonding electrons divided by two. In Table 3-2 are listed the bond orders for the molecules discussed above as predicted by the VB and MO treatments and those deduced experimentally. It can be seen that except for O_2 the two theories yield results in equally good agreement with experiment.

TABLE 3-2

Bond Orders in Some Simple Homonuclear Diatomic Molecules

Molecule	VB theory	MO theory	Experiment
Li_2	1	1	1
Be_2	0 (or 2)	0	0 (?)
B_2	1 (or 3)[a]	1	1
C_2	2	2	2
N_2	3	3	3
O_2	$\left\{ \begin{array}{l} 2 \text{ (diamagnetic)} \\ 1 \text{ (paramagnetic)} \end{array} \right\}$	2 (paramagnetic)	2 (paramagnetic)
F_2	1	1	1
Ne_2	0	0	0

[a] However, VB theory would predict that all electron spins are paired, whereas they are not.

3-10. Heteronuclear Diatomic Molecules

The treatment of heteronuclear diatomic molecules by LCAO-MO theory is not fundamentally different from the treatment of homonuclear diatomics, except that the MO's are not symmetric with respect to a plane perpendicular to and bisecting the internuclear axis. The MO's are still constructed by forming linear combinations of atomic orbitals on the two atoms, but since the atoms are now different we must write them $\phi_A + \lambda\phi_B$, where λ is not in general equal to ± 1. Thus these MO's will not in general represent nonpolar bonding. As examples let us consider HCl, CO, and NO.

In treating HCl we find it necessary to mention explicitly another factor influencing the stability of a bonding MO. Even if two atomic orbitals are capable of combining from the point of view of symmetry, the extent to which they will actually mix—that is, lose their individuality and merge to form a bonding and an antibonding MO—will depend upon whether their energies are comparable to begin with. If their energies are vastly different, they will scarcely mix at all. Mathematically, the two MO's would be

$$\psi_b = \phi_A + \lambda\phi_B$$

$$\psi_a = \phi_B - \lambda\phi_A$$

where λ would be very small so that $\psi_b \approx \phi_A$ and $\psi_a \approx \phi_B$. In other words, when the energies are not similar, we can treat ϕ_A and ϕ_B as though they do not mix at all. This is more or less what occurs in HCl. The H $1s$ orbital and the $Cl(2p\sigma)$ orbital mix fairly effectively to form a bonding and an antibonding MO, but the $Cl(2p\pi)$ and $2s$ orbitals are so much lower in energy than any other hydrogen orbitals such as $2s$ or $2p\pi$ that no significant mixing occurs. Thus we call the $2p\pi$ and $2s$ orbitals of Cl in this case nonbonding because they neither help nor hinder the bonding to a significant extent.

The heteronuclear molecule CO may be regarded as a perturbed nitrogen molecule. C and O, differing in atomic number by only two, have atomic orbitals which are quite similar; the formation of MO's will therefore be almost the same as shown in Figure 3-12 for a homonuclear diatomic, although the energies of the two sets of atomic orbitals will not now match exactly. In fact, the oxygen orbitals will be somewhat more stable, so that they will contribute more to the bonding MO's than will the carbon orbitals, whereas the carbon orbitals will contribute more to the antibonding MO's. Thus, although the ten electrons are comprised of six from oxygen and four from carbon, we can explain the low polarity of the molecule because eight of them are in bonding orbitals where they are held closer to O than to C, thus tending to neutralize the greater nuclear charge of the oxygen core.

The electron configuration of NO can easily be deduced by either removing one electron from O_2 or adding one to N_2. It thus has an unpaired electron in the π^* orbitals. NO readily loses this electron to form the NO^+ ion, which is found to have a stronger bond than does NO. Although the removal of an electron in this way usually results in bond weakening (for example, H_2 is more strongly bound than H_2^+) and is not easily accomplished, the contrary results in this case are easily accounted for since the electron concerned is an antibonding electron. In VB theory the electronic structure of NO can only be accounted for by Pauling's special postulate of a three-electron bond (3-VIII) and the corollary postulate that a three-

$$: N : O :$$

(3-VIII)

electron bond is half as strong as a two-electron bond. This second postulate can be rationalized in MO theory since if we have a bonding and an
antibonding MO as in Figure 3-10, the binding energy which results from
placing two electrons in the bonding MO is about halved when we place a
third electron in the antibonding MO. The NO molecule is a good example
of cases in which MO theory seems to give a good qualitative picture of
the bonding more straightforwardly than does VB theory, although there
are other cases where the reverse is true.

3-11. Polyatomic Molecules

MO theory is chiefly used for those polyatomic molecules in which
multiple bonding occurs. We have already considered how NO_2^- is formulated in VB theory as a resonance hybrid (3-V). In MO theory it can be

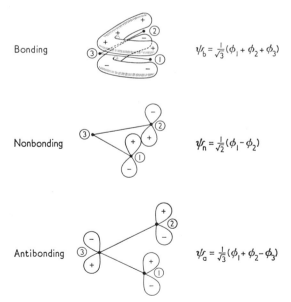

$$\text{(3-Va)} \qquad\qquad \text{(3-Vb)}$$

treated in the following way. We first assume that a set of σ bonds is
formed using four electrons and that several other electron pairs are non-

Bonding

$$\psi_b = \frac{1}{\sqrt{3}}(\phi_1 + \phi_2 + \phi_3)$$

Nonbonding

$$\psi_n = \frac{1}{\sqrt{2}}(\phi_1 - \phi_2)$$

Antibonding

$$\psi_a = \frac{1}{\sqrt{3}}(\phi_1 + \phi_2 - \phi_3)$$

Fig. 3-14. Approximate shapes of the π MO's in nitrite ion, NO_2^-.

bonding. Thus we write a framework of nuclei and σ electrons (3-IX).

(3-IX)

There are still four electrons to be assigned and each of the three atoms has an empty $p\pi$ orbital (one whose nodal plane coincides with the molecular plane). If we start with three atomic orbitals it must be possible to combine them into three molecular orbitals. A discussion of the methods by which the correct combinations are derived would be beyond the scope of this text, but their approximate forms are illustrated for the present case in Figure 3-14. ψ_1 is bonding, having the lowest energy, ψ_2 is nonbonding, and ψ_3 is antibonding. If we place our four remaining electrons in this set of π MO's, the configuration will be $(\psi_b)^2(\psi_n)^2(\psi_a)^0$. The net energy is thus favorable to bonding. Note that in general these MO's are linear combinations of all three atomic orbitals, and this description of the bonding does not therefore refer to *localized* electron pair bonds, but to *delocalized* electrons moving in MO's which extend over the entire molecule. Moreover, from the nature of the occupied MO's, ψ_b and ψ_n, it is obvious that the distribution of the four π electrons is symmetric in the two NO links. This description is sometimes symbolized by 3-X, where the dashed line indicates bonding due to delocalized electrons in molecular orbitals.

(3-X)   (3-XI)   (3-XII)

Benzene is described in VB theory as a resonance hybrid of the Kekulé, Dewar, and other canonical structures as we have seen. In MO theory, it is treated by assuming the formation of extensive π MO's. Each carbon atom is assumed to use its s, p_x, and p_y orbitals and three of its electrons to form the σ-bonded framework (3-XI). Each carbon atom still has a p_z orbital (which is a $p\pi$ type orbital) containing an electron. These $p\pi$ orbitals will merge into various MO's and the electrons in them will thus not be localized in definite double bonds, but will be free to wander around the circular π MO's. This view can be rendered symbolically with a dotted line (3-XII).

References

Cartmell, E., and G. W. A. Fowles, *Valency and Molecular Structure*, 2nd ed., Butterworths, London, 1961. A well-written introductory text.

Coulson, C. A., *Valence*, 2nd ed., Oxford University Press, 1961. Perhaps the best supplementary reference; it is lucidly written on a high but not too rigorous level. It leans to organic chemistry, but this will not do the student harm.

Eyring, H., J. Walter, and G. E. Kimball, *Quantum Chemistry*, Wiley, New York, 1960. More advanced and rigorous mathematical text.

Kauzman, *Quantum Chemistry*, Academic Press, New York, 1957. More advanced and rigorous mathematical text.

Pauling, L., *The Nature of the Chemical Bond*, 3rd ed., Cornell University Press, Ithaca, N. Y., 1960. This famous book is a mine of information and a Bible to the advocates of the valence bond approach. It must be remembered that it creates the impression that there is no other approach to chemical bonding and fails to indicate the many defects of this approach.

Pauling, L., and E. B. Wilson, *Introduction to Quantum Mechanics*, McGraw-Hill, New York, 1935. More advanced and rigorous mathematical text.

4

Further Properties of Atoms and Chemical Bonds

4-1. Bond Energies

We have already used the term bond energy several times, assuming that the reader's previous knowledge and/or the context would make the meaning sufficiently clear. In this section, the subject is examined more closely. For a diatomic molecule the bond energy, D, is equal to the enthalpy of the reaction

$$XY(g) = X(g) + Y(g) \qquad \Delta H = D \qquad (4\text{-}1)$$

where the molecule and the atoms are all in their ground states. To be exact, this bond energy is a function of temperature, and the best value to use would be that for the hypothetical reaction at $0°K$. The differences between the values at $0°K$. (properly denoted $D_0°$, to indicate that the temperature is $0°$ and that the diatomic molecule is in its lowest, that is, 0, vibrational state) and those at room temperature, denoted D_{300} are always small. They cannot exceed ~ 2.4 kcal. and must always be such that $D_{300} > D_0°$. For example, $D_0°$ for H_2 is 103.24, while D_{300} is 104.18 kcal./mole. For our purposes here, the differences between D_{300} and $D_0°$ values are not important, and we shall simply speak of bond dissociation energies as though they were independent of temperature and use the symbol D.

Although the bond energy of a diatomic molecule is actually an experimental datum, bond energies in polyatomic molecules must be carefully defined to be meaningful. Let us consider the simplest case, that of an AB_n type molecule where all B's are equivalently bonded to A and not to one another. BF_3 is an example. Since all of the B—F bonds are equivalent, all B—F bond energies, D_{B-F} must be equal and the relation

$$BF_3(g) = B(g) + 3F(g) \qquad \Delta H = 3D_{B-F} \qquad (4\text{-}2)$$

is obvious. Thus if we know the heats of formation of $BF_3(g)$, $B(g)$, and $F(g)$, we can readily calculate D_{B-F}. This value is called the *mean thermochemical bond energy*. However, it is *not* the energy, ΔH_1, of the process

$$BF_3(g) = BF_2(g) + F(g) \qquad \Delta H_1 \qquad \text{(4-3)}$$

since when the first bond is broken, the nature of the remaining two will necessarily be altered to some extent. Also ΔH_2 and ΔH_3

$$BF_2(g) = BF(g) + F(g) \qquad \Delta H_2 \qquad \text{(4-4)}$$
$$BF(g) = B(g) + F(g) \qquad \Delta H_3 \qquad \text{(4-5)}$$

are not likely to be equal to one another, or to ΔH_1 (eq. 4-3), or to D_{B-F}. It is, of course, true that $\Delta H_1 + \Delta H_2 + \Delta H_3 = 3D_{B-F}$, since the sum of equations 4-3, 4-4, and 4-5 is equal to equation 4-2 and Hess' law can be applied. The question of how much ΔH_1, ΔH_2, ΔH_3, and D_{B-F} will differ cannot be answered since there are not sufficient data available to calculate them all.

It is probable that the differences between successive dissociation energies and between any one of them and the mean will be fairly small so long as no one step involves a unique change in hybridization of the central atom. For example, the following data are available for H_2O:

$$H_2O(g) = 2H(g) + O(g) \qquad \tfrac{1}{2}\Delta H = D_{O-H} = \quad 109.5$$
$$H_2O(g) = H(g) + OH(g) \qquad \Delta H_1 = \sim 117$$
$$HO(g) = H(g) + O(g) \qquad \Delta H_2 = \sim 103$$

Since the oxygen atom in its ground state has the two unpaired electrons required to form the two O—H bonds in H_2O, there will be only relatively small changes in valence states in the different processes and no one of them will have any particularly large promotion energy peculiar to itself. In the case of the mercuric halides, however, we have a quite different situation as the following data show:

$$HgCl_2(g) = Hg(g) + 2Cl(g) \qquad \tfrac{1}{2}\Delta H = D_{Hg-Cl} = 53$$
$$HgCl_2(g) = HgCl(g) + Cl(g) \qquad \Delta H_1 = 81$$
$$HgCl(g) = Hg(g) + Cl(g) \qquad \Delta H_2 = 25$$

Whereas breaking the first ClHg—Cl bond results in only a small change in the state of the Hg atom, when the second bond, Hg—Cl, is broken the mercury atom drops from some sort of sp state into its s^2 ground state, releasing considerable energy which partially offsets the energy required to break the second bond. Hence, $\Delta H_2 \ll \Delta H_1$.

The type of molecule in which the concept of a bond energy is rather loosely defined is the commonest type, namely, one in which two or more different kinds of bonds exist. This may be obvious, as in ethane, where there are six bonds of one kind (C—H bonds) and one of another kind (the C—C bond), or it may be a little subtler, as in PCl₅, which has the structure shown in 4-I. The two axial P—Cl bonds are not symmetrically

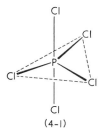

(4-I)

equivalent to the three equatorial P—Cl bonds, and so there is no reason to suppose that they have the same strength and energy. In cases such as this there is no unique way of assigning bond energy values. In C_2H_6, for example, we can only be sure that $6D_{C-H} + D_{C-C}$ must equal the energy of atomization of C_2H_6, that is,

$$C_2H_6(g) = 2C(g) + 6H(g) \qquad \Delta H = 6D_{C-H} + D_{C-C}$$

but this gives us one equation in two unknowns so that we know only that

$$D_{C-C} = \Delta H - 6D_{C-H} \qquad (4\text{-}6)$$

but not the absolute values of D_{C-C} and D_{C-H}. Indeed, it is important to recognize that no such absolute values are defined, if by defined we mean experimentally measurable. However, meaningful and useful magnitudes have been deduced for these quantities in roughly the following way, in which we keep in touch with reality by demanding internal consistency in our values. We may evaluate a mean C—H bond energy in methane since there are enough experimental data to tell us the energy of the process

$$CH_4(g) = C(g) + 4H(g) \qquad \tfrac{1}{4}\Delta H = D_{C-H}$$

If we now assume the same value of D_{C-H} in C_2H_6, we can calculate D_{C-C} from equation 4-6. Now it has also proved possible to measure the energy of the process

$$C_2H_6(g) = 2CH_3(g)$$

and we must expect this energy to agree fairly well with the value of D_{C-C} we have calculated. In fact, it does within a few per cent. If we then consider processes such as

$$CH_3(CH_2)_nCH_3(g) = (n + 2)C(g) + (2n + 6)H(g)$$

we should expect their energies to be calculable by summing up the appropriate number of D_{C-C}'s and D_{C-H}'s. In fact, we can even refine our treatment by allowing D_{C-H} for a methylene group to differ slightly from

D_{C-H} for a methyl group if we wish to be fancy. It turns out that by taking a large body of data and judiciously juggling the magnitudes of the various bond energies a set of average values which reproduce experimental energies of atomization to within a few per cent can be deduced. Similar procedures can be carried out with molecules other than hydrocarbons, although the supply of data is generally more restricted. In this way, the average bond energies in Table 4-1 were obtained.

TABLE 4-1

Some Representative Average Bond Energy Values at 25°C.
(In kcal./mole of bonds)

A. *Single Bond Energies*[a]

H	C[a]	N	O	F	Si	P	S	Cl	Br	I	
104	99	93	111	135	70	76	81	103	88	71	H
	83	70	84	105	69	63	62	79	66	57	C[a]
		38	48	65	—	50*	—	48	58(?)	—	N
			33	44	88	84*	—	49	—	48	O
				37	129	117	68	44	61	—	F
					42	51*	54	86	69	51	Si
						51	55*	79	65	51	P
							51	60	51	—	S
								58	52	50	Cl
									46	43	Br
										36	I

B. *Multiple Bond Energies*

C=C	146	C=N	147	C=O	177	N=N	100
C≡C	200	C≡N	213	C≡O	256	N≡N	226

[a] Energies of all bonds involving carbon are based on a value of 172 kcal./mole as the heat of sublimation of graphite. Starred values are estimated using electronegativity differences.

It should be noted that the energies of multiple bonds are generally higher than those for single bonds, as we would expect, but that a double bond is not, in general, quite twice as strong as a comparable single bond or a triple bond quite three times as strong.

4-2. Electronegativities

The qualitative concept of electronegativity is one to which most chemists subscribe, but the attempt to define it *quantitatively* has produced endless disputation, haggling, and plain finagling for twenty years or so. It is probable that as a quantitative concept it is much less reliable than its most passionate champions claim, but not as useless as its arch-detractors maintain. The original qualitative definition of Pauling, which is difficult to improve upon, is: "Electronegativity is the power of an atom *in a molecule* to attract electrons to itself." It is not, however, the same as electron affinity, as will be seen.

Suppose we consider a bond A—B between dissimilar atoms A and B. From the viewpoint of VB theory this will be a resonance hybrid (4-II).

$$A—B \leftrightarrow A^-B^+ \leftrightarrow A^+B^-$$
$$\text{(4-IIa)} \quad \text{(4-IIb)} \quad \text{(4-IIc)}$$

If A is considerably more electronegative than B, then 4-IIc probably contributes negligibly and may be ignored. The contribution of 4-IIb may be expected to bear a relation to the magnitude of the difference in the electronegativities so that if the contribution and the relation were known we could calculate electronegativity differences. Pauling has proposed the following procedure for doing this.

TABLE 4-2

Bond Energy Data Used to Estimate Electronegativities by Pauling's Method
(In kcal./mole)

A	B	D_{A-A}	D_{B-B}	$\sqrt{D_{AA}D_{BB}}$	D_{A-B}	Δ^a	$\Delta^{1/2}$
F	Br	37	46	41	62	21	4.6
Si	F	50	37	43	135	92	9.6
Si	Br	50	46	48	73	25	5.0

$^a \Delta = D_{A-B} - \sqrt{D_{A-A}D_{B-B}}.$

Consider the data in Table 4-2. The various bond dissociation energies are the values estimated as described above from thermodynamic data for F_2, Br_2, FBr, SiF_4, and $SiBr_4$. The treatment of these data is dictated by the following argument. Note that in each case D_{A-B} is greater than the geometric mean of D_{A-A} and D_{B-B}. This mean energy is taken as the (hypothetical) A—B bond energy if the A—B bond were purely covalent, that is, represented only by canonical form 4-IIa. The differences, Δ's, are identified as "ionic resonance energies" due to resonance of 4-IIa with 4-IIb. It is assumed that the greater the electronegativity difference the more ionic resonance there will be, and hence the larger will be the value of Δ. However, Δ is not proportional to the electronegativity differences $x_A - x_B$. Thus

$$(x_F - x_{Si}) - (x_{Br} - x_{Si}) = (x_F - x_{Br})$$

but

$$92 - 25 \neq 21$$

However, in general, the quantities $\Delta^{1/2}$ do seem to be additive or approximately so. Thus, in the present case

$$9.6 - 5.0 = 4.6$$

Therefore, Pauling set up a table of relative electronegativities using the relation

$$x_A - x_B = K\Delta^{1/2}$$

The constant K was taken as $23^{-1/2}$ (that is, the Δ's were expressed in e.v.), since this gives numbers in the convenient range of 0 to $\sim$4 for the differences. As with electrode potentials, where only differences can be measured, it is necessary to fix one point arbitrarily and for this purpose it is assumed that the most electronegative element, fluorine, has $x_F = 4$. Of course, since Pauling worked out the first electronegativity scale in this way, bond energy values have been revised and electronegativities recalculated. The values listed in Table 4-3 as "Pauling electronegativities" were calculated by Pauling's method but are not, in general, his exact original values.

Among the dozens of other methods proposed for estimating experimentally or calculating electronegativity values, we shall mention only two. Mulliken showed by theoretical arguments that the tendency of an atom *in a molecule* to compete with another atom to which it is bound in attracting the shared electrons should be proportional to $(I + A)/2$, that is, to the average of its ionization potential and its electron affinity. Physically this is quite reasonable since we should expect that the over-all ability of an atom to attract shared electrons might be the average of quantities related to the tendencies of the free atom to hold its own electrons and to attract additional electrons. It is found that when the I and A values are expressed in electron volts the Mulliken electronegativity values can be adjusted to give the least mean deviation from Pauling's by dividing them by 3.15. Representative Mulliken electronegativities are listed in Table 4-3.

Rather recently, an empirical method of computing electronegativities has been proposed by Allred and Rochow which seems to have certain advantages stemming precisely from its complete and strict empiricism. They propose formulating Pauling's qualitative definition of electronegativity in the following way. An electron in a bond is assumed to be attracted by one of the two nuclei according to Coulomb's law

$$\text{Force} = \frac{Z^* e^2}{r^2}$$

where Z^* is the effective nuclear charge which the electron feels and r is its mean distance from the nucleus. Z^* is estimated using a set of shielding parameters derived many years ago by Slater, and r is taken as the covalent radius of the atom, which for a homonuclear diatomic molecule is half the internuclear distance. (Covalent radii are discussed on page 93.) In order to relate the calculated forces, which are "absolute electronegativities," to Pauling's arbitrary and relative value, the forces are plotted against Pauling's electronegativities, the best straight line is drawn through the points, and from the slope and intercept of this line the following equation for Allred and Rochow's electronegativities is obtained:

$$x_{\text{AR}} = 0.359 \frac{Z^*}{r^2} + 0.744$$

A complete set of Allred-Rochow values is given in Table 4-3.

Inspection of Table 4-3 reveals one disadvantage of Mulliken's method. There are relatively few elements for which the electron affinities needed for calculation of the Mulliken electronegativity are known. To a lesser extent, lack of accurate thermal data limits the applicability of the Pauling method. This is especially true of the transition metals for which it is difficult to estimate values of metal–metal single bonds and also of metal–halogen bonds. Attempts have been made to estimate electronegativities of these elements by making what are virtually guesses of metal–halogen bond energies and using dubious estimates of metal–metal bond energies, and the results are of questionable significance. Allred and Rochow's method has the advantage of wide applicability.

Our discussion so far has perhaps created the impression that the electronegativity of an atom is a fixed and immutable constant. This is quite false, and it is probable that failure to recognize the variability of electronegativity is at the root of much of the past controversy about the subject. The main and most obvious cause of variation of the electronegativity of an element from one compound or bonding situation to another is the variability in its valence state, and this may be best appreciated by considering Mulliken's definition. For rigorous application of Mulliken's definition, one should take, not the I and A values applying to the ground state atom but those applying to the valence state of the atom in a particular compound, and these will vary with the nature of the valence state.

TABLE 4-3

Electronegativities of the Elements

(Values in bold type are calculated using the Allred-Rochow formula; those in italics are estimated by Pauling's method and those in Roman type are calculated by Mulliken's method.)

1	2	3	4	5	6	7	8	9	10	11	12	13	14	15	16	17	18
H **2.1**																	He
Li **0.97** *1.0*	Be **1.47** *1.5*											B **2.01** *2.0* 2.01	C **2.50** *2.60* 2.63	N **3.07** *3.05*	O **3.50** *3.50* 3.17	F **4.10** *3.90* 3.91	Ne
Na **0.94** *0.9*	Mg **1.23** *1.2*											Al **1.47** *1.5* 1.81	Si **1.74** *1.90* 2.44	P **2.06** *2.15* 2.33	S **2.44** *2.60* 2.41	Cl **2.83** *3.15* 3.00	Ar
K **0.91** *0.8*	Ca **1.04** *1.0*	Sc **1.20** *1.3*	Ti **1.32** *1.6*	V **1.45**	Cr **1.56**	Mn **1.60**	Fe **1.64**	Co **1.70**	Ni **1.75**	Cu **1.75** *1.36*	Zn **1.66** *1.49*	Ga **1.82**	Ge **2.02** *1.90*	As **2.20** *2.10* 1.75	Se **2.48** *2.55* 2.23	Br **2.74** *2.95* 2.76	Kr
Rb **0.89** *0.8*	Sr **0.99** *1.0*	Y **1.11** *1.3*	Zr **1.22**	Nb **1.23**	Mo **1.30**	Tc **1.36**	Ru **1.42**	Rh **1.45**	Pd **1.35** *1.36*	Ag **1.42** *1.36*	Cd **1.46** *1.49*	In **1.49** 1.95	Sn **1.72** *1.90*	Sb **1.82** *2.05* 1.65	Te **2.01** *2.30* 2.10	I **2.21** *2.65* 2.56	Xe
Cs **0.86** *0.7*	Ba **0.97** *0.9*	*	Hf **1.23**	Ta **1.33**	W **1.40**	Re **1.46**	Os **1.52**	Ir **1.55**	Pt **1.44** *1.36*	Au **1.42** *1.36*	Hg **1.44** *1.4*	Tl **1.80**	Pb **1.55**	Bi **1.67**	Po **1.76**	At **1.96**	Rn
Fr **0.86** *0.7*	Ra **0.97** *0.9*	**															

* La **1.08** | Ce **1.06** | Pr **1.07** | Nd **1.07** | Pm **1.07** | Sm **1.07** | Eu **1.01** | Gd **1.11** | Tb **1.10** | Dy **1.10** | Ho **1.10** | Er **1.11** | Tm **1.11** | Yb **1.06** | Lu **1.14**

** Ac **1.00** | Th **1.11** | Pa **1.14** | U **1.22** | Np **1.22** | Pu **1.22** | Am | Cm | Bk | Cf | Es | Fm | Md | No
──── ~1.2 (estimated) ────→

For example, if nitrogen is in the valence state s^2p^3 its Mulliken electronegativity is 2.33, whereas if it is in the state sp^4 the x_M value is 2.55. The former is given in Table 4-3 since the valence state of N in its common trivalent compounds is probably nearest to s^2p^3. It is clearly absurd to assume that the electronegativity of an element is independent of its valence, for S in SCl_2 must surely have a different electronegativity from S in SF_6. Clearly, an atom will have a greater attraction for electrons when it is in a high oxidation state than when it is in a low one. Thus, the numbers in Table 4-3 should not be taken as exact measures of electronegativities but only as rough guides, perhaps as the median numbers in a range for each element.

4-3. Bond Lengths and Covalent Radii

The lengths of bonds, that is, the internuclear distances in molecules, can be measured in many ways, and a considerable body of such data is available. If we consider a homonuclear diatomic molecule with a single bond, such as F_2 or Cl_2, we can assign to the atoms F and Cl *covalent single bond* radii equal to one-half of the internuclear distances in the respective molecules. It is then gratifying to find that for the most part the sums of these covalent radii are equal to the internuclear distances in the interhalogens such as Cl—Br (calculated 2.13, found 2.14). For elements which do not form diatomic molecules with single bonds, other methods of estimating the radii are used. For example, the C—C distance in diamond and a host of organic molecules is found to be 1.54 ± 0.01 A., so the covalent

TABLE 4-4

Some Single Bond Covalent Radii
(In Angstrom units)

H[a]	0.28	O	0.66
C	0.77	S	1.04
Si	1.17	Se	1.17
Ce	1.22	Te	1.37
Sn	1.40	F	0.64
N	0.70	Cl	0.99
P	1.10	Br	1.14
As	1.21	I	1.33
Sb	1.41		

[a] One-half the bond length of H_2 is 0.375, but this value does not apply when H is bonded to other atoms. 0.28 was obtained by subtracting the radius of X from various H—X bond lengths.

radius of C is taken as 0.77. To obtain the covalent radius of nitrogen 0.77 is subtracted from the C—N distance in H_3C—NH_2, yielding 0.70. In this fashion a table of single bond covalent radii can be compiled (Table 4-4).

Multiple bond radii can also be obtained. For example, the triple bond radii of carbon and nitrogen can be calculated from the bond lengths in HC≡CH and N≡N, as 0.60 and 0.55, giving 1.15 for —C≡N as compared to experimental values of ∼1.16. It may be stated, as a general rule, that the higher the order of a bond between two atoms, the shorter it is. Thus, for carbon–carbon bonds the following are typical lengths: C—C, 1.54; C=C, 1.33; C≡C, 1.21. On the basis of this qualitative idea, which can be made semiquantitative for certain atom pairs, observed bond lengths may be used to infer the relative importance of various canonical forms of a resonance hybrid. Let us consider, for example, cyanogen. Three canonical structures (4-III) may be written for this. The length of the C—C bond

$$: N{\equiv}C{-}C{\equiv}N : \leftrightarrow : \overset{+}{N}{=}C{=}C{=}\overset{-}{N} : \leftrightarrow : \overset{-}{N}{=}C{=}C{=}\overset{+}{N} :$$
$$\text{(4-IIIa)} \qquad\qquad \text{(4-IIIb)} \qquad\qquad \text{(4-IIIc)}$$

is only 1.37 A., which indicates that 4-IIIb and 4-IIIc must contribute appreciably. This shortening relative to the single bond distance is explained in terms of MO theory by saying that there is appreciable C—C π bonding as well as C—N π bonding. It is also true, however, that hybridization effects are important. Thus, strictly, the C—C distance of 1.54 refers to a bond between two sp^3-hybridized carbon atoms, whereas the carbon atoms in $(CN)_2$ use sp hybrids for their σ bonds. This change of hybridization alone would produce some bond shortening, but probably does not account for it all.

This subject is unfortunately not as tidy as might be imagined from the above examples, which were especially chosen to illustrate how the system works *when it works*. There are many cases in which it leaves much to be desired. The reader might have wondered why the radius of nitrogen (0.70) was obtained from the C—N bond in methylamine instead of from the N—N bond in H_2N—NH_2, which would be more analogous to the procedure used for the halogens. The answer is simply that one-half of the N—N distance in hydrazine is 0.73, and this does not fit as consistently with the bulk of data on X—N bond lengths as does 0.70. Even more striking, however, are cases such as SiF_4, for which an Si—F distance of 1.81 would be calculated while the actual distance is ∼1.54. Again, for BF_3 the calculated distance would be ∼1.4 (the covalent radius of B is not easy to evaluate unambiguously), whereas the measured value is 1.30. Schomaker and Stevenson proposed that since these "shrinkages" generally occur in bonds between atoms of disparate electronegativities they may be due to bond strengthening and hence shortening due to ionic-covalent resonance 4-IVa ↔ 4-IVb (three similar ionic forms) and 4-Va ↔ 4-Vb

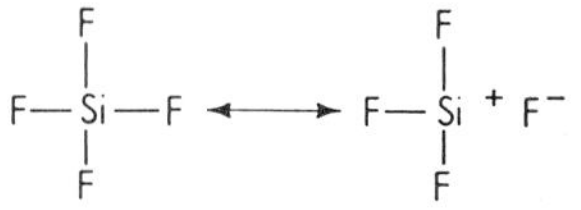

(4-IVa)   (4-IVb) 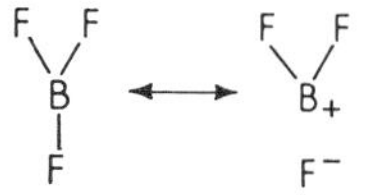   (4-Va)   (4-Vb)

(two similar ionic forms). They therefore proposed an equation known as the Schomaker-Stevenson relationship which takes account of this by making the bond distance depend on the electronegativity difference, which is an index of the ionic character of the bond. The equation they suggested is:

$$r_{A-B} = r_A + r_B - 0.09\,|x_A - x_B|$$

where r_A is the covalent radius of atom A. This relationship is not really very satisfactory except qualitatively, since it predicts too little shortening for some bonds, for example, Si—O and Si—F, and too much for others, for example, C—Cl. In the case of BF_3 the bond shortening can also be attributed to B–F double bonding since boron has a vacant p_z orbital and the fluorine atoms have filled p_z orbitals (4-VIa ↔ 4-VIb and two other similar

(4-VIa)   (4-VIb)

forms). In SiF_4 π bonding, using F $2p$ orbitals and Si $3d$ orbitals could contribute to the shortening. It is probable that *both* ionic-covalent resonance and multiple bonding contribute significantly.

In conclusion, we may say that the concept of atomic covalent radii is useful, but we cannot expect close correspondence between experimental interatomic distances and sums of these radii when the environment of either or both of the corresponding atoms differs appreciably from that of the atoms in the classes of substances used to derive the radii. Whether or not the ionicity of a bond can be related quantitatively to deviations from covalent radius sums, it does seem logical that covalent radii cannot be expected to describe appreciably ionic bonds very exactly.

4-4. Bond and Molecular Polarity

The electrical polarity of a molecule is expressed as its *dipole moment*. A system consisting of a positive charge, $+x$, and a negative charge, $-x$, separated by a distance, d, possesses a dipole moment magnitude of xd. If x is equal to the electronic charge (4.80×10^{-10} e.s.u.) and d is 1 A., $xd = 4.80$ D. (Debye) units. This unit is named after the theoretical chemist Peter Debye, who did much fundamental work on molecular polarity, and it is a convenient unit for expressing molecular dipole moments. It is important to recognize that a dipole moment is a vector quantity since it has a definite direction as well as magnitude. We shall adopt here the arbitrary convention of having the vector point in the direction of the negative end of the dipole.

The dipole moment of a molecule can be thought of as the vector sum of moments due to various parts of the molecule. These several contributions are, of course, interdependent, and no one of them can be altered without there being at least a second-order effect on the others. Let us consider first a heteronuclear diatomic molecule, such as HCl. Any such molecule must have a dipole moment since its two ends are different and only by a complex of unlikely coincidences could the various factors causing polarity cancel one another out exactly. The electronic structure of HCl can be expressed in a very simple way by writing it as an ionic-covalent resonance hybrid of two Lewis structures (4-VII). If we assume that there is no

$$\text{H} : \overset{..}{\underset{..}{\text{Cl}}} : \leftrightarrow \overset{+}{\text{H}} \quad : \overset{-}{\underset{..}{\text{Cl}}} :$$

$$\text{(4-VIIa)} \qquad \text{(4-VIIb)}$$

polarity associated with structure 4-VIIa (an assumption which will be examined and found wanting below), then it is easy to find the coefficient, λ, which we may call the *per cent ionic character*, in the expression

$$\% = \frac{(100 - \lambda)\psi_{\text{VIIa}} + \lambda\psi_{\text{VIIb}}}{100}$$

The internuclear distance in HCl is 1.27 A. If λ were 100, the dipole moment would therefore be 6.1 D. Since it is actually only 1.03 D., we conclude that $\lambda = 1.03/6.10 \approx 0.17$. Thus, we would say that there is 17% ionic character in HCl and by the same procedure calculate per cent ionic character of 43, 11, and 5 for HF, HBr, and HI, respectively. This procedure was proposed by Pauling in order to obtain a relation between electronegativity difference and per cent ionic character. By plotting the various percentages obtained above against $x_\text{X} - x_\text{H}$, where x_X is the electronegativity of the halogen atom, he obtained a smooth curve given by the equation

$$\% \text{ ionic character} = 18(x_\text{X} - x_\text{H})^{1.4}$$

and assumed that this equation is valid for other classes of compounds as well. For some, such as the alkali halides, however, it has been recognized to be inapplicable.

This procedure is now known to be full of dangers and is probably unreliable for other than qualitative work. The main sources of error are (*a*) the intrinsically polar nature of the covalent bond and (*b*) the contribution of orbital moments of unshared electrons to the total dipole moment. Both of these vitiate the initial assumption that structure 4-VIIa is intrinsically nonpolar, and we shall consider both in more detail.

1. *Polar nature of a heteronuclear bond.* If we place a proton and a Cl^+ ion—the latter being assumed, for the moment, to have spherical symmetry (hence no dipole within itself)—1.27 A. apart and then introduce the two bonding electrons between them, the system as a whole is neutral. If we place the center of gravity of the charge of these two bonding electrons exactly half way between the nuclei, then the system will have no dipole moment. However, since the hydrogen orbital is much smaller than the chlorine orbital, the center of gravity of charge for the bonding electrons will be closer to H than to Cl and a dipole will result, namely,

$$\overleftarrow{\text{H—Cl}}$$

This moment can be estimated to be $\sim$1.0 D.

2. *Orbital moments of unshared electrons.* Let us consider the internuclear axis to be the z axis of a coordinate system with the chlorine atom at the origin. If the chlorine atom uses a pure p_z orbital to form the bond, then the configuration of the remaining, unshared or nonbonding, electrons will be $s^2 p_x^2 p_y^2$, and they will contribute nothing to the polarity of the system. The s electrons are spherically distributed about the chlorine nucleus, and the p_x and p_y electrons lie more or less in a disc perpendicular

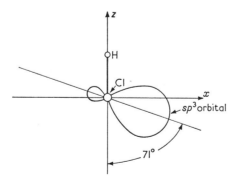

Fig. 4-1. Diagram illustrating the electrical asymmetry of electrons in an sp^3 hybrid orbital of chlorine in HCl.

to the z axis with the Cl nucleus at its center. Now let us suppose instead that the chlorine atom has full sp^3 hybridization and uses one of these hybrid orbitals to form the bond. The remaining three pairs of electrons will lie in the three equivalent hybrid orbitals, which have approximately the shape shown in Figure 4-1. It is easily seen that electrons in such an orbital are much more concentrated below the xy plane than above it, and hence there will be an *orbital dipole moment* with the vector of magnitude **v** pointing along the axis of the orbital. There is, then, a dipole moment contribution in the bond direction of $-\mathbf{v} \cos 71°$, or a total from the three such orbitals of $-3\mathbf{v} \cos 71°$, namely,

$$\underset{\text{H—Cl}}{\xrightarrow{-3\mathbf{v}\cos 71°}}$$

Now, we do not expect the chlorine atom to have full sp^3 hybridization and the unshared pairs to make this maximal contribution; rather, we expect some lesser degree of hybridization and hence some smaller contribution from the nonbonding electrons. There are various reasons for believing that there must be *some* hybridization, however.

We might follow these lines of argument further, but we shall stop here and consider what general conclusion can be drawn about the relation between molecular dipole moment and the various contributions to it, of which three principal ones have been discussed. We see first that unless we assume the intrinsic bond polarity and the orbital moments of unshared electrons exactly to balance one another out—and it is hardly likely that they will do so in all of the hydrogen halides, even if they should do so by chance in one—there is not, in general, any relation between dipole moment and per cent ionic character as had been thought. In fact, if bond polarity makes the largest contribution, then the moment could be in a direction opposite to that presumed in the simple argument which attributes the whole moment to resonance of 4-VIIa with 4-VIIb. It is perhaps worthwhile to point out that it is extremely difficult to determine the *direction* of the dipole in HCl or any similar molecule from experimental measurements, although it has been shown recently that in HI, H is positive relative to I. Although this discussion may have been a little disheartening in its inexorable regression from a state of tidy simplicity to uncertain complexity, there is, after all, nothing to be gained by pretending we understand things when we do not.

We conclude this section by considering how the net dipole moment of a polyatomic molecule can be considered to be the vector sum of various contributing dipoles. Suppose we have a regular pyramidal molecule, AB_3. Because of its symmetry, its dipole moment must lie along the three-fold axis of symmetry. If each A—B bond axis makes an angle, θ, with this symmetry axis, we might say the net molecular dipole moment, μ, is the vector sum of three equal bond moments, each of magnitude $(\mu/3)$ cos θ. Unfortunately, this picture is too simple to be satisfactory, as the following example will show.

The two pyramidal molecules NH_3 and NF_3 have dipole moments of 1.5 and 0.2 D., respectively. Knowing the bond angles ($\angle HNH = 106.75°$; $\angle FNF = 102.5°$), we would easily calculate the N—H bond moment to be $\sim$1.33 D. and the N—F bond moment to be $\sim$0.15 D. Now the trouble is that these results do not appear to be credible. In the first place, we should expect an $\overrightarrow{N—F}$ bond moment much larger than 0.15 D. Second, if we assume that only the electronegativity difference is responsible for the bond dipole, the $\overrightarrow{N—H}$ dipole should be still smaller than the $\overrightarrow{N—F}$ dipole. If we treat the N—H bond as we did the H—Cl bond and consider that despite the tendency of electronegativity to produce a moment, $\overleftarrow{N—H}$, the difference in size of the overlapping orbitals will tend to produce the opposite polarity, $\overrightarrow{N—H}$, it is still difficult to believe that the net N—H moment is $\sim$9 times the N—F moment. A satisfactory explanation of the molecular dipole moments can be developed, however, if we take account of the hybridization of the nitrogen atom and of the consequent orbital moment of the unshared electron pair on the nitrogen atom in each molecule. The observed bond angles are much larger than 90°, though not so large as 109°, and may be taken to mean that the nitrogen atom in each case is bonding the three atoms by s–p hybrid orbitals with slightly less than the amount of s character which occurs in regular sp^3 hybrids. Consequently, the unshared electrons do not occupy a pure s orbital, in which case they would be distributed spherically around the nitrogen atom and contribute nothing to the polarity of the molecules. Instead, they are in an s–p_z hybrid, so that they are more concentrated above than below the nitrogen atom. Thus, assuming the direction of the N—H bond moments to

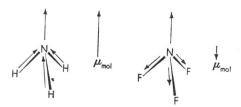

Fig. 4-2.   Diagram illustrating how the molecular dipole moment, μ_{mol}, can be regarded as a vector sum of bond moments and the lone pair moment in NH_3 and NF_3.

be as shown, the net polarity of each molecule may be accounted for as the vector sum of bond moments and the lone pair moment as shown in Figure 4-2. In general, bond moments are not directly relatable to the molecular moment by geometry alone, but hybridization and consequent orbital moments of unshared pairs must also be considered.

4-5. Molecular Vibrations and Bond Force Constants

The atoms in a molecule are never at rest, but are constantly vibrating about their equilibrium positions. If we consider a diatomic molecule, AB, the nature of this vibration is obviously such as to stretch and contract the bond relative to the equilibrium separation, r_e (4-VIII). To a good ap-

(4-VIII)

proximation, the molecule behaves like a pair of weights connected to a spring which follows Hook's law. Hook's law states that to stretch or contract the spring by Δr requires work equal to $\frac{1}{2}f(\Delta r)^2$, and the constant f is called the force constant of the spring. For the molecule we call it the force constant of the bond. This vibrating system is a harmonic oscillator and follows the usual expression relating the vibrational frequency, ν, the force constant, and the masses for a harmonic oscillator, namely:

$$\nu \ (\text{cm.}^{-1}) = \frac{1}{c}\sqrt{\frac{f}{4\pi^2\mu}} \tag{4-7}$$

where the frequency is expressed in wave numbers, c is the velocity of light, and μ is the reduced mass of the system (in grams) and is given by

$$\mu = \frac{M_A M_B}{M_A + M_B} \tag{4-8}$$

For convenience in making calculations using masses in chemical atomic weight units (for example, mass of $O = 16$, etc.), we can write

$$\nu^2 = 17.0 \times \frac{f}{\mu} \tag{4-9}$$

It therefore follows that if we can measure the vibrational frequency of the molecule, AB, we can calculate the force constant of the A—B bond.

These vibrational frequencies are determined by studying *infrared* and *Raman spectra* (collectively, *vibrational spectra*). The following description of the origin of these spectra, although inaccurate in small details, will be adequate for present purposes. When a molecule, vibrating with a frequency, ν_0, in its ground state, is bathed in radiation also of frequency ν_0, it may absorb one quantum of the radiant energy providing one condition is met. This condition is simply that the vibration of the molecule must cause a periodic variation in a dipole moment in the molecule. The transfer of energy from the radiation field to the molecule can only occur when a dipole vector in the molecule is oscillating with the same frequency as the electric vector of the radiation. This absorption of radiation gives rise to the infrared absorption spectrum. For diatomic molecules it is obvious that only a heteronuclear molecule can absorb, since a homonuclear molecule has no dipole moment in its equilibrium position, nor will any arise when the bond is stretched or contracted.

The Raman spectrum of a molecule arises in the following way. If a molecule is bathed in radiation with a frequency, ν, far in excess of its own vibrational frequency, ν_0, it practically never absorbs any of the radiant energy. Occasionally, however, it will absorb a quantum of energy, extract from it only the amount of energy corresponding to its vibrational frequency $(h\nu_0)$, and then re-emit a quantum of frequency $(\nu - \nu_0)$. The quanta re-emitted at this lower frequency are said to have undergone Raman scattering. This phenomenon was first recognized by Sir C. V. Raman, and thus bears his name. Again, as with infrared absorption, there is a limitation on the occurrence of Raman scattering, namely, that it can occur only when the molecular vibration concerned causes the polarizability of the molecule to change periodically as the vibration occurs. All diatomic molecules show such a change and therefore have Raman spectra. Clearly, for the frequency shift of the Raman-scattered radiation, we can determine the vibrational frequency of the molecule.

When a vibration causes absorption of infrared radiation, it is said to be *infrared active*; when it causes Raman scattering, it is said to be *Raman active*.

Polyatomic molecules have a number of so-called fundamental vibrational frequencies. The motions with these frequencies will, in general, involve stretchings of all the bonds and changes in all of the bond angles in the molecule, although particular vibrations often are more or less localized in one portion of the molecule. In any case, it is possible to analyze mathematically the observed set of frequencies and calculate force constants for the stretching of various bonds and also for deformation of the various bond angles.

We would certainly expect some direct, if not exactly linear, relationship to exist between the strength of a bond and its stretching force constant.

Knowing that bond strength increases with bond order, we expect bond force constants to increase with bond orders, as, in fact, they do (Table 4-5).

TABLE 4-5

Relation of Bond Force Constant and Bond Order

Bond	Stretching constant, millidynes/A.
C—C	~5.0
C=C	~9.6
C≡C	~16
C—O	~4.5
C=O	~12

However, it should not be assumed that these force constants are quantitatively characteristic of the linkages, independent of the other linkages in the molecule, for that is decidedly not so. For example, the data in Table 4-6 indicate how the force constant of a bond varies with the environ-

TABLE 4-6

Effect of Environment on Bond Force Constant

Bond	Stretching constant, millidynes/A.
≡C—H	~5.9
$\diagdown$C—H	~5.1
—C—H	~4.8
=C=O	~15.5
C=O	~12.1
—C—C≡	~5.2
—C—C—	~4.5

ment of the bond in the molecule. Actually, these small differences are extremely useful since they cause frequency variations in the absorption bands due to the stretching of the various bonds. As a result the exact position of the band can be used to infer not only the existence of a certain linkage in the molecule but also, in many cases, how that linkage is located within the molecule relative to other bonds.

4-6. Van der Waals Radii

We have discussed the distances between ions in ionic solids and pointed out that they may be considered as approximately equal to the sums of appropriate ionic radii. We have also discussed the assignment of covalent radii whose sums approximate the separations of bonded atoms in covalent molecules. There remain to be considered the distances between atoms in liquids and solids when these atoms are not bonded to one another either ionically or covalently.

Let us consider, for example, the inert gases. The fact that they can be liquefied and solidified at all proves that there are *some* forces of attraction between the atoms; at the same time the exceedingly low temperatures required to condense them proves that these forces are extremely weak. These forces are usually called van der Waals forces, after the Dutch physicist who first emphasized their importance by taking account of them in his equation of state for imperfect gases, although sometimes they are also called London forces, since their nature was first explained by Fritz London, using wave mechanics. We have mentioned them before as minor contributors to the total attractive force in ionic crystals. In crystals of the inert gases, however, there are no electrostatic forces, and these van der Waals forces are the only attractive forces. Again, as in ionic crystals, the equilibrium separation of neighboring atoms is that distance at which the attractive force is balanced by the repulsive force due to overlap of the outer portions of the electron clouds. Since this repulsive force rises very steeply and becomes important only at very short distances, the ionic radius of Br⁻ and one-half the distance of closest approach of two krypton atoms in solid krypton do not differ very much despite the differences in the nature of the attractive forces. This latter quantity—one-half the Kr—Kr separation in solid krypton—is called the van der Waals radius of krypton. The van der Waals radii are much larger than covalent radii, however. Thus, the ionic radius of Br⁻ is 1.95 A., the covalent radius of Br is 1.15 A., and the van der Waals radius of Kr is 2.00 A.

Van der Waals radii for all elements may be estimated if the distances of closest approach of their atoms to other atoms when no chemical bond exists between them are known from structural studies. For instance, in solid bromine the closest approach of nonbonded bromine atoms is 3.90 A., giving a van der Waals radius of 1.95 A. If we consider crystals consisting of molecules with permanent dipole moments, then the dipole–dipole attractions will contribute to the stability of the crystals, but the closest distance of approach of two nonbonded atoms can still be taken as the sum of their van der Waals radii. As with ionic and covalent radii, deviations from additivity occur since the basic idea is something of an oversimplification, but a set of radii has been assigned to commonly occurring nonmetallic atoms which gives the best over-all agreement with a large number of experimental data. A set of van der Waals radii computed by Pauling is given in Table 4-7.

TABLE 4-7

Van der Waals Radii of Nonmetallic Atoms
(In Angstroms)

H	1.2				
N	1.5	O	1.40	F	1.35
P	1.9	S	1.85	Cl	1.80
As	2.0	Se	2.00	Br	1.95
Sb	2.2	Te	2.20	I	2.15

Radius of a methyl group, 2.0 A.
Half thickness of an aromatic ring, 1.85 A.

4-7. Relations between Various Bond Properties

In preceding sections of this chapter, we have seen that the following qualitative rules are of general validity:

1. The greater the order of a bond, the greater is its strength.
2. The greater the strength of a bond, the greater is its force constant.
3. The greater the strength of a bond, the shorter is the internuclear distance.

All of these statements are true, with the proviso "other things being equal," which usually means that we must compare only bonds between the same atom pair in different molecules. For example, if we compare (Table 4-8) the carbon-oxygen bonds in CO_2 and CO, these rules are found to be valid.

TABLE 4-8

	CO_2	CO
Mean bond energy, kcal.	192	256
Approximate bond order	2	3
Bond force constant, millidynes/A.	15.9	19.0
C—O bond length, A.	1.16	1.13

From a combination of the second and third rules above, we might also write a fourth, redundant, rule:

4. The shorter the bond, the greater its force constant.

References*

Allred, A. L., *J. Inorg. & Nuclear Chem.*, **17**, 215 (1961). Electronegativity.

——— and A. L. Hensly, *J. Inorg. & Nuclear Chem.*, **17**, 43 (1961).

——— and E. G. Rochow, *J. Inorg. & Nuclear Chem.*, **5**, 264, 269 (1958).

Cottrell, T. L., *The Strengths of Chemical Bonds*, 2nd ed., Butterworths, London, 1958. An excellent, authoritative book dealing with methods of determination of bond energies and containing much detailed information and values.

Gaydon, A. G., *Bond Dissociation Energies*, Chapman and Hall, London, 1953.

Pritchard, H. O., and H. A. Skinner, *Chem. Revs.*, **55**, 745 (1955). A review on electronegativity.

Swarc, M., *Chem. Rev.*, **47**, 75 (1950). The determination of bond dissociation energies by pyrolytic methods.

Tables of Interatomic Distance and Configuration in Molecules and Ions, Special Publication No. 11, Chemical Society, London. An extensive compilation of structural information.

Wheatley, P. J., *The Determination of Molecular Structure*, Clarendon Press, Oxford, 1960. An excellent introduction to methods of structure determination such as X-ray diffraction, molecular spectroscopy, and nuclear resonance methods.

* The references given for Chapter 3 apply here also.

PART TWO

Chemistry of the Nontransitional Elements

5

Hydrogen

5-1. Introduction

The hydrogen atom has the simplest structure of all atoms. It consists of a nucleus of charge $+1$ with a single extranuclear electron. Three isotopes are known: ^1H, ^2H (deuterium or D), and ^3H (tritium or T). Although isotope effects are greatest for hydrogen, justifying the use of distinctive names for the two heavier isotopes, the chemical properties of H, D, and T are essentially identical except in matters such as rates and equilibrium constants of reactions. These effects are discussed later (Section 5-10). The normal form of the element is the diatomic molecule; various possibilities are H_2, D_2, T_2, HD, HT, DT.

Although the abundance on earth of molecular hydrogen is trivial, hydrogen in its compounds has one of the highest of abundances. Hydrogen compounds of all the elements other than the inert gases are known, and many of these are of transcendental importance. Water is the most important hydrogen compound; others of great significance are hydrocarbons, carbohydrates and other organic compounds, ammonia and its derivatives, sulfuric acid, sodium hydroxide, etc. Hydrogen forms more compounds than any other element.

Hydrogen forms the lightest of all gaseous molecules. It is a colorless, odorless gas, virtually insoluble in water. It is most easily prepared by the action of dilute acids on metals such as Zn or Fe and by electrolysis of water; industrially hydrogen may be obtained by thermal cracking of hydrocarbons, by the reduction of water by carbon (water gas reaction) and in other ways.

Hydrogen is not exceptionally reactive. It burns in air to form water and will react with oxygen and the halogens explosively under certain conditions. The gas at high temperatures will reduce many oxides either to lower oxides or to the metal. At elevated temperatures in the presence of suitable catalysts, it will react with N_2 to form NH_3. With most non-metals it forms hydrides. In the presence of platinum or platinum oxide catalysts, it is able to reduce, in solution in certain organic solvents (e.g., alcohol, acetic acid), a great many organic compounds; unsaturated compounds may be reduced to saturated ones, aldehydes to alcohols, certain nitrogen compounds to ammonia or amines, etc. Some of the more important reactions of H_2 are sketched in Figure 5-1. Although these hydrogen-

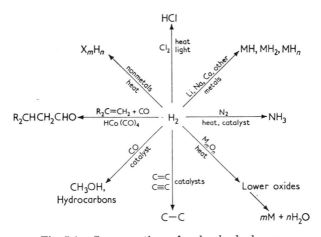

Fig. 5-1. Some reactions of molecular hydrogen.

ation reactions are heterogeneous, certain transition metal salts and complexes can react homogeneously with hydrogen at room temperature. Thus cupric acetate in quinoline can function as a hydrogenation catalyst, while Ag^+, MnO_4^-, and other ions can be homogeneously reduced by molecular hydrogen. These low temperature reactions are believed to involve the formation of a reactive bond between the transition metal and hydrogen.

The dissociation of hydrogen is highly endothermic, and this accounts in part for its rather low reactivity at low temperatures:

$$H_2 = 2H \qquad \Delta H_0^0 = 103.2 \text{ kcal./mole}$$

At high temperature, in arcs at high current density, or in discharge tubes at low hydrogen pressure, or by ultraviolet irradiation of hydrogen, atomic hydrogen can be produced. It has a short half-life (~ 0.3 second). The heat of recombination is sufficient to produce exceedingly high temperatures, and atomic hydrogen has been used for welding metals. Atomic hydrogen is exceedingly reactive chemically, being a strong reducing agent.

5-2. The Bonding of Hydrogen

The chemistry of hydrogen depends mainly on three electronic processes:

1. *Loss of the valence electron.* The $1s$ valence electron may be lost to give the hydrogen ion, H^+. This ion is merely the proton. Its small size $(r \backsim 1.5 \times 10^{-13}$ cm.$)$ relative to atomic sizes $(r \backsim 10^{-8}$ cm.$)$ and charge result in the proton having a unique ability to distort the electron cloud surrounding other atoms; the proton accordingly never exists as such, except in gaseous ion beams, and is invariably associated with other atoms or molecules in condensed phases, for example, as the H_3O^+ ion.

2. *Acquisition of an electron.* The hydrogen atom can acquire an electron, attaining the $1s^2$ structure of He, to form the hydride ion, H^-. This ion exists only in saline hydrides, such as KH or CaH_2, which are formed only by the most electropositive elements.

3. *Formation of an electron pair bond.* The hydrogen atom again attains the $1s^2$ structure by formation of an electron pair bond. This bond may be homopolar, as in the H_2 molecule, but in other cases has heteropolar nature, as, for example, in HCl.

These ways in which hydrogen can bond with other elements are discussed in more detail below. The nature of the proton and the complete absence of any shielding of the nuclear charge by electron shells allow other forms of chemical activity unique to hydrogen. Some of these are the following, which are discussed in some detail subsequently:

1. The formation of numerous compounds, often nonstoichiometric, with metallic elements, which are generally called *hydrides*, but which almost certainly do not contain hydride ions.

2. The formation of certain compounds of transition metals in which the hydrogen atom is bound directly to the metal, for example, $HCo(CO)_4$, $HRe(C_5H_5)_2$, and $(Ph_3P)_2PtClH$.

3. Formation of the *hydrogen bridge bond* in electron-deficient compounds, as in 5-I.

(5-I)

4. Formation of what is called the *hydrogen bond.*

5. Complex hydrides—$NaBH_4$, $LiAlH_4$, etc.—have certain similarities, at least in structure and stoichiometry, with other complexes such as $NaBF_4$, but are on the whole peculiar to hydrogen.

5-3. The Hydrogen Ion

For the reaction

$$H(g) = H^+(g) + e \qquad (5\text{-}1)$$

the ionization potential is 13.595 e.v. ($\Delta H = 313$ kcal./mole), which is very high by comparison with other unipositive elements such as the alkali metals and indeed many other elements; it is higher even than the first ionization potential of the inert gas Xe. It can therefore be shown that, with the possible exception of HF, bonds from hydrogen to other elements must be mainly covalent. For HF the bond energy is 5.9 e.v. For a purely ionic bond the energy can be estimated as the sum of (*1*) 13.6 e.v. to ionize H, (*2*) -3.6 e.v. to place the electron on F, and (*3*) -15.6 e.v. as an upper limit on the electrostatic energy of the ion pair H^+F^- at the observed internuclear distance in HF. The sum of these terms is -5.6 e.v. as an upper limit, which is not too far below the actual bond energy. For HCl, on the other hand, the experimental bond energy is 4.5 e.v., whereas for a purely ionic situation we would have the sum $+13.6 - 3.8 - 11.3 = -1.7$ e.v. as an upper limit. Thus purely electrostatic bonding cannot nearly explain the stability of HCl.

Hydrogen can form the hydrogen ion *only* when its compounds are dissolved in media which *solvate* protons. The solvation process thus provides the energy required for bond rupture; a necessary corollary of this process is that the proton, H^+, never exists in condensed phases, but occurs always as solvates—H_3O^+, R_2OH^+, FHF^-, etc. The order of magnitude of these solvation energies can be seen by comparing equation 5-1 with the solvation reaction in water

$$H^+(g) + xH_2O = H^+(aq) \qquad \Delta H = 256 \text{ kcal./mole}$$

Compounds which furnish solvated hydrogen ions in suitable solvents, such as water, are *acids.*

Since the most important aspect of the chemistry of the hydrogen ion is that in aqueous media, this case will be considered in more detail.

The nature of the hydrogen ion in water, which should more correctly be called the hydroxonium ion, H_3O^+, is discussed below. The hydrogen ion in water is customarily referred to as "the hydrogen ion," implying H_3O^+. The use of other terms, such as hydroxonium, is somewhat pedantic except in special cases. As a matter of convenience we shall usually write H^+ for the hydrogen ion and assume it to be understood that the ion is aquated, since in a similar manner many other cations, Na^+, Fe^{2+}, Zn^{2+}, etc., are customarily written as such, although there also it is understood that the actual species present in water are aquated species, for example, $[Fe(H_2O)_6]^{2+}$.

Water itself is weakly ionized:

$$2H_2O = H_3O^+ + OH^-$$

or

$$H_2O = H^+ + OH^-$$

Other cases of such *self-ionization* of a compound where one molecule solvates a proton originating from another are known; for example, in pure sulfuric acid

$$2H_2SO_4 = H_3SO_4^+ + HSO_4^-$$

and in liquid ammonia

$$2NH_3 = NH_4^+ + NH_2^-$$

In aqueous solutions, the hydrogen ion concentration is often given in terms of pH, defined as $\log_{10} 1/[H^+]$, where $[H^+]$ is the hydrogen ion activity, which may be considered to approximate to the molar concentration of H^+ ions in very dilute solutions.

At 25°C. the ionic product of water is

$$K_w = [H^+][OH^-] = 1 \times 10^{-14}M^2$$

This value is significantly temperature dependent. When $[H^+] = [OH^-]$, the solution is said to be neutral, and $[H^+] = 1 \times 10^{-7}M$; that is, pH = 7.0. Solutions of lower pH are acid; those of higher pH, alkaline.

The standard hydrogen electrode provides the reference for all other oxidation-reduction systems. The hydrogen half-cell or hydrogen electrode is

$$\tfrac{1}{2}H_2(g) = H^+(aq) + e$$

By definition, the potential of this system is zero ($E° = 0.000$ v.) at all temperatures when an inert metallic electrode dips into a solution of hydrogen ions of unit activity (i.e., pH = 0) in equilibrium with H_2 gas at 1 atm. pressure.

Since

$$E = \frac{RT}{nF} \ln \frac{[H^+]}{p_{H_2}^{1/2}} = -0.05916 \log \frac{[H^+]}{p_{H_2}^{1/2}} \text{ (at 298°K.)}$$

for the half-cell reaction in pure water at pH = 7 at 25°C.,

$$\tfrac{1}{2}H_2(g) = H^+(aq)(10^{-7}M) + e \qquad E°_{298} = +0.414 \text{ v.}$$

In alkaline solution (pH = 14)

$$\tfrac{1}{2}H_2(g) + OH^-(aq) = H_2O + e \qquad E^0_{298} = +0.83 \text{ v.}$$

The above potential for water shows that hydrogen will be liberated from water by reagents whose standard oxidation potentials are >0.414 v. (in absence of overvoltages, which, however, are frequently large for metals).

Thus Na will liberate hydrogen from water, since

$$Na = Na^+(aq) + e \qquad E^0_{298} = 2.1 \text{ v.}$$

Similarly, certain ions, for example, the U^{3+} ion, will be oxidized by water with the evolution of hydrogen.

$$U^{3+}(aq) = U^{4+}(aq) + e \qquad E^0_{298} = 0.61 \text{ v.}$$

Many electropositive metals or ions even if they do not liberate H_2 from water, will be oxidized by greater concentration of hydrogen ions—thus the reactions of Zn or Fe are normally used to prepare H_2 from dilute acids.

The Hydroxonium Ion, H_3O^+. Although the solvated ion H_3O^+ has long been postulated to exist and the existence of the analogous discrete NH_4^+ ion has long been known, *conclusive* evidence for H_3O^+ has only recently been obtained by nuclear magnetic resonance and infrared and Raman studies of solid hydrates of a number of acids. In these solids, the proton cannot occupy a lattice site on account of its negligible size and must hence (*a*) be present as H_3O^+ or (*b*) remain attached to some atom in the acid molecule. The ten acids that have been shown to contain H_3O^+ are listed in Table 5-1; in oxalic and some other acids, the proton or

TABLE 5-1

Constitution of Some Solid Acid Hydrates

Ordinary formula	Species actually present
$HF \cdot H_2O$	H_3O^+, F^-
$HCl \cdot H_2O$	H_3O^+, Cl^-
$HBr \cdot H_2O$	H_3O^+, Br^-
$HI \cdot H_2O$	H_3O^+, I^-
$HClO_4 \cdot H_2O$	H_3O^+, ClO_4^-
$HNO_3 \cdot H_2O$	H_3O^+, NO_3^-
$H_2PtCl_6 \cdot 2H_2O$	$2H_3O^+$, $PtCl_6^{2-}$
$H_2SO_4 \cdot H_2O$	H_3O^+, HSO_4^-
$H_2SO_4 \cdot 2H_2O$	$2H_3O^+$, SO_4^{2-}
$H_2SeO_4 \cdot H_2O$	H_3O^+, $HSeO_4^-$
$C_2O_4H_2 \cdot 2H_2O$	$C_2O_4H_2 \cdot 2H_2O$

protons have been shown to remain attached to the acid molecule. The behavior of H_3O^+ in a crystal lattice closely resembles that of NH_4^+. Thus $[H_3O][ClO_4]$ and $[NH_4][ClO_4]$ form isomorphous crystals. An important difference between H_3O^+ and NH_4^+ compounds lies in the uniformly lower melting points of the former, which results in their being of less practical importance. The structure of the H_3O^+ ion appears to be that of a rather f.at triangular pyramid with the HOH angle about 115°. Very recently it has been demonstrated that in solution H_3O^+ binds three more water molecules fairly strongly, presumably attracting an oxygen atom to each of its rather positive hydrogen atoms, so that the aqueous "hydrogen ion" is best represented as $[H_9O_4]^+$ with the kind of structure shown in 5-II. It

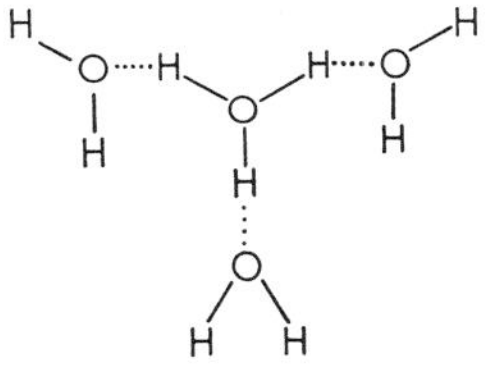

(5-II)

must be noted that the lifetime of an individual H_3O^+ ion in water is exceedingly short, $\sim 10^{-13}$ second, since all of the protons are undergoing rapid exchange.

HYDRIDES

5-4. The Hydride Ion, H⁻; Saline Hydrides

The formation of the unipositive ion H^+ (or H_3O^+, etc.) suggests that hydrogen should be classed with the alkali metals in the periodic table. On the other hand, the formation of the hydride ion might suggest an analogy with the halogens. Such attempts at classification of hydrogen with other elements can be misleading. Hydrogen has a very low electron affinity and the tendency to form the negative ion is much lower than for the more electronegative halogen elements. This may be seen by comparing the energetics of the formation reactions

$$\frac{1}{2}H_2(g) \rightarrow H(g) \qquad \Delta H = 52 \text{ kcal./mole}$$
$$H(g) + e \rightarrow H^-(g) \qquad \Delta H = -16 \text{ kcal./mole}$$

$$\frac{1}{2}H_2(g) + e \rightarrow H^-(g) \qquad \Delta H = +36 \text{ kcal./mole}$$

$$\frac{1}{2}Br_2(g) \rightarrow Br(g) \qquad \Delta H = 27 \text{ kcal./mole}$$
$$Br(g) + e \rightarrow Br^-(g) \qquad \Delta H = -82 \text{ kcal./mole}$$

$$\frac{1}{2}Br_2(g) + e \rightarrow Br^-(g) \qquad \Delta H = -55 \text{ kcal./mole}$$

Thus, owing to the endothermic character of the H^- ion, only the most electropositive metals—the alkalies and alkaline earths—form saline or salt-like hydrides, such as NaH and CaH$_2$. The ionic nature of the compounds is shown by their high conductivity just below or at the melting point and by the fact that on electrolysis of solutions in molten alkali halides hydrogen is liberated at the *anode*.

X-ray and neutron diffraction studies show that in these hydrides the H^- ion has a crystallographic radius between those of F^- and Cl^-. Thus the electrostatic lattice energies of the hydride and the fluoride and chloride of a given metal will be similar. These facts and a consideration of the Born-Haber cycles lead us to conclude that *only* the most electropositive metals *can* form ionic hydrides, since in these cases relatively little energy is required to form the metal ion.

The known saline hydrides and some of their physical properties are given in Table 5-2. The heats of formation of the saline hydrides, com-

TABLE 5-2

The Saline Hydrides and Some of Their Properties

Salt	Heat of formation, kcal./mole	M—H distance, A.	Apparent radius of H^-, A.[a]
NaCl type crystal structure			
LiH	21.7	2.04	1.26
NaH	13.5	2.44	1.46
KH	13.8	2.85	1.52
RbH	~12[b]	3.02	1.53
CsH	19.9	3.19	1.54
Orthorhombic crystal structure			
CaH$_2$	46.6	—[c]	—
SrH$_2$	42.2	—	—
BaH$_2$	41.0	—	—

[a] See text.

[b] This value appears to be out of line and may be in error.

[c] There are two different sets of M—H neighbors in this lattice with separations differing by ~0.3 A.

pared with those of the alkali halides, which are about 100 kcal./mole, reflect the inherently small stability of the hydride ion.

For the relatively simple two-electron system in the H^- ion, it is possible to calculate an effective radius for the free ion, the value 2.08 A. having been obtained. It is of interest to compare this with some other values, specifically, 0.93 A. for the He atom, ~0.5 A. for the H atom, 1.95 A. for the crystallographic radius of Br^-, and 0.30 A. for the covalent radius of hydrogen, as well as with the values of the "apparent" crystallographic radius of H^- given in Table 5-2. The latter are obtained by subtracting the Goldschmidt radii of the metal ions from the experimental M—X distances. The value 2.08 A. for the radius of free H^- is at first sight surprisingly large, being more than twice as large as that for He. This results from the facts that the H^- nuclear charge is only half that in He and that the electrons repel each other and screen each other ($\sim$30%) from the pull of the nucleus. It will be seen in Table 5-2 that the apparent radius of H^- in the alkali hydrides never attains the value 2.08 A. and also that it decreases markedly with decreasing electropositive character of the metal. The generally small size is probably attributable in part to the easy compressibility of the rather diffuse H^- ion and partly to a certain degree of covalence in the bonds.

Chemical Properties of Saline Hydrides. The saline hydrides are white crystalline substances of generally high reactivity, best prepared by direct reaction of the metal with hydrogen gas at temperatures up to $\sim$700°C. They can be dissolved in molten alkali halides and on electrolysis of such a solution, for example, CaH_2 dissolved in LiCl + KCl at 360°C., hydrogen is released at the anode. LiH alone can be melted without decomposition.

A key to the reactivity of these hydrides lies in the formalism of regarding H—H as the exceedingly weak parent acid (an extrapolation back from HCl, strong, and HF, weak) of the MH salts. Thus H^- and its salts react instantly and completely with any substance affording even the minutest traces of H^+, such as water, according to the reaction

$$NaH + H^+ = Na^+ + H_2$$

For the half reaction $H^- = \frac{1}{2}H_2 + e$, the value $E° = +2.25$ v. has been estimated.

As would be expected from the above, the saline hydrides are excellent reducing agents. LiH and CaH_2 are often used in preparative chemistry for this purpose, and CaH_2 also serves as a drying agent, although the complex hydrides like $LiAlH_4$ or $NaBH_4$ (see below) are most generally useful. Several of the saline hydrides ignite spontaneously in ordinary air, perhaps owing to initial exothermic hydrolysis by traces of water vapor. Thermal decomposition at high temperatures gives the metal and hydrogen.

5-5. Covalent Compounds of Hydrogen

The most numerous of hydrogen compounds are those in which it forms electron pair bonds with other elements; the number of carbon compounds of hydrogen is legion, and most of the less metallic elements form numerous hydrogen derivatives. Many of these compounds are volatile, being either gases or liquids.

The chemistry of many of these compounds is highly dependent upon the nature of the element to which hydrogen is bonded; particularly dependent is the degree to which the compounds behave as acids under various conditions (this matter is discussed on pages 134–140). A few general remarks about covalent hydrogen compounds are pertinent here.

Except in H_2 itself, where the electronegativity difference is zero and the resonance structures $H^+H^- \leftrightarrow H^-H^+$ are of equal weight and contribute a few per cent, all H—X bonds will possess some polar character. As will be seen subsequently, important chemical differences arise from reversal of orientation of the H—X bond dipole. In spite of the heteropolar nature of H—X bonds and in spite of the possibility of ionization and acid behavior on dissolution in a polar solvent, many compounds in this class are properly called covalent hydrides. Thus, although HCl behaves as a strong acid on dissolution in water, in nonpolar solvents, for example, in benzene, it is not dissociated and it is itself a gas. In condensed phases of such covalent hydrides there are only van der Waals forces between the molecules (in some special cases hydrogen bonding occurs).

The strength of H—X bonds and the thermal stability of covalent hydrides seem to depend on the electronegativities and size of the element X. The variation in bond strength in some binary hydrides is shown in Figure 5-2. There are a fairly smooth *decrease* in bond strength with *in-*

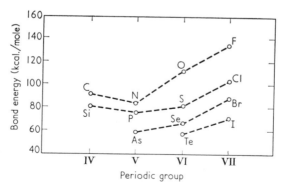

Fig. 5-2. Variation in mean H—X bond energies.

creasing Z in a periodic group and a general *increase across* any period. Thermal stability is only a crude guide to bond strength, but is useful where precise bond energies are unknown. Thermal stability, in the sense of resistance to the reaction

$$H_nX \rightarrow \tfrac{n}{2}H_2 + \tfrac{1}{2}X_x$$

invariably decreases with increasing Z. Generally, for two elements of about equal electronegativity, the *heavier* element forms the less stable hydride. Thus the stability orders $CH_4 > H_2S$ and $PH_3 > TeH_2$.

The relation of H—X bond strength to acidity in aqueous solution will be discussed on pages 138–140.

For the vast majority of covalent hydrogen compounds the chemical shifts observed in high resolution nuclear magnetic resonance spectra, which roughly indicate the electron density surrounding the proton, are of the order of a few parts per million (p.p.m.) compared to water. There is, however, a class of compounds in which the chemical shift is abnormally large—from 10 to 30 p.p.m. relative to water—suggesting unusual diamagnetic shielding of the proton. All of these compounds have a hydrogen atom bonded *directly to a transitional metal*, for example, $HCo(CO)_4$, $HW(CO)_3(C_5H_5)$, $HRe(C_5H_5)_2$, and $[(C_6H_5)_3P]_2PtClH$. The four compounds given here behave, respectively, as a strong acid, a weak acid, a base (cf. NH_3), and a neutral molecule, and there is no correlation between acid function and the proton resonance position. The nature of the M—H bonds in compounds of these types is discussed in Section 27-7.

The volatile boron hydrides (e.g., B_2H_6, B_4H_{10}) are unusual in that they are electron-deficient hydrides possessing hydrogen bridges. Their structures are discussed in Chapter 10.

5-6. Complex Hydrides of Boron, Aluminum, and Gallium

The only complex hydrides of nontransition elements known at the present time are formed by boron, aluminum, and gallium and occur as salts (not necessarily ionic) of hydride anions, for example, $Na[BH_4]$, $Li[AlH_4]$, $Li[GaH_4]$, $U(BH_4)_4$, $Al(BH_4)_3$, and $Na[BH(OCH_3)_3]$. All of these XH_4^- *ions* are believed to be tetrahedral since this structure has been established for the BH_4^- ion. Thus they may be considered formally as complexes with the central atom coordinated by four H^- ions, somewhat analogous to the BF_4^- ion.

The discovery and study of this type of compound ($LiAlH_4$ in particular) by H. I. Schlesinger, H. C. Brown, and others rank among the most important developments in inorganic chemistry in view of the broad usefulness of these hydrides as reductants and sources of H^- ion.

The chemistry of these substances may be understood through consideration of an equilibrium (probably hypothetical) representing their formation (eq. 5-2). The XH_3 group behaves as an electron acceptor and the

$$H:^- + \overset{\displaystyle H}{\underset{\displaystyle H}{\overset{..}{\underset{..}{X}}}} : H = \left[\overset{\displaystyle H}{\underset{\displaystyle H}{H : \overset{..}{\underset{..}{X}} : H}} \right]^- \qquad (5\text{-}2)$$

$$(X = B, Al, Ga)$$

hydride ion as an electron donor. It might then be expected that the thermal and chemical stabilities of the three anions would vary according to the known ability of the elements X to act as acceptors. This order is $B > Al > Ga$. The experimental facts bear this out in general. For example, the hydrolysis of the XH_4^- ions

$$4H_2O + XH_4^- \rightarrow 4H_2 + X(OH)_3 + OH^-$$

is probably initiated by reaction of XH_4^- with H^+ to form H_2 and XH_3, the latter then reacting further. In effect, XH_3 is competing with the acceptor H^+ for the hydride ion. Thus, sodium borohydride is quite soluble in water, undergoing only a slight initial decomposition which renders the solution basic and prevents further hydrolysis. It is, of course, completely hydrolyzed in acid, but Na salts of AlH_4^- and GaH_4^- are rapidly and often explosively hydrolyzed by water alone.

The stability and other properties of a given XH_4^- salt depend also on the *nature of the cation*. While $NaBH_4$ is completely ionic (Na^+, BH_4^-), most other borohydrides and the salts of AlH_4^- and GaH_4^- (of the latter few are known) show considerable covalent character. If the cation, as in $Be(BH_4)_2$ or $Al(BH_4)_3$, has considerable acceptor power, it will tend to distort the XH_4^- groups, especially AlH_4^- and GaH_4^-, where the central metal is of somewhat lower acceptor ability. Thus, as an admittedly extreme example, $Al(BH_4)_3$ is a very reactive, unstable liquid (m.p. $-64.5°C.$), very soluble in organic solvents. $Be(BH_4)_3$ is a solid, but sublimes at $90°C.$ and is insoluble in nonpolar media. The more covalent complex hydrides are rapidly, often explosively, hydrolyzed by water and ignite in air. Structural studies required to specify clearly the nature of the bonding in these covalent compounds are lacking, but it is believed that there is hydrogen bridging between XH_4 groups and the cations similar perhaps to that postulated in BeH_2 and MgH_2 and known to exist in the boron hydrides.

The principal use of these complex hydrides is as reducing agents in both organic and inorganic chemistry. The most generally used materials are $LiAlH_4$ and $Na(K)BH_4$, which are soluble in certain ethers like diethylene glycol dimethyl ether (only $LiAlH_4$ is soluble in diethyl ether), and are relatively easy to handle and store. $LiAlH_4$ accomplishes many otherwise tedious or difficult reductions, such as the direct reduction of —COOH to —CH_2OH. It is widely useful for preparing other hydrides by the general reaction

$$4MX + LiAlH_4 \rightarrow 4MH + LiX + AlX_3$$
$$(X = \text{halogen, } OCH_3, \text{ etc.})$$

$LiAlH_4$ itself is a nonvolatile, crystalline solid, white when pure, but as usually seen, grey. It is stable to $\sim 120°C$. It is prepared according to the reaction

$$4LiH + AlCl_3 \rightarrow LiAlH_4 + 3LiCl$$

and is available commercially. It is also possible to make mixed complex hydrides

$$LiAlH_4 + ROH \rightarrow LiAlH(OR)_3 + 3H_2$$

some of which are useful for special reduction reactions.

5-7. Other Hydrides

We have so far discussed compounds in which the state of the hydrogen is rather definitely known. Hydrogen does, in fact, form some sort of "compound" with nearly every other element, but with those to be discussed here the nature of the substance is not always well understood. A rough attempt to classify the various types of hydrogen compounds, which are all loosely called "hydrides," is shown in Figure 5-3. The hydrides of

H																	He
Li	Be											B	C	N	O	F	Ne
Na	Mg											Al	Si	P	S	Cl	Ar
K	Ca	Sc	Ti*	V*	Cr*	Mn*	Fe*	Co*	Ni*	Cu	Zn	Ga	Ge	As	Se	Br	Kr
Rb	Sr	Y	Zr	Nb	Mo*	Tc*	Ru*	Rh*	Pd*	Ag	Cd	In	Sn	Sb	Te	I	Xe
Cs	Ba	La–Lu Hf	Ta*	W*	Re*	Os*	Ir*	Pt*	Au	Hg	Tl	Pb	Bi	Po	At	Rn
Fr	Ra	Ac	U	Pu													
Saline hydrides		Transition metal hydrides										Borderline hydrides	Covalent hydrides				

Fig. 5-3. A classification of the hydrides. The starred elements are those for which complex molecules or ions containing M—H bonds are known.

beryllium and *magnesium*, BeH_2 and MgH_2, seem to represent a transition between the ionic and covalent hydrides. Both are white nonvolatile solids, insoluble in organic media. They appear to be polymerized, and it has been suggested that this is effected by hydrogen bridging (5-III)

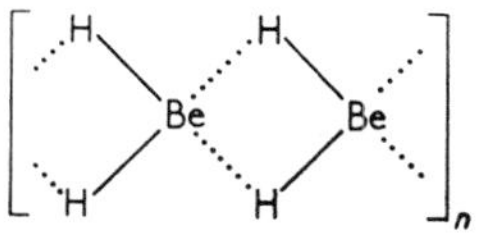

$$(5\text{-III})$$

similar to that in the boranes. Both react violently with water, alcohols, and active hydrogen in general, and both, like the saline hydrides, are powerful reducing agents.

The larger group of borderline hydrides are mostly of a very uncertain nature. Copper hydride, CuH, seems to be a definite compound, but hydrides of the other elements are certainly unstable and difficult to prepare and perhaps nonexistent. CuH is a red-brown solid with some reducing properties, insoluble in and apparently stable toward water, although decomposed by acids to liberate hydrogen.

The *transition metal binary hydrides* are commonly grouped as a class as a matter of convenience rather than because of any uniformity in properties. In fact, a very wide range of behavior toward hydrogen is shown by the various elements in this group. Metal–hydrogen systems involving scandium, yttrium, some of the lanthanides, uranium, and plutonium have been well studied, and the behavior seems well established.

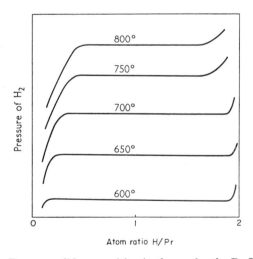

Fig. 5-4.   Pressure-solid composition isotherms for the Pr–H system.

The data shown in Figure 5-4 for the H—Pr system are typical of the elements La, Ce, Pr, Nd, and Sm. The plateaus represent regions in which two phases, Pr and PrH_2, coexist, the latter having the fluorite structure. In the regions to the extreme left, hydrogen merely dissolves in the metal. Failure of the plateaus to reach the full H/Pr ratio of 2.00 probably means that there is a short range, between H/Pr of about 1.8 and H/Pr of 2.00, in which the PrH_2 phase can exist in a hydrogen-deficient condition. Further absorption of hydrogen seems to involve the solution of hydrogen in the PrH_2 phase. With Gd and Pr the behavior in the M to MH_2 range is the same, but between MH_2 and MH_3 a third hexagonal MH_3 phase appears. Although it is true that in general specimens of these hydrides containing only one phase and having a perfectly stoichiometric composition are not isolated, perfectly well-defined hydride phases, MH_2 and MH_3, do exist. The MH_2 phases are grey solids which react with water and acids to produce hydrogen. They have metallic properties, presumably because there is still one unused valence electron per metal atom which may occupy electronic conduction bands in the solid. The heats of formation of the MH_2 phases are of the order of 40–50 kcal./mole. *Uranium hydride*, UH_3, which is a black pyrophoric powder, is formed by direct action of hydrogen on the metal. The phase relations in the U—H system show no UH_2 phase (*plutonium*, on the other hand, does also show a PuH_2 phase), and UH_3 is stoichiometric. It has a rather complex structure. UH_3 is formed quite exothermically, $\Delta H_f^0 = -30.8$ kcal./mole.

Titanium, *zirconium*, and presumably *hafnium* absorb hydrogen exothermically, giving nonstoichiometric materials with compositions such as $TiH_{1.7}$ and $ZrH_{1.9}$. The lattice changes on uptake of such quantities of hydrogen, but the phase relations have not been extensively studied. TiH_x and ZrH_x have industrial utility as reducing agents. The remaining metals in the transition group seem to have little affinity for hydrogen and do not form any well-defined binary hydrides. Several, including Fe, Co, and Ni, were reported to give black pyrophoric hydrides, such as NiH_2, when suspensions of their salts in Grignard reagents were treated with hydrogen, but more recent work indicates that there are probably no such compounds. *Palladium*, alone of the group VIII metals, absorbs appreciable amounts of hydrogen gas, but it is not known with certainty whether well-defined hydride phases exist.

THE HYDROGEN BOND

5-8. Experimental Evidence

Substances containing hydrogen bound to the most electronegative elements frequently exhibit properties best explained by assuming that the hydrogen atom has a small but significant affinity for other electronegative atoms while remaining strongly bonded to the first one. This relatively weak secondary bond is called the *hydrogen bond*. We shall employ the following notation for a hydrogen bond between an H atom bonded initially to atom X and another atom Y:

$$X\text{——}H\cdots Y$$

Some of the main lines of experimental evidence showing the existence of and defining the properties of the hydrogen bond are:

1. *Molecular association.*   If the boiling points of the covalent hydrides (along with those of the inert gases and the group IV hydrides for comparison) are plotted against molecular weight as in Figure 5-5, it is at once

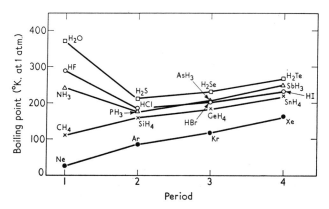

Fig. 5-5.   Boiling points of some molecular hydrides.

obvious that the boiling points of H_2O, HF, and NH_3 are out of line in a direction indicating some additional intermolecular attraction not significantly operative in the other substances.   In Figure 5-6 are shown the heats of vaporization of the same substances plotted against position in the

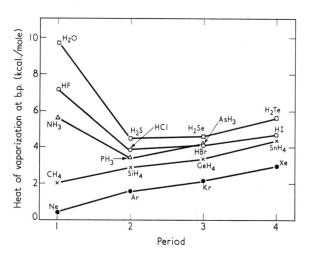

Fig. 5-6.   Heats of vaporization of some molecular hydrides.

periodic table. In both plots it is evident that only the hydrides of F, O, and N have significant intermolecular attraction owing to the existence of strong hydrogen bonds, with HCl showing evidence of slight deviation. Suffice it to say that all experimental evidence indicates that hydrogen bonds are most important when the elements X and Y are F, O, N, or Cl. As Figures 5-5 and 5-6 indicate, methane exhibits no significant hydrogen bonding. However, if the carbon to which hydrogen is bound is also bonded to sufficiently electronegative groups, as in $HCCl_3$ and HCN, then intermolecular hydrogen bonding can occur.

Figure 5-6 also shows the order of magnitude of the forces with which we are dealing, namely, energies of 1–10 kcal./mole, as compared to the range 50–100 kcal./mole for ordinary chemical bonds. We have not yet shown proof that the above effects are indeed due to the type of hydrogen bond symbolized above. Another well-known and clear-cut case of molecular association which throws considerably more light on the details is the dimerization of carboxylic acids.

Let us consider specifically the acetic acid dimer. At 160°C. the dissociation constant of the dimer is

$$[CH_3COOH]_2(g) = 2CH_3COOH(g) \qquad K_p(g) = 1.8 \text{ atm.}$$

From the temperature dependence of this constant the enthalpy of association is found to be 13.8 kcal./mole of dimer. Further, infrared and electron diffraction studies indicate that the dimer has the configuration shown in Figure 5-7.

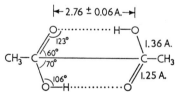

Fig. 5-7.   Structure of the acetic acid dimer.

2. *X-ray and neutron diffraction studies.* Even though the position of hydrogen atoms themselves cannot generally be determined directly by X-rays, X-ray diffraction studies have provided much knowledge about hydrogen bonds. As an example, the structure (Fig. 5-8) of orthoboric acid, H_3BO_3, was found to consist of loosely bounded parallel sheets with the indicated geometry. The study of H_3BO_3 is exceptional in giving any indication of the hydrogen positions. Generally only the over-all X to Y distance is measured. Thus structural studies do not generally answer the question of where the proton is placed along the XY axis, or even whether

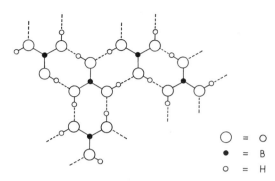

O = O
● = B
o = H

Fig. 5-8.   Structure of boric acid showing hydrogen bonds.

the X—H····Y grouping is indeed linear. Nevertheless, the XY distances alone are significant, since they are shorter than would be found for adjacent but nonhydrogen-bonded XY pairs. Thus in crystalline $NaHCO_3$, there are four kinds of O—O distances (between O's of different bicarbonate anions) having the values 2.55, 3.12, 3.15, and 3.19 A. The last three are all approximately equal to twice the van der Waals radius of oxygen, but the first, 2.55 A., corresponds to the hydrogen-bonded pair, O—H····O. Although X-ray diffraction seldom allows hydrogen atoms to be located with any accuracy because of their low scattering ability, neutron diffraction measurements on substances whose X-ray structure is known can locate the hydrogen positions. This is due to the greater scattering of neutrons of thermal energies ($\sim$0.1 e.v.) by the nuclei. For example, neutron diffraction has shown that in potassium hydrogen phenylacetate, where the O—H····O bond length was known to be 2.55 A., the hydrogen atom is midway between the oxygen atoms.

3. *Entropy data.* We shall begin directly with a particular example, namely, ice. The structure of ice is such that each oxygen atom is surrounded tetrahedrally by four hydrogen atoms, two of which are covalently bonded to it, the other two being bonded to other oxygens but forming hydrogen bonds to the oxygen atom under consideration. Because of the existence of an extended, three-dimensional structure, it is possible for each oxygen to have the four hydrogen atoms around it paired off into two near and two far neighbors in several ways, two of which are illustrated in Figure 5-9. Now, entropy is defined, statistically, by the equation

$$S = -R \ln W$$

where R is the gas constant ($\sim$2.0 cal./deg.) and W is the probability of the state of the system. As the temperature of a system approaches absolute zero, it tends to assume the state of lowest energy, and if there is only

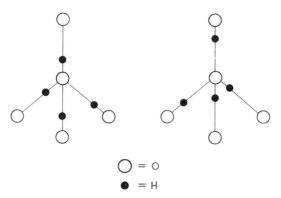

Fig. 5-9. Two possible configurations about an oxygen atom in ice.

one state, of lower energy than all others, the probability of the system being in that state at 0°K. will be 1. Hence $S_0{}^0 = -R \ln 1 = 0$, which is the substance of the third law of thermodynamics. If, however, the above model of ice is correct—that is, if hydrogen bonds are, in fact, unsymmetrical—then there will be more than one way of arranging the H atoms to give each oxygen atom two near and two far neighbors, so that the probability of any one arrangement being frozen in as the temperature is lowered will be less than 1 and the entropy of the crystal of ice will be greater than 0. By an argument which will not be given here, it can be shown that the probability of any particular arrangement (in the sense required by the above equation) is $\frac{2}{3}$, giving the frozen-in entropy the value 0.81. Experimentally, from a comparison of thermodynamic and spectroscopic entropies, the value 0.81 ± 0.05 is obtained, giving excellent confirmation of the unsymmetrical model. It should be clear that if the OHO groups were symmetrical, then no zero point configurational entropy could occur.

Similar confirmation of the consequences of an unsymmetrical hydrogen bond has been obtained for other crystals, for example, KH_2PO_4 and $Ag_2H_3IO_6$.

Notably, there is no residual entropy found for $KHF_2(K^+(FHF)^-)$. Moreover, nuclear resonance studies confirm the symmetrical arrangement in the FHF⁻ ion. In addition, it is believed that OHO bond in nickel(II) dimethylglyoxime (5-IV) may be symmetrical or very nearly so. In the solid the planar entities like that shown in 5-IV are stacked so that there is strong interaction, tantamount to metal–metal bonding, between the nickel atoms of adjoining units. There appears to be some correlation between the strength and degree of symmetry of hydrogen bonds.

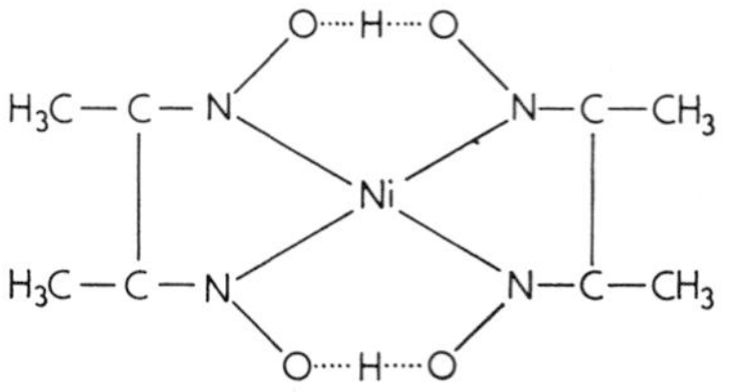

(5-IV)

Lastly, we may note that the existence of the ClHCl⁻ ion has recently been indicated when the cation is very large as in Cs(ClHCl) and $(CH_3)_4N(ClHCl)$. Whether this hydrogen bond is symmetrical or not is as yet unknown.

4. *Infrared evidence.* When the grouping X—H bond enters into hydrogen bond formation with the atom Y, the X—H stretching frequency $(cm.^{-1})$ is *lowered*. This is caused not so much by a weakening of the X—H bond as by a general flattening of the bottom of the potential well in which the proton moves. There is a fairly smooth relation between the XY distance and the X—H stretching frequency. Thus infrared studies provide a convenient diagnostic test for hydrogen bonding.

Depression of the X—H stretching frequency shows the existence of hydrogen bonding in many cases where it seems likely that a bent X—H····Y grouping may exist. An example of this type is *o*-nitrophenol (5-V). Another case, of importance in the following theoretical discussion,

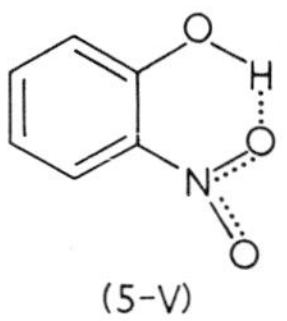

(5-V) 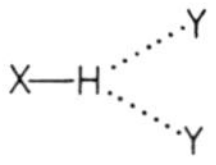   (5-VI)

is that of the $(HF)_n$ polymer, which has the zigzag arrangement shown in Figure 5-10. Bifurcated hydrogen bonds, that is, the arrangement 5-VI,

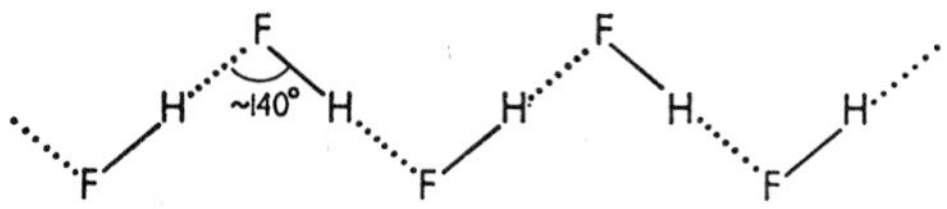

Fig. 5-10.   Structure of the hydrogen-bonded polymer of HF.

are quite rare but have been found in a few instances. Some examples of the parameters involved in H bond formation are given in Table 5-3.

TABLE 5-3

Some Parameters of Hydrogen Bonds

Bond	Compound	Bond energy, kcal./mole	Depression of stretching frequency, cm.$^{-1}$	Bond length,[a,b] A.
F—H—F	KHF_2	~27	2690	2.26
F—H····F	$(HF)_n$	6.7	700	2.55
O—H····O	$(HCOOH)_2$	7.1	~600	2.67
O—H····O	Ice	4.5	~400	2.76
N—H····N	Melamine	~6	~120	3.00
N—H····Cl	$N_2H_4 \cdot HCl$	?	~460	3.12

[a] The distance between the hydrogen-bonded atoms X and Y.

[b] For compounds with "short" hydrogen bonds, 2.44 A. or less, the protons appear to be symmetrically located; many compounds have anomalous infrared spectra with intense bands.

5-9. Theory of Hydrogen Bonding

In order to account for the existence of hydrogen bonds we must consider the possible contributions of covalent bonding, resonance, and electrostatic attraction and attempt to assess the importance of each. In short, we must ask how much each of the possible canonical structures 5-VII, 5-VIII, and 5-IX contributes to the bond energy. It is certain that

$$\overset{\delta^-}{X}\!\!-\!\!\overset{\delta^+}{H}\!\!-\!\!\!-\!\!\!-\!\!\overset{\delta^-}{Y}$$

(5-VII)

Covalence

$$X\!\!-\!\!H \quad :Y \quad \leftrightarrow \quad X\overset{-}{:} \quad H\!\!-\!\!\!-\!\!\!-\!\!\overset{+}{Y}$$
(5-VIIIa)   (5-VIIIb)

Resonance

$$\overset{\delta^-}{X}\!\!-\!\!\overset{\delta^+}{H}\!\cdots\!\overset{\delta^-}{Y}$$

(5-IX)

Electrostatic attraction

structure 5-VII, involving the coexistence of two covalent bonds to hydrogen, is completely negligible. In the first place, it would require the use of the $2s$ or $2p$ orbitals of hydrogen, and these are of such high energy as to be essentially useless for bonding. Moreover, if 5-VII were to contribute effectively, we should expect a nearly symmetrical bond when X = Y, and this would be in contradiction to the facts.

Modern theoretical work on the subject is concerned with the relative contributions of 5-VIII and 5-IX and leads to the conclusion that the resonance represented by 5-VIII is of importance *only* for the *strongest, shortest bonds*. It has been calculated, for example, that in an O—H····O bond with the O—O distance 2.78 A. and the O—H distance 1.0 A. (fairly typical parameters), structure 5-VIIIb appears in the over-all wave function to the extent of only about 4%. Thus, we proceed on the assumption that the hydrogen bond is *basically electrostatic;* but this then raises another question. If, as according to Lennard-Jones and Pople, unshared electron pairs are concentrated along the direction of hybrid orbitals, will the proton approach the atom Y preferentially along these directions? In other words, does the proton see the atom Y as a structureless concentration of negative charge or as an atomic dipole? The answer to this question is not entirely clear cut, because in most cases where the angle θ in 5-X is

(5-X)

in accord with the latter idea, it is possible to attribute this to steric requirements, as in carboxylic acid dimers or *o*-nitrophenol, or it can be equally well explained on the simpler theory as in the case of HCN polymers which are linear. However, the case of the $(HF)_n$ polymer seems to lend strong support to the hypothesis of preferred directions, since there appears to be no other reason why the structure should not be linear.

Recent infrared studies have shown that hydrogen bonding can also occur between any polar X^-—H^+ group and a highly polarizable atom or molecule. Thus, although pure HBr and HI show no significant tendency to associate by hydrogen bonding because there is too little electronegative character to the halogen atoms in these molecules, a strongly positive hydrogen, such as that found, for example, in a phenol OH group, will form strong hydrogen bonds to the polarizable Br and I atoms in many compounds. Hence, instead of the initial attraction between $H(\delta^+)$ and $Y(\delta^-)$ there is attraction between $H(\delta^+)$ and the negative end of a dipole induced in the polarizable atom, Y, *viz.,*

$$\overset{\delta^-}{X}—\overset{\delta^+}{H}····\overset{\delta^--\delta^+}{Y}—$$

Other interesting examples of this dipole–induced dipole type of hydrogen bond are those formed between very polar $\overset{\delta^-}{X}—\overset{\delta^+}{H}$ groups, especially O—H

Fig. 5-11. Examples of intramolecular hydrogen bonding of OH groups to polarize
π electron clouds.

groups, and polarizable multiple bonds such as isolated double bonds and
benzene rings, (Fig. 5-11) and, in a few cases, transition metal atoms.

SPECIAL PROPERTIES OF THE HYDROGEN ATOM
AND THE HYDROGEN MOLECULE

5-10. The Isotopes of Hydrogen: Deuterium and Tritium

Naturally occurring hydrogen contains 0.0156% deuterium, while
tritium occurs naturally in only minute amounts believed to be of the
order of 1 in 10^{17}.

Tritium is formed continuously in the upper atmosphere by cosmic ray-
induced nuclear reactions. Thus, fast neutrons arising from cosmic ray
reactions can produce tritium by the reaction $^{14}N(n, {}^3H)^{12}C$. Tritium is
radioactive (β^-, 12.4 years) and is believed to be the main source of the
minute traces of ^3He found in the atmosphere. It can be made artificially
in nuclear reactors, for example, by the reaction of thermal neutrons with
lithium $^6Li(n, \alpha)^3H$. It is available commercially for use as a tracer in reaction mechanism studies.

Deuterium as D_2O is separated from water by fractional distillation or
electrolysis and by utilization of very small differences in the free energies
of the H and D forms of different compounds, the H_2O–H_2S system being
particularly favorable in large scale use:

$$HOH(l) + HSD(g) = HOD(l) + HSH(g) \qquad K \approx 1.01$$

Deuterium oxide is commercially available in ton quantities and is used
as a moderator in nuclear reactors both because it is effective in reducing
the energies of fast fission neutrons to thermal energies and because deuterium has a much lower capture cross section for neutrons than has hydrogen and hence does not reduce appreciably the neutron flux. Deuterium is
also widely used in the study of reaction mechanisms and in spectroscopic
studies.

Isotope Effects. For many years deuterium and more recently tritium have found wide application as tracers. Usually the value of a tracer arises from the fact that, although its difference in mass or its radioactivity permits its detection, it is chemically identical with the ordinary atoms of the element. For most elements a change of one or several mass units in the nucleus is such a small percentage change that, owing to the indirect way in which nuclear mass can affect chemical behavior, the chemical differences between isotopes are not detectable. However, for the lightest elements, C, N, and especially H, reactions involving different isotopes do proceed at slightly but measurably different rates. In biological systems the substitution of deuterium for hydrogen can alter the delicately balanced processes substantially. In the case of deuterium the difference is not so great as to detract from its use as a tracer, although occasionally caution is necessary in the interpretation of data. Tritium, however, is so much heavier than H that one cannot assume *as a matter of course* that any given tritium compound will react by exactly the same path as its hydrogen analog. However, it is fair to say that even for hydrogen the chemistry of all isotopes is basically the same.

5-11. Ortho and Para Hydrogen

Molecular hydrogen exhibits the phenomenon of ortho and para forms to a marked degree. This is not peculiar to hydrogen, but will occur with all homonuclear diatomic molecules in which the nuclei have spin. In ortho hydrogen the nuclear spins are aligned, and in para hydrogen they are opposed. The equilibrium between the two forms as a function of temperature is shown in Figure 5-12. The interconversion of the two forms

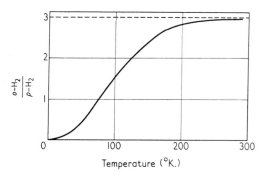

Fig. 5-12.   Equilibrium ratio $o\text{-}H_2/p\text{-}H_2$ as a function of temperature.

is not thermally activated to any appreciable extent until temperatures high enough to cause dissociation and recombination are reached. Hence, if hydrogen is prepared at any given temperature, the equilibrium ortho/ para ratio characteristic of that temperature persists at other temperatures indefinitely unless the interconversion is catalyzed. This may be done by adsorption on activated charcoal or through the influence of very strong magnetic fields such as those encountered by hydrogen adsorbed on the surface of a paramagnetic material. In fact, the latter process has recently been utilized for the measurement of paramagnetism. It will be noted from Figure 5-12 that by equilibrating on a catalyst at a very low temperature essentially pure para hydrogen can be made, but that it is not possible in this way to obtain pure ortho hydrogen. Very recently, ortho and para hydrogen have been separated by gas chromatography. The two forms differ very slightly in certain physical properties such as thermal conductivity, which provides a method of analysis. They are chemically equivalent, however.

The reason why the existence of ortho and para forms is of greater importance for hydrogen than for other diatomic molecules arises because of the very low mass in the following way. The total molecular wave function can be written

$$\psi_T = \psi_e \psi_i \psi_v \psi_r \psi_{ns}$$

where ψ_T must, according to Pauli's principle, be antisymmetric. Now the product $\psi_e \psi_i \psi_v$, if the molecules are in electronic and vibrational ground states, is symmetric so that for ψ_{ns} symmetric (o-H_2) ψ_r is antisymmetric, and vice versa, since there must be an odd number of antisymmetric ψ_i's to make ψ_T antisymmetric. Furthermore, only those rotational states having j even are symmetric, only those having j odd are antisymmetric. For most molecules the moment of inertia is so large that the separation of rotational states is small relative to kT even at low temperatures; thus both ortho and para molecules populate a host of rotational states in an almost classical distribution, and there is then practically no difference in their energy or specific heat. For H_2, however, with its uniquely small moment of inertia, only the lowest few states are populated even at room temperature, so that at and below 300°K. the differences in energy and heat capacity of ortho and para hydrogen molecules (i.e., those in the states $J = 0, 2$ and $J = 1, 3$, respectively) are uniquely large.

We may note, finally, that for D_2, on account of the different spin of the nucleus, the ortho-para relationship is the *opposite* of that in H_2. The ortho form is the more stable and can be obtained pure at low temperatures.

STRENGTHS OF PROTONIC ACIDS IN WATER

Protonic acids are substances which ionize to give an anion and a proton solvated by the solvent, which is to say in water, $[H_{2n+1}O_n]^+$. For the present, discussion will be explicitly limited to strengths of acids in water. The strength of an acid is dependent not only on the nature of the acid itself, but also on the medium in which it is dissolved; as an extreme example, nitric acid is an acid in water

$$HNO_3 + nH_2O = [H^+{}_{2n+1}O_n]^+ + NO_3^-$$

whereas in liquid hydrogen fluoride it functions quite differently, behaving as a base (H^+ acceptor):

$$HNO_3 + nHF = [H_2NO_3]^+ + [F_nH_{n-1}]^-$$

Protonic acids may be broadly classed into two groups. There are oxy acids in which the acidic protons are bound to oxygen, which in turn is bound to a central atom, that is, X—O—H, and binary acids in which protons are directly bound to a central atom, X—H.

TABLE 5-4

Strengths of Oxy Acids, H_nXO_m, in Water

$(m - n)$	Examples	$-\text{Log } K_1$ (pK$_1$)	$-\text{Log } K_2$ (pK$_2$)	$-\text{Log } K_3$ (pK$_3$)
0	HClO	7.50	—	—
	HBrO	8.68	—	—
	H_3AsO_3	9.22	?	?
	H_4GeO_4	8.59	13	?
	H_6TeO_6	8.80	?	?
	[H_3PO_3	1.8	6.15	—]
	H_3BO_3	9.22	?	?
1	H_3PO_4	2.12	7.2	12
	H_3AsO_4	3.5	7.2	12.5
	H_5IO_6	3.29	6.7	$\sim$15
	H_2SO_3	1.90	7.25	—
	H_2SeO_3	2.57	6.60	—
	$HClO_2$	1.94	—	—
	HNO_2	3.3	—	—
	[H_2CO_3	6.38 (3.58)	10.32	—]
2	HNO_3	Large neg. value	—	—
	H_2SO_4	Large neg. value	1.92	—
	H_2SeO_4	Large neg. value	2.05	—
3	$HClO_4$	Very large neg. value	—	—
	$HMnO_4$	Very large neg. value	—	—
[$-1(?)$	H_3PO_2	2	?	?]

5-12. Oxy Acids

For oxy acids certain useful generalizations may be made concerning (a) the magnitude of K_1 and (b) the ratios of successive constants, K_1/K_2, K_2/K_3, etc. The value of K_1 seems to depend upon the charge on the central atom. Qualitatively it is very reasonable to suppose that the greater the positive charge, the more will the process of proton loss be favored on electrostatic grounds. It has been found that if this positive charge is taken to be the so-called formal charge, semiquantitative correlations are possible. The formal charge in an oxy acid, H_nXO_m, is computed in the following way, assuming the structure of the acid to be $O_{m-n}X(OH)_n$. Each X—(OH) bond is formed by sharing one X electron and one OH electron and is thus *formally* nonpolar. Each X—O bond is formed using two X electrons and thus represents a net loss of one electron by X. Therefore, the formal positive charge on X is equal to the number of X—O bonds, hence equal to $(m - n)$. It may be seen from the data in Table 5-4 that, with the exception of the acids listed in brackets, which are special cases to be discussed presently, the following relations between $(m - n)$ (or formal positive charge on X) and the values of K_1 hold:

For $m - n = 0$,
$$pK_1 \sim 8.5 \pm 1.0 \ (K \sim 10^{-8} \text{ to } 10^{-9})$$
For $m - n = 1$,
$$pK_1 \sim 2.8 \pm 0.9 \ (K \sim 10^{-2} \text{ to } 10^{-4})$$
For $m - n \gtrless 2$,
$$pK_1 \ll 0$$

that is, the acid is very strong. It will also be noted that the difference between successive pK's is 4–5 with very few exceptions, only one of which (H_5IO_6) is large.

H_3PO_3 obviously is out of line with the other acids having $m - n = 0$ and seems to fit fairly well in the group with $m - n = 1$. This is, in fact, where it belongs, since there is independent evidence (Section 20-16) that its structure is $OPH^*(OH)_2$ with H^* bonded directly to P. Similarly, H_3PO_2 has a pK_1 which would class it with the $m - n = 1$ acids where it, too, belongs since its structure is $OP(H^*)_2(OH)$, with the two H^* hydrogen atoms directly bound to P.

Carbonic acid is exceptional in that the directly measured pK_1, 6.38, does not refer to the process

$$H_2CO_3 = H^+ + HCO_3^-$$

since carbon dioxide in solution is only partly in the form of H_2CO_3, but largely present as more loosely hydrated species, $CO_2(aq)$. When a correction is made for the equilibrium

$$CO_2(aq) + H_2O = H_2CO_3(aq)$$

the pK_1 value of 3.58 is obtained which falls in the range for other $m - n = 1$ acids.

Before leaving the subject of oxy acids, we may note that many metal ions whose solutions are acidic may be regarded as oxy acids. Thus, although the hydrolysis of metal ions is often written as shown here for Fe^{3+}

$$Fe^{3+} + H_2O = Fe(OH)^{2+} + H^+$$

it is just as valid thermodynamically and much nearer to physical reality to recognize that the ferric ion is coordinated by water molecules, very likely six, and write

$$[Fe(H_2O)_6]^{3+} = [Fe(H_2O)_5(OH)]^{2+} + H^+ \qquad K_{Fe^{3+}} \approx 10^{-3}$$

From this formulation it becomes clear why the ferrous ion, with a lower positive charge, is less acidic or, in alternative terms, less hydrolyzed than the ferric

$$[Fe(H_2O)_6]^{2+} = [Fe(H_2O)_5(OH)]^+ + H^+ \qquad K_{Fe^{2+}} \ll K_{Fe^{3+}}$$

It should be noted that one cannot necessarily compare the acidity of the divalent ion of one metal with that of the trivalent ion of *another* metal in this way, however. There appears to be no good general rule concerning the acidities of hydrated metal ions at the present time, although some attempts have been made at correlations.

5-13. General Theory of Ratios of Successive Constants

It was pointed out many years ago by Niels Bjerrum that the ratios of successive acid dissociation constants could be accounted for in a nearly quantitative way by electrostatic considerations. Consider any bifunctional acid, HXH,

$$HXH = HX^- + H^+ \qquad K_1$$
$$HX^- = X^- + H^+ \qquad K_2$$

There is a purely statistical effect which can be considered in the following way. For the first process dissociation can occur in two ways (i.e., there are two protons, either of which may dissociate), but recombination in only one; whereas in the second process dissociation can occur in only one way, but recombination in two (i.e., the proton has two sites to which it may return and hence twice the probability of recombining). Thus, on purely statistical grounds one would expect $K_1 = 4K_2$. Bjerrum observed that for the dicarboxylic acids, $HOOC(CH_2)_nCOOH$, the ratio K_1/K_2 was always greater than four, but decreased rapidly as n increased (see Table 5-5). He suggested the following explanation. When the two points of

TABLE 5-5

K_1/K_2 Ratio for Dicarboxylic Acids,
$HOOC(CH_2)_nCOOH$

n	K_1/K_2
1	1120
2	29.5
3	17.4
4	12.3
5	11.2
6	10.0
7	9.5
8	9.3

attachment of protons are close together in the molecule, the negative charge left at one site when the first proton leaves strongly restrains the second one from leaving by electrostatic attraction. As the separation between the sites increases, this interaction should diminish.

By making calculations using the Coulomb law,* Bjerrum was able to obtain rough agreement with experimental data. The principal difficulty in obtaining quantitative agreement lies in a choice of dielectric constant since some of the lines of electrostatic force run through the molecule ($D \sim 1$-10), others through neighboring water molecules (D uncertain), and still others through water having the dielectric constant (~ 82) of pure bulk water. More recently, Kirkwood and Westheimer were able to get nearly quantitative agreement with the data by making very elaborate calculations which take into account the variability of the dielectric constant. The important point here for our purposes is to recognize the physical principles involved without necessarily trying to obtain quantitative results.

Thus, the large separations in successive pK's for the oxy acids are attributable to the electrostatic effects of the negative charge left by the dissociation of one proton upon the remaining ones. In bifunctional binary acids, where the negative charge due to the removal of one proton is concentrated on the very atom to which the second proton is bound, the sepa-

---

* $F \propto q_1 q_2 / Dr^2$, where F is the force; q_1 and q_2 the charges, separated by r; and D is the dielectric constant of the medium between them.

ration of the constants is extraordinarily great. K_1 and K_2 for H_2S are $\backsim 10^{-7}$ and $\backsim 10^{-14}$, respectively, whereas for water we have

$$H_2O = H^+ + OH^- \qquad K_1 = 10^{-14}$$
$$OH^- = H^+ + O^{2-} \qquad K_2 < 10^{-36} \text{ (est.)}$$

5-14. Binary Acids

Factors determining the strengths of binary acids may best be discussed in terms of a thermodynamic cycle. Consider an acid, HX, which dissociates in solution according to the equation

$$HX(aq) = H^+(aq) + X^-(aq)$$

The dissociation constant, K, is related to the change in Gibbs free energy by the relation

$$\Delta F = -RT \ln K$$

and the free energy change is in turn related to the changes in enthalpy and entropy via the relation

$$\Delta F = \Delta H - T\Delta S$$

in which R is the gas constant and T is the absolute temperature, which we shall take to be 298°C. in the following discussion. The magnitudes of ΔH and ΔS for the dissociation may be related to the ΔH's and ΔS's for other basic processes involving HX, the atoms H and X, and the ions H^+ and X^- by the thermodynamic cycle shown in Figure 5-13.

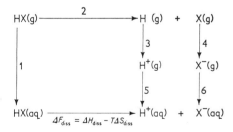

Fig. 5-13. Thermodynamic cycle for dissociation of a binary acid, HX.

The enthalpy of dissociation is given by

$$\Delta H_{\text{diss}} = -\Delta H_1 + \Delta H_2 + \Delta H_3 + \Delta H_4 + (\Delta H_5 + \Delta H_6)$$
$$(+D) \quad (+I) \quad (-A)$$

where the subscripts refer to the various stages in the cycle; and customary symbols for several of these have been noted in parentheses. Thus, ΔH_2 is the dissociation energy (intrinsically positive since energy is consumed), ΔH_3 is the ionization potential (again intrinsically positive), and ΔH_4 is the negative of the electron affinity. Similarly, the entropy of dissociation is a corresponding algebraic sum of the ΔS's for each step. The relevant thermodynamic data for the four halogen acids are presented in Tables 5-6 and 5-7, and the final computed values ΔH, ΔS, ΔF, and K in Table 5-8.

TABLE 5-6

Enthalpies Related to Dissociation of the Halogen Acids
(In kcal./mole)

Acid	$-\Delta H_1$	ΔH_2 (D)	ΔH_3 (I)	ΔH_4 $(-A)$	$\Delta H_5 + \Delta H_6$	ΔH_{diss}
HF	$+11.5$	134.6	315.0	-82.0	-381.9	-3.0
HCl	$+4.2$	103.2	315.0	-87.3	-348.8	-13.7
HBr	$+5.0$	87.5	315.0	-82.0	-340.7	-15.2
HI	$+5.5$	71.4	315.0	-75.7	-330.3	-14.1

TABLE 5-7

Entropy Changes Related to Dissociation of the Halogen Acids
(In cal./mole-deg.)

Acid	ΔS_1	ΔS_2	$\Delta S_3 + \Delta S_5$	$\Delta S_4 + \Delta S_6$	ΔS_{diss}
HF	$+23$	$+23.8$	-27.4	-40.2	-20.8
HCl	$+18$	$+22.3$	-27.4	-26.3	-13.4
HBr	$+19$	$+21.8$	-27.4	-22.5	-9.1
HI	$+20$	$+21.2$	-27.4	-17.0	-3.2

TABLE 5-8

Free Energy Changes of Equilibrium Constants for Dissociation of Halogen Acids

Acid	Calculated				Expt'l K^a
	ΔH_{diss}	ΔS_{diss}	ΔF_{diss}	K	
HF	-3.0	-20.8	3.2	10^{-3}	7×10^{-4}
HCl	-13.7	-13.4	-9.5	10^7	$\sim 10^7$
HBr	-15.2	-9.1	-12.5	10^9	$>10^7$
HI	-14.1	-3.2	-13.1	10^9	$>10^7$

[a] K's for HCl, HBr and HI are estimated from conductivities in nonaqueous solvents.

It will be seen that the values for the various ΔH's and ΔS's have combined to give K's in satisfactory agreement with experimental values. Thus, by using the thermodynamic cycle we are able to account for the well-known but perhaps surprising fact that HF is a far weaker acid than HCl, HBr, and HI in aqueous solution.

Let us examine the data in Tables 5-6, 5-7, and 5-8 to see if we can find any particularly conspicuous causes for this. First, from Table 5-8 we see that the low value of K for HF results principally from the low value of $-\Delta H_{diss}$ and to a lesser extent from the high value of ΔS_{diss}. In order to trace back the causes of the low value of $-\Delta H_{diss}$ we observe in Table 5-6 that it is due primarily to the relatively high energy of dissociation of HF and also to the relatively low electron affinity of fluorine. Although both of these are partially offset by the relatively high heat of solvation of the small F^- ion (ΔH_6), the net result is to make the enthalpy less favorable by $\backsim 11$ kcal./mole for dissociation of HF. If ΔH_{diss} for HF were -14 kcal./mole, K would be $\backsim 10^6$. From Table 5-7 we can also see that the relatively high negative value of the entropy of solvation of F^- (ΔS_6; remember that ΔS_5 is for H^+ and consequently the same in all four acids) also reduces the dissociation constant. In summary, it can be said that the favorable enthalpy and unfavorable entropy of solution of F^- about balance one another out, and the weakness of HF can be attributed mainly to the relatively great strength of the HF bond.

The foregoing discussion and thermodynamic analysis of the strengths of the halogen acids only illustrate the principles governing the strengths of all binary acids.

References

Advances in Catalysis and Related Subjects, Academic Press, New York, 1948———. This series of volumes contains much information on hydrogenations.

Bell, R. P., *The Proton in Chemistry*, Cornell University Press, Ithaca, N. Y., 1960. A lucid account of hydrogen ions in solution and acid-base behavior.

Britton, H. S., *Hydrogen Ions*, 4th ed., Chapman Hall, London, 1955.

Emmett, P. H., ed., *Catalysis*, Vols. III–V, Reinhold, New York, 1955–57 These volumes cover various aspects of hydrogenation and other reactions involving hydrogen.

Frankenberg, W. G., V. I. Komarewsky, and E. K. Rideal, eds., *Advances in Catalysis*, Academic Press, New York, annually from 1948. These volumes discuss various aspects of hydrogenation and other reactions involving hydrogen.

Gold, V., *pH Measurement*, Methuen, London, 1950.

Gold, V., and D. P. N. Satchell, *Quart. Revs. (London)*, **9**, 51 (1955). Isotope effects.

Green, M. L. H., *Angew. Chem.*, **72**, 719 (1960). A review of molecular compounds and ions with transition metal to hydrogen bonds.

Hadzi, D., ed., *Hydrogen Bonding*, Pergamon Press, New York, 1959.

Halpern, J., *Quart. Revs. (London)*, **10,** 463 (1956); *J. Phys. Chem.*, **63,** 398 (1959). Reactions of hydrogen in homogeneous solutions.

Hurd, D. T., *Introduction to the Chemistry of the Hydrides*, Wiley, New York, 1952. A general survey.

Janz, G. J., and S. S. Danyluk, *Chem. Revs.*, **60,** 209 (1960). Conductivities of hydrogen halides in anhydrous polar organic solvents.

Murphy, G. M., ed., *Production of Heavy Water*, National Nuclear Energy Series, Vol. VIII-4F, McGraw-Hill, New York, 1955.

Pimentel, G. C., and A. L. McClellan, *The Hydrogen Bond*, Freeman and Co., San Francisco, 1960. A thorough, readable book with extensive tables of data and bibliography.

Siegel, B., *J. Chem. Educ.*, **38,** 484 (1961). A review of the reactions of atomic hydrogen.

Steacie, F. W. R., *Atomic and Free Radical Reactions*, 2nd ed., American Chemical Society Monograph, No. 125, Reinhold, New York, 1954. Chemistry of atomic hydrogen.

Westheimer, F. H., *Chem. Revs.*, **61,** 265 (1961). Hydrogen and deuterium isotope effects.

Wiberg, K. B., *Chem. Revs.*, **55,** 713 (1955). Isotope effects.

6

The Inert Gases and Enclosure Compounds

GENERAL REMARKS

6-1. Group Trends

The atoms of inert gases—also called rare gases or noble gases—all have valence shells which are closed octets (or, in the case of He, the duet). These closed shells are extremely stable, as is shown by the high ionization potentials (Table 6-1). The elements are chemically inert, low-boiling

TABLE 6-1

Some Properties of the Inert Gases

	Outer shell configuration	Atomic number	1st ionization potential, e.v.	Boiling point, °K. (at 1 atm.)
He	$1s^2$	2	24.58	4.18
Ne	$2s^2 2p^6$	10	21.56	27.13
Ar	$3s^2 3p^6$	18	15.76	87.29
Kr	$4s^2 4p^6$	36	14.00	120.26
Xe	$5s^2 5p^6$	54	12.13	166.06
Rn	$6s^2 6p^6$	86	10.75	208.16

gases. They form, of necessity, monatomic gases whose physical properties vary systematically with size. Their boiling points are generally low, decreasing rapidly with decreasing molecular weight. The boiling point of helium is the lowest of any known substance, and liquid helium is extensively used as a coolant for experimentation near the absolute zero. All of the elements except helium also solidify 2–7° below their boiling points at 1 atm.; helium will solidify only under a pressure of >25 atm. at ~ 1°K.

Solid helium crystallizes in a hexagonal close-packed lattice, whereas Ne, Ar, Kr, and Xe crystallize in a cubic close-packed (face-centered cubic) lattice. For nondirectional van der Waals forces, the packing of identical spheres would have been expected to give the hexagonal close-packed arrangement, and this packing is observed in He, which has only s electrons. The other elements, although spherically symmetrical in the gas, also have p electrons in filled orbitals. Calculations have shown that the most probable configuration of a group of eight electrons has four pairs at the corners of a tetrahedron. Internal correlation of four electron pairs might affect the structure adopted because the pattern of nearest neighbors is different for the hexagonal and cubic structures and also the general repetition pattern is different. As there are no bonding electrons in the inert gases, the differences in the crystal structure then probably result from small differences in the van der Waals lattice forces due to the distribution of electron density when filled p electrons are present. It may be noted that methane also packs in the cubic close-packed way, presumably for a similar reason.

The effect of the weak induced dipole or van der Waals forces in the condensed phases which increase with the number of electrons present is shown also by the steady increases in the boiling point and in heat of vaporization, ΔH_v^0, with increasing Z. The larger atoms have a greater polarizability and hence stronger van der Waals forces between them. The magnitude of these forces is shown by the ΔH_v^0 values (Table 6-2).

TABLE 6-2

Heats of Vaporization of Inert Gases
(In kcal./mole)

He	0.022
Ne	0.44
Ar	1.50
Kr	2.31
Xe	3.27
Rn	4.3

THE ELEMENTS

6-2. Occurrence, Isolation, and Applications

The inert gases occur as minor constituents in the atmosphere (Table 6-3). Helium is also found as a component (up to $\sim 7\%$) in certain natural

TABLE 6-3

Atmospheric Content of Inert Gases
(In per cent by volume)

He	5.24×10^{-4}
Ne	1.82×10^{-3}
Ar	0.934
Kr	1.14×10^{-3}
Xe	8.7×10^{-6}

hydrocarbon gases in the United States; this helium undoubtedly originated from decay of radioactive elements in rocks, and certain radioactive minerals contain occluded helium which can be released on heating. All isotopes of radon are radioactive and are occasionally given specific names (e.g., actinon, thoron) derived from their source in the radioactive decay series. The isotope with the longest half-life (^{222}Rn, 3.825 days; α) is formed in decay of radium and is normally obtained by pumping off the gas from radium chloride solutions. Ne, Ar, Kr, and Xe are commercially obtainable as products of fractionation of liquid air.

The main uses of the gases are in welding (argon provides an inert atmosphere), in gas-filled electric light bulbs, radio tubes and Geiger counters (argon) and in discharge tubes (neon); radon has been used therapeutically as an α particle source in the treatment of cancer.

Some of the inert gases arise as products of radioactive decay in minerals, and the amount present can be used to determine the age of the specimen. For example, in the course of the decay of ^{238}U, eight α particles are produced. These can easily acquire electrons to form He atoms by oxidizing other elements present. If the rock is sufficiently impermeable, the total He remains trapped therein. If the amounts of trapped helium and remaining ^{238}U are measured, the age of the specimen can be calculated, for one-eighth of the atoms of He represent the number of ^{238}U atoms which have decayed. (A correction must be applied for thorium, which also decays by α emission and generally occurs in small amounts with uranium.) Argon arises in potassium-containing minerals by electron capture decay of ^{40}K. A complication arises here since ^{40}K also decays by β^- emission to ^{40}Ca, and the accuracy of the age determination in this case depends on the accuracy of our knowledge of the branching ratio of ^{40}K, which at present is only moderate.

6-3. Chemical Properties of the Inert Gases

All of these elements are chemically inert, as the group name implies. They form no chemically bound compounds, since with high ionization potentials and negligible electron affinities they can neither lose nor gain any electrons in ordinary chemical processes. Under spectroscopic conditions—in electric discharges or in electron bombardments—molecular species such as He_2^+ are observed. These exist only because one or more electrons are removed, breaking up the stable closed shells so that bonding can occur (see Chapter 3 for discussion of the electronic structure of the He_2^+ ion). All such species are very short-lived even in the gas phase, and none of them can be isolated.

The solubility of the inert gases in water is fairly high (of the order of 8–40 ml./liter at 20°C.), increasing with increasing atomic weight. The solubility is attributable to dipole–induced dipole forces, the larger atoms being more soluble since they are more easily polarized by the surrounding water molecules.

Excepting helium and neon, the gases form crystalline hydrates of variable formula, but with the number of water molecules per gas atom approaching six with increasing Z. The dissociation pressures of these hydrates at 0°C. increase from 1 atm. for radon to 98.5 atm. for argon. These hydrates are to be regarded as enclosure compounds (see below) in which the gas atom is trapped in a cage formed by hydrogen-bonded water molecules.

The possibility of the heavier inert gas atoms behaving as electron pair donors led to attempts to prepare compounds with the strong acceptor BF_3. Several compounds with argon were reported on somewhat tenuous evidence, but further studies of argon and xenon with a variety of acceptors including BF_3 and $B(CH_3)_3$ indicate that no such compounds exist.

The gases can be adsorbed or absorbed by some metal lattices and, with the exception of He, on active charcoal at liquid air temperature. The latter type of adsorption has been employed in fractional separations of the gases. The gases can also be separated by gas chromatography using other solid adsorbents. Helium diffuses quite rapidly through pyrex or borosilicate glass and can be separated from other gases in this way; for the handling of helium in glass systems, soft or soda glass must be used.

6-4. Properties of Liquid Helium

Naturally occurring helium is essentially all ⁴He, although ³He occurs to the extent of $\sim 10^{-7}$ atom %. ³He can be made in greater quantities by nuclear reactions and by β^- decay of tritium.

Liquid ^{3}He appears to be a normal liquid, but ^{4}He exhibits astonishing properties not possessed by any other substance known. The liquid formed at 4.12°K. is called HeI and is a normal liquid. On further cooling at 1 atm. a second form, called HeII, appears, the equilibrium temperature being 2.178°K. This transition temperature is called the λ point and varies slightly with pressure. The transition from HeI to HeII is accompanied by discontinuous changes of some physical properties. HeII has a viscosity at least as low as the most sensitive methods of measurement can detect and is superconducting. It forms exceedingly thin films, only a few hundred atoms thick, which flow apparently without friction. If the levels in two concentric vessels are unequal, it will flow from one to the other, even going uphill where necessary. Some workers have referred to HeII as a fourth state of matter. No fully satisfactory theoretical explanation of these properties has yet been devised.

6-5. Enclosure Compounds

The most important and most easily prepared "compounds" of the inert gases are those in which the gases are trapped within cavities in crystalline lattices of suitable organic or inorganic compounds. There are several types of these enclosure compounds, but the one of most interest to us here is that known as cage or *clathrate* compounds (Latin *clathratus*, "enclosed or protected by cross bars or grating").

Crystallization of solutions of quinol (o-dihydroxybenzene, o-$C_6H_4(OH)_2$) in water or alcohol under an inert gas pressure of 10–40 atm. produces crystals, often up to 1 cm. in length, which are readily distinguishable from the crystals of ordinary quinol* (α-quinol), even visually. These crystals contain the inert gas trapped in the lattice of β-quinol. On dissolving the crystals in water, or on heating, the gas is released. The crystals are stable and can be kept for years.

Such trapping of the gases is made possible by the occurrence of cavities in the crystal lattices of certain compounds. X-ray analysis indicates that in β-quinol, three quinol molecules form an approximately spherical cage of free diameter ∼4 A. with the quinol molecules being bound together by hydrogen bonds (Fig. 6-1). The free volumes are in the form of isolated

---

* o-Quinol exists in three crystalline modifications, the ordinary form being α-quinol. One of the other modifications is the β form which gives the lattice cages in clathrate compounds. The pure form can be obtained by crystallization from n-propyl alcohol by addition of a seed crystal of the argon clathrate; the seed can be removed subsequently from the mass by inspection. The pure β form has empty cages; it transforms spontaneously into the thermodynamically more stable α-quinol on standing.

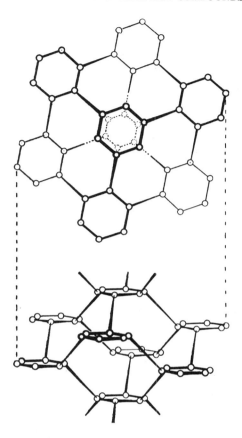

Fig. 6-1. Manner of hydrogen bonding of quinol molecules in β-quinol. *Above:* In plane each regular hexagon denotes six hydrogen bonds between oxygen atoms. Hexagons at different levels are represented by different line thickness. The tapered lines, representing the O—O axis of a quinol molecule, show the method of linking to form an infinite three-dimensional cagework. Each taper points downward from the observer. *Below:* Perspective drawing corresponding to above. The hexagons denote the hydrogen bonds; the longer lines connecting different hexagons denote the O—O axis of the quinol molecule. (Reproduced with permission from D. E. Palin and H. M. Powell, *J. Chem. Soc.*, **1947**, 208.)

cavities, and the apertures leading from one cage to another through the crystal are very small in diameter. Molecules trapped within these cavities during formation of the crystal are unable to escape. As a molecule approaches the cage walls, it will experience repulsive forces.

Since three quinol molecules are required to form each cavity, the limiting ratio of quinol to trapped atom or molecule for the composition of clathrates is 3:1. This ratio is reached for acetonitrile, but for the inert gases various composition ranges may be obtained depending on conditions —for example, $C_6H_4(OH)_2/Kr$, 3:0.74; $C_6H_4(OH)_2/Xe$, 3:0.88—and normally the cages are incompletely filled.

Since the free diameter of the quinol cage in a clathrate compound is ~4 A., only molecules of appropriate size may be expected to be trapped. Thus, although CH_3OH forms quinol clathrates, C_2H_5OH is too large and does not. On the other hand, not all small molecules may form clathrates. Helium does not, the explanation being that the He atom is too small and can escape between the atoms of the quinol molecules which form the cage. Similarly, neon has not been obtained in a quinol clathrate as yet. Water, although of a suitable size, also does not form a clathrate; in this case the explanation cannot be a size factor, but may lie in the ability of water molecules to form hydrogen bonds which enables them to approach the cage walls and thus escape through gaps in the walls.

Quinol clathrates have been prepared enclosing O_2, NO, CH_4, SO_2,* HCl, HBr, Ar, Kr, Xe, HCOOH, HCN, H_2S, CH_3OH, and CH_3CN.

As noted above, the so-called inert gas hydrates are in reality clathrate compounds, H_2O providing the host lattice. When solidified in the presence of the inert gases Ar, Kr, and Xe under pressure (and also certain other gases of small molecular size such as chlorine, sulfur dioxide, and methyl chloride), water forms a very open cubic structure with 46 H_2O per unit cell. Each unit cell contains six medium-sized holes and two small holes. The open structure is stabilized only when some or all of these holes are occupied by the gas molecules. Complete filling of only the medium holes by atoms X would lead to a "formula" $X \cdot 7.67H_2O$, while complete filling of all of the holes would lead to $X \cdot 5.76H_2O$. This structure of the host lattice is often called the gas hydrate structure. There is another open structure often formed in the presence of larger, usually liquid substances (e.g., ethyl chloride, chloroform), and hence called the liquid hydrate structure, in which the unit cell consists of an open arrangement of 136 water molecules with eight large holes and sixteen small ones. Pauling has recently proposed that the anesthetic effect of some substances such as $CHCl_3$ is due to the formation of liquid hydrate crystals in brain tissue.

The formation of enclosure compounds has a number of useful applications. Argon can be separated from neon by clathrate formation, and enrichment of Xe over Kr can be obtained.

Clathrate compounds can be utilized to study the physical properties of isolated molecules under conditions where measurements could not nor-

* It may be noted that the SO_2–quinol clathrate was discovered by Wohler in 1848, although the nature of the solid was not elucidated until the recent work of Powell

mally be made. Thus the magnetic susceptibility of the oxygen molecule in β-quinol has been measured at temperatures from 1 to 20°K. Nitric oxide can be studied similarly.

Certain compounds other than β-quinol can be used as substrates for clathrate formation and, as with quinol, some of these have preparative or analytical value. Thus nickel cyanide in ammonium hydroxide solution crystallizes with enclosed benzene and similar substances. In one crystallization of $Ni(CN)_2NH_3 \cdot C_6H_6$, benzene of $99.992 \pm 0.002\%$ purity was obtained.

(6-I)

The compound trithymotide, $C_{33}H_{36}O_6$ (6-I), has been resolved into its d and l forms by formation of clathrates of formula $2C_{33}H_{36}O_6R$, where R can be benzene, chloroform, or numerous hydrocarbons. If d- or l-trithymotide is crystallized with some solvent, R, which is itself a dl mixture, cavities of the d or l crystal enclose preferentially the d or l form of the solvent molecule. sec-Butyl bromide has been resolved in this way.

Although not classifiable as clathrate compounds, many other crystalline substances have holes, channels, or honeycomb structures which allow inclusion of foreign molecules, and many studies have been made in this field. Urea is an example of an organic compound which in the crystal has parallel continuous uniform capillaries; it may be utilized to separate straight chain hydrocarbons from branched chain ones, the latter being unable to fit into the capillaries.

Among inorganic lattices which can trap molecules, the best known are the crystalline zeolites, which are aluminosilicates. These are the so-called "molecular sieves" which are discussed in Section 19-6.

References

Cook, G. A., ed., *Argon, Helium, and the Rare Gases*, 2 vols., Interscience, New York, 1961. A comprehensive source book.

Keesom, W. H., *Helium*, Elsevier, New York, 1942.

Mandelcorn, L., *Chem. Revs.*, **59**, 827 (1959). A comprehensive review on clathrate compounds.

7

The Elements of the First Short Period

7-1. General Nature of the Elements

At He, $Z = 2$, the $1s$ shell is filled, and the next element, Li, $Z = 3$, has a single electron in the $2s$ orbital. With increasing Z, in Be, B, C, N, O, and F, the electrons successively fill the $2s$ and $2p$ levels until the next closed configuration, $1s^2 2s^2 2p^6$, is reached at neon. The seven elements Li–F are often referred to as the elements of the *first short period* of the periodic table. They constitute the first members of the *groups* of elements in the table.

Although these elements have some properties in common with the heavier elements of their respective groups—which is, of course, to be expected in view of the similarity in the outer electronic structures of the gaseous atoms (e.g., N, $2s^2 2p^3$; P, $3s^2 3p^3$)—they nevertheless show highly individual behavior in many important respects. For example, the normal state of nitrogen is as gaseous N_2 molecules, whereas P, As, and Sb form tetraatomic molecules, such as P_4, and are solids at room temperature. There are, in several cases, sufficiently striking differences between the first and succeeding members of a group to detract considerably from the usefulness of regarding these first members as prototypes for their *congeners*. Whereas Li, Be, O, and F show, on the whole, more important similarities than important differences with respect to their congeners, B, C, and especially N have chemical resemblances to their congeners which, aside from parallel oxidation states, are more formal than real. For example, stoichiometrically analogous halides, oxides, and oxy acids of N and P are otherwise almost completely unrelated, whereas those of P are fairly similar to those of As and Sb. We have, accordingly, chosen to treat the first short period separately, proceeding thereafter to consider the remaining elements by groups.

The increase in nuclear charge and the consequent changes in the extra-

150

nuclear arrangement of electrons in going from Li to F result in extremes of physical and chemical character. Some important physical properties

TABLE 7-1

Some Physical Properties of Elements in the First Short Period

Element	Normal state	Melting point, °C.	Boiling point, °C.
Li	Silvery white, soft metal[a]	179	1340
Be	Grey, fairly hard metal[b]	1285	2970
B	Crystalline solid[c] or brownish amorphous powder	~2300	?
C	Colorless, hard crystals (diamond) grey, unctuous solid (graphite)	3847	?
N	Colorless diatomic gas	−210.5	−195.8
O	Colorless diatomic gas	−218.9	−182.96
F	Very pale yellow gas	−223	−187

[a] Body-centered cubic lattice; atomic radius, 1.56 A.

[b] Hexagonal close-packed lattice; atomic radius, 1.05 A.

[c] Boron has at least four polymorphic forms; grey tetragonal boron-I has a unit cell containing icosahedra of boron atoms.

of the elements are given in Table 7-1. The range of chemical properties can be briefly indicated as follows:

Lithium is a low-melting, highly electropositive metal, and its chemistry is mainly that of the Li^+ ion in the solid state and in solution.

Beryllium is also metallic, but is less electropositive and reactive than Li; the discrete Be^{2+} ion does not exist in solution or lattices even in BeF_2 or BeO, there being a great tendency for Be to form at least partially covalent bonds.

Boron is essentially nonmetallic in the elemental state; it does not form simple B^{3+} cations, and its compounds contain predominantly covalent bonds. It has an extensive chemistry in combination with oxygen (borates) and with carbon in organoboron compounds and forms a unique series of hydrides.

Carbon is completely nonmetallic. Its chemistry is dominated by the formation of four covalent bonds; multiple bonds are also readily formed.

Nitrogen exists normally as the diatomic gas N_2, which is very unreactive because of the great strength of the $N \equiv N$ triple bond. Its compounds are covalent, usually involving three single bonds, although multiple bonds also occur. Under special circumstances the nitride ion, N^{3-}, can exist.

Oxygen normally exists as a paramagnetic, diatomic gas. It forms well-defined oxide ions, O^{2-}, in many crystals and OH^- ions in crystals and in solution (where they are doubtless hydrated via hydrogen bonds). Oxides may also be covalent, for example, SO_3.

Fluorine is a diatomic gas and is extremely reactive. It forms both ionic compounds containing F^- ions and covalent compounds containing X—F bonds; owing to the high electronegativity of fluorine, these bonds generally have considerable ionic character.

7-2. Ionization Potentials, Electron Affinities, and Electronegativities

The first ionization potentials of the gaseous atoms increase, though not monotonically, from Li to F as shown in Figure 7-1 and Table 7-2. The

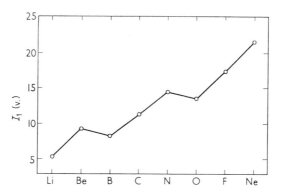

Fig. 7-1.   First ionization potentials of the elements Li–Ne.

low ionization potential of Li is in accord with the fact that its chemistry is dominated by electron loss to form the Li^+ ion. The first (9.32 e.v.) and second (18.21 e.v.) ionization potentials of Be are sufficiently high that total loss of both electrons to give Be^{2+} ions does not occur; BeX bonds (even Be—F) therefore have appreciable covalent character, and "Be^{2+} ions" in solution are strongly aquated to give $[Be(OH_2)_4]^{2+}$ and more complicated hydrolyzed species. For the succeeding elements, the absence of any simple cations under any conditions is to be expected from the high ionization potentials.

The I's of the elements B, C, N increase regularly, but they are all lower than the values which would be predicted by extrapolation from Li and Be. This is because p electrons are less penetrating than s electrons; they are therefore shielded by the s electrons and are more easily removed. Another discontinuity occurs between N and O. This one is due to the fact that

TABLE 7-2

Electronic Properties of the Elements Li–Ne

	Li	Be	B	C	N	O	F	Ne
Electronic structure								
$1s$	↑↓	↑↓	↑↓	↑↓	↑↓	↑↓	↑↓	↑↓
$2s$	↑	↑↓	↑↓	↑↓	↑↓	↑↓	↑↓	↑↓
$2p$			↑	↑ ↑	↑ ↑ ↑	↑↓ ↑ ↑	↑↓ ↑↓ ↑	↑↓ ↑↓ ↑↓
First ionization potential, e.v.	5.390	9.320	8.296	11.264	14.54	13.614	17.42	21.559
Electron affinity,[a] e.v.	0.54	~0.6	~0.2	~1.7	N^-: ~0.0 N^{3-}: ~−24	O^-: ~2.3 O^{2-}: −6.8	3.63	—
Electronegativities	1.0	1.5	2.0	2.6	3.1	3.5	4.0	
Unpaired electrons	1	0	1	2	3	2	1	0
Normal valence	1	2	3	4	3	2	1	0
Typical compounds	LiCl LiC_3H_7	$BeCl_2$ $BeSO_4$	BCl_3 $B(OH)_3$	CH_4 CCl_4	NH_3 NF_3 Li_3N	H_2O $NaOH$ $(CH_3)_2O$	ClF KF CF_4	

[a] Most of these numbers are estimates with rather wide and indefinite uncertainties and should not be taken too literally. Those for F^-, O^{2-}, and Li^- are fairly accurate.

the $2p$ shell is half full (i.e., is $p_x p_y p_z$) at N, and the p electrons added in O, F, and Ne are all going into p orbitals already singly occupied. Hence, they are partly repelled by the p electron already present in the same orbital and are thus less tightly bound. This phenomenon is the same one discussed in explaining the basis of Hund's first rule (page 22).

Like the ionization potentials, the electron affinities rise from Li to F, and the atoms become more electronegative, as indicated in Table 7-2. The consequent tendency toward anion formation becomes noticeable at carbon, which forms C_2^{2-} and other polyatomic anions, although the existence of C^{4-} ions is uncertain. N^{3-} ions are stable in some ionic nitrides, whereas O^{2-} and F^- ions are common and important. F^- is stable in water, whereas O^{2-} is immediately hydrolyzed:

$$O^{2-} + H_2O = 2OH^-$$

7-3. Formation of Electron Pair Bonds

Single Bonds. Table 7-2 recapitulates the previously discussed (Chapter 3) fact that the elements Be, B, and C have fewer unpaired electrons in their ground state atoms than the number of electron pair bonds they normally form. This has been explained in terms of promotion to valence states having the requisite numbers of unpaired electrons. Similar promotions are, of course, also required for the congeners of these elements.

There is an important empirical rule, which has a theoretical basis, concerning the valence of these elements. This is the *octet rule*. It states that these atoms tend to be surrounded by eight electrons in their compounds and, more rigorously true, are never surrounded by more than eight electrons (in the valence shell).

Let us consider the idea that eight valence shell electrons are a maximum. This means that the maximum number of electron pair bonds is four. In the first row atoms, only the orbitals of the second principal shell can be used for bond formation because any other free orbitals are of far too high energies to be useful. For example, phosphorus, with the configuration $3s^2 3p^3 3d^0$, can be excited to a valence state of configuration $3s^1 3p^3 3d^1$ with an expenditure of energy so modest that the heat of formation of the two additional bonds will more than compensate for it. On the other hand, promotion of nitrogen, $2s^2 2p^3$, to any state with five unpaired electrons, such as $2s^1 2p^3 3d^1$, would require such an enormous promotion energy that it could not be offset by the additional bond formation energy. The same type of argument can be made for all of the elements of the first short period. Thus all of them have only four orbitals energetically suitable for bond formation, cannot form more than four electron pair bonds, and can be surrounded by no more than eight electrons in the valence shell.

In the case of carbon the valence of four can be attained by promotion from the $2s^2 2p^2$ state to the $2s 2p^3$ state. For nitrogen, only three of the five electrons can possibly be unpaired, in oxygen only two, and in fluorine only one, so that these elements are limited to valences of 3, 2, and 1, respectively. On the other side of carbon, namely, in Li, Be, and B, the valences are less than four, not for lack of four low energy orbitals but for lack of electrons to occupy those orbitals. Thus by electron sharing, these elements can exhibit valences of only 1, 2, and 3, respectively.

However, the atoms with four energetically useful orbitals and fewer electrons have a strong drive to use their unoccupied orbitals. Also, atoms with too many electrons have a tendency to utilize these electrons. Thus compounds of boron, such as BCl_3, BF_3, and $B(CH_3)_3$, readily form adducts with nitrogen compounds such as NH_3, $N(CH_3)_3$, etc., as illustrated in Figure 7-2; boron makes use of an available but empty orbital, and nitro-

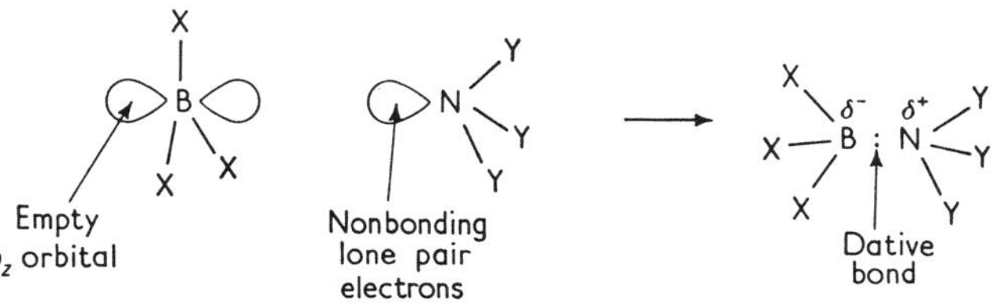

Fig. 7-2. The formation of a dative bond between boron in a BX_3 acceptor and nitrogen in a NY_3 donor.

gen makes use of an "idle" pair of electrons. Oxygen compounds, ethers, for example, which have unshared electron pairs also function as *donors* with boron compounds in which boron functions as an *acceptor*. The bond formed is called a *dative bond* (dative meaning "giving"). The number of atoms surrounding a given atom, X, is called the *coordination number* of X. The maximum coordination number of first row elements is four. Carbon attains this by forming four bonds since its valence is also four. Boron frequently attains maximum coordination by functioning as an acceptor, nitrogen by functioning as a donor. Oxygen *tend* to increase its coordination number from two to as high as four, but there are not a great many instances in which it gets beyond three. Beryllium, however, usually achieves four coordination by binding two donor atoms in addition to forming two ordinary covalent bonds.

The reason why some atoms succeed in increasing their coordination numbers from three to four, but seldom from two to four, can be understood if we consider the polar nature of the dative bond. The donor molecule and the acceptor molecule are both electrically neutral. When the dative bond is formed, the donor atom has, in effect, lost an electron charge, rendering it positive, since it then has only half ownership of an electron pair which formerly belonged entirely to it. The acceptor atom, conversely, now has an extra negative charge. This would be true for complete sharing of the electron pair (7-I); lesser polarity is introduced if the electron pair is still more the property of the donor atom than the acceptor (7-II), in which case we indicate only charges δ^+ and δ^- on the atoms.

$$\overset{-e}{\text{B}} : \overset{+e}{\text{N}} \qquad\qquad \overset{\delta^-}{\text{B}} \ldots : \overset{\delta^+}{\text{N}}$$

$$\text{(7-I)} \qquad\qquad \text{(7-II)}$$

This charge separation can only be accomplished by doing work against coulomb forces, which we must assume is more than compensated by the bond energy when a stable system results. However, if we take a case where one donor bond has already been formed (7-III), we see that the

$$\text{R}\!-\!\overset{\overset{\delta^+}{\cdot\cdot}}{\text{O}} \overset{\delta^-}{:}\text{BX}_3$$
$$|$$
$$\text{R}$$
$$\text{(7-III)}$$

other unshared pair on oxygen is further restrained by the positive charge on O arising in the dative bond already formed. There is thus much more coulombic work to be done in forming a second dative bond and apparently enough to make this process energetically unfavorable. Of course, steric hindrance between the first acceptor and a second would also militate against addition of a second. It will be noted that this electrostatic argument is basically the same as that used by Niels Bjerrum to explain the relative values of dissociation constants in a polyfunctional acid (Chapter 5). Be^{2+} probably achieves four-fold coordination in aqueous solution, as $[Be(H_2O)_4]^{2+}$. In this case it is likely that the forces between Be^{2+} and H_2O are mainly ion–dipole coulomb forces rather than $Be{\leftarrow}O$ dative bonding forces. There are many other beryllium compounds in which the metal atom does become four coordinate.

Multiple Bonds. The elements C, N, and O characteristically form multiple bonds with themselves and with one another. Their congeners do not, however (or at least only to a minor degree and by different mechanisms as in P=O, S=C, and S=O). We have seen that a multiple bond can be viewed, in MO theory, as a σ bond plus one or two π bonds, and we have seen how the π orbitals of two atoms can overlap to give π bonding MO's. The reasons why Si, P and S do not characteristically form double bonds, in contrast to C, N, and O, have not been fully elucidated. The most probable reason is that in order to approach closely enough to get good overlap of $p\pi$ atomic orbitals, the heavier atoms would encounter large repulsive forces due to overlapping of their filled inner shells, whereas the small compact inner shell of the first row elements (i.e., just $1s^2$) does not produce this repulsion. At any rate, multiple bond formation is an important feature of the elements of the first short period but not, significantly, of their congeners.

7-4. Fajans' Views on Covalent Bonding

Many years ago Fajans pointed out that when two ions, A^+ and B^-, are juxtaposed, there will be an interaction over and above their coulombic attraction, namely, an interaction due to mutual *polarization*. Fajans pointed out that the smaller and more highly charged a cation is, the more it will tend to distort the charge distribution in a neighboring anion. A reasonably quantitative measure of this polarizing power of the cation is its charge/radius ratio. At the same time the polarizability of an anion will increase with its size and charge. Other things being equal, the larger of two anions will be more polarizable because the outer electrons are farther from the nucleus. At the same time, the more negative of two isoelectronic anions (e.g., O^{2-}, F^-) will be larger and more polarizable because the extra electron–electron repulsion expands the electron cloud. Since cations are usually small and compact relative to anions, the polarization of the cation by the anion is considered to be relatively negligible in most cases (CsF is probably an exception). We may therefore expect the shapes of the free ions and of closely juxtaposed ions to be somewhat as represented in Figure 7-3.

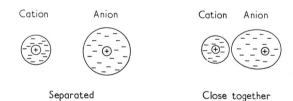

Fig. 7-3.   Schematic diagram showing how a small cation polarizes the electron cloud of a large anion.

Fajans further proposed that covalent bonding could be considered as a case of ionic bonding in which the polarization of the anions is so extreme as to give an appreciable increase in electron density between the nuclei.

Although this view is severely limited insofar as quantitative treatment is concerned, and is not in general a substitute for the quantum mechanical treatment of covalent bonding, it has certain merits as a conceptual approach to bonds which are mainly ionic, with a little covalence.

As examples of applications of Fajans' ideas, let us consider the melting points of some "ionic" halides of the alkaline earths (Table 7-3). Note

TABLE 7-3

Melting Points and Ionic Radii of Some Alkaline Earth Halides

| Compound | Radius, A. | | Melting point, °C. |
	Cation	Anion	
$BeCl_2$	0.31	1.81	405
$MgCl_2$	0.65	1.81	712
CaF_2	0.99	1.36	1392
$CaCl_2$	0.99	1.81	772
$CaBr_2$	0.99	1.95	730
CaI_2	0.99	2.16	575
$SrCl_2$	1.13	1.81	872
$BaCl_2$	1.35	1.81	960
$RaCl_2$	1.50 (est.)	1.81	~1000

that the melting points of chlorides rise steadily as the cation size increases, whereas those of the calcium halides decline steadily as the anion size increases. In other words, in general, the melting points vary inversely with the amount of polarization of the anion by the cation. It is also found that the greater the possibility of polarization, the lower is the heat of sublimation (to aggregates of ions) and the greater is the solubility in nonpolar solvents. LiCl, for example, is soluble in numerous organic liquids, whereas NaCl and other alkali chlorides are not. The reason for this kind of behavior is as follows. In the solid, where each anion is symmetrically surrounded by cations, polarization of the anions is not important because the various pulls in different directions by the cations balance out by symmetry. Thus the polarizability of the anion and the polarizing power of the cation have little effect on the lattice energy. However, for the ion pairs or other aggregates (e.g., $(LiI)_n$) in the gas phase, in solution, or in the melt, the polarizations contribute appreciably to the stability; hence, these phases have an "extra" stability relative to the crystals, with resultant higher solubilities and lower melting points and sublimation energies.

As will be seen in subsequent discussions, the first row elements, especially Li, Be, and B, have certain chemical resemblances to the second members of the next groups, that is

Thus, for example, when the properties of lithium compounds differ from those of the corresponding compounds of the other alkali metals, they frequently resemble those of magnesium compounds.

This phenomenon, sometimes referred to as the *"diagonal relationship,"* has been explained on Fajans' principles. Although Na^+ and Mg^{2+} are isoelectronic and Li^+ and Na^+ have the same charge, the resemblances between Li^+ and Mg^{2+} are also great because both are much more polarizing than Na^+. Similarly, Be and Al have many similarities, such as the formation of halogen-bridged halide dimers (7-IV and 7-V), a type of

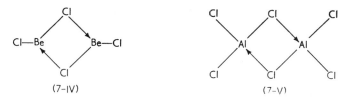

(7-IV)   (7-V)

compound not formed by Mg. However, this diagonal relationship is perhaps best kept in the back of the mind and not overemphasized. For example, the charge/radius ratio of Li^+ (1.47) differs less from that of Na^+ (1.05) than from that of Mg^{2+} (3.08). Also, the basic idea that covalent bonds are due only to distortion of ions is a vast oversimplification.

Reference

Bent, H. A., *Chem. Revs.*, **61**, 275 (1961). A review on the structure of, and hybridization in, compounds of the first row elements.

8

Lithium

8-1. Valence and Bonding

The lithium atom has a single valence electron, and lithium is the first member of the closely allied group I or alkali metals, Li, Na, K, Rb, Cs, (Fr), all of which have a single electron in an s orbital outside an inert gas core (distinction from Cu, Ag, Au). The chemistry of these elements is accordingly the simplest of any group. Here also, the similarity between the first member and its congeners is rather great, although the uniquely small size of the lithium atom and ion does lead to some notable differences in chemical behavior which will be detailed below. The low ionization potential (5.39 e.v.) results in the ready formation of the Li^+ ion, which exists as such in crystalline salts, for example, LiCl. In solutions the ion is doubtless heavily solvated and may be written $Li^+(aq)$ in water. Lithium can also form covalent bonds, Li—X. The vapor of the metal, although predominantly monatomic, contains about 1% of the diatomic molecule Li_2 near the boiling point. These molecules are detected by their characteristic band spectrum. Although to a first approximation the Li—Li bond might be considered as due to s–s overlap, more detailed study indicates that there is some s–p hybridization, which gives a bond with $\sim$14% p character. The Li—Li bond energy, 27 kcal./mole, is rather low and the Li—Li distance is 2.67 A. There are lithium compounds, such as C_2H_5Li and C_3H_7Li, which behave like typical covalent compounds, being quite volatile and soluble in nonpolar solvents. There is no evidence for oxidation states other than $+1$, nor would they be expected in view of the inert gas configuration of Li^+ and the very high second ionization potential (75.2 e.v.).

Some typical lithium compounds are listed in Table 8-1.

TABLE 8-1

Some Typical Lithium Compounds and Their Properties

Compound	Color and form	Melting point, °C.	Solubility
Li	Silvery white, soft metal	179	Liquid NH_3 and certain amines
Li_2O	White solid (CaF_2 structure)	1700	Reacts with H_2O to give LiOH
LiOH	White, tetragonal crystals	450	12.8 g./100 g. of H_2O at 20°C.
LiF	White, cubic crystals	842	Sp. sol. H_2O (0.27 g./100 g. at 18°C.)
LiCl	White, cubic crystals	614	V. sol. H_2O, methanol
Li_2CO_3	White, monoclinic crystals	723	1.5 g./100 g. of H_2O at 0°C.
$LiNO_3$	White, trigonal crystals	264	55.7 g./100 g. of H_2O at 0°C.; pyridine
$LiClO_4$	White, rhombic crystals	236	V. sol. H_2O; sol. alcohols, ethers
LiH	White, crystalline (NaCl structure)	668[a]	Insol. ethers, hydrocarbons
$LiCH_3$	White, crystalline	—	Insol. benzene, ligroin
LiC_2H_5	Colorless crystals	90	Sol. benzene, ligroin
LiC_6H_5	Colorless powder	—	Sl. sol. benzene

[a] Freezing point.

8-2. Comparison of Lithium and Its Congeners

Although, as stated above, Li in most ways has properties typical of all group I metals, there are some differences to be noted and accounted for. Certain divergences are at the same time resemblances to the chemistry of Mg. The anomalies of Li result mainly from the small size of the atom and the ion; the polarizing power of Li^+ is the greatest of all the alkali ions and leads to a singularly great tendency toward solvation and covalent bond formation.

1. The reactivity of the group I metals toward all chemical reagents except nitrogen increases with increasing electropositive nature (Li → Cs). Li is usually the least reactive. Li is only rather slowly attacked by water at 25°C., whereas Na reacts vigorously, K inflames, and Rb and Cs react explosively. With liquid Br_2, Li and Na barely react, whereas the others do so violently. Lithium will not liberate the weakly acidic hydrogen in $C_6H_5C \equiv C—H$, whereas the other alkali metals do so. However, with N_2, it is uniquely reactive to give Li_3N (note Mg also reacts to give Mg_3N_2). At 25°C. the reaction is slow, but is rapid on heating. Both Li and Mg can be used to remove nitrogen from other gases. Finally, metallic lithium is harder and higher melting than the other group I metals.

2. Lithium hydride, LiH, is far more stable than the other group I hydrides and can be melted without decomposition (f.p. $668 \pm 1°C.$); it is unaffected by oxygen below red heat, by chlorine, or by HCl. The heat of formation of LiH is greater than those of the other alkali metal hydrides (cf. Chapter 5). These facts have led to some confusion because in some places it is stated that Li is more reactive toward hydrogen (and also carbon) than the other alkalies. This is not so, since Li reacts with H_2 at 700–800°C., whereas the others react at 350–400°C. For carbon, the statement is more nearly correct—both Li and Na react directly with carbon on heating to form the *acetylides* Li_2C_2 and Na_2C_2. The heavier alkalies also react with carbon, but give nonstoichiometric interstitial compounds where the metal atoms enter between the planes of carbon atoms in the lamellar graphite structure. This difference may be attributed to size requirements for the metal both in the ionic acetylides (M^+, $C_2{}^{2-}$) and in the penetration of the graphite.

3. Only lithium oxide, Li_2O, is formed on burning the metal in air or oxygen. The other alkali oxides, M_2O, react further giving peroxides, M_2O_2, and (with K, Rb, and Cs) superoxides, MO_2. This difference may again be attributed to the small size of Li^+ which makes it unable to stabilize the larger anions relative to the O^{2-} ion.

4. Lithium hydroxide, LiOH, unlike the other hydroxides, MOH, decomposes at red heat to Li_2O (cf. Mg, Ca, etc.); NaOH, KOH, etc., sublime unchanged, mainly as dimers. LiOH is also considerably less soluble in water (4 moles/liter at 10°C.) than NaOH (12 moles/liter at 10°C.) or other alkali hydroxides.

5. Lithium hydrosulfide, LiSH, is not stable under ordinary conditions, whereas other MSH compounds are.

6. Lithium carbonate, Li_2CO_3, is relatively thermally unstable with respect to LiO and CO_2 compared to the other alkali carbonates (cf. $MgCO_3$). This is because the small Li^+ ion makes the Li_2O lattice more stable compared with the Li_2CO_3 lattice than are the other M_2O lattices compared to the M_2CO_3 lattices.

7. Lithium is the only alkali metal to form an imide, Li_2NH. This is a very reactive substance formed by heating the amide, $LiNH_2$

$$2LiNH_2 = Li_2NH + NH_3$$

8. Lithium alkyls and aryls are usually liquids or low-melting solids soluble in hydrocarbons. Methyllithium, CH_3Li, is less fusible and soluble and thus resembles the alkyls and aryls of the other alkalies; it is almost certainly polymeric.

9. The solubilities of various lithium salts resemble those of Mg salts

and often differ noticeably from those of the other group I elements. Thus, while LiCl, LiBr, and LiI are highly soluble in H_2O, LiF is relatively insoluble and can be precipitated by ammoniacal ammonium fluoride (like Mg^{2+}). LiCl, LiBr, and particularly LiI are quite soluble in oxygenated organic solvents (like Mg^{2+}); also, $LiClO_4$ (like Mg^{2+}, Ca^{2+}, Sr^{2+}, and Ba^{2+} perchlorates) is remarkably soluble in oxygenated organic solvents such as alcohol, acetone, or ethyl acetate. $NaClO_4$ is less soluble by factors of 3–12, whereas $KClO_4$, $RbClO_4$, and $CsClO_4$ have solubilities only 10^{-3} of these. Since the spherical ClO_4^- ion is virtually nonpolarizable and the alkali metal perchlorates form ionic crystals, the high solubility of $LiClO_4$ is most likely attributable to strong solvation of the Li^+ ion. Magnesium perchlorate, $Mg(ClO_4)_2$, which has solubility properties similar to $LiClO_4$, is a very effective drying agent, also because of strong solvation of the cation. LiBr in hot concentrated solution has the unusual property of dissolving cellulose. LiBr and also $LiClO_4$ form ammoniates with ammonia or amines.

10. Lithium *sulfate*, Li_2SO_4, in contrast to the other M_2SO_4 salts, does not form alums. It is also not isomorphous with the other sulfates. Lithium *sulfite*, Li_2SO_3, is also unusual in that it oxidizes in moist air or when moist, with evolution of heat.

THE ELEMENT

8-3. Occurrence, Isolation, and Properties

The most important lithium minerals are lepidolite, $Li_2(F, OH)_2Al_2$ $(SiO_3)_3$ and spodumene, $LiAl(SiO_3)_2$. Two isotopes of Li occur in nature: ^6Li, 7.30% and ^7Li, 92.7%.

In view of the high positive standard potential

$$Li = Li^+(aq) + e \qquad E^0 = +3.02 \text{ v.}$$

the metal cannot be made by electrolysis of aqueous solutions of lithium salts; this produces the hydroxide. The metal can be obtained by electrolysis of a fused salt, usually LiCl, or by electrolysis of LiCl in pyridine, ethanol, or acetone. It is soft, silver white, and much less reactive than the other alkali metals. Freshly cut surfaces tarnish in air owing to oxide and nitride formation, but the reaction with water is not so vigorous as to inflame the hydrogen.

The metal is relatively light, the density being 0.53 g./cm³. It has the highest melting and boiling points, 179 and 1317°C., and also the longest liquid range of all the alkali metals. It also has an extraordinarily high specific heat (0.784 cal./g. °C. at 0°C.). These properties make it an excellent coolant in heat exchangers, but it is also very corrosive—more so than the other liquid alkalies—which is a great practical disadvantage. It is also used to deoxidize, desulfurize, and generally de-gas copper and copper alloys. It is extensively used in the preparation of organolithium compounds, as well as LiH and $LiAlH_4$.

Like other electropositive metals, lithium dissolves in liquid ammonia and in various amines (e.g., ethylamine) to give blue solutions which conduct electricity. The nature of such solutions is discussed in more detail elsewhere (Section 16-3), but we may state here that their properties are consistent with the existence of solvated Li^+ ions and solvated electrons. Solutions of lithium in amines, particularly in ethylenediamine, $H_2NCH_2CH_2NH_2$, are powerful reducing agents used in organic chemistry.

The reactions of lithium metal are summarized in Table 8-2.

TABLE 8-2

Some Reactions of Lithium Metal

Reagent	Products
Water, slow at 25°C.	LiOH, H_2
Oxygen, 100°C.	Li_2O
Hydrogen, 700–800°C.	LiH
Nitrogen, 25–200°C.	Li_3N
Ammonia (liquid) and certain amines	Blue solutions catalytically (Fe) decomposed to amide, $LiNH_2$, which on heating gives imide, Li_2NH
Alkyl, aryl halides in petrol or ether	Organolithium compounds, RLi
Alcohols	Alkoxides, ROLi, $+H_2$
Nonmetals, heating	Li_2C, Li_2S, Li_3P, etc.
Isoprene, butadiene, styrene	Polymerized

LITHIUM COMPOUNDS

8-4. Ionic Salts; the Hydrated Li^+ Ion

The stoichiometries and general properties are mostly similar to those of the other alkali metals, with the exceptions already discussed above.

Salts with common anions such as Cl^-, SO_4^{2-} are highly ionic under all conditions. Thus the fused salts conduct electricity. Owing to its small size, the Li$^+$ ion has a large hydration energy, and it is often hydrated in its solid salts when the same salts of other alkalies are unhydrated, viz., LiClO$_4 \cdot$3H$_2$O. For salts of *strong* acids, the lithium salt is usually the *most* soluble in water of the alkali metal salts, whereas for *weak* acids the lithium salts are usually *less* soluble than those of the other alkalies.

Lithium fluoride is a white crystalline solid, only slightly soluble in water (0.27 g./100 g. at 18°C.) and insoluble in alcohol. It is used in welding fluxes and as massive crystals in infrared spectrometers because of its excellent dispersion in the range 4000–1600 cm.$^{-1}$. Lithium chloride is the most common lithium salt. It is very soluble in water and moderately soluble in oxygenated or basic organic liquids, such as alcohols, ketones, esters, and pyridine. Such substances doubtless strongly solvate the lithium ion, thus overcoming the lattice forces.

The vapors of the halides contain polymeric species—mainly dimers and trimers; for [LiF]$_2$ and [LiF]$_3$, the dissociation energies are 58.9 and 38.3 kcal./mole, respectively. (LiCl)$_2$ has been shown to be a planar, diamond-shaped molecule in the gas phase.

The *hydrated ion*, Li$^+$(aq), occurs both in solution and in some hydrous salts. Although the number of water molecules strongly bound to Li$^+$ in water cannot be estimated very exactly, it is certain that an ion with a very small crystallographic radius has a very large hydrated radius because it binds dipolar water molecules very effectively. Thus the Li$^+$(aq) ion in water doubtless has a larger effective radius than Cs$^+$(aq) (3.40 A. vs. 2.28 A., estimated). In spite of the strong solvation in solution crystalline hydrates seldom have more than four H$_2$O molecules per Li$^+$ ion, and exceptions are very likely owing to hydration of anions. As with [Be(H$_2$O)$_4$]$^{2+}$ the Li—OH$_2$ forces are probably for the most part ion–dipole and very little covalent. Lithium salts in solution generally deviate from ideal solution behavior, yielding solutions of abnormal colligative properties such as very low vapor pressure, freezing point, etc.

Lithium hydroxide formed in solution from Li$_2$O or directly from Li is a strong base like all alkali hydroxides. It absorbs CO$_2$ from the air, either in solution or in the solid state, to form Li$_2$CO$_3$. Since LiOH is a strong base, lithium salts of weak acids (Li$_2$CO$_3$, Li$_2$S, etc.) are hydrolyzed in solution and give pH's >7. LiOH is less soluble (4 moles/liter, at 0°C.) than NaOH (12 moles/liter, at 0°C.).

The metal reacts directly with most nonmetallic and some metallic elements, but the products are of no special interest. The nitrogen compounds LiNH$_2$, Li$_2$NH, and Li$_3$N are known; they are hydrolyzed to ammonia by water. The hydride and borohydride have been discussed in Chapter 5; the latter is soluble not only in water but in ethers such as tetrahydrofuran and is a very useful reducing agent. The borohydride also forms ammonia solvates.

8-5. Organolithium Compounds

One of the largest uses of metallic lithium, industrially and in the laboratory, is for the preparation of organolithium compounds. These are of great importance and utility; in their reactions they generally resemble the well-known Grignard reagents (Mg), although they are usually more reactive. The preparation is best accomplished using an alkyl or aryl

$$C_2H_5Cl + 2Li = C_2H_5Li + LiCl \tag{8-1}$$

chloride (eq. 8-1) in benzene or petroleum; ether solutions can be used, but these solvents are attacked slowly by the lithium compounds. Metal–

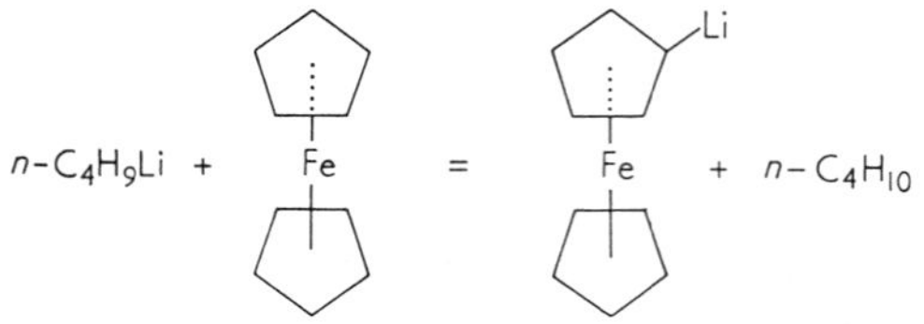

$$(8-2)$$

$$(8-3)$$

hydrogen exchange (eq. 8-2), metal-halogen exchange (eq. 8-3), and metal–metal exchange (eq. 8-4) may also be used.

$$2Li + R_2Hg = 2RLi + Hg \tag{8-4}$$

Organolithium compounds all react rapidly with oxygen, being usually spontaneously flammable in air, with liquid water, and with water vapor. However, lithium bromide and iodide form solid complexes of stoichiometry $RLi(LiX)_{1-6}$ with the alkyls, and these solids are stable in air.

Organolithium compounds are among the very few alkali metal compounds which have properties—solubility in hydrocarbons or other nonpolar liquids and high volatility—typical of covalent substances. They are generally liquids or low-melting solids, but their structures are not clearly known. Molecular association is an important structural feature; for example, ethyllithium is about a six-fold polymer in nitrobenzene. The insolubility and low volatility of methyllithium is attributed to extensive polymerization. The nature of the forces binding the molecules into polymeric aggregates is not known, but these forces may be similar to those in the beryllium and aluminum alkyls (Section 11-7).

References

Braude, E. A., in J. W. Cook, ed., *Progress in Organic Chemistry*, Vol. III, Butterworths, London, 1955, p. 172. A review of organolithium compounds in organic chemistry.
Foote Mineral Co., Philadelphia 4, Pa. Various bulletins containing physical and chemical data on lithium and its compounds.
Laidler, D. S., *Lithium and Its Compounds* (Royal Institute of Chemistry, Monograph No. 6), London, 1957. Describes the occurrence, manufacture, uses, alloys, and compounds.
Lithium Corp. of America, Minneapolis 2, Minn. Various bulletins containing physical and chemical data on lithium and its compounds.

9

Beryllium

9-1. Covalent Bond Formation; Stereochemistry; Coordination Number

The electron configuration of the gaseous beryllium atom is $1s^2 2s^2$. The increased nuclear charge over that in lithium, coupled with the fact that the $2s$ electrons only partially shield one another, has two effects: (*1*) The Be atom has a metallic radius of only 0.89 A., much smaller than metallic Li's 1.22 A. (*2*) The ionization potentials of Be, 9.32 and 18.21 e.v., are much higher than that of Li (5.39 e.v.), making Be far less electropositive in all its chemical behavior than Li. In fact, there are no crystalline compounds or solutions in which Be^{2+} ions exist as such. All compounds whose structures have been determined, even those with the most electronegative elements, such as BeO and BeF_2, have at least partial covalent bonding. Atoms of the other elements of group II, Mg, Ca, Sr, Ba, and Ra, have electronic structures similar to that of Be. However, the greater size of these atoms reduces the effect of the nuclear charge on the valence electrons. Thus their ionization potentials are lower than those of Be; they are, in general, more electropositive, and the ionic nature of their compounds steadily increases in descending the group. Though some Mg compounds show covalent character, compounds of Ca, Ba, Sr, and Ra are all essentially ionic.

Some typical beryllium compounds and their properties are listed in Table 9-1.

As a result of the small size, high ionization potentials, and high sublimation energy of beryllium, the lattice or hydration energies are insufficient for essentially complete charge separation and the formation of simple Be^{2+} ions. On the other hand, to allow the formation of two covalent

168

TABLE 9-1

Some Representative Beryllium Compounds and Their Properties

Compound	Color and form	Melting point, °C.	Solubility
Be	Fairly hard, grey metal	1285	Dil. acids and alkalies
BeO	White infusible powder	2570	Slowly in fused acid salts
Be(OH)$_2$	White solid	—	Acids and bases
BeF$_2$	Transparent, glassy solid	803	H$_2$O
BeCl$_2$	White solid; sublimable	405	Hydrolyzed by H$_2$O
[Be(H$_2$O)$_4$]SO$_4$	Colorless octahedra	−H$_2$O at ∼200	H$_2$O
Be(C$_2$H$_5$)$_2$	Colorless liquid	—	Many organic solvents
BeH$_2$	White nonvolatile solid	—	Insol. organic solvents; reacts with H$_2$O
Be$_4$O(OCOCH$_3$)$_6$	White crystalline solid	283	Nonpolar organic solvents, e.g., CCl$_4$

bonds, —Be—, it is clear that unpairing of the two $2s$ electrons is required. Where free BeX$_2$ molecules occur, the Be atom is promoted to a state in which the two valence electrons occupy two equivalent sp hybrid orbitals and the X—Be—X system is linear. However, in such a linear molecule the Be atom has a coordination number of only two and there is a strong tendency for Be to achieve maximum (four-fold) coordination, or at least three-fold coordination. Maximum coordination is achieved in several ways:

1. Polymerization may occur through bridging, as in solid BeCl$_2$ (Fig. 9-1). The coordination of Be is not exactly tetrahedral since the Cl—Be—Cl

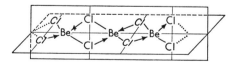

Fig. 9-1.   Structure of polymeric BeCl$_2$ in crystal.

angles are only 98°, which means that the BeCl$_2$Be units are somewhat elongated in the direction of the chain axis. In such a situation steric factors are very important in determining the exact sizes of the angles. Presumably, if the angle were opened to 109°, any improvement in bond strength would be insufficient to counterbalance the increase in Be—Be repulsion energy. Beryllium chloride readily sublimes; at high temperatures (∼750°C.) it consists of essentially all monomeric, linear BeCl$_2$ molecules, but at lower temperatures there are appreciable amounts ($\sim$20% at 560°C.) of the dimer, in which Be is three-coordinate.

2. By functioning as acceptors, many beryllium compounds attain maximum coordination of the metal atom. Thus the chloride forms etherates, $Cl_2Be(OR_2)_2$, and complex ions such as BeF_4^{2-} and $[Be(H_2O)_4]^{2+}$ exist.

3. In chelate compounds, such as the acetylacetonate (9-I), four approximately tetrahedral bonds are formed. Actually, resonance makes all of the C—O and Be—O bonds equivalent, and we cannot really speak of the two dative and the two ordinary covalent bonds implied by structure 9-I.

(9-I)

4. It has been found from X-ray structural studies that the packing in crystals is almost invariably such as to give Be a coordination number of four with a tetrahedral (or nearly so) configuration. Thus, in BeO there are BeO_4 tetrahedra. Be_2SiO_4 is exceptional among the orthosilicates of the alkaline earths, the rest of which have structures giving the metal ion octahedral coordination, in having the Be atoms tetrahedrally surrounded by oxygen atoms. It may be noted in passing that Be with F gives compounds often isomorphous with oxygen compounds of silicon; thus BeF_2 is isomorphous with cristobalite, SiO_2, $BaBeF_4$ with $BaSiO_4$, and $NaBeF_3$ with $CaSiO_3$, and there are five different corresponding forms of Na_2BeF_4 and Ca_2SiO_4.

Three-coordinate Be occurs in some cases, for example, the gaseous dimers Be_2Cl_4, Be_2Br_4, and $Be_2(CH_3)_4$. In Be phthalocyanin, the metal is perforce surrounded by four nitrogen atoms in a plane. There is some question whether the second pair of nitrogen atoms are truly coordinated to the metal atom since Be cannot form planar orbitals into which these donors could donate. This compound constitutes an example of a *forced configuration* since the Be atom is held strongly in a rigid environment.

9-2. Resemblances between Beryllium and Aluminum

Although, as seen, most simple beryllium salts are mainly covalent, it is possible to estimate an ionic radius for Be^{2+} of $\sim$0.31 A. With this value the charge/radius ratio is ~6.5, greater than for any other cation (except H^+, which does not occur in crystals, and B^{3+}, which is wholly hypothetical). Al^{3+} has nearly as high a charge/radius ratio, namely, ~6.0, and from Fajans' point of view some chemical similarities between the two may be expected. Such similarities do in fact exist, and this is probably the best example of the "diagonal relationship." Among the striking similarities are:

1. Metallic Be, like Al, is rather resistant to acids unless finely divided or amalgamated owing to the formation of an inert and impervious oxide film on the surface. Thus, although the potential

$$Be = Be^{2+}(aq) + 2e \qquad E^0 \text{ (calc.)} = 1.85$$

would indicate rapid reaction with dilute acids (and even H_2O; cf. Chapter 5), the rate of attack depends greatly also on the source and fabrication of the metal. For very pure metal the relative dissolution rates are $HF > H_2SO_4 \sim HCl > HNO_3$. The metal dissolves rapidly in $3M$ H_2SO_4 and in $5M$ NH_4F, but very slowly in HNO_3.

It may be noted that the Be potential is considerably below those of the other alkaline earth metals, showing that the high heat of sublimation and ionization potentials of Be are not as fully compensated by the hydration energy of the ion as with the other metals.

2. The metal dissolves in strong bases to give what is called the "beryllate" ion:

$$Be + 2OH^- = BeO_2^{2-} + H_2$$

Aluminum dissolves similarly to give "aluminate" ions, AlO_2^{2-}. Neither of these formulas for the ions is representative of the true species, which are probably four and six coordinated, respectively. There is also evidence that "beryllate" solutions contain polymeric anions such as $Be_2O_3^{2-}$ as well as hydrated and hydroxy-bridged species. Both Be and Al oxides and hydroxides are amphoteric, dissolving readily in sodium hydroxide solutions.

3. BeO resembles Al_2O_3 in being extraordinarily high melting (m.p. 2570°C.) and nonvolatile as well as extremely hard. BeO is polymorphic and converts into a second form above ~800°C. This high temperature form is virtually insoluble in aqueous acids or bases and is only difficultly soluble in fused salts such as $KHSO_4$ or KOH. Curiously, it dissolves rather readily in a hot sirup of concentrated sulfuric acid and ammonium sulfate. The low temperature form of BeO has the Be atoms tetrahedrally coordinated by O (wurtzite structure), whereas the other alkaline earth oxides all have the NaCl structure. In Al_2O_3 aluminum is six coordinate.

THE ELEMENT

9-3. Occurrence, Isolation, and Properties

The most important beryllium mineral is beryl, $Be_3Al_2(SiO_3)_6$, which often occurs as large hexagonal prisms. Beryllium, like lithium, is made by electrolysis of the fused chloride. However, since $BeCl_2$ is covalent and has a very low electrical conductivity, about 10^{-3} that of NaCl, the latter salt is added to the melt. Beryllium amalgam, a very air-sensitive liquid or paste, depending on the concentration, can be obtained by electrolysis of fused NaCl and $BeCl_2$ with a mercury cathode in an argon atmosphere.

The grey metal is rather light (1.86 g./cm.³) and quite hard and brittle. Since the absorption of electromagnetic radiation, X-rays, for example, depends on the electron density in matter, beryllium has the lowest stopping power per unit mass thickness of all suitable construction materials and is used for "windows" in X-ray apparatus. It is also added as an antioxidant to copper and phosphor bronzes and as a hardener to copper.

Beryllium has a much lower chemical reactivity than lithium. Some of its reactions are given in Figure 9-2.

BERYLLIUM COMPOUNDS

9-4. Halides, Oxy Salts, and Binary Compounds of Beryllium

Beryllium *fluoride* is obtained as a glassy hygroscopic mass by heating $(NH_4)_2BeF_4$. The melt is a poor conductor of electricity. It is glassy in form like silica, having randomly oriented chains of $\cdots F_2BeF_2Be\cdots$ with F bridges. Thus the structure is similar to those of $BeCl_2$ and $BeBr_2$ except that the packing of the chains is disordered. BeF_2 is readily soluble in water.

Fluoroberyllates can be made by dissolving BeO in concentrated solutions of acid fluorides or fusing it with an acid fluoride such as NH_4HF_2, and they contain tetrahedral $BeF_4{}^{2-}$ ions. This ion has a crystal chemistry much like that of $SO_4{}^{2-}$ and corresponding salts, for example, $PbSO_4$ and $PbBeF_4$, usually have similar structures and solubilities. The ion is partially hydrolyzed in solution unless a large excess of F^- is present. As well as K_2BeF_4, the KF–BeF_2 system also has K_3BeF_5, $KBeF_3$, and KBe_2F_5 phases.

Beryllium *chloride* is prepared by passing CCl_4 over BeO at 800°C. It dissolves in water very exothermically, and a hydrate, $[Be(H_2O)_4]Cl_2$, can be crystallized from HCl solutions of the salt. It also dissolves in many donor solvents (R_2O, ROH, RCOH) as noted previously. There is evidence of chloroberyllate ions, for example, in Na_2BeCl_4 from study of the phase diagrams of alkali chloride–$BeCl_2$ systems, but this ion is rather unstable and does not exist in solution.

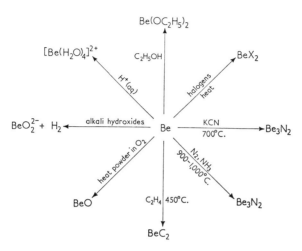

Fig. 9-2. Some reactions of beryllium.

Salts of *oxy acids* are known. $[Be(H_2O)_4]SO_4$ can be dehydrated at 400°C. to $BeSO_4$, which is very stable and does not decompose below 580°C. The nitrate, $[Be(H_2O)_4](NO_3)_2$, melts in its own water at 60.5°C.

Other noteworthy compounds are: the *sulfide*, BeS, which has the zinc blende structure and is insoluble in water (although all other alkaline earth sulfides and Al_2S_3 are rapidly hydrolyzed by water); Be_3N_2, a white crystalline powder or colorless crystals hydrolyzed by water; $BeCO_3$, which is unstable and can be kept only in an atmosphere of CO_2. The addition of soluble carbonates to aqueous solutions of beryllium salts gives basic carbonates of unknown structures.

Beryllium *hydride*, BeH_2, not obtainable by direct reaction, may be made in other ways, for example, by action of $LiAlH_4$ on $(CH_3)_2Be$ or by thermal decomposition of $[(CH_3)_3C]_2Be$. The latter method appears to give the purest product ($\sim$96%) which is stable to $\sim$240°C. and reacts only slowly and incompletely with water at 50°C.; the less pure products react vigorously. The general properties of BeH_2 suggest that it is polymeric with hydrogen bridging (see page 121).

9-5. Aqueous Chemistry of Beryllium

In concentrated acid solutions beryllium appears to exist as $[Be(H_2O)_4]^{2+}$ ions, and these occur (or probably occur) in several salts which have been mentioned above. The water in such salts is rather firmly bound; [Be $(H_2O)_4]Cl_2$, for example, loses no water over P_2O_5.

Solutions of all beryllium salts are acid owing to hydrolysis of the beryllium ion. It has also long been known that solutions of beryllium salts can dissolve considerable amounts of beryllium oxide or hydroxide. The reason for this appears to be that beryllium readily forms oxo and hydroxo complexes with Be—O—Be and Be—OH—Be bridges. In the precipitation of $Be(OH)_2$ some interesting effects have been observed. If n be the number of OH^- ions added per Be^{2+} ion, solutions remain clear up to $n = 1$. When $n > 1$, precipitation commences. With halide solutions precipitation is complete at $n = 2$, but with other ions precipitation is complete at $n = 1.8$–1.9, indicating that such precipitates of beryllium "hydroxide" contain SO_4^{2-}, NO_3^-, or ClO_4^- ions.

That precipitation occurs *only* when $n > 1$ suggests that there are $[Be(OH)^+]_n$ species which are soluble. Electrometric titration studies have, in fact, shown that in dilute solutions ($<0.050M$) the main species is $[Be(OH)]_3^{3+}$, and an equilibrium constant has been estimated

$$3Be^{2+} + 3H_2O = [Be(OH)]_3^{3+} + 3H^+ \qquad pK = -8.66$$

At very low concentrations of beryllium there is some evidence for Be_2OH^{3+} and $Be(OH)_2$, but none for $[Be(OH)]_2^{2+}$ or $[Be(OH)]_4^{4+}$. All the equilibria appear to be established rapidly. In view of the propensity of beryllium for four coordination, the structure of the $[Be(OH)]_3^{3+}$ species is thought to be (9-II). An open structure seems less likely in view of the stability of

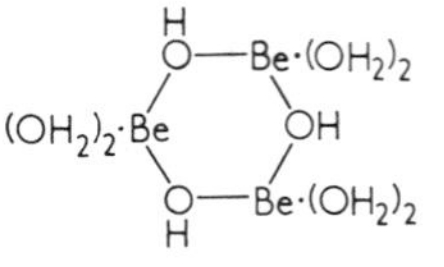

(9-II)

the trimer. The other hydroxy species may be formulated as 9-III and

$$\begin{array}{cc} (H_2O)_3Be\text{—}O\text{—}Be(H_2O)_3 & (H_2O)_2Be(OH)_2 \\ (9\text{-III}) & (9\text{-IV}) \end{array}$$

9-IV. It is possible that the beryllate ion with only one Be atom in solution is actually $[Be(OH)_4]^{2-}$, but this has not been proved.

9-6. Beryllium Complexes

Some of these have been mentioned already such as the $BeF_4{}^{2-}$ and $[Be(H_2O)_4]^{2+}$ ions, the etherates, alcoholates, and similar complexes with oxygenated organic compounds (e.g., $(R_2O)_2BeCl_2$). The tetrahedral chelate complex with acetylacetone (page 170) is only one example of many electrically neutral complexes formed with β-keto enols and β-keto esters.

Beryllium also forms some nitrogen complexes. The tetraammine, $[Be(NH_3)_4]Cl_2$, is very stable thermally, but is rapidly decomposed by water, an indication that oxygen is a stronger donor to beryllium than is nitrogen. Dimethylamine reacts with BeH_2 to give a trimer, $\{[(CH_3)_2N]_2Be\}_3$, which probably contains a six-membered ring with alternating Be and N atoms.

One of the most interesting types of beryllium complex is that of general formula $Be_4O(OCOR)_6$, formed by refluxing $Be(OH)_2$ with carboxylic acids. The resulting compounds are volatile crystalline substances, soluble in nonpolar solvents—even alkanes—and in many polar solvents other than water and lower alcohols. They are inert to water, but hydrolyzed by dilute acids. In solution they are un-ionized and monomeric. X-ray study has shown that they have the structures illustrated in Figure 9-3. The cen-

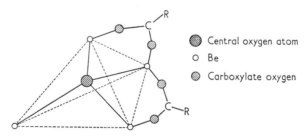

Fig. 9-3.   The structure of the carboxylate complexes $Be_4O(OOCR)_6$. Only two RCOO groups are shown.

tral oxygen atom is tetrahedrally surrounded by the four beryllium atoms (this being one of the few cases, excepting solid oxides, in which oxygen is four coordinate), and each beryllium atom is tetrahedrally surrounded by four oxygen atoms. Zinc also forms such complexes as does the ZrO^{2+} ion with benzoic acid. The zinc complexes are rapidly hydrolyzed by water in contrast to those of beryllium. The acetate complex has been utilized as a means of purifying beryllium by solvent extraction from an aqueous solution into an organic layer. It has also been shown that when $BeCl_2$ is dissolved in N_2O_4 in ethyl acetate, crystalline $Be(NO_3)_2 \cdot 2N_2O_4$ is obtained.

On heating at 50°C. this gives $Be(NO_3)_2$, which at 125°C. decomposes to N_2O_4 and volatile $Be_4O(NO_3)_6$. The structure of the latter appears to be similar to that of the acetate but with bridging nitrate groups. The basic nitrate is insoluble in nonpolar solvents.

9-7. Organoberyllium Compounds

These are obtained by reaction of beryllium halides with Grignard reagents or with lithium alkyls or aryls. They are mostly liquids or low-melting solids of high reactivity, being spontaneously flammable in air and violently hydrolyzed by water.

The methyl compound, $(CH_3)_2Be$, is polymerized in a manner (9-V) reminiscent of the $BeCl_2$ polymer, although the bridge bonding is rather

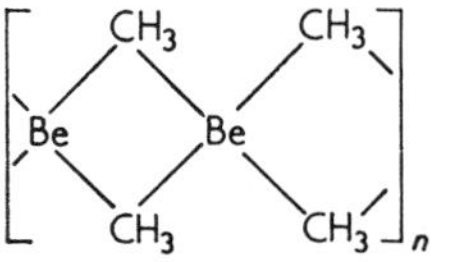

(9-V) 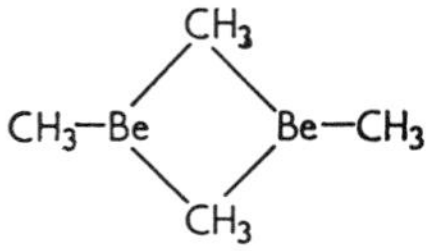   (9-VI)

different and will be discussed later (page 232). In the vapor phase di-methylberyllium is mostly dimeric (9-VI); again there is a geometrical similarity to the chloride dimer. The higher alkyls are less highly poly-merized, the diethyl being less polymerized than $(CH_3)_2Be$, and the diisopropyl compound being definitely a dimer in benzene. This lower degree of polymerization has been attributed to the more electropositive character of substituted carbon atoms and may also be due to steric hindrance. Since these compounds are not coordinately saturated, the polymeric structures can be split by strong donors and, for example, the methyl compound gives with $(CH_3)_3N$, $(CH_3)_3\overset{+}{N}—\overset{-}{Be}(CH_3)_2$ which is stable even as a vapor.

Pyrolysis of diisopropylberyllium at 200°C. gives a polymeric alkyl-beryllium hydride, a colorless, nonvolatile oil.

$$n(i\text{-}C_3H_7)_2Be \xrightarrow{200°C.} [(i\text{-}C_3H_7)BeH]_n + nC_3H_6$$

Pyrolysis of di-*tert*-butylberyllium at $> 100°C.$ gives essentially pure BeH_2 (see page 173) and isobutene.

Beryllium alkyls (and also halides) give colored complexes with 2,2'-dipyridyl, for example, $dipyBe(C_2H_5)_2$, which is bright red; the colors of these and similar complexes with aromatic amines given by beryllium, zinc, cadmium, aluminum, and gallium alkyls are believed to be due to electron transfer from the M—X bond to the lowest unoccupied orbital of the amine. Thus Be—X bonds appear to be acting as donors to the excited state of the complex.

9-8. Unipositive Beryllium

The difference between the first and second ionization potentials might suggest that there is a possibility of obtaining univalent beryllium. It has been claimed that the dissolution of beryllium anodes provides evidence for Be⁺ as an intermediate. However, further studies have shown that disintegration of the metal occurs during dissolution so that the apparent effect is one of the metal going into solution in the +1 state—too much metal is lost for the amount of current passed. The anode sludge, a mixture of Be and $Be(OH)_2$, had been considered to be due to disproportionation of Be⁺, but photomicrography indicates that the beryllium in the sludge is merely due to spallation.

There is some evidence for Be^I in fused chloride melts, for example,

$$Be + Be^{II} = 2Be^I$$

but no compound has yet been isolated.

Reference

Darwin, F. E., and J. H. Buddery, *Beryllium* (No. 7 of *Metallurgy of the Rarer Metals*), Butterworths, London, 1960.

10

Boron

GENERAL REMARKS

10-1. Electronic Structure and Bonding

The first ionization potential of boron, 8.296 e.v., is rather high, and the next two are much higher. Thus the total energy required to produce B^{3+} ions is far more than would be compensated by lattice energies of ionic compounds or by hydration of such ions in solution. Consequently, simple electron loss to form a cation plays no part in boron chemistry. Instead, covalent bond formation is of major importance, and boron compounds usually resemble those of other nonmetals, notably silicon, in their properties and reactions.

Despite the $2s^2 2p$ electronic structure, boron is always trivalent and never monovalent. This is because the total energy released in formation of three bonds in a BX_3 compound exceeds the energy of formation of one bond in a BX compound by more than enough to provide for promotion of boron to a hybridized valence state of the sp^2 type. This matter has been treated at length in Chapter 3, where it has also been shown that the three sp^2 hybrid orbitals lie in one plane at angles of 120°. It would therefore be expected, and is indeed found, without exception, that all monomeric, three-covalent boron compounds (trihalides, trialkyls, etc.) are planar with X—B—X bond angles of 120°.

It has proved troublesome to determine the covalent radius for trigonally hybridized boron very exactly, but estimates place it between 0.85 and 0.90 A. On this basis, there are apparently substantial shortenings of many B—X bonds, and this has occasioned much discussion. For example, the estimated B—F, B—Cl, and B—Br distances would be ~1.52, ~1.87, and ~1.99, whereas the actual distances in the respective trihalides are 1.30, 1.75, and 1.87 A. There appear to be three factors responsible for the shortness of the bonds.

178

1. Formation of $p\pi-p\pi$ bonds using filled $p\pi$ orbitals of the halogens and the vacant $p\pi$ orbital of boron. This is probably most important in BF_3, but of some significance in BCl_3 and BBr_3 as well.

2. Strengthening and hence shortening of the B—X bonds by ionic-covalent resonance (the effect emphasized in the Schomaker-Stevenson relationship). It is certainly in BF_3 that this will be of greatest importance, because of the large electronegativity difference. Evidence that this is important, in addition to the dative $p\pi-p\pi$ bonding, is afforded by the fact that even in BF_3 complexes such as $(CH_3)_3\overset{+}{N}\overset{-}{B}F_3$ and $BF_4{}^-$, where the $p\pi-p\pi$ bond must be largely or totally absent, the B—F bonds are still apparently shortened (1.41–1.43 A.).

3. It is also possible that because of the incomplete octet in boron, repulsions between nonbonding electrons are somewhat less than normal, permitting closer approach of the bonded atoms.

10-2. Electron Deficiency; Acceptor Behavior

In BX_3 compounds the boron octet is incomplete. In other words, boron has a low-lying orbital which it does not use in bonding owing to a shortage of electrons. Although partial use is made of it in the boron halides through B—X multiple bonding, BX_3 molecules are nevertheless electron deficient. The alkyls and halides of aluminum relieve this electron deficiency by forming dimers with alkyl or halogen bridges, but the boron compounds do not. The reason or reasons for this difference are not known with certainty. The size factor may be important for BCl_3 and BBr_3, since the small boron atom may be unable to coordinate strongly to four atoms as large as Cl and Br. The fact that $BCl_4{}^-$ and $BBr_4{}^-$ ions are stable only in crystalline salts of large anions such as Cs^+ or $(CH_3)_4N^+$ might suggest this. The fact that a certain amount of B—X $p\pi-p\pi$ bond energy would have to be sacrificed would also detract from the stability of dimers relative to monomers. The size factor cannot be controlling for BF_3, however, since $BF_4{}^-$ is quite stable. Here, the donor power of the fluorine already bonded to another boron atom may be so low that the energy of the bridge bonds would not be sufficient to counterbalance the energy required to break the B—F π bonding in the monomer. Phenomena of this nature are often difficult to explain with certainty.

An important consequence of the electron-deficient nature of BX_3 compounds is their ability to behave as acceptors (Lewis acids), in which boron achieves its maximum coordination with approximately sp^3 hybridization. Thus, various Lewis bases, such as amines, phosphines, ethers, and sulfides, form 1:1 complexes with BX_3 compounds. The following are representative of the addition compounds formed: $(CH_3)_3NBCl_3$, $(CH_3)_3PBH_3$, $(C_2H_5)_2OBF_3$, $(C_2H_5)_2SB(CH_3)_3$.

It is important to note that there is good evidence that the relative strengths of the boron halides as Lewis acids are in the order $BBr_3 \geq BCl_3 > BF_3$. This order is the opposite of what would be expected both on steric grounds and from electronegativity considerations, but can be explained in terms of the boron-halogen π bonding. In an addition compound this π bonding is largely or completely lost so that addition compounds of the trihalide with the strongest π bonding will be the most destabilized by loss of the energy of π bonding. Calculations indicate that the π bonding energies of the trihalides are in the order $BF_3 \gg BCl_3 > BBr_3$.

Boron also completes its octet by forming anions such as BF_4^-, BH_4^-, $[HB(OR)_3]^-$, and $[B(C_6H_5)_4]^-$ and chelate complexes such as 10-I. It has been proven that the four bonds to boron in such chelates are approxi-

(10-I)   (10-II)

mately tetrahedral (and certainly not planar) since, with ligands which themselves are sufficiently unsymmetrical, the complex ions may be resolved into optical isomers. Thus the borosalicylate ion (10-II) has been resolved by fractional crystallization of the diasterioisomeric salts formed with optically active strychnine.

10-3. Comparison with Silicon and Aluminum

Elemental boron has properties which place it on the borderline between metals and nonmetals. It is a semiconductor, not a metallic conductor. Chemically, boron must be classed as a nonmetal, and in general its chemistry resembles that of silicon much more closely than that of aluminum or its other congeners, Ga, In, and Tl. The main resemblances to Si and differences from Al are the following:

1. The similarity and complexity of the boric and silicic acids is notable. Boric acid, $B(OH)_3$, is weak but definitely an acid. It has no amphoteric properties, whereas $Al(OH)_3$ is mainly basic with some amphoteric behavior.

2. The hydrides of B and Si are volatile, spontaneously flammable, and

readily hydrolyzed, whereas Al forms only a solid, polymeric material of uncertain structure. However, structurally, the boron hydrides are unique, having unusual stoichiometries and configurations and unusual bonding because of their electron-deficient nature.

3. The ready hydrolysis of the boron halides (not BF_3) gives $B(OH)_3$, just as the silicon halides readily hydrolyze to silicic acid. The aluminum halides are only partially hydrolyzed in water.

4. B_2O_3 and SiO_2 are similar in their acidic nature, as evidenced by their facility in dissolving metallic oxides to form borates and silicates, and both readily form glasses which are difficult to crystallize. Certain oxy salts of B and Si are structurally similar, specifically the linear $(BO_2)_x$ and $(SiO_3)_x$ ions in metaborates and pyroxene silicates, respectively.

5. However, despite dimerization of the halides of Al and Ga and of the alkyls of Al, they behave as acceptors and form adducts similar to those given by boron halides and alkyls, for example, $Cl_3\overset{-}{Al}\overset{+}{N}(CH_3)_3$. Aluminum, like boron, also forms volatile alkoxides such as $Al(OC_2H_5)_3$, which are similar to borate esters, $B(OR)_3$.

THE ELEMENT

10-4. Occurrence, Isolation, and Properties

Boron occurs in quite substantial deposits of soluble borates such as borax, $Na_2B_4O_7 \cdot 10H_2O$, particularly in desert areas of India and California. Boric acid is present in volcanic steam and can be recovered under suitable conditions.

Natural boron consists of two isotopes, ^{10}B (18.83%) and ^{11}B (81.17%). Both these nuclides have spin, and nuclear magnetic resonance studies have proved quite fruitful in elucidating structures of boron compounds.

^{10}B can be enriched in the laboratory by reactions such as

$$^{11}BF_3 \cdot O(C_2H_5)_2(l) + {}^{10}BF_3(g) = {}^{10}BF_3 \cdot O(C_2H_5)_2(l) + {}^{11}BF_3(g)$$
$$^{11}BF_3 \cdot anisole(l) + {}^{10}BF_3(g) = {}^{10}BF_3 \cdot anisole(l) + {}^{11}BF_3(g)$$

It is exceedingly difficult to prepare elemental boron in a high state of purity because of its high melting point and the corrosive nature of the liquid. It can be prepared in quantity but low purity (95–98%) in an amorphous form by reduction of B_2O_3 with Mg followed by vigorous washing of the material so obtained with alkali, hydrochloric acid, and hydrofluoric acid. This amorphous boron is a dark powder which may contain some microcrystalline boron, but also contains oxides and borides. It is available commercially.

Crystalline boron (α-rhombohedral), of purity closely approaching 100%, has been prepared in small amounts by pyrolysis of BI_3 at 800–1000°C. on a tantalum filament, and the tetragonal-I polymorph is obtained by passing highly purified BBr_3 vapors in a stream of hydrogen over a hot tungsten or tantalum wire:

$$BBr_3 + \tfrac{3}{2}H_2 = B + 3HBr$$

With low partial pressures of BBr_3 ($\sim$18 mm.) and filament temperatures of 1300–1500°C., the boron condenses on the wire in the form of macroscopic crystals. Both plates and needles were found, but these were later shown to have identical internal structure. These are black and barely transmit light even in very thin sections. They have a metallic luster, but their electrical conductivity is more nearly that of a nonmetal. Also, the conductivity rises with temperature (factor of $\sim$100 from 20 to 600°C.) which is typical of nonmetallic solids but the reverse of normal metallic behavior. Crystalline boron is extremely hard, being apparently second only to diamond in hardness among the elements (diamond, 10.0 on Moh's scale; B, $\sim$9.2).

Crystalline boron is extremely inert chemically. It is unaffected by boiling HCl or HF, only slowly oxidized by hot, concentrated nitric acid when finely powdered, and either not attacked or only very slowly attacked by many other hot concentrated oxidizing agents.

Although a dozen or more polymorphic forms of boron have been claimed, it is now believed that there are only four well-defined, distinct phases. These are tetragonal-I, tetragonal-II, α-rhombohedral, and β-rhombohedral. The structures of the tetragonal-I and α-rhombohedral polymorphs are known in detail. Both contain B_{12} icosahedra, a grouping which appears especially characteristic of boron since it persists in boron carbide, $B_{12}C_3$, and fragments of it occur in some of the boron hydrides. β-rhombohedral boron is obtained by crystallization of the melt. Its structure is not yet known in detail, but studies to date indicate that the icosahedral unit may not be present. Tetragonal-II boron has only recently been made by reduction of BBr_3 with H_2 on tungsten or rhenium filaments at 1540°C. Its structure is unknown.

BORON COMPOUNDS

10-5. Borides

Compounds of boron with elements less electronegative than itself are usually called borides. Borides of most metals are known, with some exceptions such as Ag, Zn, Hg, Tl, Sn, and Pb. Borides can be prepared in a number of ways, of which the simplest, in principle, is by direct combination of the elements at a high temperature (ca. 2000°C.). Another advantageous method is by electrolysis of a solution of the metal oxide plus some of the metal halide in fused B_2O_3. It is believed that the metal is first liberated, some of it reducing the boron, which then combines with more metal precipitating the boride.

The stoichiometries of borides are usually inexplicable in terms of the usual conceptions of valence, and when their structures (insofar as they are known) are considered, this becomes understandable.

Representative borides are listed in Table 10-1.

TABLE 10-1

Representative Compounds Illustrating Various Stoichiometries of Borides

Cu_2B_2	MgB_2	AlB_2	SiB_3	VB	CrB	MnB	Fe_2B
	CaB_6	AlB_{12}	SiB_6	VB_2	CrB_2	MnB_2	FeB
	SrB_6	YB_6	TiB	NbB_2	Cr_3B_2		Co_2B
	BaB_6	LaB_6	TiB_2	TaB_2	MoB_2		CoB
		CeB_4	ZrB		Mo_3B_4		CoB_2
		CeB_6	ZrB_2		WB		Ni_2B
		PrB_6	ThB_4		WB_2		Ni_3B_2
			ThB_6		UB_2		NiB
					UB_4		NiB_2
					UB_{12}		Pt_2B

Some of the important boride structures which are known are the following:

1. In FeB, zigzag chains of boron atoms snake through a close-packed lattice of iron atoms.

2. The borides AlB_2, TiB_2, ZrB_2, VB_2, MnB_2, NbB_2, and TaB_2 are isomorphous, and their structures consist of planes of hexagonally arranged boron atoms with the metal atoms disposed between these layers in an ordered array.

3. In several tetraborides, for example, CeB_4, ThB_4, and UB_4, the metal atoms are arranged in planes, and holes between these layers are filled by boron atoms.

4. Most hexaborides are isomorphous and contain octahedral B_6 groups. These and the metal atoms are then packed in a cubic, CsCl-like structure with the B_6 groups lying in the centers of cubes of metal atoms. There appears to be no strong bonding of the metal atoms to the B_6 octahedra

since the borides have conductances and magnetic properties similar to those of the pure metals.

5. Magnesium boride was long thought to be Mg_3B_2, but phase studies of the Mg–B system have now shown that the only compound is MgB_2. Unlike other borides, this compound is readily hydrolyzed by water giving boron hydrides (not B_2H_6, however).

The principal chemical and physical properties of typical borides are: (a) they are highly refractory and generally approach diamond in hardness; (b) they generally have metallic conductivity; (c) they are mostly chemically inert toward nonoxidizing acids and stable in air up to fairly high temperatures, but strong oxidizing agents attack most of them, and they are readily decomposed by strong oxidizing alkalies such as fused peroxides.

Boron nitride, which can be obtained by interaction of boron with ammonia at white heat, is a slippery white solid with a layer structure very similar to that of graphite (Fig. 11-2). The units, instead of being hexagonal carbon rings, have alternate B and N atoms 1.45 A. apart with angles of 120° (sp^2 at B). The distance between the sheets is 3.34 A. The analogy of C—C and B—N further discussed below is heightened by the conversion of graphite-like BN under high temperature and pressure to a cubic form with a diamond-like structure. This form is extremely hard and will scratch diamond. The nitride is stable in air but slowly hydrolyzed by water.

10-6. Oxy Compounds of Boron

Boron compounds with oxygen are very important; with the possible exception of fluorine, boron seems to have its greatest affinity for oxygen. Boron always occurs oxygenated in nature, mainly as borates, and most boron compounds on burning or hydrolysis are converted to oxide, boric acid, or borates.

The structures of oxy compounds of boron are based on either a planar BO_3 unit with 120° angles or, less commonly, a tetrahedral BO_4 unit.

Boron Oxides. The principal oxide, B_2O_3, is obtained by fusing boric acid. It usually forms a glass and is one of the most difficult substances to crystallize. Its most important chemical feature is its acidity. With water it gives boric acid, and it readily dissolves many metal oxides when fused to give borate glasses. In glassy P_2O_3 there exist randomly oriented three-dimensional networks of BO_3 groups, each oxygen being bonded to two boron atoms. The crystal is quite different. Here there are BO_4 tetrahedra, two sets of which form two types of interconnected spiral chains; three B—O bonds are equivalent, but the fourth is somewhat longer. The reluctance of B_2O_3 to crystallize is probably due to the difficulty of transforming one three-dimensional network into another.

Boron also forms a well-established lower oxide, $(BO)_x$. The structure of the solid compound is unknown, but it seems certain that it contains B—B bonds and B—O—B bonds. At 1300–1500°C. it vaporizes to B_2O_2 molecules. It is obtained by heating $B_2(OH)_4$ at 250°C. and 0.5 mm. pressure. $B_2(OH)_4$ is itself obtained in fair yield by acid hydrolysis of $((CH_3)_2N)_2BB(N(CH_3)_2)$ and in essentially quantitative yield by reaction of neutral water with $(RO)_2BB(OR)_2$ $(R = C_2H_5$ or $i\text{-}C_3H_7)$. $(BO)_x$ reacts with BCl_3 at 200°C. to give B_2Cl_4. Since B_2Cl_4 is definitely known to have the Cl_2BBCl_2 structure (page 193), and the substances hydrolyzed are virtually certain to have B—B bonds, it seems virtually certain that the intermediate compounds, $B_2(OH)_4$ and $(BO)_x$, also have B—B linkages.

Boric Acid. The acid, $B(OH)_3$, or its salts are formed by hydrolysis of boron halides, hydrides, etc.; the acid forms white needle-like crystals in which there are $B(OH)_3$ units linked together by hydrogen bonds to form layers of nearly hexagonal symmetry (see Fig. 5-8, page 126). It was at one time believed that the hydrogen atoms were midway between the oxygen atoms, but recent work has shown that the hydrogen bonds are unsymmetrical. The layers in the crystal are 3.18 A. apart, which accounts for the pronounced basal cleavage.

Some reactions of boric acid are given in Figure 10-1.

Boric acid is moderately soluble in water with a large negative heat of solution so that the solubility increases markedly with temperature. It is

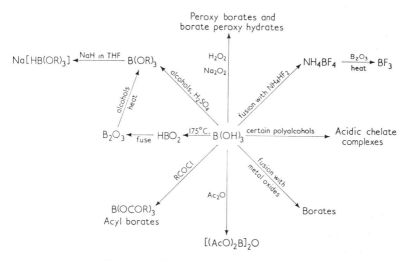

Fig. 10-1. Some reactions of boric acid.

a very weak and exclusively monobasic acid which acts not as a proton donor but as a Lewis acid, accepting OH^-:

$$B(OH)_3 + H_2O = B(OH)_4^- + H^+ \quad pK = 9.00$$

At concentrations $\leq 0.025M$, essentially only mononuclear species $B(OH)_3$ and $B(OH)_4^-$ are present; but at higher concentrations the acidity increases, and pH measurements are consistent with the formation of polymeric species such as

$$3B(OH)_3 = B_3O_3(OH)_4^- + H^+ + 2H_2O \quad pK = 6.84$$

There is also good evidence that polymers are present in mixed solutions of boric acid and borates:

$$2B(OH)_3 + B(OH)_4^- = B_3O_3(OH)_4^- + 3H_2O \quad K = 110$$

There are probably some other polymers of similar type present, but the predominant species appears to be the ring polymer 10-III. Rings of this

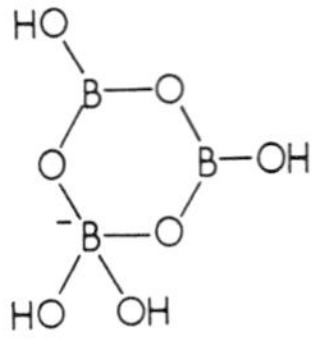

(10-III)

sort have been characterized in crystalline borates such as $Cs_2O \cdot 2B_2O_3$. The equilibria in solution are rapidly established as shown, for example, by rapid exchange between boric acid labeled with ^{18}O and borates.

The strength of boric acid can be greatly increased by the addition of polyhydroxy compounds to the solutions. Glycerol and mannitol are used for analytical purposes, the boric acid being then titratable with strong bases. This effect is due to the formation of complexes of type 10-IV and

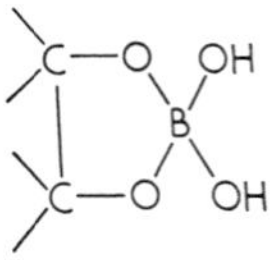

(10-IV)

others. Steric considerations are very critical in the formation of these complexes. Thus 1,2- and 1,3-diols in the *cis* form only, such as *cis*-cyclopentane-1,2-diol, are active, and only *o*-quinols react. Indeed, the ability of a diol to affect the acidity of boric acid is a useful criterion of the configuration where *cis-trans* isomers are possible.

Borates. Many borates occur naturally, usually in hydrated form. Anhydrous borates can be made by fusion of boric acid and metal oxides, and hydrated borates can be crystallized from aqueous solutions. The stoichiometry of borates, for example, $KB_5O_8 \cdot 4H_2O$, $Na_2B_4O_7 \cdot 10H_2O$, CaB_2O_4, and $Mg_7Cl_2B_{16}O_{30}$, gives little idea of the structures of the anions, which are cyclic or linear polymers formed by linking together of BO_3 and/or BO_4 units by sharing oxygen atoms. The main principles for determining these structures are similar to those of silicates, to which the borates are structurally and often physically similar in forming glasses. It is interesting to note that in contrast to the borates, the carbonate ion of superficially similar structure forms no polymeric species; this is probably attributable to the formation of strong $C\!-\!O$ π bonds.

(10-V) (10-VI)

Examples of complex anhydrous borate anions are the ring anion (10-V) in $K_3B_3O_6$ and the infinite chain anion (10-VI) in CaB_2O_4.

Hydrated borates also contain polyanions in the crystal, but not all the known polyanions exist as such in solutions; only those containing one or more BO_4 groups appear to be stable. The structures are best correlated by the following assumptions:

1. Both trigonal BO_3 and tetrahedral BO_4 groups are present, the ratio of BO_4 to total B being equivalent to the ratio of the charge on the anion to total boron. Thus $KB_5O_8 \cdot 4H_2O$ has one BO_4 and four BO_3, whereas $Ca_2B_6O_{11} \cdot 7H_2O$ has four BO_4 and two BO_3 groups.

2. The basic structure is a six-atom ring whose stability depends on the presence of one or two BO_4 groups. Anions which do not have BO_4 groups, such as metaborate, $B_3O_6^{3-}$, or metaboric acid, $B_3O_3(OH)_3$, hydrate rapidly and lose their original structures. The fact that certain complex borates can be precipitated or crystallized from solution does not constitute evidence for the existence of such anions in solution, since other less complex anions can readily recombine during the crystallization process. [11]B nuclear resonance and other evidence has shown that both BO_3 and BO_4 groups are present in a variety of hydrated crystalline borates.

3. Other discrete and chain polymer anions can be formed by linking of two or more rings by shared tetrahedral boron atoms, in some cases with dehydration (cf. metaborate below).

Some known structures are $KB_5O_8 \cdot 4H_2O$ (10-VII) and borax, $Na_2B_4O_7 \cdot 10H_2O$ (10-VIII).

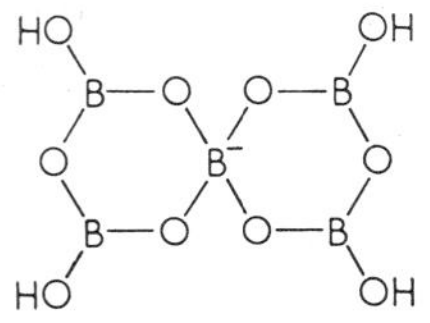

(10-VII) 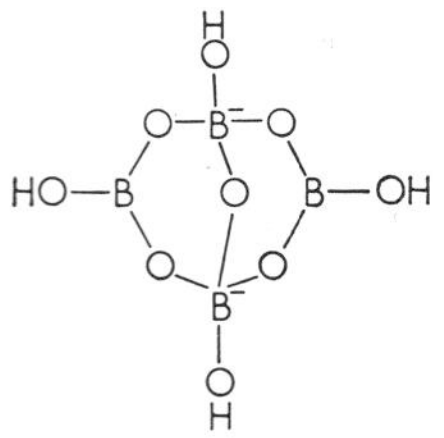   (10-VIII)

Simple sharing of one oxygen by two BO_3 units would give $[O_2BOBO_2]^{4-}$; this so-called pyroborate anion has been shown to exist in $Co_2B_2O_5$. Also, the compound referred to as boron acetate, prepared by the reaction

$$2B(OH)_3 + 5(CH_3CO)_2O = (CH_3COO)_2BOBOCOCH_3)_2 + 6CH_3COOH$$

has a pyroborate-like structure. Boron phosphate, obtained by the reaction of boric and phosphoric acids, BPO_4, has tetrahedral boron with B—O—P bonds.

Treatment of borates with hydrogen peroxide or of boric acid with sodium peroxides leads to products variously formulated as $NaBO_3 \cdot 4H_2O$ or $NaBO_2 \cdot H_2O_2 \cdot 3H_2O$, which are extensively used in washing powders because they afford H_2O_2 in solution. The crystal structure has been found to contain $[B_2(O_2)_2(OH)_4]^{2-}$ units with two peroxy groups bridging the tetrahedral boron atoms.

Metaborates. On heating, boric acid loses water stepwise:

$$B(OH)_3 \underset{H_2O}{\overset{\text{heat}}{\rightleftarrows}} HBO_2 \underset{H_2O}{\overset{\text{heat}}{\rightleftarrows}} B_2O_3$$

Metaboric acid, HBO_2, exists in three modifications, the one obtained depending on the conditions of preparation; metaborate anions of at least two types exist in crystals. Orthorhombic HBO_2—I has cyclic, trimeric units (10-IX) which are bound together by hydrogen bonds; monoclinic-II contains chains with both three- and four-coordinated boron.

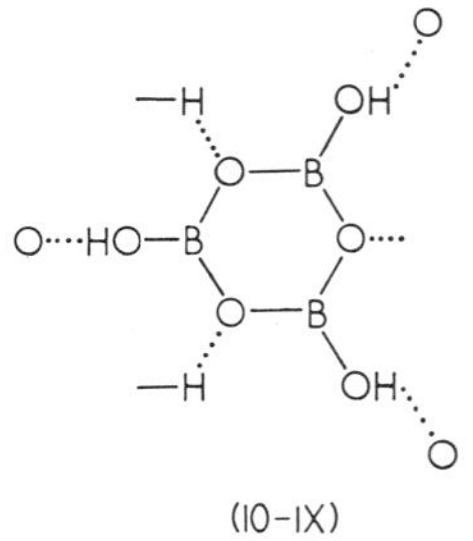

(10-IX)

10-7. Trihalides of Boron

Compounds of the type BX_3 exist for all of the halogens. On mixing any two of the halides, BF_3, BCl_3, BBr_3, at room temperature, a redistribution of halogen atoms occurs rather rapidly to produce a mixture of the original pure halides with the mixed halides in about statistical proportions. Thus, for example, we have the equilibrium

$$BF_3 + BCl_3 = BFCl_2 + BF_2Cl$$

A nuclear resonance study of the mixture of all three halides has established the existence of BFClBr. There is some reason to believe that these redistribution reactions take place via the transitory formation of dimers (10-X), although the concentration of dimers in any simple or mixed halide

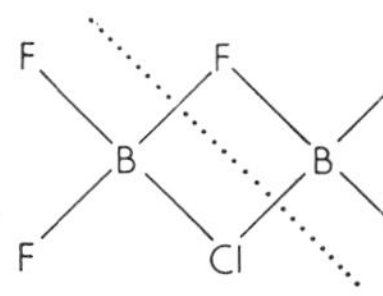

(10-X)

system must be exceedingly low. There is a report (1891) that the mixed halides $BBrI_2$ and BBr_2I can be isolated. If true, this might be due to the great difficulty of dimer formation in a system with the very large halogens. No other mixed halides have been isolated, however.

Some reactions of the halides are summarized in Figure 10-2.

Boron trifluoride is the most important of the halides. It is a pungent, colorless gas (b.p. $-101°C.$) prepared by heating B_2O_3 with NH_4BF_4 or with CaF_2 and concentrated H_2SO_4.

BF_3 reacts with water to form two "hydrates," which may be written $BF_3 \cdot H_2O$ and $BF_3 \cdot 2H_2O$, melting at 10.18 and 6.36°C., respectively. It has been shown by nuclear resonance studies that they are un-ionized in the solid state. For the monohydrate, we may assume that the structure is that of a normal adduct (10-XI). This species presumably also exists in

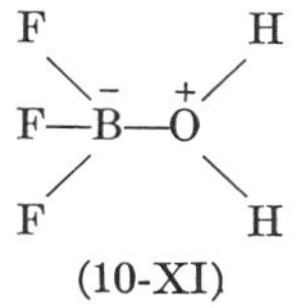

(10-XI)

the solid dihydrate, but the manner in which the second H_2O is held is at

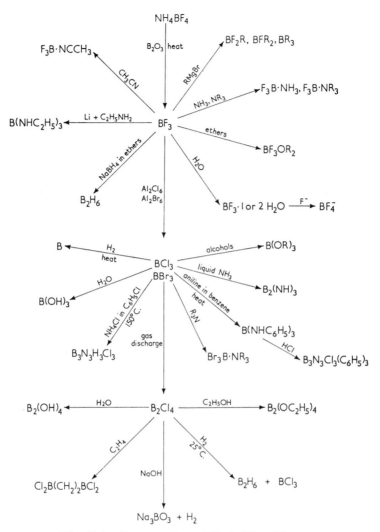

Fig. 10-2. Some reactions of the halides of boron.

present unknown. Both of these hydrates are partially dissociated into ions in their liquid phases, presumably as follows:

$$2(BF_3 \cdot H_2O) = [H_3O^+ - BF_3]^+ + [BF_3OH]^-$$
$$BF_3 \cdot 2H_2O = H_3O^+ + [BF_3OH]^-$$

Above about 20°C. they decompose extensively, giving off BF_3. The $[BF_3OH]^-$ ion is called the hydroxytrifluoroborate ion. The mode of dissociation of the monohydrate is similar to the autoprotolysis of pure H_2SO_4, that is,

$$2H_2SO_4 = H_3SO_4^+ + HSO_4^-$$

When relatively small amounts of BF_3 are passed into water, a solution of fluoroboric acid (not isolable as a pure substance) is obtained.

$$4BF_3 + H_2O = 3H_3O^+ + 3BF_4^- + B(OH)_3$$

There is also some hydrolysis of the fluoroborate ion to produce HF and hydroxyfluoroborate ion.

$$BF_4^- + H_2O = [BF_3OH]^- + HF \qquad K = 2.3 \times 10^{-3}$$

Boron trifluoride is one of the most avid acceptors—that is, strongest Lewis acids—known, and readily unites with water, ethers, alcohols, amines, phosphines, etc., to form adducts. BF_3 is commonly available as its diethyl etherate, $(C_2H_5)_2\overset{+}{O}\overset{-}{B}F_3$. Because of its potency as a Lewis acid, BF_3 is widely used to promote various organic reactions, such as (a) ethers or alcohols + acids → esters + H_2O or ROH; (b) alcohols + benzene → alkyl benzenes + H_2O; (c) polymerization of olefins and olefin oxides; and (d) Friedel-Crafts-like acylations and alkylations. In the first two cases, the effectiveness of BF_3 must depend on its ability to form an adduct with one or both of the reactants, thus lowering the activation energy of the rate-determining step in which H_2O or ROH is eliminated by breaking of C—O bonds. However, the exact mechanisms of these reactions are not at present known, nor are those of the olefin and olefin oxide polymerizations.

In the case of the Friedel-Crafts-like reactions, isolation of certain intermediates at low temperatures has provided a fairly definite idea of the function of the BF_3. Thus, the ethylation of benzene by ethyl fluoride proceeds as in equation 10-1. With benzene, HF, and BF_3, compound

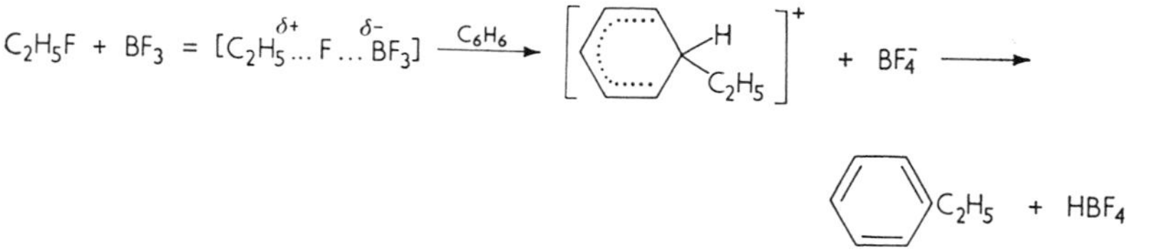

10-XII can be isolated at low temperatures. It will be seen that the BF_3 is not really "catalytic," but must be present in the stoichiometric amount since it is consumed in the process of tying up the HF as HBF_4.

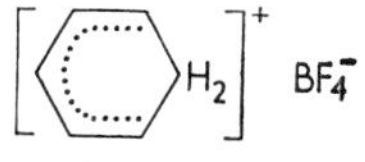

(10-XII)

Solid salts of tetrafluoroboric acid are readily isolated, those of NH_4^+ and many metals such as the alkalies and alkaline earths being commercially available. Ammonium fluoroborate may be prepared in a dry way by fusing NH_4HF_2 with B_2O_3. $B(OH)_3$ also readily dissolves in HF to form solutions of fluoroboric acid:

$$B(OH)_3 + 4HF = H_3O^+ + BF_4^- + 2H_2O$$

Fluoroboric acid is a strong acid. The fluoroborate ion has a tetrahedral structure, and fluoroborates closely resemble the corresponding perchlorates in their crystal structures and solubilities.

Boron trichloride is a liquid at room temperature under slight pressure (b.p. 12.5°C.), whereas the *bromide* boils at 90°C. Both fume in moist air and are completely hydrolyzed by water,

$$BCl_3 + 3H_2O = B(OH)_3 + 3HCl$$

The compounds are prepared by direct interaction of the elements at elevated temperatures.

The rapid hydrolysis by water could indicate that these halides are stronger Lewis acids than BF_3. In fact, the molar heats of solution of the trihalides in nitrobenzene and the heats of reaction with pyridine in nitrobenzene show that under these conditions the electron acceptor strength increases $BBr_3 > BCl_3 > BF_3$.

The *iodide* is a white solid (m.p. 43°C.). It is explosively hydrolyzed by water. It is prepared by the action of iodine on $NaBH_4$ or of HI on BCl_3 at red heat.

Tetrachloroborates are obtained by addition of BCl_3 to alkali chlorides at high pressures, by cold milling at room temperatures, or by the reaction

$$[(C_2H_5)_4N]^+ Cl^- + BCl_3 \xrightarrow{CHCl_3} [(C_2H_5)_4N]^+ BCl_4^-$$

The stability of these salts and the corresponding tetrabromoborates and tetraiodoborates is greatest with the largest cations. With a given cation, the stability order is $MBCl_4 > MBBr_4 > MBI_4$, tetraiodoborates occurring only with the largest cations. Mixed ions such as BF_3Cl^- also exist.

10-8. Lower Halides of Boron

Diboron tetrachloride, B_2Cl_4, is prepared by passing a discharge through BCl_3 vapor between mercury electrodes or, better, by the reaction of $(BO)_x$ with BCl_3. It is a colorless liquid which ignites in air and decomposes above 0°C. partially to B_4Cl_4 and other nonvolatile chlorides such as $(BCl_{0.9})_n$ and $(BCl_{0.6})_n$. X-ray study of the solid has shown that the

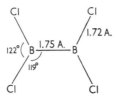

Fig. 10-3. Planar structure of B_2Cl_4 determined by X-ray study.

molecule has the *planar* structure shown in Figure 10-3. By contrast, spectroscopic and electron diffraction study of the vapor indicate that the molecule is not planar. This may be due to torsional motion about the B—B bond, but further work is required to settle this point. This compound, with its long B—B bond, can be considered analogous to the isoelectronic species $C_2O_4^{2-}$ and N_2O_4.

B_2F_4 is a gas, extremely explosive in the presence of oxygen, which may be solidified at $-56°C$. The structure of the molecule in the crystal is analogous to that of B_2Cl_4, the molecule being planar. The F—B—F angles are $120 \pm 2.5°$, the B—F distance is 1.32 ± 0.03 A., and the B—B distance is 1.67 ± 0.05 A. Owing to the errors in the B—B distance measurements in both molecules, it is not certain that this distance in B_2F_4 is significantly shorter than in B_2Cl_4. If it really is, there is uncertainty as to the reason.

Tetraboron tetrachloride, B_4Cl_4, is a pale yellow, fairly volatile solid. It has a novel structure (Fig. 10-4). The B_4 arrangement is tetrahedral,

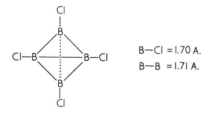

Fig. 10-4. Structure of B_4Cl_4.

and the B—Cl axes are colinear with the axes of the tetrahedron. This molecule is an example of an electron-deficient molecule (like the boranes to be discussed later). There are insufficient electrons for all of the B—B bonds and the B—Cl bonds to be two-electron bonds. It is assumed that the B—Cl bonds are normal electron pair bonds, whereas the tetrahedral boron skeleton is held together by multicenter bonds (see page 201).

Recently the compound to which the formula $(BCl_{0.9})_n$ is generally assigned in the literature has been shown to be B_8Cl_8. The boron atoms are

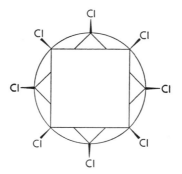

Fig. 10-5.   Structure of B_8Cl_8.

at the apexes of a distorted square antiprism with a chlorine atom bonded to each one (Fig. 10-5).

10-9. The Boranes or Boron Hydrides

In a remarkable series of papers from 1912 to 1936, Alfred Stock and his co-workers characterized the boron hydrides—or boranes, as they are now called—B_2H_6, B_4H_{10}, B_5H_9, B_5H_{11}, B_6H_{10}, and $B_{10}H_{14}$. Only recently have additional hydrides, B_9H_{15} and $B_{10}H_{16}$, been characterized. Other hydrides, for example, B_3H_7, B_6H_{12}, and B_9H_{13}, have been reported but are not well characterized. With the exception of diborane, B_2H_6, which was prepared by thermal cracking of higher boranes, Stock prepared the hydrides by the action of acid on magnesium boride, MgB_2. He obtained in this way a mixture of very reactive, air-sensitive, if not spontaneously flammable, compounds. In order to separate them and study their physical and chemical properties, Stock pioneered the methods of manipulation and study of compounds in glass high vacuum systems.

Until quite recently, the boranes were of interest primarily because of their unusual stoichiometries and structures. However, they have been recently intensely studied as potential high energy fuels; despite their inconvenient properties, their desirability as fuels is evident from the following comparison of the heats of combustion of B_2H_6 and C_2H_6:

$$B_2H_6 + 3O_2 = B_2O_3 + 3H_2O \qquad \Delta H = -482 \text{ kcal./mole } (-17.5 \text{ cal./g.})$$
$$C_2H_6 + 3.5O_2 = 2CO_2 + 3H_2O \qquad \Delta H = -232 \text{ kcal./mole } (-7.8 \text{ cal./g.})$$

Preparation.   The original Stock method is no longer used except for B_6H_{10} which is not obtainable in the cracking processes discussed below.

Diborane is now the starting point for the preparation of other boranes and is obtained in essentially quantitative yields by reaction of metal hydrides with boron trifluoride, the most convenient method being to drop boron trifluoride etherate into a solution of sodium borohydride in diethylene glycol dimethyl ether (diglyme).

$$3NaBH_4 + 4BF_3 = 3NaBF_4 + 2B_2H_6$$

Other hydrides which can be used are LiH and $NaBH(OCH_3)_3$. Diborane can also be obtained by the reaction of BCl_3 with hydrogen over a Cu–Al catalyst at 450°C.

Higher boranes are obtained by "cracking" reactions. All boranes undergo complex, reversible reactions at 100–250°C. which are similar to the well-known cracking and hydroforming processes in hydrocarbon systems except that they proceed at lower temperatures and without catalysts. It is believed that the mechanisms involve borine, BH_3, as an intermediate. The higher boranes (B_6H_{10} excepted) are made by heating diborane with

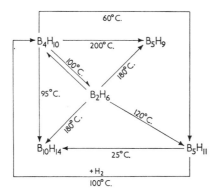

Fig. 10-6.   Interconversion of boranes.

hydrogen under specific conditions. Figure 10-6 illustrates the general nature of the processes.

Properties. Some important properties of the boranes are given in Table 10-2. In general, these compounds can be divided into two groups of formulas: B_nH_{n+4} and B_nH_{n+6}; the members of the first group are thermally relatively stable, whereas those of the second group are thermally rather unstable. All are hydrolyzed by water at various rates, but alkalies cause rapid hydrolysis to yield borate and hydrogen.

For present purposes, the chemical reactions of diborane (Fig. 10-7) may be considered as representative of those of boranes in general, although some decided differences do exist. Thus HCl reacts slowly with B_2H_6 and B_4H_{10} to form chlorinated boranes, but does not react with the pentaboranes or decaborane; chlorine reacts only slowly with decaborane at

TABLE 10-2

Important Properties of Boranes

Name	Formula	Melting point, °C.	Boiling point, °C.	Reaction with air at 25°C.	Thermal stability	Reaction with water
Diborane	B_2H_6	−165.5	−92.5	Spontaneously flammable	Fairly stable at 25°C.	Instant hydrolysis
Tetraborane	B_4H_{10}	−120	18	Not spontaneously flammable if pure	Decomposes fairly rapidly at 25°C.	Hydrolysis in 24 hours
Pentaborane-9	B_5H_9	−46.6	48	Spontaneously flammable	Stable 25°C.; slow decomposition 150°C.	Hydrolyzed only on heating
Pentaborane-11	B_5H_{11}	−123	63	Spontaneously flammable	Decomposes very rapidly at 25°C.	Rapid hydrolysis
Hexaborane	B_6H_{10}	−65	—	Stable	Slow decomposition at 25°C.	Hydrolyzed only on heating
Enneaborane	B_9H_{15}	−20	—	Stable	—	—
Decaborane	$B_{10}H_{14}$	99.7	213 (extrap.)	Very stable	Stable at 150°C.	Slow hydrolysis

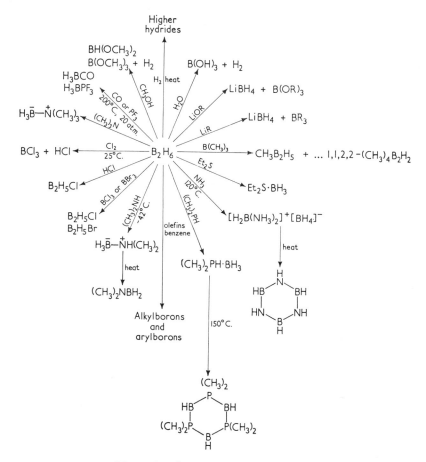

Fig. 10-7. Some reactions of diborane.

room temperature to give monochloro- and dichlorodecaboranes, but reacts violently with the others to give BCl₃. All of the boranes react with amines. B₂H₆ reacts with dimethylamine at 0°C. to form $(CH_3)_2NHBH_3$ or with trimethylamine to give $(CH_3)_3NBH_3$. Pentaborane-9 reacts with trimethylamine to give $(CH_3)_3NB_5H_9$, which on heating yields $(CH_3)_3NBH_3$.

Borine itself, BH₃, cannot be isolated and has not actually been detected by any physical means. Estimates for the reaction

$$B_2H_6 = 2BH_3$$

give $K_p = {\sim}10^{-5}$ atm. at 155°C. and $\Delta H_{273°} = -28$ kcal./mole. Much of the chemical behavior of diborane and other boranes suggests BH₃ as an intermediate, and adducts of BH_3 with certain donors are known, for example, H_3BCO and H_3BPF_3.

10-10. Configuration and Bonding of the Boranes

The structures of the boranes are of great interest. The stoichiometries are most unusual and inexplicable on "normal" ideas of bond formation. The boranes, in fact, are one of the most important classes of *electron-deficient* compounds, which means that there are more stable, potentially bonding orbitals available than there are electrons to form electron pair bonds using all such orbitals. Before discussing the theory of valence involved here, it will be necessary to describe the actual molecular configurations of the boranes.

Diborane. The structure of diborane, B_2H_6, was a matter of contention for many years. The arguments were concerned with the possibility of an ethane-like structure, $H_3B—BH_3$, which could only be rationalized by a rather *ad hoc* postulate of "bond no-bond" resonance and covalent-ionic resonance (10-XIII) or a structure involving hydrogen bridges be-

$$
\begin{array}{ccc}
\text{H\ \ H} & & \text{H}^+\ \text{H} \\
|\ \ \ | & & |\ \ \ | \\
\text{H}^+\quad \text{B—B}^-\text{—H} & \leftrightarrow & \text{H—B—B}^-\text{—H}\quad \text{etc.} \\
|\ \ \ | & & |\ \ \ | \\
\text{H\ \ H} & & \text{H\ \ H} \\
\text{(10-XIIIa)} & & \text{(10-XIIIb)}
\end{array}
$$

tween the boron atoms (10-XIV), as was first suggested by Dilthey in 1921. Universal acceptance of the bridged structure in spite of much excellent

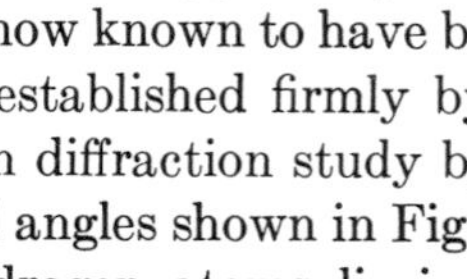

(10-XIV)

evidence for it was delayed by the apparently conflicting evidence of certain electron diffraction results now known to have been incorrectly interpreted.

The structure was first established firmly by W. C. Price by infrared measurements, and electron diffraction study by Hedberg and Schomaker has given the distances and angles shown in Figure 10-8. The boron atoms and the four terminal hydrogen atoms lie in the same plane; the two bridging hydrogen atoms lie symmetrically above and below this plane. Among the other physical data supporting the bridged structure we may note the following:

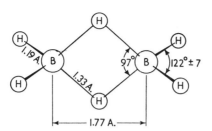

Fig. 10-8.   Structure of diborane.

1. There is a very high barrier to rotation of the two ends of the molecule against one another about the B—B axis. In an ethane-like molecule the barrier would be expected to be very low.

2. Nuclear resonance study has clearly shown the presence of two hydrogens of one type and four of another. This is consistent with the bridge model but inconsistent with the ethane-like model where all six hydrogens would be equivalent.

Additional evidence comes from studies of derivatives of diborane, for example, from the microwave spectrum of B_2H_5Br.

Higher Boranes.   The configurations of the higher boranes are shown in Figure 10-9. Details (angles and distances) and the evidence for them

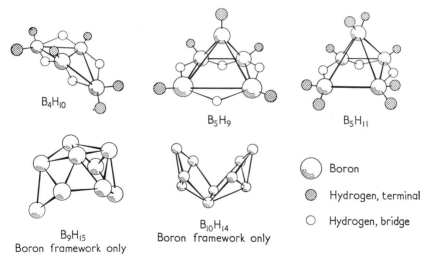

Fig. 10-9.   Structures of some boranes.

are given by Lipscomb, who has done much of the recent work on the structures and bonding in boranes.

Bonding in the Boranes. In order to account for the bonding in the boranes, chemists were compelled to broaden their views of chemical bonding. Thus these compounds—along with a few other electron-deficient compounds—have a very important role in the development of valence theory. Moreover, the development of theories to cover these bonding problems has taken place mostly within the past decade. The first impetus in this work was given by Bell and Longuet-Higgins, who proposed the idea of a "three-center bond," and it has been carried through in application to the other boranes by Lipscomb and his co-workers. The following account is necessarily brief and superficial.

From the MO viewpoint, in a normal covalent bond between two atoms, each atom supplies one orbital and one electron. The orbitals combine to form a bonding orbital and an antibonding orbital, and the electrons pair up and occupy the bonding MO. Such a bond between two atoms may be called a *two-center bond*. Suppose now that we have three atoms, each with an available orbital, but with only two electrons altogether. It is found from relatively simple calculations that these three atomic orbitals will combine to give at most one bonding orbital, and one decidedly antibonding orbital, with the third MO being nonbonding or perhaps somewhat anti-bonding. The two electrons will, of course, occupy the bonding orbital, and we then have a *three-center bond*. This bonding orbital binds all three atoms together. Before proceeding further in theory, let us see how this idea enables us to explain the bonding in B_2H_6.

In B_2H_6 we have two BH_2 fragments united by hydrogen bridges. Let us begin by supposing that in each BH_2 fragment there exist ordinary two-center, two-electron B—H bonds (10-XV). Thus each boron atom

$$\cdot B \underset{H}{\overset{H}{}}$$

(10-XV)

has only one electron left. Let us now consider the bridging arrangement, BHB. The hydrogen atom has one electron and one useful orbital, namely, its 1s orbital. Each boron atom will also have an orbital available (to be

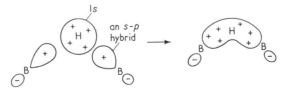

Fig. 10-10.   Sketch showing overlap of orbitals to form a three-center BHB bond.

specified in more detail presently). We may envision the formation of a three-center bonding MO as shown in Figure 10-10. An identical three-center bonding MO will be formed in the other bridging system, BHB. We now have two three-center bonding MO's. Altogether we have four electrons: one from each BH_2 group and one from each hydrogen atom. These four electrons now occupy the two bonding MO's, and the bridge bonding system is complete.

We may now discuss the nature of the s–p hybrid orbitals* contributed by boron to the bridging system in more detail. From the measured H—B—H angle of 122° we can infer that boron is using some sort of s–p hybrid orbitals. It is then possible, by assuming that these two hybrid orbitals point *exactly* in the directions of the hydrogen atoms, to calculate that the boron atom has two more s–p hybrids, which would make an angle of 101 ± 7° (Fig. 10-11). Note that this calculated angle agrees

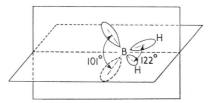

Fig. 10-11. The orbitals used by a boron atom in B_2H_6.

within the errors of experiment and calculation with the observed H(bridge)—B—H(bridge) angle of 97 ± 3°.

In some of the higher boranes a somewhat different three-center bond exists, namely, between three boron atoms. The type discussed above has been called an "open" three-center bond, and this second type may be

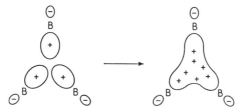

Fig. 10-12. Sketch showing overlap of orbitals to form a closed, three-center BBB bond.

called a "closed" three-center bond. Figure 10-12 is a rough physical picture of its formation.

---

* We use s–p to mean *some* form of hybrid made up of s and p orbitals, reserving sp to denote the linear, equivalent hybrids formed by equal s and p contributions. Thus sp, sp^2, sp^3, and all intermediate schemes are s–p hybrids.

Both two-center and three-center bonds are merely simple special cases of *multicenter bonds* which may be four-, five-, and in general n-centered; the MO's may be considered as linear combinations of the atomic orbitals of all the atoms involved, and they may be visualized in the same manner as has been illustrated for the three-center bonds above. Multicenter bonds may be expected to exist only in electron-deficient molecules, that is, where there are more usable atomic orbitals than there are electrons to use them all in forming two-center bonds. In general, where we have n atomic orbitals and m electrons, the following cases arise:

1. $m = n$, as in the hydrocarbons. In C_2H_6, for example, there are fourteen atomic orbitals, which are combined to produce seven bonding orbitals. There are also fourteen electrons, or seven pairs, to occupy these seven bonding orbitals, and we can thus write the usual description of ethane, with seven two-center, two-electron bonds (10-XVI).

$$\begin{array}{c} \text{H H} \\ \cdot\cdot \;\; \cdot\cdot \\ \text{H} : \text{C} : \text{C} : \text{H} \\ \cdot\cdot \;\; \cdot\cdot \\ \text{H H} \end{array}$$

(10-XVI)

2. $m > n$, as in NH_3 or H_2O. In NH_3 we have seven orbitals and four electron pairs. Six of the orbitals combine to form three bonding orbitals (and three antibonding orbitals), while a fourth orbital remains unused in bonding. Thus there are three pairs of bonding electrons and a pair of "lone" or nonbonding electrons, in accordance with our usual picture of the electronic structure of NH_3 (10-XVII)

$$\begin{array}{c} \text{H} \\ \cdot\cdot \\ : \text{N} : \text{H} \\ \cdot\cdot \\ \text{H} \end{array}$$

(10-XVII)

3. $m < n$. In these cases, where energetically possible, multicenter orbitals will be formed. Thus, to recapitulate the case of B_2H_6, there are altogether fourteen atomic orbitals and twelve electrons. Eight orbitals (two from each boron and the orbitals from the four terminal hydrogen atoms) are combined to form four bonding orbitals of the two-center type in which eight of the electrons are housed. The remaining six orbitals are combined into two three-center bonding orbitals (and four three-center non- or antibonding MO's) which are occupied by the remaining four electrons.

Space does not permit us to discuss the bonding in the higher boranes in any detail. From Figure 10-9, however, it may be seen that the hydrogen bridge bond, the ordinary B:H bond, and the closed three-center bond between three boron atoms are all important. In addition, there are still higher order multicenter bonds, namely, a five-center bond in B_5H_9 and two six-center bonds in B_9H_{15}. Note also that in the higher boranes, the configurations of the boron atoms are fragments of the icosahedron which occurs in elemental boron in some cases (B_9H_{15} in particular) and of the octahedron in others (e.g., B_5H_9). In the recently discovered $B_{10}H_{16}$ there is also a direct B—B bond; and two tetragonal pyramidal five-boron units, each like B_5H_9, are linked together at apical borons.

That there are inadequacies in the electronic theories and/or in our experimental knowledge is shown by the fact that a number of theoretically possible boranes are not known experimentally. Further, an explanation of the relative thermal stabilities and chemical reactivities of the boranes in terms of their electronic and geometrical structures has not progressed very far as yet.

10-11. Derivatives of the Boranes

The chemistry of compounds derived from or related to the boron hydrides is already extensive and is increasing rapidly. In fact, if organo-boron derivatives are included, this chemistry is tending to become as complex and varied as that of carbon compounds.

Borohydride Ions. The most common borohydride ion is BH_4^-, and a great variety of compounds of the type $M[BH_4]_n$ are known. Substituted borohydrides, for example, $M[BH(OCH_3)_3]$, are also known. Borohydrides of many elements—the alkalies, Be, Mg, Al, Ti, Zr, Th, U, etc.—have been made. The compounds are prepared by reactions of the following types:

$$4NaH + B(OCH_3) \xrightarrow{225-275°C.} NaBH_4 + 3NaOCH_3$$
$$NaH + B(OCH_3)_3 \xrightarrow{THF*} NaBH(OCH_3)_3$$
$$2LiH + B_2H_6 \xrightarrow{ether} 2LiBH_4$$
$$AlCl_3 + 3NaBH_4 \xrightarrow{heat} Al(BH_4)_3 + 3NaCl$$
$$UF_4 + 2Al(BH_4)_3 \longrightarrow U(BH_4)_4 + 2AlF_2BH_4$$
$$2TiCl_4 + 8LiBH_4 \longrightarrow 2Ti(BH_4)_3 + 8LiCl + B_2H_6 + H_2$$

The alkali borohydrides are nonvolatile, crystalline, salt-like compounds, stable in dry air. The most common salt is $NaBH_4$, which is widely used as a reducing agent or preparative source of hydride ion; it is insoluble in diethyl ether, but is soluble in tetrahydrofuran and still more soluble in diethylene glycol dimethyl ether, which is often used as the reaction medium. Some features of the chemical behavior of borohydrides and

* THF = tetrahydrofuran.

such similar complex hydrides as $[AlH_4]^-$ have been mentioned previously (Chapter 5, page 119). However, borohydrides have some specific characteristics, an important one being that they can be used for liberating diborane *in situ*, for example, from $NaBH_4$ and HCl, BCl_3 or $AlCl_3$, $NaBH_4$ and HCl in ether, or alternatively $LiAlH_4$ and BF_3 etherate. *In situ* preparation of diborane is important in hydroboronation reactions of olefins, and these are of particular interest in organic chemistry for, among other uses, the anti-Markownikoff *cis* hydration of olefins (eq. 10-2). A

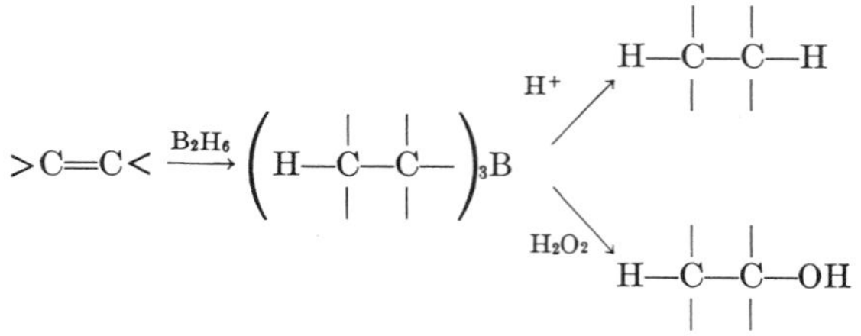

$$>C=C< \xrightarrow{B_2H_6} \left(H-\overset{|}{\underset{|}{C}}-\overset{|}{\underset{|}{C}}-\right)_3 B \begin{cases} \xrightarrow{H^+} H-\overset{|}{\underset{|}{C}}-\overset{|}{\underset{|}{C}}-H \\ \xrightarrow{H_2O_2} H-\overset{|}{\underset{|}{C}}-\overset{|}{\underset{|}{C}}-OH \end{cases} \tag{10-2}$$

modification of the hydroboronation reaction using triethylamine (or pyridine) borine can give reactions such as equation 10-3.

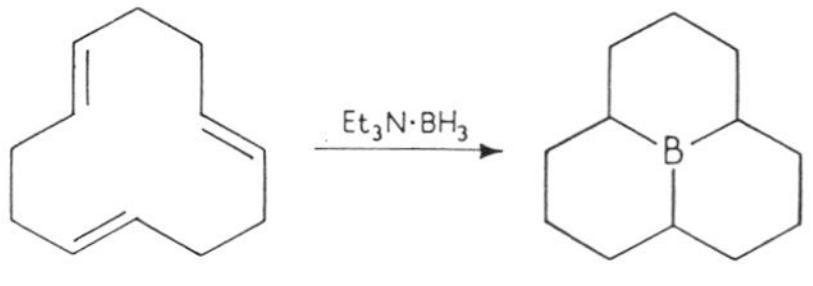

$$\xrightarrow{Et_3N \cdot BH_3} \tag{10-3}$$

With decreasing electropositivity of the metal, the covalent character of the borohydrides increases and essentially covalent compounds are known. Thus, $Al(BH_4)_3$ is a volatile liquid (b.p. 44.5°C.) which detonates in the vapor when exposed to traces of water vapor. The volatile borohydrides are generally unstable, decomposing at various rates, even at room temperature, and all are very reactive compounds.

The structures of the borohydrides are interesting. The ionic borohydrides contain discrete BH_4^- ions, which are tetrahedral. Some borohydrides are isomorphous with ammonium halides, for example, $CsBH_4$, the Cs^+ ion replacing the Cl^- ion and the BH_4^- ion replacing the NH_4^+ ion in NH_4Cl. In $LiBH_4$ the tetrahedron is distorted by the attraction of the small, positive Li ion for the hydrogen atoms closest to it. This tendency toward distortion becomes dominant in the covalent hydrides, where definite hydrogen bridge bonds, like those in the boranes, exist. The volatile aluminum borohydride is such a case, and the bonding in the Al—H—B bridges can be described in terms of three-center MO's, as in the boranes. Another example of a bridged borohydride is that of the

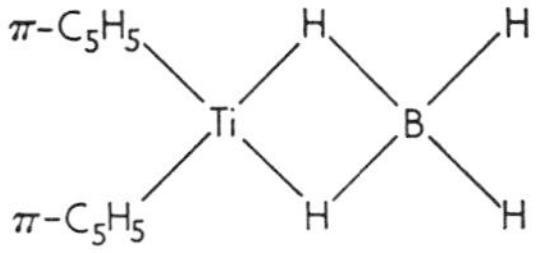

(10-XVIII)

π-cyclopentadienyltitanium compound (10-XVIII). There are a number of other borohydride ions which are related to the polynuclear boranes, among them $B_3H_8^-$, $B_{10}H_{13}^-$, and $B_{12}H_{12}^{2-}$, some of which are remarkably stable and have an independent chemistry of their own.

Compounds with Boron Bonded to Other Elements. Diborane has proved to be a useful starting material for the preparation of compounds containing boron bound to N, As, P, O, S, C, etc. Here, again, the chemistry is extensive and complex, and only a selection of important types of compounds will be presented.

There are some very interesting compounds of boron with the group V elements, especially nitrogen. Of particular interest are certain boron–nitrogen compounds which are isoelectronic and isostructural with carbon

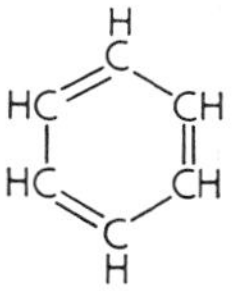

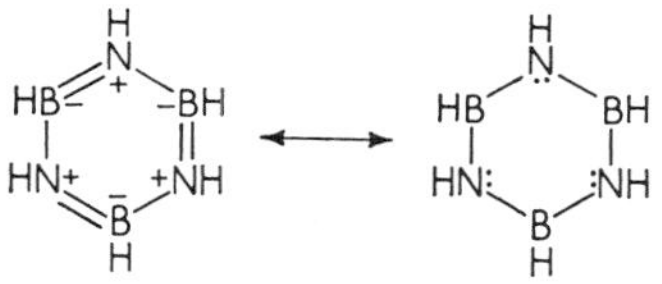

compounds. As examples, consider benzene (10-XIX) and borazine (10-XX) and isobutene (10-XXI) and β,β'-dimethylaminoborine (10-XXII).

$$(CH_3)_2C{=}CH_2$$
(10-XXI)

$$(CH_3)_2B{-}\overset{..}{N}H_2 \leftrightarrow (CH_3)_2\overset{-}{B}{=}\overset{+}{N}H_2$$
(10-XXIIa) (10-XXIIb)

Borazine, or *borazole*, $B_3N_3H_6$ (b.p. 63°C.), has the superficial resemblance to benzene which is indicated, and does resemble it in some of its physical and chemical properties. However, in benzene the C⋯C bonds are non-polar and the nucleus is very resistant to addition reactions, whereas the borazine nucleus, because of its polarities, is fairly reactive. Thus it readily adds three molecules of H_2O, CH_3OH, CH_3I, or HCl, the more negative group generally attaching itself to the boron atoms (eq. 10-4). Borazine also

$$B_3N_3H_6 + 3HCl =$$

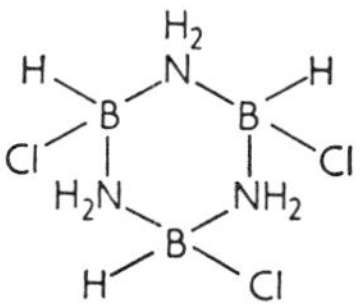

(10-4)

decomposes slowly on standing and is hydrolyzed at high temperatures to $B(OH)_3$ and NH_3. It may be conveniently prepared by heating together ammonium chloride and BCl_3, the initial product being the B-chloro-borazine, which is then reduced with sodium borohydride in a polyether

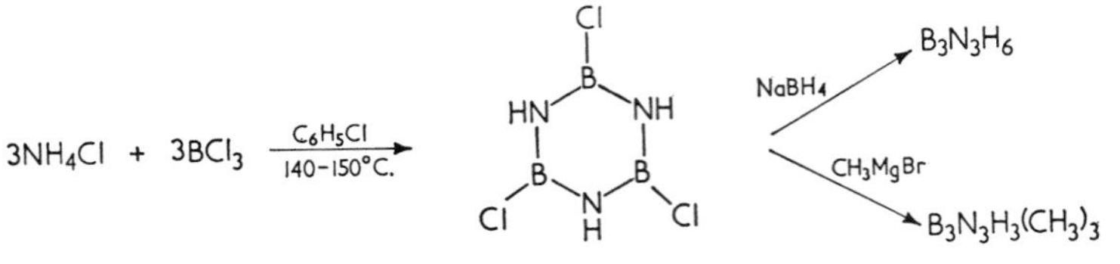

$$3NH_4Cl + 3BCl_3 \xrightarrow[140-150°C.]{C_6H_5Cl} \text{(borazine ring)} \quad \begin{array}{c} \xrightarrow{NaBH_4} B_3N_3H_6 \\ \\ \xrightarrow{CH_3MgBr} B_3N_3H_3(CH_3)_3 \end{array} \quad (10\text{-}5)$$

(eq. 10-5). N-Alkylated borazines may also be obtained by starting with alkylammonium halides (eq. 10-6). Borazine and substituted borazines

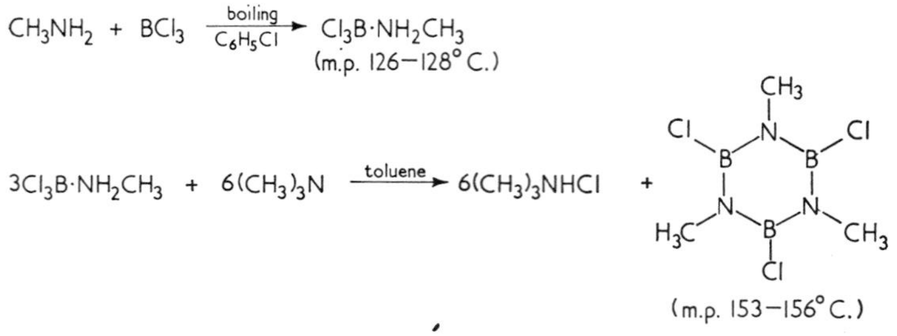

$$CH_3NH_2 + BCl_3 \xrightarrow[C_6H_5Cl]{boiling} Cl_3B \cdot NH_2CH_3$$
$$\text{(m.p. 126-128° C.)}$$

$$3Cl_3B \cdot NH_2CH_3 + 6(CH_3)_3N \xrightarrow{toluene} 6(CH_3)_3NHCl + \text{(ring structure)} \quad (10\text{-}6)$$
$$\text{(m.p. 153-156° C.)}$$

can also be made by treating sodium borohydride with ammonium or alkylammonium chlorides in triethylene glycol dimethyl ether. The B—Cl bonds can often be subsequently alkylated by Grignard reagents.

Diborane and ammonia under the proper conditions react to produce the so-called diammoniate of diborane which has recently been shown to be $[H_2B(NH_3)_2]^+[BH_4]^-$. This, on heating, produces borazine. On heating mixtures of ammonia and diborane, a compound, B_2H_7N or $B_2H_5NH_2$, can be obtained, and by using mono- and disubstituted (but not trisubstituted) amines similar compounds such as $B_2H_5(CH_3NH)$, $B_2H_5(CH_3NSiH_3)$, etc., are produced. These compounds, called aminodiboranes, have been shown to have the 10-XXIII type of structure.

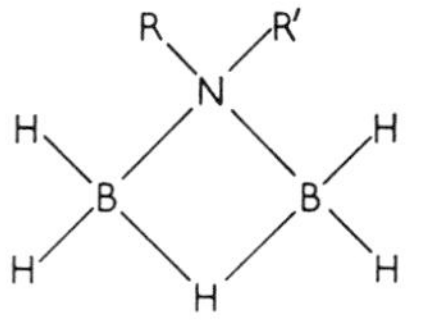

(10-XXIII) 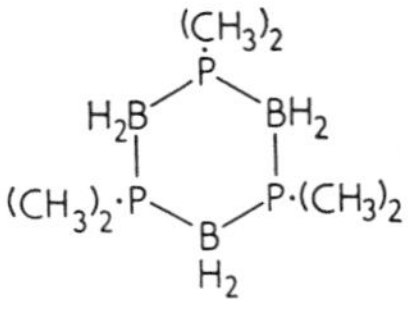   (10-XXIV)

In view of the extensive aminoboron chemistry, studies have been made of boron–phosphorus and boron–arsenic chemistry. One of the notable

B—P compounds is $[(CH_3)_2PBH_2]_3$, which has the cyclic structure 10-XXIV. The arsenic analog is also known. This compound and its arsenic analog are extraordinarily stable and inert, a fact which has been attributed to a drift of electron density from the BH_2 groups into the *d* orbitals of P or As. This has the effect of reducing the hydridic nature of the hydrogen atoms, making them less susceptible to reaction with protonic reagents, and also of offsetting the $\overset{-}{B}—\overset{+}{P}$, $\overset{-}{B}—\overset{+}{As}$ polar character, which the σ bonding alone tends to produce. These cyclic compounds are inorganic analogs of cyclohexanes such as $C_6(CH_3)_{12}$.

Diboron–nitrogen derivatives can be obtained by the reaction

$$[(CH_3)_2N]_2BCl + Na(dispersion) = [(CH_3)_2N]_2B—B[N(CH_3)_2]_2$$

Apart from B_2Cl_4 few compounds with B—B bonds are known. Tetra(dimethylamino)diboron is stable in dry air at 200 and in oxygen at 100°C., although B_2Cl_4 decomposes slowly at room temperature and reacts rapidly with oxygen even at −78°C.

Organoboron Compounds. Some organoboron compounds, $(CH_3)_3B$, $(CH_3O)_3B$, etc., have already been mentioned in passing. Hundreds of boron compounds containing organic groups bonded either directly to

TABLE 10-3

Types of Alkyl and Aryl Boron Acids and Derivatives

	Boronic	Boronous
Acid	$R—B(OH)_2$	$R_2B(OH)$
Ester	R—B(OH)(OR′)	R_2BOR'
	R—B(OR)(OR)	
Anhydride		$R_2B—O—BR_2$

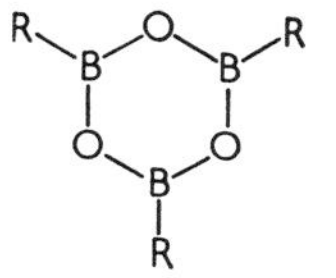

boron or indirectly via other atoms such as O and N are known. One important series of compounds is the alkyl and aryl orthoborates, $B(OR)_3$, and their complexes such as $Na[HB(OR)_3]$, the trialkoxy borohydrides. These may be thought of as derived from $B(OH)_3$. There are, then, also the classes of compounds shown in Table 10-3, and finally the trialkyl or triaryl borons, R_3B. The lower alkyl borons are very reactive substances which will inflame in air. Aryls and hydroxy derivatives are stable in air. Sulfur analogs of many of the oxy compounds also exist. The boronic acids can be made in various ways, for example,

$$BF_3 \cdot O(C_2H_5)_2 + C_6H_5MgBr \longrightarrow C_6H_5BF_2 \xrightarrow{H_2O} C_6H_5B(OH)_2$$

and are quite stable and water soluble. Their acidities depend upon the nature of the alkyl or aryl group. Dehydration of a boronic acid by heating yields a boronic anhydride:

$$3RB(OH)_2 = (RBO)_3 + 3H_2O$$

These boronic anhydrides, also called boroxines, have been shown to have trimeric, cyclic structures with planar rings of alternating boron and oxygen atoms. The alkyl groups are also in the plane of the ring.

Lastly, we may mention that if boron halides are reacted with four moles of a Grignard reagent or other metal alkyl or aryl, the trialkyl or triaryl boron first produced will add another alkyl or aryl group forming an anion of the type BR_4^-.

$$3RM + BX_3 = R_3B + 3MX$$
$$R_3B + RM = (M^+)(BR_4^-)$$

Perhaps the most important such compound is sodium tetraphenylborate, $Na[B(C_6H_5)_4]$. The sodium compound is moderately soluble in water, but tetraphenylborates of larger cations such as K^+, Rb^+, Cs^+, or $(CH_3)_4N^+$ are insoluble and suitable for gravimetric analysis.

References

Booth, H. S., and L. Audrieth, *Boron Trifluoride and Its Derivatives*, Wiley, New York, 1949.

Brown, H. C., and B. C. Subba Rao, *J. Am. Chem. Soc.*, **82**, 681 (1960). B_2H_6 as a reagent in organic chemistry.

Dale, J., *J. Chem. Soc. (London)*, **1961**, 910, 922. On structures of borate anions and alcohol complexes.

Edwards, J. O., and V. Ross, *J. Inorg. & Nuclear Chem.*, **15**, 329 (1960). Structural principles for borates.

Gerrard, W., *The Organic Chemistry of Boron*, Academic Press, New York–London, 1961. An excellent account of the more organic aspects of boron chemistry such as boric esters and alkyls.

Greenwood, N. N., and R. L. Martin, *Quart. Revs. (London)*, **8,** 1 (1954). Halides of boron.

Heal, H. G., *Royal Institute of Chemistry Lectures, Monographs, and Reports*, No. 1, London, 1960. A review of general advances in boron chemistry.

Hoard, J. L., and A. E. Newick, *J. Am. Chem. Soc.*, **82,** 70 (1960). Allotropy of boron.

Lappert, M. F., *Chem. Revs.*, **56,** 959 (1956). Organoboron compounds.

Lipscomb, W. W., in H. J. Emeléus and A. G. Sharpe, eds., *Advances in Inorganic Chemistry and Radiochemistry*, Vol. 2, Academic Press, New York, 1960, p. 279. Structural chemistry of boranes and their derivatives.

Matkovitch, U. I., *J. Am. Chem. Soc.*, **83,** 1804 (1961). Interstitial compounds of boron.

Palchak, R. J. F., J. H. Norman, and R. E. Williams, *J. Am. Chem. Soc.*, **83,** 3380 (1961). Decaborane chemistry.

Sharp, D. W. A., *Advances in Fluorine Chemistry*, Vol. I, Butterworths, London, 1960. Fluoroboric acids and their derivatives.

Sheldon, J. C., and B. C. Smith, *Quart. Revs. (London)*, **14,** 200 (1960). Borazole and related compounds.

Sillén, L. G., *et al.*, *Acta. Chem. Scand.*, **1,** 1034 (1957). Boric acids and borates in solution.

Stone, F. G. A., *Quart. Revs. (London)*, **9,** 174 (1955); also in H. J. Emeléus and A. G. Sharpe, eds., *Advances in Inorganic Chemistry and Radiochemistry*, Vol. 2, Academic Press, New York, 1960, p. 279. General chemistry of boranes and their derivatives.

Topchiev, A. V., S. V. Zavgorodnii, and Y. M. Paushkin (trans. J. Greaves), *Boron Fluoride and Its Compounds as Catalysts in Organic Chemistry*, Pergamon Press, London, 1959. A comprehensive account of BF_3 reactions.

11

Carbon

There are more known compounds of carbon than of any other element except hydrogen. Indeed the chemistry of carbon is so extensive and so important that it constitutes, in itself, that branch of the whole field of chemistry known as organic chemistry.

The electronic structure of the carbon atom in its ground state is $1s^2 2s^2 2p^2$, with the two $2p$ electrons unpaired following Hund's rule. In order to account for the normal four covalence of carbon, we must consider that it is promoted to a valence state based on the configuration $2s 2p_x 2p_y 2p_z$. This has been discussed in detail in Chapter 3. The ion C^{4+} does not arise in any normal chemical processes; the C^{4-} ion may possibly exist in some carbides. In general, however, carbon forms covalent bonds.

Some cations, anions, and radicals of moderate stability can occur, and there is abundant evidence from the study of organic reaction mechanisms for transient species of these types. Cations of the type $R_1R_2R_3C^+$ are called *carbonium* ions. The triphenylmethyl carbonium ion was one of the first to be discovered and is a fairly typical example. It doubtless owes its stability primarily to the fact that the positive charge is highly delocalized, as indicated by canonical structures of the type 11-Ia–d. It behaves in

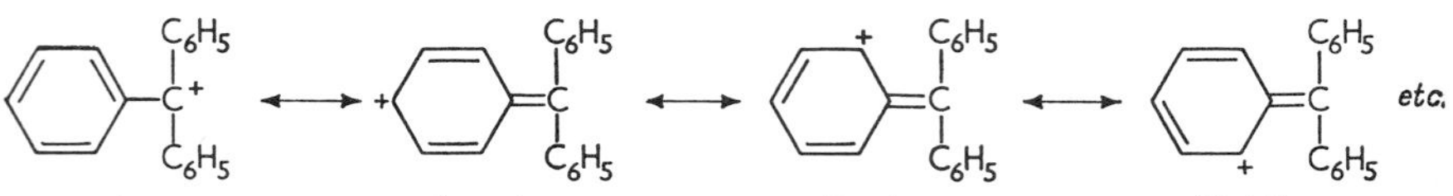

$$(II-Ia) \quad\longleftrightarrow\quad (II-Ib) \quad\longleftrightarrow\quad (II-Ic) \quad\longleftrightarrow\quad (II-Id) \quad etc.$$

some respects like other large univalent cations (Cs^+, R_4N^+, R_4As^+, etc.) and forms insoluble salts with large anions, such as BF_4^-, $GaCl_4^-$. There is good evidence that the cation has a propeller-like arrangement for the phenyl groups which are bound to the central carbon atom by sp^2 trigonal plane bonds.

Anions of the type $R_1R_2R_3C^-$ are called *carbanions*. Like carbonium ions they generally have no permanent existence, except in cases where the negative charge can be effectively delocalized. The triphenylmethyl

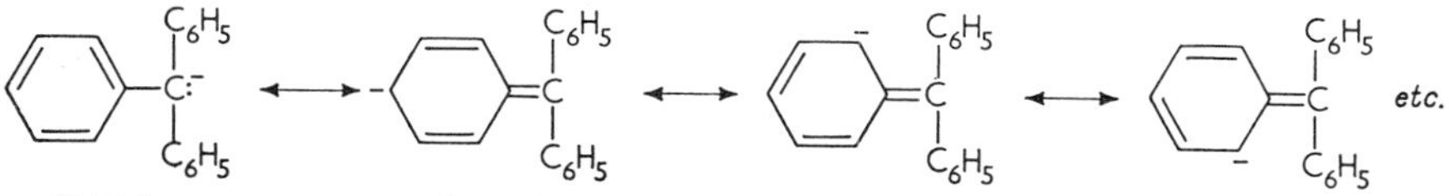

(II-IIa)   (II-IIb)   (II-IIc)   (II-IId)

carbanion (11-II) is a good example, as is also the cyclopentadienyl anion (11-III). In fact, since the negative charge in this case is equally delocal-

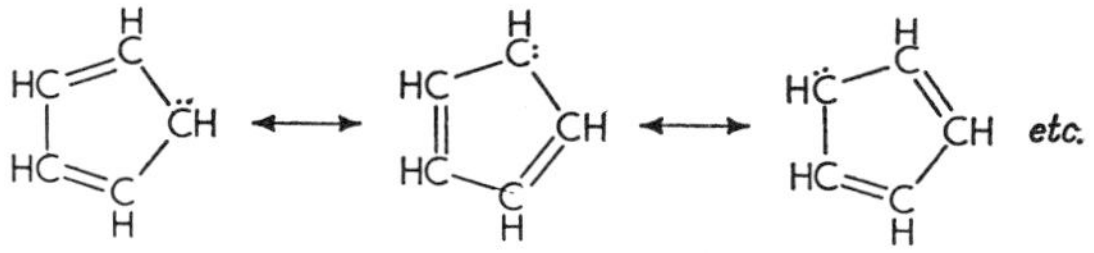

(II-IIIa)   (II-IIIb)   (II-IIIc)

ized on all of the carbon atoms, the anion is a regular plane pentagon and the π-electron density distribution can be well represented by 11-IV.

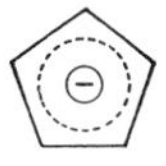

(II-IV)

There are also a number of radicals which are fairly long-lived, such as the celebrated triphenylmethyl radical. Here again the stability is due mainly to delocalization—in this case of the odd electron—as in the representative canonical structures 11-V. Note that in both of the ions and in

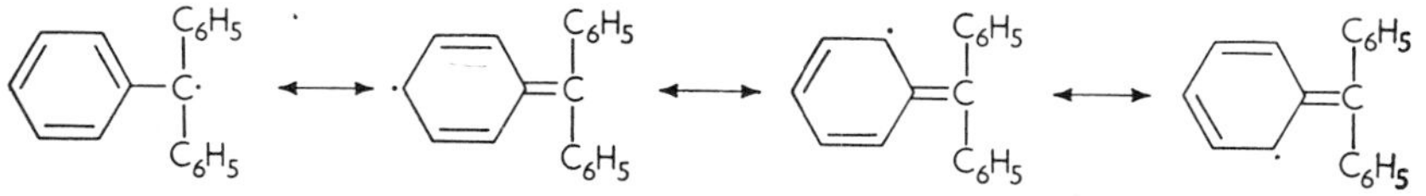

(II-Va)   (II-Vb)   (II-Vc)   (II-Vd)

the radical this resonance stabilization is possible only because of the ability of the unique carbon atom to form strong double bonds with the carbon atoms in the phenyl groups. If, as stated, it is the resonance effect which causes $(C_6H_5)_3C^+$ and $(C_6H_5)_3C\cdot$ to be stable, then we should not expect $(C_6H_5)_3Si^+$, $(C_6H_5)_3Si$, $(C_6H_5)_3Ge^+$, $(C_6H_5)_3Ge \ldots (C_6H_5)_3Pb^+$, and $(C_6H_5)_3Pb$ to be stable since Si, Ge, Sn, and Pb are unable, according to independent evidence, to form the required double bonds. In point of fact $(C_6H_5)_6Si_2$, $(C_6H_5)_6Ge_2$, $(C_6H_5)_6Sn_2$, and $(C_6H_5)_6Pb_2$ do not dissociate to form $(C_6H_5)_3M$ radicals, and compounds such as $(C_6H_5)_3MCl$ are only partially or negligibly ionic.

Carbon is one of the few elements for which *catenation* is a key feature in its chemistry. By catenation is meant the formation of chains of identical atoms. Such chains may also be closed into rings. Obviously, only an element with a valence of at least two which forms rather strong bonds with itself will do this. Carbon forms chains and rings not only with

$$R—(C=C—)_nR \qquad\qquad R—(C\equiv C—)_nR$$
$$\text{(11-VI)} \qquad\qquad\qquad \text{(11-VII)}$$

carbon–carbon single bonds but also with multiple bonds (11-VI, 11-VII, and 11-VIII). Sulfur is probably the element with the next greatest

(11–VIII)

tendency to catenation; it forms rings and chains in the elemental state and in the class of compounds known as sulfanes:

$$Y—S_n—Y$$
$$(n = 1\text{–}15;\ Y = \text{halogen, H, } SO_3, \text{ etc.})$$

However, the sulfanes are relatively unstable toward heat and oxidation. Silicon also has some tendency to catenation, the silanes $H(SiH_2)_nH$ with n from 1 to 6 being known. However, the stability of these compounds is very low compared to their carbon analogs. In the heavier elements of group IV—Ge, Sn, and Pb—the tendency to catenation and the stability of the bonds decrease rapidly, but, even for tin and lead, compounds with metal–metal bonds are known, for example $(CH_3)_3Sn—Sn(CH_3)_3$.

The unusual stability of catenated carbon compounds, compared with those of Si and S (the elements with the next greatest tendencies to catenation), can be appreciated by considering the bond energy data shown in Table 11-1. Thus the simple *thermal* stability of C—C—C— . . . chains is

TABLE 11-1

Bond Energies of Carbon, Silicon, and Sulfur

Bond	Energy, kcal./mole	Bond	Energy, kcal./mole
C—C	83	C—O	84
Si—Si	42	Si—O	88
S—S	51	S—O	Not known quantitatively, but certainly rather high

high because of the intrinsic strength of C—C bonds. The relative stabilities toward oxidation follow from the fact that for carbon C—C and C—O bonds are of comparable stability, whereas for Si, and probably also S, the bond to oxygen is considerably stronger. Thus, given the necessary activation energy, compounds with a number of Si—Si links are converted very exothermically to compounds with Si—O bonds.

THE ELEMENT

Naturally occurring carbon has the isotopic composition ^{12}C, 98.89%; ^{13}C, 1.11%. In addition, traces of ^{14}C exist, and this radioisotope provides the basis for the radiocarbon dating technique. ^{14}C is produced in the upper atmosphere by slow neutron capture by nitrogen atoms—$^{14}N(n,p)^{14}C$—and it decays by β^- emission with a half-life of 5570 years. Before the nuclear age this upper atmosphere process was presumably the only source of ^{14}C, and it was probably present in the atmosphere (as CO_2) at a constant, steady-state concentration determined by the relative values of the rate of production and the total rate of removal (e.g., by consumption of the CO_2 by plants, by radioactive decay, etc.). The half-life is sufficiently long that ^{14}C in atmospheric CO_2 will become thoroughly mixed into all carbon-containing systems which are in equilibrium with atmospheric CO_2, namely, carbonic acid and dissolved carbonates and, of special importance, living organisms. When the organisms die they are no longer able to take up further ^{14}C, and that which is present diminishes by radioactive decay. Thus from a knowledge of the concentration now present in objects of organic origin (estimated from β^- counting) and the steady-state concentration of ^{14}C when they lived one can estimate when the organism lived (or, more precisely, died). The method has been well calibrated using objects of known ages, and the uncertainties are of the order of 5% of the age.

11-1. Allotropy of Carbon: Diamond; Graphite

The two forms of carbon, diamond and graphite, differ in their physical and chemical properties because of differences in the arrangement and bonding of the atoms. Diamond is denser than graphite (diamond: 3.51 g./cm.³; graphite: 2.22 g./cm.³), but graphite is the more stable, by 0.58 kcal./mole at 0°K. and 0.45 kcal./mole at 300°K. and 1 atm. pressure. From the densities it follows that in order to transform graphite into diamond pressure must be applied, and from the known thermodynamic properties of the two allotropes it can be estimated that they would be in equilibrium at 300°C. under a pressure of ⌣15,000 atm. Of course, equilibrium might not be rapidly attained at this temperature. Indeed it is just this slowness in reaching equilibrium which allows the diamond structure to persist under ordinary conditions.

The energy required to vaporize graphite to a monatomic gas is an important quantity, since it enters into the estimation of the energies of all bonds involving carbon. It is not easy to measure directly because, even at very high temperatures, the vapor contains appreciable fractions of C_2, C_3, etc. Spectroscopic studies established that the value had to be either ⌣124, ⌣137, or 171.7 kcal./mole depending on the actual nature of the process measured spectroscopically. Recently, the composition of vapors has been determined mass spectrographically with sufficient accuracy to show that the low values are unacceptable. Hence it is now certain that the exact value is 171.7 kcal./mole at 300°K. In using older tables of bond energies, attention should be paid to what value was used for the heat of sublimation of graphite.

Diamond. The diamond is one of the hardest solids known. This and the higher density are explicable in terms of the structure, which was one of the first to be determined by X-ray diffraction study. In the diamond lattice, each carbon atom is tetrahedrally surrounded by four other carbon atoms at a distance of 1.54 A. This reticulated structure extends throughout each entire crystal so that each one is in effect a giant "molecule." This structure also accounts for many other properties of diamond. Its melting and boiling points are unknown but presumably extraordinarily high. It is also a nonconductor of electricity, since all of the electrons are firmly held in the carbon–carbon bonds.

The diamond structure can be produced from graphite carbon only by the application of high pressures. Furthermore, in order to get an appreciable rate of conversion, high temperatures are necessary. Naturally occurring diamonds must have been formed when such conditions were provided by geological processes. Since at least 1880, recognition of these requirements has led many workers to attempt the production of synthetic diamonds. Until 1955 all such attempts ended in failure, inadequately proved claims, and even in a bogus report of success. Modern knowledge of the thermodynamics of the process indicates that none of the conditions of temperature and pressure reported could have been sufficient for success. Figure 11-1 shows the equilibrium transition temperature as a function of pressure for the graphite–diamond system and also the region in which the successful synthesis is carried out. This region covers approximately the

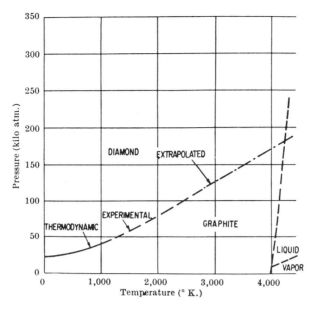

Fig. 11-1.   Carbon phase diagram (H. P. Bovenkerk *et al.*, *Nature*, **184**, 1094 (1959)).

range 2000–4000°K., 60–120 kilo atm. However, even in this region, with such high temperatures, no significant rate of conversion of graphite to diamond is attained without the use of catalysts, which, in this process, may be any one of the metals Cr, Mn, Fe, Co, Ni, Rh, Pd, Os, Ir, Pt, or Ta. It appears that a thin film of molten metal forms on the graphite, dissolving some and reprecipitating it as diamond, which is less soluble. So far, diamonds up to 0.1 carat of high industrial though not gem quality have been produced.

The chemical reactivity of diamond is much lower than that of carbon in the form of macrocrystalline graphite or the various amorphous forms. Diamond can be made to burn in air by heating to 600–800°C.

Graphite.   Graphite has a layer structure as indicated in Figure 11-2. The separation of the layers is 3.35 A., which is about equal to the sum of van der Waals radii and indicates that the forces between layers should be relatively slight. Thus the observed softness and particularly the lubricity of graphite can be attributed to the easy slippage of these layers over one another. It will be noted that within each layer each carbon atom is surrounded by only three others. After forming one σ bond with each neighbor, each carbon atom would still have one electron and these are paired

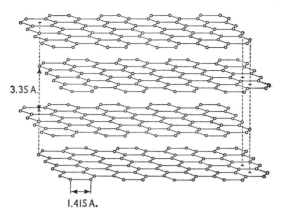

Fig. 11-2.   The normal structure of graphite.

up into a system of π bonds (11-IX). Resonance with other structures
having different but equivalent arrangements of the double bonds makes

(11-IX)

all C—C distances equal at 1.415 A. This is a little longer than the C—C
distance in benzene, where the bond order is 1.5, and agrees with the
assumption that the bond order in graphite is ∽1.33.

Actually two modifications of graphite exist, differing in the ordering of
the layers. In no case do the carbon atoms of one layer lie directly over
those in the next layer, but, in the structure shown in Figure 11-2, carbon
atoms in every other layer are superposed. This type of stacking, which
may be designated (ABAB . . .), is apparently the most stable and exists
in the commonly occurring hexagonal form of graphite. There is also a
rhombic form, frequently present in naturally occurring graphite, in which
the stacking order is (ABCABC . . .); that is, every third layer is superposed. It seems that local areas of rhombic structure can be formed by
mechanical deformation of hexagonal crystals and can be removed by
heat treatment.

The many forms of so-called amorphous carbon such as charcoals, soot, and lampblack, are all actually microcrystalline forms of graphite. In some soots the microcrystals are so small that they contain only a few unit cells of the graphite structure. The physical properties of such materials are mainly determined by the nature and magnitude of their surface areas. The finely divided forms, which present relatively vast surfaces with only partially saturated attractive forces, readily adsorb large amounts of gases and solutes from solution.

Although Si, Ge, and Sn also occur with the diamond structure, the graphite structure is peculiar to carbon, presumably because only carbon has marked ability to form double bonds.

The very loose, layered structure of graphite makes it possible for many molecules and ions to penetrate between the layers. The resulting interstitial or lamellar compounds of graphite are of sufficient interest to merit extended discussion.

11-2. Lamellar Compounds of Graphite

There are two basic types of lamellar compounds: those in which the graphite, which has good electrical conductivity, becomes nonconducting and those in which high electrical conductivity remains and is enhanced. Only two substances of the first type are known, namely, graphite oxide and graphite fluoride.

Graphite oxide is prepared by treating graphite with strong oxidizing agents such as mixtures of concentrated nitric and sulfuric acids or fuming nitric acid and potassium perchlorate or potassium permanganate. Graphite oxide is not obtained as a definite reproducible substance of fixed composition. Oxygen/carbon ratios approach but never exceed 1:2, and the material invariably contains hydrogen. The structure of graphite oxide is still rather uncertain, but the following are important features:

1. The presence of the oxygen causes the layer separation of the graphite to increase to 6–7 A. in thoroughly dried samples. The product readily absorbs water, acetone, dioxane, and alcohols with resultant swelling, the interlayer spacing increasing to as much as 19 A. with some of the alcohols.

2. The oxygen atoms are believed to be bound in C—O—C ether-like bridges between meta positions of the hexagonal rings, in keto groups, and the corresponding enol forms, $\diagdown C{=}O$ and $\diagdown C{-}OH$. These hydroxy groups are fairly acidic and may be esterified and methylated.

3. As a result of the formation of four covalent bonds by all or most of

the carbon atoms, it is believed that the layers become buckled, although certain proof of this is lacking. Formation of four covalent bonds, thus tying up all of the electrons, and buckling of the layers would account for the loss of the electrical conductivity, which in graphite takes place by the ready movement of electrons through the delocalized π orbitals in the layers. Graphite oxide is thus an aliphatic compound.

Graphite fluoride is the only other nonconducting compound of graphite and is obtained by direct reaction, which is occasionally explosive, of fluorine and graphite. The reproducibility of the preparation is poor, but products with C/F ratios up to 1:0.99, white in color, have been obtained. More commonly it is grey with a lower fluorine content. As with graphite oxide, the layer spacing is increased, typically to $\backsim$8 A. This is about equal to the sum of two C—F bond lengths (1.4 A.) plus two van der Waals radii of fluorine ($\backsim$2.6 A.), and it is believed that ideally the compound should have the composition $(CF)_n$ with each carbon atom forming a C—F bond (in accord with the infrared spectrum which shows only one C—F band) and three C—C bonds. Although the layers should be buckled because of the tetrahedral carbon bonding, certain proof has not been obtained.

In the *electrically conducting lamellar compounds*, various atoms, molecules, and ions are inserted or intercalated between the carbon sheets. A large number of the compounds form spontaneously on bringing graphite and the reactant into contact. Thus the heavier alkali metals K, Rb, and Cs, the halogens Cl_2 and Br_2, and a great variety of halides, oxides, and sulfides of metals, for example, $FeCl_3$, UCl_4, FeS_2, and MoO_3, form spontaneous lamellar compounds.

A smaller group of compounds are formed by electrolysis of the reactant using a graphite anode. For example, with sulfuric acid, the following reaction occurs:

$$C_m + 3H_2SO_4 = C_mHSO_4 \cdot 2H_2SO_4 + H^+ + e$$

the value of m depending on the amount of current passed. In these compounds the graphite layers remain planar. The gross composition of a compound does not necessarily fix its internal nature, since two factors relate this with the gross composition. First, the composition depends upon the concentration of invading reactant in the invaded layers; second, it depends upon what fraction of the layers are invaded. Definite stages of invasion have been observed; in many cases there is considerable long-range order, every nth layer being invaded, the intervening ones being untouched.

The manner in which the invading reactant species increase the conductivity of the graphite is not definitely settled, but apparently they do so by either adding electrons to or removing electrons from the conduction levels of graphite itself. They thus either increase the number of electrons or the number of positive holes which carry current by moving in these conduction levels. The alkali metals, for example, must add electrons, some of them therefore being present in the graphite as ions,

$$C_m K_n \qquad\qquad C_m{}^{x-}K_x{}^+K_{n-x}$$
Stoichiometry $\qquad$ Ionic nature

As another example, in a ternary compound in which both chlorine and $AlCl_3$ are present, the state of ionization may be represented by the following:

$$C_m Cl_n(AlCl_3)_p \qquad C_m{}^{x+}(AlCl_4)_x{}^-Cl_{n-x}(AlCl_3)_{p-x}$$
Stoichiometry $\qquad$ Ionic nature

In most cases at least, the extent of ionization appears to be only fractional.

There is some evidence that compounds whose lattices, like graphite, can expand—BN, AlB_2, and $CrCl_3$—can also act as host lattices for oxides, sulfides, and chlorides.

CARBIDES

The term carbide is applied to those compounds in which carbon is combined with elements of lower or about equal electronegativity. Thus compounds with oxygen, sulfur, phosphorus, nitrogen, halogens, etc., are not considered in this category, and by convention neither are those with hydrogen. The reasonableness of this division will become apparent as the nature of the carbides is discussed. They are usually considered to be of three types: (*1*) the salt-like carbides, formed chiefly by the elements of groups I, II, and III; (*2*) the interstitial carbides formed by most transition metals, especially those in groups IV, V, and VI, and (*2a*) a borderline type formed by a few of the transition metals with small atomic radii; and (*3*) covalent carbides, SiC and B_4C.

The general preparative methods for carbides of all three types include (*a*) direct union of the elements at high temperature (2200°C. and above); (*b*) heating a compound of the metal, particularly the oxide, with carbon; and (*c*) heating the metal in the vapor of a suitable hydrocarbon. Carbides of Cu, Ag, Au, Zn, and Cd, also commonly called acetylides, are prepared by passing acetylene into solutions of the metal salts; with Cu, Ag, and Au, ammoniacal solutions of salts of the unipositive ions are used to obtain Cu_2C_2, Ag_2C_2, and Au_2C_2 (uncertain), whereas with Zn and Cd, the acetylides ZnC_2 and CdC_2 are obtained by passing acetylene into petrol solutions of dialkyl compounds. The Cu and Ag acetylides are explosive, being sensitive to both heat and mechanical shock.

1. *Salt-like carbides.* The most electropositive metals form carbides having physical and chemical properties which indicate that they are essentially ionic. They form colorless, transparent crystals and are decomposed by water and/or dilute acids at ordinary temperatures. The liberated anions are immediately hydrolyzed too, and hydrocarbons are thus evolved. There are ionic carbides containing C^{4-} and C_2^{2-} ions and one which, it has been inferred, contains C_3^{4-} ions.

Carbides containing C^{4-} ions evolve methane on hydrolysis and can be called methanides. Be_2C and Al_4C_3 are of this type. Thus the hydrolysis of the latter may be written:

$$Al_4C_3 + 12H_2O = 4Al(OH)_3 + 3CH_4$$

The structure of Be_2C is rather simple, being the antifluorite structure (see Fig. 2-4, page 46) with the beryllium atoms replacing F^- in CaF_2 and carbon atoms replacing Ca^{2+}. The structure of Al_4C_3 is quite complicated; the details need not concern us except insofar as it is found that the carbon atoms occur singly.

Carbides containing C_2^{2-} ions are rather common. Normally they evolve only acetylene on hydrolysis and are thus called acetylides. The metals Li–Cs and Cu–Au give M_2C_2 compounds; the metals Be–Ba and Zn and Cd give MC_2. Boron forms a covalent carbide to be discussed later, whereas Al and Ce give carbides of the formula $M_2(C_2)_3$. Other lanthanides exhibit divalence, the metals Y, La, Ce, Pr, Nd, and Sm giving compounds of the type MC_2. It is noteworthy that although CaC_2 (C—C, 1.20 A.) is an insulator, LaC_2 (C—C, 1.28 A.) and UC_2 (C—C, 1.34 A.) are metallic conductors; one or more of the electrons from the formally $+2$ ion are believed to be in an antibonding orbital of the C_2^{2-} ion which may overlap with a conduction band in the solid state. There are miscellaneous other acetylides also having the metals in unusually low oxidation states, such as ThC_2, UC_2, and VC_2. It has been found that those carbides in which the metal atoms are in their normal oxidation states evolve only acetylene on hydrolysis and the reactions may be written:

$$CaC_2 + 2H_2O = Ca(OH)_2 + HCCH$$
$$Al_2C_6 + 6H_2O = 2Al(OH)_3 + 3HCCH$$

The acetylides of thorium and the lanthanides, however, evolve only 50–70% C_2H_2 along with C_2H_4, CH_4, and H_2. Aside from the notable absence of C_2H_6, these results may be explained by recognizing that the metals, which are in low and unstable valence states, will be further oxidized by the water with the production of hydrogen which can lead to the formation of C_2H_4, CH_4, and H_2 in the products. For example,

$$LaC_2 + 2H_2O = La(OH)_2 + HCCH$$

$$La(OH)_2 + H_2O = La(OH)_3 + \tfrac{1}{2}H_2$$

$$HCCH \xrightarrow{H_2} \begin{cases} H_2CCH_2 \\ CH_4 \end{cases}$$

All of the acetylides so far examined structurally have sodium chloride-like lattices. Most have the CaC_2 structure in which the $[C—C]^{2-}$ ions lie lengthwise in the same direction along the cell axes, thus causing a distortion from cubic symmetry to tetragonal symmetry with one axis longer than the other two. In thorium carbide, the C_2^{2-} ions are lying flat in parallel planes in such a way that two axes are equally lengthened with respect to the third. These structures are shown in Figure 11-3.

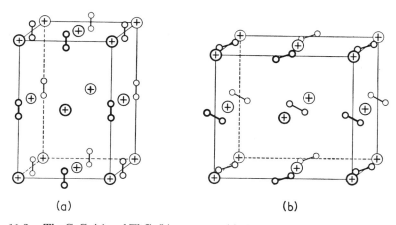

(a)   (b)

Fig. 11-3. The CaC_2 (a) and ThC_2 (b) structures (the latter is somewhat simplified here).

2. *Interstitial carbides.* In interstitial carbides, carbon atoms occupy the octahedral holes in close-packed arrays of metal atoms. The characteristics of interstitial carbides, namely, very high melting points (3000–4800°C.), great hardness (7–10, mostly 9–10, on Moh's scale), and metallic electrical conductivity, are thus easily explainable. The free electron structure and other characteristic properties of the pure metal are not fundamentally altered by insertion of the carbon atoms into some of the interstices of the metal lattice; at the same time, the carbon atoms further stabilize the lattice thus increasing hardness and raising the melting point. The ability of the carbon atoms to enter the interstices without appreciably

distorting the metal structure requires that the interstices, and hence the metal atoms, be relatively large, and it can be estimated that a metal atom radius of ᴖ1.3 A. or greater is required.

The metals Cr, Mn, Fe, Co, and Ni have radii somewhat smaller than 1.3 A., and they do not therefore form typical interstitial carbides. Instead, the metal lattices are appreciably distorted and the carbon atoms interact directly with one another. The structures can be roughly described as having carbon chains (with C—C distances ᴖ1.65 A.) running through very distorted metal lattices. The carbides Cr_3C_2 and M_3C (M = Mn, Fe, Co, Ni) are rather easily hydrolyzed by water and dilute acids to give a variety of hydrocarbons (even liquid and solid ones and, in the case of Fe_3C, free carbon) and hydrogen. They are thus transitional between the typical ionic and interstitial carbides.

3. *Covalent carbides.* Although other carbides, for example, Be_2C, are at least partially covalent, the two elements which approach carbon closely in size and electronegativity, namely, Si and B, give completely covalent compounds. Silicon carbide, SiC, technically known as carborundum, is an extremely hard, infusible, and chemically stable material made by reducing SiO_2 with carbon in an electric furnace. It occurs in three structural modifications, in all of which there are infinite three-dimensional arrays of Si and C atoms, each tetrahedrally surrounded by four of the other kind. Interestingly, no evidence has ever been obtained for a germanium carbide of this or any other type.

Boron carbide, B_4C, also an extremely hard, infusible, and inert substance, and made by reduction of B_2O_3 with carbon in an electric furnace, has a very unusual structure. The carbon atoms occur in linear chains of three, and the boron atoms in icosahedral groups of twelve (as in crystalline boron itself). These two units are then packed together in a sodium chloride-like array. There are, of course, covalent bonds between carbon atoms and boron atoms as well as between boron atoms in different icosahedra.

SIMPLE MOLECULAR COMPOUNDS

In this section we shall discuss a few simple compounds which are neither carbides, organometallic compounds, nor compounds of the kinds which are mainly if not exclusively in the province of organic chemistry. With the above restrictions, we are left only with the simpler compounds of carbon with the elements of groups V, VI, and VII. Some important compounds and their principal properties are listed in Table 11-2.

TABLE 11-2

Some Simple Compounds of Carbon

Compound	Melting point, °C.	Boiling point, °C.	Remarks
CF_4	−185	−128	Very stable
CCl_4	−23	76	Moderately stable
CBr_4	93	190	Decomposes slightly on boiling
CI_4	171	—	Decomposes before boiling; can be sublimed under low pressure
COF_2	−114	−83	Easily decomposed by H_2O
$COCl_2$	−118	8	"Phosgene"; highly toxic
$COBr_2$	—	65	Fumes in air; $COBr_2 + H_2O \rightarrow CO_2 + 2HBr$
$CO(NH_2)_2$	132	—	Decomposes on heating to $NH_4^+NCO^-$
CO	−205	−190	Odorless and toxic
CO_2	−57 (5.2 atm)	−79	
C_3O_2	—	−7	Evil-smelling gas
COS	−138	−50	Flammable; slowly decomposed by H_2O
CS_2	−109	46	Flammable and toxic
$(CN)_2$	−28	−21	Very toxic; colorless
HCN	−13.4	25.6	Very toxic; high dielectric constant (116 at 20°C.) for the associated liquid

11-3. Carbon Halides

Carbon tetrafluoride is an extraordinarily stable compound. It is the end product in the fluorination of any carbon-containing compound. A useful laboratory preparation, for example, involves the fluorination of silicon carbide. The SiF_4 also formed is removed easily by passing the mixture through 20% NaOH solution; the CF_4 is quite unaffected, whereas the SiF_4 is immediately hydrolyzed:

$$SiF_4 + 8OH^- = SiO_4^{4-} + 4F^- + 4H_2O$$

This phenomenon is a good illustration of the differences which frequently exist between a compound of an element in the first short period and seemingly analogous compounds of its congeners. The difference in this case is due to the fact that, in CF_4, carbon is coordinately saturated—that is, it has no orbitals with which to coordinate OH^- ions as a first step in the process of hydrolysis—whereas silicon in SiF_4 has $3d$ orbitals available, and by means of these is rapidly attacked.

Carbon tetrachloride is a commonly used solvent; it is fairly readily photochemically decomposed and also quite often readily transfers chloride ion to various substrates, CCl_3 radicals often being formed simultaneously at high temperatures (300–500°C.). It is often used to convert oxides to chlorides. Although it is thermodynamically unstable with respect to hydrolysis, the absence of any acceptor orbitals on carbon makes attack very difficult.

Carbon tetrabromide is a pale yellow solid at room temperature. It is insoluble in water and other polar solvents, soluble in some nonpolar solvents such as benzene.

Carbon tetraiodide is a bright red crystalline material possessing an odor like that of iodine. Both heat and light cause decomposition to iodine and tetraiodoethylene. It is insoluble in water and alcohol, though attacked by both at elevated temperatures, and soluble in benzene. It may be prepared by the following reaction

$$CCl_4 + 4C_2H_5I \xrightarrow{AlCl_3} CI_4 + 4C_2H_5Cl$$

The increasing instability, both thermal and photochemical, of the carbon tetrahalides with increasing weight of the halogen correlates with a steady decrease in the C—X bond energies:

C—F, 105;   C—Cl, 79;   C—Br, 66;   C—I, 57 kcal./mole

The *carbonyl halides*, COX_2 (X = F, Cl, and Br), are all hydrolytically unstable substances. $COCl_2$ is phosgene, an extremely poisonous gas. Mixed carbonyl halides such as COClBr are also known. The compound $CO(NH_2)_2$ is urea. The molecular structures of both urea and phosgene have been determined. In each case the C—O bond length is somewhat longer than the expected value for a C=O double bond, whereas the N—C and Cl—C distances are somewhat shorter than expected for single bonds. These facts lead to the conclusion that these molecules should be viewed as resonance hybrids (11-X and 11-XI).

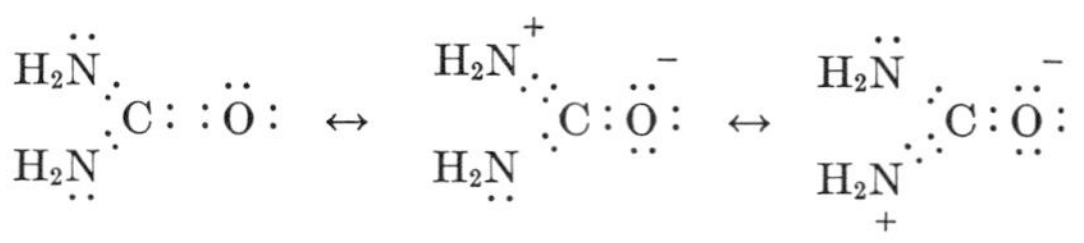

(11-Xa)   (11-Xb)   (11-Xc)

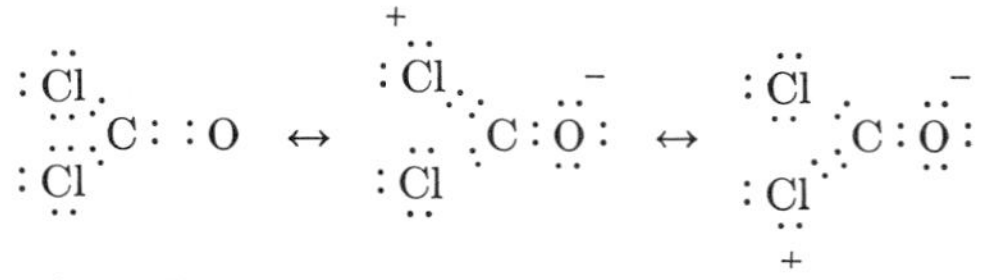

(11-XIa)   (11-XIb)   (11-XIc)

11-4. Carbon Oxides

There are five reported oxides of carbon: CO, CO_2, C_3O_2, C_5O_2, and $C_{12}O_9$. The last one is the anhydride of mellitic acid (11-XII) and will not be discussed further.

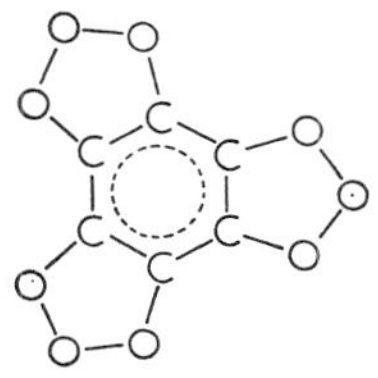

(11-XII)

Carbon monoxide is formed when carbon is burned with a deficiency of oxygen. At all temperatures, the following equilibrium exists, but is not rapidly attained at ordinary temperatures

$$2CO(g) = C(s) + CO_2(g)$$

The reaction

$$C + H_2O = CO + H_2$$

is important commercially, the equimolar mixture of CO and H_2 being called water gas. A convenient laboratory preparation of CO is by the action of concentrated sulfuric acid on formic acid,

$$HCOOH \xrightarrow{-H_2O} CO$$

Although CO is an exceedingly weak Lewis base, one of its most important properties is the ability to act as a donor ligand toward transition metals giving *metal carbonyls*. For example, nickel metal reacts with CO to form $Ni(CO)_4$, and iron reacts under more forcing conditions to give $Fe(CO)_5$; many other metal carbonyls and mixed carbonyl complexes are known and are discussed in Chapter 27 in detail. Briefly, however, the ability of CO to form bonds to transition metal atoms is attributed to the fact that, in addition to a very weak dative bond, $O{\equiv}C{\rightarrow}M$, there exists "back-bonding" by the donation of electrons in metal d orbitals to the incompletely filled π orbitals of the CO, as indicated in 11-XIIIb.

$$\bar{M} : C : : : \overset{+}{O} : \leftrightarrow M : : C : : \overset{..}{O} :$$
(11-XIIIa)   (11-XIIIb)

Transition metal salts are used in a variety of catalytic reactions in which carbon monoxide is incorporated into organic compounds and carbonyl complexes are probably intermediates in these reactions.

Carbon dioxide is obtained by combustion of carbon in the presence of excess oxygen or by treating carbonates with dilute acids. Its important properties should already be familiar.

Carbon suboxide, C_3O_2, is an interesting but relatively little known substance which is formed by dehydrating malonic acid with P_2O_5 in vacuum at 140–150°C. or, better, by pyrolysis of diacetyl tartaric anhydride (eq. 11-1). It is an evil-smelling gas, with a normal boiling point of $-7°C$.

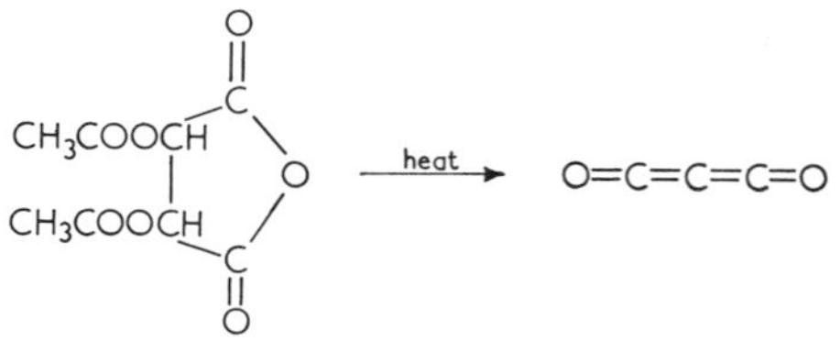

$$O=C=C=C=O \qquad \text{(11-1)}$$

Although there is still some room for doubt, it appears most likely from various structural and spectral studies that the C_3O_2 molecule is completely linear. The bond distances are C—C, 1.30 A. (theory for C=C, 1.33), and C—O, 1.20 A. (theory for C≡O, 1.22). It is supposed that linearity of the molecule and the observed bond lengths are attributable to resonance among the canonical structures 11-XIV.

$$O=C=C=C=O \leftrightarrow \overset{+}{O}\equiv C-C\equiv C-\overset{-}{O} \leftrightarrow \overset{-}{O}-C\equiv C-C\equiv\overset{+}{O}$$
$$\text{(11-XIVa)} \qquad \text{(11-XIVb)} \qquad \text{(11-XIVc)}$$

C_5O_2 has been claimed, but others have disputed the claim and its existence must at present be considered uncertain. Note that if resonance of the above type is an important stabilizing factor, then oxides of the type C_nO_2 would be expected only for n odd, so that C_5O_2 would be theoretically possible, whereas C_2O_2 and C_4O_2, which are unknown, would not.

"Carbonic Acids." Carbon monoxide is formally the anhydride of formic acid, but its solubility in water and bases is slight. On heating with alkalies, however, it will react to give the corresponding formate. C_3O_2 is the anhydride of malonic acid. It combines very vigorously with water to produce the acid and with ammonia and amines to produce malondiamides.

$$C_3O_2 + 2H_2O = HOOCCH_2COOH$$
$$C_3O_2 + 2NHR_2 = R_2NCOCH_2CONR_2$$

Carbon dioxide is the anhydride of the most important simple acid of carbon, "carbonic acid." For many purposes, the following acid dissociation constants are given for aqueous "carbonic acid":

$$\frac{[H^+][HCO_3^-]}{[H_2CO_3]} = 4.16 \times 10^{-7}$$

$$\frac{[H^+][CO_3^{2-}]}{[HCO_3^-]} = 4.84 \times 10^{-11}$$

The equilibrium quotient in the first equation above is not really correct. It assumes that all CO_2 dissolved and undissociated is present as H_2CO_3, which is not true. In actual fact, the greater part of the dissolved CO_2 is only loosely hydrated, so that the correct first dissociation constant, using the "true" activity of H_2CO_3, has a value of about 2×10^{-4}. As has been noted in Chapter 5, this value is more nearly in agreement with what one would expect for an acid with the structure $(HO)_2CO$.

The rate at which CO_2 comes into equilibrium with H_2CO_3 and its dissociation products when passed into water is measurably slow, and this indeed is what has made possible an analytical distinction between H_2CO_3 and the loosely hydrated $CO_2(aq.)$. This slowness is of great importance in biological, analytical, and industrial chemistry. By the addition of HCl to dispersed $NaHCO_3$ in anhydrous ether at $-30°C.$, it has been shown that the anhydrous acid H_2CO_3 exists in ether solution at $-30°C.$ as a stable entity. An etherate, $H_2CO_3(C_2H_5)_2O$, which decomposes above $-10°C.$ can be precipitated at $-78°C.$ as white crystals.

Carbamic acid, also called aminoformic acid, can be regarded as derived from carbonic acid by substitution of —NH_2 for —OH; it has the structural formula 11-XV. This is only one example of the existence of compounds

$$\begin{array}{c} \text{HO} \\ \diagdown \\ \qquad C{=}O \\ \diagup \\ \text{H}_2\text{N} \end{array}$$

(11-XV)

which are related in this way; —NH_2 and —OH are isoelectronic and virtually isosteric and frequently give rise to isostructural compounds. If the second OH in carbonic acid is replaced by NH_2, we have urea. Carbamic acid is not known in the free state, but many salts are known, all of which, however, are unstable to water. Thus the carbamate anion is not obtainable in aqueous solution.

$$H_2NCO_2^- + H_2O = NH_4^+ + CO_3^{2-}$$

11-5. Other Compounds

1. *Cyanogen.* A colorless, poisonous, and water-soluble gas, cyanogen is formed by heating $Hg(CN)_2$ or by the reaction

$$2Cu^{2+} + 4CN^- = 2CuCN + (CN)_2$$

It is quite stable despite the fact that it is unusually endothermic with an enthalpy of formation of $+71$ kcal./mole. At $400-500°C.$ it polymerizes to paracyanogen, a solid polymer which reverts to $(CN)_2$ at $800-850°C.$, but decomposes above this temperature. The structure of $(CN)_n$ has been

(II–XVI)

inferred from infrared spectroscopy to be 11-XVI. Cyanogen is slowly hydrolyzed by water, in part giving 11-XVII, which indicates that the

$$H_2N—C—C—NH_2$$
$$\overset{\|}{O} \ \ \overset{\|}{O}$$

(11-XVII)

order of atoms must be NCCN. This is fully confirmed by physical studies, in particular by structural investigations which give the following data: the molecule is symmetrical and linear with the C—C distance equal to 1.37 A. and the C—N distance equal to 1.16 A. The C—C distance is much less than that expected (1.54) for the electronic structure N≡C—C≡N. In valence bond theory we can explain this by considering other canonical structures, for example, the resonance 11-XVIII. Cyan-

$$:N::\ :C:C:\ :\ :N:\ \leftrightarrow\ :\overset{=}{N}:\ :C:\ :C:\ :\overset{+}{N}:\ \leftrightarrow\ :\overset{+}{N}:\ :C:\ :C:\ :\overset{=}{N}:$$

(11-XVIIIa) (11-XVIIIb) (11-XVIIIc)

ogen dissociates into CN radicals, and CN^- ions may be thought of as deriving from $(CN)_2$ just as halide ions X^- are derived from X_2. In fact, $(CN)_2$ is one of several substances called *pseudohalogens*, which will be discussed later when the halogens are discussed (Chapter 22).

2. *Hydrogen cyanide.* This compound, HCN, like the hydrogen halides, is a covalent, molecular substance, but capable of dissociation in aqueous solution. It is an extremely poisonous (though less so than H_2S), colorless gas and is evolved when cyanides are treated with acids. It condenses at 25.6°C. to a liquid with a very high dielectric constant (~116). Here, as in similar cases, such as water, the high dielectric constant is due to association of intrinsically very polar molecules by hydrogen bonding. Liquid HCN is unstable and can polymerize violently in the absence of stabilizers. The solid tetrameric polymer has been shown to be diaminomaleonitrile. In aqueous solution HCN is a very weak acid ($K = 2.1 \times 10^{-9}$). The CN^- ion is of great importance as a ligand in the complexes of many transitional and related (e.g., Zn, Cd, Hg) metals. For ionic cyanides such as NaCN, which has the rock salt structure, the CN^- ion is spherically symmetrical because of free rotation and has a radius of 1.92 A.

3. *Carbon disulfide and thiocarbon compounds.* Carbon disulfide is prepared by direct interaction of the elements and is a pale yellow liquid

which is extensively used as a solvent. It is also used to prepare carbon tetrachloride:

$$CS_2 + Cl_2 = CCl_4 + S_2Cl_2$$

A similar diselenide is obtained by the action of CH_2Cl_2 on molten selenium; it has a worse smell than CS_2, but, unlike it, is nonflammable.

The action of ammonium hydroxide on CS_2 gives red solutions from which orange and yellow crystals of $(NH_4)_2CS_3$ and $(NH_4)_2CS_4$ can be obtained. The action of alcoholic HCl on the thiocarbonate gives the acid H_2CS_3, a red liquid.

If CS_2 is treated with various primary or secondary amines in sodium hydroxide solution, dithiocarbamates of general formula 11-XIX are obtained; these soluble salts form a large number of metal complexes and are of great industrial importance as catalysts in the vulcanization of rubber. If sodium alkoxides are used instead of amines, xanthates (11-XX), which have similar properties, are obtained.

(II-XIX)   (II-XX)

ORGANOMETALLIC COMPOUNDS

11-6. General Survey of Types

Organometallic compounds are those in which organic groups (radicals or molecules) are bound *directly* to metal atoms. Thus we do not include in this category compounds in which carbon-containing moieties are bound to a metal via some other atom such as oxygen, nitrogen, or sulfur. For example, $(C_3H_7O)_4Ti$ is not considered to be an organometallic compound, whereas $C_6H_5Ti(OC_3H_7)_3$ is, because in the latter there is one direct linkage of the metal to carbon. Although organic groups can be bound through carbon, in one way or another, to virtually all the elements in the periodic table, excluding the inert gases, the term organometallic is usually rather loosely defined and organo compounds of decidedly nonmetallic elements such as B, P, and Si are often included in the category. Specific compounds are discussed in the sections on the chemistry of the individual elements since the organo derivatives are usually just as characteristic of any element as are, say, its halides or oxides. However, it is pertinent to make a few general comments here on the various types of compounds.

1. Ionic Compounds of Electropositive Metals. The organometallic compounds of highly electropositive metals are usually ionic in nature. Thus the alkali metal derivatives, with the exception of those of lithium (Chapter 8, page 166) which are fairly covalent in nature, are insoluble in hydrocarbon solvents and are very reactive toward air, water, etc. The alkaline earth metals Ca, Sr, and Ba give poorly characterized compounds which are even more reactive and unstable than the alkali salts. The stability and reactivity of ionic compounds are determined in part by the stability of the organic anion. Compounds containing unstable anions (e.g., $C_nH_{2n+1}^-$) are generally highly reactive and often unstable and difficult to isolate. However, where reasonably stable anions (see page 211) exist, the metal derivatives are more stable and less reactive (e.g., $(C_6H_5)_3C^-Na^+$ and $(C_5H_5^-)_2Ca^{2+}$). The only organo derivatives of such highly electropositive elements as scandium and the lanthanides (Chapter 31) are of this type, with the cyclopentadienide ion, for example, $(C_5H_5)_3Nd$.

2. σ-Bonded Compounds. Organo compounds in which the organic residue is bound to a metal by a normal two-electron covalent bond (albeit in some cases with appreciable ionic character) are formed by most metals of lower electropositivity and, of course, by nonmetallic elements. The normal valence rules apply in these cases, and partial substitution of halides, hydroxides, etc., by organic groups is possible, as in $(CH_3)_3SnCl$, $(CH_3)SnCl_3$, etc.

In most of these compounds, bonding is predominantly covalent and the chemistry is organic-like, although there are many differences in detail due to factors such as use of higher d orbitals or donor behavior as in R_4Si, R_3P, R_2S, etc., incomplete valence shells or coordinative unsaturation as in R_3B or R_2Zn, and effects of electronegativity differences between M—C and C—C bonds.

It was long believed that the transition metals of the d type could not, except in a few special cases, form σ bonds to carbon. This view is no longer held (see Chapter 28). Although it is true that few binary organo compounds (R_nM) have been characterized, it is now well established that σ-bonded compounds can be formed by the transition elements provided that other ligands, usually though not always π-bonding ligands, are present. The first-known extensive group of compounds of this type had π-C_5H_5 and CO groups present, for example, π-$C_5H_5Mo(CO)_3C_2H_5$, but several other types are now recognized.

3. Nonclassically Bonded Compounds. The organometallic field has presented some very challenging problems since there are several classes of compounds whose structures have been found to be unexpected and novel and which cannot be treated on normal valence considerations. The more important are the following:

Bridge-bonded alkyl compounds: This type of compound is exemplified by the polymeric alkyls of Be, Al, and Pt; the lithium alkyls probably fall in this category.

Sandwich-bonded compounds: These are compounds which have a delocalized "aromatic" ring system bound symmetrically to a transition metal so that all M—C distances are identical. They involve overlap of ring π electron density and certain d orbitals of the metal. The main classes are those with the cyclopentadienyl, benzene, and tropylium entities bound to a metal. The name "sandwich" was first used in connection with the structure of the molecule now known as ferrocene, $C_{10}H_{10}Fe$, where the iron atom lies between two planar C_5H_5 rings. In the case of the cyclopentadienyl radical, the prefix π is used to denote symmetrical bonding and to make a distinction from σ-bonded C_5H_5 groups.

Olefin and acetylene compounds: These compounds, like those discussed in the preceding paragraph, are characteristic of the transition metals. They also involve interaction of π electron density of the hydrocarbon with d orbitals. Olefins of various types and acetylenes can be directly bound to a metal atom. In addition, acetylenes can undergo reactions with metal carbonyls in which the acetylene group is modified, for example, by linking to carbon monoxide to give quinone, cyclopentadienone, or lactone groupings which are bound to the metal atom.

Since the sandwich-bonded, olefin, and acetylene types of compounds are specific to transition metals and the bonding results from the special properties of d orbitals, these types are discussed separately in Chapter 28. The *bridge-bonded compounds* are conveniently discussed here.

11-7. Electron-Deficient Bridged Alkyls

The elements B, Al, Ga, In, and Tl all form fairly stable but reactive alkyls and aryls. The most striking feature of the compounds of this series is the dimerization of the aluminum lower alkyls.

The alkyls of boron, gallium, and thallium(III) are monomeric, as are all those of indium except for trimethylindium which does polymerize. It is tetrameric in benzene and is associated in the solid state where its structure is complicated, tetrameric units being linked together by rather long bonds. Unlike the methyl bridges in $(CH_3)_2Be$, $(CH_3)_6Al_2$, or $(CH_3)_4Pt$ discussed below, the $CH_3\cdots In—CH_3$ bridges are unsymmetrical. The reasons for this exceptional behavior are not too clear.

Trimethylaluminum (a liquid) is a dimer, $Al_2(CH_3)_6$, in benzene solution and appreciably dimerized in the vapor phase. Triethylaluminum and tri-*n*-propylaluminum are also dimeric in benzene solution but much more highly dissociated in the vapor phase than is $Al(CH_3)_3$. Triisopropylaluminum is monomeric in benzene solution. Presumably in this last case steric hindrance prevents dimerization (or could, whatever the nature of the bridge bonding). The beryllium alkyls have been found to be highly polymeric, and methylplatinum derivatives are tetramers; these compounds have bridging alkyl groups. The structures of $[(CH_3)_2Be]_n$ and $[(CH_3)_3Al]_2$ as determined by Rundle and his co-workers are shown in Figure 11-4. The important feature of these structures is the bridging by methyl groups.

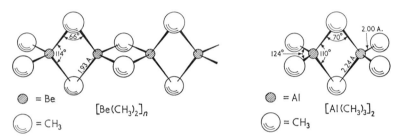

Fig. 11-4. Structures of $[Be(CH_3)_2]_n$ and $[Al(CH_3)_3]_2$ as found by X-ray diffraction.

It should first be emphasized that although these structures are geometrically similar to those of the corresponding chlorides, the nature of the bridge bonding must be essentially different. In the chlorides there is no deficiency of electrons, and we may consider that the equality of the bridge bonds is due to resonance of type 11-XXI.

$$\underset{(11-XXIa)}{\text{Cl}} \longleftrightarrow \underset{(11-XXIb)}{\text{Cl}}$$

In the case of the methyl-bridged compounds, there is an electron deficiency. In attempting to write classical Lewis structures we could get only as far as 11-XXII, where the question marks indicate that there is no way within the classical framework of valence theory, which recognizes only two-center bonds, to account for the additional metal–carbon bonds. At one time structures such as 11-XXIII were discussed, but the meaning of

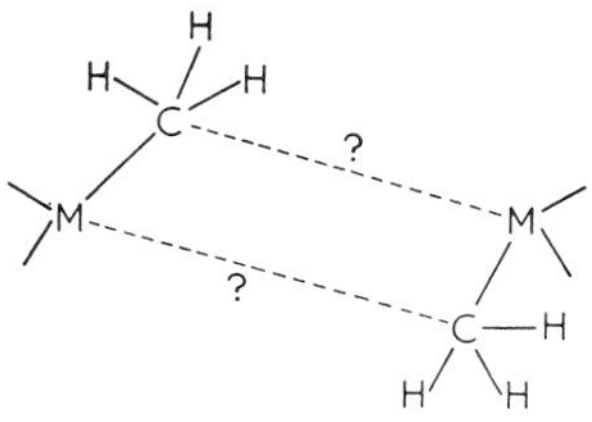

(II-XXII)

the dotted lines—that is, the nature of the hydrogen–metal interaction they imply—was obscure. The structure data now available, of course, rule out any such idea since the M—C—M groupings are shown to be symmetrical.

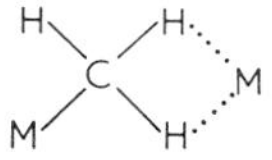

(II-XXIII)

The solution to this problem of methyl bridging lies in the recognition of multicenter bonding as in the case of the boranes (Chapter 10). In $[Al(CH_3)_3]_2$, for example, each aluminum atom is assumed to be hybridized in a manner approximating to, but not exactly, the tetrahedral sp^3 hybridization. It then uses two of these orbitals and two of its electrons to form two normal two-center bonds to the terminal methyl groups. The $(CH_3)_2Al$ fragments then have two hybrid orbitals and one electron each free for further bonding. The bridging methyl groups are normal methyl groups and therefore have one empty sp^3 (approximately) hybrid orbital and one electron available for further bonding. These fragments then combine in much the same way as the $2BH_2\cdot$ and $2H\cdot$ in B_2H_6. The methyl orbital and one orbital from each of the aluminum atoms overlap to form a three-center bonding orbital which is occupied by two electrons. A schematic representation of the overlap of these orbitals is in Figure 11-5. Inspection of Figure 11-4 shows that the metal–carbon–metal angles are quite small, 70 and 66°. From Figure 11-5 the reason for this may be deduced. The hybrid orbital of carbon is directed and condensed rather strongly along the C—C axis. Consequently, in order for the aluminum orbitals to overlap well with it, the axes of their orbitals must not make too great an angle with the C—C axis. Hence the small Al—C—Al and Be—C—Be angles. In $[Be(CH_3)_2]_n$ all methyls are bridging, and the nature of this bonding is in principle exactly the same as in the trimethyl-aluminum dimer. It should be noted that the metal orbitals doubtless overlap one another to some extent, as indicated in Figure 11-5. This means, in effect, that there is some direct metal–metal bonding. According to present views, this is not, however, the dominant factor in the bridge bonding (see discussion of the methyl platinum compounds below).

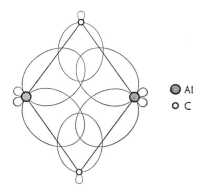

Fig. 11-5.   Orbital overlaps in $[Al(CH_3)_3]_2$.

The curious fact that none of the alkyls of the group III elements except those of aluminum are dimerized (although there is some evidence for very slight dimerization of $(CH_3)_3Ga$) has not yet been satisfactorily explained. It has been proposed that for the heavier metals, the small M—C—M angles required to secure good overlap would introduce large repulsions between the bulky metal atoms, but this cannot explain why $(CH_3)_3B$ does not dimerize, especially since hydrogen bridging is quite important in the boranes.

In 1907 it was found that platinic chloride, $PtCl_4$, reacts with a methyl Grignard reagent to yield the so-called trimethylplatinum chloride. The corresponding bromide and iodide were also prepared. Curiously, no analogous compounds have ever been isolated with any other alkyl or aryl group. More recently $(CH_3)_4Pt$ has also been prepared. All of these compounds are tetrameric, and their structures (Fig. 11-6) are quite interesting. The $[(CH_3)_3PtX]_4$ compounds have halogen bridges, which are unusual in being between three metal atoms. Halogen bridges between two metal atoms are relatively common. However, the most startling structure is that of $[(CH_3)_4Pt]_4$ in which there are methyl bridges between three Pt atoms. The nature of the bridge bonding here can be formulated in a manner similar to that in the aluminum and beryllium methyls except that four-center bonds must be used. In $[(CH_3)_4Pt]_4$ the platinum atoms are too far apart for any effective Pt—Pt bonding, and this provides evi-

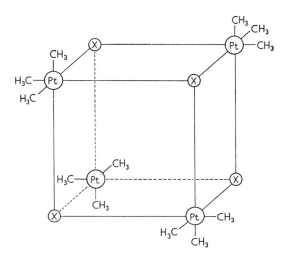

$\bigotimes$ = Halogen or CH_3

Fig. 11-6. Structure of the tetramers $[(CH_3)_3PtX]_4$ (X = Cl, Br, I, CH_3).

dence that methyl bridge bonding in itself can be strong enough to hold polymeric molecules of this sort together. Trimethylplatinum derivatives of β-diketones are also unusual in that it has been found that the "active methylene" group in the diketone can be bound to platinum. An example of this is the dimeric compound shown in Figure 30-19 (page 857) in which the platinum atom is octahedrally coordinated by three methyl groups, two oxygen atoms, and the carbon of the active methylene group of acetylacetone.

References

Brotherton, T. K., and J. W. Lynn, *Chem. Revs.*, **59**, 841 (1959). Cyanogen and its chemistry.

Coates, G. E., *Organometallic Compounds*, 2nd ed., Methuen, London, 1960. An excellent general text, but silicon, phosphorus, and arsenic compounds are not treated.

Croft, R. C., *Quart. Revs. (London)*, **14**, 1 (1960). Intercalation compounds of graphite.

Hall, H. Tracy, *J. Chem. Educ.*, **38**, 484 (1961). Review on the synthesis of diamonds.

Hennig, G. R., "Chemistry of Graphite Compounds," in F. A. Cotton, ed., *Progress in Inorganic Chemistry*, Vol. I, Interscience, New York–London, 1959, p. 125.

Kern, D. M., *J. Chem. Educ.*, **37**, 14 (1960). An excellent review on the hydration of CO_2, the CO_2–carbonate equilibrium and kinetics.

Rochow, E. G., O. T. Hurd, and R. N. Lewis, *The Chemistry of Organometallic Compounds*, Wiley, New York, 1957. A general survey.

Rüdorff, W., in H. J. Emeléus and A. G. Sharpe, eds., *Advances in Inorganic Chemistry and Radiochemistry*, Vol. 2, Academic Press, New York, 1959, p. 224. Chemistry of graphite compounds.

Ubbelohde, A. R. J. P., and F. A. Lewis, *Graphite and Its Crystal Compounds*, Oxford University Press, 1961.

Williams, H. E., *Cyanogen Compounds*, 2nd ed., Arnold, London, 1960. A detailed account of most C—N compounds including cyanides.

Metal-Organic Compounds (*Advances in Chemistry Series*, No. 23), American Chemical Society, Washington, D. C., 1959. A collection of papers on various aspects, technical and otherwise, such as preparation of organolithium compounds, organoboron compounds, organoaluminum compounds, etc.

Zeiss, H. H., ed., Organometallic Chemistry ACS Monograph No. 147 Reinhold, New York, 1960. A collection of review articles on metal-carbon bonding, vinylmetallics, organoaluminum compounds, and cyclopentadienyl metal compounds, transition metal alkyls, and metal carbonyls.

12

Nitrogen

GENERAL REMARKS

12-1. Introduction

The electronic structure of the nitrogen atom in its ground state is $1s^2 2s^2 2p^3$, with three $2p$ electrons distributed among the p_x, p_y, and p_z orbitals with spins unpaired. Nitrogen forms an exceedingly large number of compounds, most of which are to be considered organic rather than inorganic. In its compounds, nitrogen is one of the most electronegative elements, only oxygen and fluorine exceeding it in this respect.

The nitrogen atom has five valence electrons, and the completed octet can be achieved in several ways:

1. *Electron gain to form the nitride ion, N^{3-}.* This ion occurs only in the salt-like nitrides of the most electropositive elements, for example, Li_3N. Many other nitrides exist, but they are not ionic and do not contain the nitride ion. Nitrides in general are discussed later in this chapter.

2. *Formation of electron pair bonds.* The octet can be completed either by the formation of three single bonds, as in NH_3 or NF_3, or by multiple bond formation as in nitrogen itself, $:N:::N:$, azo compounds, $—\overset{..}{N}::\overset{..}{N}—$,

nitro compounds, $—N\diagup\!\!\!\!\overset{O}{\diagdown\!\!\!\!\diagdown O}$, etc.

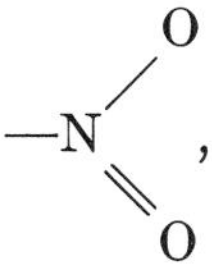

3. *Formation of electron pair bonds with electron gain.* The completed octet is achieved in this way in ions such as the amide ion, NH_2^-, and the imide ion, NH^{2-}.

4. *Formation of electron pair bonds with electron loss.* Nitrogen can form four bonds provided an electron is lost to give positively charged ions R_4N^+

such as NH_4^+, $N_2H_5^+$, and $(C_2H_5)_4N^+$. The ions are probably better regarded as being formed by the protonation of the lone pair,

$$H_3N : + H^+ = [NH_4]^+$$

or generally

$$R_3N : + R^+X^- = R_4N^+X^-$$

Failure to Achieve Octet. In NO and NO_2 there are an odd number of electrons. Consequently, it is impossible for all atoms to have complete octets. It is, of course, impossible to say that the odd electron is localized on one atom or another, but for the molecule as a whole there is at least one electron shell which is not closed; satisfactory valence descriptions are provided by molecular orbital theory.

Valence of Nitrogen. Compounds of nitrogen in all the possible formal oxidation states from -3 to $+5$ are known. In the chemistry of nitrogen, and in the chemistry of covalent compounds generally, the oxidation state concept is only a formalism, useful, for example, in balancing equations, but not to be taken literally. The various formal oxidation states arise *only* because of covalent bond formation by nitrogen, and there are no grounds whatever for considering nitrogen as a cation in the positive oxidation states or as an anion in the negative ones. The positive oxidation states are found only in oxygen and fluorine compounds (owing, of course, to the purely arbitrary convention that we allow only O and F to have negative oxidation states). Some examples are N_2O_5 ($+5$), NO_2 ($+4$), HNO_2 ($+3$), NO ($+2$), N_2O ($+1$), N_2 (0), NH_2OH (-1), N_2H_4 (-2), and NH_3 (-3).

12-2. Types of Covalence in Nitrogen; Stereochemistry

In common with other first row elements, nitrogen has only four orbitals available for bond formation, and a maximum of four bonds may be formed. However, since formation of three electron pair bonds completes the octet, $:N(:R)_3$, and the nitrogen atom then possesses a lone pair of electrons, four covalent bonds can only be formed by either (*a*) coordination, as in donor-acceptor complexes (e.g., $F_3\overset{-}{B}—\overset{+}{N}(CH_3)_3$) or in amine oxides (e.g., $(CH_3)_3\overset{+}{N}—\overset{-}{O}$), or (*b*) loss of an electron, as in ammonium ions. This loss of an electron gives a valence state configuration for nitrogen (as N^+) with four unpaired electrons in sp^3 hybrid orbitals analogous to that of neutral carbon, while, as noted above, gain of an electron (as in NH_2^-) leaves only two electrons for bond formation. In this case, the nitrogen atom (as N^-) is isoelectronic with the neutral oxygen atom, and angular bonds are formed. We can thus compare, sterically, the following isoelectronic species:

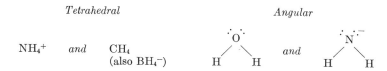

It may be noted that the ions NH_2^-, OH^-, and F^- are isoelectronic and have comparable sizes. The amide, imide, and nitride ions, which can be considered as members of the isoelectronic series NH_4^+, NH_3, NH_2^-, NH^{2-}, N^{3-}, occur as discrete ions only in salts of highly electropositive elements.

In all nitrogen compounds where the atom forms two or three bonds, there remain, respectively, two or one pair of nonbonding electrons, also called lone pairs. As will be discussed more generally in Chapter 15, these nonbonding electron pairs have a profound effect on the stereochemistry. Thus, the stereochemistry about an atom with a filled octet depends on the spatial distribution of *four* pairs of electrons, whether all four pairs are bonding electrons (as in CX_4) or not (as in NH_3, or NH_2^-, or H_2O). Furthermore, the lone pairs are responsible for the donor properties of the atom possessing them. To illustrate the important chemical consequences of nonbonding electron pairs in nitrogen chemistry, we shall consider one of the most important types of molecule, namely, NR_3, as exemplified by NH_3 and amines.

Three-Covalent Nitrogen. With only one known exception—$N(SiH_3)_3$, to be discussed later—molecules of this general type are invariably pyramidal. The bond angles vary depending on the groups attached to the nitrogen atom. In NH_3 the H—N—H angle is 106.75°, in NF_3 it is 102.5°, and in $(CH_3)_3N$ it is ~108°. If the N—X bonds were formed using pure $2p$ orbitals of nitrogen, as might have been expected from the electron configuration, $1s^2 2s^2 2p^3$, the bond angles would be more nearly 90°. Although in the past expansion of the angles from 90° has been attributed to repulsions between the groups bound to nitrogen, this effect is now known to be inadequate to explain the considerably larger angles which are found. It is more appropriate to consider that nitrogen uses hybrid orbitals. These will be approximately sp^3 tetrahedral hybrids, but, since the various bond angles differ from each other, and none is an exact tetrahedral angle, the hybrids are slightly different. The important point is that the lone pair electrons are not in a pure $2s$ orbital, as they would be if nitrogen used pure $2p$ orbitals for bonding. Thus, rather than being spherically distributed about the nitrogen nucleus, these electrons are in a hybrid orbital and are therefore concentrated in a definite region of space as shown in Figure 12-1.

Fig. 12-1. R_3N molecule showing the lone pair electron distribution.

This view also provides an explanation of the difference in dipole moments of NH_3 and NF_3 (see page 99). The availability of this lone pair, due to their being in the projecting hybrid orbital, also accounts for the fact that R_3N: molecules are good donors, both in compounds like $R_3\overset{+}{N}$—$\overset{-}{B}X_3$, where the "dative" bond is highly covalent, and in complexes such as $[Zn(NH_3)_4]^{2+}$, where the dative bond is predominantly electrostatic. Similarly, this concentration of negative charge in a restricted region about the nitrogen helps make hydrogen bonding in ammonia, H_2N—H····:NH_3, quite strong.

It is to be noted that in a pyramidal R_3N compound of the kind $NRR'R''$ there should exist nonsuperposable mirror images, that is, optically active isomers. No such optical isomers have ever been isolated, however, because molecules of this type have a mode of vibration known as inversion, in which the nitrogen atom oscillates through the plane of the three R groups, much as an umbrella can turn inside out. Inversion has been shown not to occur in solid ammonia since the lone pair is involved in hydrogen bonding to other molecules. In order for the nitrogen atom to cross from one side of the plane to the other (to go from one equilibrium position, say, $+r_0$, to the other, $-r_0$, in Figure 12-2a), the molecule goes through a state of higher potential energy, as shown in the potential energy curve (Fig. 12-2b). However, this "potential energy barrier" to inversion is only 6 kcal./mole, and the frequency of the oscillation is 2.387013×10^{10}

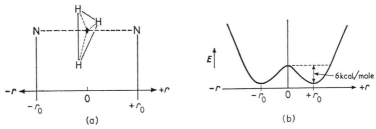

Fig. 12-2. Diagrams illustrating the inversion in NR_3 compounds (see text).

c.p.s. (cycles per second) in NH_3. A lower, but still very high, inversion frequency would be expected in any R_3N molecule, which explains why it is impossible to isolate any optical isomers. It has been estimated that a barrier of at least 20 kcal./mole would be necessary in order to make the rate of interconversion sufficiently slow.

Multiple Bonding in Nitrogen and Its Compounds. Like its neighbors carbon and oxygen, nitrogen readily forms multiple bonds, differing in this respect from its heavier congeners, P, As, Sb, and Bi. Nitrogen thus forms many compounds for which there are no analogs with the heavier elements. Thus, whereas phosphorus, arsenic, and antimony form tetrahedral molecules, P_4, As_4, Sb_4, nitrogen forms the multiple-bonded diatomic molecule $:N{\equiv}N:$, with an extremely short internuclear distance (1.094 A.) and very high bond strength. The multiple bonding in nitrogen has already been discussed in both the VB and MO approximations in Chapter 3. Nitrogen also forms triple bonds to carbon (in $-C{\equiv}N:$) and to oxygen (in $:\overset{\cdot}{N}{\equiv}O:$, the odd electron being in an antibonding orbital).

In compounds where nitrogen forms one single and one double bond, the grouping $X-\overset{\cdot\cdot}{N}{=}Y$ is nonlinear. This can be explained by assuming that nitrogen uses a set of sp^2 orbitals, two of which are used to form σ bonds to X and Y, while the third houses the lone pair. A π bond to Y is then formed using the nitrogen p_z orbital. In certain cases, stereoisomers result from the nonlinearity, for example, *cis*- and *trans*-azobenzenes (12-Ia and

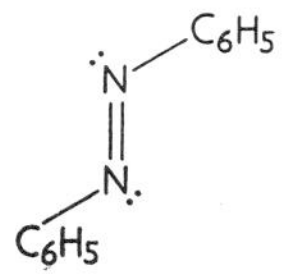

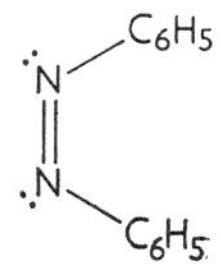

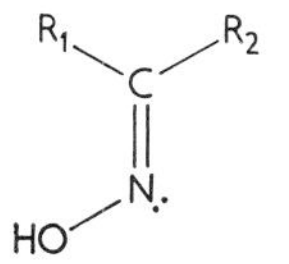

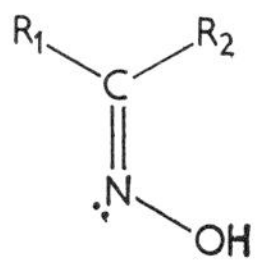

(12-Ia)   (12-Ib)   (12-IIa)   (12-IIb)

12-Ib) and the oximes 12-IIa and 12-IIb. These do not readily interconvert, although they do so more easily than do *cis* and *trans* olefins.

Multiple bonding occurs also in oxy compounds. For example, NO_2^- (12-III) and NO_3^- (12-IV) can be regarded as resonance hybrids in the

(12-IIIa)   (12-IIIb)

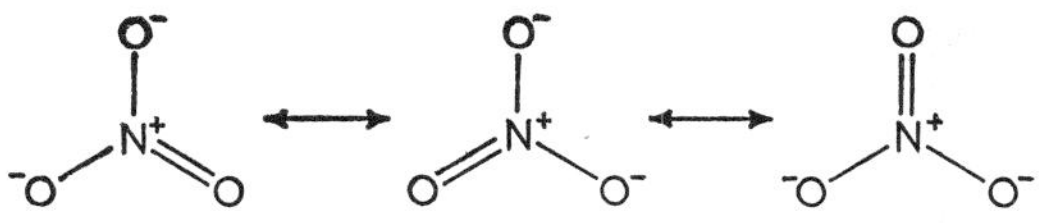

(12-IVa)   (12-IVb)   (12-IVc)

VB approach. From the MO viewpoint, one considers the existence of a π MO extending symmetrically over the entire ion and containing the two π electrons.

An unusual but significant case of multiple bonding occurs in trisilylamine, $N(SiH_3)_3$. This compound differs from trimethylamine (a) in being a very weak base (measured in terms of its ability to form donor-acceptor complexes; e.g., $(H_3Si)_3\overset{+}{N}{-}\overset{-}{B}F_3$ decomposes above $-40°C$.) and (b) in being *planar* rather than pyramidal. These observations can be explained by supposing that nitrogen forms dative π bonds to the silicon atoms. In the planar state of $N(SiH_3)_3$, the nonbonding electrons of nitrogen would occupy the $2p_z$ orbital, if we assume that the N—Si bonds are formed using sp_xp_y trigonal hybrid orbitals of nitrogen. Silicon has empty $3d$ orbitals, which are of low enough energy to be able to interact appreciably with the nitrogen $2p_z$ orbital. Thus, the N—Si π bonding is due to the kind of overlap indicated in Figure 12-3. It is the additional bond strength to be

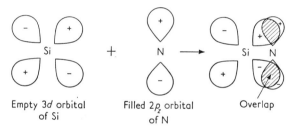

Empty $3d$ orbital of Si   Filled $2p_z$ orbital of N   Overlap

Fig. 12-3.   Formation of $d\pi-p\pi$ bond between Si and N in trisilylamine.

gained by this $p\pi{\rightarrow}d\pi$ bonding which causes the NSi_3 skeleton to take up a planar configuration, whereas with $N(CH_3)_3$, where the carbon has no low energy d orbitals, the σ bonding alone determines the configuration, which is pyramidal as expected. Another case of N—Si $p\pi{\rightarrow}d\pi$ bonding

$$H_3\overset{\frown}{Si} - N = C = S$$

(12-V)

occurs in silyl isothiocyanate (12-V), which has a linear Si—N—C—S grouping, whereas in $H_3C{-}\overset{..}{N}{=}C{=}S$ the C—$\overset{..}{N}$=C linkage is bent as would normally be expected. Tetrasilylhydrazine has been shown to be much less effective a donor than $(CH_3)_4N_2$; its structure is not completely certain, but appears to be a staggered one similar to gaseous B_2Cl_4.

Donor Properties of Three-Covalent Nitrogen; Four-Covalent Nitrogen.   As noted above, the formation of tetrahedral sp^3 (or approximately) bonds to nitrogen occurs in cations, R_4N^+, and in amine oxides,

$R_3\overset{+}{N}$—$\overset{-}{O}$; and the dipolar nature of NR_3 compounds has been discussed in terms of the occupancy of a hybrid orbital by the unshared pair, which confers donor properties on most R_3N: compounds. In donor-acceptor compounds, for example, $R_3\overset{+}{N}$—$\overset{-}{B}X_3$, the N—B bond is polar as indicated; the degree of polarity is influenced by the relative electronegativities of the donor and acceptor atoms, but some polarity will always exist because of the higher effective nuclear charge of the donor atom. Multiple bonds cannot be formed between the acceptor atom and nitrogen (regardless of the acceptor atom)—that is, no contribution of the form $X{=}N\overset{\diagup}{\underset{\diagdown}{}}$ is possible—in view of the strict limit of four covalence for nitrogen. This situation contrasts strongly with that for phosphorus and arsenic derivatives, for example, R_3P: and R_3As:, because these elements possess low-lying d orbitals that are capable of back acceptance from a suitable partner. Thus, the amine oxides can only be written $R_3\overset{+}{N}$—$\overset{-}{O}$, whereas the phosphine oxides have a considerable multiple bond character, and $R_3P{=}O$ represents a good approximation to the electronic structure.

Catenation. Unlike carbon and a few other elements, nitrogen has little tendency for catenation. N—N bonds are rather weak, the N—N bond energy in hydrazine being about 32 kcal./mole. There are a few types of compounds containing chains of three or more nitrogen atoms with some multiple bonds such as R_2N—N$=$NR_2, R_2N—N$=$N—NR_2, $RN{=}N$—$N(R)$—NR_2, $RN{=}N$—(R)—$N{=}NR$, and even $RN{=}N$—$N(R)$—N$=$N—$N(R)$—N$=$NR, where R represents an organic radical (some R's may be H, but known compounds contain only a few H's). There are also cyclic compounds containing rings with up to five consecutive nitrogen atoms. Many of these compounds are not particularly stable, and all are traditionally in the realm of organic chemistry.

Hydrogen Bonding. Since it is one of the most electronegative elements, nitrogen, along with oxygen, fluorine, and to a lesser extent, chlorine, extensively enters into hydrogen bond formation in its hydrogen compounds.

THE ELEMENT

12-3. Occurrence and Properties

Nitrogen occurs in nature mainly as the inert diatomic gas N_2 (m.p. 63.1°K., b.p. 77.3°K.), which comprises 78% by volume of the earth's atmosphere. Naturally occurring nitrogen consists of ^{14}N and ^{15}N with an absolute ratio $^{14}N/^{15}N = 272.0$. ^{15}N is often useful as an isotopic tracer, and it has been found possible to prepare nitric acid containing up to 99.8% ^{15}N by taking advantage of the preferential concentration of ^{15}N in HNO_3 in the system

$$^{15}NO(g) + H^{14}NO_3(aq) = {}^{14}NO(g) + H^{15}NO_3(aq)$$

The equilibrium distribution of ^{15}N favors HNO_3 by only a very minute fraction, owing to the extremely slight effect of the mass differences on the free energies of the two compounds. Thus, the exchange system operates so that the equilibration is carried automatically through thousands of stages in much the same way as two liquids with only a slight boiling point difference are separated by distillation through a fractionation column with thousands of theoretical plates. The $H^{15}NO_3$ produced can be used to prepare any desired ^{15}N-labeled nitrogen compound.

The heat of dissociation of nitrogen is extremely large:

$$N_2(g) = 2N(g) \qquad \Delta H = 225.8 \text{ kcal./mole}; K_{25°C.} = 10^{-120}$$

Because the reaction is endothermic, the equilibrium constant increases with increasing temperature, but still, even at 3000°C. and ordinary pressures, there is no appreciable dissociation. The great strength of the $N{\equiv}N$ bond is principally responsible for the chemical inertness of N_2 and for the fact that most simple nitrogen compounds are endothermic even though they may contain strong bonds. Nitrogen is notably unreactive when compared with other systems containing triple bonds, such as $X{-}C{\equiv}C{-}X$, $:C{\equiv}O:$, and $X{-}C{\equiv}N:$, because N_2 has (a) no polarity and (b) an appreciably higher ionization potential than these other systems. Thus, both $-C{\equiv}C-$ and $-C{\equiv}N$ groups are known to serve as donors by using their π electrons, and $:C{\equiv}O:$ functions as a donor (with reinforcement of the σ bond by back-bonding (see Chapter 27, page 614)) using the unshared electron pair on carbon. N_2 will do neither of these things, so far as is known.

Nitrogen is obtained commercially by liquefaction and fractionation of air; when so prepared it usually contains some argon and, depending on the quality, upwards of $\sim$30 p.p.m. of oxygen. The oxygen may be removed by admixing with a little hydrogen and treating with a platinum catalyst, by passing the gas over hot copper or other metal, or by bubbling through aqueous solutions of Cr^{2+} or V^{2+} ions. Spectroscopically pure nitrogen is best prepared by thermal decomposition of sodium or barium azides, for example,

$$2NaN_3 = 2Na + 3N_2$$

The only reactions of N_2 at room temperature are with metallic lithium to give Li_3N and with nitrogen-fixing bacteria, either free-living or symbiotic on root nodules of clover, peas, beans, etc. The mechanism by which these bacteria fix nitrogen is still completely unknown, although it is believed that the terminal reduction product is ammonia.

At elevated temperatures nitrogen becomes more reactive, especially when catalyzed, typical reactions being:

$$N_2(g) + 3H_2(g) = 2NH_3(g) \qquad K_{25°C.} = 10^3 \, atm.^{-2}$$
$$N_2(g) + O_2(g) = 2NO(g) \qquad K_{25°C.} = 5 \times 10^{-31}$$
$$N_2(g) + 3Mg(s) = Mg_3N_2(s)$$
$$N_2(g) + CaC_2(s) = C(s) + CaNCN(s)$$

Active nitrogen has been known for many years to result from passing discharges through nitrogen. This gas has a persistent golden-yellow afterglow and is chemically very reactive. After years of study and discussion, during which such species as an ozone-like N_3 were considered, it has recently been established by mass spectroscopic and other studies that active nitrogen contains nitrogen atoms in their ground state. Because of quantum restrictions these atoms recombine to produce N_2 only slowly, giving off the characteristic radiation.

NITROGEN COMPOUNDS

12-4. Nitrides

As with carbides, there are three general classes, although the nitrides have not been as extensively studied structurally.

Ionic nitrides are formed by Mg, Ca, Ba, Sr, Zn, Cd, Li, and Th. Their formulas correspond to what would result from combination of the normal metal ions with N^{3-} ions. So far as is known they are all essentially ionic compounds and are properly written as $Ca_3^{2+}N_2^{3-}$, $Li_3^+N^{3-}$, etc. Nitrides of the M_3N_2 type are often anti-isomorphous with M_2O_3-type oxides. This does not, however, necessarily mean that, like the oxides, they are ionic. However, their ready hydrolysis to ammonia and the metal hydroxides makes this seem likely. The ionic nitrides are prepared by direct union of the elements or by loss of ammonia from amides on heating, for example,

$$3Ba(NH_2)_2 \rightarrow Ba_3N_2 + 4NH_3$$

There are various covalent "nitrides"—BN, S_4N_4, P_3N_3, etc.—the properties of which vary greatly depending upon the element with which nitrogen is combined. Such substances are therefore discussed under the appropriate element.

The transition metals form interstitial nitrides that are analogous to the interstitial borides and carbides in their constitution and properties. The nitrogen atoms occupy interstices in the close-packed metal lattices. These nitrides are often not exactly stoichiometric (being nitrogen deficient), and they are metallic in appearance, hardness, and electrical conductivity, since the electronic band structure of the metal persists. Like the interstitial borides and carbides, they are chemically very inert, extremely hard, and very high melting. A representative compound, VN, melts at 2570°C. and has a hardness between 9 and 10. Interstitial nitrides are usually prepared by heating the metals in ammonia at 1100–1200°C.

12-5. Nitrogen Hydrides

Ammonia. On a laboratory scale, ammonia, NH_3, may be prepared either by treatment of an ammonium salt with a base

$$NH_4X + OH^- = NH_3 + H_2O + X^-$$

or by hydrolysis of an ionic nitride. The latter method provides a convenient way of preparing ND_3:

$$Mg_3N_2 + 6D_2O = 3Mg(OD)_2 + 2ND_3$$

On the industrial scale ammonia is obtained by the Haber process in which the reaction

$$N_2(g) + 3H_2(g) = 2NH_3(g) \qquad \Delta H = -11 \text{ kcal./mole}; K_{25°C.} = 10^3 \text{ atm.}^{-2}$$

is carried out in the presence of a catalyst at pressures of 10^2–10^3 atm. and temperatures of 400–550°C. Although the equilibrium is most favorable at low temperature, even with the best available catalysts (iron alloys) elevated temperatures are required to obtain a satisfactory rate of conversion.

Ammonia is a colorless pungent gas with a normal boiling point of -33.35°C. and a freezing point of -77.8°C. The liquid has a large heat of evaporation (327 cal./g. at the boiling point) and is therefore fairly easily handled in ordinary laboratory equipment. Liquid ammonia resembles water in its physical behavior, being highly associated because of the polar nature of the molecules and strong hydrogen bonding. Its dielectric constant ($\sim$22 at -34°C.; cf. 81 for H_2O at 25°C.) is sufficiently high to make it a fair ionizing solvent. A system of nitrogen chemistry with many analogies to the oxygen system based on water has been built up, the foundations being largely due to Franklin. Thus, we have the comparable self-ionization equilibria:

$$2NH_3 = NH_4^+ + NH_2^-   \quad K_{-50°C.} = [NH_4^+][NH_2^-] = \sim10^{-30}$$
$$2H_2O = H_3O^+ + OH^-   \quad K_{25°C.} = [H_3O^+][OH^-] = 10^{-14}$$

Table 12-1 presents a simple comparison of the ammonia and water systems.

TABLE 12-1

	Ammonia system		Water system	
	Class of compound	Example	Class of compound	Example
Acids	$NH_4^+X^-$	$NH_4^+Cl^-$	$H_3O^+X^-$	$H_3O^+Cl^-$
Bases	Amides	$Na^+NH_2^-$	Hydroxides	Na^+OH^-
	Imides	$Li_2^+NH^{2-}$	Oxides	$Li_2^+O^{2-}$, $Mg^{2+}O^{2-}$
	Nitrides	$Mg_3^{2+}N_2^{3-}$		

Liquid ammonia has lower reactivity toward electropositive metals than H_2O. Such metals generally react immediately with water to produce hydroxide, evolving hydrogen, although some alkali metals form blue solutions, but these are fleeting even at 0°C. Liquid ammonia, on the other hand, readily dissolves many electropositive metals (the alkali metals, Ca, Sr, Ba, and some of the lanthanide metals) to give blue solutions containing metal ions and solvated electrons (see also page 316). Such solutions are stable for long periods and are useful as powerful reducing agents. However, they do react slowly—or rapidly in the presence of catalysts such as transition metal salts—to liberate hydrogen, for example,

$$Na + NH_3 = NaNH_2 + \tfrac{1}{2}H_2$$

Chemical Reactions of Ammonia. Perhaps the two most important reactions of ammonia are those with oxygen and with water.

Ammonia will burn in pure oxygen but only under certain conditions. Normal combustion in air gives mainly water and oxygen according to equation 12-1. However, ammonia can be made to react with oxygen as

$$4NH_3(g) + 3O_2(g) = 2N_2 + 6H_2O \quad K_{25°C.} = 10^{228} \qquad (12\text{-}1)$$

shown in equation 12-2, despite the fact that the process of equation 12-1 is thermodynamically much more favorable. This is accomplished by

$$4NH_3 + 5O_2 = 4NO + 6H_2O \quad K_{25°C.} = 10^{168} \qquad (12\text{-}2)$$

carrying out the reaction at 750–900°C. in the presence of a platinum or platinum–rhodium catalyst which selectively catalyzes the second reaction. This process, known as the Ostwald process, is used industrially. It can easily be demonstrated in the laboratory by introducing a piece of glowing platinum foil into a jar containing gaseous NH_3 and O_2; the foil will continue to glow because of the heat of reaction 12-2, which occurs only on the surface of the metal, and brown fumes will appear owing to the reaction of NO with excess oxygen to produce NO_2. Industrially, the mixed oxides of nitrogen are then absorbed in water to form nitric acid:

$$2NO + O_2 = 2NO_2$$
$$3NO_2 + H_2O = 2HNO_3 + NO, \text{ etc.}$$

Thus, the sequence in industrial utilization of atmospheric nitrogen is as follows:

$$N_2 \xrightarrow[\substack{\text{Haber} \\ \text{process}}]{H_2} NH_3 \xrightarrow[\substack{\text{Ostwald} \\ \text{process}}]{O_2} NO \xrightarrow{O_2 + H_2O} HNO_3(aq)$$

Ammonia is extremely soluble in water. It is possible to isolate two stable crystalline hydrates at low temperatures, $NH_3 \cdot H_2O$(m.p. 194.15°K.) and $2NH_3 \cdot H_2O$ (m.p. 194.32°K.), in which the NH_3 and H_2O molecules are linked by hydrogen bonds. The substances contain neither NH_4^+ and OH^- ions nor discrete NH_4OH molecules. Thus, $NH_3 \cdot H_2O$ has chains of H_2O molecules linked by hydrogen bonds (2.76 A.). These chains are cross linked by NH_3 into a three-dimensional lattice by OH····N (2.78 A.) and O····H—N bonds (3.21–3.29 A.). In aqueous solution ammonia is probably hydrated in a similar manner. Although aqueous solutions are commonly referred to as solutions of the weak base NH_4OH, called "ammonium hydroxide," this is to be discouraged, since there is no evidence that undissociated NH_4OH exists and there is reason to believe that it probably does not. Solutions of ammonia are best described as NH_3(aq), with the equilibrium written as

$$NH_3(aq) + H_2O = NH_4^+ + OH^- \quad K_{25°C.} = \frac{[NH_4^+][OH^-]}{[NH_3]} = 1.81 \times 10^{-5} (pK_b = 4.75)$$

In an odd sense NH_4OH might be considered a *strong* base since it is completely dissociated in water. A $1N$ solution of NH_3 is only $0.0042N$ in NH_4^+ and OH^-.

Nuclear magnetic resonance measurements show that the hydrogen atoms of NH_3 readily exchange with those of water by the process

$$H_2O + NH_3 = OH^- + NH_4^+$$

but there is no exchange in the vapor phase or in the liquid if water is completely removed.

Ammonium Salts. There are many rather stable crystalline salts of the NH_4^+ ion; most of them are water soluble like alkali metal salts. Salts of strong acids are fully ionized, and the solutions are slightly acidic:

$$NH_4Cl = NH_4^+ + Cl^- \quad K \approx \infty$$
$$NH_4^+ + H_2O = NH_3 + H_3O^+ \quad K_{25°C.} = 5.5 \times 10^{-10}$$

Thus, a $1M$ solution will have a pH of ~ 4.7. The constant for the second reaction is sometimes called the hydrolysis constant; however, it may equally well be considered as the acidity constant of the cationic acid NH_4^+, and the system regarded as an acid–base system in the following sense:

$$NH_4^+ + H_2O = H_3O^+ + NH_3(aq)$$
$$\text{Acid} \quad \text{Base} \quad \text{Acid} \quad \text{Base}$$

Ammonium salts generally resemble those of potassium and rubidium in solubility and, except where hydrogen bonding effects are important, in structure, since the three ions are of comparable radii: $NH_4^+ = 1.43$ A., $K^+ = 1.33$ A., $Rb^+ = 1.48$ A. The ammonium ion is, of course, tetrahedral.

Many ammonium salts volatilize with dissociation around 300°C., for example,

$$NH_4Cl(s) = NH_3(g) + HCl(g) \quad \Delta H = 42.3 \text{ kcal./mole}; K_{25°C.} = 10^{-16}$$

Some salts which contain oxidizing anions decompose on heating, with oxidation of the ammonia to N_2O or N_2 or both. For example:

$$NH_4NO_3(s) = NH_3(g) + HNO_3(g) \qquad \Delta H = \quad 44.2 \text{ kcal./mole}; K_{25°C.} = 10^{-16}$$
$$\text{(12-3)}$$
$$NH_4NO_3(s) = N_2(g) + 2H_2O(g) + \tfrac{1}{2}O_2(g) \quad \Delta H = -28.3 \text{ kcal./mole}; K_{25°C.} = 10^{48}$$
$$\text{(12-4)}$$
$$NH_4NO_3(s) = N_2O(g) + 2H_2O(g) \qquad \Delta H = -8.84 \text{ kcal./mole}; K_{25°C.} = 10^{30}$$
$$\text{(12-5)}$$

At low temperatures NH_3 and HNO_3 are formed reversibly; at higher temperatures irreversible decomposition occurs exothermically, giving mainly N_2O, although some N_2 and HNO_3 are formed, the latter catalyzing the decomposition of the nitrate under some conditions. Ammonium nitrate in bulk has been known to explode spontaneously; when it is used in explosives, the operative reaction is 12-4.

Derivatives of Ammonia. There are an enormous number of compounds which can be considered as derived from ammonia by replacement of hydrogen atoms with other organic and inorganic radicals. Most of them, such as amines and amides, are properly considered as organic compounds and will not concern us further here. We may note, however, that tetra-alkylammonium cations, R_4N^+, are often of use in inorganic chemistry where large, univalent cations are required. They are prepared generally by the following reaction:

$$R_3N + RI = R_4N^+I^-$$

and I^- may be replaced with the anion of interest in various metathetical reactions. Some important "inorganic" derivatives of ammonia are discussed in succeeding sections.

Hydrazine. Hydrazine, N_2H_4, may be thought of as derived from ammonia by replacement of a hydrogen atom by the —NH_2 group. It might therefore be expected to be a base, but somewhat weaker than NH_3, which is the case. Of course, it is a bifunctional base:

$$N_2H_4(aq) + H_2O = N_2H_5^+ + OH^- \qquad K_{25°C.} = 8.5 \times 10^{-7}$$
$$N_2H_5^+(aq) + H_2O = N_2H_6^{2+} + OH^- \qquad K_{25°C.} = 8.9 \times 10^{-16}$$

Anhydrous N_2H_4 (m.p. 2°C., b.p. 114°C.) is a fuming colorless liquid with a high dielectric constant ($\epsilon = 52$ at 25°). It is surprisingly stable in view of its endothermic nature:

$$N_2(g) + 2H_2(g) = N_2H_4(l) \qquad \Delta H_f° = 12.0 \text{ kcal./mole}$$

It will burn in air, however, with considerable evolution of heat

$$N_2H_4(l) + O_2(g) = N_2(g) + 2H_2O(l) \qquad \Delta H = 148.6 \text{ kcal./mole}$$

which accounts for a recent upsurge of interest in it and certain of its alkylated derivatives as potential rocket fuels.

Two series of hydrazinium salts are obtainable, those of $N_2H_5^+$ and those of $N_2H_6^{2+}$. The former are stable in aqueous solution, simply ionizing to $N_2H_5^+$ and X^-, whereas, owing to the low value of K_2 for N_2H_4, the latter are immediately hydrolyzed (cf. hydrolysis of sulfides, for example, Na_2S):

$$N_2H_6X_2 + H_2O = N_2H_5^+ + H_3O^+ + 2X^- \qquad K = 11$$

However, the diacid salts can be obtained by crystallization from aqueous solution containing a large excess of the acid, since they are usually less soluble than the monoacid salts.

As another consequence of its basicity, hydrazine, like NH_3, can form coordination complexes with both Lewis acids and metal ions. Just as with respect to the proton, electrostatic considerations (and in these cases, also steric considerations) militate against bifunctional behavior. Although some polymeric complexes having hydrazine bridges (12-VI) have been postulated, generally only one nitrogen atom is coordinated.

(12–VI)

Aqueous hydrazine is a powerful reducing agent in basic solution; one reaction which is quantitative with some oxidants (e.g., I_2) is

$$4OH^- + N_2H_4(aq) = N_2 + 4H_2O + 4e \qquad E° = +1.16 \text{ v.}$$

However, NH_3 and HN_3 are also obtained under various conditions. Air and oxygen, especially when catalyzed by polyvalent metal ions in basic solution, produce hydrogen peroxide:

$$2O_2 + N_2H_4(aq) = 2H_2O_2(aq) + N_2$$

but further reaction will occur in presence of metal ions:

$$N_2H_4 + 2H_2O_2 = N_2 + 4H_2O$$

In acid solution, hydrazine can reduce halogens:

$$N_2H_4(aq) + 2X_2 = 4HX + N_2$$

The *preparation* of hydrazine has been the subject of much study. Many reactions produce it in small amounts under certain conditions, for example,

$$N_2 + 2H_2 = N_2H_4$$
$$N_2O + 2NH_3 = N_2H_4 + H_2O + N_2$$
$$2NH_3(g) + \tfrac{1}{2}O_2 = N_2H_4 + H_2O$$
$$N_2O + 3H_2 = N_2H_4 + H_2O$$

However, none of these has ever been developed into a practical method because there are competing, and thermodynamically more favorable, reactions, such as

$$2NH_3 + \tfrac{3}{2}O_2 = N_2 + 3H_2O$$
$$2NH_3 + 3N_2O = 4N_2 + 3H_2O$$
$$N_2O + H_2 = N_2 + H_2O$$

These are good illustrations of the effect of the great stability of N_2 on nitrogen chemistry.

The only practical method for preparing hydrazine in quantity, especially on a commercial scale, is the Raschig synthesis, discovered in the first decade of this century. The over-all reaction, carried out in aqueous solution, is

$$2NH_3 + NaOCl = N_2H_4 + NaCl + H_2O$$

Actually, the reaction proceeds in two steps. The first one, which is fast, produces chloramine, NH_2Cl:

$$NH_3 + NaOCl = NaOH + NH_2Cl \qquad (12\text{-}6)$$

The chloramine then reacts slowly with further ammonia:

$$NH_3 + NH_2Cl + NaOH = N_2H_4 + NaCl + H_2O \qquad (12\text{-}7)$$

However, there is a competing and parasitic reaction which is rather fast once some hydrazine has been formed:

$$2NH_2Cl + N_2H_4 = 2NH_4Cl + N_2 \qquad (12\text{-}8)$$

In order to obtain appreciable yields, it is necessary, as Raschig discovered, to add some gelatinous material, usually glue or gelatin, to the reaction mixture. It is now known that this serves two essential purposes. First, it sequesters heavy metal ions which catalyze reaction 12-8 at the expense of 12-7. Even the part per million or so of Cu^{2+} in ordinary water will almost completely prevent the formation of hydrazine if no catalyst is used. However, although addition of simple sequestering agents (e.g., ethylenediaminetetraacetic acid), in the absence of glue or gelatin, was shown to be beneficial, it was found that the glue or gelatin must serve a second function, namely, to catalyze reaction 12-7 but not 12-8. Under proper conditions, yields of 60–70% are obtained. By distillation hydrazine is obtained as a dilute aqueous solution which may be concentrated to ∼85% by further distillation. From this solution anhydrous hydrazine may be obtained by further distillation over NaOH or KOH. Alternatively, hydrazine sulfate, $N_2H_6SO_4$, may be precipitated from the dilute solution obtained in the Raschig process. On treating this with liquid ammonia, ammonium sulfate is almost quantitatively precipitated

$$N_2H_6SO_4 + 2NH_3 = N_2H_4 + (NH_4)_2SO_4$$

and the hydrazine is easily obtained by stripping the ammonia after filtration.

Structurally, hydrazine resembles hydrogen peroxide. From the fact that the molecule has a dipole moment of about 1.85 Debye units, the *trans* structure must be ruled out. The equilibrium configuration is probably the *gauche* form (Fig. 12-4b); a completely eclipsed form seems unlikely, al-

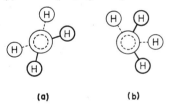

(a)   (b)

Fig. 12-4.   Structure of hydrazine (see text).

though it has not been positively disproved. The N—N distance is 1.47 ± 0.02 A., the N—H distance ∼1.04 A., and the HNH and NNH angles ∼110°.

Hydrazoic Acid and Azides.   Although hydrazoic acid, HN_3, is a hydride of nitrogen in a formal sense, it has no essential relationship to NH_3 and N_2H_4. The sodium salt is prepared by the reactions

$$3NaNH_2(l) + NaNO_3 \xrightarrow{175°C.} NaN_3 + 3NaOH + NH_3$$
$$2NaNH_2(l) + N_2O(g) \xrightarrow{190°C.} NaN_3 + NaOH + NH_3$$

while the free acid can be obtained in solution by the reaction

$$N_2H_5^+ + HNO_2 \xrightarrow{aq. soln.} HN_3 + H^+ + 2H_2O$$

Many other oxidizing agents attack hydrazine to form small amounts of HN_3 or azides. Free hydrazoic acid, obtainable by distillation from aqueous solutions, is a colorless liquid, boiling at 37°C., and "fearfully and dangerously explosive." In water it is a weak acid ($K_{25°C.} = 1.8 \times 10^{-5}$). Azides of many metals are known. Salts of heavy metals are generally explosive; those of Pb, Hg, and Ba explode on being struck sharply and are used in detonation caps. Azides of electropositive metals are not explosive and, in fact, decompose smoothly and quantitatively when heated to 300°C. or higher, for example,

$$2NaN_3(s) = 2Na(l) + 3N_2(g)$$

Azide ion also functions as a ligand in complexes of transition metals. In general, N_3^- behaves rather like a halide ion and is commonly considered as a pseudohalide, although the corresponding pseudohalogen $(N_3)_2$ is not known.

The azide ion itself is symmetrical and linear (N—N distance 1.16 A.), and its electronic structure may be represented in valence bond theory as:

$$: \overset{..}{\underset{..}{N}} : : \overset{+}{N} : : \overset{..}{\underset{..}{N}} : \quad \leftrightarrow \quad : N : : : \overset{+}{N} : \overset{2-}{\underset{..}{N}} : \quad \leftrightarrow \quad : \overset{2-}{\underset{..}{N}} : \overset{+}{N} : : : N :$$

In covalent azides, on the other hand, the symmetry is lost as is evident in

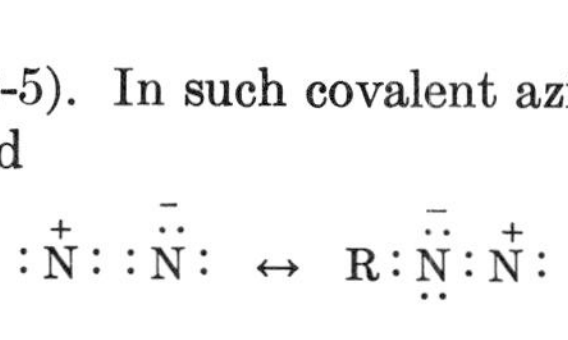

Fig. 12-5.   Structure of HN_3 and CH_3N_3.

HN_3 and CH_3N_3 (Fig. 12-5). In such covalent azides the electronic structure is a resonance hybrid

$$R : \overset{..}{\underset{..}{N}} : : \overset{+}{N} : : \overset{..}{\underset{..}{N}} : \quad \leftrightarrow \quad R : \overset{..}{\underset{..}{N}} : \overset{+}{N} : : : N :$$

Hydroxylamine. As hydrazine may be thought of as derived from ammonia by replacement of one hydrogen by NH_2, so hydroxylamine, NH_2OH, is obtained by replacement of H by OH. Like hydrazine, hydroxylamine is a weaker base than NH_3:

$$NH_2OH(aq) + H_2O = NH_3OH^+ + OH^- \qquad K_{25°C.} = 6.6 \times 10^{-9}$$

Hydroxylamine is prepared by reduction of nitrates or nitrites either electrolytically or with SO_2. In order to obtain good yields by either method, conditions of reaction must be very closely controlled. Free hydroxylamine is a white solid (m.p. 33°C.) which must be kept on ice to avoid decomposition. It is normally encountered as an aqueous solution and in the form of its salts, especially $[NH_3OH]Cl$, $[NH_3OH]NO_3$, and $[NH_3OH]_2SO_4$, which are stable, water-soluble, white solids. Although hydroxylamine can serve as either an oxidizing or a reducing agent, it is usually used as the latter. It has properties which, in many ways, lie between those of ammonia, H_2N—H, and water, H—OH, as its formula, H_2N—OH, might suggest. It can serve as a ligand in complexes (e.g., $Zn(NH_2OH)_2Cl_2$), probably coordinating through nitrogen.

12-6. Oxides of Nitrogen

The known oxides of nitrogen are listed in Table 12-2.

TABLE 12-2

Oxides of Nitrogen

Formula	Name	Color	Remarks
N_2O	Nitrous oxide	Colorless	Rather unreactive
NO	Nitric oxide	Gas, colorless; liquid and solid, blue	Moderately reactive
N_2O_3	Dinitrogen trioxide	Blue solid	Extensively dissociated as gas
NO_2	Nitrogen dioxide	Brown	Rather reactive
N_2O_4	Dinitrogen tetroxide	Colorless	Extensively dissociated to NO_2 as gas and partly as liquid
N_2O_5	Dinitrogen pentoxide	Colorless	Unstable as gas; ionic solid
NO_3; N_2O_6	—	—	Not well characterized and quite unstable

Nitrous Oxide. Nitrous oxide, N_2O, can be obtained by thermal decomposition of ammonium nitrate

$$NH_4NO_3 = N_2O + 2H_2O$$

or hydroxylamine. The former method is often employed since the only contaminant other than water (removable with a cold trap) is NO, which can be removed by passage through ferrous sulfate solution. The gas is also produced in the reduction of nitrites and nitrates under certain conditions and by decomposition of hyponitrites.

Nitrous oxide is relatively unreactive, being inert to the halogens, alkali metals, and ozone at room temperature. At higher temperatures it decomposes to nitrogen and oxygen, reacts with alkali metals and many organic compounds, and will support combustion. It has a moderate solubility in cream, and, apart from its anesthetic role, its chief commercial use is as the propellant gas in "whipped" cream bombs.

Its structure is well established; it has a linear NNO grouping and can be considered as a resonance hybrid,

$$:\overset{..}{\underset{}{N}}::\overset{+}{N}::\overset{..}{O}: \leftrightarrow :N:::\overset{+}{N}:\overset{..}{O}:$$

Nitric Oxide. Nitric oxide, NO, is formed in many reactions involving reduction of nitric acid and solutions of nitrates and nitrites. For example, with $8N$ nitric acid:

$$8HNO_3 + 3Cu = 3Cu(NO_3)_2 + 4H_2O + 2NO$$

For laboratory preparation of reasonably pure NO a very suitable reaction is the following:

$$2NaNO_2 + 2FeSO_4 + 3H_2SO_4 = Fe_2(SO_4)_3 + 2NaHSO_4 + 2H_2O + 2NO$$

Commercially it is obtained by catalytic oxidation of ammonia as already noted. Direct combination of the elements occurs only at very high temperatures, and in order to isolate the small amounts so formed (a few volume per cent at 3000°C.) the equilibrium mixture must be rapidly chilled. Although this reaction has been much studied, it has not been developed into a practical commercial synthesis.

Nitric oxide is an odd molecule in that it has an unpaired electron. However, its behavior is atypical for an odd molecule since it is not colored (although in the liquid and solid phases it has a blue color) and the molecules do not show a *marked* tendency to associate via electron pairing. The high Trouton constant (27) indicates that *some* association occurs in the liquid, and the solid has been found to consist of loose dimers with the structure shown in Figure 12-6.

Fig. 12-6.   Structure of nitric oxide dimer.

Not unrelated to the fact that, for an odd molecule, NO is relatively stable and unreactive is its unusual magnetic behavior. This stems from a combination of factors not found in any other case. The odd electron has an orbital momentum of one unit about the molecular axis. The spin momentum of one-half may couple either with or against this orbital momentum, yielding a ground state which is diamagnetic or an excited state which is paramagnetic. It happens that the energy difference between these states is only 352 cal./mole, whereas kT at room temperature is $\sim$600 cal./mole. In fact, down to quite low temperatures kT is greater than or comparable with this separation so that the distribution of molecules between the diamagnetic and paramagnetic states is markedly influenced by temperature, and the molecule *appears* to have a temperature-dependent magnetic moment. The diamagnetism of the solid at low temperatures does not, therefore, imply the existence of strong *inter*molecular spin coupling.

Among the important chemical reactions of nitric oxide are those of oxidation and reduction. It reacts instantly with oxygen, forming brown NO_2:

$$2NO + O_2 = 2NO_2$$

Thus, it must be handled out of contact with air. It reacts with F_2, Cl_2, and Br_2 but not I_2 to give the nitrosyl halides XNO (see page 267). It is oxidized to nitric acid by several strong oxidizing agents; the reaction with permanganate is quantitative and provides a method of analysis. It is reduced to N_2O by SO_2 and to NH_2OH by chromous ion in acid solution.

Although the electronic structure of NO may be considered in the valence bond theory as a resonance hybrid (12-VII), with 12-VIIa predominating, it is advantageous to use molecular orbital theory in this case.

$$: \overset{\cdot}{N} : : \overset{\cdot\cdot}{O} : \leftrightarrow : \overset{-}{\underset{}{N}} : : \overset{+}{\underset{}{O}} :$$

(12-VIIa)   (12-VIIb)

NO contains one more electron than does N_2, and according to simple MO theory (pages 74–80) this extra electron occupies an antibonding π MO. The consequences of this are (a) that the theoretical bond order is 2.5 (0.5 less than the 3 for nitrogen), which agrees fairly well with the observed bond distance of 1.14 A. (estimated for double and triple bonds 1.18 and 1.06 A., respectively), (b) that removal of this electron ought not to be too difficult, and (c) that the NO^+ ion produced should have a stronger N—O bond than does NO itself. In fact, the ionization potential of 9.5 e.v. is appreciably lower than for similar molecules (e.g., N_2, CO), and the stronger N—O bond is evidenced by an N—O stretching frequency of 2200 cm.$^{-1}$ in NO^+ as compared to 1840 cm.$^{-1}$ in NO.

The theoretical prediction that the *nitrosonium ion*, NO^+, should be readily formed is abundantly confirmed experimentally, and the ion has an extensive and interesting chemistry which can be only briefly summarized here. When N_2O_3 or N_2O_4 is dissolved in concentrated sulfuric acid, the ion is formed:

$$N_2O_3 + 3H_2SO_4 = 2NO^+ + 3HSO_4^- + H_3O^+$$
$$N_2O_4 + 3H_2SO_4 = NO^+ + NO_2^+ + 3HSO_4^- + H_3O^+$$

The compound $NO^+HSO_4^-$, nitrosonium bisulfate, is an isolable compound which is an important intermediate in the lead chamber process for manufacture of sulfuric acid. That it has the salt-like constitution indicated has been shown by electrolysis, conductivity studies, and cryoscopic measurements. The compounds $NO^+ClO_4^-$ and $NO^+BF_4^-$, both isostructural with the corresponding ammonium and H_3O^+ compounds, are known as well as a host of others such as $(NO)_2PtCl_6$, $NOFeCl_4$, $NOAsF_6$, $NOSbF_6$, and $NOSbCl_6$. Many may be made in the following general way, using a nitrosyl halide,

$$ClNO + SbCl_5 = NO^+SbCl_6^-$$

All such salts are readily hydrolyzed

$$NO^+ + H_2O = H^+ + HNO_2$$

and must be prepared and handled under anhydrous conditions.

The NO^+ ion is isoelectronic with CO, and, like CO, but to a somewhat lesser extent and sometimes under somewhat different conditions, will form bonds to metals. Thus, for example, analogous to nickel carbonyl, $Ni(CO)_4$, there is the isoelectronic $Co(CO)_3NO$. These transition metal nitrosyl complexes are discussed in more detail later (Section 27-6), but we may note here that the compound responsible for the brown ring in the test for nitrates is a nitrosyl complex of iron(I) with the formula $[Fe^I(H_2O)_5NO]^{2+}$.

Dinitrogen Trioxide. This oxide, N_2O_3, exists pure only in the solid state at low temperatures; in the liquid and vapor it is largely dissociated:

$$N_2O_3(g) = NO(s) + NO_2(g)$$

The oxide is formally the anhydride of nitrous acid, and dissolution of an equimolar mixture of NO and NO_2 in alkalies gives virtually pure nitrite. Nitrogen tracer studies have shown rapid exchange between NO and NO_2 consistent with the above equilibrium. Condensation of gaseous NO + NO_2 gives N_2O_3 as a blue liquid which freezes to a blue solid. It can be made by the action of As_2O_3 on HNO_3. The solid is believed to have two forms, an unstable one of structure ONONO and the other with an N—N bond.

Nitrogen Dioxide and Dinitrogen Tetroxide. These two oxides, NO_2 and N_2O_4, are in a strongly temperature-dependent equilibrium:

$$2NO_2 \quad = \quad N_2O_4$$

Brown	Colorless
Paramagnetic	Diamagnetic

In the solid state, the oxide is wholly N_2O_4; in the liquid, partial dissociation occurs and we can consider the liquid (m.p. $-11.2°C.$) as a dilute solution of NO_2 in N_2O_4; in the vapor at $100°C.$, the composition is $90\%\ NO_2$, $10\%\ N_2O_4$.

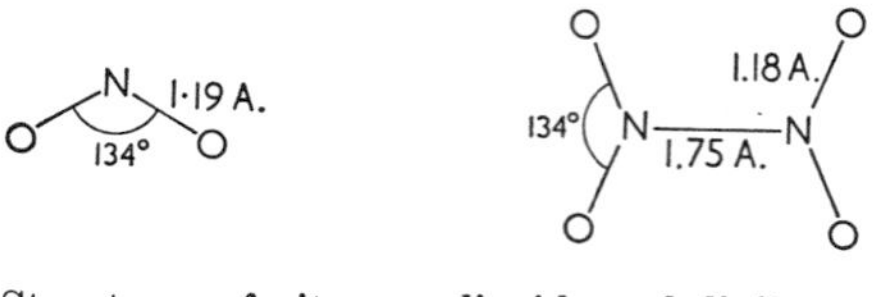

Fig. 12-7.   Structures of nitrogen dioxide and dinitrogen tetroxide.

The monomer has an angular structure, whereas the dimer is planar in all three phases (Fig. 12-7). The structure of N_2O_4 is surprising. The NO_2 fragments scarcely differ in their dimensions from NO_2 itself. Moreover, although the N—N bond is extraordinarily long (N—N distance in hydrazine 1.47 A.), there is evidence that the equilibrium configuration of the molecule is planar with a rather high barrier to internal rotation. This last fact is difficult to reconcile with the existence of an N—N σ bond, and it has been suggested that the N—N bond is a π bond. However, since π bonds without accompanying σ bonds are otherwise unknown, and it is no easier to see why a π bond should be so very long, the bonding here must be considered something of a puzzle. NO_2 itself is an odd molecule, but here its properties, color, and ready dimerization to colorless and diamagnetic N_2O_4 are what would be expected for an odd molecule. NO_2 can also lose its odd electron fairly readily to give NO_2^+, the *nitronium ion*, of which more will be said below.

The mixed oxides are obtained by heating metal nitrates, for example,

$$Pb(NO_3)_2 = PbO + 2NO_2$$

by oxidation of nitric oxide in air, and by reduction of nitric acid and nitrates by metals and other reducing agents. The gases are highly toxic and attack metals rapidly. They react with water,

$$2NO_2 + H_2O = HNO_3 + HNO_2$$

the nitrous acid decomposing, particularly on warming

$$3HNO_2 = HNO_3 + 2NO + H_2O$$

The oxides are fairly strong oxidizing agents comparable in strength to bromine:

$$2HNO_2 = N_2O_4 + 2H^+ + 2e \qquad E^0 = -1.07\ v.$$

The mixed oxides, "nitrous fumes," are used in organic chemistry as selective oxidizing agents.

Dinitrogen tetroxide has been extensively studied as a nonaqueous solvent. The electrical conductivity of the liquid is quite low. It forms molecular addition compounds with a great variety of nitrogen, oxygen, and aromatic donor compounds. Systems involving liquid N_2O_4 mixed with an organic solvent are often very reactive; for example, they dissolve relatively noble metals to form nitrates, often solvated with N_2O_4. Thus copper reacts vigorously with N_2O_4 in ethyl acetate to give crystalline $Cu(NO_3)_2 \cdot N_2O_4$, from which anhydrous, volatile (at 150–200°C.) cupric nitrate is obtained (see page 755). Some of the compounds obtained in this way may be formulated as nitrosonium salts, for example, $Zn(NO_3)_2 \cdot 2N_2O_4$ as $(NO^+)_2[Zn(NO_3)_4]^{2-}$, although conclusive proof of such structures is lacking.

In anhydrous acids, N_2O_4 dissociates ionically, as in H_2SO_4 above, and in anhydrous HNO_3 almost completely:

$$N_2O_4 = NO^+ + NO_3^-$$

The dissociation in H_2SO_4 is complete in dilute solution; at higher concentrations undissociated N_2O_4 is present, and at very high concentrations nitric acid is formed:

$$N_2O_4 + 3H_2SO_4 = NO^+HSO_4^- + HNO_3 + HSO_4^- + SO_3 + H_3O^+$$

The $NOHSO_4$ actually crystallizes out. The detailed mechanism and intermediates are undoubtedly complex, and the system is not yet completely unraveled.

Dinitrogen Pentoxide. This oxide, N_2O_5, which forms colorless crystals, is usually obtained by dehydration of nitric acid with P_2O_5; the oxide is not too stable (sometimes exploding) and is distilled in a current of ozonized oxygen.

$$2HNO_3 + P_2O_5 = 2HPO_3 + N_2O_5$$

It is, conversely, the anhydride of nitric acid:

$$N_2O_5 + H_2O = 2HNO_3$$

It is deliquescent, readily producing nitric acid by the above reaction. The gaseous compound probably has structure 12-VIII, and N—O—N π

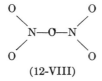

(12-VIII)

bonding would be expected to favor a completely planar configuration, but the structure is not completely certain.

In the solid, "N_2O_5" is $NO_2^+NO_3^-$, that is, nitronium nitrate. From study of this substance it is found that the nitronium ion is linear and symmetrical with the N—O distance equal to 1.154 A. (cf. CO_2 which is isoelectronic, linear, and symmetrical, with C—O distance of 1.163 A.). The nitrate ion, as in common nitrates, is symmetrical and planar.

As with N_2O_4, ionic dissociation occurs in anhydrous H_2SO_4, HNO_3, or H_3PO_4 to produce NO_2^+, for instance,

$$N_2O_5 + 3H_2SO_4 = 2NO_2^+ + 3HSO_4^- + H_3O^+$$

Other Oxides. The oxides NO_3 and N_2O_6 have been reported as products of the reaction of O_3 with N_2O_5 and F_2 with HNO_3, respectively. There is some spectroscopic and chemical evidence for their existence, but they have not been isolated.

12-7. Oxy Acids of Nitrogen

Hyponitrous Acid. Hyponitrites, the salts of hyponitrous acid, $H_2N_2O_2$, are formed by treating NH_2OH with amyl nitrite in ethanol containing $NaOC_2H_5$. Reduction of nitrites with sodium amalgam also gives hyponitrites. The silver salt is insoluble in water, and the ion is commonly isolated as the silver salt. The sodium salt and also the free acid can be obtained as white crystals, the latter from the silver salt on treatment with HCl in ether. The acid is weak and decomposes in the solid and in solution to give N_2O. Hyponitrites of the alkalies react with CO_2 to give N_2O.

Infrared spectra of the silver, sodium, and mercury hyponitrites have shown that the anion has the *trans* configuration (12-IX).

$$\left[\begin{array}{c} O \\ \diagup \\ N=N \\ \diagup \\ O \end{array} \diagdown O \right]^{2-}$$

(12-IX)

Hyponitrites undergo various oxidation-reduction reactions in acid and alkaline solutions, depending on conditions; they usually behave as reducing agents, however.

There is a compound called *nitramide*, which is also a weak acid ($K_{25°C} = 2.6 \times 10^{-7}$) and is an isomer of hyponitrous acid. Its structure has been shown to be 12-X.

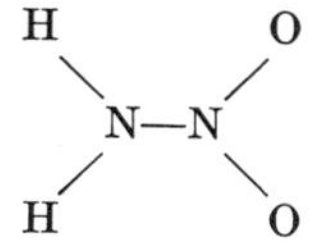

$$\begin{matrix} H & & O \\ & \diagdown & \diagup \\ & N\!\!-\!\!N & \\ & \diagup & \diagdown \\ H & & O \end{matrix}$$

(12-X)

Nitrous Acid. Solutions of nitrous acid, HNO_2, are easily made by acidifying solutions of nitrites. The aqueous solution can be obtained free of salts by the reaction

$$Ba(NO_2)_2 + H_2SO_4 = 2HNO_2 + BaSO_4 \downarrow$$

Nitrous acid is a weak acid with a dissociation constant at 25°C. of 6.0 × 10^{-6}. The free liquid acid is unknown, although the acid can be obtained in the vapor phase; the *trans* form has been shown to be more stable than the *cis* form by about 0.5 kcal./mole. In the gas phase the following equilibrium is established:

$$NO + NO_2 + H_2O = 2HNO_2 \qquad K_{25°C.} = 1.74 \text{ atm.}^{-1}$$

Aqueous solutions of nitrous acid are unstable and decompose rapidly when heated, according to the equation:

$$3HNO_2 = HNO_3 + H_2O + 2NO$$

This reaction is reversible.

Nitrites of the alkali metals may be prepared by thermal decomposition of the nitrates, for example,

$$NaNO_3 = NaNO_2 + \tfrac{1}{2}O_2$$

or, better, by heating with a reducing agent such as carbon, lead, iron, etc.

Nitrous acid is used in the well-known preparation of diazonium compounds in organic chemistry. Numerous organic derivatives of the NO_2 group are known. They are of two types: nitrites, R—ONO, and nitro compounds, R—NO_2. Similar tautomerism occurs in some inorganic complexes, in which either oxygen or nitrogen is the actual donor atom when NO_2^- is a ligand.

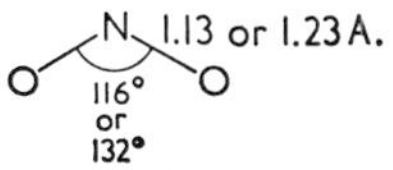

$$O \diagdown \underset{\substack{116° \\ or \\ 132°}}{\diagup N \diagdown} \diagup O \qquad 1.13 \text{ or } 1.23 \text{A.}$$

Fig. 12-8.   Structure of NO_2^- in ionic nitrites.

The NO_2^- ion in ionic nitrites has a bent structure (Fig. 12-8). The uncertainty in the exact parameters is surprising, but the two sets of results have been reported by different workers, and the discrepancy has not yet been resolved. The bent structure is readily explicable in terms of the resonance 12-XI or, in MO theory, by assuming N forms three sp^2

(12-XIa)   (12-XIb)

hybrid orbitals, one housing an unshared pair and the other two being used in σ bonding to the oxygens. The p_z orbitals of N and O are used for π bond formation.

Nitric Acid. Nitric acid, HNO_3, and its salts are the most important oxy compounds of nitrogen. The acid is now almost invariably made by converting atmospheric nitrogen to ammonia, oxidizing ammonia catalytically to NO, and absorbing the NO in presence of oxygen in water.

Anhydrous nitric acid is a colorless liquid boiling at 84.1°C. and freezing to a crystalline solid at -41.59°C. The pure acid auto-ionizes:

$$2HNO_3 = NO_2^+ + NO_3^- + H_2O$$

the molar concentration of each species being 0.51 at -10°C. In dilute aqueous solution nitric acid is strong, being about 93% dissociated in $0.1M$ solution. The normal "concentrated" aqueous acid ($\sim70\%$ by weight) is colorless, but often becomes yellow as a result of photochemical decomposition to give NO_2:

$$2HNO_3 \overset{h\nu}{\to} 2NO_2 + H_2O + \tfrac{1}{2}O_2$$

So-called "fuming" nitric acid contains dissolved NO_2 (in excess of the amount which can be hydrated to $HNO_3 + NO$). Concentrated nitric acid is a powerful oxidizing agent; of the metals, only Au, Pt, Rh, and Ir are unattacked, although a few other metals such as Al, Fe, and Cr are rendered "passive." The exact nature of this passivity is not known, but the formation of an impervious oxide film probably plays some part. Magnesium alone can liberate H_2 and only initially at that, the attack on metals involving reduction of nitrogen. Gold and the platinum metals are attacked by aqua regia (~3 parts conc. $HCl + 1$ part conc. HNO_3) which contains free chlorine and ClNO. The complexing action of the chloride ions is also important in making aqua regia more effective than nitric acid. Nonmetals are usually oxidized by concentrated nitric acid to oxides or oxy acids. The oxidizing power of nitric acid is, however, very dependent on concentration, and below about $2M$ the acid has virtually no oxidizing power.

The gaseous nitric acid molecule has a planar structure, although hindered rotation of OH relative to NO_2 probably occurs (Fig. 12-9).

Nitrates of practically all metallic elements are known. They are fre-

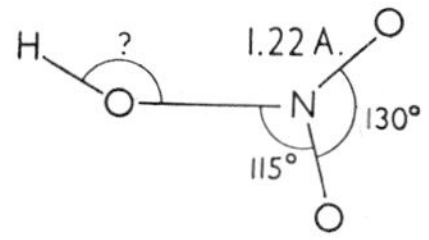

Fig. 12-9. Structure of nitric acid in vapor.

quently hydrated and are mostly soluble in water. They are decomposed on heating, being strong oxidizing agents at high temperatures; with the exception of the alkali nitrates, which pyrolyze to give nitrites, and ammonium nitrate, which gives N_2O and H_2O, nitrates pyrolyze to give O_2, NO_2, and the metal oxide. In neutral solution, nitrates can be reduced only with difficulty. The mechanism of the reduction is still obscure. Al or Zn in alkaline solution produce NH_3.

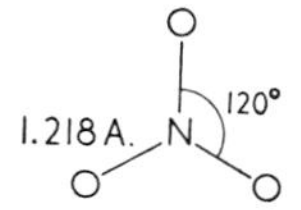

Fig. 12-10. Structure of the nitrate ion.

The nitrate ion is planar and symmetrical (Fig. 12-10). This structure may be explained in valence bond theory as a resonance hybrid (12-XII),

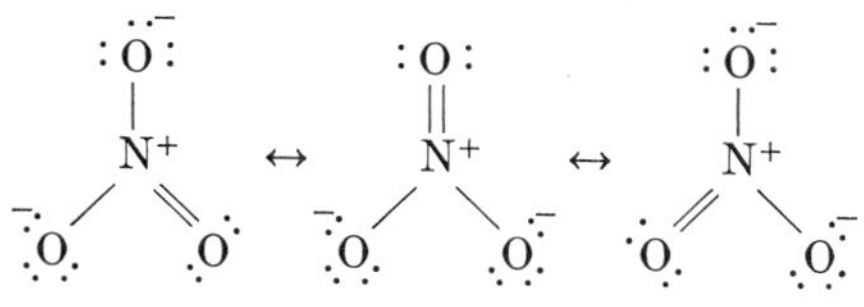

(12-XIIa)   (12-XIIb)   (12-XIIc)

or in molecular orbital theory by assuming that nitrogen forms three σ bonds using sp^2 hybrid orbitals and that the p_z orbitals of nitrogen and the three oxygen atoms combine to form a π MO, housing two electrons.

Nitrate ion has rather poor complexing ability, though not as poor as perchlorate. However, a fair number of complexes are known in which the nitrate ion is unidentate, coordinating through one oxygen atom, viz., $M \leftarrow ONO_2$. It is believed that in some other instances (e.g., in some uranyl complexes) the nitrate ion may be bidentate, viz.,

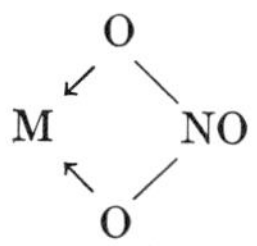

The uranyl complexes are of considerable importance in the extraction of uranium from aqueous nitric acid into various organic solvents in the form of neutral species thought to be of the type $(UO_2)(NO_3)_2$ (solvent)$_2$.

Nitric acid has the ability to nitrate many organic compounds, especially in the presence of concentrated sulfuric acid. This property is associated with the dissociation of the acid to produce the nitronium ion, NO_2^+.

The Nitronium Ion. This ion, NO_2^+, is directly involved not only in the dissociation of nitric acid itself but in nitration reactions and in solutions of nitrogen oxides in nitric and other strong acids. Various early physical measurements by Hantsch gave evidence for dissociation of HNO_3 in sulfuric acid. Thus "HNO_3" in H_2SO_4 shows no vapor pressure, and cryoscopic studies gave a van't Hoff i factor of 3. Hantsch proposed therefore:

$$HNO_3 + 2H_2SO_4 = H_3NO_3^{2+} + 2HSO_4^-$$

More recent work has shown that Hantsch's suggestion is not correct in detail, but that ionic dissociation does occur. This work was undertaken by Hughes and Ingold and others to find an explanation for the enormous increases in the rate of nitration of aromatic compounds by HNO_3–H_2SO_4 mixtures as the concentration of the sulfuric acid is increased and to account for variations in rate in other media. For example, the rate of nitration of benzene increases by 10^3 on going from 80% H_2SO_4 to 90% H_2SO_4. Detailed kinetic data, in sulfuric acid, nitromethane, and glacial acetic acid solutions, were explicable only by the postulate that the NO_2^+ ion was the attacking species. The origin of the NO_2^+ ion can be explained, for example, by ionizations of the following types:

$$2HNO_3 = NO_2^+ + NO_3^- + H_2O$$
$$HNO_3 + H_2SO_4 = NO_2^+ + HSO_4^- + H_2O$$

The importance of the first type is reflected in the fact that addition of ionized nitrate salts to the reaction mixture will retard the reaction. The actual nitration process can then be formulated as equation 12-10. The

dissociation of nitric acid in various media has been confirmed by cryoscopic studies, and nitrogen oxides have also been found to dissociate to produce nitronium ions as noted above. Spectroscopic studies have confirmed the presence of the various ions in such solutions. For example, the NO_2^+ ion can be identified by a Raman line at 1400 cm.$^{-1}$.

Final confirmation of the existence of nitronium ions has been obtained by isolation of nitronium salts which have a symmetrical N—O stretching frequency at 1396 cm.$^{-1}$ and a bond length of 1.10 A. Thus, from HNO_3 and $HClO_4$ in nitromethane a mixture of the perchlorates $NO_2^+ClO_4^-$ and $H_3O^+ClO_4^-$ can be obtained by crystallization. Other reactions leading to crystalline nitronium salts are:

$$N_2O_5 + HClO_4 = [NO_2^+ClO_4^-] + HNO_3 \qquad (12\text{-}11)$$
$$N_2O_5 + FSO_3H = [NO_2^+FSO_3^-] + HNO_3 \qquad (12\text{-}12)$$
$$HNO_3 + 2SO_3 = [NO_2^+HS_2O_7^-] \qquad (12\text{-}13)$$

Reactions 12-11 and 12-12 are really just metatheses, since N_2O_5 in the solid and in anhydrous acid solution is $NO_2^+NO_3^-$. Reaction 12-13 is that between an acid anhydride, SO_3, and a base(!), $NO_2^+OH^-$ (cf. $2NaOH + SO_3 = Na^+_2SO_4^{2-} + H_2O$).

Nitronium salts are crystalline and thermodynamically stable, but very reactive chemically. They are rapidly hydrolyzed by moisture; in addition $NO_2^+ClO_4^-$, for example, reacts violently with organic matter, but can actually be used to carry out nitrations in nitrobenzene solution.

Pernitrous Acid. The reactions of H_2O_2 with HNO_2 at low acidity, ozone with sodium azide, and a mixture of NO and NO_2 with H_2O_2 have been shown to produce pernitrous acid, HOONO. In acid solutions the brownish yellow color of the free acid is only transient, but quite stable alkaline solutions of the pernitrite ion can be obtained by mixing a slightly acidified solution of H_2O_2 with a solution of $NaNO_2$ and immediately making the mixture alkaline. The reactions can be written

$$HONO + HOOH \longrightarrow HOONO + H_2O \xrightarrow{OH^-} OONO^- + 2H_2O$$

Evidence from chemical reactions shows that in the decomposition of pernitrous acid free radicals are produced, since, for example, the polymerization of methyl methacrylate, which is known to be free-radical initiated, takes place. With aromatic hydrocarbons both hydroxylation and nitration occur, the former due to OH radicals and the latter by reaction of aryl radicals with NO_2.

12-8. Halogen Compounds of Nitrogen

Binary Halides. There are only four binary halides known as pure substances: N_2F_2, N_2F_4, NF_3, and NCl_3.

Nitrogen trifluoride, together with dinitrogen difluoride, is obtained by electrolysis of ammonium fluoride in anhydrous HF. Dinitrogen tetrafluoride, together with N_2F_2, is obtained by homogeneous reaction of NF_3 with mercury in an electric discharge or by heterogeneous reduction of NF_3 by hot metals. With copper reactor packing as catalyst, ammonia and fluorine diluted with nitrogen have been found to react smoothly and exothermically. Excess fluorine gives only NF_3, but with excess ammonia N_2F_2 and N_2F_4 are also formed. If a T-shaped reactor is used, difluoroamine, NHF_2, can be obtained.

Nitrogen trifluoride is a very stable and inert gas (b.p. $-129°C.$). It is not affected by water and most other reagents at room temperature and does not decompose on heating in the absence of reducing metals. On heating in presence of metals such as copper, the metal is fluorinated and N_2F_4 is obtained. The NF_3 molecule has a pyramidal structure but a very low dipole moment (see page 99), and it appears to be totally devoid of donor properties.

N_2F_2 is also a gas and it occurs in two isomeric forms. The more stable of these has been shown to have a planar, *trans* FNNF configuration; the less stable isomer is believed to have the corresponding *cis* structure although the possibility of its being F_2NN has not been conclusively ruled out.

N_2F_4, also a gas (b.p. $-73°$), is best prepared by the reaction of NF_3 with copper mentioned above. Microwave study has shown that its structure is similar to that of hydrazine. It is interesting that N_2F_4 dissociates in the gas and liquid phases according to the equation:

$$N_2F_4 = 2NF_2$$

The enthalpy of dissociation is about 19 kcal./mole, and the NF_2 radical appears surprisingly stable. Evidently, it must be added to the list of relatively stable odd molecules (which includes, *inter alia*, NO, NO_2, and ClO_2).

Nitrogen trichloride is formed in the chlorination of slightly acid ammonium chloride solutions as a pale yellow oil, b.p. $\sim71°C$. It is an exceedingly explosive and treacherous compound above its boiling point, in light, or in the presence of organic compounds. Unlike the fluoride ($\Delta H_f^0 = -26$ kcal./mole), the chloride is endothermic ($\Delta H_f = 55.4$ kcal./mole) and is also different in being readily hydrolyzed to NH_3 and HOCl.

The tribromide and triiodide of nitrogen have not been isolated except as ammoniates. $NBr_3 \cdot 6NH_3$, a purple solid, formed by treatment of ammonia with bromine at $-95°C.$, decomposes explosively above $-70°C.$ to give nitrogen, ammonia, and ammonium bromide. $NI_3 \cdot nNH_3$ ($n = 1$–12, depending inversely upon temperature of preparation) are known as black crystals; $NI_3 \cdot NH_3$ is explosive and hydrolyzed readily by water.

Haloamines. These are compounds of the type H_2NX and HNX_2, where H may be replaced by an alkyl radical also. Only H_2NCl, chloramine, HNF_2, and H_2NF have been isolated; $HNCl_2$, H_2NBr, and $HNBr_2$ probably exist but are quite unstable. It is believed that, on chlorination of aqueous ammonia, $NHCl_2$ forms at pH >8.5, $NHCl_2$ at pH 4.5–5.0, and NCl_3 at pH <4.4.

Oxy Halides. There are two series of these which might be formally considered as salts of the nitronium and nitrosonium ions, but since they are, in fact, quite covalent compounds, they were not discussed under the chemistry of these ions. The known compounds and some of their properties are listed in Tables 12-3 and 12-4.

TABLE 12-3

Physical Properties of Nitrosyl Halides

	FNO[a]	ClNO	BrNO
Color of gas	Colorless	Orange-yellow	Red
Melting point, °C.	−133	−65	−56
Boiling point, °C.	−60	−6	∼0
Structure	Bent	Bent	Bent
X—N distance, A.	1.52	1.95 ± 0.01	2.14 ± 0.02
N—O distance, A.	1.13	1.14 ± 0.02	1.15 ± 0.04
X—N—O angle, deg.	110	116 ± 2	114

[a] Uncertainties in structure parameters not known.

TABLE 12-4

Physical Properties of Nitryl Halides

	FNO_2	$ClNO_2$
Color of liquid	Colorless	Colorless
Melting point, °C.	−166	−145
Boiling point, °C.	−72	−16
Structure	Planar	Planar
X—N distance, A.	1.35	1.79
N—O distance, A.	1.23	1.25
X—N—O angle, deg.		
O—N—O angle, deg.	125 (assumed)	125 (assumed)

The nitrosyl halides can all be obtained by direct union of the halogens with nitric oxide and also in other ways. They are increasingly unstable in the series FNO, ClNO, BrNO. ClNO is always slightly impure, decomposing (to Cl_2 and NO) to the extent of about 0.5% at room temperature, and BrNO is decomposed to ∼7% at room temperature and 1 atm.

All three are reactive and are powerful oxidizing agents, able to attack many metals. All decompose on treatment with water producing HNO_3, HNO_2, NO, and HX. Their structures indicate that they are covalent molecules, the main resonance structure being 12-XIII. Alternatively, from

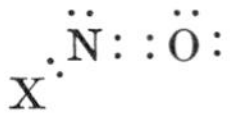

$$\overset{..}{\underset{X}{.\overset{..}{N}::\overset{..}{O}:}}$$

(12-XIII)

a molecular orbital viewpoint, nitrogen may be considered to have sp_xp_y hybridization, forming σ bonds to X and O and having an unshared pair, and then a π bond, using its p_z orbital, to oxygen.

The only known nitryl halides are FNO_2 and $ClNO_2$. The former is conveniently prepared by treatment of liquid NO_2 with fluorine. $ClNO_2$ is not obtainable by direct reaction of NO_2 and Cl_2, but is easily made in excellent yield by the reaction:

$$ClSO_3H + HNO_3(\text{anhydrous}) \xrightarrow{0°C.} ClNO_2 + H_2SO_4$$

Both compounds are quite reactive; both are decomposed by water:

$$XNO_2 + H_2O = HNO_3 + HX$$

Their structures are not fully known, but it has been established with certainty that they are planar (12-XIV), as valence considerations would suggest.

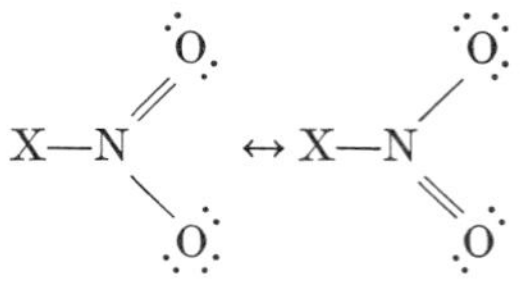

(12-XIVa)   (12-XIVb)

References

Addison, C. C., and J. Lewis, *Quart. Revs. (London)*, **9**, 115 (1955). Chemistry of nitric oxide with particular reference to its metal complexes.

Audrieth, L.F., and J. Kleinberg, *Non-Aqueous Solvents: Application as Media for Chemical Reactions*, Wiley, New York, 1953. Use of liquid ammonia as a solvent system.

Audrieth, L. F., and B. J. A. Ogg, *The Chemistry of Hydrazine*, Wiley, New York, 1951.

Beckman, L. J., W. A. Fessler, and M. Kise, *Chem. Revs.*, **48**, 319 (1951). Chemistry of nitrosyl chloride.

Brotherton, T. K., and J. W. Lynn, *Chem. Revs.*, **59**, 841 (1959). Synthesis and chemistry of cyanogen.

Clark, F., *Hydrazine*, Mathieson Chemical Company, 1953.

Evans, B. L., A. D. Yoffee, and P. Gray, *Chem. Revs.*, **59**, 515 (1959). Chemistry of azides.

Franklin, E. C., *The Nitrogen System of Compounds (American Chemical Society Monograph*, No. 68), Reinhold, New York, 1935. A classic volume containing much information on ammonia and related compounds.

George, J. W., "Halides and Oxyhalides of the Elements of Groups Vb and VIb," in F. A. Cotton, ed., *Progress in Inorganic Chemistry*, Vol. II, Interscience, New York–London, 1960, p. 33.

Gray, P., *Royal Institute of Chemistry Monograph*, No. 4, London, 1958. Chemistry of N_2O_4.

Jennings, K. R., and J. W. Linnett, *Quart. Revs. (London)*, **57**, 1179 (1957). Spectroscopic and chemical properties of active nitrogen.

Lewis, J., *Sci. Progr.*, **47**, 206 (1959). Chemistry of nitric oxide with particular reference to its metal complexes.

Orville-Thomas, W. J., *Chem. Revs.*, **57**, 1179 (1957). Valence bonding in nitrogen compounds.

Reed, R. A., *Royal Institute of Chemistry Lectures*, No. 5, London, 1957. Hydrazine and its derivatives.

Stern, S. A., J. T. Mullhaupt, and W. B. Kay, *Chem. Revs.*, **60**, 185 (1960). An exhaustive review on the physical properties of nitric acid.

Symposium on Inorganic Chemistry of Nitrogen, Chem. Soc. (London), Spec. Publ., No. 10 (1957). Nitronium compounds, chemistry of N_2O_4, synthesis of H_2SO_4 by NO catalysis, halogen derivatives of ammonia.

Turney, T. A., and G. A. Wright, *Chem. Revs.*, **59**, 497 (1959). Nitrous acid and nitrosation.

Yost, D. M., and H. Russell, *Systematic Inorganic Chemistry (of the 5th and 6th Group Elements)*, Prentice-Hall, New York, 1946. Selected topics in nitrogen chemistry, brilliantly expounded.

13

Oxygen

GENERAL REMARKS

13-1. Types of Oxides

The oxygen atom has the electronic structure $1s^2 2s^2 2p^4$. Oxygen forms compounds with all of the elements except the inert gases, and it combines directly with all of the other elements except the halogens and a few noble metals, either at ordinary or at elevated temperatures. The earth's crust contains about 50% by weight of oxygen. Most inorganic chemistry is concerned with its compounds, if only in the sense that so much chemistry involves the most important oxygen compound—water.

As a first row element, oxygen follows the octet rule, and the closed shell configuration can be achieved in ways which are similar to those for nitrogen, namely, by (a) electron gain to form O^{2-}, (b) formation of two single covalent bonds (e.g., R—O—R) or a double bond (e.g., O=C=O), (c) gain of one electron and formation of one single bond (e.g., in OH^-), and (d) formation of three or four covalent bonds (e.g., R_2OH^+, etc.).

There are a variety of binary oxygen compounds of disparate natures. The range of physical properties is attributable to the range of bond types from essentially ionic to essentially covalent. Some typical oxides and their properties are listed in Table 13-1.

The formation of the oxide ion, O^{2-}, from molecular oxygen requires the expenditure of a considerable energy, 227 kcal./mole;

$$\tfrac{1}{2}O_2(g) = O(g) \qquad \Delta H = 59.2 \text{ kcal./mole}$$
$$O(g) + 2e = O^{2-}(g) \qquad \Delta H = 168 \text{ kcal./mole}$$

Moreover, in the formation of an ionic oxide, energy must be expended in vaporizing and ionizing the metal atoms. Nevertheless, many ionic oxides exist and are very stable because the energies of lattices containing the

270

TABLE 13-1

Some Typical Oxides

Compound	Nature	Properties
	Crystalline Oxides	
CaO	White solid; m.p. 2580°C.	Ionic lattice; basic
SiO_2	Colorless crystals; m.p. 1710°C.[a]	Infinite three-dimensional lattice; acidic
BeO	White solid; m.p. 2570°C.	Semi-ionic; amphoteric
$Th_{0.7}Y_{0.3}O_{1.85}$	White crystalline solid	Fluorite lattice with some O^{2-} missing. Typical mixed metal oxide
$FeO_{0.95}$	Black solid	Fe^{2+} and some Fe^{3+} ions in interstices of hex. c.p. oxide lattice
	Molecular Oxides	
CO	Colorless gas	Inert; no acid or basic properties
SO_2	Colorless gas	Acid anhydride
OsO_4	Pale yellow, volatile solid; m.p. 41°C.	Readily reduced to Os
Cl_2O_7	Explosive, colorless oil	Anhydride of $HClO_4$

[a] β-Crystobalite; see page 357.

relatively small (1.40 A.), doubly charged oxide ion are quite high. In fact, the lattice energies are often sufficiently high to allow the ionization of metal atoms to unusually high oxidation states. Many metals form oxides in oxidation states not encountered in their other compounds, except perhaps in fluorides or some complexes. Examples of such higher oxides are MnO_2, AgO, and PrO_2. Many of these higher ionic oxides are nonstoichiometric.

In some cases the lattice energy is still insufficient to permit complete ionization, and oxides having substantial covalent character, such as BeO or B_2O_3, are formed. Finally, at the other extreme there are numerous oxides, such as CO_2, the nitrogen and phosphorus oxides, SO_2, SO_3, etc., which are essentially covalent molecular compounds. Such compounds are gases or volatile solids or liquids. Even in "covalent" oxides, unusually high *formal* oxidation states are often found, as in OsO_4, CrO_3, SO_3, etc.

In terms of chemical behavior, it is convenient to classify oxides according to their acid or base character in the aqueous system.

Basic Oxides. Although X-ray studies show the existence of discrete oxide ions, O^{2-} (and also peroxide, O_2^{2-}, and superoxide, O_2^-, ions, to be discussed presently), these ions cannot exist in any appreciable concentrations in aqueous solution owing to the hydrolytic reaction:

$$O^{2-}(s) + H_2O = 2OH^-(aq) \qquad K > 10^{22}$$

We have also for the ionic per- and superoxide ions:

$$O_2^{2-} + H_2O = HO_2^- + OH^-$$
$$2O_2^- + H_2O = O_2 + HO_2^- + OH^-$$

Thus only those ionic oxides which are insoluble in water are inert to water. Ionic oxides function, therefore, as *basic anhydrides*. When insoluble in water, they usually dissolve in dilute acids, for example,

$$MgO(s) + 2H^+(aq) = Mg^{2+}(aq) + H_2O$$

although in some cases, MgO being one, high temperature ignition produces a very inert material, quite resistant to acid attack.

Acidic Oxides. The covalent oxides of the nonmetals are usually acidic, dissolving in water to produce solutions of acids. They are termed *acid anhydrides*. Insoluble oxides of some less electropositive metals of this class will generally dissolve in bases. Thus,

$$N_2O_5(s) + H_2O = 2H^+(aq) + 2NO_3^-(aq)$$
$$Sb_2O_5(s) + 2OH^- + 5H_2O = 2Sb(OH)_6^-$$

Basic and acidic oxides will often combine directly to produce salts, such as

$$Na_2O + SiO_2 \xrightarrow{\text{fusion}} Na_2SiO_3$$

Amphoteric Oxides. These oxides behave acidically toward strong bases and as bases toward strong acids:

$$ZnO + 2H_3O^+ = Zn^{2+} + 3H_2O$$
$$ZnO + 2OH^- + H_2O = Zn(OH)_4^{2-}$$

Other Oxides. There are various other oxides, some of which are completely inert, dissolving in neither acids nor bases, for instance, N_2O and MnO_2.

There are also many oxides which are nonstoichiometric. These commonly consist of arrays of close-packed oxide ions with some of the interstices filled by metal ions. However, if there is variability in the oxidation state of the metal, nonstoichiometric materials result. Thus ferrous oxide probably never has the composition FeO, but is usually something in the range $FeO_{0.9}$–$FeO_{0.95}$, depending on the manner of preparation. There is an extensive chemistry of mixed metal oxides.

It may also be noted that when a given element forms several oxides, the oxide with the element in the highest formal oxidation state (usually meaning more covalent) is more acidic (*cf.* the rules for dependence of acid dissociation constants on formal charge in Chapter 5). Thus, for chromium we have: CrO, basic; Cr_2O_3, amphoteric; and CrO_3, fully acidic.

The Hydroxide Ion. Discrete hydroxide ions, OH^-, exist only in the hydroxides of the most electropositive elements such as the alkali metals and alkaline earths. For such an ionic material, dissolution in water results in formation of aquated metal ions and hydroxide ions:

$$M^+OH^-(s) + nH_2O = M^+(aq) + OH^-(aq)$$

and the substance is a strong base. In the limit of an extremely covalent M—O bond, dissociation will occur to varying degrees as follows:

$$MOH + nH_2O = MO^-(aq) + H_3O^+(aq)$$

and the substance must be considered an acid. Amphoteric hydroxides are those in which there is the possibility of either kind of dissociation, the one being favored by the presence of a strong acid

$$M\text{—}O\text{—}H + H^+ = M^+ + H_2O$$

the other by strong base

$$M\text{—}O\text{—}H + OH^- = MO^- + H_2O$$

because the formation of water is so highly favored:

$$H^+ + OH^- = H_2O \qquad K_{25°C.} = 10^{14}$$

Similarly, hydrolytic reactions of many metal ions can be written

$$M^{n+} + H_2O = (MOH)^{(n-1)+} + H^+$$

However, in view of the fact that such ions are coordinated by water molecules, a more realistic equation is

$$M(H_2O)_x{}^{n+} = [M(H_2O)_{x-1}(OH)]^{(n-1)+} + H^+$$

Thus we may consider that the more covalent the M—O bond tends to be, the more acidic are the hydrogen atoms in the aquated ion, but at present there are no extensive correlations of the acidities of aquo ions with properties of the metal.

The hydroxide ion has the ability to form bridges between metal ions. Thus there are various compounds of the transition and other metals containing OH bridges, for example, $[(NH_3)_3Co(OH)_3Co(NH_3)_3]Cl_3$. This bridging is accomplished in the same way as is done by Cl or F, that is, as in 13-I.

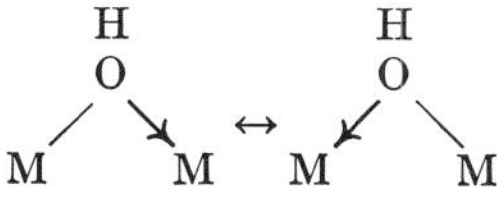

(13-Ia)   (13-Ib)

The formation of hydroxy bridges occurs at an early stage in the precipitation of hydrous metal oxides. In the case of Fe^{3+}, precipitation of

$Fe_2O_3 \cdot xH_2O$—commonly, but not rigorously correctly, written $Fe(OH)_3$—proceeds through the stages:

$$[Fe(H_2O)_6]^{3+} \xrightarrow{-H^+} [Fe(H_2O)_5OH]^{2+} \longrightarrow [(H_2O)_4Fe(OH)_2Fe(H_2O)_4]^{4-} \xrightarrow{-xH^+}$$

$$pH < 0 \qquad\qquad 0 < pH < 2 \qquad\qquad \sim2 < pH < \sim3$$

$$\text{colloidal } Fe_2O_3 \cdot xH_2O \xrightarrow{-yH^+} Fe_2O_3 \cdot zH_2O \text{ ppt.}$$

$$\sim3 < pH < \sim5 \qquad\qquad pH < \sim5$$

Analogous to the OH^- ion are the alkoxide ions, OR^-. These are even stronger bases as a rule, being immediately hydrolyzed by water:

$$OR^- + H_2O = OH^- + ROH$$

A considerable number of metal alkoxides are known, many stoichiometrically analogous to the metal hydroxides, for example, $Ti(OH)_4$ and $Ti(OR)_4$. These compounds are quite reactive, and as R becomes large they become essentially organic in their physical properties; such alkoxides are usually polymeric, with coordination numbers greater than those indicated by the simple stoichiometry, owing to the existence of OR bridge groups.

13-2. Covalent Compounds; Stereochemistry of Oxygen

Two-Coordinate Compounds. The normal coordination number of oxygen is two, and in most of its compounds it forms two single bonds, as in water, ethers, alcohols, etc. In all such compounds there are two pairs of nonbonding electrons which play a role in the stereochemistry. In order to account for the fact that the X—O—X bond angles are all more nearly equal to the tetrahedral angle than to the 90° expected if oxygen used two pure p orbitals for bonding, it is assumed that the oxygen orbitals are hybridized in a manner approximating to sp^3, tetrahedral. Thus, as in trivalent nitrogen compounds, the unshared electrons are not distributed symmetrically about the oxygen atom, but occupy directed hybrid orbitals. In R_3N compounds the R—N—R angles seem always to be less than 109°; it has been proposed that this is because repulsion between nonbonding electron pairs and bonding pairs is greater than repulsion between two pairs of bonding electrons, which, in turn, is attributed to the fact that the bonding pairs may be more densely concentrated in the bond directions. What degree of truth there may be in this view is not certain, but in some oxygen compounds the angles exceed 109°; consider OCl_2 ($\sim113°$), $(CH_3)_2O$ (111°), and ozone (127°). It should be noted that there is no good reason to suppose that the central atom tends to form four equivalent sp^3

hybrid orbitals and that all deviations of bond angles from the exact tetrahedral angles must be due to other forces. If all four orbitals are not to be
used in identical ways, there is no reason why they should inherently tend
to be identical. Thus, the various bond angles in R_3N and R_2O compounds
can simply be taken to imply slightly varying degrees of hybridization, all
of which, however, are much closer to sp^3 than to p^2 or p^3 (i.e., the use of
pure p orbitals by the central atom).

Three-Coordinate Compounds. Compounds in this class are mainly
oxonium ions—that is, H_3O^+, R_2OH^+, ROH_2^+, R_3O^+—and donor-acceptor
complexes with Lewis acids such as 13-II. The formation of oxonium ions

$$C_2H_5$$
$$\diagdown \overset{+}{O}-\overset{-}{B}F_3$$
$$\diagup$$
$$C_2H_5$$

(13-II)

is quite analogous to the formation of ammonium ions, NH_4^+, RNH_3^+,
$\ldots R_4N^+$.

As would be expected on the assumption of approximately sp^3 hybridization of the oxygen orbitals, three-coordinate oxygen compounds are
pyramidal.

Various instances have been noted already in which R_2O compounds
behave as donors. In hydrated cations water, which may be regarded as
the prototype R_2O compound, behaves as a donor, for example, in
$[Be(OH_2)_4]^{2+}$, although the bond strength in many such hydrates may be
appreciably if not largely due to ion–dipole attraction. The mechanism of
hydrolysis of many covalent halides such as $SiCl_4$ presumably involves
initial formation of a donor bond from H_2O (or OH^-) to the central atom.

Four-Coordinate Oxygen. Although the maximum coordination
number for oxygen is four, it is seldom attained. Oxide ions are often
four coordinate in ionic or partially ionic oxides. In the compounds
$OM_4(OCOR)_6$, where M is Be or Zn, oxygen is four coordinate (see Fig. 9-3,
page 175). Doubtless the O—M bonds here have considerable ionic character and, though four coordinate, the oxygen atom is not truly four covalent.

Multiple Bonding. Like nitrogen, oxygen has considerable ability to
form double bonds. These may be of the $p\pi$–$p\pi$ type as in ketones, carboxylic acids, CO, CO_2, N_2O, NO, etc., and in the resonance structures
making up the true electronic states of such species as NO_2^- and NO_3^-.

It is also possible for oxygen to form dative $d\pi$–$p\pi$ double bonds to second
and third row elements similar in the nature of the overlaps involved to

those discussed for $(H_3Si)_3N$. In disiloxane, $(SiH_3)_2O$, the Si—O—Si bond angle is very large; the exact value is not known, but it is definitely $\gg 150°$. This may be attributed to the tendency of the filled $p\pi$ orbitals of oxygen to overlap with empty $d\pi$ orbitals on Si. In the limit this would lead to an Si—O—Si angle of 180°. In phosphine oxides, R_3PO, and sulfoxides, R_2SO, there is doubtless some $p\pi$–$d\pi$ bonding; that is, the actual state of the P—O or S—O bonds is described by a resonance between 13-IIIa and 13-IIIb, where one pair of electrons in 13-IIIb is in a bonding orbital formed

$$\overset{+}{R_3P} : \overset{..}{\underset{..}{O}} : \quad \leftrightarrow \quad R_3P : : \overset{..}{\underset{..}{O}}$$

(13-IIIa)   (13-IIIb)

by $p\pi$–$d\pi$ overlap. With amine oxides this is, of course, not possible, and

the NO bond is essentially just $\overset{+}{N} : \overset{..}{\underset{..}{O}} :$. Certain transition metal complexes

also have oxygen bridges, M—O—M, which are linear, for example $[Cl_5Ru$—O—$RuCl_5]^{4-}$; the magnetic properties and structure can only be explained by $d\pi$–$p\pi$ bonding through the oxygen atom.

Oxy Acids and Oxy Anions. Oxygen occurs in an immense number of oxy acids and oxy anions of various types. The bonds are mainly covalent with varying degrees of partial ionic character and also varying degrees of multiple bond character. Common monomeric oxy anions are NO_3^-, SO_4^{2-}, CrO_4^{2-}, MnO_4^-, CO_3^{2-}, etc. There are polymeric anions such as $S_2O_7^{2-}$, $Cr_2O_7^{2-}$, and $P_2O_7^{4-}$, having oxygen bridges as well as more highly polymerized species, linear, cyclic, and three dimensional as in silicates. There are also a few dimeric anions—for example, $P_2O_6^-$ and $S_2O_4^{2-}$—in which there are no bridges.

Catenation. As with nitrogen, and even more so, catenation is limited. In peroxides and superoxides there are two consecutive oxygen atoms, and in ozone three, but longer chains are unknown. Sulfur and selenium have a much greater tendency to catenation, sulfur being probably second only to carbon in this respect.

THE ELEMENT

13-3. Occurrence, Properties, and Allotropes

Oxygen occurs in nature in three isotopic species: ^{16}O (99.64%), ^{17}O (0.04%), and ^{18}O (0.20%). All three are stable. The rare isotopes, particularly ^{18}O, can be concentrated by fractional distillation of water, and concentrates containing up to $\sim$90% ^{18}O are commercially available. ^{18}O has been widely used as a tracer in studying reaction mechanisms of oxygen compounds.

Elemental oxygen occurs in two allotropic forms; the common, stable O_2 and the endothermic ozone, O_3. O_2 is paramagnetic in the gaseous, liquid, and solid states and has the rather high dissociation energy of 117 kcal./mole. As has been discussed (page 55), the valence bond theory would most naturally predict that the molecule would have the electronic structure $\overset{..}{:}O\overset{..}{:}\,:O\overset{..}{:}$ which, while accounting for the strong bond, fails to account for the paramagnetism. Alternatively, but only as an after-the-fact rationalization, we might write $\overset{..}{:}O\overset{..}{:}O\overset{..}{:}$ to account for the presence of two unpaired electrons; but then we should scarcely expect as high a bond energy as is found, since the N—N, O—O, and F—F single bond energies are, respectively, 32 (in N_2H_4), 33 (in H_2O_2), and 37 (in F_2) kcal./mole. However, simple molecular orbital theory straightforwardly predicts a bond order of 2 *and* the presence of two unpaired electrons, with the electron configuration: $[\sigma(s)]^2[\sigma^*(s)]^2[\sigma(p)]^2[\pi]^4[\pi^*]^2$, where the two π^* electrons will be unpaired in this doubly degenerate orbital following Hund's rule. The structure $:O\overset{.}{\underset{.}{::}}O:$ has been suggested to account for the bond energy and paramagnetism (recall that a three-electron bond has approximately one-half the strength of a two-electron bond), but in order to accept it one must ignore the octet rule, ordinarily considered an integral part of the VB approach in first row elements. Like NO, which has one unpaired electron in an antibonding (π^*) MO, oxygen molecules associate only weakly, and true electron pairing to form a symmetrical O_4 species apparently does not occur even in the solid. Both liquid and solid O_2 are pale blue in color.

The other allotrope of elemental oxygen is *ozone*, O_3. This is usually prepared by the action of a silent electric discharge upon O_2; concentrations up to 10% O_3 can be obtained in this way. Ozone gas is perceptibly blue. Pure ozone can be obtained by fractional liquefaction of O_2–O_3 mixtures. There is a two-phase liquid system; one with 25% ozone is stable, but a deep purple phase with 70% ozone is explosive, as is the deep blue pure liquid (b.p. $-112°C$.). The solid (m.p. $-250°C$.) is black-violet. Small quantities of ozone are formed in electrolysis of dilute sulfuric acid, in some chemical reactions producing elemental oxygen, and by action of ultraviolet light on O_2. Ozone occurs in traces in the upper atmosphere, the maximum concentrations being at an altitude of $\sim$25 km. It is diamagnetic. It is very exothermic,

$$O_3 = \tfrac{3}{2}O_2 \qquad \Delta H = -34.0 \text{ kcal./mole}$$

but decomposes only slowly at 250°C. in absence of catalysts and ultra-violet light.

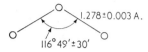

Fig. 13-1. The structure of ozone, O_3.

The structure of O_3 is shown in Figure 13-1. Since the O—O bond distances are 1.49 A. in HOOH (single bond) and 1.21 A. in O_2 (∽ double bond), it is apparent that the O—O bond in O_3 must have considerable double bond character. Four reasonable resonance structures (13-IV) may be written, with 13-IVa and 13-IVb predominating. In molecular

(13-IVa)　　　　(13-IVb)　　　　(13-IVc)　　　　(13-IVd)

orbital theory the existence of strong, delocalized π bonding can be invoked.

The chemical reactivities of O_2 and O_3 differ vastly. Although O_2 will combine directly with practically all other elements, it will do so only at elevated temperatures in most cases, but ozone is a powerful oxidizing agent and reacts with many substances under conditions where O_2 will not. The reaction

$$O_3 + 2KI + H_2O = I_2 + 2KOH + O_2$$

is quantitative and can be used for the determination of ozone.

The following oxidation potentials indicate the strengths of O_2 and O_3 as oxidizing agents in aqueous solution:

$$
\begin{array}{ll}
2H_2O = O_2 + 4H^+ + 4e & E^0 = -1.229 \text{ v.} \\
4OH^- = O_2 + 2H_2O + 4e & E^0 = -0.401 \text{ v.} \\
2H_2O = O_2 + 4H^+ (10^{-7} M) + 4e & E^0 = -0.815 \text{ v.} \\
O_2 + H_2O = O_3 + 2H^+ + 2e & E^0 = -2.07 \text{ v.} \\
O_2 + 2OH^- = O_3 + H_2O + 2e & E^0 = -1.24 \text{ v.} \\
O_2 + H_2O = O_3 + 2H^+ (10^{-7} M) + 2e & E^0 = -1.65 \text{ v.}
\end{array}
$$

In acid solution, O_3 is exceeded in oxidizing power only by fluorine, atomic oxygen, OH radicals, and a few other such species. It can also be seen that neutral water when saturated with O_2 is a fairly good oxidizing agent. For example, although Cr^{2+} is just stable toward oxidation in pure water, in air-saturated water it is rapidly oxidized; Fe^{2+} is oxidized (only slowly in acid, but rapidly in base) to Fe^{3+} in presence of air, although in air-free water Fe^{2+} is quite stable,

$$Fe^{2+} = Fe^{3+} + e \qquad E^0 = -0.77 \text{ v.}$$

The slowness of many oxygen oxidations in acid solution is attributable to the initial reduction to H_2O_2 with HO_2^- as an intermediate if one-electron reducing agents are present

$$H_2O_2 = O_2 + 2H^+ + 2e \qquad E^0 = -0.682$$
$$OH^- + HO_2^- = O_2 + H_2O + 2e \qquad E^0 = 0.076$$

Oxygen is readily soluble in organic solvents, and merely pouring such liquids in air serves to saturate them with oxygen. This should be kept in mind when determining the reactivity of air-sensitive materials in solution in organic solvents.

A few substances are known which can act as reversible carriers of molecular oxygen; that is, they take up and release O_2 reversibly. These compounds are metal chelates (Section 25-3). Such metal complexes, when bound to protein molecules as prosthetic groups, are indispensable in life processes, notably respiration, and are found in living organisms. Hemoglobin and the hemocyanins are natural carriers; heme prosthetic groups contain an iron atom bound in a porphine derivative. There are several synthetic oxygen-carrying complexes known which provide model systems for the natural carriers. Examples of these are cobalt–histidine and cobalt–salicylaldehyde–ethylenediimine complexes, which carry oxygen both in the solid state and in solution; the nature of the bonding of oxygen to the complex is believed to be as in a peroxo bridge, —O—O—.

Manganese(II) phthalocyanine has also been shown to take up oxygen reversibly. The oxygen is possibly bound to the metal in a manner similar to that in heme complexes, which is believed to be of the type shown in the resonance structure 13-Va, but it is also possible that bonding to the metal can occur using π electrons from the double bond (13-Vb) as in olefin

$$
\begin{array}{cc}
\overset{\displaystyle \cdot \cdot O \cdot}{\underset{\displaystyle }{\Big/\Big/}} & \\
\cdot \cdot O_+ & O{=}O \\
\Big| & \downarrow \\
M & M \\
(13\text{-Va}) & (13\text{-Vb})
\end{array}
$$

complexes of transition metals (see Chapter 28). The bonding of oxygen in reversible oxygen-carrying complexes is not well understood.

OXYGEN COMPOUNDS

In view of the fact that virtually all of the elements except the inert gases form oxygen compounds, most of these compounds are described in treating the chemistry of the other elements. Water and the hydroxonium ion have already been discussed (Chapter 5). A few important compounds and classes of compounds will be mentioned here.

13-4. Oxygen Fluorides, OF_2, O_2F_2, O_3F_2, and O_4F_2

Since fluorine is more electronegative than oxygen, it is logical to call OF_2 and O_2F_2 oxygen fluorides rather than fluorine oxides, although the latter names are sometimes seen. OF_2 is prepared either by passing fluorine rapidly through 2% sodium hydroxide solution or by electrolysis of fluorosulfonic acid (FSO_3H) in liquid HF using a nickel anode. It is a pale yellow gas (m.p. -224, b.p. $-145°C.$) and extremely poisonous. It is relatively unreactive. It can be mixed with H_2, CH_4, or CO without reaction, although sparking causes violent explosion. Mixtures of OF_2 with Cl_2, Br_2, and I_2 explode at room temperature. It is fairly readily hydrolyzed by base:

$$OF_2 + 2OH^- = O_2 + 2F^- + H_2O$$

It reacts more slowly with water, but explodes with steam:

$$OF_2 + H_2O = O_2 + 2HF$$

The molecule has a bent symmetrical structure with an O—F distance of 1.418 A. and an F—O—F angle of 103.2°.

Other oxygen fluorides, O_2F_2, O_3F_2, and O_4F_2, have been reported. These are formed on passing electric discharges through mixtures of O_2 and F_2 in a quartz tube at $-180°C.$ and 10–20 mm. pressure. The yellow solid, O_2F_2, melts at $-160°C.$ to a red liquid boiling with decomposition at $\sim -57°C.$ O_3F_2, a blood-red compound (m.p. 83°K.), decomposes at $-157°C.$ to $O_2 + O_2F_2$. O_4F_2 is reddish brown and decomposes above $-73°C.$

13-5. Hydrogen Peroxide, H_2O_2

Hydrogen peroxide used to be commonly prepared in dilute solution by treatment of barium peroxide with acid; BaO_2 is obtained by the action of air or oxygen upon BaO at 500°C. Hydrogen peroxide is obtained by electrolytic processes which involve the formation of peroxydisulfate ion and its subsequent hydrolysis. Sulfuric acid or ammonium sulfate–sulfuric acid solutions are electrolyzed at high current density (~ 1 amp./dm.²) using electrode materials (usually Pt) with high overvoltages for O_2 evolution. Although the detailed mechanism of the process is not quite certain, stoichiometrically we have:

$$2HSO_4^- = S_2O_8^{2-} + 2H^+ + 2e \qquad E^0 = -2.18 \text{ (acid)}$$
$$2SO_4^{2-} = S_2O_8^{2-} + 2e \qquad E^0 = -2.06 \text{ (neutral)}$$

An optimum residence time for the solution and low temperature ($-20°C.$) are used to minimize the hydrolytic reaction (eq. 13-1) in the cell and con-

$$H_2S_2O_8 \quad + \quad H_2O \quad = \quad H_2SO_5 \quad + \quad H_2SO_4 \quad (13\text{-}1)$$
Peroxydisulfuric   Peroxymonosulfuric
acid   acid; "Caro's" acid

sequent loss of product by decomposition reactions (eqs. 13-2a, b)

$$2H_2O_2 = 2H_2O + O_2 \qquad\qquad (13\text{-}2a)$$
$$H_2SO_5 + H_2O_2 = H_2SO_4 + H_2O + O_2 \qquad (13\text{-}2b)$$

The peroxydisulfuric acid solution is hydrolyzed separately

$$H_2S_2O_8 + H_2O = H_2SO_5 + H_2SO_4 \quad \text{(fast)}$$
$$H_2SO_5 + H_2O = H_2O_2 + H_2SO_4 \quad \text{(slow)}$$

and the H_2O_2 is rapidly removed by distillation at high temperature and low pressure. Dilute solutions of H_2O_2 so obtained are then concentrated by vacuum distillation to 28–35% by weight. Higher concentrations, 90–99%, are commercially achieved by further, multistage fractionation. Such concentrated materials are very susceptible to metal-ion catalyzed decomposition and it is necessary to add inhibitors such as sodium pyrophosphate or stannate and to store them in pure aluminum ($>99.6\%$) containers.

Hydrogen peroxide is also produced on a large scale by autoxidation of an anthraquinol, such as 2-ethylanthraquinol (13-VI), in a cyclic con-

(13-VI)

tinuous process. Hydrogen from the cracking of butane is used to reduce the quinone using Pd on an inert support in free suspension. H_2O_2 is extracted from the oxygenated organic solution by countercurrent columns and the aqueous product contains about 20% H_2O_2. The process needs only H_2, atmospheric oxygen, and water as major raw materials; it is cheaper to operate than the electrolytic method.

Pure H_2O_2 is a pale blue, syrupy liquid, boiling at 150.2°C. and freezing at $-0.89°C.$ It resembles water in many of its physical properties. The pure liquid has a dielectric constant at 25°C. of 93 and a 65% solution in water has a dielectric constant of 120. Thus both the pure liquid and its aqueous solutions are potentially excellent ionizing solvents, but its utility in this respect is limited by its strongly oxidizing nature and its ready decomposition in the presence of even traces of many heavy metal ions according to the equation:

$$2H_2O_2 = 2H_2O + O_2 \tag{13-3}$$

In dilute aqueous solution it is more acidic than water,

$$H_2O_2 = H^+ + HO_2^- \qquad K_{20°C.} = 1.5 \times 10^{-12}$$

Its oxidation-reduction chemistry in aqueous solution is summarized by the potentials of the following reactions:

$$2H_2O = H_2O_2 + 2H^+ + 2e \qquad E^0 = -1.77 \text{ v.}$$
$$H_2O_2 = O_2 + 2H^+ + 2e \qquad E^0 = -0.68 \text{ v.}$$
$$3OH^- = HO_2^- + H_2O + 2e \qquad E^0 = -0.87 \text{ v.}$$

from which it can be seen that hydrogen peroxide is a strong oxidizing agent in either acid or basic solution; only toward very strong oxidizing agents such as MnO_4^- will it behave as a reducing agent.

Dilute or 30% hydrogen peroxide solutions are widely used as laboratory oxidants. In acid solution oxidations with hydrogen peroxide are most often slow, whereas in basic solution they are usually fast. Decomposition of hydrogen peroxide according to reaction 13-3, which may be considered a self-oxidation, occurs most rapidly in basic solution; hence excess H_2O_2 may best be destroyed in basic solution by heating.

The oxidation of H_2O_2 in aqueous solution by Cl_2, MnO_4^-, Ce^{4+}, etc., and the catalytic decomposition caused by Fe^{3+}, I_2, MnO_2, etc., have been studied. In both cases, by using labeled H_2O_2, it has been shown that the oxygen produced is derived entirely from the peroxide and not from water. This suggests that oxidizing agents do not break the O—O bond, but simply remove electrons. In the case of oxidation by chlorine, a mechanism of the following kind is consistent with the lack of exchange of ^{18}O between H_2O_2 and H_2O:

$$Cl_2 + H_2{}^{18}O_2 \rightarrow H^+ + Cl^- + H^{18}O^{18}OCl$$
$$H^{18}O^{18}OCl \rightarrow H^+ + Cl^- + {}^{18}O_2$$

The molecule H_2O_2 has a skew, chain structure (Fig. 13-2). There is only a low barrier to internal rotation about the O—O bond. In the liquid state H_2O_2 is even more highly associated via hydrogen bonding than is H_2O.

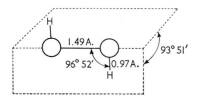

Fig. 13-2. The structure of hydrogen peroxide.

13-6. Peroxides, Peroxy Compounds, and Superoxides

Simple *ionic peroxides* containing O_2^{2-} ions are known for many of the more electropositive elements. On treating such substances with water or dilute acid, hydrogen peroxide is obtained. A typical and important metal peroxide is sodium peroxide, Na_2O_2, which is widely used as a source of H_2O_2 and for oxidations.

A large number of *organic peroxides* are known. Many ethers take up oxygen from the atmosphere (autoxidation) forming peroxy ethers which are often dangerously explosive. Care should be taken to remove peroxides from ether solvents (treat with Na or LiAlH$_4$) before distillation. Peroxy-carboxylic acids—for example, peracetic acid, $CH_3CO \cdot OOH$—may be prepared by action of hydrogen peroxide on acid anhydrides. These peroxy acids are useful as oxidizing agents and as sources of free radicals. Benzoyl peroxide is moderately stable and is widely used as a polymerization initiator and for other purposes.

Many *peroxy acids*, acids in which —O— is replaced by —O—O—, are known. The peroxysulfates (13-VIII and 13-X) are among the most im-

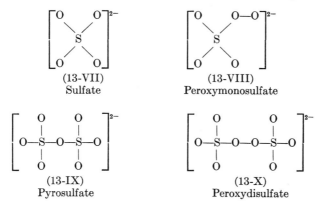

(13-VII)	(13-VIII)
Sulfate	Peroxymonosulfate
(13-IX)	(13-X)
Pyrosulfate	Peroxydisulfate

portant inorganic ones, and the peroxycarboxylic acids are also widely useful. All peroxy acids yield H_2O_2 on hydrolysis. Peroxydisulfate, as the ammonium salt, is commonly used as a strong oxidizing agent, for example, to convert Mn^{2+} to MnO_4^- or Ce^{3+} to Ce^{4+}. These reactions are slow in the absence of silver ion as a catalyst. This catalytic activity is due to the reaction of silver ion directly with the peroxydisulfate, the resulting Ag^{3+} ion then rapidly oxidizing the Mn^{2+} or Ce^{3+}:

$$S_2O_8^{2-} + Ag^+ = 2SO_4^{2-} + Ag^{3+}$$

It is important to make the distinction between true peroxy compounds which contain —O—O— groups and compounds which contain hydrogen peroxide of crystallization such as $2Na_2CO_3 \cdot 3H_2O_2$ or $Na_4P_2O_7 \cdot nH_2O_2$.

The action of oxygen at pressures near atmospheric on the metals K, Rb, Cs, Ca, Sr, and Ba produces very dark-colored crystalline solids, such as KO_2 and $Ba[O_2]_2$, termed *superoxides*. Treatment of Na_2O_2 with oxygen at 300 atm. and 500°C. gives NaO_2. The paramagnetism of the compounds corresponds to the presence of one unpaired electron per two oxygen atoms and requires a formulation of, for example, the potassium compound, as $K^+O_2^-$. In the superoxide ion, O_2^-, there would be one unpaired electron, and crystal structure determinations show the existence of such discrete O_2^- ions. The compounds KO_2, RbO_2, and CsO_2 crystallize in the CaC_2 structure (Fig. 11-3a), which is a distorted NaCl structure. NaO_2 is cubic owing to a disorder in the orientation of the O_2^- ions. The superoxides are very powerful oxidizing agents. They react vigorously with water

$$2O_2^- + H_2O = O_2 + HO_2^- + OH^-$$

Materials of composition approximating to M_2O_3 (M = alkali metal) are almost certainly mixtures of peroxide and superoxide, and there is no evidence for the existence of an O_3^{2-} ion.

However, it has been recently shown that alkali metals can give ozonides which contain the O_3^- ion; there is also some evidence that this ion may be formed during the decomposition of H_2O_2 in alkaline solution. O_3^- is paramagnetic and appears to be bent, as is ClO_2, which it resembles in its electronic structure.

References

Bradley, D. C., "Metal Alkoxides," in F. A. Cotton, ed., *Progress in Inorganic Chemistry*, Vol. II, Interscience, New York–London, 1960, p. 303.
——— in *Metal Organic Compounds* (*Advances in Chemistry Series*, No. 23), American Chemical Society, Washington, D. C., 1959. On metal alkoxides.
Brewer, L., *Chem. Revs.*, **52**, 1 (1953). A comprehensive survey of thermodynamic properties of oxides.
——— and G. M. Rosenblatt, *Chem. Revs.*, **61**, 257 (1961). Dissociation energies of gaseous oxides, MO_2.
Dole, M., *Chem. Revs.*, **51**, 263 (1952). Chemistry of isotopes of oxygen.
Hawkins, E. G. E., *Quart. Revs.* (*London*), **4**, 25 (1950). Organic peracids and reactions of organic peroxides.
Schumb, W. C., C. N. Satterfield, and R. L. Wentworth, *Hydrogen Peroxide* (American Chemical Society Monograph, No. 128), Reinhold, New York, 1955. A recent and highly comprehensive discussion of all phases of the chemistry of hydrogen peroxide and related compounds.
Swan, D., *Chem. Revs.*, **45**, 1 (1949). Organic peracids and reactions of organic peroxides.

Ward, R., "Mixed Metal Oxides," in F. A. Cotton, ed., *Progress in Inorganic Chemistry*, Vol. I, Interscience, New York–London, 1959, p. 465. Comprehensive review of mixed metal oxides including their physical properties.

Yost, D. M., and H. Russell, *Systematic Inorganic Chemistry (of the 5th and 6th Group Elements)*, Prentice-Hall, New York, 1946. Excellent coverage of selected aspects of oxygen chemistry.

14

Fluorine

GENERAL REMARKS

14-1. Introduction

Fluorine is a greenish diatomic gas, F_2. It is the most chemically reactive of all the elements, a fact which for a long time hindered its isolation. Fluorine combines directly at ordinary or elevated temperatures with all of the elements other than oxygen, nitrogen, and the inert gases, often with extreme vigor. It also attacks many other compounds, particularly organic compounds, breaking them down to fluorides; organic materials often inflame and burn in the gas.

The great reactivity of the element is in part attributable to the weakness of the F—F bond in the fluorine molecule, and reactions of atomic fluorine are strongly exothermic. Although the value of the *dissociation energy* long proved difficult to measure accurately, a value of 37.7 ± 0.2 kcal./mole now appears well established. This value is lower than those of the other halogens. The most satisfactory reason for this weakness is that it is due to repulsion between nonbonding electrons; in the other halogens, the longer bond distances and tighter bonding of inner shell electrons tend to reduce this repulsion. A further reason has been suggested: the bonds in the other halogens are strengthened by some multiple bond character due to their ability, denied to fluorine, of being able to use outer d orbitals for such bonding.

Fluorine is the most electronegative of all the elements. Its ionization potential, 401 kcal./g.-atom, combined with the dissociation energy, leads to the standard heat of formation of the gaseous F^+ ion of 420 kcal./g.-atom (*cf.* Cl^+, 327; Br^+, 301; I^+, 268). Thus even solvated cationic species are unlikely, and no evidence whatever exists for a positive oxidation state of fluorine.

The *electron affinity* of fluorine is 83.5 ± 2 kcal./g.-atom. This value is somewhat surprising, since one might have expected fluorine to have the highest electron affinity of all the halogens rather than one between those of chlorine (88) and bromine (82). This low value is, however, an inescapable consequence of the low dissociation energy of fluorine, since the electron affinities of the halogens have been obtained from Born-Haber cycles. Indeed, for some years a higher bond energy was advocated for F_2 in order to obtain a higher electron affinity, but the present bond energy and hence the relatively low electron affinity are now indisputable.

14-2. Types of Fluorides

The fluorine compounds of the elements are essentially of two main types, ionic and covalent, in all of which fluorine has a complete octet; examples are given in Table 14-1.

TABLE 14-1

Some Typical Fluorine Compounds

Compound	Nature	Properties
HF	Colorless liquid; b.p. 19°C.	H-bonded polymer
CaF_2	Colorless crystals; m.p. 1360°C.	Insoluble in water; fluorite structure
KHF_2	Colorless crystals; m.p. 239°C.	Soluble in water, dissociated
SbF_3	White solid; m.p. 292°C.	Hydrolyzes in H_2O; soluble in methanol
MoF_6	Colorless liquid; m.p. 17.5°C.; b.p. 35°C.	Hydrolyzed instantaneously
K_2OsF_6	Pale yellow crystals	Sparingly soluble in water
BrF_3	Yellow liquid	Explodes with water and vigorously fluorinates many compounds
SF_4	Colorless gas; m.p. −121°C.	Hydrolyzes in H_2O
SF_6	Colorless gas; m.p. −56°C.	Stable to water and most reagents
CF_3I	Colorless gas; b.p. −22.5°C.	Alcoholic KOH → CHF_3
CF_3COOH	Colorless liquid; b.p. 72.4°C.	Strong acid; miscible with water
$(—CF_2—CF_2—)_n$	Translucent greasy solid	Very stable to all chemical reagents
$P(CF_3)_3$	Colorless liquid; b.p. 17.5°C.	Donor molecule
$CF_3CCl_2CFClCF_3$	Colorless liquid; b.p. 98°C.	Insoluble in water; stable to oxidants

Ionic Fluorides. These contain the F^- ion. The relatively small radius of F^-, 1.36 A., is almost identical with that of the oxide, O^{2-}, ion

(1.40 A.), consequently, many fluorides and oxides are ionic with similar formulas and crystal structure, for example, CaO and NaF. The compounds of the other halogens with the same formula usually form quite different lattices and may even give molecular lattices. Thus chlorides and other halides often resemble sulfides, just as the fluorides often resemble oxides. In several cases the fluorides are completely ionic, whereas the other halides are covalent; for example, CdF_2 and MgF_2 have the CaF_2 lattice (nearly all difluorides have the fluorite or rutile structures), but $CdCl_2$ and $MgCl_2$ have layer lattices with the metal atoms octahedrally surrounded by chlorine atoms. These differences also show up in the solubilities in water.

Covalent Fluorides. Covalent fluorides of many elements exist, and it is obvious that in view of the high electronegativity of fluorine such bonds have very considerable ionic character. It may be noted that fluorine shows the lowest affinity toward oxygen, which is not surprising in the light of their high electronegativities.

The high electronegativity of fluorine and its ability to withdraw electron density to itself is demonstrated by facts such as (a) CF_3COOH is a very strong acid, (b) $(CF_3)_3N$ has no basic properties, and (c) CF_3 derivatives are attacked much less readily by electrophilic reagents in anionic substitutions than are CH_3 compounds.

The coordination number of fluorine seldom exceeds 1. However, several cases of fluorine atoms acting as bridges and being two coordinate are known; thus, in BeF_2 glass BF_4 tetrahedra are joined together by shared fluorine atoms, and in SbF_5, a viscous liquid, polymeric species also occur. The best-documented cases of fluorine bridging occur in $K^+[(C_2H_5)_3Al-F-Al(C_2H_5)_3]^-$, in which the Al—F—Al group is linear and symmetrical and the Al—F distance is equal to 1.80 ± 0.06 A., and in BeF_2 (page 172).

An important feature in the formation of fluorides is that in reactions with fluorine or with powerful fluorinating agents such as BrF_3, the elements usually give the highest known or maximum oxidation state; as noted previously, only oxides in comparable oxidation states are known. Thus silver gives AgF_2; the platinum metals give RuF_5, PtF_6, and OsF_6; and iodine gives IF_7.

Hydrogen bonding. Along with N and O, fluorine often engages in hydrogen bond formation. The hydride HF is consequently abnormal compared to the other halogen HX compounds, just as NH_3 and H_2O are abnormal. In the liquid and vapor state HF is polymeric; the structure has been noted previously (see page 128). HF gives complex ions such as HF_2^- and $H_2F_3^-$. Although the formula for the bifluoride ion is often written $[F-H-F]^-$ to indicate that it is linear and symmetrical, this may create the erroneous impression that hydrogen is forming two electron pair bonds. The electron structure of this ion can be expressed in terms of resonance theory as a hybrid (14-I); or it may be considered in terms of the

$$[\overset{-}{F}\cdots\overset{\delta^+}{H}-\overset{\delta^-}{F}] \leftrightarrow [\overset{\delta^-}{F}-\overset{\delta^+}{H}\cdots\overset{-}{F}]$$
$$\text{(14-Ia)} \qquad\qquad \text{(14-Ib)}$$

concept of three-center bonds where two fluorine σ orbitals and the hydrogen $1s$ orbital combine to form three-center orbitals, one bonding (B), one antibonding (A), and one nonbonding (NB), which are populated $(B)^2(NB)^2(A)^0$.

The ability of fluorine to form hydrogen bonds is also shown by the hydration of certain fluorides, whereas the other halides are more commonly anhydrous. It must be noted, however, that the other halides do show some tendency to hydrogen bond formation, as evidenced by the behavior of $CHCl_3$ and the existence of salts with Cs^+, $[NR_4]^+$, and other large monovalent cations of stoichiometry $RHCl_2$.

Bond Distances and Bond Energies in Covalent Fluorides. Because of the low dissociation energy of fluorine, the heats of formation of fluorine compounds in their standard states are such that most fluorine compounds are strongly exothermic; this is the opposite of the situation with nitrogen compounds where the bond in N_2 is very strong. Further, because of the high electronegativity of fluorine, ionic-covalent resonance contributes substantially to the bond energies. In addition, small atoms such as fluorine can form stronger bonds owing to better overlap of their electron density, and π bonding is much more likely to occur for this reason. Multiple bond formation by fluorine is certainly one of the contributing factors to the shortness of many bonds in involving fluorine—for example, in BF_3 and SiF_4—when compared to those formed by the other halogens.

Organic Fluorine Derivatives. A vast number of organic compounds are now known in which hydrogen atoms are replaced by fluorine atoms. Examples are $CF_3CCl_2CFClCF_3$, $CF_2{=}CF_2$, $CF_3C{\equiv}CCF_3$, $C_3F_7CH_2NH_2$, and $CF_3PO_3H_2$.

Many of these compounds have chemical and physical properties strikingly different from the hydrogen analogs or from the analogous compounds of the other halogens where these exist. The C—F bond energy is indeed very high (103.4 kcal./mole), but organic fluorides are not necessarily particularly thermodynamically stable; indeed, some of the stabilities of fluorine derivatives must be attributed to the impossibility of expansion of the octet of fluorine and the inability of, say, water to coordinate to fluorine or carbon as the first step in hydrolysis, whereas with chlorine this may be possible using outer d orbitals.

THE ELEMENT

14-3. Occurrence, Isolation, and Properties

Fluorine is rather widespread in nature, occurring as insoluble fluorides of electropositive metals, notably as fluorspar, CaF_2; cryolite, Na_3AlF_6; and fluorapatite, $3Ca_3(PO_4)_2Ca(F,Cl)_2$.

The estimated standard oxidation potential of F^- ($E° = -2.85$ v.) clearly indicates why early attempts to prepare the element by electrolytic methods in aqueous solution suitable for chlorine ($E° = -1.36$ v.) failed. The element was first isolated in 1886 by Moissan, who pioneered the chemistry of fluorine and its compounds. The gas is obtained by electrolysis of fluorides in media with no other anions present. Anhydrous HF is nonconducting, but the addition of anhydrous KF gives conducting solutions. The most commonly used electrolytes are KF·2–3HF, which is molten at 70–100°C., and KF–HF, which is molten at 250–270°C. The electrolyte can be regenerated when the melting point begins to be too high by resaturation with HF from a storage tank. There have been many designs for fluorine cells; these are constructed of steel, copper, or Monel metal, which become coated with an unreactive layer of fluoride, and steel or copper cathodes with ungraphitized carbon anodes are used. Although fluorine is often handled in metal apparatus, it can be handled in the laboratory in glass apparatus provided traces of HF, which attacks glass rapidly, are removed. This is achieved by passing the gas through sodium or potassium fluorides with which HF forms the bifluorides.

FLUORINE COMPOUNDS

14-4. Hydrogen Fluoride and Its Salts

Hydrogen Fluoride. Hydrogen fluoride, HF, is made by the action of concentrated H_2SO_4 on CaF_2 and is the principal source of fluorine and its compounds. It is commercially available in tanks. The liquid has a high dielectric constant (83.6 at 0°C.), and it is polymeric owing to hydrogen bonding. After water, it is one of the most generally useful of solvents; indeed, in some respects it surpasses water as a solvent for both inorganic and organic compounds, the latter often forming highly conducting solutions owing to their ionization. Very pure HF has a very low conductivity,

1.6×10^{-6} ohm^{-1} cm.$^{-1}$ at 0°C. The self-ionization equilibria in liquid HF are

$$2HF \rightleftarrows H_2F^+ + F^-$$
$$F^- + HF \rightleftarrows HF_2^- \ (H_2F_3^-, \ H_3F_4^-, \text{ etc.})$$

so that fluoride ion is the conjugate base, and fluorides behave as bases in the HF solvent system.

In aqueous solution, the equilibria are

$$HF + H_2O \rightleftarrows H_3O^+ + F^- \qquad K_1 = 7.2 \times 10^{-4}$$
$$F^- + HF \rightleftarrows F_2H^- \qquad K_2 = 5.1$$

The weakness of HF as an acid in *dilute* aqueous solution is in great contrast to that of other hydrogen halides; this point is discussed elsewhere (page 140). In 5–15M solutions ionization into H_3O^+, HF_2^-, and more complex species ($H_2F_3^-$, $H_3F_4^-$, etc.) occurs, and HF becomes a strong acid. The formation of these stable anions in liquid HF accounts for the extremely strong acidity of the pure substance. Only a few substances, such as BF_3, AsF_5, SbF_5, and SnF_4, which are among the strongest fluoride ion acceptors, will function as "acids" in the liquid:

$$SbF_5 + 2HF = H_2F^+ + SbF_6^-$$

Such solutions can dissolve many metals. Other strong acids such as nitric acid actually behave as bases in liquid HF,

$$HNO_3 + HF = H_2NO_3^+ + F^-$$

HNO_3 behaving as a proton acceptor. Other reactions can be found to illustrate amphoteric behavior, solvolysis, or complex formation in liquid HF.

Metal Fluorides; the Fluoride Ion. Many metals show their highest oxidation state in the fluorides and many of them are often salt-like in their properties. Let us consider the Born-Haber cycle in equation 14-1.

$$M(s) \xrightarrow{\ S\ } M(g) \xrightarrow{\ I_4\ } M^{4+}(g)$$
$$\searrow$$
$$MX_4(s) \qquad (14\text{-}1)$$
$$\nearrow$$
$$2X_2(g) \xrightarrow{\ 2D\ } 4X(g) \xrightarrow{\ 4A\ } 4X^-(g)$$

The value of $(A - D/2)$, the energy change in forming 1 g.-ion of X$^-$ from $\frac{1}{2}$ g.-mole of X_2, is ~60 kcal. for all of the halogens, and S is small compared to I_4 in all cases. Although the structure of MX_4 and hence the lattice energy may not be known to allow us to say whether $4(E - D/2)$ plus the lattice energy will compensate for $(I_4 + S)$, we can say that the lattice energy and hence the potential for forming an ionic halide in a high oxidation state will be greatest for fluoride, since, generally, for a given cation size the greatest lattice energy will be available for the smallest anion, that is, F^-.

However, for very high oxidation states, which are formed notably with transition metals, for example, WF_6 or OsF_6, the energy available is quite insufficient to allow ionic crystals with, say, W^{6+} or Os^{6+} ions; consequently such fluorides are gases, volatile liquids, or solids resembling closely the covalent fluorides of the nonmetals. The question as to whether a metal fluoride will be ionic or covalent cannot be reliably predicted, and the distinction between the types is not always sharp.

As noted previously, ionic oxides can also be obtained in high oxidation states, sometimes even higher than the fluorides, for example, MnF_3 and MnO_2. Fluorides in high oxidation states (unless the covalence maximum is attained) are often hydrolyzed by water, the important factors here being the greater stability of the ionic oxides and also the low dissociation of HF in aqueous solution. Thus, for example,

$$RuF_5 + H_2O \rightarrow RuO_2 + RuO_4 + HF$$

Many simple fluorides of metals in lower oxidation states are obtained by dissolving the oxides, carbonates, etc., in HF and drying the product, or by dry reaction. Higher fluorides, such as AgF_2 or CrF_4, usually require the use of elemental fluorine on the metal or a lower fluoride or other salt; bromine trifluoride has also been widely used as a fluorinating agent in place of fluorine.

The lanthanide elements and actinide elements in the $+3$ and $+4$ oxidation states give insoluble fluorides from aqueous solution. Fluorides of Li, Ca, Sr, and Ba also are sparingly soluble, the lithium compound being precipitated by ammonium fluoride. Lead gives a sparingly soluble salt, PbClF, which can be used for gravimetric determination of F^-.

CaF_2 is used for prisms in infrared spectrometers since it gives better resolution than NaCl in the region 1500–4000 cm.$^{-1}$. NH_4F differs from other ammonium halides in having a wurzite rather than a rock salt or CsI structure; each nitrogen atom forms four tetrahedral N—H—F bonds of length 2.69 A. Although the N—H stretching frequency is lowered from 3300 to 2820 cm.$^{-1}$ here, the N—H bond length is the same as in NH_4Cl.

Acid Fluorides.   The alkali metal fluorides with HF give various acid fluorides; the structure of HF_2^- has been noted before. These salts are prepared by mixing the appropriate proportions of the constituents; examples are $KF \cdot 4HF$ (m.p. $72°C.$), $KF \cdot 3HF$ (m.p. $65.8°C.$), and $KF \cdot HF$ (m.p. $239°C.$).

Polymeric Fluorides.   Several fluorides do not form simple ionic lattices. Rather, owing to the high charge/radius ratio of the cation, they give more covalent MF bonds and form macromolecules of which beryllium fluoride is a notable example.

Fluoro Anions. Many metals and nonmetals form complex fluoro anions, if the simple fluoride is coordinatively unsaturated; some fluorides, for instance BF_3 and PF_5, are extremely strong F^- ion acceptors. Fusion of simple fluorides often gives the complex fluoro anions, as does the action of BrF_3 or F_2 on complex chlorides. A simple general method is the reaction of ammonium fluoride with metal bromides in acetone solution to give complexes such as NH_4MnF_3, NH_4BiF_4, and $(NH_4)_3InF_6$. Examples of other reactions leading to the formation of fluoro anions are:

$$3NaF + AlF_3 \xrightarrow{\text{fuse}} Na_3AlF_6$$
$$B(OH)_3 + 4HF(aq) \longrightarrow BF_4^- + H^+ + 3H_2O$$
$$SO_3 + HF(l) \longrightarrow HSO_3F$$
$$KBr + Ru \xrightarrow{BrF_3} KRuF_6$$

Many of the complex fluorides of metals are hydrolyzed by water; this is particularly true where higher oxidation states are involved. The factors governing the stability of fluoro anions are similar to those noted previously for simple fluorides.

The complex fluoro acids are all exceedingly strong. In fact, it would be impossible for, say, HBF_4 to be otherwise without involving either pentavalent boron or divalent fluorine. In this case, study of the $HF-BF_3$ system shows that there is *no* 1:1 compound formed; that is, HBF_4 does not exist. If a solvent molecule is present to combine with the proton, compound formation can be observed as with $H_3O^+BF_4^-$. A similar situation exists with other fluoro anions, for example, PF_6^-.

14-5. Inorganic Molecular Fluorides

The molecular fluorides of both metals and nonmetals are usually gases or volatile liquids; analogs with the other halogens are often lacking, the reason being partly the size factor which with fluorine permits higher coordination numbers and partly the factors discussed above concerning the stability of higher oxidation states and covalent bond formation. Where the central atom has suitable vacant orbitals available, and especially if the polarity of the single bonds M—F would be such as to leave a considerable positive charge on M, as in, say, SF_6, multiple bonding can occur using filled p orbitals of fluorine for overlap with vacant orbitals of the central atom. The volatility of molecular fluorides is due to the absence of intermolecular bonding other than van der Waals forces, since the polarizability of fluorine is very low and no suitable outer orbitals exist for other types of attraction.

Where the fluoride gives the maximum covalence, as in CF_4 or SF_6, the compounds are exceedingly inert chemically. In other cases, rapid hydrolysis occurs in water or stable fluoro anions are formed; thus SeF_6 hydrolyzes on heating, and TeF_6 hydrolyzes at room temperature to $Te(OH)_6$, although SF_6 is inert to water.

The particular fluorides, where of interest, are discussed under the respective elements. Fluorine compounds of the other halogens are discussed under interhalogen compounds (page 461), but it is convenient to note here *perchloryl fluoride*. This compound, first made in 1952, is now produced in ton quantities as a powerful oxidizing agent. It is a stable gas, b.p. $-47.5°C$., inert and noncorrosive at room temperature. It has the highest dielectric constant of any known gas. The compound is prepared by the reaction

$$NaClO_4 + FSO_3H \xrightarrow{\text{warm}} FClO_3 + NaHSO_4$$

With aqueous ammonia, perchloryl fluoride reacts to give the ions $NClO_3^-$ and $HNClO_3^-$ which can be precipitated as explosive Rb or Cs salts.

14-6. Organic Fluorine Compounds

A vast number of organic fluorine compounds exist. They are prepared in a variety of ways, principally as follows:

1. *Replacement of other halogens using metal fluorides*. The driving force for a reaction

$$R-Cl + MF = R-F + MCl$$

depends in part on the free energy difference of MF and MCl, which is approximately equal to the difference in lattice energies. Since lattice energies are proportional to the reciprocal of the interionic distance, the increase in free energy when MCl is formed from MF is proportional to the difference of the reciprocals of the sums of the ionic radii in MF and MCl. Thus the larger the cation M, the less is the amount of free energy for the above reaction, and the fluorine-exchanging ability increases with increasing metal ion radius in isomorphous compounds. For AgF, the difference in lattice energies is small owing to contributions of nonionic bonding in AgCl, so that AgF is a very powerful fluorinating agent.

Other fluorinating agents, each having particular advantages under given conditions, are AgF_2, CoF_3, SbF_3 (+ $SbCl_5$ catalyst), HgF_2, KHF_2, ZnF_2, AsF_3, etc. Examples of some fluorinations are

$$PCl_3 + AsF_3 \xrightarrow{25°C.} PF_3 + AsCl_3$$
$$C_6H_5CCl_3 + SbF_3 \longrightarrow C_6H_5CF_3 + SbCl_3$$

Nonmetal fluorides are also often effective. Sulfur tetrafluoride is a particularly useful and selective fluorinating agent for organic oxygen compounds where, for example, $\diagdown$C$=$O groups are converted to $\diagdown$CF$_2$ groups.

2. *Hydrogen replacement using fluorides or fluorine.* Under controlled conditions, usually in the vapor phase, fluorine or cobaltic fluoride can be used, for example,

$$(CH_3)_3N \xrightarrow{\text{CoF}_3} (CF_3)_3N + (CF_3)_2NF + CF_3NF_2 + NF_3$$
$$C_6H_6 + F_2 \xrightarrow[265°C.]{\text{copper catalyst}} C_6F_{12}$$

A special case of this type of substitution, which is widely used in the laboratory and commercially, is the electrolysis of compounds in liquid HF at a voltage below that required for the liberation of fluorine. Steel cells with nickel anodes and steel cathodes are used. Organic compounds, as noted before, often give conducting solutions in liquid HF and are fluorinated at the anode, usually into a perfluoro derivative. Examples of electrolytic fluorinations are

$$(C_2H_5)_2O \rightarrow (C_2F_5)_2O$$
$$C_8H_{18} \rightarrow C_8F_{18}$$
$$(CH_3)_2S \rightarrow CF_3SF_5 + (CF_3)_2SF_4$$
$$(C_4H_9)_3N \rightarrow (C_4F_9)_3N$$

Other methods sometimes used are the addition of HF to multiple bonds and thermal decomposition of aromatic diazonium fluoroborates, for example,

$$CCl_2{=}CCl_2 \xrightarrow[25°C.]{\text{PbO}_2 + \text{HF}} CCl_2HCCl_2F$$
$$C_6H_5N_2Cl \xrightarrow{\text{NaBF}_4} C_6H_5N_2BF_4 \xrightarrow{\text{heat}} C_6H_5F + N_2 + BF_3$$

The C—F bond is very stable, and fluorocarbon compounds tend to decompose on heating by breaking C—C bonds in contrast to the hydrocarbons where C—H bonds are broken. The stability of C_nF_{2n+2} compounds is in part due to the fact that the fluorine atoms so block the carbon atoms that attack on C—C or C—F bonds via attack on the carbon atoms is virtually impossible for steric reasons.

The replacement of H by F leads to increased density, but not to the same extent as with other halogens. Completely fluorinated derivatives, C_nF_{2n+2}, have very low boiling points for their molecular weights and low intermolecular forces; the weakness of these forces is also shown by the very low coefficient of friction for polytetrafluoroethylene, $(CF_2—CF_2)_n$.

Commercially important organic fluorine derivatives are chlorofluorocarbons, which are used as nontoxic, inert refrigerants, aerosol bomb propellants, and heat transfer agents, and fluoroolefins, used as monomers for free-radical-initiated polymerizations to oils, greases, etc., and also as chemical intermediates.

The fluorinated carboxylic acids are notable first for their strongly acid nature—for example, for CF_3COOH, $K_a = 5.9 \times 10^{-1}$, whereas CH_3COOH has $K_a = 1.8 \times 10^{-5}$. Second, many standard reactions of carboxylic acids can be made leaving the fluoroalkyl group intact, as in equation 14-2.

$$C_3F_7COOH \xrightarrow[C_2H_5OH]{H_2SO_4} C_3F_7COOC_2H_5 \xrightarrow{NH_3} C_3F_7CONH_2 \begin{array}{c} \xrightarrow{P_2O_5} C_3F_7CN \\ \searrow_{LiAlH_4} \\ C_3F_7CH_2NH_2 \end{array} \qquad (14\text{-}2)$$

Trifluoroacetic anhydride obtained by action of P_2O_5 on the acid is widely used in organic chemistry as an acylating agent in presence of acid.

The $C_nF_{2n+1}COOH$ acids can be converted to *perfluoroalkyl halides* by, for example, the action of I_2 on the silver salt. These halides are relatively reactive, undergoing free radical reactions on heating or on irradiation, although, because of the very strong electron-attracting nature of the perfluoroalkyl groups, they fail to show many of the common nucleophilic reactions of alkyl halides. They do not, for example, readily form Grignard reagents. The activation energy for the reaction

$$CF_3I = CF_3 \cdot + I \cdot$$

is only 1.7 kcal./mole. CF_3I is an important intermediate for preparation of trifluoromethyl derivatives. Thus the reaction of CF_3I and similar compounds with metals and nonmetals has led to an extensive range of CF_3 derivatives, for example,

$$CF_3I + P \xrightarrow{heat} (CF_3)_nPI_{3-n}$$

References

Cady, G. H., *Proc. Chem. Soc. (London)*, **1960**, 133. Review on fluorocarbons and perfluoroalkyl compounds.

Clark, H. C., *Chem. Revs.*, **58**, 869 (1958). Physical and chemical properties of halogen fluorides and other covalent fluorides.

Eméleus, H. J., *Proc. Chem. Soc. (London)*, **1960**, 234. Review on fluorocarbons and perfluoroalkyl compounds.

Haszeldine, R. N., and A. G. Sharpe, *Fluorine and Its Compounds*, Methuen, London, 1951. A small book on general fluorine chemistry with particular reference to organic derivatives, BrF_3, etc.

Mellor, J. W., *Comprehensive Treatise of Inorganic Chemistry*, Vol. II, Suppl. I, Part I, Longmans, Green, New York–London, 1956.

Peacock, R. D., "Some Fluorine Compounds of the Transition Metals," in F. A. Cotton, ed., *Progress in Inorganic Chemistry*, Vol. II, Interscience, New York–London, 1960, p. 193.

Sharpe, A. G., *Quart. Revs. (London)*, **9**, 49 (1957). An excellent brief article on inorganic fluorine chemistry.

Simons, J. H., ed., *Fluorine Chemistry*, Vols. I–III, Academic Press, New York, 1954. Fairly comprehensive reference books on special topics in fluorine chemistry.

Stacey, M., J. C. Tatlow, and A. G. Sharpe, eds., *Advances in Fluorine Chemistry*, Vols. I and II, Butterworths, London, 1960 and 1961. A series of annual review volumes covering all aspects of fluorine chemistry.

15

Molecular Stereochemistry In Compounds of Nontransition Elements

15-1. Introduction

We have now completed our discussion of those elements of the first short period which strictly obey the octet rule. Several of them also have a strong tendency to form multiple bonds. The stereochemistry of their compounds is governed by these two facts. In the chapters immediately following we shall discuss the chemistry of the remaining nontransitional elements, that is, the congeners of the elements of the first short period. For many of these elements the presence of low-lying d orbitals means that the number of electron pairs in the valence shell may exceed four; that is, the octet rule no longer holds rigorously and is indeed very often violated. In addition, for these heavier atoms, participation in double bond formation by the use of $p\pi$ orbitals is much less important than for their congeners in the first short period, whereas they can use low-lying $d\pi$ orbitals to participate in varying degrees of multiple bonding. Thus the stereochemistry of molecular compounds of the heavier elements is somewhat more varied and complex.

However, in compounds of all *nontransition* elements, there are three guiding principles in understanding and predicting molecular structures: (*1*) use of hybrid rather than pure hydrogen-like orbitals by atoms in forming bonds, (*2*) that unshared pairs of electrons occupy hybrid orbitals in much the same way as do the shared (bonding) pairs and they therefore play an essential role in determining the necessary hybridization scheme, and (*3*) that repulsions between various electron pairs will have secondary but noticeable effects. Regarding the last principle we may reason that a pair of electrons held by only one atom will constitute a larger and more diffuse charge cloud than that due to an electron pair held between two atoms bonded together by that electron pair. Thus, other things being

298

equal, it would be expected that the various electron pair repulsions would increase in the order: bonding-bonding, bonding-nonbonding, nonbonding-nonbonding.

In discussing molecular structures here, we shall be primarily concerned with the configuration of a group of atoms all bound to a common central atom. If we make the usual assumption* that the bonds lie along the internuclear axes, then we may rephrase the question of why the central atom in a compound, say sulfur in SF_4, is surrounded by the four fluorine atoms in a particular way to the question of why the sulfur atom has a set of four bonding orbitals in these particular directions. Thus we are actually concerned with the question of *directed valence* in an atom to which several other atoms are bound—in general, the atom A in a molecule of the type AB_n. We shall find that it is the electronic structure of atom A itself that basically determines the structure of the compound AB_n and that the nature of the atom B will have only a secondary effect.

In the following sections we shall deal first with compounds having central atoms with octets and then with compounds having central atoms which contain more than eight electrons in their valence shells.

15-2. Directed Valence in Atoms with Octets

To a certain extent this section will be a review and codification of principles mentioned already in discussions of the elements of the first short period. However, we shall also deal with heavier elements in compounds where they have octets. First we shall consider the cases where all valence shell electrons are present either as unshared pairs or in single bonds and then those cases where some of the valence shell electrons are in multiple bonds formed by the atom using its p orbitals.

Molecules with Only Single Bonds. In Table 15-1 are listed some representative molecules of the types AB_2, AB_3, and AB_4, where the central atom A has an octet of electrons in its valence shell. It will be seen that the bond angles lie in the range 91–115° with all but one between 91 and $\sim107°$. In NH_3 and H_2O the angles come closest to the tetrahedral angle of 109°28′. As already noted in several places, current theoretical work indicates that the best explanation for these bond angles involves the assumption that the central atom, O or N, tends to assume sp^3 hybridization. However, because the bonding and nonbonding electron pairs are not equivalent, we might expect that the orbitals holding the unshared

* This is only an assumption in many cases, though not all, and the idea of some bonds being at least a little "bent" cannot be summarily dismissed in sophisticated valence theory.

TABLE 15-1

Structural Parameters in Some AB_2, AB_3, and ACB_3 Molecules
in Which Atom A Has an Octet

Molecule	Bond angle, deg.	Molecule	Bond angle, deg.
NH_3	107	OCl_2	$\sim$111
		ClO_2	$\sim$117
PH_3	94	OF_2	102
AsH_3	92	POF_3	103 (FPF)
SbH_3	91	SO_2F_2	93 (FSF)
H_2O	105	PSF_3	100 (FPF)
H_2S	92	SCl_2	$\sim$102
NF_3	103		
PF_3	104		
PCl_3	100		
PBr_3	$\sim$100		
AsF_3	102		
$AsCl_3$	98		
$SbCl_3$	104		
$SbBr_3$	$\sim$96		
SbI_3	$\sim$98		

pairs and the orbitals used in bonding would not be exactly equivalent to one another. The deviations of the angles are toward values less than 109°28'. It has been suggested that the bonding pairs are more concentrated along the internuclear axes so that the lone pairs tend to occupy relatively more space. Thus the hybridization is such as to give bonding orbitals with a somewhat smaller angle between them in order that the best energetic compromise may be reached between maximizing bond strengths and minimizing interelectronic replulsions. Once again, we may repeat that it has been shown that the electrostatic forces of repulsion between the relatively positive hydrogen atoms in NH_3 and H_2O would be insufficient to account for an expansion from 90° if we had assumed that the central atoms preferred using pure p orbitals for bonding.

It is striking that, on going from NH_3 to PH_3, the angle drops sharply to $\sim$94° and then to $\sim$92° in AsH_3 and SbH_3. Similarly, the HSH angle is only $\sim$92°. This could result from the ability of the heavier elements to form stronger bonds to hydrogen using nearly pure p orbitals. Similarly, in halides, especially fluorides, the angles are generally much below the tetrahedral value indicating increased p character in the bonding orbitals and decreased p character in the orbitals holding lone pairs. There appears to be some evidence from microwave studies that the contribution of d

character in H_2S and other non-first-row compounds is of the same order as the s character and can lower the angle in H_2S to about 90°.

It has been pointed out—and is apparent from the data in Table 15-1 —that smaller angles usually occur in those molecules in which the central atom is less electronegative than the atoms to which it is bound. This can be explained by considering that the configuration of lowest potential energy is determined not only by the dependence of overlap, and hence intrinsic bond strength, on the angles but also by the variation of repulsive energy between the various electron pairs (i.e., lone pair–bonding pair, lone pair–lone pair, and bonding pair–bonding pair repulsions). As the bonding electrons in AB_3, for example, are drawn further away from A, the bonding pair–bonding pair repulsion will lessen, permitting some closing up of the bond angles in order to decrease lone pair–bonding pair repulsions. It is not known whether this hypothesis is correct, but it seems reasonable and in agreement with observation. The large bond angle in ClO_2 has not been explained with certainty; steric repulsion may be principally responsible.

Molecules with Multiple Bonds. In molecules in which there are *multiple bonds*, but with all atoms obeying the octet rule, it is possible to predict the symmetry of the molecules quite reliably either by valence bond theory or by molecular orbital theory; at the same time neither approach used in the simple forms to be described below can be counted on to give angles to within better than 10–15° or so.

From the valence bond point of view, we may consider, as before, that in any atom having an octet of electrons these will be arranged so that a pair of electrons tends to be centered around each apex of a tetrahedron. Now, in a molecule like ethane, we have found that the structure is correctly predicted by treating the C—C single bond as corresponding to the sharing of an apex by two tetrahedra about the carbon atoms. This approach may be extended to the cases of double and triple bonds. A *double bond* is considered to result from the sharing of a common edge by two tetrahedra. Thus, for example, in the general case of an ABX=YCD type molecule the structure should be as shown in Figure 15-1, with the angles AXY, CYX, etc., equal to about 125° and the angles AXB and CYD equal to about 109°. Note that this approach predicts qualitatively that the entire molecule should be planar and provides a kind of mechanical analogy for remember-

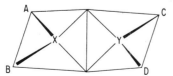

Fig. 15-1. The formation of a double bond by sharing a common edge of two tetrahedra.

ing that rotation about a double bond is strongly hindered. This most general formulation includes cases where A, B, C, and D are all atoms as in ethylenes as well as cases in which one, two, or three of them are only unshared pairs as in $R_2C=N(OH)$, $Cl_2C=O$, $C_6H_5N=N(OH)$, or $ClN=O$.

From the point of view of molecular orbital theory, molecules with double bonds can be treated in the following way, taking again the general case $ABX=YCD$. Each of the atoms X and Y is assumed to possess a set of hybrid orbitals approximating to, and let us for simplicity at the outset say exactly, sp^2, made up of the atomic orbitals, s, p_x, and p_y. One of these on each atom, X and Y, is used to form an X—Y σ bond. The remaining two are used to house electron pairs either in bonds to the atoms A, B, C, and D or to house unshared pairs of electrons. Finally, the p_z orbitals on X and Y, each containing one electron, combine to form an X—Y π bond. Again, therefore, we would predict coplanarity of the $ABX=YCD$ skeleton and, because of the π bond, a strong hindrance to internal rotation. If we keep to our original assumption that the hybridization of X and Y is exactly sp^2, then we must expect *all* bond angles to be 120°. But, considering X, for example, this assumption is over-restrictive since there is no reason why the orbitals used by X to bind the three different groups, A, B, and Y, should be exactly equivalent. If they are not, then deviations of the bond angles from 120° may be expected.

In order to test the utility of these two approaches, both of which lead to identical predictions regarding symmetry and substantially the same predictions as to the order of magnitude of the bond angles, we may refer to some data on representative molecules assembled in Table 15-2.

TABLE 15-2

Structures of Some Molecules of the Type $ABX=YCD$

Molecule	A	B	X	Y	C	D	Planar	Bond angle, deg.			
								YXA	YXB	XYC	XYD
$H_2C=CH_2$	H	H	C	C	H	H	Yes	120	120	120	120
$Cl_2C=CCl_2$	Cl	Cl	C	C	Cl	Cl	Yes	123	123	123	123
$H_2N=NO_2$	H	H	N	N	O	O	Yes	Unknown		115	115
$(CH_3)_2C=N(OH)$	C	C	C	N	O	—	Yes	131	113	111	—
$[ON=NO]^{2-}$	O	—	N	N	O	—	Yes	Unknown			
ClNO	Cl	—	N	O	—	—	Yes	116	—	—	—
BrNO	Br	—	N	O	—	—	Yes	114	—	—	—
$Cl_2C=O$	Cl	Cl	C	O	—	—	Yes	124	124	—	—
$F_2C=O$	F	F	C	O	—	—	Yes	~124	~124	—	—
HFC=O	H	F	C	O	—	—	Yes	Unknown	122	—	—

There remains one other case of double bond formation by atoms with octets, namely, the general case A=X=B. From the valence bond approach we should predict linearity for such an arrangement, that is, an AXB angle of 180° as shown in Figure 15-2. Using the molecular orbital

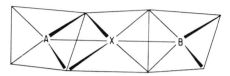

Fig. 15-2. Formation of two double bonds according to the valence bond view.

approach, we reach precisely the same conclusion by the following analysis. The atom X uses two sp hybrid orbitals to form σ bonds to the atoms A and B. It then has two p orbitals, at right angles to one another in a plane perpendicular to the AXB axis, which can combine with corresponding orbitals on A and B to form π bonds. This is illustrated in Figure 15-3.

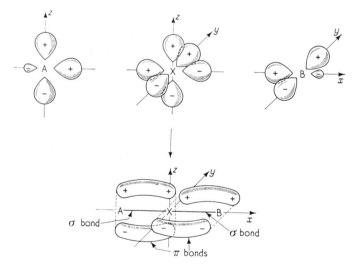

Fig. 15-3. Formation of two double bonds according to the molecular orbital view.

In each case one would also predict great hindrance to rotation of A relative to B. A few examples of molecules of this sort which substantiate the prediction are:

H₂C=C=O (ketene): $\widehat{CCO}$ = 180°; $\widehat{HCH}$ = 123°
O=C=O: Linear
N=N=O (in resonance with (N≡N—O): Linear
O=C=C=C=O: Linear
H₂C=C=CH₂ (allene): $\widehat{CCC}$ = 180°; $\widehat{HCH}$ = 117°
H—N=C=O: $\widehat{NCO}$ = 180°; $\widehat{HNC}$ = 126°
H—N=C=S: $\widehat{NCS}$ = 180°; $\widehat{HNC}$ = 131°

Now let us consider *triple bonds*, for which the general case would be A—X≡Y—B. In valence bond theory we consider the triple bond as the sharing between X and Y of a tetrahedron face. As can be seen in Figure 15-4, this leads to the prediction that the A—X≡Y—B chain should be

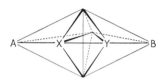

Fig. 15-4. Formation of a triple bond according to the valence bond view.

completely linear. Taking a molecular orbital approach, we assume that atoms X and Y each use linear *sp* hybrid orbitals to form the σ bonds A—X—Y and X—Y—B. Then there remain, on both X and Y, pairs of *p* orbitals at right angles to one another and in planes perpendicular to the AXYB axis which overlap to form two π bonds (Fig. 15-5). Thus, again,

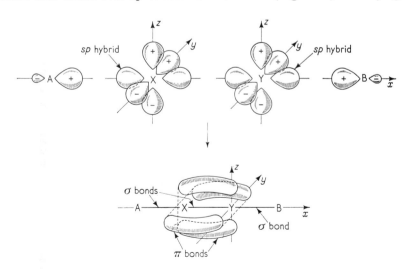

Fig. 15-5. Formation of a triple bond according to the molecular orbital view.

both approaches have given the same prediction as to symmetry, and all available data indicate that this prediction is correct. Thus, for example, acetylene and all its derivatives, for example, $N\equiv C-C\equiv CH$, $Cl-C\equiv C-H$, $CH_3-C\equiv C-CH_3$, etc., are linear, as are $HC\equiv N$, $N\equiv C-C\equiv N$, and others.

Before concluding this section, a few additional remarks are in order lest too optimistic a view of the state of simple structural theory be given. The above ideas have their limitations and involve in their application further complications. The chief limitation is that except in the cases such as the AXB angle in $A=X=B$ and the AXY and XYB angles in $A-X\equiv Y-B$, *exact* bond angles cannot be predicted. To take a concrete example, for a molecule of the type $X_2C=CX_2$ the XCX angles are never exactly 125.5° as predicted by valence bond theory or 120° as predicted by the molecular orbital treatment in the above simple forms and, moreover, they vary with the nature of the atoms X. Thus in $H_2C=CH_2$ the HCH angle is 119.9°, and in $H_2C=CBr_2$ the BrCBr angle is 113.5°. Such variability is actually to be expected, just as in the case of molecules without multiple bonds. In terms of the valence bond approach it simply means that the four electron pairs do not lie at the corners of a perfectly regular tetrahedron, and, since the environments at the various corners are not identical, we should not be surprised at the lack of precise regularity. Similarly, in terms of the molecular orbital treatment, the deviations from 120° bond angles simply mean that the carbon atoms do not use three equivalent sp^2 hybrid orbitals, but that those used to form the σ bonds to the atoms X differ somewhat from the one used to form the σ bond to carbon, and that the variation in the orbitals depends somewhat on the identity of the atoms X. It is quite reasonable to expect such variation.

In molecules where several resonance forms are important, there is some additional complexity. It sometimes happens that all important canonical forms predict *exactly* the same bond angles, and the interpretation remains perfectly cleancut. Examples of this are 15-I and 15-II. The next most

$$: \overset{..}{\underset{..}{N}}=\overset{+}{N}=\overset{..}{O}: \quad \leftrightarrow \quad : N\equiv \overset{+}{N}-\overset{\overline{..}}{\underset{..}{O}}:$$

(15-Ia)   (15-Ib)

$$: N\equiv C-C\equiv N: \quad \leftrightarrow \quad : \overset{\overline{..}}{N}=C=C=\overset{+}{N}: \quad \leftrightarrow \quad : \overset{+}{N}=C=C=\overset{\overline{..}}{\underset{..}{N}}:$$

(15-IIa)   (15-IIb)   (15-IIc)

complicated case is one in which two or more important canonical forms require the same general symmetry, but not exactly the same bond angles. A typical example of this would be carbonyl chloride (15-III). All three

$$
\underset{\text{Cl}}{\overset{\text{Cl}}{\diagdown}}\text{C}{=}\text{O} \leftrightarrow \underset{\text{Cl}}{\overset{\overset{+}{\text{Cl}}}{\diagdown}}\text{C}{-}\text{O}^- \leftrightarrow \underset{\underset{+}{\text{Cl}}}{\overset{\text{Cl}}{\diagdown}}\text{C}{-}\text{O}^-
$$

(15-IIIa)   (15-IIIb)   (15-IIIc)

resonance structures require planarity, and the molecule is indeed planar, but each would be most stable with a somewhat different set of bond angles. The actual angles must be assumed to be the best compromise energetically. In the case of the nitrate ion we use the valence bond description shown in 15-IV. Now, no one of the energetically equivalent

$$
\overset{\text{O}}{\underset{}{\overset{\|}{\text{N}}}} \leftrightarrow \overset{\text{O}}{\underset{}{\overset{|}{\text{N}}}} \leftrightarrow \overset{\text{O}}{\underset{}{\overset{|}{\text{N}}}}
$$

(15-IVa)   (15-IVb)   (15-IVc)

structures 15-IVa–c, *if* it existed, would have the three-fold symmetry which the nitrate ion actually has, but, of course, we must remember that the canonical structures are hypothetical. They must be assumed to have the geometry of the actual molecule, even though the distribution of the electrons is less symmetrical.

In concluding this section, we may briefly consider the relation between the valence bond and molecular orbital treatments of multiple bonding which have been shown to be equally good in accounting for the symmetry of molecules with multiple bonds. Although both seem about equally useful, we might ask the question: Are both equally valid fundamentally?

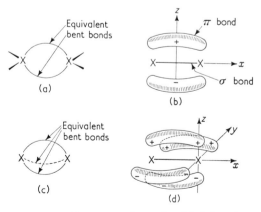

Fig. 15-6. Representations of multiple bonds.

In other words, is there any basic theoretical reason for preferring Figure 15-6a over 15-6b as a description of a double bond, or Figure 15-6c over 15-6d as a description of a triple bond, or can one choose whichever is handiest for a particular purpose?

The answer is that in quantitative calculations both formulations can be shown to be correct to a fairly high degree of approximation. In fact, the two bent bonds in Figure 15-6a are mathematically *equivalent* to the $(\sigma + \pi)$ combination in Figure 15-6b, and the three bent bonds in Figure 15-6c are mathematically *equivalent* to the $(\sigma + 2\pi)$ combination in Figure 15-6d. It happens, particularly in organic chemistry, that the $(\sigma + \pi)$ formulation of multiple bonding has certain conceptual advantages and has a certain vogue at present, but it is not fundamentally any more *correct* than the valence bond formulation. It is well to develop facility in using both concepts in considering possible structures for molecules.

15-3. Directed Valence in Atoms with Valence Shells of More Than Eight Electrons

The nontransition elements in groups IV, V, VI, and VII of the second and higher periods form various compounds in which their valence shells are occupied by more than four electron pairs, counting both shared and unshared pairs. The molecular structures encountered in such compounds are often unusual at first sight, but essentially all of them are explicable and to a considerable degree predictable. Let us first consider molecules of the type AB_n where the number of electron pairs in the valence shell of A is equal to n; that is, all pairs are bonding pairs.

The first stage beyond the octet is the decet, in molecules of general formula AB_5. In order for A to house five electron pairs, it must have five bonding orbitals. Its ns and three np orbitals provide the components of only four hybrid bonding orbitals. In order to make five, an additional atomic orbital of the lowest possible energy must also be used. This will presumably be one of the nd orbitals. Thus, the bonding orbitals will be some kind of sp^3d hybrids. As noted on page 70, there are two sorts of sp^3d hybrids possessing some degree of symmetry: $sp^3d_{z^2}$, in which the five hybrids are directed to the apices of a trigonal bipyramid, and $sp^3d_{x^2-y^2}$ (or sp^3d_{xy}), in which they are directed to the corners of a square pyramid. It is difficult to predict with any certainty which set will give the more stable compound in any given case, but experimental evidence indicates that it will generally be the $sp^3d_{z^2}$ set, since all known structures are of the trigonal bipyramid type, as in PCl_5 (gas), PF_5, and $SbCl_5$.

In compounds of type AB_6, where all valence shell electrons of atom A are bonding electrons, atom A must have six hybrid orbitals, and these may reasonably be expected to be of the octahedral sp^3d^2 type. Thus, such molecules should be octahedral, and all of them which are known do indeed have this structure. These include such molecules and ions as SF_6, SeF_6, TeF_6, PF_6^-, $SnCl_6^{2-}$, SiF_6^{2-}, etc., as well as F_5S—SF_5, in which each sulfur atom is octahedrally surrounded by five fluorine atoms and a sulfur atom.

Molecules or ions of type AB_7 with fourteen electrons in the valence shell orbitals of atom A are quite rare. They could only be of the following types: AB_7, where A is in group VII; AB_7^-, where A is in group VI; AB_7^{2-}, where A is in group V; or AB_7^{3-}, where A is in group IV. There are no examples known of the ions, and only one neutral molecule, namely, IF_7. The seven bonding orbitals used by iodine are most likely some sort of sp^3d^3 hybrids, although it is not impossible that $4f$ orbitals might play some part in the hybridization. Even assuming that $4f$ orbitals may be neglected, there are various possible arrangements depending upon which three d orbitals are used. The most symmetrical possibility would be a pentagonal bipyramid, and this is the structure of IF_7 in both the vapor and crystalline states, although in the crystal there is significant distortion.

We can now consider the class of molecules in which the valence shell of atom A in an AB_n molecule contains ten, twelve, or fourteen electrons and also more than n electron pairs; in other words, cases in which there are unshared electron pairs on the central atom.

Let us first consider molecules of type AB_4 in which there is *one unshared pair* on atom A. There are a fair number of such molecules known, and all those for which the structures have been established are listed in Table 15-3.

TABLE 15-3

Structures of AB_4 Molecules in Which There Is One Unshared Pair on Atom A

Molecule	Distance, A.		Angle, deg.	
	A—B	A—B'	BAB	B'AB'
SF_4	Molecular parameters unknown, but symmetry of structure shown to be as in Fig. 15-7			
SeF_4	~1.76	~1.76	180–200	~120
$(C_6H_5)_2SeCl_2$	Se—Cl: 2.30 ± 0.05	Se—C: ?	180 ± 5	?
$(C_6H_5)_2SeBr_2$	Se—Br: 2.52 ± 0.05	Se—C: 1.91 ± 0.03	180 ± 3	110 ± 10
$TeCl_4$	~2.33	~2.33	~170	90–120
$(C_6H_5)_2TeBr_2$	Te—Br: 2.682	Te—C: 2.18	178	95 ± 1
$(CH_3)_2TeCl_2$	Te—Cl: 2.51 ± 0.04	Te—C: 2.09 ± 0.03	172.3 ± 0.3	98.2 ± 1.1
$[IO_2F_2]^-$	I—F: 2.0 ± 0.1	I—O: 1.93 ± 0.05	~180	100 ± 7

The interbond angles, where known, are quoted with reference to the labeling of angles in Figure 15-7, which shows the type of structure char-

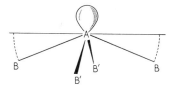

Fig. 15-7. The general structure of molecules of the types AB_4 or AB_2C_2 where atom A has an unshared pair of electrons.

acteristic of all such molecules so far as is known. Although such a relatively unsymmetrical structure seems a little surprising, it may be explained in the following way. We assume that the central atom uses a set of sp^3d trigonal bipyramid orbitals for holding the five electron pairs in its valence shell and that the unshared pair occupies one of the equatorial orbitals. Ideally, this would mean that the BAB angle should be 180° and the B'AB' angle should be 120°. As in previous cases, we can expect only that the actual angles will approximate to these values. The data in Table 15-3, most of which are not extremely accurate, indicate that the above view enables one to predict the correct symmetry and approximately the correct bond angles. The tendency of the B'—A—B' angles to be much less than 120° may be explained by assuming that the nonbonding pair–bonding pair repulsions are greater than bonding pair–bonding pair repulsions.

We may extend the same analysis to account for the structures of AB_3 and AB_2 systems in which atom A has altogether five electron pairs in its valence shell.

There are three known examples of the AB_3 case (two unshared pairs), namely, ClF_3, BrF_3, and ICl_3, the structures of which are shown in Figure 15-8. The molecular parameters given for ClF_3 and BrF_3 are the extremely accurate ones determined by microwave studies of the gases. X-ray studies show only slight and insignificant variations in the crystalline materials. ICl_3 exists only as a solid and has the dimeric structure shown. The structures of ClF_3 and BrF_3 can be accounted for by assuming that the Cl and Br atoms use a set of sp^3d trigonal bipyramid orbitals to house three pairs of bonding electrons and two unshared pairs, the latter occupying equatorial orbitals. $(ICl_3)_2$ will be discussed presently.

The known AB_2 systems are the various trihalide anions such as I_3^-, Br_3^-, ICl_2^-, IrB_2^-, $ClBr_2^-$, $BrCl_2^-$, $FIBr^-$, and $ClIBr^-$. All of these are linear and have the heaviest atom in the middle. By a natural extension of the preceding analysis, we may suppose that again the central atom has

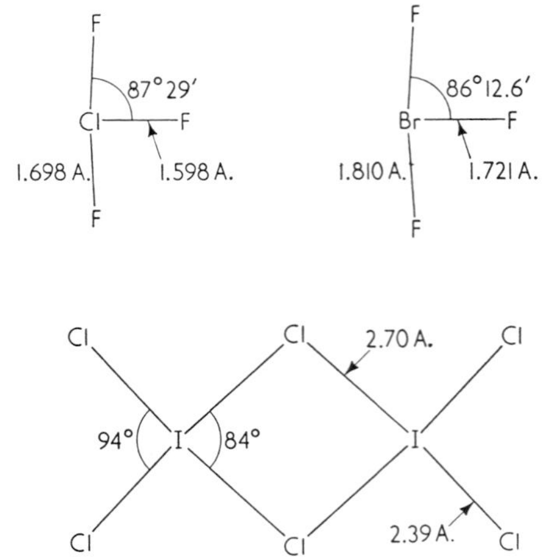

Fig. 15-8.   The structures of ClF_3, BrF_3, and I_2Cl_6.

a set of sp^3d, trigonal bipyramid hybrid orbitals of which the axial ones are used in bond formation and the equatorial ones hold the unshared pairs.

In concluding the discussion of compounds with central atoms having ten-electron valence shells, it may be well to point out clearly that, although there is a consistent scheme to account for the structures, it is actually more empirical than theoretical. In the first place, there is no substantial theoretical basis for preferring the trigonal bipyramid to the square pyramid type of sp^3d hybridization. It is only from the experimental data themselves that we know that the former is the correct choice; that is, no examples of regular square pyramidal structure (i.e., with the central atom in or inside the basal plane) have *yet* been found. Second, we again are unable to explain with any certainty why it is always the *equatorial orbitals which hold the unshared pairs*. Actually we might have expected the opposite since in PCl_5 it is found that the axial P—Cl bonds are substantially weaker than the equatorial ones; one would suppose that in case one or the other type of orbital were to be unused in bonding it would be the one expected to give the weaker bond. Indeed, it may be seen in ClF_3 and BrF_3 that the "axial" bonds are longer and presumably weaker than the "equatorial" one. Of course, it must be true that when *all* factors are considered the structures actually found are those giving the lowest free energy.

Let us now proceed to molecules AB_n in which the central atom A has twelve electron pairs in the valence shell with one or more being unshared.

Those known to exist are of the types AB_5 with one unshared pair and AB_4 with two unshared pairs. The known AB_5 types are BrF_5 and IF_5. The structure of the former is rather definitely established to be as shown in Figure 15-9. The structure of IF_5 has not been determined conclusively,

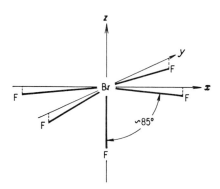

Fig. 15-9. The structure of BrF_5.

but the infrared, Raman, and nuclear resonance spectra strongly suggest that it is analogous. These structures can easily be explained assuming that the central atom uses a set of sp^3d^2, octahedral hybrid orbitals with one containing an unshared pair. The bond angles of ⌣85° may be assumed to result from the fact that repulsions between the lone pair electrons and those in the four equivalent Br—F bonds are greater than those between the Br—F bonding electrons in adjacent bonds. The ion $SbF_5{}^{2-}$ and other five-coordinate Sb^{III} compounds also have a square pyramidal structure with the metal atom outside the basal plane (see Chapter 20).

Of AB_4 species with twelve valence shell electrons on atom A, several mixed halide anions have been reported, but only for the $ICl_4{}^-$ and $BrF_4{}^-$ ions is structural information available. The former has been conclusively shown to be planar, and there is evidence that the latter is also. The planar structure may be explained by assuming sp^3d^2 hybridization of the central atom with the unshared pairs occupying *trans* positions in the octahedron. Assuming again that since nonbonding electron pairs form a more diffuse cloud than bonding pairs, it is reasonable that they would occupy *trans* rather than *cis* positions in order to minimize repulsion between electron pairs.

Finally, we may return to $(ICl_3)_2$, the structure of which has already been given. This may be explained by assuming that each iodine atom has a twelve-electron valence shell (seven of its own, one from each terminal Cl, and three from the pair of bridging chlorines) and that again the unshared pairs take *trans* positions in the octahedra.

15-4. Concluding Remarks

The foregoing survey deals with essentially all known types of AB_n compounds for which there is structural information. The explanation of the observed structures is in terms of three principles, as mentioned in the introduction: (*1*) use of a set of hybrid orbitals by the central metal atom, (*2*) placement of shared *and* unshared pairs in these orbitals on an *approximately* equal footing, and (*3*) the assumption that, other things being equal, electron pair repulsions increase in the order: bonding-bonding, bonding-nonbonding, nonbonding-nonbonding. Although other *ad hoc* assumptions must also be made in several cases, the entire approach is internally consistent and at least serves the purpose of reducing the problem of remembering a large number of structures to one of remembering a considerably smaller number of rules from which they may all be deduced.

References

Gillespie, R. J., *J. Am. Chem. Soc.*, **82,** 5978 (1960). Hydrides and halides of groups V and VI.

—— *Can. J. Chem.*, **39,** 318 (1961). Bond lengths and angles in nontransition metal octahedral and trigonal bipyramidal compounds.

—— and R. S. Nyholm, in W. Klyne and P. B. D. de la Mare, eds., *Progress in Stereochemistry*, Vol. II, Academic Press, New York, 1958, p. 261. A general account of inorganic stereochemistry for nontransition and also transition elements.

——, *Quart. Revs. (London)*, **7,** 339 (1957). Another account of inorganic stereochemistry for nontransition and transition elements.

Nyholm, R. S., in W. Klyne, ed., *Progress in Stereochemistry*, Vol. I, Academic Press, New York, 1954, p. 322. A general account of inorganic stereochemistry for nontransition and also transition elements.

Searcy, A. W., *J. Chem. Phys.*, **31,** 1 (1959). A review on the stereochemical effects of unshared pairs of electrons.

Walsh, A. D., in W. Klyne, ed., *Progress in Stereochemistry*, Vol. I, Academic Press, New York, 1954, p. 1. Brief description of experimental methods and tables of data for small molecules.

16

The Group I Elements: Na, K, Rb, Cs

GENERAL REMARKS

16-1. Introduction

The chemistry of the first member of the group I elements (the alkalies), lithium, has been described previously (Chapter 8); in many respects it is a prototype for the other members, although it has characteristic differences, which have already been discussed, because of its small atomic and ionic radii. The elements Na, K, Rb, and Cs have the simplest of all elemental chemistries (excepting the inert gases) since the atoms have only a single s electron outside an inert-gas core. The electronic configurations, ionization potentials, and standard electrode oxidation potentials are listed in Table 16-1. The low ionization potentials for the outer electrons and the fact that the resulting M^+ ions have inert-gas configurations and are thus spherical and of relatively low polarizability result in the

TABLE 16-1

Some Properties of Group I Metal Atoms

Element	Atomic number	Electronic configuration	Ionization potentials, e.v.		E^0, for $M(s) = M^+(aq) + e$, v.
			1st	2nd	
Li	3	[He]$2s$	5.390	75.62	3.02
Na	11	[Ne]$3s$	5.138	47.29	2.71
K	19	[Ar]$4s$	4.339	31.81	2.92
Rb	37	[Kr]$5s$	4.176	27.36	2.99
Cs	55	[Xe]$6s$	3.893	23.4	3.02
Fr	87	[Rn]$7s$	?	?	?

chemistry of these elements being essentially that of their $+1$ ions. No other oxidation states are known, nor are they to be expected considering the magnitudes of the second ionization potentials.

Although the chemistry of the elements is predominantly ionic, some degree of covalent bonding occurs in certain cases. The gaseous diatomic molecules—Na_2, Cs_2, etc.—are covalently bonded, and the bonds to oxygen, nitrogen, and carbon in various chelate and organometallic compounds doubtless have some slight covalent character. The tendency to covalence is greatest with lithium and least with cesium, as would be expected from the charge/radius ratios.

The element *francium* is formed in the natural radioactive decay series and in appropriate artificial nuclear reactions. All of its isotopes are radioactive with short half-lives. Precipitation reactions and solubility and ion exchange studies have shown that the ion behaves as would be expected from its position in the group.

It is to be noted also that the isotope ^{40}K (β^-, K; 16.1×10^8 y; 0.0119% abundance) occurs in potassium in nature. Use is made of this in age determinations of potassium-containing minerals; the unusual abundance of ^{40}Ar in the earth's atmosphere is due to its formation by K-capture decay of ^{40}K. Rubidium is also naturally radioactive owing to ^{87}Rb (β^-, 6×10^{10} y; 27.2% abundance).

Of all the groups in the periodic table, the group I (alkali) metals, including lithium, show most clearly and with least complication the effect of increasing size and mass on chemical and physical properties. Thus all of the following *decrease* through the series: (a) melting points and heats of sublimation of the metals; (b) lattice energies of all salts except those with the very smallest anions (because of irregular radius ratio effects); (c) the effective hydrated radii and the hydration energies (see Table 16-2); (d) the ease of thermal decomposition of nitrates and carbonates; (e) strength of the covalent bonds in the M_2 molecules; (f) heats of formation of fluorides, hydrides, oxides, and carbides (because of higher lattice energies with the smaller cations). Other trends can readily be found.

The elements copper, silver, and gold, the so-called coinage metals, are sometimes treated with the sodium group. The only justification for this procedure is that the atom of each of these elements has a single s electron outside of a closed shell. In this case, however, the closed shell is a d shell of the penultimate principal level. Although these elements do have $+1$ oxidation states, their over-all chemical resemblance to the sodium group is very slight. They are best considered as close relatives of the transition metals, which they resemble in much of their chemistry, such as formation of complexes, variable oxidation state, etc.

It is pertinent to note that there are other ions which have chemical behavior closely resembling the group I ions:

1. The most important of these are the ammonium ions, NH_4^+, RNH_3^+ . . . R_4N^+. NH_4^+ has an ionic radius (1.43 A.) close to those of K^+ and Rb^+, and its salts generally resemble those of potassium quite closely in their solubilities and crystal structures.

2. In the +1 oxidation state, thallium, as Tl^+, behaves in certain respects as an alkali metal ion (although in others more like Ag^+). Its ionic radius (1.51 A.) is comparable to that of Rb^+, although it is more polarizable. Thus thallous hydroxide is a water-soluble, strong base, which absorbs carbon dioxide from the air to form the carbonate. The sulfate and some other salts are isomorphous with the alkali metal salts.

3. A variety of other types of monopositive, essentially spherical cations often behave like alkali metal ions of comparable size. For example, the very stable di(π-cyclopentadienyl)cobalt(III) ion and its analogs with similar "sandwich" structures have precipitation reactions similar to those of Cs^+, and $[(\pi\text{-}C_5H_5)_2Co]OH$ is a strong base which absorbs carbon dioxide from the air and forms insoluble salts with large anions.

THE ELEMENTS

16-2. Preparation and Properties

The metals are obtained by electrolysis of fused salts or salt mixtures. Because there is only one valence electron per metal atom, the binding energies in the close-packed metal lattices are relatively weak and the metals are consequently very soft and have low melting points (Na, 97.5; K, 63.7; Rb, 38.5; Cs, 28.5°C.). Liquid alloys of the alkali metals are known, the most important being the Na–K alloys. The eutectic mixture in this system contains 77.2% K and melts at $-12.3°C$. This alloy, which has a wide liquid range and high specific heat, has been considered as a coolant for nuclear reactors.

Studies of the spectra of group I metal vapors at about the boiling points of the metals show the presence of $\sim 1\%$ of diatomic molecules whose dissociation energies decrease with increasing atomic number (Na_2, 17.3; K_2, 11.8; Rb_2, 10.8; Cs_2, 10.4 kcal./mole). These molecules provide the most unambiguous cases of covalent bonding by the alkalies.

All of the alkali metals are highly electropositive and react with most other elements directly. The reactivities toward air and water increase down the group; sodium effervesces with water, but the hydrogen evolved is not usually ignited; the heavier elements react explosively. In air sodium and potassium tarnish rapidly, and the other metals must be handled in an inert atmosphere as must Na–K alloys. Although Li, Na, K, and Rb are silvery in appearance, Cs has a distinct golden yellow cast.

The metals dissolve vigorously and exothermically in mercury, forming amalgams. Sodium amalgam (commonly symbolized by Na/Hg) is a liquid when dilute in sodium or a solid when rich in sodium; it is quite useful as a strong reducing agent.

Sodium metal may be dispersed by melting on various supporting solids such as sodium carbonate, Kieselguhr, etc., or by high speed stirring of a suspension of the metal in various hydrocarbon solvents held just above the melting point of the metal. Dispersions of the latter type are commercially available; they may be poured in air, and they react with water only with effervescence. They are often used synthetically where sodium shot or lumps would react too slowly. In addition, these dispersions can be converted by hydrogen to suspensions of sodium hydride, which are also commercially available as intermediates for preparation of other hydrides, for example, $NaBH_4$, for reductions, etc.

16-3. Solutions in Liquid Ammonia, Amines, and Ethers

The group I metals, and to a lesser extent Ca, Sr, Ba, and a few other electropositive metals, are soluble in liquid ammonia and in certain amines to give solutions which are blue when dilute. These solutions conduct electricity *electrolytically*, and measurements of transport numbers of the carriers suggest that the main current carrier is the *solvated electron*, by which is implied electrons which are free from their parent sodium atoms and occupy cavities in the liquid. At higher alkali metal concentrations the solutions are copper colored and have a metallic luster, and various physical data such as their exceedingly high electrical conductivities, indicate that they are very similar to liquid metals.

In spite of a great deal of experimental and theoretical work the nature of these solutions is still not understood in detail. Paramagnetic resonance experiments have confirmed the presence of "free" electrons, however; also variations in the absorption spectrum and magnetic susceptibility with concentration have been interpreted to mean that the "free" electrons occur in at least two conditions. Some are single electrons which give rise to paramagnetism and to an absorption band at ⌣15,000 A. owing to transitions among quantized levels in their solvent cages. There are also electron pairs which have their spins paired and are therefore diamagnetic and give rise to an absorption band at ⌣7000 A. Thus, crudely, the following equilibria are thought to exist, although there may be others:

$$Na(s) \text{ (dispersed)} = Na \text{ (in solution)} = Na^+ + e$$
$$2e = e_2$$

This view is also consistent with the densities of the solutions, which are much less than that of liquid ammonia.

The physical and chemical properties required of the solvent to make possible the formation of such solutions are not fully understood. It can be said that high dielectric constant and fairly strong donor properties appear to be necessary, though perhaps not alone sufficient; in ether solvents (see below) steric factors are important.

Ammonia has long been known to give blue solutions, but the solubility of metals in water, although discovered by Fernelius in 1935, has only recently been confirmed. Thus, with air-free water at 0°C., potassium dissolves to give a blue solution having an absorption band at ∽6500 A.; such solutions are of course quite unstable, decomposing as expected with the liberation of hydrogen. Considerably more stable solutions of K, Rb, and Cs in various ethers have been obtained. Tetrahydrofuran, ethylene glycol dimethyl ether, and other methyl polyethers are among the best. The general properties of these solutions, insofar as they have been determined in view of the attack on the solvents, appear to be similar to those of the amine and liquid ammonia solutions; the alkali metal concentrations in saturated solutions are, however, only ∽10^{-4} g.-atom/liter.

The ammonia and amine solutions of alkali metals are widely used preparatively in both organic and inorganic chemistry. Thus lithium in methylamine shows great selectivity in its reducing properties, but both this reagent and lithium in ethylenediamine are quite powerful and will reduce aromatic rings to cyclic monoolefins. Sodium in liquid ammonia is probably the most widely used system for preparative purposes. The solution is moderately stable, but decomposition

$$Na + NH_3(l) = NaNH_2 + \tfrac{1}{2}H_2$$

can occur photochemically and by catalysis by transition metal salts. Sodium amide can be conveniently prepared by treatment of sodium with liquid ammonia in the presence of a trace of ferric chloride. Amines react similarly:

$$Li(s) + CH_3NH_2(l) \xrightarrow{50-60°C.} LiNHCH_3(s) + \tfrac{1}{2}H_2$$

Some further remarks may be made concerning the function of the solvent and the nature of the species in these solutions of group I metals. The dielectric constant of the solvent is important, to say the least, in the same way as in the solution of an ionic solid, namely, to diminish the forces of attraction between the oppositely charged particles—in this case, M^+ ions and electrons. Furthermore, if the solvent molecules immediately surrounding these particles will interact strongly with them, the energy of the system will be further lowered. The detailed nature of the interaction of the electrons with the surrounding solvent molecules is still debatable, but it is fairly certain that the metal ions are solvated in the same way as they would be in a solution of a metal salt in the same solvent. It is therefore pertinent to discuss here the $[Na(NH_3)_4]^+$ ion which is formed on treatment of NaI with liquid ammonia. $[Na(NH_3)_4]I$ is a liquid of fair thermal stability. It freezes at 3°C. and at 25°C. has an equilibrium pressure of NH_3 of 420 mm.; thus it must be kept in an atmosphere of ammonia with at least this pressure at 25°C. The infrared and Raman spectra indicate the complex ion $[Na(NH_3)_4]^+$ to be tetrahedral with Na—N bonds about as strong as the Zn—N bonds in $[Zn(NH_3)_4]^{2+}$ or the Pb—C bonds in $Pb(CH_3)_4$. Bending and rocking frequencies, however, are quite low, suggesting that the Na—N bonding is mainly due to ion-dipole forces. Thus it may be assumed that Na^+ and other metal ions in the liquid ammonia, amine, and ether solutions are strongly solvated in the same way. The well-known effectiveness of tetrahydrofuran and ethylene and diethylene glycol dimethyl ethers ("glyme" and "diglyme," respectively) as media for reactions involving sodium may be due in part to the slight solubility of the metal, but the solvation of ions by ether molecules undoubtedly provides the most important contribution. Indeed, in several instances crystalline etherates have been isolated, for example, $[Na\ diglyme_2][Ta(CO)_6]$ and $[K\ diglyme_3][Mo(CO)_5I]$.

COMPOUNDS OF THE GROUP I ELEMENTS

The group I metals react directly with most nonmetals to give one or more binary compounds; they also form numerous alloys and compounds with other metals such as Pb and Sn. Many of these compounds are described under the appropriate element, although a few classes will be treated here.

16-4. Oxides

Sodium rapidly tarnishes in dry air, and the heavier metals are increasingly readily attacked to give oxides. On combustion at atmospheric pressure lithium gives only the oxide Li_2O; sodium gives the peroxide Na_2O_2; and potassium, rubidium, and cesium give the superoxides, MO_2.

Na_2O_2 will take up further oxygen at elevated pressures and temperatures to form NaO_2. The per- and superoxides of the heavier alkalies can also be prepared by passing stoichiometric amounts of oxygen into their liquid ammonia solutions, and ozonides, MO_3, are also known. The structures of the ions O_2^{2-}, O_2^-, and O_3^- and of their alkali salts have already been discussed (Chapter 13). The increasing stability of the per- and superoxides as the size of the alkali ions increases is noteworthy and is a typical example of the stabilization of larger anions by larger cations through lattice energy effects.

Owing to the highly electropositive character of the alkali metals, the various oxides (and also sulfides and similar compounds) are readily hydrolyzed by water according to the following equations:

$$M_2O + H_2O = 2MOH$$
$$M_2O_2 + 2H_2O = 2MOH + H_2O_2$$
$$2MO_2 + 2H_2O = O_2 + 2MOH + H_2O_2$$

The oxide Cs_2O has the antifluorite structure and is the only known oxide with this type of lattice. An abnormally long Cs—Cs distance and short Cs—O distance imply considerable polarization of the Cs^+ ion.

The *hydroxides*, MOH, are white crystalline solids soluble in water and in alcohols. They can be sublimed unchanged at 350–400°C., and the vapors consist mainly of dimers $(MOH)_2$. KOH at ordinary temperatures is monoclinic with each K surrounded by a distorted octahedron of O atoms and the OH groups form a zigzag hydrogen-bonded chain with O—H$\cdots$O = 3.35 A. The breaking of these bonds results in the formation of the cubic high temperature form.

Sodium peroxide is obtainable commercially as a yellowish powder containing $\sim$10% NaO_2. It can be recrystallized, quickly, from concentrated aqueous solutions as $Na_2O_2 \cdot 8H_2O$.

16-5. Ionic Salts

Salts of the bases, MOH, with virtually all acids are known. For the most part they are colorless, crystalline, ionic solids. Those which are colored owe their color to the anions, except in special cases. The colors of metal ions are due to absorption of light of proper energy to excite electrons to higher energy levels; for the alkali ions with their very stable inert gas configurations, the energies required to excite electrons to the lowest available empty orbitals could be supplied only by quanta far out in the vacuum ultraviolet (the transition $5p^6 \rightarrow 5p^56s$ in Cs^+ occurs at about 1000 A.). However, colored crystals of compounds such as NaCl are sometimes encountered. This is due to the presence of holes and free electrons in the lattice, called color centers, and such chromophoric disturbances can be produced by irradiation of the crystals with X-rays and nuclear radiations. The color results from transitions of the electrons between energy levels in the holes in which they are trapped. These electrons behave in principle similarly to those in solvent cages in the liquid ammonia solutions, but the energy levels are differently spaced and consequently the colors are different and variable. Small excesses of free metal atoms produce similar effects.

The structures and stabilities of the ionic salts are determined in part by the lattice energies and by radius ratio effects, which have been discussed in Chapter 2. Thus the large Cs^+ ion can accommodate eight near-neighbor Cl^- ions, and its structure is different from that of NaCl where the smaller cation Na^+ can accommodate only six near neighbors.

The salts are generally characterized by high melting points, by electrical conductivity of the melts, and by ready solubility in water. There are a few salts which are not appreciably water soluble, and thus there are a few important *precipitation reactions* of the group I ions. These are generally with large anions, and the larger the group I cation, the more numerous are its insoluble salts. Thus sodium has very few insoluble salts; the mixed sodium zinc and sodium magnesium uranyl acetates (e.g., $NaZn(UO_2)_3(CH_3COO)_9 \cdot 6H_2O$), which may be precipitated almost quantitatively under carefully controlled conditions from dilute acetic acid solutions, are useful for analysis. The perchlorates and hexachloroplatinates of K, Rb, and Cs are rather insoluble in water and virtually insoluble in 90% ethanol. These heavier ions may also be precipitated by cobaltinitrite ion, $[Co(NO_2)_6]^{3-}$, and various other large anions. $NaB(C_6H_5)_4$, which is moderately soluble in water, is a useful reagent for precipitating the tetraphenyl borates of K, Rb, and Cs from neutral or faintly acid aqueous solutions, and quantitative gravimetric determinations of these ions may be made in this way.

The group I salts are seldom hydrated when the anions are small, as in the halides, because the hydration energies of the ions are insufficient to compensate for the energy required to expand the lattices.

The large size of the Cs^+ and Rb^+ ions frequently allows them to form ionic salts with rather unstable anions, such as various polyhalide anions (page 463) and the superoxides already mentioned.

Apart from solvates, there are very few complexes of the alkali metal ions, although a number of chelate complexes which are soluble in organic compounds have been obtained using oxygenated ligands such as salicylaldehyde and benzoylacetone. As in the case of the solvates, the bonding is essentially electrostatic in these complexes.

The M^+ Ions in Solution. The group I ions are hydrated in solution to rather indeterminate degrees. X-ray scattering studies have indicated that the primary hydration shell of K^+ contains four water molecules. Since Na^+ forms the very stable $[Na(NH_3)_4]^+$ ion in liquid ammonia, it is probable that it too has a primary hydration sphere of four water molecules. Nothing definite is known about the Rb^+ and Cs^+ ions. It is quite possible that they, especially Cs^+, might have six water molecules in the first hydration shell. However, electrostatic forces are still operative beyond the first hydration sphere, and additional water molecules will be bound in layers of decreasing definiteness and strength of attachment. Apparently, the larger the cation itself, the less it binds additional outer layers so that, although the crystallographic radii increase down the group, the

TABLE 16-2

Data on Hydration of Aqueous Group I Ions

	Li⁺	Na⁺	K⁺	Rb⁺	Cs⁺
Crystal radii,[a] A.	0.60	0.95	1.33	1.48	1.69
Hydrated radii (approx.), A.	3.40	2.76	2.32	2.28	2.28
Approximate hydration numbers[b]	25.3	16.6	10.5	—	9.9
Hydration energies, kcal./mole	123	97	77	70	63
Ionic mobilities (at ∞ dil., 18°C.)	33.5	43.5	64.6	67.5	68

[a] For six coordination.
[b] From transference data.

hydrated radii decrease as shown in Table 16-2. Also, the hydration energies, as defined by the equation

$$M^+(g) + H_2O(l) = M(aq)^+$$

decrease. The decrease in the size of the hydrated ions is manifested in various ways. The mobility of the ions in electrolytic conduction increases, and also the strength of binding to ion exchange resins generally increases.

In a cation exchange resin, two cations compete for attachment at anionic sites in the resin, as in the following equilibrium:

$$A^+(aq) + [B^+R^-](s) = B^+(aq) + [A^+R^-](s)$$

where R represents the resin and A^+ and B^+ the cations. Such equilibria have been measured quite accurately, and the order of preference of the alkali cations is usually $Li^+ < Na^+ < K^+ < Rb^+ < Cs^+$, although irregular behavior does occur in some cases. This may be explained if we assume that the binding force is essentially electrostatic and that under ordinary conditions the ions are hydrated within the water-logged resin about as they are outside of it. Then the ion with the smallest hydrated radius (which is the one with the largest "naked" radius) will be able to approach most closely to the negative site of attachment and will hence be held most strongly according to the Coulomb law.

The reasons for the deviations from this simple pattern as well as selective passage of certain ions through cell walls are not properly understood, and factors other than mere size are doubtless important.

16-6. Organometallic Compounds

Only organo compounds of sodium, and to a much lesser extent potassium, are of importance, and both are less important than the lithium compounds. The derivatives are all essentially ionic and are not soluble to any appreciable extent in hydrocarbons; they are exceedingly reactive, being sensitive to air and hydrolyzed vigorously by water. Although alkyl and particularly aryl sodium derivatives can be prepared for *in situ* use as reaction intermediates, they are seldom isolated. More important are the compounds formed by acidic hydrocarbons such as cyclopentadiene, indene, acetylenes, etc. These are obtained by interaction with sodium in liquid ammonia or, more conveniently, sodium dispersed in tetrahydrofuran, glyme, diglyme, or dimethylformamide.

$$C_5H_6 + Na = C_5H_5^-Na^+ + \tfrac{1}{2}H_2$$
$$RC{\equiv}CH + Na = RC{\equiv}C^-Na^+ + \tfrac{1}{2}H_2$$

Certain unsaturated hydrocarbons can form highly colored anions when treated with sodium or potassium in tetrahydrofuran at low temperatures; thus benzene gives the yellow benzenide ion, $C_6H_6^-$, which can be detected spectroscopically and by electron spin resonance. Anions of this type can be obtained when the negative charge can be delocalized over a conjugated organic radical. Other aromatic compounds such as ketones, triphenylphosphine oxide, triphenylarsine, and azobenzene also form anions.

References

Jackson, C. B., ed., *Liquid Metals Handbook*, 3rd ed. (Sodium, NaK Suppl.), Atomic Energy Commission and Bureau of Ships, Dept. of Navy, Washington, D. C., 1955.

Jolly, W., "Metal-Ammonia Solutions," in F. A. Cotton, ed., *Progress in Inorganic Chemistry*, Vol. I, Interscience, New York–London, 1959, p. 235. The nature of the solutions of alkali metals in liquid ammonia.

Kaufmann, D. W., *Sodium Chloride* (American Chemical Society Monograph, No. 145), Reinhold, New York, 1960. An encyclopedic account of salt.

Stern, K. H., and E. S. Amis, *Chem. Revs.*, **59,** 1 (1959). Ionic size, a comprehensive review on radii in crystals and solutions.

Symons, M. C. R., *Quart. Revs. (London)*, **13,** 99 (1959). The nature of the solutions of alkali metals in liquid ammonia.

—— and W. T. Doyle, *Quart. Revs. (London)*, **14,** 62 (1960). Color centers in alkali, halides.

17

The Group II Elements: Mg, Ca, Sr, Ba, Ra

GENERAL REMARKS

17-1. Introduction

As noted previously (Chapter 9), the first-row member of group II, beryllium, has unique chemical behavior; it also has a predominantly covalent chemistry in contrast to the other members now to be considered, which are predominantly ionic. Magnesium, the second-row element, does not stand in as close a relationship with the heavier members as might have been expected; it has considerable tendency to covalent bond formation, which is consistent, from Fajans' viewpoint, with the following values of the charge to radius ratios: Be^{2+}, 17 (est.); Mg^{2+}, 3.3; Ca^{2+}, 1.8; Sr^{2+}, 1.2; Ba^{2+}, 1.0; Ra^{2+}, 0.7. Its chemistry is intermediate between that of beryllium and that of the closely allied series Ca–Ra. For instance, like beryllium, its hydroxide can be precipitated from aqueous solutions, whereas hydroxides of the other elements are all moderately soluble.

The metal atomic radii are smaller than those of the adjacent group I metals due to the increased nuclear charge; the number of bonding electrons in the metals is twice as great so that the metals have higher melting and boiling points and greater densities.

All the elements in this group are highly electropositive metals, however, as is shown by their high chemical reactivities, their ionization potentials, their standard electrode potentials, and, for the heavier ones, the ionic nature of their compounds. Important numerical constants such as those mentioned are collected in Table 17-1. Although the energies required to vaporize and ionize these atoms to the M^{2+} ions are considerably greater than those required to produce the M^+ ions of the group I elements, the high lattice energies in the solid salts and the high hydration energies of the M^{2+}(aq) ions compensate for this with the result that the electrode

TABLE 17-1

Some Physical Parameters for the Group II Elements

Element	Electron configuration	Ionization potentials, e.v.		E^0 for $M(s) = M^{2+}(aq) + 2e$, v.	Ionic radii, A.
		1st	2nd		
Mg	[Ne]$3s^2$	7.64	15.03	+2.37	0.65
Ca	[Ar]$4s^2$	6.11	11.87	+2.87	0.94
Sr	[Kr]$5s^2$	5.69	10.98	+2.89	1.10
Ba	[Xe]$6s^2$	5.21	9.95	+2.90	1.29
Ra	[Rn]$7s^2$	5.28	10.10	+2.92	1.50

potentials of the group II metals are rather similar to those of the group I metals. As with group I ions, various experimental data suggest that the radii of the hydrated ions are greatest for those with the smallest crystallographic radii.

All of the M^{2+} ions are smaller and considerably less polarizable than the isoelectronic M^+ ions. Thus deviations from complete ionicity in their salts due to polarization of the cations is even less important. However, for Mg^{2+} and, as noted, to an exceptional degree for Be^{2+}, polarization of anions by the cations does produce a degree of covalence for compounds of Mg and makes covalence characteristic for Be.

Calcium, strontium, barium, and radium form a closely allied series in which the chemical and physical properties of the elements and their compounds vary systematically with increasing size in much the same manner as in group I, the ionic and electropositive nature being greatest for Ra. Again the larger ions can stabilize certain large anions: the peroxide and superoxide ions, polyhalide ions, etc. Some examples of systematic group trends in the series Ca–Ra are: (a) hydration tendencies of the crystalline salts increase; (b) solubilities of sulfates, nitrates, chlorides, etc. (fluorides are an exception) decrease; (c) solubilities of halides in ethanol decrease; (d) thermal stabilities of carbonates, nitrates, and peroxides increase; (e) rates of reaction of the metals with hydrogen increase. Other similar trends can be found.

All isotopes of _radium_ are radioactive, the longest-lived isotope being ^{226}Ra (α; ⌒1600 yr.). This isotope is formed in the natural decay series of ^{238}U and was first isolated by the Curies. Once widely used in radiotherapy, it is now being supplanted by much cheaper radioisotopes made in nuclear reactors.

It may be noted that isotopically pure ^{87}Sr (99%) is found in some minerals, such as certain Canadian micas, where it is formed by β^- decay of ^{87}Rb.

The elements Zn, Cd, and Hg, which have two electrons outside of filled penultimate d shells, are also classed in group II. Although the difference between the calcium and zinc subgroups is marked, Zn, and to a lesser extent Cd, show some resemblance to Mg in their chemistry. We shall discuss these elements separately, but it may be noted here that Zn, which has the lowest second ionization potential in the Zn, Cd, Hg group, still has a value (17.89 e.v.) similar to that of Be (18.21 e.v.) and its standard electrode potential ($+0.49$ v.) is considerably less positive than that of Mg.

There are a few ions in other parts of the periodic table with properties similar to those of Sr^{2+} or Ba^{2+}. Thus bivalent europium, Eu^{2+}, has a radius very similar to that of Ba^{2+}. Its hydroxide is a strong base, and its sulfate is insoluble in water, resembling the barium analogs. Because of this fortuitous chemical similarity, europium is frequently found in nature in group II minerals, and this is indeed a good example of the geochemical importance of such chemical similarity. Sm^{2+} and Yb^{2+} are also similar to Ba^{2+}, but they are much more readily oxidized than is Eu^{2+} and cannot persist in aqueous solution.

THE ELEMENTS

17-2. Occurrence, Isolation, and Properties

The group II elements are widely distributed in minerals and in the sea. They occur in substantial deposits such as dolomite, $CaCO_3 \cdot MgCO_3$; carnallite, $MgCl_2 \cdot KCl \cdot 6H_2O$; barytes, $BaSO_4$; etc. Calcium is the second most abundant metal terrestrially. Radium occurs in low concentration in uranium ores as a product of radioactive decay.

Magnesium is produced in several ways. An important source is dolomite from which, after calcination, the calcium is removed by ion exchange using sea water, the equilibrium being favorable because of the lower solubility of $Mg(OH)_2$ relative to $Ca(OH)_2$:

$$Ca(OH)_2 \cdot Mg(OH)_2 + Mg^{2+} = 2Mg(OH)_2 + Ca^{2+}$$

The most important process for preparation of magnesium is the electrolysis of fused halide mixtures (e.g., $MgCl_2 + CaCl_2 + NaCl$) from which the least electropositive metal, Mg, is deposited. It may also be obtained by reduction of MgO or of calcined dolomite ($MgO \cdot CaO$). The latter is heated with ferrosilicon

$$CaO \cdot MgO + FeSi = Mg + Ca \text{ and Fe silicates}$$

and the magnesium distilled out. MgO can be heated with coke at 2000°C. and the metal deposited by rapid quenching of the high temperature equilibrium which lies well to the right:

$$MgO + C = Mg + CO$$

Calcium and the other metals are made only on a relatively small scale by electrolysis of fused salts or reduction of the halides with sodium.

Radium is isolated in the processing of uranium ores; after coprecipitation with barium sulfate, it can be obtained by fractional crystallization of a soluble salt.

Magnesium is a greyish white metal with a surface oxide film which protects it to some extent chemically—thus it is not attacked by water despite the favorable potential unless amalgamated. It is readily soluble in dilute acids and is attacked by most alkyl and aryl halides in ether solution to give Grignard reagents. Calcium and the other metals are soft and silvery, resembling sodium in their chemical reactivities although somewhat less reactive. These metals are also soluble, though less readily and to a lesser extent than sodium, in liquid ammonia, giving blue solutions of a similar nature to those of the group I metals. These blue solutions are also susceptible to decomposition with the formation of the amides and have other chemical reactions similar to those of the group I metal solutions. They differ, however, in that moderately stable metal ammines such as $Ca(NH_3)_6$ can be isolated on removal of solvent at the boiling point.

COMPOUNDS OF THE GROUP II ELEMENTS

17-3. Binary Compounds

Oxides. The oxides, MO, are obtained most readily by calcination of the carbonates. They are white crystalline solids with ionic, NaCl-type lattices. Magnesium oxide is relatively inert, especially after ignition at high temperatures, but the other oxides react with water, evolving heat, to form the hydroxides. They also absorb carbon dioxide from the air. Magnesium hydroxide is insoluble in water ($\sim 1 \times 10^{-4}$ g./liter at 20°C.) and can be precipitated from Mg^{2+} solutions; it is a much weaker base than the Ca–Ra hydroxides, although it has no acidic properties and unlike $Be(OH)_2$ is insoluble in excess hydroxide. The Ca–Ra hydroxides are all soluble in water, increasingly so with increasing atomic number ($Ca(OH)_2$, ~ 2 g./liter; $Ba(OH)_2$, ~ 60 g./liter at ~ 20°C.) and all are strong bases.

As for the group I cations, there are no optical transitions in the electronic spectra of the M^{2+} ions and they are all colorless. Colors of salts are thus due only to colors of the anions or to lattice defects. For example, the oxides are often obtained with defects, and BaO crystals up to 1 cm. $\times$ 2 mm. have been grown in vacuum with are deep red due to $\sim 0.1\%$ excess of metal in the lattice.

Hydrides. The Ca–Ba group give ionic hydrides, MH_2 and MXH (Chapter 5), by direct reaction under fairly mild conditions. MgH_2 is also obtained by direct reaction using hydrogen under pressure, as a light grey powder stable in air; the product prepared by pyrolysis of magnesium alkyls is much more reactive, however. If the Ca–Ba hydrides are heated to $\sim 900°$C. with their halides in an atmosphere of hydrogen, stable, mica-like solids, melting at 660–860°C., of stoichiometry MXH are obtained. These are compounds, not mixed crystals, and have the PbClF structure. The MgClH from the reaction of RMgX with diborane gives only a crystalline dietherate with tetrahydrofuran from which the ether cannot be removed.

Carbides. All of the metals in the Ca–Ba series or their oxides react directly with carbon in an electric furnace to give the carbides MC_2. These are ionic acetylides whose general properties (hydrolysis to $M(OH)_2$ and C_2H_2, structures, etc.) have already been discussed in Chapter 11. Magnesium at $\sim 500°$C. gives MgC_2 but at 500–700°C. with excess carbon Mg_2C_3 is formed, which on hydrolysis gives $Mg(OH)_2$ and propyne and is presumably ionic, that is, $(Mg^{2+})_2(C_3^{4-})$. Neutron diffraction on CaC_2 shows the presence of the acetylide ion with C—C = 1.20 A.

Other Compounds. Direct reaction of the metals with other elements can lead to binary compounds such as borides, silicides, arsenides, sulfides, etc. Like the corresponding group I compounds, many of these are ionic and are rapidly hydrolyzed by water or dilute acids. At $\sim 300°$C., magnesium reacts with nitrogen to give colorless, crystalline Mg_3N_2 (resembling Li and Be in this respect). The other metals also react, but their nitrides are much less stable.

17-4. Salts, Aqueous Solutions, and Complexes of the M^{2+} Ions

Magnesium. In contrast to beryllium, the anhydrous halides and other salts are essentially ionic in nature due to the larger size of the Mg^{2+} ion. In water the hydrated ion (most likely, $[Mg(H_2O)_6]^{2+}$) binds the water in the first coordination sphere much less strongly than does Be in $[Be(H_2O)_4]^{2+}$, and the aquo ion is not perceptibly acidic. The hydration energy, however, is still sufficiently high that magnesium salts usually crystallize from water as rather stable hydrates. $Mg(ClO_4)_2$ is an excellent drying agent. Most magnesium salts are water soluble; the fluoride, however, is only sparingly soluble.

Calcium, Strontium, Barium, and Radium. Although calcium salts are usually hydrated and the anhydrous halides are deliquescent, the tendency to form hydrates as well as the solubilities in water decrease with increasing size. This can be shown to be due to the fact that with increasing size the hydration energies decrease more rapidly than the lattice energies. The fluorides vary inversely in solubility, Ca < Sr < Ba, because the unusually small size of the F^- ion relative to the large M^{2+} ions causes polarization effects to become increasingly important in stabilizing the lattices as the cations increase in size. The carbonates are all rather insoluble; sulfates of Sr, Ba, and Ra are very insoluble, the solubility products of both carbonates and sulfates decreasing with increasing cation size. Calcium sulfate has a hemihydrate, $2CaSO_4 \cdot H_2O$ (plaster of Paris) which readily absorbs more water to form the very sparingly soluble $CaSO_4 \cdot 2H_2O$ (gypsum). In the latter there are two S—O distances of 1.479 and 1.497 A., the latter being those to which the lattice water is hydrogen bonded.

In aqueous solution the $M^{2+}(aq)$ ions are not at all hydrolyzed.

Rather weak *complexes* can be formed by the lighter group II elements. Thus although the magnesium halides do not have strong acceptor properties, these, the alkyls, and the Grignard species will form complexes with donor molecules, particularly oxygen compounds. Thus $MgBr_2$ and MgI_2 are soluble in alcohols, ketones, and ethers; magnesium perchlorate is also quite soluble in such solvents.

Of the other ions only Ca shows a tendency to similar behavior, calcium chloride being readily soluble in alcohols and carboxylic acids.

In aqueous solution, oxygen chelate compounds, among the most important being those of the ethylenediaminetetraacetate (EDTA) type, can give complexes in alkaline solution, such as

$$Ca^{2+}(aq) + EDTA^{4-} = [Ca(EDTA)]^{2-}$$

The complexing of calcium by EDTA and also by polyphosphates is of some importance not only for removal of calcium ions from water but in analysis, for example for the volumetric estimation of calcium using EDTA.

Only rather weak ammonia and amine complexes are known for Mg^{2+} and Ca^{2+}. Thus anhydrous $MgCl_2$ will absorb NH_3 to give an easily dissociated complex $[Mg(NH_3)_6]Cl_2$.

17-5. Unipositive Magnesium

Although the ionization potentials of the group II elements might suggest the possibility of isolable stable compounds with unipositive ions, this is not the case. Calculations using Born-Haber cycles clearly demonstrate that, because of the much greater lattice energies of MX_2 compounds, MX compounds would be quite unstable with respect to disproportionation

$$2MX = M + MX_2$$

However, in the case of magnesium there is some evidence that Mg^+ ions may be formed under some conditions; they are only short-lived, however. The evidence comes mainly from studies on anodic dissolution of magnesium in aqueous salt solutions and in organic donor solvents such as pyridine containing sodium iodide. It is found, for example, that in aqueous solutions hydrogen is evolved near or at the anode, and more detailed studies have shown that Mg^+ ions must be present. It is possible to use electrically generated Mg^+ ions as reducing agents for a variety of organic compounds.

17-6. Organometallic Compounds

Where they are known, organometallic compounds of Ca, Sr, and Ba are highly ionic and are of little importance. However, the magnesium derivatives are of very great importance since the Grignard reagents, "RMgX," are undoubtedly the most widely used of all organometallic compounds. They are made by direct interaction of magnesium with an organic halide, RX, in a donor solvent, usually an ether.

$$Mg + RX = \text{"RMgX"}$$

While the reactions of Grignard reagents are in keeping with the formulation "RMgX," the pure unsolvated species of this formula cannot be obtained. Although the question of the precise nature of the species present in Grignard solutions is not completely settled, they appear to be mixtures or complexes of the R_2Mg derivatives with MgX_2 solvated by the ether or other donor solvent molecules.

The dialkyl and aryl magnesium derivatives can often be isolated in a pure state; their reactions are generally similar to those of Grignard reagents, and they are hydrolyzed by water and sensitive to air. The colorless crystalline ionic cyclopentadienide, $Mg(C_5H_5)_2$, has been shown to have the same "sandwich" configuration as ferrocene (Chapter 28); it can be readily made by the direct action of cyclopentadiene vapor on heated magnesium or by thermal decomposition of cyclopentadienylmagnesium halides.

References

Kharasch, M. S., and O. Reinmuth, *Grignard Reactions of Non-Metallic Substances*, Constable and Co., London, and Prentice-Hall, New York, 1954.

Pannell, E. V., *Magnesium: Its Production and Use*, Pitman, London, 1948.

Rausch, M. D., W. E. Ewen, and J. Kleinberg, *Chem. Revs.*, **57**, 417 (1957). Use of Mg^+ as a reducing agent in organic chemistry.

Yoffe, S. T., and A. N. Nesmeyanov, *Handbook of Magnesium Organic Compounds*, Vols. I–III, Pergamon Press, London.

18

The Group III Elements: Al, Ga, In, Tl

GENERAL REMARKS

18-1. Electronic Structures and Valences

The electronic structures and some other important fundamental properties of the elements are listed in Table 18-1.

TABLE 18-1

Some Properties of the Group III Elements

| Element | Electronic structure | Ionization potentials, e.v. | | | | E^0, v.[a] |
		1st	2nd	3rd	4th	
B	$[He]2s^2 2p$	8.30	25.15	37.92	259.30	Not measurable
Al	$[Ne]3s^2 3p$	5.98	18.82	28.44	119.96	1.66
Ga	$[Ar]3d^{10}4s^2 4p$	6.00	20.43	30.6	63.8	0.53
In	$[Kr]4d^{10}5s^2 5p$	5.79	18.79	27.9	57.8	0.342
Tl	$[Xe]4f^{14}5d^{10}6s^2 6p$	6.11	20.32	29.7	50.5	-0.72[b]

[a] For $M(s) = M^{3+}(aq) + 3e$.
[b] $Tl = Tl^+ + e$, $E^0 = +0.34$ v.

As might be expected, the trivalent state is important for all members of the group, but the univalent state becomes more prominent as the group is descended. Indeed, the Tl^I–Tl^{III} relationships are the dominant feature of the chemistry of thallium. For the other elements, however, the univalent state is accessible only by special means, and univalent compounds are seldom encountered.

18-2. Group Trends

Aluminum and its congeners, Ga, In, and Tl, are considerably larger than boron (atomic radii of Al and B being 1.26 and 0.88 A., respectively), and hence they are much more metallic and ionic in their character. Elemental aluminum itself is clearly metallic, but it is nevertheless still on the borderline (like beryllium) between ionic and covalent character in its compounds. So also are Ga, In, and Tl. Although electronegativity values are not particularly useful in interpreting the chemistry of these rather metallic elements, the available values (Allred-Rochow) are: B, 2.01; Al, 1.47; Ga, 1.82; In, 1.49; Tl, 1.44. The irregularity of the sequence is discussed on page 348.

The so-called *inert pair* effect first makes itself evident in this group, although it is adumbrated in the low reactivity of mercury, and it is much more pronounced in groups IV and V. The term inert pair refers to the resistance of a pair of s electrons to be lost or to participate in covalent bond formation. Thus mercury is difficult to oxidize, allegedly because it contains only an inert pair $(6s^2)$, Tl readily forms Tl^I rather than Tl^{III} because of the inert pair in its valence shell $(6s^26p)$, etc. The concept of the inert pair does not actually tell us anything about the ultimate reasons for the stability of certain lower valence states, but it is useful as a label and is often encountered in the literature. The relative stabilities of oxidation states differing in the presence or absence of the inert pair are further discussed in Chapter 19.

THE ELEMENTS

18-3. Occurrence, Isolation, and Properties

Aluminum, the commonest metallic element in the earth's crust, occurs widely in nature in silicates such as micas and feldspars, as the hydrated oxide (bauxite), and as cryolite (Na_3AlF_6). The other three elements are found only in trace quantities. Traces of gallium and indium are found in aluminum and zinc ores, but the richest sources contain less than 1% of gallium and still less indium. Traces of thallium are widely distributed; the element is usually recovered from flue dusts from the roasting of certain sulfide ores, mainly pyrites.

Aluminum is prepared on a vast scale from bauxite. This is purified by dissolution in sodium hydroxide and reprecipitation using carbon dioxide. It is then dissolved in molten cryolite at 800–1000°C. and the melt electrolyzed. Aluminum is a hard, strong, white metal with a high oxidation potential. It is nevertheless resistant to corrosion because a hard, tough film of oxide forms on the surface. Thick oxide films, some with the proper porosity when fresh to trap particles of pigment, are often electrolytically applied to aluminum, thus imitating but improving upon nature. Aluminum is soluble in dilute mineral acids, but is passivated by concentrated nitric acid. If the protective effect of the oxide film is overcome, by scratching or by amalgamation, for example, rapid attack even by water can occur. The metal is attacked under ordinary conditions by hot alkali hydroxides, halogens, and various nonmetals. Highly purified aluminum is quite resistant to acids and is best attacked by hydrochloric acid containing a little cupric chloride or in contact with platinum, some H_2O_2 also being added during the dissolution.

Gallium, indium, and *thallium* are usually obtained by electrolysis of aqueous solutions of their salts; for Ga and In this possibility arises because of large overvoltages for hydrogen evolution on these metals. They are soft, white, comparatively reactive metals, dissolving readily in acids; however, thallium dissolves only slowly in sulfuric and hydrochloric acids since the Tl^I salts formed are only sparingly soluble. Gallium, like aluminum, is soluble in sodium hydroxide. The elements react rapidly at room temperature, or on warming, with the halogens and with nonmetals such as sulfur.

The melting points of the elements are: Al, 660; Ga, 29.8; In, 157; Tl, 304°C. The exceptionally low melting point of gallium has no simple explanation. Since its boiling point (2070°C.) is not abnormal, gallium has the longest liquid range of any known substance and finds use as a thermometer liquid.

CHEMISTRY OF THE TRIVALENT STATE

18-4. Aqueous Chemistry

Both $Al(OH)_3$ and $Ga(OH)_3$ are amphoteric. The following approximate constants have been reported:

$$Al(OH)_3(s) = Al^{3+} + 3OH^- \qquad K \approx 5 \times 10^{-33}$$
$$Al(OH)_3(s) = AlO_2^- + H^+ + H_2O \qquad K \approx 4 \times 10^{-13}$$
$$Ga(OH)_3(s) = Ga^{3+} + 3OH^- \qquad K \approx 5 \times 10^{-37}$$
$$Ga(OH)_3(s) = GaO_2^- + H^+ + H_2O \qquad K \approx 10^{-15}$$

Both aluminum and gallium metals dissolve in acid to give Al^{3+} and Ga^{3+} and in base to give AlO_2^-, aluminate, and GaO_2^-, gallate ions. It should be noted that these MO_2^- ions have no real existence as such, either in solutions or in solid "aluminates" and "gallates." The latter are generally ionic solids, whereas the structures of the species in solution remain uncertain. It is reasonable to suppose, however, that aluminate and gallate ions in aqueous solution are four- or six-coordinate species such as $[M(OH)_4]^-$ or $[M(OH)_4(H_2O)_2]^-$. The oxides and hydroxides of indium and thallium are not amphoteric, but purely basic.

The M^{3+} ions almost certainly exist in aqueous solution as octahedral $[M(H_2O)_6]^{3+}$ ions which are moderately acidic. For the reaction

$$[M(H_2O)_6]^{3+} = [M(H_2O)_5(OH)]^{2+} + H^+$$

the following constants have been determined: $K_A(Al)$, 1.12×10^{-5}; $K_A(Ga)$, 2.5×10^{-3}; and $K_A(In)$, 2×10^{-4}. Although too much emphasis must not be placed on these exact numbers, the orders of magnitude are important, for they show that aqueous solutions of the M^{III} salts are subject to extensive hydrolysis. Indeed, salts of weak acids—sulfides, carbonates, cyanides, acetates, etc.—of these elements cannot exist in aqueous solution or in contact with water for they are completely hydrolyzed.

Not much is known about the formation of *complexes* by the trivalent ions in aqueous solution. Because of the ready hydrolysis of the aquo ions, there are, of course, no complexes formed with ammonia or amines. The gallates and aluminates may be regarded as hydroxide complexes. The only important halide complexes appear to be the fluoride complexes of aluminum which are remarkably stable. All six species from AlF^{2+} to AlF_6^{3-} are formed, and the equilibrium and kinetic behavior of the system have been carefully studied.

18-5. Oxygen Compounds

Stoichiometrically speaking, there is only one oxide of aluminum, alumina, Al_2O_3. However, this simplicity is compensated by the occurrence of various polymorphs, hydrated species, etc., the formation of which depends on the conditions of preparation. We consider first the forms of anhydrous Al_2O_3. There are two of these, α-Al_2O_3 and γ-Al_2O_3.* Since various other trivalent metals (Ga, Fe) form oxides which crystallize in these same two structures, it is worthwhile to describe them in detail. In α-Al_2O_3 the oxide ions form a hexagonally close-packed array and the aluminum ions are distributed symmetrically among the octahedral interstices. The γ-Al_2O_3 structure is sometimes regarded as a "defect"

* "β-Al_2O_3" is actually $Na_2O \cdot 11Al_2O_3$.

spinel structure, that is, as having the structure of spinel (see below) with a deficit of cations.

α-Al_2O_3 is stable at high temperatures and also indefinitely metastable at low temperatures. It occurs in nature as the mineral corundum and may be prepared from γ-Al_2O_3 or any hydrous oxide by heating above 1000°C. γ-Al_2O_3 is obtained by dehydration of hydrous oxides at low temperatures ($\sim$450°C.). α-Al_2O_3 is very hard and resistant to hydration and attack by acids, whereas γ-Al_2O_3 readily takes up water and dissolves in acids. The Al_2O_3 which forms on the surface of the metal has still another structure, namely, a defect rock salt structure; there is an arrangement of Al and O ions in the rock salt ordering with every third Al ion missing.

There are several important hydrated forms of alumina corresponding to the stoichiometries $AlO \cdot OH$ and $Al(OH)_3$. Addition of ammonia to a boiling solution of an aluminum salt produces a form of $AlO \cdot OH$ known as böhmite, which may be prepared in other ways also. A second form of $AlO \cdot OH$ occurs in nature as the mineral diaspore. The true hydroxide, $Al(OH)_3$, is obtained as a crystalline white precipitate when carbon dioxide is passed into alkaline solution of "aluminates."

The gallium oxide system quite closely resembles the aluminum oxide system, affording a high temperature α- and a low temperature γ-Ga_2O_3 and definite hydrous oxides, $GaO \cdot OH$ and $Ga(OH)_3$. The trioxide is formed by heating the nitrate, the sulfate, or the hydrous oxides which are precipitated from Ga^{III} solutions by the action of ammonia. β-Ga_2O_3 contains both tetrahedrally and octahedrally coordinated gallium with Ga—O distances of 1.83 and 2.00 A., respectively. Indium gives yellow In_2O_3, which is known in only one form, and a hydrated oxide, $In(OH)_3$. Thallium has only one form, the brown-black Tl_2O_3; this oxide begins to lose oxygen at about 100°C. to give Tl_2O. The action of NaOH on Tl^{III} salts gives what appears to be the oxide, whereas with Al, Ga, and In the products are basic salts.

Aluminum, gallium, and thallium, form mixed oxides with other metals which are of some interest. There are, first, aluminum oxides containing only small traces of other metal ions. These include ruby (Cr^{3+}) and blue sapphire (Fe^{2+}, Fe^{3+}, and Ti^{4+}). Synthetic ruby, blue sapphire, and white sapphire (gem quality corundum) are now produced synthetically in large quantities. Second, and perhaps more important, are mixed oxides containing macroscopic proportions of other elements, such as the minerals *spinel*, $MgAl_2O_4$, and crysoberyl, $BeAl_2O_4$. The spinel structure is of great importance, for it is adopted by an enormous number of mixed oxides of the type $M^{II}M_2^{III}O_4$, including some such as Mn_3O_4, Fe_3O_4, and Co_3O_4 in which the M^{II} and M^{III} ions are of the same atomic number. In $MgAl_2O_4$ the oxide ions are arranged in a cubic close-packed array. One-half of all the octahedral holes in this array are occupied by Al^{3+} ions, and one-fourth of all the tetrahedral holes by Mg^{2+} ions. More will be said later of the spinel structure and of the properties of other mixed oxides which have it. Compounds of the formula M^ITlO_2 are also mixed oxides.

18-6. Halides

All four halides of each element are known with one probable exception. It has been shown that the compound TlI_3 obtained by adding iodine to thallous iodide is not thallium(III) iodide, but rather thallium(I) triiodide, $Tl^I(I_3)$. This situation may be compared with the nonexistence of iodides of other oxidizing cations such as Cu^{2+} and Fe^{3+}, except that here a lower valent compound fortuitously has the same stoichiometry as the higher valent one.

The other thallium(III) halides are genuine but very unstable. The chloride loses chlorine at about 40°C. and above to give the monochloride, and the tribromide loses bromine at even lower temperatures to give first a compound which may be $Tl^I[Tl^{III}Br_4]$. The fluoride is stable to about 500°C.; but, compared to the fluorides of the other group III elements, this is rather poor stability. These facts provide a very good illustration of the way in which the stability of the lower valence state dominates thallium chemistry.

The halides of the remaining elements, Al, Ga, and In, form fairly homologous groups. The fluorides are all high-melting solids, whereas the chlorides, bromides, and iodides all have low melting points (Table 18-2).

TABLE 18-2

Melting Points of the Trihalides of Al, Ga, and In
(In °C.)

X	AlX_3	GaX_3	InX_3
Fluoride	1290	950 (subl.)	1170
Chloride	193 (1700 mm.)[a]	78	586
Bromide	98	122	436
Iodide	180	212	210

[a] Sublimes at 760 mm. at 180°C.

Although it is reasonable to expect that the metal–fluorine bonds have a greater intrinsic tendency to be ionic than do other metal–halogen bonds, the pattern of melting points shown in Table 18-2 is best explained in terms of coordination numbers and structures. The Al^{3+}, Ga^{3+}, and In^{3+} cations are sufficiently large to prefer a coordination number of six toward the relatively small fluorine atom. In order to achieve this, they adopt structures which are infinitely extended arrays of metal and fluorine atoms. Whether these are best regarded as ionic lattices or as giant polymers in which the bonds are significantly ionic is a moot point. Whether strictly covalent (as in diamond) or highly ionic (as in NaCl), such an infinitely extended structure would lead to a high melting point. The other halides have quite different structures. Evidently, with the larger halogen atoms, Cl, Br, and I, a coordination number of four is best for the metal atoms and so the dimeric structures, of which that for aluminum bromide (Fig. 18-1) is typical, are formed. Naturally, a crystal containing such distinct molecules with no strong forces between them has a low melting point.

These covalent, dimeric structures persist in the vapor phase at temperatures not too far above the boiling points. At sufficiently high temperatures, however, dissociation into planar, triangular monomers, analogous to the boron halides, occurs. There is some evidence that for gallium iodide this dissociation is very extensive even at the boiling point. The group III halides dissolve readily in many nonpolar solvents such as benzene, in which they remain dimeric. The enthalpies of dissociation, $Al_2X_6(g) = 2AlX_3(g)$, have been measured and are 11–15 kcal./mole. As Figure 18-1 shows, the configuration of halogen atoms about each metal

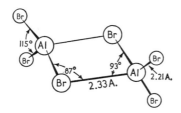

Fig. 18-1.   The structure of the aluminum bromide dimer.

atom is roughly, though far from exactly, tetrahedral. The formation of such dimers is attributable to the tendency of the metal atoms to complete their octets. The dimers may be split by reaction with donor molecules whereby complexes of the type R_3NAlCl_3 are formed. The halides dissolve in water dissociating into M^{3+} and X^- ions; from such solutions hydrates containing hexaquo ions, for example, $[Al(H_2O)_6]Cl_3$, may be obtained.

18-7. Other Salts and Compounds

The group III elements form various other compounds such as carbides, nitrides, phosphides, sulfides, and salts of oxy acids.

Aluminum *carbide*, Al_4C_3, is formed from the elements at temperatures of 1000–2000°C. It reacts instantly with water to produce methane, and X-ray studies have shown it to contain discrete carbon atoms (C—C = 3.16 A.); for these reasons it is sometimes considered to be a "methanide," that is, a salt containing C^{4-}, but this is perhaps an oversimplification.

The *nitrides* AlN, GaN, and InN are known. Only aluminum reacts directly with nitrogen. GaN forms on reaction of Ga with NH_3 and InN by pyrolysis of $(NH_4)_3InF_6$. All have a wurzite structure (Fig. 23-1, page 475). They are fairly hard and stable, as might be expected from their close structural relationship to diamond and the diamond-like BN.

Gallium *phosphide* can be obtained as pale orange single crystals by the reaction of phosphorus and Ga_2O vapor at 900–1000°C.; it behaves as a semiconductor.

Al, Ga, In, and Tl do *not* form any hydrides analogous to those of boron except for the MH_4^- ions and some $[R_nMH_{4-n}]^-$ ions. Some not too well-characterized solid binary hydrides, such as $(AlH_3)_n$ obtained by the addition of $AlCl_3$ to $LiAlH_4$ in ether, have been reported, but little is known with certainty concerning their structures and properties. There is reason to suppose that the larger size of Al, Ga, In, and Tl makes the formation of hydrogen bridges of the type occurring in the boranes impossible and that this accounts, at least in part, for the absence of comparable series of hydrides.

Salts of most strong *oxy acids* are well known and are obtained as hydrates from aqueous solutions. It is likely that all contain the hexaquo metal ions. Once again we encounter a class of aluminum compounds which are of importance because they are structural prototypes and give their name to a large group of analogous compounds formed by other elements. These are the *alums*. They have the general formula $MAl(SO_4)_2 \cdot 12H_2O$ in which M is practically any common univalent cation except for Li^+, which is too small to be accommodated without loss of stability of the structure. The crystals are made up of $[M(H_2O)_6]^+$, $[Al(H_2O)_6]^{3+}$, and two SO_4^{2-} ions. There are actually three structures, all cubic, consisting of the above ions, but differing slightly in details depending on the size of the univalent ion. Salts of the same type, $M^I M^{III}(SO_4)_2 \cdot 12H_2O$, and having the same structures are formed by many other trivalent metal ions, including those of Ti, V, Cr, Mn, Fe, Co, Ga, In, Rh, and Ir, and all such compounds are referred to as alums. The term is used so generally that those alums containing aluminum are designated, in a seeming redundancy, as aluminum alums.

The four elements form *alkoxides*, but only those of aluminum, particularly the isopropoxide, which is widely used in organic chemistry as a reducing agent for aldehydes and ketones, are of importance. They can be made by the reactions

$$Al + ROH \xrightarrow[\substack{\text{catalyst,} \\ \text{warm}}]{1\% \text{ HgCl}_2} (RO)_3Al + \tfrac{3}{2}H_2$$

$$AlCl_3 + 3RONa \longrightarrow (RO_3)Al + 3NaCl$$

The alkoxides hydrolyze vigorously with water and are polymeric in solution in inert organic solvents.

18-8. Complexes

Complexes containing both octahedrally and tetrahedrally coordinated metal ions are known, the former being decidedly more numerous and characteristic for Ga, In, and Tl and the latter somewhat more so for Al.

Aluminum forms octahedral complexes with some neutral ligands, giving such complex cations as $[Al(H_2O)_6]^{3+}$ and $\{Al[OS(CH_3)_2]_6\}^{3+}$, and with fluoride ion. There are many salts of the AlF_6^{3-} ion known, among which is the technologically important compound cryolite. The structure of cryolite (Fig. 18-2) is of some interest since it is adopted by many other

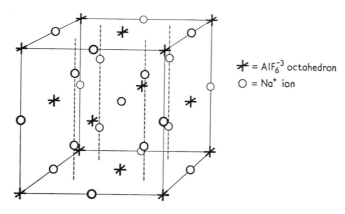

$\text{✳} = AlF_6^{-3}$ octahedron
$O = Na^+$ ion

Fig. 18-2.   The cubic structure of cryolite, Na_3AlF_6.

compounds containing small cations and large octahedral anions and, in its *anti* form, by many salts of the same type as $[Co(NH_3)_6]I_3$. It is closely related to the structures adopted by many compounds of the types

$M_2^+[AB_6]^{2-}$ and $[XY_6]^{2+}Z_2^-$. These latter two structures are essentially the fluorite and antifluorite structures (see Fig. 2-4, page 46), except that the anions (or cations) are octahedra whose axes are oriented parallel to the cube edges. The unit cell contains four formula units. Addition of four cations per unit cell, one at the center of the cube and one at the midpoint of each edge, gives the cryolite structure. Other complex fluorides of aluminum, such as Tl_2AlF_5 and NH_4AlF_4, also contain octahedrally coordinated aluminum. In the former the octahedra are joined at corners to form chains (Fig. 18-3a), and in the latter they share corners (but not edges

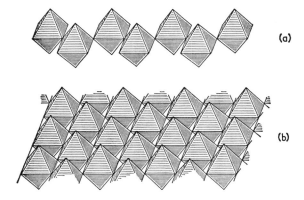

(a)

(b)

Fig. 18-3. Diagrams showing how AlF_6^{3-} octahedra combine by sharing corners in the compounds (a) Tl_2AlF_5 and (b) NH_4AlF_4.

on account of the high charge on Al^{3+}) to form sheets (Fig. 18-3b). Basic aluminum acetate has a structure similar to that of the basic acetates of chromium(III) and iron(III) and is probably $[Al_3(OH)_2(OCOCH_3)_6]^+$. It has been suggested that there is a central oxygen atom and three metal atoms in a plane with bidentate acetate groups bridging the metal atoms.

Aluminum forms no octahedral complexes with the larger halogens, but

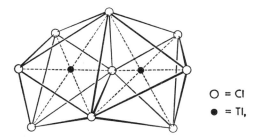

O = Cl
● = Tl,

Fig. 18-4. The structure of the binuclear complex anions $[Tl_2Cl_6]^{3-}$ and $[W_2Cl_9]^{3-}$.

its congeners do. Salts of the complex anions $[GaCl_6]^{3-}$ and $[InCl_6]^{3-}$ are fairly numerous, and some salts of the anions $[GaBr_6]^{3-}$, $[InBr_6]^{3-}$, $[TlCl_6]^{3-}$, $[TlBr_6]^{3-}$, and $[TlI_6]^{3-}$ are known. Thallium alone forms the interesting binuclear ion $[Tl_2Cl_9]^{3-}$, which has the structure shown in Figure 18-4, in which two octahedra share a face. The most important octahedral complexes of the group III elements are those containing chelate rings. Typical of these are the β-diketone complexes (18-I and 18-II), the catechol

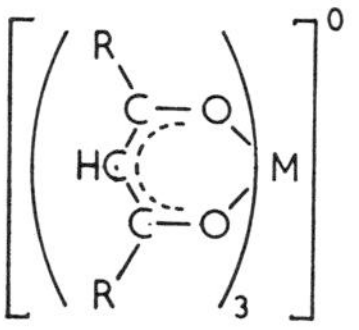

(18-I) 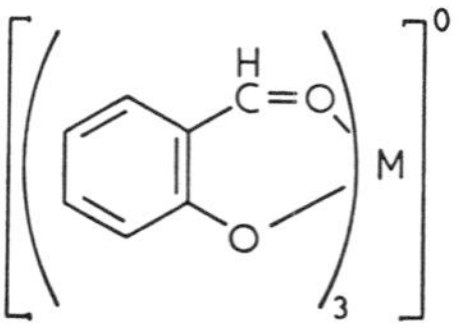   (18-II)

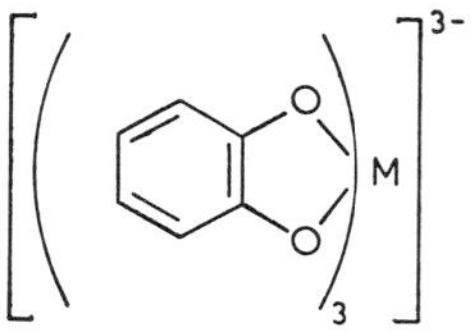

(18-III) 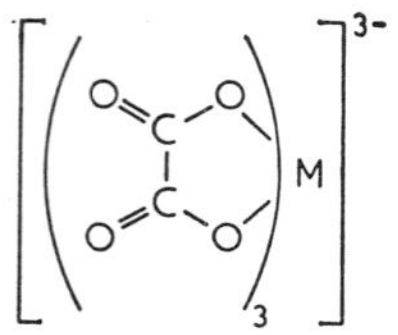   (18-IV)

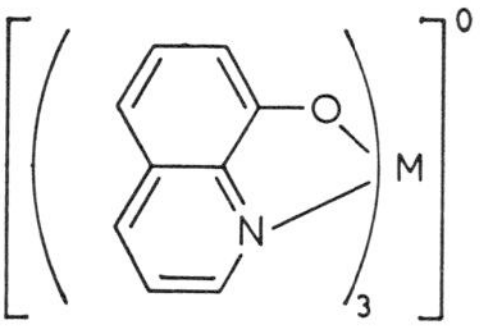

(18-V)

(18-III) and dicarboxylic acid (18-IV) complexes, and the 8-hydroxy-quinoline (18-V) complexes. The neutral complexes dissolve readily in organic solvents, but are insoluble in water. The acetylacetonates (18-I, $R = CH_3$) have low melting points ($> 200°C.$) and vaporize without decomposition. The anionic complexes are isolated as the salts of large univalent cations. The 8-hydroxyquinolinates are used for analytical purposes.

Tetrahedral complexes are much rarer than the octahedral ones and are formed mainly by Al and Ga salts. $[AlCl_4]^-$ and $[GaCl_4]^-$ ions are fairly common, but the tetrahedral complexes are mostly formed by addition of neutral donors to AlX_3 and GaX_3. The neutral donors may be ammonia, amines, ethers, alcohols, ketones, phosphines, thioethers, etc., and complexes of the general types $\overset{+}{L}\overset{-}{Al}X_3$ and $\overset{+}{L}\overset{-}{Ga}X_3$, with approximately tetrahedral coordination of Al and Ga, are formed. The formation of $[AlCl_4]^-$

and $[AlBr_4]^-$ ions is, of course, essential to the functioning of Al_2Cl_6 and Al_2Br_6 as Friedel-Crafts catalysts, since in this way the necessary carbonium ions are simultaneously formed:

$$RCOCl + AlCl_3 \rightarrow RCO^+ + [AlCl_4]^- \text{ (ion pair)}$$
$$RCO^+ + C_6H_6 \rightarrow [RCOC_6H_6]^+ \rightarrow RCOC_6H_5 + H^+$$

18-9. Organometallic Compounds

Those of aluminum are by far the most important and best known. They may be prepared by the classical reaction of aluminum with the appropriate organomercury compound:

$$2Al + 3R_2Hg \rightarrow 2R_3Al \text{ (or } [R_3Al]_2) + 3Hg$$

In more recently developed methods, useful for large-scale work, Al reacts with alkyl halides giving alkyl aluminum halides (dimeric due to halide bridging) which can be thermally cracked to give, upon fractionation, the trialkyls, for example,

$$4Al + 6EtBr \longrightarrow Et_4Al_2Br_2 + Et_2Al_2Br_4 \xrightarrow[\text{distil}]{\text{heat}} [Et_3Al]_2 + Al_2Br_6$$

Alternatively, an alloy of aluminum with a very electropositive metal such as Mg may be used and the trialkyl aluminum compound obtained directly:

$$Al_2Mg_3 + 6EtCl \rightarrow [Et_3Al]_2 + 3MgCl_2$$

The ethyl derivative is also made by the high pressure reaction:

$$Al + 3C_2H_4 + \tfrac{3}{2}H_2 \rightarrow Al(C_2H_5)_3$$

some diethylaluminum hydride being formed also:

$$2(C_2H_5)_3Al + Al + \tfrac{3}{2}H_2 \rightarrow 3(C_2H_5)_2AlH$$

The aluminum alkyls are all extremely reactive liquids, inflaming in air and explosively sensitive to water. Moreover, all of those with lower alkyl groups are dimerized. (The nature of the electron-deficient bond ng in these dimers has been discussed on page 231.) The trialkyl aluminum compounds are Lewis acids combining with many donors such as amines, phosphines, and ethers to give tetrahedral complexes. They also combine with alkyl lithium compounds to give tetraalkyl aluminate ions:

$$(C_2H_5)_3Al \cdot O(C_2H_5)_2 + LiC_2H_5 \rightarrow Li[Al(C_2H_5)_4] + (C_2H_5)_2O$$

Triethylaluminum, the sesquichloride $(C_2H_5)_3Al_2Cl_3$, and alkyl hydrides are used together with transition metal halides or alkoxides or organometallic complexes as catalysts (e.g., Ziegler catalysts) for the polymerization of ethylene, propylene, and a great variety of other unsaturated compounds. These polymerizations are often stereospecific, giving crystalline oriented polypropylenes, for example. The alkyls are also used as alkylating agents.

The organometallic compounds of gallium and indium resemble those of aluminum in most respects, but they have been much less extensively investigated. They are similarly acceptors, and the order of acceptor character has been roughly established to be $B < Al > Ga > In > Tl$. One signal point of difference is the lack of dimerization of the alkyls of B, Ga, In, and Tl at ordinary temperatures, with the exception of the unusual polymerization of trimethylindium (see page 231). Thallium forms no stable Tl^I organometallic compounds with the exception of the insoluble polymeric TlC_5H_5, which is precipitated by adding aqueous TlOH to cyclopentadiene; a similar In compound is also known. Derivatives of Tl^{III} are known which are generally similar in character to those of Ga and In, but the trialkyls and triaryls are unstable and reactive. However, Tl gives very stable ionic derivatives of the type R_2TlX (X = halogen, sulfate, nitrate, etc.), which resemble mercury compounds R_2Hg, being unaffected by air and water. The ion $(CH_3)_2Tl^+$ in aqueous solution has been shown by Raman spectroscopy to have a linear skeleton C—Tl—C, as would be expected since it is isoelectronic with C—Hg—C. Other salts are ionic in the crystal, again with linear ions.

LOWER VALENT COMPOUNDS

18-10. Lower Valences of Aluminum, Gallium, and Indium

Since the elements have the outer electron configurations ns^2np, it is natural to consider whether monovalent ions might be capable of existence. It may be recalled that there is no evidence for B^I under chemically important conditions.

To date there is no evidence that compounds containing Al^I exist at ordinary temperatures. Anodic oxidation of aluminum at high current densities evidently produces lower valent aluminum ions, either Al^I or Al^{II}, or both, but they are ephemeral. There is no doubt that *gaseous* Al^I halide molecules exist at high temperatures, and their spectroscopic properties are well known. In the chloride system the equilibrium

$$AlCl_3(g) + 2Al(s) = 3AlCl(g)$$

has been thoroughly studied and its use in purifying aluminum proposed. The reaction proceeds to the right at high temperatures, but reverses readily at low temperatures. Similarly, it has been shown that gaseous

Al_2O and AlO molecules exist above 1000°C., but no solid oxides containing lower valent aluminum have been shown definitely to exist under ordinary conditions. It is doubtful if the reported solid AlI is authentic, and no serious claim has ever been made for the existence of other monohalides.

The existence of a number of Ga^I compounds is quite certain. The "dihalides," $GaCl_2$, $GaBr_2$, and GaI_2, have all been shown to have the structure $Ga^I[Ga^{III}X_4]$, and the Ga^I ion can be obtained without the simultaneous presence of any Ga^{III} in the compounds $Ga^I[AlX_4]$. The gallium(I) tetrahalogallates(III) are prepared by reducing the trihalides with gallium metal. The monohalides have also been prepared, but are difficult to obtain pure. Ga_2S is also an authentic Ga^I compound. GaS and $GaSe$ have been shown to contain trivalent gallium with Ga—Ga bonds. The oxide Ga_2O exists at high temperatures similarly to Al_2O.

There is some evidence that unstable Ga^I species are important in the dissolution of gallium in perchloric acid. This postulation accounts for the stoichiometries observed and for the fact that gallium is one of the few reagents to reduce perchloric acid:

$$Ga + H^+ = Ga^+ + \tfrac{1}{2}H_2$$
$$4Ga^+ + 8H^+ + ClO_4^- = 4Ga^{3+} + Cl^- + 4H_2O$$

Some delayed reducing ability of gallium dissolved in HCl has been reported.

Although it appears that lower valent indium compounds are more stable, as a class, than those of gallium, they are less well characterized. InF_2 appears to exist, but its structure is unknown. The monohalides, $InCl$, $InBr$, and InI, exist. $InCl_2$ does not appear to exist as a distinct compound, but a phase, In_2Cl_3, for which the structure $In_3^I[In^{III}Cl_6]$ has been suggested, is stable. In_2O appears to be an authentic In^I compound, but its structure remains unknown.

No Ga^I or In^I species are stable in aqueous solution.

18-11. Thallium(I)

With thallium, the unipositive state is quite stable. In aqueous solution it is distinctly more stable than Tl^{III}:

$$Tl^+ = Tl^{3+} + 2e \qquad E^0 = -1.28 \text{ v.}$$

The thallous ion is not very sensitive to pH, although the thallic ion is extensively hydrolyzed to $TlOH^{2+}$ and the colloidal oxide even at pH 1–2.5.

The colorless thallous ion has a radius of 1.44 A., which can be compared with those of K^+, Rb^+, and Ag^+, (1.33, 1.48, and 1.26 A.), since in its chemistry this ion resembles either the alkali or argentous ions. The yellow hydroxide is thermally unstable, giving the black oxide, Tl_2O, at about

100°C. The latter and the hydroxide are readily soluble in water to give strongly basic solutions which absorb carbon dioxide from the air; TlOH is a weaker base than KOH, however. Many thallous salts have solubilities somewhat lower than the corresponding alkali salts, but otherwise are similar to and quite often isomorphous with them. Examples of such salts are the cyanide, nitrate, carbonate, sulfate, phosphates, perchlorate, and alums. Thallous solutions are exceedingly poisonous and in trace amounts cause loss of hair.

Thallous sulfate, nitrate, and acetate are moderately soluble in water, but—except for the very soluble TlF—the halides are sparingly soluble. The chromate and the black sulfide, Tl_2S, which can be precipitated by hydrogen sulfide from weakly acid solutions, are also insoluble. Thallous chloride also resembles silver chloride in being photosensitive, darkening on exposure to light. It is insoluble in ammonia, however, unlike silver chloride; in general, thallous complexes, with the exception of those with oxygen and sulfur ligands, are scarce.

The two isotopes, ^{203}Tl and ^{205}Tl (70.48%), both have nuclear spin, and nuclear magnetic resonance signals are readily detected for thallium solutions or for solids. In solution both Tl^I and Tl^{III} resonances are markedly dependent on concentration and on the nature of anions present; such data have shown that thallous perchlorate is highly dissociated, but salts of weaker acids and TlOH have been shown to form ion pairs in solution.

The Tl^I–Tl^{III} system has been intensively studied because, superficially, it provides an example of a two-electron transfer oxidation-reduction couple. Although Tl^{II} has not been characterized in isolable compounds, the kinetic data are best interpreted by postulating a Tl^{II} intermediate. A similar intermediate is believed to occur in the reduction of Tl^{III} solutions, for example,

$$Tl^{III} + Fe^{II} = Tl^{II} + Fe^{III}$$
$$Tl^{II} + Fe^{II} \rightarrow Tl^I + Fe^{III}$$

References

Stone, F. G. A., *Chem. Revs.*, **88**, 101 (1958). Stability relationships in analogous molecular addition compounds of group III elements (including boron).

Thomas, C. A., *Anhydrous Aluminum Chloride in Organic Chemistry*, Reinhold, New York, 1941.

Ziegler, K., in Sir A. R. Todd, ed., *Perspectives in Organic Chemistry*, Interscience, New York–London, 1956. Use of organoaluminum compounds in syntheses.

——, *International Conference on Coordination Chemistry*, *Chem. Soc. (London)*, *Spec. Publ. No. 13* (1959). Use of organoaluminum compounds in syntheses.

——, in H. H. Zeiss, ed., *Organometallic Chemistry* (American Chemical Society Monograph No. 147), Reinhold, New York, 1960, p. 194. Organoaluminum compounds.

19

The Group IV Elements: Si, Ge, Sn, Pb

GENERAL REMARKS

19-1. Group Trends and Stereochemistry

The general trend from electronegative to electropositive character with increasing atomic number which is found in several groups is strikingly evident in group IV. Carbon is strictly nonmetallic; silicon is chemically essentially nonmetallic; germanium is a metalloid; tin and lead are truly metallic although their oxides, especially those of tin, are amphoteric.

However, although this trend in metallic character is continuous, it is not regular. There is scarcely any more striking example of an enormous discontinuity in general properties between the first and second row elements followed by a relatively smooth change toward more metallic character thereafter than in this group. Little of the chemistry of silicon can be inferred from that of carbon. Some properties of the elements are given in Table 19-1.

TABLE 19-1

Some Properties of the Group IV Elements

Element	Electronic structure	Ionization potentials, e.v.				Electro-negativities	Covalent radius, A.
		1st	2nd	3rd	4th		
C	$[He]2s^22p^2$					2.55	0.77
Si	$[Ne]3s^23p^2$	8.1	16.3	33.5	45.1	1.90	1.17
Ge	$[Ar]3d^{10}4s^24p^2$	8.1	15.9	34.1	45.5	2.01	1.22
Sn	$[Kr]4d^{10}5s^25p^2$	7.3	14.5	30.5	39.4	1.96	1.41
Pb	$[Xe]4f^{14}5d^{10}6s^26p^2$	7.4	15.0	32	42.1	2.33	1.54[a]

[a] Ionic radius of Pb^{2+}, 0.84.

The tendency to *catenation* decreases markedly down the group. Silicon has some tendency, germanium very little, and tin and lead form no known compounds in which Sn or Pb is bound to more than one other Sn or Pb atom. This low and rapidly diminishing tendency to catenation has already been mentioned and ascribed partly to diminishing strength of the C—C, Si—Si, Ge—Ge, Sn—Sn, and Pb—Pb bonds. The energies of these bonds are believed to be about as follows:

C—C   83 kcal./mole   Ge—Ge   40 kcal./mole
Si—Si 53 kcal./mole   Sn—Sn   37 kcal./mole

The strengths of single covalent bonds between group IV atoms and other atoms generally decrease in going down the group, as can be seen from Table 19-2; it will be noticed that in some cases there is an initial

TABLE 19-2

Some Average Bond Energies

Group IV[a] element	Energy of bond, kcal./mole, with						
	H	C	F	Cl	Br	I	O
C	99	83	116	81	68	51	85
Si	75	76	135	91	74	55	108
Ge	74	71		85	68	50	
Sn	71	68		82	65	47	

[a] Data derived mainly from MX_4 type compounds which are unstable or nonexistent when M = Pb.

rise from C to Si followed by a decrease. These energies do not, of course, reflect the ease of heterolytic breaking of bonds which is the usual way in chemical reactions; thus, for example, in spite of the high Si—Cl or Si—F bond energies, compounds containing these bonds are highly reactive. Since the charge separation in a bond is a critical factor, the bond ionicities must also be considered in order to interpret the reactivities toward nucleophilic reagents. Thus SiCl bonds are much more reactive than SiC bonds because, though stronger, they are more polar, $Si^{\delta+}$—$Cl^{\delta-}$, rendering the silicon more susceptible to attack by a nucleophile such as OH^-.

It will be noted from Table 19-1 that the electronegativities for the sp^3-hybridized elements do not decrease monatomically as might have been expected following the trend usually observed in the groups. The order C > Pb > Ge > Sn > Si has been obtained by a variety of different methods and appears to be significant. A similar anomalous order occurs in group III. This alternation has been attributed to the effects of the filling of the d, and later f, shells in the transition elements and in the lanthanides, which affects the screening of the valence electrons in the elements following them.

In group IV there is a certain amount of chemical behavior which supports the above order, although, owing to the numerous factors which affect chemical behavior, good correlations solely with electronegativity cannot be expected. However, it can be noted that Zn and hydrochloric acid reduce only germanium halides to the hydrides, which suggests a higher electronegativity for Ge than for Si or Sn. Also, 15% NaOH does not affect GeH_4 or SnH_4, while SiH_4 is rapidly hydrolyzed by water containing a trace of OH^-, which is consistent with, though not necessarily indicative of, the Ge—H or Sn—H bonds either being nonpolar or having the positive charge on hydrogen. Finally, we note that germanium halides are hydrolyzed in water only slowly and reversibly.

There is a gradual and steady increase in the stability of the II oxidation state relative to the IV state, so that, although the former is virtually nonexistent with carbon, and, as far as we know, with silicon, it appears definitely with germanium and with lead is the dominant state. Inspection of Table 19-1 clearly shows that this trend cannot be explained exclusively in terms of ionization potentials, since these are essentially the same for all of the group IV elements; the "inert pair" concept is not particularly instructive either.

The other factors which undoubtedly do govern the relative stabilities of the oxidation states are promotion energies and bond strengths for covalent compounds and lattice energies for ionic compounds. Taking first the former, it is rather easy to see why the divalent state becomes stable if we remember that the M—X bond energies generally decrease in the order Si—X, Ge—X, Sn—X, Pb—X(?). Referring to the promotion energy diagram for methane (page 61), we see that the factor which stabilizes CH_4 relative to $CH_2 + H_2$, despite the much higher promotional energy required in forming CH_4, is the great strength of the C—H bonds and the fact that two more of these are formed in CH_4 than in CH_2. Thus if we have a series of reactions $MX_2 + X_2 = MX_4$ in which the M—X bond energies are decreasing, it is obviously possible that this energy may eventually become too small to compensate for the $M^{II} \rightarrow M^{IV}$ promotion energy and the MX_2 compound becomes the more stable. For ionic compounds matters are not so simple, but since the sizes of the (real or hypothetical) ions, M^{2+} and M^{4+}, will increase down the group, it is possible that lattice energy differences will no longer favor the M^{4+} compound relative to the

M^{2+} compound in view of the considerable energy expenditure required for the process

$$M^{2+} = M^{4+} + 2e$$

Of course there are few compounds of the types MX_2 or MX_4 which are entirely covalent or ionic (almost certainly no ionic MX_4 compounds) so that the above arguments are oversimplifications, but they indicate roughly the factors involved.

Stereochemistry. With the exception of a few compounds of the heavier elements, such as bisthiourealead(II) chloride, in which the lead atoms are seven-coordinate, and the $SnCl_5^-$ ion, the normal coordination numbers in this group are 4 and 6 and the respective geometries are tetrahedral and octahedral.

Tetrahedral stereochemistry implies the possibility of optical isomerism, and this has been realized in the case of silicon by resolution of compounds such as $SiCH_3 \cdot C_2H_5 \cdot C_6H_5 \cdot C_6H_4COOH$.

Multiple Bonding. Silicon, germanium, tin, and lead do not form $p\pi$ multiple bonds either to themselves or to other elements, whereas carbon has a profound tendency to do so. Thus there are numerous classes of carbon compounds such as olefins, ketones, imides, etc., which have no analogs among silicon and the heavier elements. Purely stoichiometric analogs such as CO_2, SiO_2, $(CH_3)_2CO$, $(CH_3)_2SiO$ exist, but they are totally different kinds of substances structurally. For example, dehydration of the silanol $R_2Si(OH)_2$ gives not a ketone analog but a disiloxane R_2Si (OH)—O—$Si(OH)R_2$ and silicones $(R_2SiO)_n$.

However, there is considerable evidence that in certain bonds to silicon, notably with O and N, there is some $d\pi$–$p\pi$ double bond character. This has been mentioned previously in the discussion of $N(SiH_3)_3$ (page 242). This type of multiple bond character is evidenced also by the rather large bond angles in siloxanes and by the much stronger acidity and hydrogen bonding of silanols such as $(CH_3)_3SiOH$ compared to $(CH_3)_3COH$; this can be ascribed to Si—O π bonding involving one of the two unshared pairs of the silanol oxygen and the $3d$ orbital of Si to give a situation somewhat similar electronically to the nitrogen atom in an imine $R_2C=N$—H. The fact that one unshared pair still remains on the oxygen is consistent with the fact that *base* character of the silanol is not much lowered in spite of its stronger acidity, compared to the alcohol.

Although discussion is outside the scope of this book, it may be noted that studies of the mechanism of substitution at tetrahedral silicon atoms also provide some evidence for the involvement of d orbitals. Thus the energy to reach the transition states in substitution reactions involving a five-coordinate intermediate appear lower than would be expected without use of the silicon d orbitals.

THE ELEMENTS

19-2. Occurrence, Isolation, and Properties

Silicon is second only to oxygen in weight percentage of the earth's crust ($\sim$28%) and is found in an enormous diversity of silicate minerals. Germanium, tin, and lead are relatively rare elements ($\sim$10^{-3} weight %), but are well known because of their technical importance (a recent development for Ge) and the relative ease with which they are obtained from natural sources in the cases of tin and lead.

Silicon is obtained in the ordinary commercial form by reduction of SiO_2 with carbon or CaC_2 in an electric furnace. Similarly germanium is prepared by reduction of the dioxide with carbon or hydrogen. Among the important recent commercial uses of silicon and germanium, and indeed the one which has made germanium a commercially important element, is their use as semiconductors, especially in transistors. For this purpose exceedingly high purity materials are required, and special methods are required to obtain usable materials. For silicon, methods vary in detail but the following general procedure is followed.

1. Ordinary, "chemically" pure Si is converted, by direct reaction, to a silicon halide or to $SiCl_3H$. This is then purified (of B, As, etc.) by fractional distillation in quartz vessels.

2. The SiX_4 is then reconverted to elemental silicon by reduction with hydrogen in a hot tube or on a hot wire, when X is Cl or Br

$$SiX_4 + 2H_2 = Si + 4HX$$

or by direct thermal decomposition on a hot wire when X is I. Very pure Si can also be obtained by thermal decomposition of silane.

3. Pure silicon is then made "super-pure" (impurities $<$10^{-9} atom %) by zone refining. In this process a rod of metal is heated near one end so that a cross-sectional wafer of molten silicon is produced. Since impurities are more soluble in the melt than they are in the solid they concentrate in the melt and the melted zone is then caused to move slowly along the rod by moving the heat source. This carries impurities to the end. The process may be repeated. The impure end is then removed.

Super-pure germanium is made in a similar way. Germanium chloride is fractionally distilled and then hydrolyzed to GeO_2, which is then reduced with hydrogen. The resulting metal is zone melted.

Tin and lead are obtained from their ores in various ways, commonly by reduction of their oxides with carbon. Further purification is usually effected by dissolving the metals in acid and depositing the pure metals electrolytically.

Silicon is ordinarily rather unreactive but not so much so as diamond. It is attacked by halogens giving tetrahalides, and by alkalies giving solutions of silicates. It is not attacked by acids except hydrofluoric; presumably the stability of SiF_6^{2-} provides the driving force here. Rather recently a highly reactive form of silicon has been prepared by the reaction:

$$3CaSi_2 + 2SbCl_3 = 6Si + 2Sb + 3CaCl_2$$

For example, it reacts with water to give SiO_2 and hydrogen. It has been suggested that this form is a graphite-like allotrope, but proof is as yet lacking, and its reactivity may be due to a state of extreme subdivision as in certain reactive forms of amorphous carbon.

Germanium is quite similar to but somewhat more reactive than silicon. It will dissolve in concentrated sulfuric and nitric acids. Tin and lead are more reactive. They dissolve in several acids, are rapidly attacked by halogens, and are slowly attacked by cold alkali, and rapidly by hot, to form stannates and plumbites. Lead often appears to be much more noble and unreactive than would be indicated by the potential

$$Pb^0 = Pb^{2+} + 2e \qquad E^0 = +0.1 \text{ v.}$$

This low reactivity can be attributed to high overvoltage for hydrogen and also in some cases to insoluble surface coatings. Thus lead is not dissolved by dilute sulfuric and concentrated hydrochloric acids.

19-3. Allotropic Forms

There is only one proven form of elemental silicon, and its structure is the same as that of diamond. The same is true of germanium. The graphite structure is peculiar to carbon, which is understandable since such a structure requires the formation of $p\pi$–$p\pi$ bonds and silicon and germanium are unable to engage in such bonding.

Tin has three crystalline modifications, with the following equilibrium transition temperatures

$$\alpha\text{-Sn} \underset{\text{"grey"}}{\overset{13.2°C.}{\rightleftarrows}} \beta\text{-Sn} \underset{\text{"white"}}{\overset{161°C.}{\rightleftarrows}} \gamma\text{-Sn} \overset{232°C.}{\rightleftarrows} Sn(l)$$

α-Tin, or grey tin (density at 20°C. = 5.75), has the diamond structure. This form is unstable above 13.2°C. and is transformed to β-tin or white tin (density at 20°C. = 7.31) which has a metallic nature; γ-tin is also metallic. In the metallic forms there exist distorted close-packed arrangements of the metal atoms. The approach to ideal close packing accounts for the considerably greater density of the β-metal compared to the diamond form.

The most metallic of the group IV elements, lead, exists only in a cubic, metallic form. This is a reflection of both its preference for divalence rather than tetravalence and of the relatively low stability of the Pb—Pb bond.

COMPOUNDS OF THE GROUP IV ELEMENTS

19-4. Hydrides

The known hydrides of the elements Si, Ge, Sn, and Pb are listed in Table 19-3.

TABLE 19-3

Hydrides of the Group IV Elements

Si	Ge	Sn	Pb
SiH_4 (b.p. $-112°C$.) Silane	GeH_4 (b.p. $-90°C$.) Germane	SnH_4 Stannane	PbH_4 Plumbane
Si_2H_6 Disilane	Ge_2H_6		
Si_3H_8 Trisilane	Ge_3H_8		
Si_4H_{10}[a] Tetrasilane	Ge_4H_{10}		
Si_5H_{12}[a] Pentasilane	Ge_5H_{12}		
Si_6H_{14}[a] Hexasilane	Ge_6H_{14}[b]		
$(SiH)_n$	Ge_7H_{16}[b] Ge_8H_{18}[b]		

[a] Isomers known.
[b] Characterized by gas chromatography.

While for carbon the stoichiometrically analogous alkanes, C_nH_{2n+2}, occur without known limit on n, the hydrides of the other elements form very limited series due to the weakness of the metal–metal bonds. So far as is known, the compounds in Table 19-3 all have structures based upon a tetrahedral disposition of bonds about the metal atoms. The nomenclature is given in the table for the silanes and follows the same pattern for the germanes.

The *silanes*, also commonly called silicon hydrides, have been most extensively studied, especially by Stock and his students in the first third of this century. The preparative procedure used by Stock is the sulfuric or phosphoric acid hydrolysis of magnesium silicide, Mg_2Si, which is easily prepared by heating silicon and magnesium together in absence of air. The hydrolysis gives a mixture of the six silanes, in the approximate proportions: 40% SiH_4, 30% Si_2H_6, 15% Si_3H_8, 10% Si_4H_{10}, 5% Si_5H_{12} and Si_6H_{14}, with perhaps traces of still higher members of the series; the over-all yields based on Si converted to volatile hydrides is about 25%. The individual silanes can be separated by fractional distillation or by vapor phase chromatography; the latter method has allowed separation of the isomers. Monosilane is now most conveniently prepared by the action of lithium aluminum hydride on silicon tetrachloride.

The important physical and chemical properties of the silanes are the following. All are colorless. The boiling points rise steadily with increasing molecular weight so that Si_3H_8 is a liquid at room temperature. All are very reactive; they are spontaneously flammable in air,

$$Si_4H_{10} + \tfrac{13}{2}O_2 = 4SiO_2 + 5H_2O$$

They are stable toward neutral or acid water, but in the presence of base, even the traces provided by glass vessels, they are rapidly hydrolyzed in a manner typical of compounds containing hydridic hydrogen (the electronegativity of hydrogen is greater than that of silicon; cf. also the hydrolysis of the boranes):

$$Si_2H_6 + (4 + 2n)H_2O \equiv 2SiO_2 \cdot nH_2O + 7H_2$$
$$\text{(Hydrous silica)}$$

The silanes are strong reducing agents. They react explosively with halogens at room temperature, but controlled replacement of H by Br or Cl may be effected in the presence of AlX_3 to give halosilanes such as SiH_3Cl. The ease of thermal decomposition of the silanes increases with increasing number of Si—Si links; thus the higher silanes decompose slowly although SiH_4 and Si_2H_6 are indefinitely stable at room temperature.

A great variety of alkyl and other substituted silanes are known, and silyl compounds containing the SiH_3 group have been much studied.

The reactivity of the Si—H bond toward water and oxygen is much the same in whatever compound it may occur. Si—H bonds have an ionic contribution Si^+H^-, in contrast to that of the C—H bond, C^-H^+, and react accordingly.

The hydrides of germanium are rather similar to the silanes in their general properties. They are not as flammable as the silanes, but they are rapidly oxidized by oxygen to GeO_2 and H_2O, increasingly so with increasing molecular weight. They are also far more stable to hydrolysis than are the silanes, monogermane being stable even to $\sim 30\%$ alkali. Like the silanes they are produced upon acid hydrolysis of Mg_2Ge but here GeH_4 constitutes almost the entire product. GeH_4 can also be prepared in 75% yield by reduction of an acidic aqueous solution of GeO_2 with $NaBH_4$.

For tin and lead only SnH_4 and PbH_4 are known. SnH_4 can be prepared by reduction of $SnCl_4$ with $LiAlH_4$ in ether at $-30°C$. It is a gas which decomposes slowly at room temperature and very rapidly at $\sim 150°C$. Stannane is stable toward 15% sodium hydroxide solution and dilute acids. It is attacked by some oxidizing agents such as $HgCl_2$. Plumbane is not very well characterized. It forms in minute quantities on acid hydrolysis of Mg–Pb alloys or in cathodic reduction of lead salts. Although the monohydrides are unstable, comparatively stable alkylated hydrides R_nMH_{4-n} are known for tin and lead; they are prepared from the corresponding chlorides by treatment with $LiAlH_4$.

19-5. Halides

All of the possible group IV tetrahalides are known except for $PbBr_4$ and PbI_4. In addition, silicon forms a number of catenated halides; with fluorine, bromine, and iodine Si_2X_6 is the highest, but with chlorine the entire series up to Si_6Cl_{14} is known. Only one catenated halide of germanium, Ge_2Cl_6, is known, and with tin and lead none have been prepared. A number of mixed halides of silicon such as SiF_3I, $SiCl_2Br_2$, $SiFCl_2Br$, are known, although the ultimate one, $SiFClBrI$, which would exist in enantiomorphs, has never been obtained.

The nonexistence of $PbBr_4$ and PbI_4 can be attributed to the inability of Br_2 and I_2 to oxidize Pb^{II} to Pb^{IV}, or, what is equivalent, to the reducing powers of Br^- and I^-. Even $PbCl_4$ must be kept at low temperatures to prevent decomposition into $PbCl_2$ and Cl_2.

The silicon halides, except SiF_4, are immediately and completely hydrolyzed by water to give "silicic acid." Germanium tetrachloride and $GeBr_4$ are also hydrolyzed, but in 6–9M acid there is an equilibrium involving species such as $[Ge(OH)_nCl_{6-n}]^{2-}$, and from concentrated acid solutions the tetrahalide can be distilled and separated. Stannic and plumbic chlorides are also not completely hydrolyzed except in dilute solution, and in excess acid complex ions such as $SnCl_6^{2-}$ and $SnCl_5^-$ are known.

Silicon and germanium tetrafluorides with water give hydrous oxides, but the main product, and in excess hydrofluoric acid the only product, is the fluoro anion, SiF_6^{2-} or GeF_6^{2-}. Tin(IV) fluoride is a white solid subliming at 705°C.; the tin is octahedrally coordinated by four bridging and two non-bridging fluorine atoms. PbF_4 is also salt-like.

For silicon only, a number of *oxy halides* are known largely through the work of Schumb and co-workers. Compounds of the type $Cl_3SiO(SiCl_2O)_n$ $SiCl_3$ were first obtained by the action of a mixture of chlorine and oxygen on silicon at red heat, and the analogous oxybromides were made in a similar manner. Members of both series up to $n = 4$ have been characterized. The oxychlorides may also be obtained by controlled hydrolysis of $SiCl_4$ with moist ether. The oxychlorides but not the oxybromides can be esterified with ethanol to yield compounds of the general formula $(EtO)_3SiO—[Si(OEt)_2O]_n—Si(OEt)_3$. In addition to these linear oxy halides there are cyclic ones such as $(SiOX_2)_4$ in which there is an eight-membered ring of alternate Si and O atoms.

By careful hydrolysis of Si_2Cl_6 in ether, compounds containing alternate Si—Si and Si—O—Si links can be obtained; these are typified by $Cl_3Si—SiCl_2—O—SiCl_2—SiCl_3$.

19-6. Oxygen Compounds of Silicon

Silica. Silicon dioxide, also commonly called silica, occurs in several crystallographic forms. In all of them, with a possible exception noted later, the silicon is tetrahedrally surrounded by, and bound to four oxygen atoms by, single bonds doubtless having considerable ionic character. The crystal symmetries and equilibrium interconversion temperatures of the various polymorphs are shown in Figure 19-1. In crystobalite the silicon atoms are placed as are the atoms in the diamond structure, with the oxygen atoms midway between each pair. In quartz and tridymite, there are helices so that these forms have optical isomers. Enantiomorphic crystals of quartz are easily recognized and mechanically separated. Interconversion of quartz, tridymite, and cristobolite requires breaking and reforming of bonds; consequently, the activation energies of these transformations are high, and they occur only very slowly. Thus all three forms are found in nature, although, of course, only one, α-quartz, is thermodynamically stable at ordinary temperatures. The other forms are metastable. This phenomenon of metastability is often encountered; examples noted previously in this

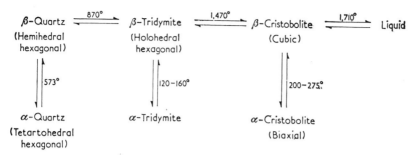

Fig. 19-1. The crystallographic forms of silica.

text include diamond relative to graphite, pure o- or p-hydrogen, etc. The interconversions of the α and β forms of each basic structural type occur without bond breaking and hence rapidly and at rather low temperatures.

Slow cooling of molten silica or heating any form of solid silica to the softening temperature gives an amorphous material which is glassy in appearance and is indeed a glass in the general sense, that is, a material with no long range order but rather a disordered array of polymeric chains, sheets, or three-dimensional units.

Silica in any form is rather unreactive. It resists attack by chlorine, bromine, hydrogen, and most acids and metals at ordinary and slightly elevated temperatures. It is attacked by fluorine, hydrofluoric acid, and alkalies.

It has recently been claimed that on heating a mixture of Si and SiO_2 in vacuum at 1200–1500°C. and condensing the vapors on a cold surface a fibrous form of SiO_2 with a structure like that of SiS_2 can be obtained. The material was stated to be unstable, changing slowly to tridymite. The hydrolysis of silanes or $SiCl_4$ or acidification of soluble silicates gives the so-called "silicic acid"; this is a gel-like hydrated oxide.

Silicates. When alkali metal carbonates are fused with silica ($\sim$1300°C.), CO_2 is driven off and a complex mixture of alkali silicates is obtained. When the mixtures are rich in alkali, the products are soluble in water, but with low alkali contents they become quite insoluble. Presumably the alkali-rich mixtures contain mainly silicates with low molecular weights such as Na_4SiO_4, $Na_{2n}(SiO_3)_n$, $Na_2Si_2O_5$, which are soluble, whereas those rich in SiO_2 contain very large, polymeric anions.

Most of our understanding of silicate structures comes from studies of the many naturally occurring (and some synthetic) silicates of heavier metals. In such substances the basic unit of structure is the SiO_4 tetrahedron. These tetrahedra occur singly, or by sharing oxygen atoms, in small groups, in small cyclic groups, in infinite chains, or in infinite sheets.

Simple Orthosilicates. A few silicates are known in which there are simple, discrete SiO_4^{4-}, orthosilicate, anions. In such compounds the associated cations are coordinated by the oxygen atoms, and various structures are found depending on the coordination number of the cation. In phenacite, Be_2SiO_4, and willemite, Zn_2SiO_4, the cations are surrounded by a tetrahedrally arranged set of four oxygen atoms. There are a number of compounds of the type M_2SiO_4, where M^{2+} is Mg^{2+}, Fe^{2+}, Mn^{2+}, or some other cation with a preferred coordination number of six, in which the SiO_4^{4-} anions are so arranged as to provide interstices with six oxygen atoms at the apices of an octahedron in which the cations are found. In zircon, $ZrSiO_4$, the Zr^{4+} ion is eight-coordinate although not all Zr—O distances are equal. It may be noted that, although the M—O bonds are probably more ionic than the Si—O bonds, there is doubtless some covalent character to them, and these substances should not be regarded as literally ionic in the sense $[M^{2+}]_2[SiO_4^{4-}]$ but rather as somewhere between this extreme and the opposite extreme of infinite giant molecules. There are also other silicates containing discrete SiO_4 tetrahedra.

Other Discrete, Noncyclic Silicate Anions. The simplest of the condensed silicate anions—that is, those formed by combining two or more SiO_4 tetrahedra by sharing of oxygen atoms—is the pyrosilicate ion, $Si_2O_7^{6-}$. Substances containing this ion are actually quite rare, the only documented examples being thortveitite, $Sc_2Si_2O_7$, and hemimorphite, $Zn_4(OH)_2Si_2O_7 \cdot H_2O$.

Cyclic Silicate Anions. Only two such ions are known, namely, $Si_3O_9^{6-}$ and $Si_6O_{18}^{12-}$, the structures of which are shown schematically in Figure 19-2. It should be clear that the general formula for any such ion must be

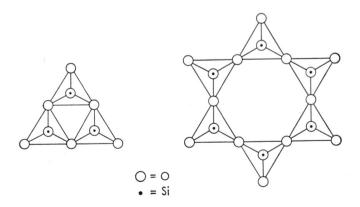

$\bigcirc$ = O
$\bullet$ = Si

Fig. 19-2. Examples of cyclic silicate anions.

benitoite

$Si_nO_{3n}^{2n-}$. The ion $Si_3O_9^{6-}$ occurs in bentonite, $BaTiSi_3O_9$, and wollastonite, $CaSiO_3$. The ion $Si_6O_{18}^{12-}$ occurs in beryl, $Be_3Al_2Si_6O_{18}$.

Infinite Chain Anions. These are of two main types, the *pyroxenes*, which contain single-strand chains of composition $(SiO_3^{2-})_n$ (Fig. 19-3)

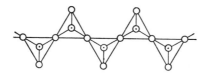

Fig. 19-3. A linear chain silicate anion.

and the *amphiboles* which contain double-strand, crosslinked chains or bands of composition $(Si_4O_{11}^{6-})_n$. Note that the general formula of the anion in a pyroxene is the same as in a silicate with a cyclic anion. Silicates with this general stoichiometry are often, especially in older literature, called "metasilicates." There is actually no metasilicic acid nor any discrete metasilicate anions. With the exception of the few "metasilicates" with cyclic anions, such compounds contain infinite chain anions.

Examples of pyroxenes are enstatite, $MgSiO_3$, diopside, $CaMg(SiO_3)_2$, and spodumene, $LiAl(SiO_3)_2$, an important lithium ore. In the latter there is one unipositive and one tripositive cation instead of two dipositive cations. Indeed the three compounds cited illustrate very well the important principle that, within rather wide limits, *the specific cations or even their charges are unimportant so long as the total positive charge is sufficient to produce electroneutrality.* This may be easily understood in terms of the structure of the pyroxenes in which the $(SiO_3)_n$ chains lie parallel and are held together by the cations which lie between them. Obviously the exact identity of the individual cations is of minor importance in such a structure.

A typical amphibole is tremolite, $Ca_2Mg_5(Si_4O_{11})_2(OH)_2$. Although this would not seem to be absolutely necessary, amphiboles apparently always contain some hydroxyl groups which are attached to the cations. Aside from this, however, they are structurally similar to the pyroxenes, in that the $(Si_4O_{11}^{6-})_n$ bands lie parallel and are held together by the metal ions lying between them. Like the pyroxenes and for the same reason, they are subject to some variability in the particular cations incorporated.

Because of the strength of the $(SiO_3)_n$ and $(Si_4O_{11})_n$ chains in the pyroxenes and amphiboles and the relative weakness and lack of strong directional properties in the essentially electrostatic forces between them via the metal ions, we might expect such substances to cleave most readily in directions parallel to the chains. This is in fact the case, dramatically so in the various asbestos minerals which are all amphiboles.

Infinite Sheet Anions. When SiO_4 tetrahedra are linked into infinite two-dimensional networks as shown in Figure 19-4, the empirical formula

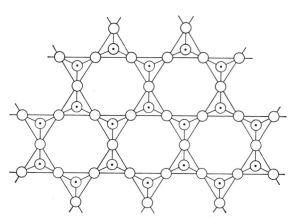

Fig. 19-4.   A sheet silicate anion.

for the anion is $(Si_2O_5{}^{2-})_n$. Many silicates have such sheet structures with the sheets bound together by the cations which lie between them. Such substances might thus be expected to cleave readily into thin sheets, and this expectation is confirmed in the micas which are silicates of this type.

Framework Minerals. The next logical extension in the above progression from simple $SiO_4{}^{4-}$ ions to larger and more complex structures would be to three-dimensional structures in which *every* oxygen is shared between two tetrahedra. The empirical formula for such a substance would be simply $(SiO_2)_n$; that is, we would have silica. However, if, in such a three-dimensional framework structure, some silicon atoms are replaced by aluminum atoms, the framework must be negatively charged and there must be other cations uniformly distributed through it. Aluminosilicates of this type are the feldspars, zeolites, and ultramarines which (excepting the last) are among the most widespread, diverse, and useful silicate minerals in nature. Moreover, many synthetic zeolites have been made in the laboratory and several are manufactured industrially for use as ion exchangers and "molecular sieves." The feldspars are the major constituents of igneous rocks and include such minerals as orthoclase, $KAlSi_3O_8$, which may be written $K[(AlO_2)(SiO_2)_3]$ to indicate that one-fourth of the oxygen tetrahedra are occupied by Al atoms, and anorthite, $CaAl_2Si_2O_8$ or $Ca[(AlO_2)_2(SiO_2)_2]$, in which half of the tetrahedra are AlO_4 and half SiO_4.

The ultramarines are synthetically produced silicates which are strongly colored. In addition to cations sufficient to balance the negative charge of the $[(Si,Al)O_2]_n$ framework these substances contain additional cations and anions such as Cl^-, $SO_4{}^{2-}$, and S^{2-}. The framework of the ultramarines is rather open, permitting fairly ready exchange of both cations and anions. The exact reasons for their colors are not certain. Apparently certain the cations and anions, perhaps S^{2-} especially, are responsible.

Undoubtedly the most important and interesting framework silicates are the zeolites. Their most important characteristic is the openness of the $[(Al,Si)O_2]_n$ framework (Figs. 19-5, 19-6, and 19-7). It is this characteristic

Fig. 19-5. The arrangement of AlO_4 and SiO_4 tetrahedra which gives the cubo-octahedral cavity in some zeolites and feldspathoids (R. M. Barrer, *Colston Papers*, Vol. X, Butterworths, London, 1958).

which makes possible their principal uses: (a) as ion exchangers and (b) as selective adsorbants or "molecular sieves." There are many natural zeolites, some of which have been synthesized, and also several dozen synthetic ones not known to occur in nature. The general composition is always of the type $M_{x/n}[(AlO_2)_x(SiO_2)_y]\cdot zH_2O$ where n is the charge of the metal cation, M^{n+}, which is usually Na^+, K^+ or Ca^{2+} and the z is the number of moles of water of hydration, which is highly variable.

The zeolites function as cation exchangers because when a zeolite con-

Fig. 19-6. Cubo-octahedral cavities linked in tetrahedral coordination as in faujasite or Linde molecular sieve type 13X (R. M. Barrer, Physical Chemistry of Some Nonstoichiometric Phases, *10th Solvay Conference*, Brussels, 1956).

taining a particular cation, say A^+, is placed in a solution containing another cation, say B^+, an equilibrium distribution of each cation between the zeolite and the aqueous phases will be set up. The equilibrium distribution is achieved rapidly since the porous structure makes possible rapid passage of ions in and out. Because in general one ion will have a slightly greater preference for the zeolite environment than the other, it will tend to concentrate there. The naturally occurring zeolites were the first ion exchangers discovered; they now have heavy competition for this purpose from the synthetic organic exchange resins which are made for both cation and anion exchange.

The use of zeolites as selective adsorbants is a recent and rather fascinating development. One of the synthetic ones which has been rather thoroughly investigated will serve as a good example for discussion. By slow crystallization under definite, well controlled conditions of a sodium aluminosilicate gel of proper composition, the crystalline compound $Na_{12}[(AlO_2)_{12}(SiO_2)_{12}] \cdot 27H_2O$ may be obtained. In this hydrated form it can be used as a cation exchanger in basic solution. To obtain the "molecular sieve," the water of hydration is removed by heating in vacuum to 350°C. The crystalline substance is of cubic symmetry. The AlO_4 and SiO_4 tetra-

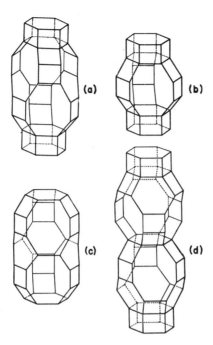

Fig. 19-7. Cavities of different dimensions in (a) chabazite, $(Ca,Na_2O)Al_2O_3 \cdot 4SiO_2 \cdot 6H_2O$; (b) gmelinite, $(Na_2,Ca)O \cdot Al_2O_3 \cdot 4SiO_2 \cdot 6H_2O$; (c) erionite, $(Ca,Mg,Na_2,K_2)O \cdot Al_2O_3 \cdot 6SiO_2 \cdot 6H_2O$; and (d) levynite, $CaO \cdot Al_2O_3 \cdot 4SiO_2 \cdot 6H_2O$ (R. M. Barrer and I. S. Kerr, *Trans. Faraday Soc.*, **55**, 1919 (1959)).

hedra are linked together so as to form a ring of eight oxygen atoms on each face of the unit cube and an irregular ring of six oxygen atoms across each corner. In the center of the unit cell is a large cavity about 11.4 A. in diameter which is connected to six identical cavities in adjacent unit cells by the eight-membered rings which have inner diameters of about 4.2 A. In addition, the large cavity is connected to eight smaller cavities, about 6.6 A. in diameter, by the six-membered rings, which provide openings about 2.0 A. in diameter. In the hydrated form all of the cavities contain water molecules. In the anhydrous state these same cavities may be occupied by other molecules brought into contact with the zeolite, providing such molecules are able to squeeze through the apertures connecting the cavities. Molecules within the cavities then tend to be held there by attractive forces of electrostatic and van der Waals types. Thus the zeolite will be able to absorb and strongly retain molecules just small enough to enter the cavities. It will not absorb at all those too big to enter, and it will absorb weakly very small molecules or atoms which can enter but also leave easily.

For example, the zeolite under discussion will absorb straight-chain hydrocarbons but not branched-chain or aromatic ones.

19-7. Oxygen Compounds of Germanium, Tin, and Lead

Oxides and Hydroxides. The oxides GeO_2, SnO_2, and PbO_2 are all well characterized compounds. GeO_2 exists in two forms, one with a cristobolite lattice and the other with a rutile (TiO_2) lattice; the radius ratio is that at which the change should occur theoretically. SnO_2 exists in three different modifications of which the rutile form (in the mineral cassiterite) is most common and important. It has long been known that the hydrous SnO_2 obtained by slow, low-temperature hydrolysis of Sn^{IV} in solution (α-oxide) is readily soluble in acids or bases, whereas that obtained by high temperature hydrolysis or by the action of nitric acid on the metal (β-oxide) is quite inert. Actually, X-ray studies show that both have the rutile structure, with adsorbed water, and the differences in reactivity must be due to differences in particle sizes, nature of the surfaces of the particles, etc. PbO_2 occurs only with the rutile structure.

There is no evidence for any stoichiometric hydroxides $M(OH)_4$, and materials so considered in the older chemical literature are best written $MO_2 \cdot nH_2O$ where n may be about 2, but is not in general sharply defined.

The basicity of the MO_2 oxides increases as the group is descended. As we have seen, SiO_2 is purely acidic. GeO_2 is not as strongly so, but is not appreciably basic either, although in concentrated HCl solution the tetrachloride is formed. SnO_2 is definitely amphoteric. PbO_2 is not well characterized in this respect since it is rather inert.

Oxy Anions. Germanates, stannates, and plumbates are all known, although these classes of compounds have not been studied nearly so extensively as have the silicates. Both metagermanates, $M_2^I GeO_3$, and orthogermanates, for example, Mg_2GeO_4, have been obtained in crystalline form, and have been shown to have structures analogous to the corresponding meta- and orthosilicates. Crystalline alkali metal stannates and plumbates can be obtained as trihydrates, for instance, $K_2SnO_3 \cdot 3H_2O$. Actually such materials are not simply hydrated "meta" stannates or plumbates, but contain the anions $Sn(OH)_6^{2-}$ and $Pb(OH)_6^{2-}$ in which Sn and Pb are surrounded octahedrally by six OH^- ions. No silicates containing $Si(OH)_6^{2-}$ ions have ever been reported, but a few germanates, $Fe[Ge(OH)_6]$, for example, are known. In the latter, the Fe and Ge atoms are arranged as in the rock salt lattice and each is surrounded by a distorted octahedron of oxygen atoms.

19-8. Organometallic Compounds

There is a very extensive chemistry of the group IV elements bound to carbon. The organosilicon derivatives are the most extensive and best studied, but certain tin and lead compounds are of importance. Although the Si—C bond dissociation energy is quite high, silicon compounds are more reactive than the carbon compounds. This is true, first, because the Si—C bond is somewhat polar, Si^+C^-, so that nucleophilic attack on Si or electrophilic attack on C can occur, and second, as noted previously, because displacement reactions of silicon are facilitated by its ability to utilize $3d$ orbitals.

The tetraalkyl and aryl silicons are thermally very stable; thus $(C_6H_5)_4Si$ boils about 530°C. without decomposition. The alkyl and aryl silicon halides are of special importance because of their hydrolytic reactions. They may be obtained by normal Grignard procedures from $SiCl_4$, or, in the case of the methyl derivatives, by the Rochow process in which methyl chloride is passed over a heated, copper-activated silicon

$$CH_3Cl + Si(Cu) \rightarrow (CH_3)_nSiCl_{4-n}$$

The halides are liquids which are readily hydrolyzed by water, usually in an inert solvent. In certain cases, the *silanol* intermediates R_3SiOH, $R_2Si(OH)_2$, and $RSi(OH)_3$ can be isolated, but the diols and triols usually condense under the hydrolysis conditions to *siloxanes* which have Si—O—Si bonds. The exact nature of the products depends on the hydrolysis conditions and linear, cyclic, and complex crosslinked polymers of varying molecular weights can be obtained. Controlled hydrolysis of the alkyl halides in suitable ratios can give products of particular physical characteristics. The polymers may be liquids, rubbers, or solids which have in general high thermal stability, high dielectric strength, and resistance to oxidation and chemical attack.

Examples of simple siloxanes are $Ph_3SiOSiPh_3$ and the cyclic trimer or tetramer $(Et_2SiO)_{3(or\ 4)}$; the linear polymers contain —SiR_2—O—SiR_2—O— chains, whereas the crosslinked sheets have the basic unit

The commercial "silicone" polymers usually have $R = CH_3$, but other alkyl or phenyl groups may be incorporated for special purposes.

Germanium, tin, and lead form similar alkyl and aryl compounds. For a given type of compound in the series, the Pb compounds are the least stable thermally and chemically as would be expected from the increasing weakness and polarity of the M—C bonds. Germanium compounds are not particularly important, but aryl and alkyl tin compounds have acquired some technical importance. The most unusual feature of the organotin compounds is the ionization of some of the R_3SnX and R_2SnX_2 compounds in water to give species such as $(CH_3)_3Sn(OH_2)_n^+$. There is some infrared and other evidence that in crystals of the salts such as $(CH_3)_3SnF$ and $(CH_3)_2Pb(OCOCH_3)_2$ there are linear $(CH_3)_2Sn^{2+}$ and planar $(CH_3)_3Sn^+$ and $(CH_3)_3Pb^+$ ions.

The most important organolead compound is the tetraethyl, which is made on a very large scale for use as an antiknock agent in gasoline. It is a viscous and highly toxic liquid obtained by the reaction of ethyl bromide with sodium-lead alloy. The tetramethyl compound is also manufactured for use as an antiknock agent.

19-9. Complexes

Silicon forms a limited number of complexes. With fluoride ion, the stable fluorosilicate ion SiF_6^{2-} is obtained. In view of the formation of this ion, the hydrolysis of SiF_4 is incomplete

$$2SiF_4 + 2H_2O = SiO_2 + SiF_6^{2-} + 2H^+ + 2HF$$

No corresponding anions are given by the other halogens. With β-diketones, silicon forms cationic complexes such as the octahedral acetylacetonate ion (19-I). This ion should exist in d and l optical isomers, and indeed

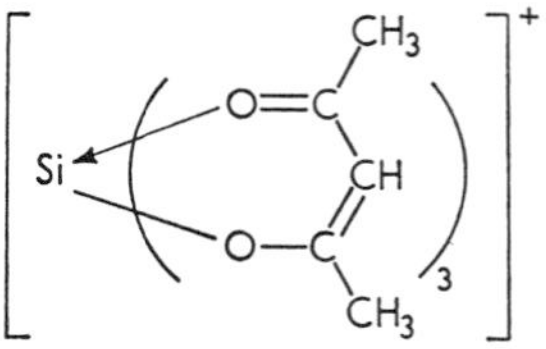

(19—I)

fractional crystallization of the diastereoisomeric salts with an optically active base has allowed their resolution.

Germanium forms both GeF_6^{2-} and $GeCl_6^{2-}$ ions and with acetylacetone forms the octahedral cation like that of silicon. Tin gives SnF_6^{2-}, $SnCl_6^{2-}$, $SnBr_6^{2-}$, and SnI_6^{2-} salts. It also forms complex anions of the types $R_2SnX_4^{2-}$, $R_2SnX_3^-$, and $R_3SnX_3^{2-}$, where R is an alkyl group. The thiostannate ion which is formed when SnS_2 is dissolved in excess S^{2-} is written as SnS_3^{2-}, but its true structure is unknown. Lead forms complex halide ions with F^- and Cl^-; both are readily hydrolyzed by water.

The tetrahalides of Si, Ge, and Sn also form addition compounds with certain donors, especially oxygen and nitrogen donors. One example is dipyridinegermanium tetrachloride which has a *trans* octahedral structure. Some 1:1 complexes, for example, $SiCl_4N(CH_3)_3$, are known, but it is not certain whether these are five-coordinate or are salts as in the case of $[H_3SiN(CH_3)_3]^+I^-$.

19-10. Other Compounds

Silicon–Nitrogen Compounds. The action of ammonia on $SiCl_4$ gives a white amide, $Si(NH_2)_4$, which on heating gives an imide and finally silicon nitride, Si_3N_4. The latter occurs in two forms differing only in the sequence in which the planes of like atoms are linked in a layer lattice. A number of substituted silylammonium compounds are known, for example, $(SiH_3)_3N$ and $[(CH_3)_3Si]_3N$.

Sulfides. A lead disulfide is not known, but for the other elements direct interaction of the elements gives MS_2. The silicon and germanium compounds are colorless crystals hydrolyzed by water. The structures of SiS_2 and GeS_2 are chains of tetrahedral MS_4 linked by the sulfur atoms (see page 416). SnS_2 has a CaI_2 lattice, each Sn atom having six sulfur neighbors. Thiostannates, for example, Na_2SnS_3, are also known. Stannic sulfide is precipitated from aqueous solutions containing Sn^{IV} by hydrogen sulfide.

Alkoxides, Esters, and Oxy Salts. All four elements form alkoxides, for example, $Si(OC_2H_5)_4$, and esters, for example, $Pb(OCOCH_3)_4$. The latter, lead tetraacetate, which is obtained by the action of acetic acid on Pb_3O_4 or by electrolytic oxidation of Pb^{II} in carboxylic acids is used in organic chemistry as a strong, but selective, oxidizing agent.

The tetravalent elements do not form oxy salts with the exception of tin(IV) sulfate, $Sn(SO_4)_2 \cdot 2H_2O$, which can be crystallized from the solutions obtained by oxidation of Sn^{II} sulfate. It is extensively hydrolyzed in water. Although solutions of tin nitrate are stable, attempts to evaporate them can give violent explosions. A solid, highly explosive salt, probably $Sn(OH)_4(NO_3)_2$, has been obtained, however.

19-11. Lower Valences

The term lower valence indicates the use of fewer than four electrons in bonding. Thus although the oxidation state of carbon in CO is usually taken to be 2, this is only a formalism and carbon uses all four valence electrons in bonding. For carbon, true divalence is never found in stable compounds, and the same is true for silicon; however, chemically stable divalent states are found for the other group IV elements.

At high temperature only, divalent silicon species have been identified. Thus SiO is formed in the vapors over a mixture of SiO_2 and Si at high temperatures; species such as $SiCl_2$ and SiS are also found in vapors. There is evidence that such compounds are thermodynamically unstable at ordinary temperatures.

With germanium the existence of divalent compounds at ordinary temperatures is well established although they are only moderately stable. Those known are GeS, $GeCl_2$, $GeBr_2$, and GeI_2. GeF_2 has never been isolated with certainty. A yellow, amphoteric hydroxide, "$Ge(OH)_2$," chemically similar to "$Sn(OH)_2$," is precipitated from solutions containing Ge^{IV} in various ways, for example, by addition of base after reduction with zinc in 25% H_2SO_4 or by reduction with hypophosphorus acid. The wet precipitate is readily oxidized by air to GeO_2. However, the hydrous material can be completely dehydrated by heating to $\sim$650°C. in a nitrogen atmosphere to yield black crystals. It is possible that these are only metastable since it has been reported that, at higher temperature, the phase diagram of the GeO_2–Ge system does not indicate the existence of a GeO phase. GeS is made by reducing GeS_2 with hydrogen or ammonia, or by the reaction

$$GeS_2 + Ge = 2GeS$$

whereby black crystals resembling in appearance those of iodine are obtained.

The germanium(II) halides are quite well established substances. The chloride may be prepared by passing $GeCl_4$ vapors over heated germanium metal, the dichloride being isolated in the cold part of the apparatus. It rather readily disproportionates, however,

$$2GeCl_2 = Ge + GeCl_4$$

beginning about 75°C. and being completely decomposed at $\sim$450°C. It can be dissolved in concentrated HCl, and on addition of Cs^+ or Rb^+ ions the salts $CsGeCl_3$ and $RbGeCl_3$ are obtained. $GeBr_2$ and GeI_2 are also known. Both tend to disproportionate at elevated temperatures. Neither has been reported to form complex salts like those of $GeCl_2$. GeI_2 has been examined by X-rays and is found to have the CdI_2 structure.

For tin and lead the II oxidation state becomes progressively more important until with lead it is dominant. It may be noted that the ease of addition of chlorine to the dichlorides of Ge, Sn, and Pb reflects the relative stabilities of their II oxidation states:

$$GeCl_2 + Cl_2 = GeCl_4 \quad \text{(uncontrollably rapid)}$$
$$SnCl_2 + Cl_2 = SnCl_4 \quad \text{(slow)}$$
$$PbCl_2 + Cl_2 = PbCl_4 \quad \text{(only under forcing conditions)}$$

The divalent states of tin and lead provide the only cationic aqueous chemistry in group IV, since the existence of 4+ ions is very dubious. Divalent tin halides are essentially covalent in nature, and Pb^{2+} ions certainly occur in PbF_2.

In aqueous solution Sn^{2+} and Pb^{2+} will give precipitates (soluble in excess to give stannites and plumbites) with OH^- ion, commonly called hydroxides and written $Sn(OH)_2$ and $Pb(OH)_2$. However, neither of these is a stoichiometric compound. They are both actually hydrous oxides, $SnO \cdot xH_2O$ and $PbO \cdot xH_2O$, where x is rather variable. There is some evidence that the composition of the tin product is probably $Sn_5O_3(OH)_4$, but it also always contains some Sn^{IV} owing to reduction of OH^- by Sn^{II}. On heating, the water can be completely removed, passing through colored stages where there may well be OH^- ions in the lattice, to give the anhydrous oxides SnO and PbO, the former blue-black and the latter yellow to brown in color. A metastable, red SnO, which is readily converted to the normal oxide by pressure or by excess OH^-, can be obtained by the action of sodium phosphite on hydrous stannous oxide. PbO occurs in two crystalline modifications, both of which are isostructural with the tin ores. In the stable SnO structure the Sn or Pb ion is coordinated by four oxide ions at four of the five apices of a trigonal bipyramid, the fifth position being occupied by the unshared pair.

Lead alone forms an oxide containing the metal in both the II and IV states. This is Pb_3O_4, red lead, which has been shown conclusively to be a distinct compound and not a mere mixture of $2PbO + PbO_2$ although in much of its ordinary chemistry it behaves as though it might be. There are $Pb^{IV}O_6$ octahedra in chains sharing opposite edges linked by Pb^{II} atoms each bound to three oxygens.

The halides and some of the oxy salts are known for Sn^{2+} and Pb^{2+}, for example, $SnCl_2 \cdot 2H_2O$ and $Pb(NO_3)_2$. Anhydrous $SnCl_2$ has angular (95°) bonds in accord with the expected structure for a molecule with a lone pair (Chapter 15). In the dihydrate, there is still a nonbonding pair which is stereochemically important. The structure contains a pyramidal arrangement of two chlorine atoms and one water about the sp^3-hybridized tin. The other water molecule, which is readily lost at 80°C., is outside the coordination sphere. There are thus alternate layers of $Sn(H_2O)Cl_2$ and H_2O molecules hydrogen-bonded in the lattice.

The stannous ion is extensively hydrolyzed in aqueous solution

$$Sn^{2+} + H_2O = SnOH^+ + H^+ \qquad K = 10^{-2}$$

and excess acid must be present to prevent the precipitation of basic salts such as $Sn(OH)Cl \cdot H_2O$. Complex halide anions such as $SnCl_4{}^{2-}$ are known. The Sn^{2+} ion is also a well known reducing agent in acid solutions (which are slowly oxidized by air).

$$Sn^{2+} = Sn^{4+} + 2e \qquad E^0 = -0.15 \text{ v.}$$

In strongly alkaline solutions so-called stannite ions are present, and these also are quite strong reducing agents.

The plumbous ion is also hydrolyzed in water. In perchlorate solutions the principal equilibria appear to be

$$Pb^{2+} + H_2O = PbOH^+ + H^+ \qquad \log K \sim -7.9$$
$$4Pb^{2+} + 4H_2O = Pb_4(OH)_6{}^{6+} + 4H^+ \qquad \log K \sim -19.5$$

The structures of the main product, $Pb_4(OH)_4{}^{4+}$, and of other less abundant polymers are not known, but they may be cyclic. With the exception of $Pb(NO_3)_2$ and $Pb(OCOCH_3)_2 \cdot 2H_2O$ (which is incompletely ionized) most lead(II) salts are insoluble in water. All lead salts can be converted to black PbS with H_2S, and all lead salts except PbS can be dissolved in excess OH^-. PbS has a rock salt lattice.

Both the Sn^{2+} and Pb^{2+} ions form complexes in aqueous solution, particularly in the presence of halide ions; in general, species from MX^+ to $MX_3{}^-$ are known.

Organometallic compounds of divalent Sn and Pb are ill defined, but the air-sensitive, thermally stable cyclopentadienyls $(C_5H_5)_2M$ are known. These crystalline compounds are believed to be covalently bound with the metal (sp^2 hybridized) to ring axes at an angle; there must of course also be a lone pair of electrons, as in the angular gaseous $SnCl_2$ molecule. The covalent nature and the symmetrical metal to ring bonding of the ferrocene type (see Chapter 26) is indicated by the symmetrical splitting of the cyclopentadienyl proton resonance lines by the tin isotopes ^{117}Sn and ^{119}Sn.

References

Allred, A. L., and E. G. Rochow, *J. Inorg. & Nuclear Chem.*, **5**, 264, 269 (1958). New electronegativity scale and application to C, Si, Ge, Sn, and Pb in homologous compounds.

Eaborn, C., *Organosilicon Compounds*, Butterworths, London, 1960.

Fessenden, R., and J. S. Fessenden, *Chem. Revs.*, **61**, 361 (1961). A review of the chemistry of silicon-nitrogen compounds.

Hersh, C. K., *Molecular Sieves*, Chapman and Hall, London, 1961.

Ingham, R. K., S. D. Rosenberg, and H. Gilman, *Chem. Revs.*, **60**, 459 (1960). Organotin compounds—an exhaustive review (924 references).

Johnson, O. H., *Chem. Revs.*, **48**, 319 (1951); **51**, 431 (1952). Organic and inorganic compounds of germanium.

Leeper, R. W., L. Summers, and H. Gilman, *Chem. Revs.*, **54**, 101 (1954). Chemistry of bivalent tin compounds.

Nowotny, H., and A. Wittman, *16th International Congress of Pure and Applied Chemistry, Experientia, Suppl.*, No. 7, 239 (1957). Syntheses and properties of inorganic germanium compounds.

Rochow, E. G., *An Introduction to the Chemistry of the Silicones*, 2nd ed., Wiley, New York, 1951.

Schick, H. L., *Chem. Revs.*, **60**, 331 (1960). High temperature vaporization properties of silica.

Stone, F. G. A., and D. Seyferth, *J. Inorg. & Nuclear Chem.*, **1**, 112 (1955). Review of use of d orbitals in silicon chemistry.

20

The Group V Elements: P, As, Sb, Bi

GENERAL REMARKS

20-1. Group Trends

The electronic structures and some other properties of the elements are listed in Table 20-1. The valence shells have a structure formally similar

TABLE 20-1

Some Properties of P, As, Sb, and Bi

	P	As	Sb	Bi
Electronic structure	$[Ne]3s^23p^3$	$[Ar]3d^{10}4s^24p^3$	$[Kr]4d^{10}5s^25p^3$	$[Xe]4f^{14}5d^{10}6s^26p^3$
Ionization potentials, e.v.				
3rd	30.15	28.0	24.7	25.4
5th	65.0	62.5	55.5	55.7
Electronegativity	2.19	2.18	2.06	2.16
Radii, A.				
Ionic	1.85 (P^{3-})		0.92 (Sb^{3+})	1.08 (Bi^{3+})
Covalent[a]	1.10	1.21	1.41	1.52

[a] For trivalent state.

to that of nitrogen, but, beyond the formal stoichiometries of some of the simpler compounds—NH_3, PH_3, NCl_3, $BiCl_3$, for example—there is little resemblance between the characteristics of these elements and those of nitrogen.

The elements P, As, Sb, and Bi show a considerable range in chemical behavior. There are some fairly continuous variations in certain properties and characteristics with increasing mass, although in several instances there is no regular trend, for example, in the ability of the +5 oxides to act as oxidizing agents. Phosphorus, like nitrogen, is essentially covalent in all of its chemistry, whereas arsenic, antimony, and bismuth show increasing metallic behavior. Although the electronic structure of the next inert gas could be achieved by electron gain, considerable energies are involved, and only phosphorus gives a compound Na_3P. The loss of valence electrons is similarly difficult to achieve because of the high ionization potentials. The $+5$ ions certainly do not exist, but for trivalent antimony and bismuth cationic behavior does occur. BiF_3 seems predominantly ionic, and salts such as $Sb_2(SO_4)_3$ and $Bi(NO_3)_3 \cdot 5H_2O$, as well as salts of the oxy ions SbO^+ and BiO^+, exist.

Some of the more important trends are shown by the oxides, which change from acidic for phosphorus to basic for bismuth, and by the halides, which have increasingly ionic character, PCl_3 being instantly hydrolyzed by water to $HPO(OH)_2$, while the other trihalides give initially clear solutions which hydrolyze to As_2O_3, $SbOCl$, and $BiOCl$, respectively. There is also an increase in the stability of the lower oxidation state with increasing atomic number; thus Bi_2O_5 is the most difficult to prepare and the least stable pentoxide.

20-2. Covalence and Stereochemistry

Although oxidation states or oxidation numbers can be and often are assigned to these elements in their compounds, they are of rather limited utility except in the formalities of balancing reactions. The important

TABLE 20-2

Number of bonds to other atoms	Orbitals used in bonding	Geometry	Examples
3	p^3 to sp^3 [a]	Pyramidal	PH_3, $AsCl_3$, $Sb(C_6H_5)_3$
4	sp^3 [b]	Tetrahedral	PH_4^+, $PO(OH)_3$, $POCl_3$
5	sp^3d	Trigonal bipyramidal	PF_5, AsF_5, $SbCl_5$
		Square pyramidal[d]	K_2SbF_5, Sb_2S_3
6	sp^3d^2 [c]	Octahedral	PF_6^-, AsF_6^-, $[Sb(OH)_6]^{3-}$
			$(SbF_5)_n$, $Bi_6O_6(OH)_3^{3+}$

[a] Lone pairs present.

[b] In some compounds, such as those with PO and PS bonds, d orbitals of P may be used in $d\pi - p\pi$ bonding.

[c] There may be considerable ionic character and hence little genuine involvement of two d orbitals.

[d] Sb is below base plane of square pyramid.

valence features concern the number of covalent bonds formed and the stereochemistries. The general types of compounds and stereochemical possibilities are given in Table 20-2. Like NR_3 compounds, the PR_3, AsR_3, and SbR_3 compounds can behave as donors (Lewis bases) owing to the presence of lone pairs. There is, however, one major difference: the nitrogen atom can have no function other than simple donation because no other orbitals are accessible, but P, As, and Sb have empty d orbitals of fairly low energy. Thus, when the atom to which the P, As, or Sb donates has electrons in orbitals of the same symmetry as the empty d orbitals, back-donation resulting in over-all multiple bond character may result. (See discussion of this phenomenon in Section 27-5). The consequences of vacant d orbitals are also quite evident on comparing the amine oxides, R_3NO, on the one hand, with R_3PO or R_3AsO on the other. In the N-oxide the electronic structure can be represented by the single canonical structure $R_3\overset{+}{N}-\overset{-}{O}$, whereas for the others the bonds to oxygen have multiple character and are represented as resonance hybrids:

$$R_3\overset{+}{P}-\overset{-}{O} \leftrightarrow R_3P{=}O \overset{?}{\leftrightarrow} R_3\overset{-}{P}{\equiv}\overset{+}{O}$$

These views are substantiated by the shortness of the P—O bonds ($\sim$1.45 as compared to $\sim$1.6 A. for the sum of the single bond radii) and by the normal bond lengths and high polarities of N—O bonds. The amine oxides are also more chemically reactive, the P—O bonds being very stable indeed, as would be expected from their strength, $\sim$127 kcal.

It will be noted in Table 20-2 that the five-coordinated compounds of these group V elements have different stereochemistries depending upon the formal valence state of the element. This is entirely in accord with the principles discussed in Chapter 15. In the pentavalent compounds (e.g., PF_5), the central atom has only the five bonding pairs in its valence orbitals and the usual trigonal bipyramidal arrangement is adopted. In the trivalent species (e.g., SbF_5^{2-}), there are six electron pairs; this anion is isoelectronic with BrF_5 and has the same structure (see p. 311) where the five bonding and one nonbonding pairs of electrons are approximately at the apices of an octahedron and the larger charge cloud of the nonbonding pair makes the F—Sb—F angles somewhat less than 90°.

Phosphorus, arsenic, and antimony also make use of their d orbitals to some extent in increasing their coordination numbers to five and six. The elements show no tendency to form multiple bonds in which $p\pi$ orbitals are used, and many of the differences between nitrogen and phosphorus chemistries in particular can be ascribed to this fact.

THE ELEMENTS

20-3. Occurrence

Phosphorus occurs in various orthophosphate minerals, notably fluoro-apatite, $3Ca_3(PO_4)_2Ca(F, Cl)_2$. Arsenic and antimony occur more widely, though in lower total abundance, and are often associated with sulfide minerals, particularly those of Cu, Pb, and Ag. Bismuth ores are rather uncommon, the sulfide being the most important; bismuth also occurs in other sulfide minerals.

20-4. Elemental Phosphorus

The element is obtained by reduction of phosphate rock with coke and silica in an electric furnace. Phosphorus volatilizes as P_4 molecules (partly dissociated above 800°C. into P_2) and is condensed under water as white phosphorus (m.p. 44.1°C., α form).

$$2Ca_3(PO_4)_2 + 6SiO_2 + 10C = P_4 + 6CaSiO_3 + 10CO$$

There are three main allotropic forms—white, red, and black; each of these is polymorphic and there are in all about eleven known modifications, some amorphous, others of somewhat indefinite identity, and most of unknown structure. In the liquid and in solid white phosphorus, there are tetrahedral P_4 molecules; below 800°C., where measurable dissociation to P_2 occurs, the element is also as P_4 molecules. The P—P distances are 2.21 A.; the P—P—P angles, of course, are 60°. The low angle indicates considerable strain, and the strain energy has been estimated to be about 23 kcal./mole. This means that the total energy of the six P—P bonds in the molecule is that much smaller than would be the total energy of six P—P bonds of the same length formed by phosphorus atoms with normal bond angles. Thus the structure of the molecule is consistent with its high reactivity.

Commercial red phosphorus is made by heating white phosphorus at 400°C. for several hours. Its nature remains to the present time uncertain. At least six modifications are thought to exist. Black phosphorus is obtained in crystalline form by heating white phosphorus either under very high pressure or at 220–370°C. for 8 days in the presence of mercury as a catalyst and with a seed of black phosphorus. This form is the only one for which the structure has been established unequivocally in detail. It consists of corrugated sheets, each phosphorus atom being bound to three

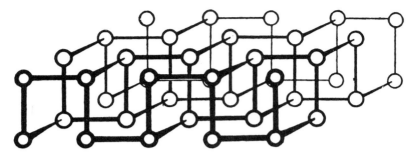

Fig. 20-1. The arrangement of atoms in the corrugated planes found in crystalline black phosphorus (J. R. Van Wazer, *Phosphorus and Its Compounds*, Vol. I, Interscience, New York–London, 1958, p. 121).

neighbors (Fig. 20-1). The atoms in adjacent layers are more weakly bound than are the atoms within a layer and the crystals are therefore flaky like graphite.

The main forms of phosphorus show considerable difference in chemical reactivity. White phosphorus is by far the most reactive form, and black phosphorus the least reactive. White phosphorus is stored under water to protect it from the air, whereas the red and black varieties are stable in air; indeed, the black form can be ignited only with difficulty. White phosphorus inflames in air and is soluble in organic solvents such as CS_2 and benzene. Some reactions of both red and white phosphorus are shown in Figure 20-2.

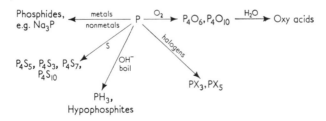

Fig. 20-2. Some typical and important reactions of red and white phosphorus.

20-5. Elemental Arsenic, Antimony, and Bismuth

These elements are obtained by reduction of their oxides with hydrogen or carbon. For As and Sb unstable yellow allotropes, presumably containing tetrahedral As_4 and Sb_4 molecules, can be obtained by rapid condensation of vapors. They are easily transformed into the stable forms, and yellow antimony is only stable at very low temperatures. Bismuth does not occur in a yellow form. The normal forms of As, Sb, and Bi are bright and metallic in appearance and have crystal structures similar to that of black phosphorus. The metals burn in air on heating to form the oxides, and they react directly and readily with halogens and some other nonmetals. They form alloys with various other metals. Dilute nonoxidizing acids are without effect on them. With nitric acid, arsenic gives arsenic acid, antimony gives the trioxide, and bismuth dissolves to form the nitrate.

BINARY COMPOUNDS

20-6. Phosphides, Arsenides, and Antimonides

Direct interaction of phosphorus with many metals and metalloids gives binary compounds of three major types: (1) volatile, molecular compounds (mostly with S, Se, and Te); (2) covalently bound complex polymers; and (3) metal-like compounds ranging from hard, essentially metallic solids to amorphous polymeric powders. Alkali phosphides (e.g., K_2P_5) are known, but it is not certain that these contain discrete phosphide ions, although considerable ionic character must be present in the bonds. The interaction of the elements at high temperatures gives Na_3P. These, as well as the phosphides of the alkaline earths, lanthanides, and other electropositive metals, are generally hydrolyzed rapidly by water to give PH_3.

Phosphides of transition metals, for example, Fe_2P, are commonly greyblack metallic substances, insoluble in water and conductors of electricity. They may also be ferromagnetic. Arsenic and antimony give similar compounds, but the tendency to form volatile molecular compounds is much less, decreasing in the order $P > As > Sb \gg Bi$.

20-7. Hydrides

All of the group V elements form gaseous hydrides of general formula MH_3 which can be obtained by treating phosphides or arsenides of electropositive metals with acids or by reduction of sulfuric acid solutions of arsenic, antimony, or bismuth with an electropositive metal or electrolytically. The stability of these hydrides falls rapidly so that stibine and bismuthine are very unstable thermally, the latter having been obtained only in trace amounts. The known average bond energies are in accord with this trend in stabilities: E_{N-H}, 93.4; E_{P-H}, 76.4; E_{As-H}, 58.6; and E_{Sb-H}, 60.9 kcal./mole.

Phosphine, PH_3, has been most thoroughly studied. The molecule is pyramidal with a P—H bond length of 1.419 A. and an HPH angle of 93.7°. Phosphine when pure is not spontaneously flammable, but often inflames owing to traces of P_2H_4 or P_4 vapor. However, it is readily oxidized by air when ignited, and explosive mixtures may be formed. It is also exceedingly poisonous. These properties account for its commercial unavailability. Unlike NH_3, it is not associated in the liquid state and it is only sparingly soluble in water; pH measurements show that the solutions are neither basic nor acidic—the acid constant is $\sim 10^{-29}$ and the base constant $\sim 10^{-25}$. It does, however, react with some acids to give phosphonium salts; one, PH_4I, is discussed further below.

Arsine, AsH_3, is extremely poisonous. Its ready thermal decomposition to arsenic, which is deposited on hot surfaces as a mirror, is utilized in tests for arsenic, for example, the well-known Marsh test. Stibine is very similar to arsine but even less stable.

All these hydrides are strong reducing agents and react with solutions of many metal ions, such as Ag^I and Cu^{II}, to give the phosphides, arsenides, or stibnides or a mixture of these with the metals. In basic solution

$$PH_3 + 3OH^- = \tfrac{1}{4}P_4 + 3H_2O + 3e \qquad E^0 = 0.89 \text{ v.}$$

Phosphorus alone forms a second hydride, P_2H_4, diphosphine. This is generally formed along with phosphine and can be condensed as a yellow liquid. It is spontaneously flammable and decomposes on standing to form polymeric, amorphous yellow solids, insoluble in common solvents and of stoichiometry approximating, but varying around, P_2H. It differs from N_2H_4 in having no basic properties.

20-8. Halides

The binary halides—that is, those compounds containing only halogen (or halogens) in addition to the group V element—are of two main types, MX_3 and MX_5. All of the trihalides excepting PF_3 may be obtained by direct halogenation, keeping the metal in excess, whereas all of the pentahalides may be prepared by treating the metals with excess of the halogens.

All four of the group V elements give all four trihalides. In addition to these sixteen compounds, some mixed halides of the types MXY_2 and MXYZ are known. Gaseous mixed halides as well as gaseous mixtures of two simple halides tend to reorganize to equilibrium mixtures of the various possible simple and mixed halides, a phenomenon which occurs often in other comparable systems, for example, in the boron halides. All of the trihalides, simple or mixed, are rapidly hydrolyzed by water and are

rather volatile; the gaseous molecules have the expected pyramidal structures. Some have lattices which are entirely molecular, but it is known
that at least some, namely, the iodides AsI_3, SbI_3, and BiI_3, crystallize in
layer lattices in which the metal atoms occupy octahedral holes between
layers of iodide ions, there being no discrete molecules. BiF_3 is also known
definitely to have an ionic lattice which is the same as that of cryolite (Fig.
18-2, page 340) if we replace each AlF_6 octahedron by Bi and each Na by F.

All of the trichlorides and trifluorides will take on additional halide ions
to form complex halo anions such as $[BiCl_5]^{2-}$, $[SbF_5]^{2-}$, $[SbCl_6]^-$, and
$[Sb_2F_7]^-$. The considerations of Chapter 15 would lead us to expect irregular
polyhedra since there are unshared electron pairs in the metal valence
shells, and in several cases this has been confirmed by X-ray studies. The
$[SbF_5]^{2-}$ ion in K_2SbF_5 has the shape of an octahedron with one apex
missing, whereas the $[Sb_2F_7]^-$ ion in $CsSb_2F_7$ has the interesting structure

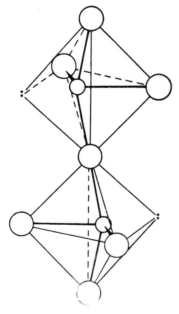

Fig. 20-3. The structure of $[Sb_2F_7]^-$ (Byström and Wilhelmi, *Arkiv Kemi*, **3,** 466 (1951)).

shown in Figure 20-3, which approximates to two trigonal bipyramids
sharing an axial apex, with an equatorial position open on each.

Some of the more important trihalides will now be described in more
detail.

PF$_3$. This is a colorless gas made by the action of AsF_3, ZnF_2, etc., on

PCl₃. One of its most interesting properties is its ability to form complexes with transition metals similar to those formed by carbon monoxide. Like CO, it is highly poisonous because of the formation of a hemoglobin complex. Unlike the other trihalides, it is hydrolyzed only slowly by water, but it is attacked rapidly by alkalies. Unlike AsF₃, it has not been observed to have any acceptor properties.

PCl₃. The most common of the phosphorus halides is a low-boiling liquid which is violently hydrolyzed by water to give phosphorous acid or, under special conditions, other acids of lower valent phosphorus. It also reacts readily with oxygen to give POCl₃. The hydrolysis of PCl₃ may be contrasted with that of NCl₃ which gives HOCl and NH₃. It is thought that this difference may be due to the ability of phosphorus to use its 3*d* orbitals to form a transition state in which water is coordinated to the phosphorus atom. Figure 20-4 illustrates some of the important reactions

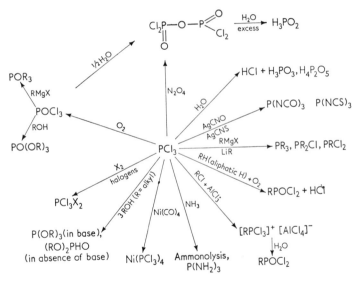

Fig. 20-4. Some important reactions of PCl₃. Many of these are typical for other MX₃ compounds as well as for MOX₃ compounds.

of PCl₃. Many of these reactions are typical of other MX₃ compounds and also, with obvious changes in formulas, of POCl₃ and other oxyhalides.

Arsenic, Antimony, and Bismuth Trihalides. Arsenic trihalides are similar to those of phosphorus in both physical and chemical properties. SbF₃, a white, readily hydrolyzed solid, finds considerable use as a moderately active fluorinating agent. Both AsF₃ and SbF₃ can function as Lewis bases and form with fluoride ion AsF₄⁻ and SbF₄⁻ as well as forming neutral complexes with some organic bases. $SbCl_3$ differs from its P and As analogs in that it dissolves in a limited amount of water to give a clear solution which, on dilution, gives insoluble oxychlorides such as $SbOCl$ and $Sb_4O_5Cl_2$. There is, however, no evidence to suggest that any simple Sb^{3+} ions exist in the solutions. $BiCl_3$, a white, crystalline solid, is hydrolyzed by water to $BiOCl$, but may be obtained from aqueous solution containing concentrated HCl since this reaction is reversible; $BiOCl$ redissolves in concentrated HCl, and $BiCl_3$ is obtained on evaporating such solutions.

Pentahalides. Of the possible pentahalides, the following are known: all of the fluorides (PF_5, AsF_5, SbF_5, and BiF_5), PCl_5, PBr_5, and $SbCl_5$. Phase studies have shown that $AsCl_5$ definitely does not exist in stable equilibrium, and it has never been isolated. As to the structures of the gaseous molecules, it has been shown conclusively that PCl_5 has the configuration of a trigonal bipyramid with the two axial bonds appreciably longer than the equatorial ones. Presumably the phosphorus atom uses $sp^3d_{z^2}$ hybrid orbitals. The structure of PF_5 has not been established with certainty, but there is some evidence to suggest that it, too, has a trigonal bipyramid structure. There is also some evidence for a trigonal bipyramid structure for gaseous and liquid $SbCl_5$, and this structure has been proved conclusively for the solid at $-30°C$. PBr_5 is known to be totally dissociated to PBr_3 and Br_2 in the vapor phase above about $35°C$.

PF_5 is easily prepared by the interaction of PCl_5 with CaF_2 at $300–400°C$. It is a very strong Lewis acid and forms complexes with amines, ethers, and other bases as well as with F^-. However, these organic complexes are less stable than those of BF_3 and are rapidly decomposed by water and alcohols. Like BF_3, PF_5 is a good catalyst, especially for ionic polymerization.

In the crystalline state both PCl_5 and PBr_5 have ionic structures: $[PCl_4]^+ [PCl_6]^-$ and $[PBr_4]^+ Br^-$. The PX_4 cations are tetrahedral and the PCl_6 anion octahedral as the principles of Chapter 15 would require. The nonformation of PBr_6^- can be attributed partly to steric factors and partly to insufficient electronegativity of Br to promote sp^3d^2 hybridization. All of the pentafluorides except BiF_5 are definitely known to react with metal fluorides to form salts containing MF_6^- ions. PCl_5 forms some addition compounds with other halides which are undoubtedly ionic in structure. For example, $PCl_5 \cdot BCl_3$ is probably $[PCl_4]^+[BCl_4]^-$, and $PCl_5 \cdot ICl$ is probably $[PCl_4]^+[ICl_2]^-$. There are many compounds known which are salts of $[AsCl_4]^+$ with large anions such as $[PCl_6]^-$, $[AlCl_4]^-$, and $[AuCl_4]^-$, although, as noted above, $AsCl_5$ does not exist. It is also known that the compounds obtained on addition of halogens to trialkyl and triaryl phosphines are ionic, $[R_3PX]^+X^-$, in the solid state.

The only arsenic pentahalide definitely known is the fluoride, which is quite similar to PF_5. The action of chlorine on AsF_3 at 0°C. gives a compound whose conductivity in excess AsF_3 suggests that it may be $[AsCl_4]^+[AsF_6]^-$.

Antimony pentafluoride is a viscous liquid which is associated even in the vapor state. These properties are due to molecular association via fluorine bridges. Nuclear magnetic resonance studies lead to the conclusion that each antimony atom is surrounded octahedrally by six fluorine atoms with two *cis* fluorines being shared with adjacent octahedra. The lengths of the chains have not been established, but probably average 5–10 units. SbF_5 also has some unusual chemical behavior. For instance, it dissolves sulfur, selenium, and tellurium, and from the solutions stable crystalline substances such as $(SbF_5)_2S$ may be isolated.

Antimony pentachloride is a fuming yellow liquid; when highly pure, however, it is colorless. It is a powerful chlorinating agent. It has been shown to form a molecular lattice with trigonal bipyramidal molecules.

Bismuth pentafluoride is made by direct fluorination of liquid bismuth at 600°C. with fluorine at low pressure. It is a white crystalline solid and an extremely powerful fluorinating agent.

The best-characterized mixed pentahalides are the compounds PF_3Cl_2 and PF_3Br_2, which are obtained by direct combination of the trifluoride and the appropriate halogen. The bromine and chlorine atoms have been shown to occupy the two axial positions of the trigonal bipyramid structures. When heated, these mixed pentahalides disproportionate into the two simple pentahalides; on standing, PF_3Cl_2 has been shown to transform slowly to $[PCl_4]^+[PF_6]^-$. Some chlorobromides are also known.

Other Halides. Phosphorus alone forms isolable halides other than the tri- and pentahalides. These are the two so-called tetrahalides P_2Cl_4 and P_2I_4, which both decompose on standing to the trihalide and nonvolatile yellow solids. Both are readily decomposed by air and water. Their structures are unknown, but it is likely that they contain P—P bonds. There is some evidence for the species Sb_2I_4 in solutions of Sb in molten SbI_3 and for BiCl and Bi_2Cl_2 in Bi–$BiCl_3$ melts.

20-9. Oxides

The following oxides of the group V elements are well characterized:

P_4O_6	As_4O_6	Sb_4O_6	Bi_2O_3
P_4O_{10}	As_2O_5	Sb_2O_5	

The reason for writing some with simplest empirical formulas and others as dimers will be explained shortly; the oxides should be compared with those of nitrogen (Chapter 12, page 254).

Doubtless the most thoroughly studied and best understood of the seven oxides mentioned above is phosphorus pentoxide (named according to its empirical formula, P_2O_5, for historical reasons), the correct molecular formula of which is P_4O_{10}, as written above. It is usually the main product of burning phosphorus and, under proper conditions with excess oxygen, is the only product. It is a white, crystalline material which sublimes at 360°C. at 1 atm., and this constitutes an excellent method of purification since the products of incipient hydrolysis, which are the commonest impurities, are comparatively nonvolatile. Phosphorus pentoxide exists in three crystalline polymorphs, in an amorphous form, and also in a glassy form. A hexagonal crystal form, known as the H-form, is obtained on sublimation. It consists of P_4O_{10} molecules with the structure shown in Figure 20-5. In this structure, the P atoms are at the corners of a tetra-

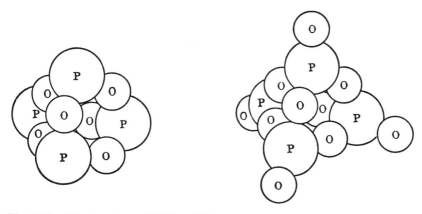

Fig. 20-5. The structures of P_4O_6 and P_4O_{10} as determined from diffraction data and bond theory (J. R. Van Wazer, *Phosphorus and Its Compounds*, Vol. I, Interscience, New York–London, 1958, p. 270).

hedron with six oxygen atoms along the edges and the remaining four lying along extended three-fold axes of the tetrahedron. The twelve P—O distances between phosphorus atoms and shared oxygen atoms are 1.62 A., which is about the P—O single bond distance, but the other four apical P—O distances are only 1.39 A. and indicate considerable $p\pi$–$d\pi$ double bonding of the kind mentioned on page 374. In the gas phase the same molecular units persist.

On heating the H-form in a closed system for 24 hours at 450°C., an orthorhombic form known as the O′-form is obtained. By heating the

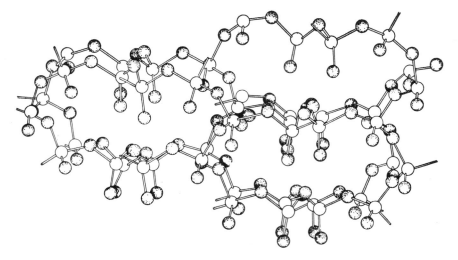

The O-form

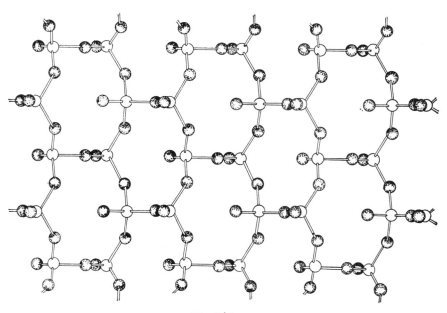

The O'-form

Fig. 20-6. Structures of the two orthorhombic forms of phosphorus pentoxide. The white balls represent phosphorus atoms and the shaded balls oxygen atoms (J. R. Van Wazer, *Phosphorus and Its Compounds*, Vol. I, Interscience, New York–London, 1958, p. 271).

H-form for only 2 hours at 400°C., a metastable orthorhombic form known as the O-form is obtained. In both of these, whose structures are shown in Figure 20-6, there are infinite sheets in which each phosphorus atom has essentially the same environment as in the P_4O_{10} molecule, namely, a tetrahedral set of bonds to three shared and one unshared oxygen atoms. When the H-form is melted, a volatile liquid of low viscosity is initially obtained, but this eventually changes into a viscous, nonvolatile liquid which is the same as or similar to that obtained directly on melting the O- or the O'-form. It thus appears that the molecular H-form melts to a molecular liquid which requires time to reorganize into a polymeric structure. The glassy solid is obtained on chilling the viscous liquid.

The most important chemical property of phosphorus pentoxide is its avidity for water. It is one of the most effective drying agents known at temperatures below 100°C. It reacts with water to form a mixture of phosphoric acids (see below) whose composition depends on the quantity of water and other conditions. Its avidity for water is so great that it will extract the elements of water from many other substances themselves considered good dehydrating agents; for example, it converts pure HNO_3 to N_2O_5 and H_2SO_4 to SO_3. It also dehydrates many organic compounds, converting amides to nitriles, for example. With alcohols it gives esters of simple and polymeric phosphoric acids depending on reaction conditions. The breakdown of P_4O_{10} with various reagents (alcohols, water, phenols, ethers, alkyl phosphates, etc.) is a very general one and is illustrative of the general reaction schemes also for the breakdown of P_4S_{10}, and also of P_4 with alkali to give PH_3, hypophosphite, etc. Thus the first reaction of an alcohol with P_4O_{10} can be written as equation 20-1, followed by further reaction at the next most anhydride-like linkage until eventually products containing only one P atom are produced (eq. 20-2).

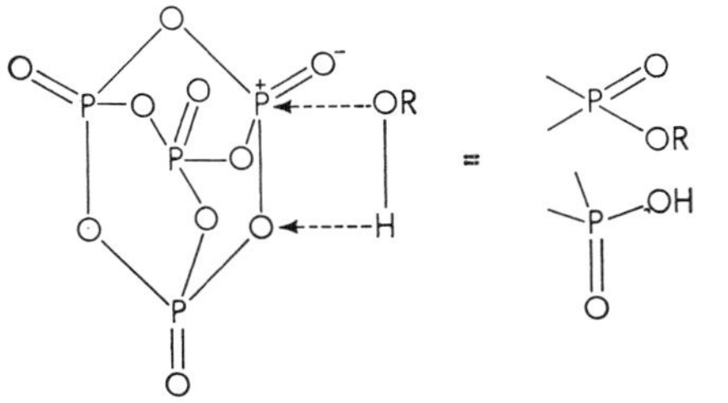

$$P_4O_{10} + 6ROH = 2(RO)_2PO \cdot OH + 2RO \cdot PO(OH)_2 \qquad (20\text{-}2)$$

The fusion of P_2O_5 with basic oxides gives solid phosphates of various types, the nature depending on experimental conditions.

The other well-characterized oxide of phosphorus is the so-called trioxide, whose true molecular formula is P_4O_6. The structure of this molecule is very similar to that of P_4O_{10} except that the four nonbridging apical oxygens present in the latter are missing. P_4O_6 is a colorless, volatile compound (m.p. 23.8, b.p. 175°C.) which forms in about 50% yield when white phosphorus is burned in a deficit of oxygen. It is difficult to separate from traces of unreacted phosphorus by distillation, but irradiation with ultraviolet light changes the white phosphorus into red, from which the P_4O_6 can be separated by dissolution in organic solvents.

On heating to temperatures above 210°C., phosphorus trioxide decomposes into red phosphorus and another oxide, PO_2. It reacts vigorously with chlorine and bromine to give the oxyhalides. It reacts with iodine in a sealed tube to give P_2I_4. It is stable to oxygen at room temperature. When it is shaken vigorously with an excess of *cold* water, it is hydrolyzed exclusively to phosphorous acid, H_3PO_3, of which it is the anhydride; P_4O_6 apparently cannot be obtained by dehydration of phosphorous acid. The reaction of phorphorus trioxide with *hot* water is very complicated, producing among other products phosphine, phosphoric acid, and elementary phosphorus; it may be noted in partial explanation that phosphorous acid itself, and all trivalent phosphorous acids generally, are thermally unstable, for example,

$$4H_3PO_3 = 3H_3PO_4 + PH_3$$

The oxide PO_2 is not very well characterized. It can be sublimed at high temperatures to give transparent crystals which are deliquescent and very soluble in water. The species present in these aqueous solutions have not been satisfactorily identified.

The oxides of arsenic are similar to those of phosphorus in most respects. Arsenic trioxide is formed on burning the metal in air. The gaseous molecules have the formula As_4O_6 and the same structure as P_4O_6. It appears that two solid forms exist. It has been shown that the ordinary form contains the same tetrahedral As_4O_6 molecules as the gas, but the structure of the second form has not been elucidated. It is soluble in various organic solvents as As_4O_6 molecules and in water to give solutions of "arsenious acid." Arsenic pentoxide, whose true molecular formula and structure are unknown, cannot be obtained by direct reaction of arsenic with oxygen. It can be prepared by oxidation of arsenic with nitric acid, followed by dehydration of the arsenic acid hydrates so obtained. It readily loses oxygen on heating to give the trioxide. It is very soluble in water, giving solutions of arsenic acid.

Antimony trioxide is also obtained by direct reaction of the metal with oxygen. In the vapor the molecular formula is Sb_4O_6, the molecules having the same tetrahedral structure as their phosphorus and arsenic analogs. The solid form which is stable up to 570°C. has a molecular lattice of such molecules; above this temperature there is another solid form with a polymeric structure. The trioxide is insoluble in water and dilute nitric and sulfuric acids, but soluble in hydrochloric and certain organic acids. It dissolves in bases to give solutions of antimonates. Antimony pentoxide is prepared by the action of nitric acid on the metal. It loses oxygen on mild heating to give the trioxide.

On heating either antimony oxide in air at about 900°C. there is formed a white, insoluble powder of stoichiometry SbO_2. The structure has been found to consist of a network of fused $Sb^{III}O_6$ and Sb^VO_6 octahedra.

The only well-established oxide of bismuth is Bi_2O_3, a yellow powder soluble in acids to give bismuth salts but with no acidic character, being insoluble in alkalies. From solutions of bismuth salts alkali or ammonium hydroxide precipitates a hydroxide, $Bi(OH)_3$, which is a definite compound. Like the oxide, this is completely basic in nature. It appears that a bismuth(V) oxide does exist, but that it is extremely unstable and has never been obtained in a completely pure state. It is obtained by the action of extremely powerful oxidizing agents on Bi_2O_3 and is a red-brown powder which rapidly loses oxygen even at 100°C.

The oxides of the group V elements clearly exemplify two important trends which are manifest to some extent in all groups of the periodic table: (1) the stability of the higher oxidation state decreases with increasing atomic number, and (2) in a given oxidation state, the metallic character of the elements, and therefore the basicity of the oxides, increase with increasing atomic number. Thus, P^{III} and As^{III} oxides are acidic, Sb^{III} oxide is amphoteric, and Bi^{III} oxide is strictly basic.

20-10. Sulfides

Phosphorus and sulfur combine directly above 100°C. to give a number of sulfides, the most important being P_4S_3, P_4S_5, P_4S_7, and P_4S_{10}. It is possible to obtain any one of these compounds in high yield by heating stoichiometric quantities of red phosphorus and sulfur for a suitable length of time at the proper temperature. A melting point diagram for the P—S system has shown that these four are probably the only binary compounds which exist under equilibrium conditions, although there is some evidence for a phase between P_4S_5 and $P_4S_{6.9}$. P_4S_3 is used commercially in matches and is soluble in organic solvents such as carbon disulfide and benzene. The structures of all four compounds are known, and in terms of the structures the above formulas do not appear as irrational as they otherwise might. P_4S_{10} has the same structure as P_4O_{10}. The others (20-I, 20-II, and 20-III) also have structures based on a tetrahedral group of phosphorus

(20-I)   (20-II)   (20-III)

atoms with sulfur atoms bonded to individual P atoms or bridging along the edges of the tetrahedron. Like P_4O_{10}, P_4S_{10} breaks down with alcohols, but with a different stoichiometry

$$P_4S_{10} + 8ROH = 4(RO)_2PS \cdot SH + 2H_2S$$

The difference is due to the fact that acids of the type $ROPS \cdot (SH)_2$ are more reactive than their oxygen analogs and react

$$ROPS \cdot (SH)_2 + ROH = (RO)_2PS \cdot SH + H_2S$$

These reactions of P_4S_{10} are extremely important commercially in that dialkyl and diaryl dithiophosphoric acids form the basis of many extreme pressure lubricants, of oil additives, and of flotation agents. Phosphorus also forms selenides and tellurides which are in many respects similar to the sulfides. The selenide P_4Se_3 has been shown to have the same structure as P_4S_3.

Arsenic forms the sulfides As_4S_3, As_4S_4, As_2S_3, and As_2S_5 by direct reaction of the elements; the last two can also be precipitated from hydrochloric acid solutions of As^{III} and As^V by hydrogen sulfide. As_2S_3 is insoluble in water and acids, but shows its acidic nature by dissolving in alkali sulfide solutions to give thio anions. As_2S_5 behaves similarly. The structures of As_4S_4 and As_2S_3 have been determined. The former has a structure similar to that of N_4S_4 (see Fig. 21-7, page 416), whereas the latter has the same structure as As_2O_3. The structure of at least one thioarsenite ion, AsS_3^{3-}, is known; it has the shape of a regular triangular pyramid.

Antimony forms the sulfides Sb_2S_3 and Sb_2S_5, both of which may be obtained either by direct combination of the elements or by precipitation with hydrogen sulfide from Sb^{III} or Sb^V solutions. Like their arsenic analogs, they are soluble in excess sulfide to give anionic thio complexes. Sb_2S_3 has a ribbon-like polymeric structure in which half the Sb atoms have the square pyramidal coordination discussed on page 379.

Bismuth forms only Bi_2S_3, which appears as a dark brown precipitate when solutions of bismuth salts, are treated with hydrogen sulfide. It is not acidic and is insoluble in alkali sulfides.

Selenides and tellurides of As, Sb, and Bi can be made. Some of these, for example, bismuth telluride, have been studied intensively as semi-conductors.

OTHER COMPOUNDS

20-11. Oxy Halides

These compounds are of various stoichiometric types. Among the most important are those of phosphorus with the general formula POX_3, the phosphoryl halides, in which X may be F, Cl, or Br. The most important one is $POCl_3$, obtainable by the reactions:

$$2PCl_3 + O_2 = 2POCl_3$$
$$P_4O_{10} + 6PCl_5 = 10POCl_3$$

The reactions of $POCl_3$ are much like those of PCl_3. The halogens can be replaced by alkyl or aryl groups using Grignard reagents, and by alkoxy groups using alcohols; hydrolysis by water yields phosphoric acid. $POCl_3$ also has donor properties toward metal ions, and many complexes are known. The distillation of the $POCl_3$ complexes of $ZrCl_4$ and $HfCl_4$ can be used to separate Zr and Hf, and the very strong $POCl_3$–Al_2Cl_6 complex has been utilized to remove Al_2Cl_6 from adducts with Friedel-Crafts reaction products. $POCl_3$ has also been shown to function as an ionizing solvent, although its self-ionization

$$2POCl_3 = POCl_2^+ + POCl_4^-$$

is small. In this system chlorides are bases, and salts of $POCl_2^+$ are acids.

The structure of all POX_3 molecules consists of a pyramidal PX_3 group with the oxygen atom occupying the fourth position to complete a distorted tetrahedron. Corresponding sulfides and selenides, PSX_3 and $PSeX_3$, are also known.

More complex oxy halides containing P—O—P bonds are known; some of these have linear structures, while some form rings. The linear compound $Cl_2(O)P$—O—$P(O)Cl_2$ is obtained either by oxidation of PCl_3 with N_2O_4 or by partial hydrolysis of $POCl_3$.

Antimony and bismuth form the important oxy halides SbOCl and BiOCl which are ionic solids, insoluble in water. They precipitate upon diluting solutions of Sb^{III} and Bi^{III} in concentrated HCl.

Only one oxyhalide of arsenic has been prepared. The reaction of fluorine with an equimolar mixture of $AsCl_3$ and As_2O_3 produces $AsOF_3$, a volatile liquid (m.p. -68, b.p. 26°C.).

20-12. Phosphonium Compounds

Although organic derivatives of the type $[MR_4]^+X^-$ are well known for M = P, As, and Sb (see page 392), only phosphorus gives the hydrogen-containing prototype, PH_4^+, and this does not form any very stable compounds. The best-known phosphonium salt is the iodide, which forms as colorless crystals on mixing gaseous HI and PH_3. The chloride and bromide are also known, but are even less stable. The dissociation pressure of PH_4Cl into PH_3 and HCl reaches 1 atm. below 0°C. The estimated basicity constant of PH_3 in water is about 10^{-25}, and phosphonium salts are completely hydrolyzed by water, releasing the rather insoluble gas PH_3:

$$PH_4I(s) + H_2O = H_3O^+ + I^- + PH_3(g)$$

Perhaps the most readily produced organic phosphonium compound is obtained by the interaction of phosphine with formaldehyde in hydrochloric acid solution:

$$PH_3 + 4CH_2O + HCl = [P(CH_2OH)_4]^+Cl^-$$

It is a white crystalline solid soluble in water and is available commercially.

20-13. Phosphonitrilic Compounds

The reaction of PCl_5 with ammonium chloride or substituted ammonium chlorides either by fusion together or on refluxing in halogenated solvents gives a series of compounds of composition $(PNCl_2)_x$. From this mixture by fractional distillation, chromatography, and other methods, the lower members can be obtained as moderately volatile, white, crystalline solids.

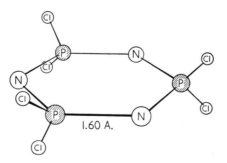

Fig. 20-7.   Structure of trimeric phosphonitrilic chloride, $(PNCl_2)_3$.

They have cyclic structures with alternating P and N atoms. The structure of the trimer is shown in Figure 20-7. While the ring in the trimer is almost planar, deviations probably being due to crystal forces, that in the tetramer is definitely puckered. The P—N distance in the trimer, $\sim$1.6 A., is shorter than a single P—N bond in the phosphoramidate Zwitterion, $[\overset{+}{N}H_3\overset{-}{PO_3}]^-$. Many derivatives of the lower members (which have some aromatic-like properties) in which some or all of the chlorine atoms are replaced by other groups, such as SCN, CH_3, C_6H_5, and other halogens, are known. Geometrical isomers can occur in substituted derivatives; also boat and chair forms have been proved for certain substituted tetramers, and other configurational isomers are possible in addition to positional isomers. Higher members appear to be linear polymers; the polymer is end-stopped with the elements of PCl_5 at one end and PCl_4 at the other. These have rubber-like properties and give X-ray diffraction patterns typical of fibers. Unfortunately, they are only temporarily and conditionally stable.

The formulas for the cyclic compounds are usually written with double bonds (20-IV and 20-V). There is, however, reason to believe that the

(20-IV)   (20-V)

amount of double bonding is not nearly this great and that delocalization of the π electrons and consequent aromatic character are very limited. It is important to note that although the nitrogen π orbitals are p orbitals, the phosphorus π orbitals must be, at least in part, d orbitals. The different symmetry properties of d orbitals plays an important part in modifying the behavior of the π electron system in these compounds relative to the π system in a compound such as a triazine where all π orbitals are p orbitals. The overlap of $d\pi$ and $p\pi$ orbitals is discussed in some detail for transition metal complexes (Chapter 27).

20-14. Organic Derivatives

For phosphorus and arsenic there is a vast chemistry involving P—C and As—C bonds. With the exception of pentaphenyl compounds of P, As, Sb, and Bi, the organo derivatives of the group V elements are compounds with only three or four bonds to the central atom. The organobismuth compounds are few and not very stable. The organo derivatives may be prepared in a great variety of ways, the simplest being by treatment of halides or oxy halides with Grignard reagents:

$$(O)MX_3 + 3RMgX = (O)MR_3 + 3MgX_2$$

The lower trialkyls are rather easily oxidized, trimethylphosphine being spontaneously flammable in air, but many of the higher members are quite stable. The R_3MO compounds, which may be obtained from the oxy halides as shown above or by oxidation of the corresponding R_3M compounds, are all very stable.

Trialkyl and triaryl phosphines, arsines, and stibines are all good donors toward the heavier transition metals and form numerous complexes with Pt, Pd, Au, etc., and also replace carbon monoxide from metal carbonyls. They use their empty d orbitals to accept electrons back from the metal atoms in these compounds. The oxides, R_3MO, also form many complexes, but they function simply as donors. Trialkyl and triaryl phosphines, arsines, and stibines generally react with alkyl and aryl halides to form quaternary salts:

$$R_3M + R'X = [R_3R'M]^+X^-$$

The stibonium compounds form with the greatest difficulty and are the least common. These quaternary salts, excepting the hydroxides, which are obtained as sirupy masses, are white crystalline compounds. The tetraphenylphosphonium and -arsonium ions are useful for precipitating large anions such as ReO_4^-, ClO_4^-, and $ZnCl_4^{2-}$.

The basicities of phosphines toward protons is of interest when compared to amines. The phosphines are less basic than amines of the same type, but for phosphines the order is tertiary > secondary > primary, whereas for amines it is commonly irregular but usually with primary > tertiary. It is believed that hybridization changes best explain the data for phosphorus. If the energy for the reaction of acid and base consists of two parts—the energy for the base to assume the sp^3 hybridization of the ion and the energy for formation of the new bond—then, since the bond angles change in going from PH_3 to PR_3 (suggesting a hybridization change $p^3 \rightarrow sp^3$) the rehybridization energy would *decrease* with increasing substitution. For amines, on the other hand, there is little or no change in bond angle, and the reverse order can be ascribed to solvation effects. If the number of R groups increases, the amount of solvation of $N-H^+$ bonds in the product decreases; thus NH_4^+ is more stabilized by solvation and thus thermodynamically favored.

One of the substituted phosphines deserves special comment. Triphenylphosphine, a white crystalline solid, now is utilized very widely in the Wittig reaction for olefin synthesis. This reaction involves the formation of alkylidene or arylidene triphenylphosphoranes from the action of butyl-lithium or other base on the quaternary halide, for example,

$$[(C_6H_5)_3PCH_3]^+Br^- \xrightarrow{\text{n-butyllithium}} (C_6H_5)_3P{=}CH_2$$

This intermediate reacts very rapidly with aldehydes and ketones to give zwitterionic compounds (20-VI) which eliminate triphenylphosphine oxide under mild conditions to give olefins (20-VII).

(20-VI)   (20-VII)

20-15. Aqueous Cationic Chemistry

Apart from the quaternary salts mentioned in the preceding section, there is no cationic chemistry of P and As. Although the reaction

$$As(OH)_3 = As^{3+} + 3OH^-$$

may occur to some slight extent, there is little direct evidence for the existence of significant concentrations of tripositive cations even in strong acid solutions.

Antimony has some definite cationic chemistry, but only in the trivalent state, the basic character of Sb_2O_5 being negligible. The Sb^{III} ion has a great tendency to hydrolyze, and cationic compounds of Sb^{III} are mostly of the antimonyl ion, SbO^+, although some of the Sb^{3+} ion, such as $Sb_2(SO_4)_3$, are known. Antimony salts readily form complexes with various acids in which the antimony forms the nucleus of an anion, for example, [Sb $(SO_4)_2]^-$, $[Sb(C_2O_4)_2]^-$, and $[Sb(OH_2)C_4H_2O_6]^-$. The last, as potassium antimony tartrate, is one of the best known of water-soluble antimony compounds.

Only for bismuth can it be said that there is an extensive true cationic chemistry, and aqueous solutions definitely containing hydrated Bi^{III} ions can be obtained. In neutral perchlorate solutions the main species is $[Bi_6O_6]^{6+}$ or its hydrated form, $[Bi_6(OH)_{12}]^{6+}$, and at higher pH $[Bi_6O_6(OH)_3]^{3+}$ is formed. From acid solution various hydrated crystalline salts such as $Bi(NO_3)_3 \cdot 5H_2O$, $Bi_2(SO_4)_3$, and double nitrates of the type M_3^{II} $[Bi(NO_3)_6]_2 \cdot 24H_2O$ can be obtained. Treatment of Bi_2O_3 with nitric acid gives bismuthyl salts such as $BiO(NO_3)$ and $BiO_2(OH)(NO_3)$. Similar bismuthyl salts are precipitated on dilution of strongly acid solutions of various bismuth compounds. Bismuthyl salts are generally insoluble in water. In solutions of Bi^{III} containing excess halide ions, BiX_4^- complexes are present.

THE OXY ANIONS

The oxy anions in both lower and higher states are a very important part of the chemistry of phosphorus and arsenic and comprise the only real aqueous chemistry of these elements. For the more metallic antimony and bismuth, oxy anion formation is less pronounced, and for bismuth only ill-defined "bismuthates" exist.

20-16. Oxy Acids and Anions of Phosphorus

All phosphorus oxy acids have P—OH bonds where the hydrogen atom is ionizable; hydrogen atoms in P—H bonds are not ionized. There are a vast number of oxy acids or ions, some of them of great technical importance; but with the exception of the simpler species, they have not been well understood structurally until quite recently.

We can attempt to deal only with some structural principles and some of the more important compounds. It is to be stressed that it is the *oxy anion* which is important, since in many cases the free acid cannot be isolated even though its salts are stable. Both lower, P^{III}, and higher, P^V, acids are known. A lower acid would normally be expected to have the P atom bound as in $P(OH)_3$, while a higher acid would be derived from $O=P(OH)_3$. Since the latter is the most stable configuration for phosphorus, this type of structure would be expected to predominate. In fact, attempts to make oxy acids based on three-covalent phosphorus fail since there is a hydrogen transfer:

$$P—OH \rightarrow H—P=O$$

Thus, with the exception of the triesters, $P(OR)_3$ (20-X), the free lower acid, mono- and disubstituted anions, and esters (20-VIII) *all* have a P—H

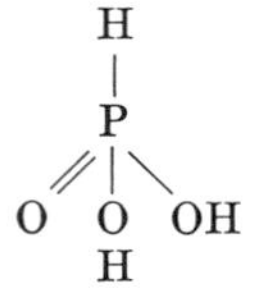

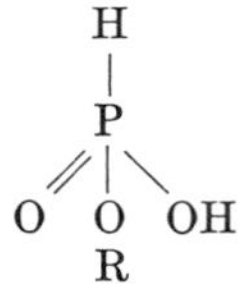

(20-VIII)	(20-IX)	(20-X)
$H_2[HPO_3]^{2-}$	Phosphite monoester	Phosphite triester

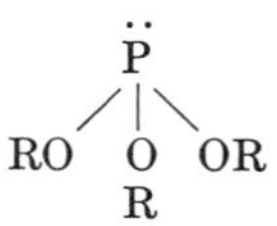

bond with four bonds (sp^3) to phosphorus. This hydrogen atom transfer in the lower oxy acids (eq. 20-3) is comparable to the keto-enol shift in carbonyl compounds (eq. 20-4), except that in the carbon case there is a

$$R{-}\overset{..}{\underset{R}{P}}{-}OH \to R{-}\overset{..}{\underset{R}{P}}{-}O^- + H^+ \to R{-}\overset{H}{\underset{R}{P^+}}{-}O^- \qquad (20\text{-}3)$$

$$\left[R{-}\overset{H}{\underset{R}{P^+}}{-}O^- \leftrightarrow R{-}\overset{H}{\underset{R}{P}}{=}O \right]$$

$$R{-}\overset{H}{\underset{H}{\overset{|*}{C}}}{-}C\overset{O}{\diagdown}_R \quad = \quad \overset{R}{\diagdown}\overset{*}{C}{=}C\overset{OH}{\diagup}_R \qquad (20\text{-}4)$$

change of hybridization at C^* from sp^3 to sp^2, whereas in the phosphorus case little change occurs. Although the free acids based on three-covalent phosphorus can exist only as transitory species, kinetic evidence suggests that they are present in concentrations of the order of 1 in 10^{12}. The keto-enol analogy can be illustrated by the reaction with sulfur. Dialkyl phosphites, $(RO)_2PHO$, do *not* add sulfur, whereas the solid derivatives, $(RO)_2PONa$, add sulfur very readily.

The fundamental structures of oxy anions containing one phosphorus atom are represented by 20-XI, 20-XII, and 20-XIII, where the structures have tetrahedral or distorted tetrahedral arrangements and the P—O bonds have some multiple character.

$$\left[H{-}\overset{H}{\underset{O}{P}}{-}O \right]^- \qquad \left[O{-}\overset{H}{\underset{O}{P}}{-}O \right]^{2-} \qquad \left[O{-}\overset{O}{\underset{O}{P}}{-}O \right]^{3-}$$

(20-XI)   (20-XII)   (20-XIII)
Hypophosphite   Phosphite   Orthophosphate

Lower Acids: *Hypophosphorous Acid, $H[H_2PO_2]$.* The salts are usually prepared by boiling white phosphorus with alkali or alkaline earth hydroxide. The main reactions appear to be:

$$P_4 + 4OH^- + 4H_2O = 4H_2PO_2^- + 2H_2$$
$$P_4 + 4OH^- + 2H_2O = 2HPO_3^{2-} + 2PH_3$$

The calcium salt is soluble in water, unlike that of phosphite or phosphate; the free acid can be made from it or obtained by oxidation of phosphine with iodine in water. Both the acid and its salts are powerful reducing agents, being oxidized to orthophosphate. The pure acid, a white crystalline solid, behaves as a monobasic acid, $K = 8.0 \times 10^{-2}$; other physical studies, such as nuclear magnetic resonance, confirm the presence of a

$\diagdown$
$\quad$PH$_2$ group. Either or both of the hydrogen atoms can be replaced, but
$\diagup$

only by indirect methods, by alkyl groups to give mono- or dialkyl *phosphonous* compounds.

Phosphorous Acid, $H_2[HPO_3]$. As noted above, this acid and its mono- and diesters have a P—H bond. The free acid is obtained by treating PCl$_3$ or P$_4$O$_6$ with water. The mono-, di-, and triesters can be obtained from reactions of alcohols with PCl$_3$ alone or in the presence of an organic base as hydrogen chloride acceptor. The presence of the P—H bond has been demonstrated by a variety of structural studies as well as by the formation of only mono and di series of salts. The pure acid is a deliquescent colorless solid (m.p. 70.1°C.; $K_1 = 5 \times 10^{-2}$). It is oxidized to orthophosphate by halogen, sulfur dioxide, and other agents, but the reactions are slow and complex.

The *phosphite triesters*, P(OR)$_3$, are notable for forming donor complexes with transition metals and other acceptors. They are readily oxidized to the respective phosphates,

$$2(RO)_3P + O_2 = 2(RO)_3PO$$

They also undergo the Michaelis-Arbusov rearrangement with alkyl or other halides,

$$P(OR)_3 + R'X = [(RO)_3PR'X] \rightarrow RO\overset{\displaystyle O}{\underset{\displaystyle OR}{\overset{\|}{-}P\overset{}{\underset{|}{-}}R'}} + RX$$
$$\qquad\qquad\quad \text{Phosphonium}$$
$$\qquad\qquad\quad \text{intermediate}$$

and it may be noted that the methyl ester undergoes easy isomerization to the dimethyl ester of methylphosphonic acid:

$$P(OCH_3)_3 = CH_3PO(OCH_3)_2$$

Higher Acids: *Orthophosphoric Acid.* This acid, H$_3$PO$_4$, commonly called phosphoric acid, is one of the oldest known and most important phosphorus compounds. The free acid is made in vast quantities, usually as 85% sirupy acid, by the direct reaction of ground phosphate rock with sulfuric acid and also by the direct burning of phosphorus and subsequent hydration of the oxide P$_4$O$_{10}$. The pure acid is a colorless crystalline solid (m.p. 42.35°C.). It is very stable and has essentially no oxidizing properties below 350–400°C. At elevated temperatures it is fairly reactive toward metals and is reduced; it will also then attack quartz.

The acid is tribasic: at 25°C., $K_1 = 0.7107 \times 10^{-2}$; $K_2 = 7.99 \times 10^{-8}$; $K_3 = \sim4 \times 10^{-13}$. The pure acid and its crystalline hydrates have tetrahedral PO_4 groups connected by hydrogen bonds (Fig. 20-8). These persist

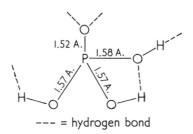

--- = hydrogen bond

Fig. 20-8. Structure of anhydrous orthophosphoric acid.

in the concentrated solutions and are responsible for the sirupy nature. For solutions of concentration less than $\sim50\%$, the phosphate anions are hydrogen-bonded to the liquid water rather than to other phosphate anions.

Phosphates of most metal ions and other cations are known. Some of these are of enormous commercial and practical importance, for example, ammonium phosphate fertilizers, alkali phosphate buffers, etc. Natural phosphate minerals are *all* orthophosphates, the major one being fluoroapatite; hydroxyapatites, partly carbonated, make up the mineral part of teeth.

Orthophosphoric acid and phosphates form complexes with many transition metal ions. The precipitation of insoluble phosphates from fairly strong acid solution ($3–6N\ HNO_3$) is characteristic of $+4$ cations such as those of Ce, Th, Zr, U, Pu, etc.

Large numbers of phosphate *esters* are known. Some of these are important technically. Thus tri-*n*-butyl phosphate is used for solvent extraction of metal ions from aqueous solutions. Other important phosphates are the sugar and glycerol phosphates.

Phosphate esters are usually prepared by reactions such as

$$O{=}PCl_3 + 3ROH = O{=}P(OR)_3 + 3HCl$$
$$Ag_3PO_4 + 3CH_3COCl = (CH_3CO{\cdot}O)_3P{=}O + 3AgCl$$

Organic phosphates are of major importance in biological processes. The sugar phosphates are important in photosynthesis, and nucleic acids contain phosphate. Examples of such phosphates are glucose-6-phosphoric acid (20-XIV) and deoxyribonucleic acid (20-XV, fragment of chain). The rates of hydrolysis of phosphate esters and of triphosphate esters (see

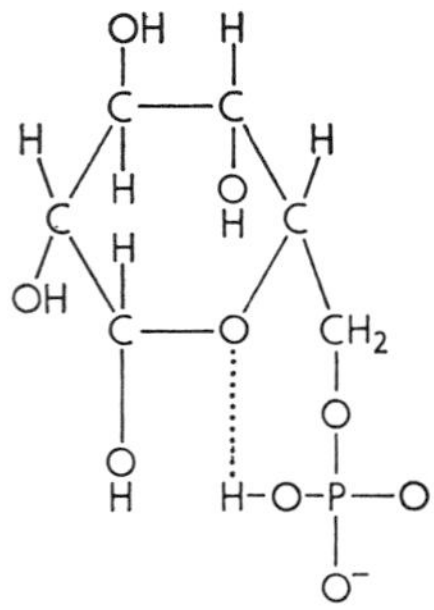

(20-XIV)

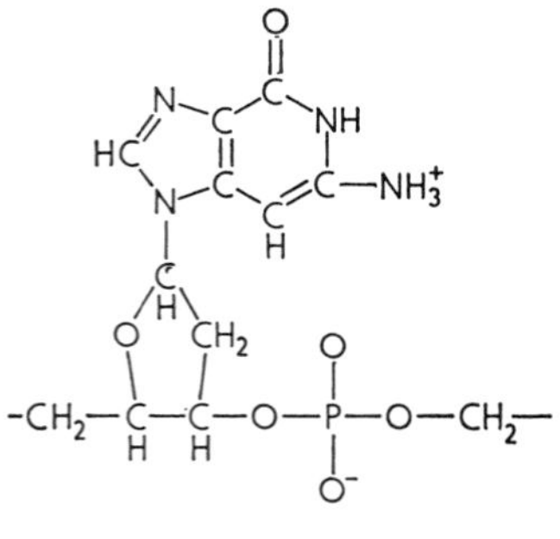

(20-XV)

below) such as adenosine triphosphate, which is basically the hydrolysis of C—O—P bonds, and the associated energy changes are of fundamental importance in biological systems, since the driving forces for many reactions are provided by the hydrolytic free energy changes. Large numbers of enzymes are known which catalyze the scission and formation of C—O—P links.

Condensed Phosphates. Condensed phosphates are those containing more than one P atom and having P—O—P bonds. We may note that the *lower* acids can also give condensed species, although we shall deal here only with a few examples of phosphates.

There are three main building units in condensed phosphates: the end unit (20-XVI) middle unit (20-XVII) and branching unit (20-XVIII).

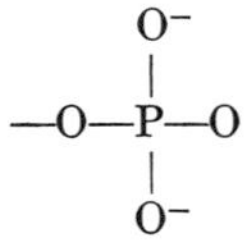

(20-XVI)	(20-XVII)	(20-XVIII)
$PO_{3.5}^{2-}$	PO_3^-	$PO_{2.5}$

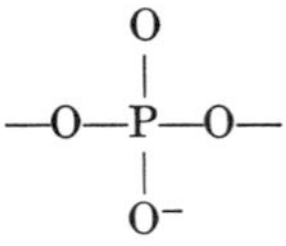

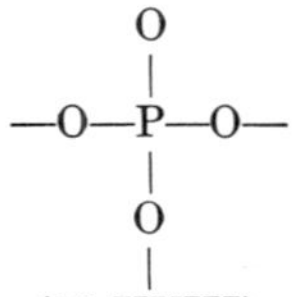

These units can be distinguished not only chemically—for example, the branching points are rapidly attacked by water—but also by the ^{31}P magnetic resonance spectra of the P atoms. These units can be incorporated into either (*a*) chain or *polyphosphates*, containing 2–10 P atoms, or (*b*) *ring* or *metaphosphates*, containing 3–7 or more P atoms. Not all possible combinations of the basic units are known. Some of the most important are:

Linear polyphosphates, which are salts of anions of general formula

$[P_nO_{3n+1}]^{(n+2)-}$. Examples are $M^I_4P_2O_7$ (20-XIX), a pyrophosphate or dipolyphosphate, and $M^I_5P_3O_{10}$ (20-XX), a tripolyphosphate.

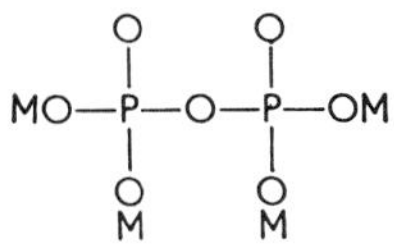

(20-XIX) 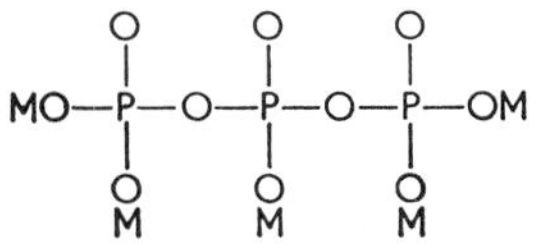   (20-XX)

Cyclic polyphosphates, which are salts of anions of general formula $[P_nO_{3n}]^{n-}$. Examples are $M_3P_3O_9$ (20-XXI), a trimetaphosphate, and $M_4P_4O_{12}$ (20-XXII), a tetrametaphosphate.

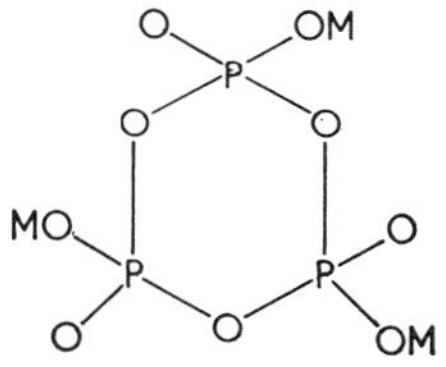

(20-XXI) 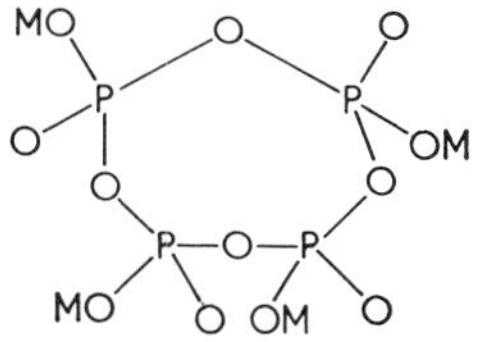   (20-XXII)

Condensed phosphates are usually prepared by dehydration of orthophosphates under various conditions of temperature (300–1200°C.) and also by appropriate hydration of dehydrated species, as, for example,

$$(n-2)NaH_2PO_4 + 2Na_2HPO_4 \xrightarrow{\text{heat}} Na_{n+2}P_nO_{3n+1} + (n-1)H_2O$$
$$\text{Polyphosphate}$$

$$nNaH_2PO_4 \xrightarrow{\text{heat}} (NaPO_3)_n + nH_2O$$
$$\text{Metaphosphate}$$

They can also be prepared by controlled addition of water or other reagents to P_4O_{10}, by treating chlorophosphates with silver phosphates, etc.

The separation of the complex mixtures of anions that can be obtained is now not too difficult using ion exchange or chromatographic procedures as illustrated in Figure 20-9.

Condensed phosphates form soluble complexes with many metals, and chain phosphates are used industrially for this purpose, for example, as water softeners.

The most important *cyclic* phosphate is *tetrametaphosphate*, which can be prepared, among other methods, by heating copper nitrate with slightly more than an equimolar amount of phosphoric acid (75%) slowly to 400°C. The sodium salt can be obtained by treating a solution of the copper salt with Na$_2$S. Slow addition of P$_4$O$_{10}$ to ice water gives ~75% of the phos-

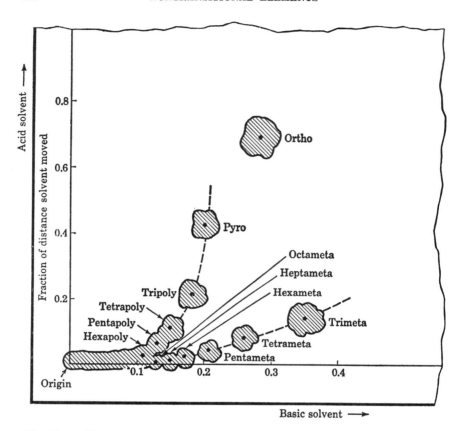

Fig. 20-9. Chromatographic separation of complex phosphate mixtures. Corner of a two-dimensional paper chromatogram showing the positions of the pentameta- through octametaphosphate rings in relation to the positions of the well-known ring and chain phosphates. The basic solvent traveled 9 in. in 24 hr., whereas the acid solvent traveled 4.5 in. in 5.5. hr. (J. R. Van Wazer, *Phosphorus and Its Compounds*, Vol. I, Interscience, New York–London, 1958, p. 702).

phorus as tetrametaphosphate. The structure (Fig. 20-10) has the possibility of boat and chair forms for the anion, and these can be distinguished chemically.

Fluorophosphates. As with many other oxy anions, fluorine can replace OH in phosphate to give mono- and difluorophosphate salts and esters. The dialkyl monofluorophosphate esters have been found to inhibit cholinesterase in the body and to be exceedingly toxic.

The completely fluorinated *hexafluorophosphate* ion, PF_6^-, can be obtained by reactions such as:

$$PCl_5 + NaCl + 6HF(l) = NaPF_6 + 6HCl$$
$$12HF + P_2O_5 = 2H^+PF_6^- + 5H_2O$$

This ion is octahedral. Appreciable covalent character of the P—F bonds is shown by the spin-spin coupling between the P and F nuclei in the NMR spectrum. Hexafluorophosphates have solubilities similar to perchlorates. They are hydrolyzed in acid but not in neutral or basic solution.

20-17. Oxy Acids and Anions of Arsenic, Antimony, and Bismuth

Arsenic. The nature of the lower acid is not firmly established, and it more likely is the hydrated oxide $As_2O_3(aq)$; it is readily oxidized, even by air. However, in salts, the *arsenite* anion is known in the ortho as well as more complex forms. *Arsenic acid*, H_3AsO_4, is obtained by treating arsenic

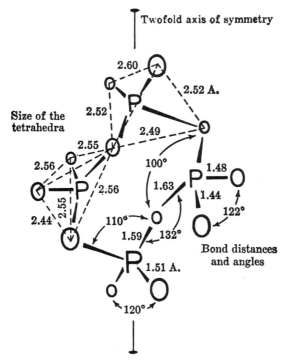

(Distances in A and angles in degrees)

Fig. 20-10. Structure of the anion in ammonium tetrametaphosphate (J. R. Van Wazer, *Phosphorus and Its Compounds*, Vol. I, Interscience, New York–London, 1958, p. 698).

with concentrated nitric acid to give white crystals, $H_3AsO_4 \cdot \frac{1}{2}H_2O$. Unlike phosphoric acid, it is a moderately strong oxidizing agent in acid solution, the potentials being

$$HAsO_2 + 2H_2O = H_3AsO_4 + 2H^+ + 2e \qquad E^0 = -0.559 \text{ v.}$$
$$H_3PO_3 + H_2O = H_4PO_4 + H^+ + e \qquad E^0 = 0.276 \text{ v.}$$

Arsenic acid is tribasic but somewhat weaker than phosphoric acid, $K_1 = 5 \times 10^{-3}$. The arsenates generally resemble orthophosphates and are often isomorphous with them.

Condensed arsenic anions are much less stable than the condensed phosphates and, owing to rapid hydrolysis, do not exist in aqueous solution. Dehydration of KH_2AsO_4 gives three forms, stable at different temperatures, of metaarsenate; one form is known to contain a linear chain polyanion.

Antimony. No lower acid is known but only the hydrated oxide $Sb_2O_3(aq)$; the antimonites are well defined salts, however. The higher acid is known only in solution, but it gives crystalline antimonates of the type $K[Sb(OH)_6]$. There do not appear to be finite SbO_4 ions under any circumstances. Some "antimonates" obtained by heating mixed oxides, for example, $M^{I}SbO_3$, $M^{III}SbO_4$, and $M_2^{II}Sb_2O_7$, contain SbO_6 octahedra and differ only in the manner of linking in the lattice. They are best regarded as mixed oxides.

Bismuth. When $Bi(OH)_3$ in strongly alkaline solution is treated with chlorine or other strong oxidizing agents, "bismuthates" are obtained, but never in a state of high purity. They can also be made, for example, by heating Na_2O_2 and Bi_2O_3 which gives $NaBi^VO_3$. Bismuthates are powerful oxidizing agents in acid solution.

References

Bent, H. A., *J. Inorg. & Nuclear Chem.*, **19**, 43 (1961). Hybridization bond angles and bond lengths in PX_3, PSX_3 and POX_3 compounds.

Berlin, K. D., and G. B. Butler, *Chem. Revs.*, **60**, 243 (1960). Preparation and properties of phosphine oxides.

Crofts, P. C., *Quart. Revs. (London)*, **12**, 34 (1958). Chemistry of compounds with P—C bonds.

Doak, G. O., and L. D. Freedman, *Chem. Revs.*, **61**, 31 (1961). Structure and properties of dialkyl phosphonates.

Frank, A. W., *Chem. Revs.*, **61**, 389 (1961). Phosphonous acids and their derivatives.

George, J. W., "Halides and Oxyhalides of the Elements of Groups Vb and VIb," in F. A. Cotton, ed., *Progress in Inorganic Chemistry*, Vol. II, Interscience, New York–London, 1960, p. 33.

Gillespie, R. J., *J. Am. Chem. Soc.*, **82,** 5978 (1960). Valence bonding in hydrides and halides.

Kosopoloff, G. K., *Organophosphorus Compounds*, Wiley, New York, 1950.

Mann, F. G., in *Progress in Stereochemistry*, Vol. 2, Butterworths, London, 1958, p. 196. Stereochemistry of N, P, As, Sb, and Bi.

Mooney, R. W., and M. A. Aia, *Chem. Revs.*, **61,** 433 (1961). Alkaline earth phosphates.

Paddock, N. L., and H. T. Searle, in H. J. Emeléus and A. G. Sharpe, eds., *Advances in Inorganic Chemistry and Radiochemistry*, Vol. 1, Academic Press, New York, 1959. Phosphonitrilic halides and their derivatives.

Van Wazer, J. R., *Phosphorus and Its Compounds*, Vol. I, Interscience, New York–London, 1958. A comprehensive account of all phases of phosphorus chemistry. Vol. II, *Technology, Biological Functions, and Applications*, 1961.

——— and C. F. Callis, *Chem. Revs.*, **58,** 1011 (1958). Complexing of metals by phosphate.

Yost, D. M., and H. Russell, *Systematic Inorganic Chemistry (of the 5th and 6th Group Elements)*, Prentice-Hall, New York, 1946. An older but very useful account of some aspects of phosphorus chemistry.

21

The Group VI Elements: S, Se, Te, Po

GENERAL REMARKS

21-1. Electronic Structures and Valences

The elements have the following outer electronic configurations:

S: [Ne]$3s^23p^4$
Se: [Ar]$3d^{10}4s^24p^4$
Te: [Kr]$4d^{10}5s^25p^4$
Po: [Xe]$4f^{14}5d^{10}6s^26p^4$

With these electronic structures, approaching as they do the configurations of the next inert gas atoms, the elements show purely nonmetallic chemistry except for polonium and to a very slight extent tellurium. Their compounds are practically all covalent ones except for the anions S^{2-}, Se^{2-}, Te^{2-} and a few complex cations, such as R_3S^+ and R_3SO^+, within which the bonding is covalent. As with other nonmetallic elements, the concept of oxidation state has only formal significance.

Some of the compounds formed by these elements can be considered to show their tendency to complete the inert gas configuration, of which they lack two electrons. Thus they form the chalconide ions, S^{2-}, Se^{2-}, and Te^{2-}, although the existence of these ions as such in chalconides of metals other than the most electropositive ones is quite unlikely. The elements also form compounds in which there are two electron pair bonds, for example, $(CH_3)_2S$, H_2S, SCl_2, etc., and ionic species in which there is one bond and one negative charge, for example, RS^-, or three bonds and one positive charge, for example, R_3S^+, can be formed.

21-2. Group Trends

There are great differences between the chemistry of oxygen and that of the other group VI elements and then more gradual variations through the sequence S, Se, Te, Po. Differences from oxygen are attributable among other things to the following:

1. The lower electronegativities of the S–Po elements lessens the ionic character of those of their compounds which are formally analogous to those of oxygen, alters the relative stabilities of various kinds of bonds, and drastically lessens the importance of hydrogen bonding.

2. The maximum coordination number is not limited to four as in the case of oxygen, since d orbitals are available for use in bonding. Thus sulfur forms several hexacoordinate compounds, for example, SF_6, and for tellurium six is actually the characteristic coordination number.

3. Sulfur (but not Se or Te) has a particular tendency to catenation so that it forms several classes of compounds having no oxygen, selenium, or tellurium analogs, for example, polysulfide ions, S_n^{2-}, sulfanes, XS_nX (where X may be H, halogen, —CN, or —NR_2), and the polysulfonic acids, $HO_3SS_nSO_3H$ and their salts. Although selenium and tellurium have by no means the same tendency to catenation as sulfur, they do form rings (Se only) and long chains in their elemental forms. These chains are of course not branched because the valence of the element is only two.

In the S–Po group gradual changes of properties are evident with increasing size, decreasing electronegativity, etc. Among these are:

1. Decreasing thermal stability of the H_2X compounds. Thus H_2Te is quite endothermic.

2. Increasing metallic character of the elements.

3. Increasing tendency to form anionic complexes such as $SeBr_6^{2-}$, $TeBr_6^{2-}$, PoI_6^{2-}.

4. Decreasing stability of compounds in high formal positive oxidation states.

5. Emergence of cationic properties for Po and, very marginally, for Te. Thus TeO_2 and PoO_2 appear to have ionic lattices and they react with hydrohalic acids to give Te^{IV} and Po^{IV} halides and PoO_2 forms a hydrate $Po(OH)_4$. There are also some ill-defined "salts" of Te and Po, such as $Po(SO_4)_2$, $TeO_2 \cdot SO_3$, etc.

Use of d Orbitals. In addition to the ability of the S–Po elements to bring d orbitals into hybridization with s and p orbitals so as to form more than four σ bonds to other atoms, sulfur particularly and also selenium appear to make frequent use of $d\pi$ orbitals to form multiple bonds. Thus, for example, in the sulfate ion, where the s and p orbitals are used in σ bonding, the shortness of the S—O bonds suggests that there must be considerable multiple bond character. The only likely explanation for this is that empty $d\pi$ orbitals of sulfur accept electrons from filled $p\pi$ orbitals of oxygen. We have cited evidence for similar $d\pi$–$p\pi$ bonding in similar phosphorus compounds, but it seems to be more prominent with sulfur and many instances will be cited later in this chapter.

THE ELEMENTS

21-3. Occurrence

Sulfur occurs widely in nature as the element, as H_2S and SO_2, in innumerable sulfide ores of metals and in the form of various sulfates such as gypsum and anhydrite ($CaSO_4$), magnesium sulfate, etc. Selenium and tellurium are much less abundant than sulfur and frequently occur as selenide and telluride impurities in metal sulfide ores. They are often recovered from flue dusts of combustion chambers for sulfur ores, particularly those of Ag and Au, and from lead chambers in sulfuric acid manufacture.

Polonium occurs in uranium and thorium minerals as a product of radioactive decay series. It was first isolated from pitchblende which contains less than 0.1 mg. of Po per ton. It is now obtained in milligram to gram quantities by irradiation of bismuth in nuclear reactors:

$$^{209}Bi(n,\gamma)^{210}Bi \rightarrow {}^{210}Po + \beta^-$$

Polonium is separated from bismuth by sublimation or in a variety of chemical ways. Several isotopes are known and all are of short half-life. The longest lived is ^{210}Po with a half-life of 138.4 days. The study of polonium chemistry is rendered quite difficult by the intense α radiation which causes damage to solutions and solids, evolves much heat, and makes necessary special handling techniques for protection of the chemist.

21-4. The Structures of Elemental Sulfur

In each of the three phases, solid, liquid and gas, the structural relationships of sulfur are complex. Despite a great deal of work there are still many uncertainties and contradictions to be found in the literature. We shall deal here only with the more important and definite facts.

Two crystalline modifications of sulfur are most common. One is the rhombic form which is stable at room temperature and the other is the monoclinic form which becomes the stable form at 95.6°C. The enthalpy of this transition is small and the process is slow. It is therefore possible by rapid heating to take rhombic sulfur up to its melting point, 112.8°C.

Monoclinic sulfur has a true melting point of 119°C., but is often observed to melt a few degrees lower due to breakdown of the S_8 molecules. Both rhombic and monoclinic sulfur contain S_8 cyclic molecules, the structure of which, as found in the rhombic form, is shown in Figure 21-1. Both forms

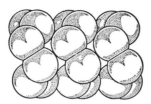

Fig. 21-1.   The structure of rhombic sulfur, in which layers of ring S_8 molecules are stacked together.

show a high solubility in organic solvents, particularly carbon disulfide. Molecular weight measurement on such solutions show that the S_8 rings persist in the solutions at ordinary temperatures.

A third crystalline modification of sulfur, called S_ρ or Engel's sulfur, can be obtained by pouring an $Na_2S_2O_3$ solution into concentrated hydrochloric acid at 0°C. and extracting with toluene, from which it crystallizes in a short time. The hexagonal crystals are not very stable, reverting to a mixture of plastic and rhombic sulfur over several hours. The crystals contain S_6 rings, which are puckered with a chair configuration. The S—S bond distance is 2.06 ± 0.02 A., identical within experimental error with that found in the S_8 ring in rhombic sulfur. The conversion to plastic and rhombic sulfur must proceed by opening and partial fragmentation of these S_6 rings to form chains and S_8 rings.

Plastic or amorphous sulfur is obtained by quenching liquid sulfur heated to 160°C. or more, for example, by pouring it into water. This material can be drawn into fibers of considerable tensile strength, and X-ray studies have shown that the fibers contain helical chains of sulfur atoms with eight sulfur atoms per cycle of the helix. Amorphous sulfur can be made in other ways, but in all cases it is insoluble in organic solvents and slowly reverts to the crystalline form.

Liquid sulfur has been the subject of much informative study. At its melting point and a little above, liquid sulfur is yellow, transparent, and mobile. Above 159°C., however, it rapidly turns brown; it becomes increasingly viscous as the temperature is further raised until at about 200°C. the viscosity again begins to fall with increasing temperature. At its boiling point of 444.60°C. it is again a rather mobile liquid. These viscosity changes as well as the temperature variation of the specific heat are shown in Figure 21-2. These facts are explained in the following way according

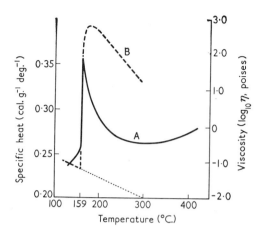

Fig. 21-2. Specific heat (A) and viscosity (B) of liquid sulfur. (Reprinted with permission from G. Gee, *Sci. Progr.*, **1955**, 193.)

to current views. The S_8 rings which originate in the crystalline solid become unstable as the temperature is raised. It has been postulated that six- and four-membered rings may form in equilibrium with the eight-membered rings, but this is not certain. Of prime importance, however, is the formation of open chains by homolytic fission of S—S bonds in the S_8 rings. Such chains are free radicals, actually diradicals, and they in turn will attack other rings and chains so that at any temperature an equilibrium between rings and chains of many lengths will eventually be set up. Paramagnetic resonance studies have definitely established the presence of the radical ends of these chains in molten sulfur. Their concentration is about 6×10^{-3} mole/liter at 300°C. It is presumed that the chains reach their greatest average length at about 200°C. where the viscosity is highest. The quantitative behavior of the system is sensitive to certain impurities, such as iodine, which can stabilize chain ends, for example, by formation of S—I bonds. In the formation of polymers, practically every S—S bond of an S_8 ring broken is replaced by an S—S bond in a linear polymer and the over-all heat of the polymerization is thus expected to be close to zero. An enthalpy of 3.2 kcal./mole of S_8 converted to polymer has been found at the critical polymerization temperature (159°C.). Figure 21-3 shows the approximate composition of liquid sulfur from its melting to its boiling point according to the most recent data.

Sulfur vapor is also known to contain various species in a temperature-dependent equilibrium. Those believed to be of greatest importance are S_8, S_6, S_4, and S_2, but except for the first and the last this is not absolutely certain nor are the structures of the intermediate ones known. Assuming, however, that these are the only species present, the vapor density data require that at 450°C. and 500 mm. pressure, for example, the

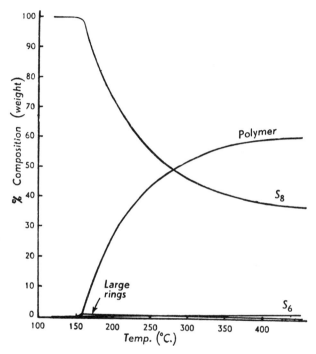

Fig. 21-3. Approximate composition of liquid sulfur showing abundances of the various species. (Reprinted with permission from G. Gee, *Sci. Progr.*, **1955**, 193.)

amounts of these species are: S_8, 54%; S_6, 37%; S_4, 5%; S_2, 4%. As the temperature is raised and/or the pressure lowered, the proportion of S_2 rises rapidly, and at very high temperatures dissociation of S_2 into atoms becomes important. If sulfur vapor at a temperature and pressure such that it contains largely S_2 is rapidly quenched in liquid nitrogen ($-193°C.$) a purple, paramagnetic solid is obtained which is unstable above $-80°C$. Since there is evidence that the S_2 molecule, like the O_2 molecule, is paramagnetic with two unpaired electrons, it has been assumed that this purple substance is made up of S_2 molecules.

21-5. The Structures of Elemental Selenium, Tellurium, and Polonium

Selenium also exists in a variety of forms, but these have been less thoroughly studied than those of sulfur, to which they apparently bear some analogies though there are some distinct differences. There are two crystalline modifications, one rhombic and one monoclinic, both of which almost certainly contain Se_8 rings since they dissolve rather freely in carbon disulfide to give solutions in which the solute molecules have the molecular weight of Se_8. Both of these forms are obtained upon evaporation of the dark red carbon disulfide solutions below about 72°C. Both are thermodynamically unstable toward a gray crystalline modification which may be obtained by (a) heating the rhombic or monoclinic forms, (b) evaporating carbon disulfide solutions above about 75°C., or (c) by slow cooling of molten selenium (m.p. 220.0°C.). This gray form, which has no analog with sulfur, contains infinite chains of selenium atoms spiraling around axes parallel to one of the crystal axes. Although there are evidently fairly strong single bonds between adjacent atoms in each chain, there is evidently weak interaction of a metallic nature between the neighboring atoms of different chains, and gray selenium is metallic in appearance and to some extent in some of its properties. It is not comparable with most true metals in its electrical conductivity in the dark, but it is markedly photoconductive.

Only one allotropic form of tellurium is definitely known, and this is silvery white, semimetallic, and isomorphous with the gray form of selenium. Like the latter it is virtually insoluble in all liquids except those with which it reacts. Gray selenium and tellurium form a continuous range of solid solutions which appear to contain chains in which Se and Te atoms alternate more or less randomly.

In selenium and tellurium vapors the concentration of paramagnetic Se_2 and Te_2 molecules and Se and Te atoms is evidently much higher under comparable conditions of temperature and pressure than that for sulfur, indicating decreased tendency toward catenation.

The trend toward greater metallic character in the group VI elements is complete at polonium. Whereas sulfur is a true insulator (specific resistivity in $\mu\Omega$-cm. $= 2 \times 10^{23}$), selenium (sp. res., 2×10^{11}) and tellurium (sp. res. 2×10^5) are intermediate in their electrical conductivities and the temperature coefficient of resistivity in all three cases is negative, which is usually considered characteristic of nonmetals, polonium in each of its two allotropes has a resistivity typical of true metals ($\sim 43\mu\Omega$-cm.) and a positive temperature coefficient. The low temperature allotrope, which is stable up to about 100°C., has a cubic structure, and the high temperature form is rhombohedral. In both forms, the coordination number is six.

21-6. Reactions of the Elements

Sulfur, selenium, and tellurium are moderately reactive substances. They burn in air, on heating, to give dioxides, SO_2, SeO_2 and TeO_2. They combine directly with the halogens and with numerous metals and non-metals. Sulfur, selenium, and tellurium are not attacked by nonoxidizing acids, but polonium will dissolve in sulfuric acid, hydrofluoric acid, hydrochloric acid, and concentrated nitric acid, which is in accord with the metallic character of Po. S, Se, and Te are attacked on heating with concentrated sulfuric acid or nitric acid. Sulfur dissolves in fuming sulfuric acid giving yellow to blue solutions which contain as yet unidentified paramagnetic species. Sulfur and selenium and, to a limited extent, tellurium dissolve in aqueous solutions of their anions, S^{2-}, Se^{2-}, and Te^{2-}, to form polyanions, S_n^{2-}, Se_n^{2-}, and Te_n^{2-}.

Sulfur and selenium react with many organic molecules. For example, saturated hydrocarbons are dehydrogenated. The reaction of sulfur with olefins is of enormous technical importance, for it results in the vulcanization (formation of sulfur bridges between chains) of natural and syn-

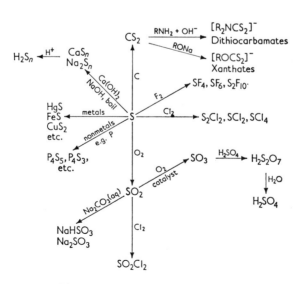

Fig. 21-4. Some reactions of sulfur.

thetic rubbers. Some important reactions of sulfur, which are also on the whole typical of selenium and tellurium, are shown in Figure 21-4.

BINARY COMPOUNDS

21-7. Hydrides

The simple hydrides, MH_2, are all gases with revolting odors and are extremely poisonous. Those of S, Se, and Te are most readily obtained by the action of acids on metal sulfides, selenides, and tellurides. H_2Po has been prepared only in trace quantities by dissolving magnesium foil plated with Po in $0.2N$ HCl. The thermal stability and bond strengths decrease rapidly from H_2S to H_2Po; in fact all but H_2S appear to be thermodynamically unstable with respect to their constituent elements. All behave as very weak acids in aqueous solution and the dissociation constants increase with increasing atomic number. The general reactivity of the simple hydrides also increases in the same direction. Only hydrogen sulfide is of general importance. It dissolves in water to give a solution about $0.1M$ under 1 atm. pressure. Its dissociation equilibria in water are:

$$H_2S + H_2O = H_3O^+ + HS^- \qquad K = 1 \times 10^{-7}$$
$$HS^- + H_2O = H_3O^+ + S^{2-} \qquad K = \sim 10^{-14}$$

Only for sulfur are higher hydrides, called *sulfanes*, known. The lower members, H_2S_2, through H_2S_6 have been isolated in a pure state, whereas higher members are so far known only in mixtures. All of the sulfanes are yellow liquids whose viscosities increase with chain length. They may be prepared in large quantities by reactions such as:

$$Na_2S_n(aq) + 2HCl(aq) \rightarrow 2NaCl(aq) + H_2S_n(l) \ (n = 4\text{--}6)$$
$$S_nCl_2(l) + 2H_2S(l) \rightarrow 2HCl(g) + H_2S_{n+2}(l)$$
$$S_nCl_2(l) + 2H_2S_2(l) \rightarrow 2HCl(g) + H_2S_{n+4}(l)$$

The oils from the first reaction can be cracked and fractionated to give H_2S_2 through H_2S_5 in a pure state, whereas the higher sulfanes are obtained from the other reactions. Although the sulfanes are all thermodynamically unstable with respect to the reaction

$$H_2S_n(l) = H_2S(g) + (n - 1)S(s)$$

these reactions are sufficiently slow that the compounds can be preserved for considerable periods of time. The sulfanes are, however, quite reactive.

21-8. Metal Chalconides

Most metallic elements react directly with S, Se, Te, and, so far as is known, Po. Often they react very readily, mercury, for example, reacting with sulfur at room temperature. Binary compounds of great variety and complexity of structure can be obtained. The nature of the products usually also depends on the ratios of reactants, temperature of reaction, and other conditions. Many elements form several compounds and sometimes long series of compounds with a given chalconide. We will give here only the briefest account of some of the most important types and we shall also, for the most part, deal only with the sulfides. These are best known and the selenides and tellurides are very often quite similar.

Ionic Sulfides. Only the more electropositive elements—alkalies and alkaline earths—form sulfides which appear to be mainly ionic. They are the only sulfides which dissolve in water and they crystallize in simple ionic lattices, for example, an antifluorite lattice for the alkali sulfides (and most other chalconides) and a rock salt lattice for the alkaline earth sulfides (and most other chalconides). Of course, the sulfide ions in aqueous solutions of these sulfides are extensively hydrolyzed:

$$S^{2-} + H_2O = SH^- + OH^- \qquad K = \sim 1$$

Aqueous solutions of polysulfides can be obtained by boiling solutions of the sulfides with sulfur. From such solutions, and also in some other ways,

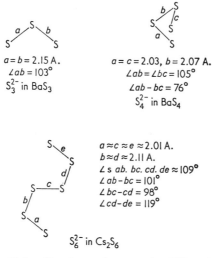

$a = b = 2.15$ A.
$\angle ab = 103°$
S_3^{2-} in BaS_3

$a = c = 2.03, b = 2.07$ A.
$\angle ab = \angle bc = 105°$
$\angle ab - bc = 76°$
S_4^{2-} in BaS_4

$a \approx c \approx e \approx 2.01$ A.
$b \approx d \approx 2.11$ A.
$\angle s\ ab.\ bc.\ cd.\ de \approx 109°$
$\angle ab - bc = 101°$
$\angle bc - cd = 98°$
$\angle cd - de = 119°$
S_6^{2-} in Cs_2S_6

Fig. 21-5. Structures of some polysulfide anions.

crystalline polysulfides may be obtained. Three polysulfides in which the existence and structure of the poly anion has been demonstrated are Cs_2S_6, BaS_3, and BaS_4. Their structures are shown in Figure 21-5.

Other Metallic Sulfides. Most metal sulfides cannot be well described by assuming them to be mainly ionic. They frequently have peculiar stoichiometries, are often nonstoichiometric phases rather than compounds in a classical sense, are often polymorphic, and many of them are alloy-like or semimetallic in behavior. Indeed, study and elucidation of the structure and bonding of heavy metal sulfides appears to be an extremely interesting but relatively neglected field of research. Metal sulfides tend to be much more covalent than metal oxides, with the result that quite often there is only limited and occasionally no stoichiometric analogy between the oxides and the sulfides of a given metal; very often, indeed possibly most of the time when there is a sulfide and an oxide of identical empirical formula, they will have different structures. To illustrate these generalizations, the following examples may be considered.

Several transition metal sulfides, for example, FeS, CoS, and NiS, adopt a structure called the nickel arsenide structure, illustrated in Figure 21-6.

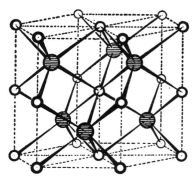

Fig. 21-6.   The structure of NiAs (As atoms shaded). The Ni atom in the center of the diagram is surrounded octahedrally by six As atoms and has also two near Ni neighbors which are coplanar with four of the As atoms. (Reprinted with permission from A. F. Wells, *Structural Inorganic Chemistry*, Clarendon Press, Oxford, 1945, p. 387).

In this structure each metal atom is surrounded octahedrally by six sulfur atoms, but also approached fairly closely by two other metal atoms. These metal–metal distances are 2.60–2.68 A. in FeS, CoS, and NiS, and at such distances there must be a considerable amount of metal–metal bonding, thus accounting for their alloy-like or semimetallic character. Note that such a structure is not in the least likely for a predominantly ionic salt, requiring as it would the close approach of dipositive ions.

Another class of metal sulfides of considerable importance are the disulfides, represented by FeS_2, CoS_2 and a number of others. All of these contain discrete S_2 units with an S—S distance almost exactly equal to that to be expected for an S—S single bond. These assume one of two closely related structures. First there is the pyrite structure named after the polymorph of FeS_2 which exhibits it. This structure may be visualized as a distorted NaCl structure. The Fe atoms occupy Na positions and the S_2 groups are placed with their centers at the Cl positions but turned in such a way that they are not parallel to any of the cube axes. The marcasite structure is very similar but somewhat less regular.

FeS is a good example of a well-characterized nonstoichiometric sulfide. It has long been known that a sample with a Fe:S ratio precisely unity is rarely encountered, and in the older literature such formulas as Fe_6S_7 and $Fe_{11}S_{12}$ have been assigned to it. The iron–sulfur system assumes the nickel arsenide structure over the composition range 50–55.5 atom % sulfur, and, when the S/Fe ratio exceeds unity, some of the iron positions in the lattice are vacant in a random way. Thus the very attempt to assign stoichiometric formulas such as Fe_6S_7 is meaningless. We are dealing not with *one* compound, in the classical sense, but with a *phase* which may be perfect, that is, FeS, or may be deficient in iron. That particular specimen which happens to have the composition Fe_6S_7 is better described as $Fe_{0.858}S$.

An even more extreme example of nonstoichiometry is provided by the Co–Te (and the analogous Ni–Te) system. Here, a phase with the nickel arsenide structure is stable over the entire composition range CoTe to $CoTe_2$. It is possible to pass continuously from the former to the latter by progressive loss of Co atoms from alternate planes (see Fig. 21-6) until, at $CoTe_2$, every other plane of Co atoms present in CoTe has completely vanished.

TABLE 21-1

Nonstoichiometry in a Metal–Sulfur system: Cr–S

Phase (ideal composition)	Structure	Range of stability
CrS	Monoclinic	$CrS_{0.95}$–CrS
Cr_7S_8	Partly disord., trigonal	$Cr_{0.88}S$–$Cr_{0.87}S$
Cr_5S_6	Trigonal	$\sim Cr_{0.85}S$
Cr_3S_4	Monoclinic	$Cr_{0.79}S$–$Cr_{0.76}S$
Cr_2S_3	Trigonal	$\sim Cr_{0.69}S$
Cr_2S_3	Rhombohedral	$\sim Cr_{0.67}S$

An example of a system in which many different phases occur (and each has a small range of existence so that each may be encountered in nonstoichiometric form) is the Cr–S system. The six phases occurring in the composition range $CrS_{0.95}$ to $CrS_{1.5}$ are shown in Table 21-1.

21-9. Other Binary Sulfides

Most nonmetallic or metalloid elements form sulfides. A number of these have been or will be discussed under the respective elements, but a few will be mentioned here. Silicon disulfide (21-I) consists of infinite chains of SiS_4 tetrahedra sharing edges (similar to the structure of BeF_2 and

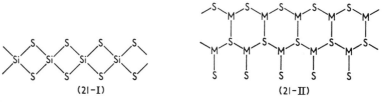

(21-I)   (21-II)

$BeCl_2$). Sb_2S_3 and Bi_2S_3 are isomorphous (21-II), forming infinite bands which are then held together in parallel strips in the crystal by weak, secondary bonds.

Sulfur nitride is obtained by the reaction of sulfur chlorides with ammonia and forms orange-yellow crystals which, though stable in air, are detonatable by shock. The chemistry of N_4S_4 has been extensively studied, and a great variety of other sulfur nitrogen compounds, for example, S_4N_3Cl, $S_4N_4H_4$, etc.) can be obtained from it. N_4S_4 and arsenic sulfide (orpiment), As_4S_4, have the similar unusual finite structures shown in Figure 21-7. Each may be regarded either as a crown shaped ring, similar

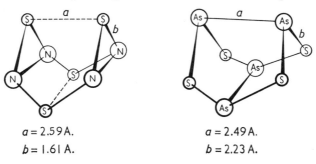

$a = 2.59 A.$ $a = 2.49 A.$
$b = 1.61 A.$ $b = 2.23 A.$

Fig. 21-7. The structures of N_4S_4 and As_4S_4.

to the S_8 ring, or alternatively as an interpenetrating combination of a square and a flattened tetrahedron. The important difference is that in tetrasulfur tetranitride the sulfur atoms form the flattened tetrahedron, whereas in tetrarsenic tetrasulfide the sulfur atoms form the square. The structure of As_4S_4 can be thought of as derived from that of pyramidal As_4 by adding sulfur bridges across four of the edges of the tetrahedron, in the same general way as the structures of the various phosphorus sulfides were rationalized (Chapter 20, page 387). Since nitrogen does not exist as a tetrahedral N_4 molecule, it is perhaps not surprising that its sulfide does not have a structure related thereto. The rather short distance between sulfur atoms not bound to the same nitrogen atom strongly suggests that there is partial S—S bonding and the S—N bond lengths imply that these bonds have an order somewhat higher than one. From the valence bond viewpoint, the molecule may be regarded as a resonance hybrid of the principal canonical forms shown in 21-III. Note that in 21-IIIe, 21-IIIf,

(21-IIIa) (21-IIIb) (21-IIIc) (21-IIId) (21-IIIe)

(21-IIIf) (21-IIIg) (21-IIIh)

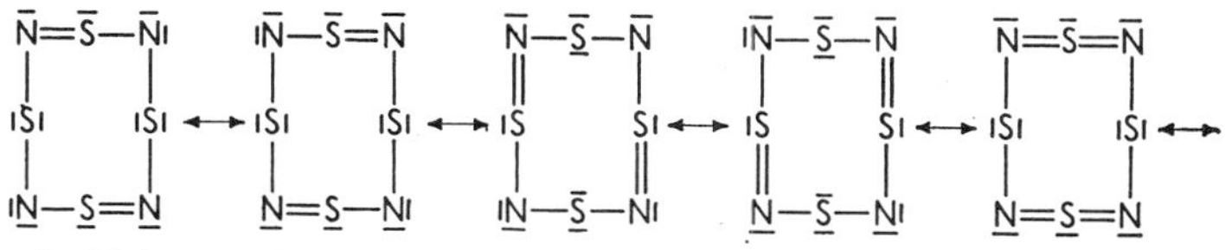

and 21-IIIh sulfur has a decet of electrons, which means that it is assumed to be using a *d* orbital.

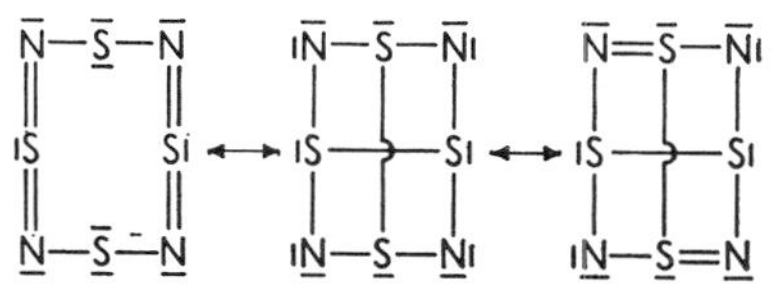

The halides obtained by halogenation of N_4S_4 are believed to have ring structures, and $N_4S_4F_4$ has been shown to have an eight-membered ring of alternating S and N atoms with the fluorine bound to sulfur.

21-10. Halides

The group VI elements form many halides. Those known, along with a few in square braces which are of uncertain existence, are listed in Table 21-2, along with their principal properties. No attempt will be made to discuss all of these compounds in detail. Instead we shall concentrate on a few which are of the greatest interest and importance.

Sulfur Fluorides. The existence of S_2F_2 and SF_2 is at present extremely doubtful. The important fluorides of sulfur are SF_4, SF_6, and

TABLE 21-2

The Group VI Binary Halides[a]

Fluorides	Chlorides	Bromides	Iodides
	Sulfur		
$[S_2F_2]$	S_2Cl_2,[b] m -80, b 138	S_2Br_2,[b] m -46, d 90	
$[SF_2]$	SCl_2, m -78, d 59		
SF_4, m -121, b -40	SCl_4, d -31		
SF_6, s -65, m -51			
S_2F_{10}, m -55, b 29			
	Selenium		
	Se_2Cl_2	Se_2Br_2, d in vapor	
	$SeCl_2$, d in vapor	$SeBr_2$, d in vapor	
SeF_4, m -10, b 106	$SeCl_4$, s 191	$SeBr_4$, exists only as solid	
SeF_6, s -47, m -35			
	Tellurium		
	$TeCl_2$, m 208, b 327	$TeBr_2$, m 210, b 339	
TeF_4, m 130	$TeCl_4$, m 225, b 390	$TeBr_4$, m 380, b 414	TeI_4, m 259,[c]
		(d in vapor)	d 100
TeF_6, s -39, m -38			
Te_2F_{10}, m -34, b 53			

[a] m = melts; b = boils; s = sublimes; d = decomposes; all temperatures given in °C.
[b] Also the dichlorosulfanes, S_nCl_2, $2 < n < 100(?)$, and dibromosulfanes, S_nBr_2, $n > 2$.
[c] Melting point obtained in a sealed tube to prevent decomposition: $TeI_4 = Te + 2I_2$.

S_2F_{10}. The direct fluorination of sulfur yields principally SF_6 and only traces of the other two. To date there is no other known source of S_2F_{10}. Sulfur tetrafluoride, SF_4, can be made in various other ways, of which the best is by reaction of SCl_2 with NaF in acetonitrile at 70–80°C. SF_4 is an extremely reactive substance, instantly hydrolyzed by water to SO_2 and HF, but its fluorinating action is quite selective. It will convert C=O and P=O groups smoothly to CF_2 and PF_2 and COOH and P(O)OH groups to CF_3 and PF_3 groups without attack on most other functional or reactive groups which may be present. It is also quite useful for converting metal oxides to fluorides which are (usually) in the same oxidation state. The structure of SF_4 is that of a trigonal bipyramid with one equatorial position occupied by a lone pair (see Chapter 15, page 308).

Aryl-substituted fluorides can be readily obtained by the reaction

$$(C_6H_5)_2S_2 + 6AgF_2 = 2C_6H_5SF_3 + 6AgF$$

which is carried out in trichloro- or trifluoromethane. The aryl sulfur trifluorides are more convenient laboratory fluorinating agents than SF_4 in that they do not require pressure above atmospheric.

Sulfur hexafluoride has almost the properties of an inert gas. It can be induced to react with other substances only under the most extreme conditions. Thus SF_6 resists molten KOH, steam at 500°C., and oxygen even in an electric discharge. It will, however, react with molten sodium at 250°C., with H_2 when sparked, and with some red hot metals. Because of its chemical inertness, high dielectric strength, and molecular weight, it is used as a gaseous insulator in high voltage generators and other electrical equipment.

The only well-established mixed halide of a group VI element can be regarded as a substituted sulfur hexafluoride, namely, SF_5Cl, a colorless gas, b.p. $-21°C$. This can be formed by reaction of S_2F_{10} with Cl_2 at 200–350°C., but is produced more effectively by the reaction of SF_4 and ClF at about 350°C. It is not nearly so inert as SF_6, being rapidly hydrolyzed by alkalies, but it is inert to acids. Another substituted sulfur hexafluoride is CF_3SF_5, which is quite unreactive.

All of these compounds are known or may be presumed to have octahedrally bonded sulfur. In SF_6 it is known that the S—F bonds are about 0.2 A. shorter than expected for S—F single bonds. Their low reactivity, particularly toward hydrolysis, which contrasts with the very high reactivity of SF_4, is presumably due to a combination of factors including high S—F bond strength and the facts that sulfur is both coordinately saturated and sterically hindered, augmented in the case of SF_6 by the lack of polarity of the molecule. The low reactivity is due more to kinetic factors than to thermodynamic stability, since the reaction of SF_6 with H_2O to give SO_3 and HF would be decidedly favorable ($\Delta F = -110$ kcal./mole), and the average bond energy in SF_4, 78 kcal./mole, is slightly higher than that of SF_6.

Disulfur decafluoride is extremely poisonous (the reason for which is not clear) being similar in its physiological action to phosgene. It is not dissolved or hydrolyzed by water or alkalies and is not generally very reactive. Its structure is such that each sulfur atom is surrounded octahedrally by five fluorine atoms and the other sulfur atom. The S—S bond is unusually long, 2.21 A., as compared to about 2.08 A. expected for a single bond, whereas the S—F bonds are, as in SF_6, about 0.2 A. shorter than anticipated for an S—F single bond. At room temperature it shows scarcely any chemical reactivity, though it will oxidize the iodide in an acetone solution of KI.

Selenium and Tellurium Fluorides. SeF_4 and TeF_4 are, like SF_4, highly reactive fluorinating agents, but their chemistry is not known in detail as yet. Selenium and tellurium hexafluorides are considerably more reactive than SF_6. In fact TeF_6 is fully hydrolyzed on contact with water for 24 hours. It is also interesting that TeF_6 has weak Lewis acidity, combining with F^- in presence of large cations to form, presumably, TeF_7^- or TeF_8^{2-}, and with trialkyl amines to form adducts of the formula $(R_3N)_2$ TeF_6. Ditellurium decafluoride is somewhat more reactive than its sulfur analog. There is as yet no report of the preparation of Se_2F_{10}, but it is presumably capable of existence.

Sulfur Chlorides. The direct action of chlorine on molten sulfur gives S_2Cl_2, an orange liquid of revolting smell. It is readily hydrolyzed to give SO_2, S, and HCl. It is used as a solvent for sulfur (giving dichlorosulfanes up to about $S_{100}Cl_2$), in the vulcanization of rubber, and occasionally as a chlorinating agent. In the vapor it has been shown to have a Cl—S—S—Cl structure, with S—S = 2.05 A., S—Cl = 1.99 A., <SSCl = 103°, and twisted out of plane in the same way as is hydrogen peroxide. The action of excess chlorine on S_2Cl_2 produces the red liquid, SCl_2, which is unstable with respect to dissociation back into S_2Cl_2 and chlorine. The tetrachloride, formed by the action of liquid chlorine on S_2Cl_2, forms yellow crystals which decompose dissociatively above −31°C.

Selenium and Tellurium Halides. These compounds are generally more stable than those of sulfur. They also differ in showing Lewis acidity, which is particularly manifested in their forming complex halides such as $K[SeF_5]$, $H_2[SeBr_6]$, $K_2[SeCl_6]$, $Cs_2[TeI_6]$ on heating the halide with hydrogen or alkali halides.

Polonium Halides. Polonium halides are similar to those of tellurium, being volatile above 150°C. and soluble in organic solvents. They are readily hydrolyzed and form complexes, for example, $Na_2[PoX_6]$, isomorphous with those of tellurium. There is tracer evidence for the existence of a volatile polonium fluoride. The metal is also soluble in hydrofluoric acid, and complex fluorides presumably exist.

21-11. Oxides

The following oxides of the group VI elements are the principal ones:

S_2O			
SO_2	SeO_2	TeO_2	$PoO_2[PoO(OH)_2]$
SO_3	SeO_3	TeO_3	

We shall not discuss the lower oxide of sulfur at any length. It is produced when a glow discharge is passed through SO_2 and in other ways, and was for several decades thought to be SO. Recent studies have shown rather conclusively that gases of this composition are equimolar mixtures of S_2O and

SO_2. S_2O is believed to have the structure SSO. It is unstable at ordinary temperatures.

The dioxides are obtained by burning the elements in air, though small amounts of SO_3 also form in the burning of sulfur. Sulfur dioxide is also produced when many sulfides are heated in air. Selenium and tellurium dioxides are also obtained by treating the metals with hot nitric acid to form H_2SeO_3 and $2TeO_2 \cdot HNO_3$, respectively, and then heating these to drive off water or nitric acid.

The dioxides differ considerably in structures. SO_2 is a gas (b.p. $-10°C.$), SeO_2 is a white volatile solid (normal sublimation temperature 315 °C.) and TeO_2 is a nonvolatile white solid. Gaseous SO_2 and SeO_2 are bent symmetrical molecules, in both cases the short S—O and Se—O bond distances imply that there is considerable multiple bonding. There is presumably $p\pi-p\pi$ bonding as indicated in the resonance structures 21-IVa and 21-IVb

(21-IVa)   (21-IVb)

as well as $p\pi-d\pi$ bonding due to the overlap of filled $p\pi$ orbitals of oxygen with vacant $d\pi$ orbitals of sulfur. SO_2 solidifies to form a molecular lattice as far as is known, but SeO_2 forms infinite chains of the type shown in Figure 21-8. As the values of the angles imply, these chains are not planar.

$$a = b = c = 1.78 \text{ A.}$$
$$\angle ab = 125°$$
$$\angle bc = 90°$$
$$\angle bd = \angle cd = 98°$$

Fig. 21-8.   Section of infinite chain of SeO_2.

TeO_2 crystallizes in two apparently ionic crystalline forms, the usual one having the rutile structure (page 46). PoO_2 also seems to exist in two ionic crystalline forms.

SO_2 has many uses, the chief one being in sulfuric acid production. It is also often used as a reducing agent, though it is not a powerful one except in basic solution where sulfite ion is formed. A fair amount of work has been done using liquid SO_2 as a nonaqueous solvent. Although it is not a good ionizing solvent (dielectric constant ≈ 12), it dissolves many substances. Self-ionization has been postulated:

$$2SO_2 = SO^{2+} + SO_3{}^{2-}$$

There is little direct evidence for this, and recent work suggests that self-ionization, if it occurs at all, plays no important role in the solvent properties of SO_2.

Of the trioxides, only sulfur trioxide is of importance. Tellurium trioxide, which can be obtained by dehydration of telluric acid, $Te(OH)_6$ reacts but slowly with water to regenerate the acid though it dissolves readily in strong base to give tellurate ions. Selenium trioxide has never been obtained in a pure state. Dehydration of selenic acid is always accompanied by some loss of oxygen, thus giving a mixture of the di- and trioxides. It is, however, quite hygroscopic, reacting readily with water to regenerate selenic acid.

Sulfur trioxide is obtained by reaction of sulfur dioxide with molecular oxygen, a reaction which is thermodynamically very favorable but extremely slow in the absence of catalysts. Platinum sponge, V_2O_5, and NO serve as catalysts under various conditions. SO_3 reacts vigorously with water to form sulfuric acid. Commercially, for practical reasons, SO_3 is absorbed in concentrated sulfuric acid, to give oleum (which is mainly pyrosulfuric acid, $H_2S_2O_7$) which is then diluted. SO_3 is also used as such for preparing sulfonated oils and alkylaryl sulfonate detergents. It is also a powerful oxidizing agent. The free molecule, as it occurs in the gas phase, has a planar, triangular structure which may be considered to be a resonance hybrid involving $p\pi$–$p\pi$ S—O bonding, as in 21-V, with additional π bonding via overlap of

(21-Va)   (21-Vb)   (21-Vc)

filled oxygen $p\pi$ orbitals with empty sulfur $d\pi$ orbitals, in order to account for the very short S—O distance of 1.43 A. In view of this affinity of S in SO_3 for electrons, it is not surprising that SO_3 functions as a fairly strong Lewis acid toward those bases which it does not preferentially oxidize.

(21-VI)

From a structural viewpoint, solid SO_3 is complex. At least three well-defined phases are known. There is first γ-SO_3, formed by condensation of vapors at $-80°C$. or below. This ice-like solid (m.p. 16.8°C.) contains cyclic trimers with structure 21-VI.

A more stable, asbestos-like phase, β-SO_3, has infinite helical chains of linked SO_4 tetrahedra (21-VII), and the most stable form, α-SO_3, which

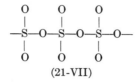

(21-VII)

also has an asbestos-like appearance, presumably has similar chains cross-linked into layers.

Liquid γ-SO_3 (b.p. 44.8°C), which is a monomer-trimer mixture, can be stabilized by the addition of boric acid. In the pure state it is readily polymerized by traces of water.

OXY ACIDS

21-12. General Remarks

S, Se, and Te form oxy acids. Those of sulfur are by far the most important and the most numerous. Some of the acids are not actually known as such, but like phosphorus oxy acids occur only in the form of their anions and salts. In Table 21-3 the various oxy acids of sulfur are grouped according to structural type. This classification is to some extent arbitrary, but it corresponds with the order in which we shall discuss these acids in the following sections. None of the oxy acids of sulfur in which there are S—S bonds have any known Se or Te analogs. With regard to a point of nomenclature, as is usual, salts of acids ending in -ous have names ending in -ite, while those of acids ending in -ic have names ending in -ate.

21-13. Sulfurous Acid

SO_2 is quite soluble in water; such solutions, which possess acidic properties, have long been referred to as solutions of sulfurous acid, H_2SO_3. Modern physical methods of study have shown, however, that H_2SO_3 is either not present or present only in infinitesimal quantities in such solutions. The so-called hydrate, $H_2SO_3\cdot\sim6H_2O$, which is equivalent to

TABLE 21-3

Principal Oxy Acids of Sulfur

Formula	Structure[b]	Name
	Acids Containing One Sulfur Atom	
H_2SO_3[a]	SO_3^{2-} (in sulfites)	Sulfurous
H_2SO_4	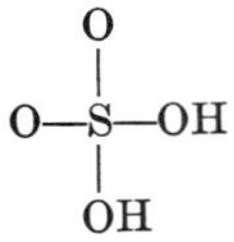 $O-\underset{\underset{OH}{\vert}}{\overset{\overset{O}{\vert}}{S}}-OH$	Sulfuric
	Acids Containing Two Sulfur Atoms	
$H_2S_2O_3$	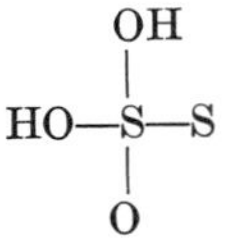 $HO-\underset{\underset{O}{\vert}}{\overset{\overset{OH}{\vert}}{S}}-S$	Thiosulfuric
$H_2S_2O_4$[a]	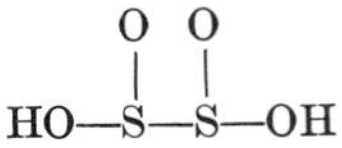 $HO-\overset{\overset{O}{\vert}}{S}-\overset{\overset{O}{\vert}}{S}-OH$	Dithionous
$H_2S_2O_5$[a]	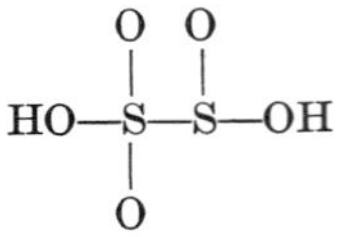 $HO-\overset{\overset{O}{\vert}}{S}-\underset{\underset{O}{\vert}}{\overset{\overset{O}{\vert}}{S}}-OH$	Pyrosulfurous
$H_2S_2O_6$	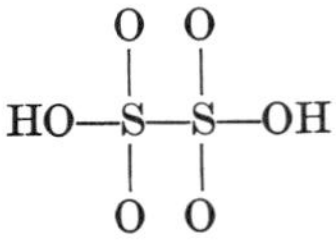 $HO-\underset{\underset{O}{\vert}}{\overset{\overset{O}{\vert}}{S}}-\underset{\underset{O}{\vert}}{\overset{\overset{O}{\vert}}{S}}-OH$	Dithionic
$H_2S_2O_7$	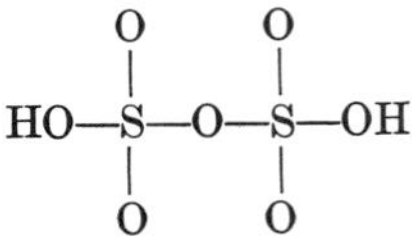 $HO-\underset{\underset{O}{\vert}}{\overset{\overset{O}{\vert}}{S}}-O-\underset{\underset{O}{\vert}}{\overset{\overset{O}{\vert}}{S}}-OH$	Pyrosulfuric
	Acids Containing Three or More Sulfur Atoms	
$H_2S_nO_6$	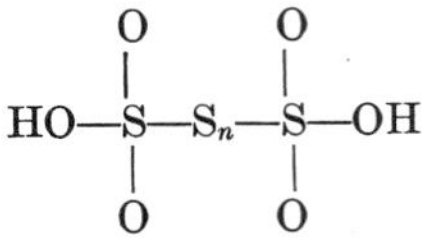 $HO-\underset{\underset{O}{\vert}}{\overset{\overset{O}{\vert}}{S}}-S_n-\underset{\underset{O}{\vert}}{\overset{\overset{O}{\vert}}{S}}-OH$	Polythionic
	Peroxy Acids	
H_2SO_5	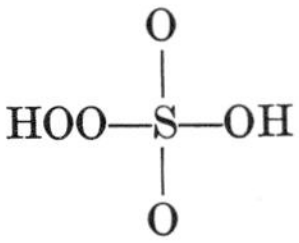 $HOO-\underset{\underset{O}{\vert}}{\overset{\overset{O}{\vert}}{S}}-OH$	Peroxymonosulfuric
$H_2S_2O_8$	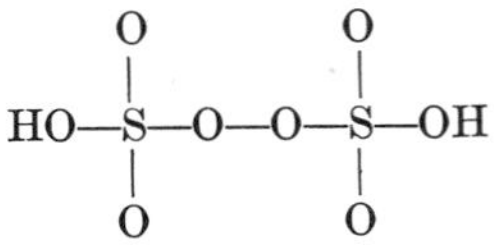 $HO-\underset{\underset{O}{\vert}}{\overset{\overset{O}{\vert}}{S}}-O-O-\underset{\underset{O}{\vert}}{\overset{\overset{O}{\vert}}{S}}-OH$	Peroxydisulfuric

[a] Free acid unknown.
[b] In most cases the structure given is inferred from the structure of anions in salts of the acid.

$SO_2 \cdot \sim 7H_2O$, contains no H_2SO_3 but is a clathrate of the same type as other gas hydrates (Chapter 6, page 148). The equilibria in aqueous solutions of SO_2 are best represented as

$$SO_2 + xH_2O = SO_2 \cdot xH_2O \text{ (hydrated } SO_2)$$
$$[SO_2 \cdot xH_2O = H_2SO_3 \qquad K \langle\langle\langle 1]$$
$$SO_2 \cdot xH_2O = HSO_3^-(aq) + H_3O^+ + (x - 2)H_2O$$

and the first acid dissociation constant for "sulfurous acid" is properly defined as follows:

$$K_1 = \frac{[HSO_3^-][H^+]}{[\text{Total dissolved } SO_2] - [HSO_3^-] - [SO_3^{2-}]} = 1.3 \times 10^{-2}$$

Although sulfurous acid itself evidently does not exist, two series of salts, the bisulfites containing HSO_3^-, and the sulfites containing SO_3^{2-}, are well known. There is unequivocal evidence that the SO_3^{2-} ion exists as such in crystals; it appears that in dilute solution the principal ion is $HOSO_2^-$, whereas at higher concentrations HSO_3^- and $S_2O_5^{2-}$ are the major species. X-ray study of Na_2SO_3 has shown that the SO_3^{2-} ion is pyramidal, as expected from the consideration in Chapter 15.

Only the alkali sulfites and bisulfites are commonly encountered; these are water soluble. On heating solid bisulfites or on passing SO_2 into their aqueous solutions, one obtains pyrosulfites, which are of some structural interest:

$$2MHSO_3 \overset{\text{heat}}{\rightleftharpoons} M_2S_2O_5 + H_2O$$
$$HSO_3^-(aq) + SO_2 = HS_2O_5^-(aq)$$

Whereas pyroacids, for example, pyrosulfuric $H_2S_2O_7$ to be discussed below, usually have oxygen bridges, pyrosulfite ion has a S—S bond and hence an unsymmetrical structure, O_2S—SO_3. Some important reactions of sulfites are shown in Figure 21-9.

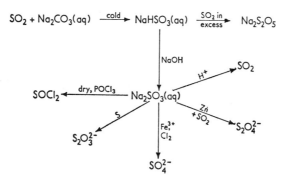

Fig. 21-9. Some reactions of sulfites.

Solutions of SO_2 and of sulfites possess reducing properties and are often used as reducing agents.

$$SO_2 \cdot xH_2O = SO_4^{2-} + 4H^+ + (x - 2)H_2O + 2e \qquad E^0 = -0.17 \text{ v.}$$
$$SO_3^{2-} + 2OH^- = SO_4^{2-} + H_2O + 2e \qquad E^0 = 0.93 \text{ v.}$$

The bisulfite ion appears to exist in the tautomeric forms of 21-VIII in

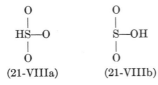

(21-VIIIa)   (21-VIIIb)

solution; tautomeric forms of diesters of sulfurous acids are well known (21-IX) and can be isolated.

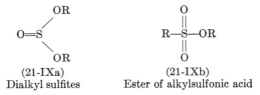

(21-IXa)   (21-IXb)
Dialkyl sulfites   Ester of alkylsulfonic acid

21-14. Selenous and Tellurous Acids

SeO_2 dissolves readily in water to give solutions which do contain selenous acid with the $OSe(OH)_2$ structure. Moreover, the solid acid, though efflorescent, can be isolated and X-ray studies have shown the presence of layers of SeO_3 groups connected by hydrogen bonds. Selenous acid forms two series of salts, biselenites and selenites. The acid and its salts are moderately strong oxidizing agents

$$H_2SeO_3 + 4H^+ + 4e = Se + 3H_2O \qquad E^0 = 0.74 \text{ v.}$$

and will oxidize SO_2, HI, H_2S, etc.

TeO_2 is virtually insoluble in water, giving very dilute solutions ($\sim 10^{-5}M$) called solutions of tellurous acid, though there is no information as to the species actually present, and no hydrated form of TeO_2 has been isolated. The dioxide does, however, dissolve in strong bases to give solutions of tellurites, bitellurites and various polytellurites which may be isolated as solids.

14-15. Sulfuric Acid

This is probably the most widely used and most important sulfur compound. It is prepared on an enormous scale by the lead chamber and contact processes. In the former, SO_2 oxidation is catalyzed by oxides of nitrogen (by intermediate formation of nitrosyl sulfuric acid, $HOSO_2ONO$); in the latter, heterogeneous catalysts such as platinum are used for the oxidation. Pure sulfuric acid, H_2SO_4, is a colorless liquid freezing at 10.37°C. The phase diagram of the H_2SO_4–H_2O system is rather complicated. A number of eutectic hydrates such as $H_2SO_4 \cdot H_2O$ (m.p. 8.5°C.) and $H_2SO_4 \cdot 2H_2O$ (m.p. -38°C.) occur. The presence of H_3O^+ ions in some of these has been demonstrated.

Sulfuric acid is a strong dibasic acid. In dilute aqueous solution the first dissociation is essentially complete, and the second dissociation constant has a value of $\sim 10^{-2}$. Sulfates and acid sulfates of virtually all electropositive elements are known. Most are soluble in water except for the sulfates of the Ca–Ra group and a few other divalent cations.

When acid sulfate salts are heated, water is first liberated, resulting in the formation of pyrosulfate ions:

$$2MHSO_4 \overset{heat}{\rightleftharpoons} M_2S_2O_7 + H_2O$$

Further heating drives off SO_3 to leave the sulfate. The pyrosulfate ion is derived from pyrosulfuric acid (oleum, fuming sulfuric acid), which is formed on passing a mole of SO_3 into a mole of H_2SO_4. The pyrosulfate ion is immediately hydrolyzed by water to two moles of sulfate. X-ray study of pyrosulfate salts has shown the structure to be O_3S—O—SO_3, with approximately tetrahedral bond angles about each sulfur atom. The sulfate and bisulfate ions themselves are, of course, tetrahedral.

Sulfuric acid is not a very strong oxidizing agent, although the concentrated (98%) acid has some oxidizing properties. Concentrated sulfuric acid usually reacts with organic matter vigorously. Most commonly it reacts so as to remove the elements of water; thus it chars most hydrocarbons. When diluted it sometimes sulfonates organic substances and often serves mainly as a reaction medium.

Pure sulfuric acid contains a number of species in equilibrium,

$$2H_2SO_4 = H_2O + H_2S_2O_7$$
$$H_2SO_4 + H_2O = H_3O^+ + HSO_4^-$$
$$H_2SO_4 + H_2S_2O_7 = H_3SO_4^+ + HS_2O_7^-$$
$$2H_2SO_4 = H_3SO_4^+ + HSO_4^-$$

A great many substances dissolve in the pure acid, often undergoing protonation, and the species present and the equilibria have been studied in many cases. Pure sulfuric acid is evidently a useful ionizing solvent in some instances, but the interpretation of cryoscopic data is often complicated.

No polysulfuric acids higher than the pyro acid are known.

21-16. Selenic and Telluric Acids

The strong oxidation of selenites or fusion of selenium with potassium nitrate gives selenic acid (or its salts). The free acid forms colorless crystals, m.p. 57°C. It is very similar to sulfuric acid in its formula, H_2SeO_4, formation of hydrates, and acid strength and in the properties of its salts, most of which are isomorphous with the corresponding sulfates and bisulfates. It differs mainly in being less stable. It evolves oxygen on heating above about 200°C. and is a strong, though usually not kinetically fast, oxidizing agent:

$$SeO_4^{2-} + 4H^+ + 2e = H_2SeO_3 + H_2O \qquad E^0 = 1.15 \text{ v.}$$

Pyroselenates exist and appear to contain the ion $[O_3SeOSeO_3]^{2-}$ in crystals, but in solution the species appears to be $[SeO_3(OH)]^-$.

Telluric acid is quite different from sulfuric and selenic acids. Its formula is $Te(OH)_6$, and X-ray studies have shown that octahedral molecules of this composition exist in the crystals. There is no evidence for the existence of $HTeO_4^-$ or TeO_4^{2-} ions under any conditions.

The acid or its salts may be prepared by oxidation of tellurium or TeO_2 by H_2O_2, Na_2O_2, CrO_3, or other powerful oxidizing agents. It is a moderately strong, but, like selenic acid, kinetically slow, oxidizing agent ($E^0 = 1.02$ v.). It is a very weak dibasic acid with $K_1 \approx 10^{-7}$, and two series of salts are known, $MTeO(OH)_5$ and $M_2TeO_2(OH)_4$.

21-17. Peroxy Acids

Two peroxy acids derived from sulfuric acid are well known. These are peroxymonosulfuric acid, H_2SO_5, and peroxydisulfuric acid, $H_2S_2O_8$. No peroxy acids containing selenium or tellurium are known.

Peroxydisulfuric acid can be obtained from its salts with alkali metal and ammonium ions. The latter can be crystallized from solutions of the sulfates after electrolysis at low temperatures and high current densities. The peroxydisulfate ion is one of the most powerful and useful oxidizing agents known. It can oxidize Mn^{II} to permanganate and Cr^{III} to chromate:

$$S_2O_8^{2-} + 2e = 2SO_4^{2-} \qquad E^0 = 2.01 \text{ v.}$$

Direct oxidation by peroxydisulfate generally proceeds slowly, but becomes rapid in the presence of catalysts, Ag^I ion being a common one. The catalytic activity of Ag^I results from its being oxidized to the Ag^{III} ion which then oxidizes the reducing agent, becoming again Ag^I. Peroxydisulfate ion is known from X-ray studies of its salts to have the structure

O_3S—O—O—SO_3, with approximately tetrahedral angles about each sulfur atom.

Peroxymonosulfuric acid, often called Caro's acid, is obtained by hydrolysis of peroxydisulfuric acid,

$$\underset{\substack{\| \\ O}}{\overset{\substack{OH \\ \|}}{O=S}}-O-O-\underset{\substack{\| \\ O}}{\overset{\substack{OH \\ \|}}{S=O}} + H_2O = \underset{\substack{\| \\ O}}{\overset{\substack{OH \\ \|}}{O=S}}-OH + \underset{\substack{\| \\ O}}{\overset{\substack{OH \\ \|}}{O=S}}-OOH$$

and also by the action of hydrogen peroxide on sulfuric acid or chlorosulfonic acid

$$H_2O_2 + H_2SO_4 = HOOSO_2OH + H_2O$$
$$H_2O_2 + HClSO_3 = HOOSO_2OH + HCl$$

Salts of this acid are generally unstable and have not been isolated in a pure state.

21-18. Thiosulfuric Acid

Thiosulfates are readily obtained by boiling sulfur with solutions of sulfites and in the decomposition of dithionites. The free acid is quite unstable at ordinary temperatures, but it has been isolated as an etherate at $-78°C$. from the reaction:

$$SO_3 + H_2S = H_2S_2O_3$$

The alkali thiosulfates are manufactured for use mainly in photography where they are used to dissolve unreacted silver bromide from emulsion. They do this by formation of complexes with silver ion, $[Ag(S_2O_3)]^-$ and $[Ag(S_2O_3)_2]^{3-}$; the thiosulfate ion also forms complexes with other metal ions.

Although there are no X-ray data on thiosulfates, the general structure of the ion is almost certainly SSO_3, since radioactive tracer studies have shown the sulfur atoms not to be equivalent. Thus when the ion is formed by union of isotopically labeled sulfur, S^*, and sulfite of normal isotopic composition

$$S^* + SO_3^{2-} = S^*SO_3^{2-}$$

and then decomposed by acid,

$$S^*SO_3^{2-} + 2H^+ = S^* + H_2SO_3$$

all of the labeled sulfur again appears as elemental sulfur, showing that the absorbed sulfur had never become chemically equivalent to the sulfur originally in the sulfite.

21-19. Dithionous (Hypo- or Hydrosulfurous) Acid

The reduction of sulfites in aqueous solutions containing excess sulfur dioxide, usually with zinc dust, gives the dithionite ion, $S_2O_4^{2-}$. Solutions of this ion are not very stable and decompose by disproportionation

$$2S_2O_4^{2-} + H_2O = S_2O_3^{2-} + 2HSO_3^-$$

as well as being oxidized by air. Decomposition is rapid in acid solution, producing then also elemental sulfur.

The zinc and sodium salts are commercially available as reducing agents in alkaline solution. They have a high potential and usually react rapidly:

$$4OH^- + S_2O_4^{2-} = 2SO_3^{2-} + 2H_2O + 2e \qquad E° = 1.12 \text{ v.}$$

In the presence of β-anthraquinone sulfonate (21-X) as a catalyst (Fieser's

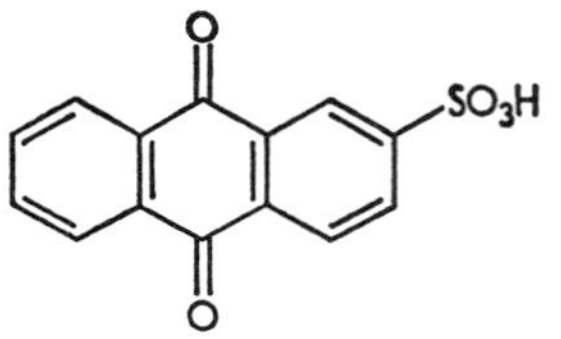

(2I-X)

solution), aqueous sodium dithionite efficiently removes oxygen from gases. The structure of the dithionite ion is known and, as Figure 21-10 shows,

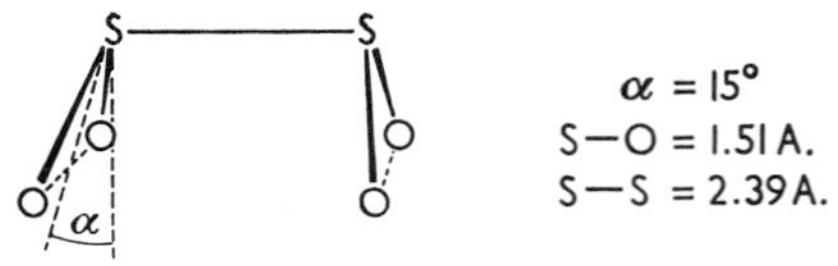

$\alpha = 15°$
$S-O = 1.51$ A.
$S-S = 2.39$ A.

Fig. 21-10.   The structure of the dithionite ion, $S_2O_4^{2-}$, in $Na_2S_2O_4$.

has several remarkable features. The oxygen atoms, which must bear considerable negative charge, are closely juxtaposed by the eclipsed configuration and by the small value of the angle α, which would be 35° for sp^3 tetrahedral hybridization at the sulfur atom. Secondly, the S—S distance is enormously longer than that to be expected for an ordinary bond formed by sulfur atoms each using an sp^3 hybrid orbital. The structure can, however, be understood in terms of valence theory. It will be noted that the S—O bond lengths are about the same as those in other compounds where considerable multiple S—O bonding is believed to occur. If we assume that there is one S—O π bond, resonating between the two S—O bonds, in each SO_2 fragment, then simple orbital accounting proceeds this way. Each sulfur atom requires: one orbital for its unshared pair, one for the S—S bond, one for each S—O σ bond, and one for the S—O π bonding, for a total of five. Hence, in addition to the $3s$ and the three $3p$ orbitals, a $3d$ orbital must be used. An appropriately chosen d orbital will combine with a p orbital to form two hybrids (Fig. 21-11) of which (a) is suitable for S—O

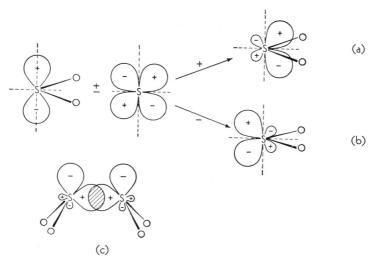

Fig. 21-11. Diagrams showing the two d–p hybrid orbitals (a and b) formed in an SO_2 group and the manner in which those of type (b) can overlap to form an S—S bond in $S_2O_4^{2-}$.

π bonding, whereas (b) is useful for S—S bond as shown in (c). It is evident that good overlap of these orbitals can only be obtained when they lie in the same plane, which means that the SO_2 groups must be eclipsed. Moreover, the angle between the S—S bond and the SO_2 planes will tend to be small because of the directional properties of the orbital (Fig. 21-11b) and the need to minimize repulsion between the unshared pairs on each sulfur atom. Finally, the unusually long S—S bond is due in part to the d character of the orbitals used to form it.

21-20. Dithionic Acid

Although $H_2S_2O_6$ might at first sight appear to be the simplest homolog of the polythionates ($S_nO_6^{2-}$) to be discussed in the next section, dithionic acid and its salts do not behave like the polythionates. Furthermore, from a structural point of view, dithionic acid should not be considered as a member of the polythionate series, since dithionates contain no sulfur atom bound only to other sulfur atoms as do $H_2S_3O_6$ and all higher homologs, $H_2S_nO_6$. The dithionite ion has the structure O_3S—SO_3 with approximately tetrahedral bond angles about each sulfur, and the shortness of the S—O bonds (1.43 A.; cf. 1.44 A. in $SO_4{}^{2-}$) again suggests considerable double bond character.

Dithionate is usually obtained by oxidation of sulfite or SO_2 solutions with manganese(IV) oxide:

$$MnO_2 + 2SO_3{}^{2-} + 4H^+ = Mn^{2+} + S_2O_6{}^{2-} + 2H_2O$$

Other oxy acids of sulfur which form as by-products are precipitated with barium hydroxide, and $BaS_2O_6 \cdot 2H_2O$ is then crystallized. Treatment of aqueous solutions of this with sulfuric acid gives solutions of the free acid which may be used to prepare other salts by neutralization of the appropriate bases. Dithionic acid is a moderately stable strong acid which decomposes slowly in concentrated solutions and when warmed. The ion itself is quite stable; solutions of its salts may be boiled without decomposition. Although it contains sulfur in an intermediate oxidation state, it resists most oxidizing and reducing agents, presumably for kinetic reasons.

21-21. Polythionates

These anions have the general formula $[O_3SS_nSO_3]^{2-}$. The free acids are not stable, decomposing rapidly into sulfur, sulfur dioxide, and sometimes sulfate. Also, no acid salts are known. The well-established polythionate anions are those with $n = 1$–4. They are named according to the total number of sulfur atoms and are thus called: $S_3O_6{}^{2-}$, trithionate; $S_4O_6{}^{2-}$, tetrathionate; $S_5O_6{}^{2-}$, pentathionate; $S_6O_6{}^{2-}$, hexathionate. It has been conclusively established in all four of these anions that there are sulfur chains, thus disposing of proposals commonly found in older literature and texts that there might be $>$S→S linkages. The conformations of the chain[8] in these anions are very similar to those of segments of the S_8 ring, whereas the configurations about the end sulfur atoms, —S—SO_3, are approximately tetrahedral.

Polythionates can be prepared in various ways. Mixtures are obtained by reduction of thiosulfate solutions with sulfur dioxide in presence of arsenic(III) oxide and also by the reaction of hydrogen sulfide with an aqueous solution of sulfur dioxide which produces a solution called Wackenroder's liquid. Although individual polythionates can be separated from these mixtures, many are better obtained by selective preparations. For example, trithionate can be made by the action of hydrogen peroxide on cold saturated sodium thiosulfate solution:

$$2S_2O_3{}^{2-} + 4H_2O_2 = S_3O_6{}^{2-} + SO_4{}^{2-} + 4H_2O$$

Tetrathionates are obtained by treatment of thiosulfates with iodine in a reaction which is widely used in the volumetric determination of iodine:

$$2S_2O_3{}^{2-} + I_2 = 2I^- + S_4O_6{}^{2-}$$

OXYHALIDES AND HALOSULFONIC ACIDS

21-22. Oxyhalides

Only sulfur and selenium are known to form well-defined oxyhalides. These are of three main types: (a) the thionyl and selenyl halides, SOX_2 and $SeOX_2$; (b) the sulfuryl halides, SO_2X_2, and their one selenium analog, SeO_2F_2; and (c) a number of more complex sulfur oxychlorides and oxy-fluorides.

The following thionyl and selenyl halides are known:

SOF_2	$SOCl_2$	$SOBr_2$	$SOFCl$
$SeOF_2$	$SeOCl_2$	$SeOBr_2$	

With the exception of thionyl fluoride, all of these compounds react rapidly, and sometimes violently, with water, being completely hydrolyzed:

$$SOCl_2 + H_2O = SO_2 + 2HCl$$

Thionyl fluoride reacts only slowly with water.

These halides may be prepared in many ways. $SOCl_2$ is usually prepared by the following reaction:

$$PCl_5 + SO_2 = SOCl_2 + POCl_3$$

SOF_2 is obtained from $SOCl_2$ by reaction with SbF_3 in presence of $SbCl_5$ (Swarts reagent):

$$3SOCl_2 + 2SbF_3 = 3SOF_2 + 2SbCl_3$$

$SOBr_2$ is also prepared from $SOCl_2$ by treatment of the latter with HBr at 0°C. $SOClF$ is usually a by-product in the preparation of SOF_2. Selenyl chloride may be obtained by reaction of SeO_2 with $SeCl_4$ in carbon tetrachloride, and the fluoride is obtained therefrom by halogen exchange with AgF or HgF_2. $SeOBr_2$ may be obtained by treating a mixture of Se and SeO_2 with bromine or by reaction of SeO_2 with $SeBr_2$.

The thionyl and selenyl halides are stable in vacuum at ordinary temperatures and below, but on strong heating they decompose, usually to a mixture of products including the dioxide, free halogen, and lower halides. The structures are pyramidal, Figure 21-12, the S and Se atoms using sets of,

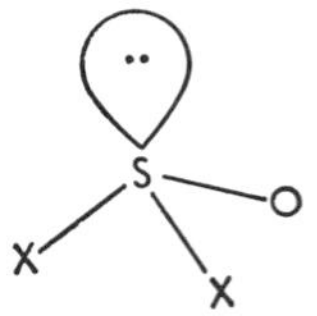

Fig. 21-12.   Structure of thionyl halides, X_2SO.

roughly, sp^3 hybrid orbitals, one of which holds the unshared pair. The S—O bonds in the thionyl halides are evidently resonance hybrids of the canonical structures 21-XI. In 21-XIb and 21-XIc the multiple bonding

$$\overset{+}{S}\!-\!\overset{-}{O} \quad\leftrightarrow\quad S\!=\!O \quad\leftrightarrow\quad \overset{-}{S}\!\equiv\!\overset{+}{O}$$
$$\text{(21-XIa)} \qquad \text{(21-XIb)} \qquad \text{(21-XIc)}$$

results from overlap of filled $p\pi$ orbitals of oxygen with empty $d\pi$ orbitals of sulfur. The net bond order appears to be about 2, as indicated by the bond distances which are ~1.45 A. as compared to ~1.7 A. expected for an S—O single bond. The bond order also increases in the order $OSBr_2$ < $OSCl_2$ < OSF_2, the more electronegative halogen causing the greater amount of oxygen-to-sulfur dative π bonding.

Thionyl chloride finds laboratory use in preparing anhydrous metal halides from oxides, hydroxides, and hydrated chlorides.

The thionyl and selenyl halides can function as weak Lewis bases, using lone pairs on oxygen and also, more surprisingly, as weak Lewis acids, using vacant d orbitals. The structure of the compound $SeOCl_2 \cdot 2py$ is shown in

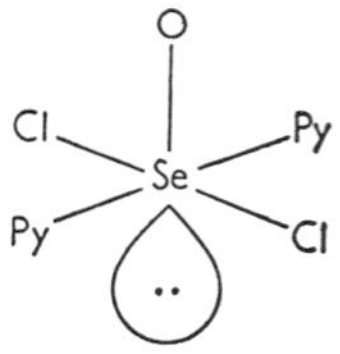

Fig. 21-13.   Structure of $SeOCl_2 \cdot 2C_5H_5N$.

Figure 21-13. It may be regarded as an octahedral structure with one unshared pair in place of an atom.

Oxyhalides of the type SO_2X_2 are called *sulfuryl halides*. Those known are SO_2F_2, SO_2Cl_2, SO_2FCl and SO_2FBr, of which sulfuryl chloride and fluoride are most important. The chloride is formed by direct reaction of

SO_2 with chlorine in the presence of a catalyst and the fluoride by thermal decomposition of barium fluorosulfonate:

$$Ba(SO_3F)_2 \underset{}{\overset{500°C.}{\rightleftarrows}} SO_2F_2 + BaSO_4$$

Sulfuryl fluoride is a chemically inert gas, unaffected by water even at 150°C., but slowly hydrolyzed by strong aqueous alkali. Sulfuryl chloride is much less stable than the fluoride, decomposing thermally below 300°C. and reacting fairly rapidly with water. It fumes strongly in moist air. It can be used as a chlorinating agent.

SeO_2F_2 has been prepared only recently by warming a mixture of barium

TABLE 21-4

Some Complex Oxyhalides of Sulfur

Compound	Structure
$S_2O_5F_2$	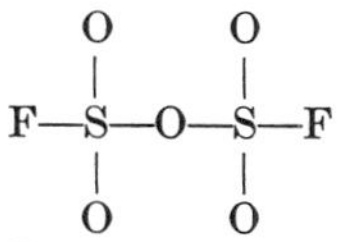 F—S—O—S—F (with O above and below each S)
$S_2O_5Cl_2$	Presumably analogous to that of $S_2O_5F_2$
SOF_4	 O=S with four F
SO_3F_2	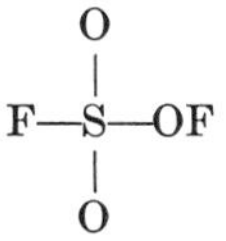 F—S—OF (with O above and O below)
SOF_6	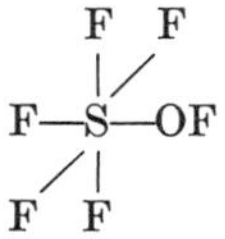 F—S—OF (with F F above and F F below)
$S_2O_6F_2$	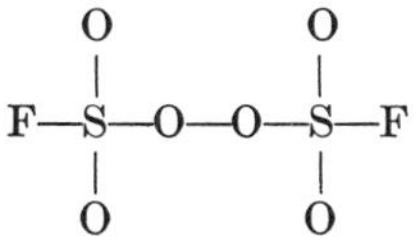 F—S—O—O—S—F (with O above and below each S)
$S_3O_8F_2$ $S_3O_8Cl_2$	Structures not known, but probably 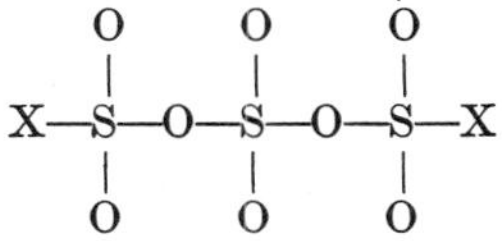 X—S—O—S—O—S—X (with O above and below each S)

selenate and fluorosulfonic acid. It is a rather reactive gas, readily hydrolyzed by water.

The sulfuryl halides are known to have distorted tetrahedral structures with S—O bonds similar to those in the thionyl halides.

Some of the more complex oxychlorides and oxyfluorides of sulfur are those shown in Table 21-4 along with their structures, where known. These structures were determined, in large part, from studies of fluorine nuclear magnetic resonance which has proved to be an extremely useful structural tool for compounds such as these.

21-23. Halosulfonic Acids

The sulfuryl halides may be considered, formally, as derivatives of sulfuric acid in which both OH groups have been replaced by halogen atoms. If only one OH group be replaced, the halosulfonic acids, FSO_3H, $ClSO_3H$, and $BrSO_3H$ are obtained. Fluorosulfonic acid is prepared by treating fuming sulfuric acid with KHF_2 or CaF_2 at $\sim 250°C$. It is a colorless liquid boiling at $169°C$. It forms many salts which are very stable and similar in their solubilities to perchlorates and fluoroborates, and mixed crystals can often be formed. The acid is very strong and only slowly hydrolyzed by water. Chlorosulfonic acid is a colorless fuming liquid, explosively hydrolyzed by water, which forms no salts and finds its chief use as a sulfonating agent in organic chemistry. It is prepared by treating SO_3 with dry HCl. Bromosulfonic acid, prepared from HBr and SO_3 in liquid SO_2 at $-35°C.$, decomposes at its melting point $(8°C.)$ into Br_2, SO_2, and H_2SO_4.

References

Abrahams, S. C., *Quart. Revs. (London)*, **10**, 407 (1956). An excellent review of the stereochemistry of S, Se, Te, Po, and O.

—— and I. Lindquist, *J. Inorg. & Nuclear Chem.*, **6**, 153 (1958). Bond distances and bond energies in group VI compounds.

Bagnall, K. W., *The Chemistry of the Rare Radioelements*, Butterworths, London, 1957. Includes an exhaustive account of polonium chemistry.

Becke-Goehring, M., in H. J. Emeléus and A. G. Sharpe, eds., *Advances in Inorganic Chemistry and Radiochemistry*, Vol. 2, Academic Press, New York, 1960, p. 159. Sulfur nitride chemistry.

——, *Quart. Revs. (London)*, **10**, 437 (1956). Sulfur nitride chemistry.

Cady, G. H., in H. J. Emeléus and A. G. Sharpe, eds., *Advances in Inorganic Chemistry and Radiochemistry*, Vol. 2, Academic Press, New York, 1960, p. 105. Fluorine-containing sulfur compounds.

Cilento, G., *Chem. Revs.*, **60**, 147 (1960). Comprehensive survey of effects of utilization of d orbitals in organic sulfur chemistry.

Cruickshank, D. W. J., *J. Chem. Soc. (London)*, 5486, **1961**. A detailed discussion of $d\pi-p\pi$ bonding in SO bonds.

Foss, O., in H. J. Emeléus and A. G. Sharpe, eds., *Advances in Inorganic Chemistry and Radiochemistry*, Vol. 2, Academic Press, New York, 1960, p. 237. A comprehensive account of compounds with S—S bonds.

George, J. W., "Halides and Oxyhalides of the Elements of Groups Vb and VIb," in F. A. Cotton, ed., *Progress in Inorganic Chemistry*, Vol. II, Interscience, New York–London, 1960, p. 33.

Gillespie, R. J., *J. Am. Chem. Soc.*, **82**, 5978 (1960). Valence and bonding in hydrides and halides.

—— and E. A. Robinson, in H. J. Emeléus and A. G. Sharpe, eds., *Advances in Inorganic Chemistry and Radiochemistry*, Vol. 1, Academic Press, New York, 1959, p. 386. Sulfuric acid as a solvent.

Parker, A. J., and N. Kharasch, *Chem. Revs.*, **59**, 583 (1959). Scission of S—S bonds.

Sulphur Manual, Texas Gulf Sulphur Co., New York, 1959.

Symposium on the Inorganic Chemistry of Sulfur, Chem. Soc. (London), Spec. Publ., No. 12 (1958).

Taller, W. N., ed., *Sulphur Data Book*, McGraw-Hill, New York, 1954.

Yost, D. M., and H. Russell, *Systematic Inorganic Chemistry (of the 5th and 6th Group Elements)*, Prentice-Hall, New York, 1946. Selected aspects of chemistry of S, Se, and Te.

22

The Group VII Elements: Cl, Br, I, and At

GENERAL REMARKS

22-1. Electronic Structures and Valences

The electronic structures of the group VII elements (halogens) are as follows:

$$F: \quad 1s^2 2s^2 2p^5$$
$$Cl: \quad [Ne]3s^2 3p^5$$
$$Br: \quad [Ar]3d^{10}4s^2 4p^5$$
$$I: \quad [Kr]4d^{10}5s^2 5p^5$$
$$At: \quad [Xe]4f^{14}5d^{10}6s^2 6p^5$$

Since the structures of the atoms are only one electron short of the inert gas configuration, the elements form the uninegative ion X^- or a single covalent bond, $-X$. The chemistries of the elements are essentially completely nonmetallic and, in the main, the properties of the elements and their compounds change steadily with decreasing electronegativity (F, 4.0; Cl, 3.0; Br, 2.8; I, 2.5). There is a much greater change between fluorine and chlorine than between the other pairs of elements, some of the factors involved here having been discussed under fluorine (Chapter 7, page 286). Although there is no extensive chemistry of positive ions, there is reasonable evidence for cationic species of chlorine, bromine, iodine, and—where studies have been possible—astatine.

Although fluorine normally forms only one bond, certain bridged fluorides, where the fluorine atom has a coordination number of two are known, for example, SbF_5, $(BeF_2)_x$, and $K^+[(C_2H_5)_3Al-F-Al(C_2H_5)_3]^-$. For the other elements, higher covalencies (with formal oxidation states up to +7) are known, but only in oxygen compounds (e.g., ClO_4^-) or in interhalogen compounds (e.g., BrF_5). Expansion of the octet through utilization of d orbitals can, in principle, allow some multiple bond character in bonds to Cl, Br, and I.

THE ELEMENTS

None of the halogens occur in the elemental state in nature because of their high reactivity. All exist as diatomic molecules, which, being homonuclear, are without permanent electrical polarity. The forces between these molecules in the condensed phases are only weak van der Waals forces. Hence the trend in melting and boiling points of the halogens parallels that in the inert gases since in both cases the same two factors are decisive, namely, increasing weight and increasing magnitude of the van der Waals forces as size and polarizability of the atoms or molecules increase. The increase in color of the elements and of their covalent compounds with increasing size is due to a progressive shift of charge-transfer bands to longer wavelengths in the absorption spectrum.

22-2. Chlorine

Chlorine is a pale green gas at ordinary temperatures, with normal boiling and freezing points of -35 and $-102°C.$, respectively. It occurs in nature mainly as sodium chloride both in sea water and in various inland salt lakes and as solid deposits originating presumably from the prehistoric evaporation of salt lakes. Chlorine is prepared in enormous quantities industrially, almost entirely by electrolysis of brine:

$$Na^+ + Cl^- + H_2O = Na^+ + OH^- + \tfrac{1}{2}Cl_2 + \tfrac{1}{2}H_2$$

It is seldom necessary to prepare chlorine in the laboratory, but, in the event that it is, the oxidation of Cl^- in acid solution by a strong oxidizing agent such as MnO_2 is a satisfactory method:

$$2Cl^- + 4H^+ + MnO_2 = Mn^{2+} + 2H_2O + Cl_2$$

Chlorine is moderately soluble in water with which it reacts (see page 447).

On passing chlorine into dilute solutions of $CaCl_2$ at $0°C.$, feathery crystals of "chlorine hydrate" are formed having the composition $Cl_2 \cdot 7.3H_2O$. This substance is a water clathrate of the gas hydrate type (see Chapter 6, page 148) having all medium holes and $\sim20\%$ of the small holes in the structure of ice filled with chlorine molecules.

Naturally occurring chlorine consists of 75.4 atom $\%$ ^{35}Cl and 24.6 atom $\%$ ^{37}Cl. Samples enriched in one or the other of these stable isotopes are obtainable, and the enriched isotope can be used as a tracer by measuring its concentration with a mass spectrometer. ^{36}Cl is an artificial radioactive isotope (β, 2×10^6 years) which is quite useful as a tracer. Both naturally occurring nuclei have spin, and nuclear resonance studies are, in principle, possible, although few have been reported to date.

More important perhaps is the fact that both nuclides have electrical quadrupole moments. Studies of the coupling of these nuclear quadrupole moments to asymmetric electrical fields in the electron distribution about the atoms have provided interesting information about the ionicity of bonds to chlorine. A brief account of the theory is as follows. We assume that only s and p orbitals need be considered. It is clear that an electron in an s orbital cannot produce any asymmetry in the field about the nucleus since the distribution of such an electron is spherically symmetric. However, unless all three p orbitals are equally populated, there will be an asymmetry in the charge distribution which will be detectable by measuring the coupling of the nuclear quadrupole with it. Now in Cl^-, the p shell is symmetrical, and the quadrupole coupling parameter should be 0. In ionic chlorides this is found to be the case. Conversely, in the free Cl atom there is an unbalance of one full electronic charge in one p orbital relative to the other two, and the coupling parameter is found experimentally to be 110.4. For various compounds intermediate values are found. In terms of a theory, which unfortunately contains the oversimplification of assuming that chlorine uses a pure p orbital for bonding and ignores the more realistic possiblility that some degree of sp and perhaps d hybridization occurs, it has been shown that there is a degree of correlation between the quadrupole coupling constants and expectations of ionicity based on electronegativity differences. Typical results are given in Table 22-1. In ClF, where the chlorine will tend to be positive, the coupling parameter indicates an aver-

TABLE 22-1

Quadrupole Coupling Constants for ^{35}Cl and Electronegativity Differences

Compound	Quadrupole coupling constants	$X_{Cl} - X_z$ (Allred-Rochow)
Cl (atom)	110.4	—
Cl_2	108.5	0
ClF	145.9	-1.3
ClI	82.5	$+0.6$
CH_3Cl	75.1	$+0.3$
GeH_3Cl	43.2	$+0.8$
SiH_3Cl	39.2	$+1.1$
TlCl	15.8	$+1.4$
NaCl	<1	$+1.8$

age of more than one vacancy in the p bonding orbital of the chlorine atom, indicating the importance of the resonance form Cl^+F^-. The value for Cl_2 is in good accord with the expected value ($\sim$110) for pure covalent bonding. It is possible also to allow for the possibility of s–p hybridization in the chlorine bonding orbital and thus to express the quadrupole coupling constant as a function of both bond ionicity and hybridization, but this becomes involved and we shall not go into it here.

22-3. Bromine

Bromine occurs in nature principally as bromide salts of the alkali and alkaline earths in much smaller amounts than, but along with, chlorine. Industrially, bromine is obtained from brines and sea water by chlorination at a pH of $\sim$3.5 and is swept out in a current of air. Laboratory methods for its preparation all involve oxidation of the bromide ion, and MnO_2 can be used in a reaction analogous to that given for chlorine on page 439.

Bromine is a dense, mobile, dark red liquid at room temperature. It freezes at $-7°C$. and boils at $58°C$. It is moderately soluble in water ($\sim$35 g./liter at 20°C.) and miscible with nonpolar solvents such as CS_2 and CCl_4.

Naturally occurring bromine consists of 50.57 atom % ^{79}Br and 49.43 atom % ^{81}Br. Both nuclei have nuclear spin and nuclear quadrupole moments, but, except for some studies of quadrupole coupling constants, these have not as yet been much studied for chemical purposes.

22-4. Iodine

Iodine is found in nature as iodide in brines and also in the form of sodium and calcium iodates. Also, various forms of marine life concentrate iodine in their systems. Production of iodine commercially involves either oxidizing I^- or reducing iodates to I^- followed by oxidation to the elemental state. Exact methods vary considerably depending on the raw materials. A commonly used oxidation reaction, and one suited to laboratory use when necessary, is, again, oxidation of I^- in acid solution with MnO_2.

Iodine is a black solid with a slight metallic luster. At atmospheric pressure it sublimes without melting. The vapor is violet. Its solubility in water is slight ($\sim$0.3 g./liter at 20°C.). It is readily soluble in nonpolar solvents such as CS_2 and CCl_4 to give violet solutions; in solvents such as benzene, unsaturated hydrocarbons, liquid SO_2, alcohols, and ketones iodine solutions are brown, and it has been shown that solvation and complex formation occur. Similar molecular complexes of chlorine and bromine, for example, with dioxane and benzene, are also known. Further, a variety of halogen complexes with donor molecules can be obtained in the solid state. These are known as "charge-transfer compounds" and have one halogen linked to the donor atom, with the second halogen pointing away, as in N····X—X.

Iodine also forms the well-known blue complex with starch where the iodine atoms are aligned in channels in the polysaccharide amylose.

Naturally occurring iodine is monoisotopic, consisting entirely of ^{127}I. This nuclide has spin and a quadrupole moment, and investigations of quadrupole coupling constants have been made for chemical purposes.

22-5. Astatine, At, Element 85

Several isotopes of element 85 have been identified as very short-lived branch products in the natural decay series of uranium and thorium. The element was first obtained in quantities sufficient to afford definite proof of its existence and a knowledge of some of its properties in 1940 by the cyclotron reaction:

$$^{209}Bi(\alpha,2n)^{211}At$$

This isotope has a half-life of 7.5 hours and decays about 60% by electron capture and about 40% by α emission. The element was named astatine from the Greek meaning unstable. About 20 isotopes are now known, the longest lived being ^{210}At with a half-life of only 8.3 hours.

Because of the short half-lives of even the most stable isotopes, macroscopic quantities cannot be accumulated. Our knowledge of its chemistry is therefore based entirely on tracer studies, which show however that it behaves about as one might expect by extrapolation from the other halogens. The element is rather volatile. It is somewhat soluble in water from which it may, like iodine, be extracted into benzene or carbon tetrachloride. It cannot, like iodine, be extracted from basic solutions.

The At^- ion is produced by reduction with SO_2 or zinc but not ferrous ion (which gives some indication of the oxidation potential of At^-). This ion is carried down in AgI or TlI precipitates. Positive oxidation states are known. Bromine and, to some extent, ferric ions oxidize it to what appears to be AtO^- or HAtO. HClO or hot $S_2O_8^{2-}$ oxidize it to an anion carried by IO_3^- and therefore probably AtO_3^-. Astatine is also carried when $(Ipy_2)^+$ salts are isolated, indicating that $[Atpy_2]^+$ can exist. In 0.1M acid, the astatine potentials appear to be

$$At^- \underline{-0.3} At^0 \underline{-1.0} HOAt(?) \underline{-1.5} AtO_3^-$$

OXIDES, OXY ACIDS, AND THEIR SALTS

22-6. Oxides

The known oxides of chlorine, bromine, and iodine are listed in Table 22-2. Oxides of fluorine have already been discussed; while these were

TABLE 22-2

Oxides of Chlorine, Bromine, and Iodine

Chlorine	Bromine	Iodine
Cl_2O	Br_2O	I_2O_4
ClO_2	Br_3O_8 or BrO_3	I_4O_9
Cl_2O_6	BrO_2	I_2O_5
Cl_2O_7	$Br_2O_7(?)$	

called oxygen fluorides because of the greater electronegativity of fluorine, those of the remaining halogens are conventionally and properly called *halogen oxides* since oxygen is the more electronegative element, although not by a very great margin relative to chlorine. All of the oxides may be formally considered as anhydrides or mixed anhydrides of the appropriate oxy acids, but this aspect of their chemistry is of little practical consequence. For the most part they are neither common nor especially important.

Chlorine Oxides. All of them are highly reactive and unstable, tending to explode under various conditions. Probably the best characterized is chlorine monoxide, Cl_2O. It is a yellowish red gas at room temperature; the liquid boils at 2°C. It explodes rather easily on heating or sparking to Cl_2 and O_2. Chlorine monoxide dissolves in water forming an orange-yellow solution which contains some HOCl, of which it is formally the anhydride. The molecule is angular and symmetrical with the O—Cl distances equal to 1.71 A. and the Cl—O—Cl angle equal to 111°. It is prepared by treating freshly prepared mercuric oxide with chlorine gas or with a solution of chlorine in carbon tetrachloride:

$$2Cl_2 + 2HgO = HgCl_2 \cdot HgO + Cl_2O$$

Chlorine dioxide is also highly reactive and liable to explode very violently. Apparently mixtures with air containing less than 50 mm. or so partial pressure of ClO_2 are safe. Actually, ClO_2 has recently been found useful as a very active oxidizing agent in certain commercial processes and is made on a fairly large scale. However, because of its explosive nature it is never shipped but produced where and as required. There are a variety of methods by which it can be made, of which the following is useful on a laboratory scale:

$$2KClO_3 + 2H_2C_2O_4 = 2ClO_2 + 2CO_2 + K_2C_2O_4 + 2H_2O$$

The CO_2 liberated serves as a diluent for the ClO_2. Commercially, the gas is made by the exothermic reaction of sodium chlorite in 4–$4.5M$ sulfuric acid containing 0.05–$0.25M$ chloride ion with sulfur dioxide

$$2NaClO_3 + SO_2 + H_2SO_4 = 2ClO_2 + 2NaHSO_4$$

ClO_2 is a yellowish gas at room temperature, and the normal boiling point of the liquid is $11°C$. It has a symmetrical bent structure with the Cl—O distances equal to 1.49 A. and the O—Cl—O angle equal to $117°$. It is to be noted that ClO_2 is an odd molecule. However, it apparently has no marked tendency to dimerize. It is soluble in water, solutions containing up to 8 g./liter being stable in the dark. In light, solutions decompose slowly to HCl and $HClO_3$. In alkaline solution a mixture of chlorite and chlorate ions is formed fairly rapidly, whereas in acid, reduction to $HClO_2$ occurs first, followed by decomposition to HCl + $HClO_3$.

Chlorine hexoxide, Cl_2O_6, forms on ultraviolet irradiation of chlorine dioxide or by the action of ozone on chlorine dioxide. It is a red oily liquid, freezing at $3.5°C$. Molecular weight determinations in carbon tetrachloride solution indicate the dimeric formula, but it has been inferred from magnetic measurements that the pure substance and its aqueous solutions are slightly dissociated to ClO_3. It is not particularly stable, decomposing even at its melting point into ClO_2 and O_2, and it reacts explosively with organic matter such as stopcock grease and other reducing agents. Chlorine hexoxide reacts with water or alkalies to give a mixture of chlorate and perchlorate ions. The structure of the molecule is unknown.

Chlorine heptoxide is the most stable of the chlorine oxides, but it, too, detonates when heated or subjected to shock. It is obtained as a colorless oily liquid by dehydration of perchloric acid with P_2O_5 at $-10°C$. followed by distillation at $85°C$., with precautions against explosions. It reacts with water and alkalies to regenerate perchlorate ion. The molecular structure of chlorine heptoxide is unknown.

Bromine Oxides. The bromine oxides have been characterized only rather recently and are still not well studied. They are all of very low thermal stability. Br_2O, a dark brown liquid freezing at $-18°C$. decomposes at an appreciable rate above $-50°C$. Br_3O_8 (also claimed to be BrO_3) is a white solid unstable above $-80°C$. except in an atmosphere of ozone. BrO_2 is a yellow solid unstable above about $-40°C.$; under certain conditions it decomposes in vacuum, evolving Br_2O, to a white solid which may be Br_2O_7.

Iodine Oxides. Of these, iodine pentoxide is the most important. When iodic acid is heated to about 200°C., white crystalline I_2O_5 is obtained.

$$2HIO_3 = I_2O_5 + H_2O \qquad (22\text{-}1)$$

It is stable up to about 300°C. where it melts with decomposition to iodine and oxygen. It is the anhydride of iodic acid and reacts immediately with water in the reverse sense of equation 22-1. It reacts as an oxidizing agent with various substances such as H_2S, HCl, and CO. One of its important uses is as a reagent for the determination of CO, the iodine which is produced quantitatively according to equation 22-2 being then determined by standard iodometric procedures:

$$5CO + I_2O_5 = I_2 + 5CO_2 \qquad (22\text{-}2)$$

The other oxides of iodine, I_2O_4 and I_4O_9, are of less certain nature. Both decompose on heating to $\sim$100°C. to I_2O_5 and iodine or to iodine and oxygen. The yellow solid I_2O_4, which is obtained by partial hydrolysis of $(IO)_2SO_4$ (discussed later), appears to have a network built up of polymeric I—O chains which are cross-linked by IO_3 groups.

22-7. Oxy Acids

The known oxy acids of the halogens are listed in Table 22-3. In general,

TABLE 22-3

Oxy Acids of the Halogens

Fluorine	Chlorine	Bromine	Iodine
None	HClO	HBrO	HIO
	HClO$_2$	HBrO$_2$(?)	—
	HClO$_3$	HBrO$_3$	HIO$_3$
	HClO$_4$	—	HIO$_4$, H$_5$IO$_6$, H$_4$I$_2$O$_9$

the chemistry of these acids and their salts is very complicated. Solutions of all of the acids and of several of the anions can be obtained by reaction of the free halogens with water or aqueous bases. We shall discuss these reactions first.

Reaction of Halogens with H_2O and OH^-. A considerable degree of order can be found in this area if full and proper use is made of thermodynamic data in the form of oxidation potentials and equilibrium constants and if the relative rates of competing reactions are also considered. The basic thermodynamic data are given in Table 22-4. From these all necessary potentials and equilibrium constants can be derived.

TABLE 22-4

Standard Electrode Potentials for Oxidation-Reduction Reactions of the Halogens
(In volts)

Reaction	Cl	Br	I
(1) $\frac{1}{2}X_2(g,l,s) + H_2O = H^+ + HOX + e$	−1.63	−1.59	−1.45
(2) $\frac{1}{2}X_2(g,l,s) + 2H_2O = 3H^+ + HXO_2 + 3e$	−1.64	—	—
(3) $\frac{1}{2}X_2(g,l,s) + 3H_2O = 6H^+ + XO_3^- + 5e$	−1.47	−1.52	−1.20
(4) $\frac{1}{2}X_2(g,l,s) + 4H_2O = 8H^+ + XO_4^- + 7e$	−1.42	—	−1.34
(5) $X^- = \frac{1}{2}X_2(g,l,s) + e$	−1.36	−1.07	−0.54[a]
(6) $X^- + 2OH^- = XO^- + H_2O + 2e$	−0.89	−0.76	−0.49
(7) $X^- + 4OH^- = XO_2^- + 2H_2O + 4e$	−0.78	—	—
(8) $X^- + 6OH^- = XO_3^- + 3H_2O + 6e$	−0.63	−0.61	−0.26
(9) $X^- + 8OH^- = XO_4^- + 4H_2O + 8e$	−0.56	—	−0.39

[a] Indicates that I^- can be oxidized by oxygen in aqueous solution.

The halogens are all to some extent soluble in water. However, in all such solutions there are species other than solvated halogen molecules, since a disproportionation reaction occurs *rapidly*. Two equilibria serve to define the nature of the solution:

$$X_2(g,l,s) = X_2(aq) \qquad K_1$$
$$X_2(aq) = H^+ + X^- + HOX \qquad K_2$$

The values of K_1 for the various halogens are: Cl_2, 0.062; Br_2, 0.21; I_2, 0.0013. The values of K_2 can be computed from the potentials in Table 22-4 to be 4.2×10^{-4} for Cl_2, 7.2×10^{-9} for Br_2, and 2.0×10^{-13} for I_2. We can also estimate from

$$X^- = \frac{1}{2}X_2 + e$$

and

$$2H_2O = O_2 + 4H^+ + 4e \qquad E^0 = -0.815$$

that the potentials for the reactions

$$X_2 + H_2O = 2H^+ + 2X^- + \frac{1}{2}O_2$$

are 2.035 for fluorine, 0.545 for chlorine, 0.25 for bromine, and −0.28 for iodine.

Thus for saturated solutions of the halogens in water at 25°C. we have the final results shown in Table 22-5. There is an appreciable concentration

TABLE 22-5

Equilibrium Concentrations in Aqueous Solutions of the Halogens, 25°C.

	Cl_2	Br_2	I_2
Total solubility	0.091	0.21	0.0013
Concentration X_2(aq), mole/liter	0.061	0.21	0.0013
$[H^+] = [X^-] = [HOX]$	0.030	1.15×10^{-3}	6.4×10^{-6}

of hypochlorous acid in a saturated aqueous solution of chlorine, a smaller concentration of HOBr in a saturated solution of Br_2, but only a negligible concentration of HOI in a saturated solution of iodine.

Note that the hypohalous acids are all weak. Their dissociation constants are: HOCl, 2×10^{-3}; HOBr, 2×10^{-9}, HOI, 1×10^{-11}. As can be readily seen, reaction of halogens with water does not constitute a suitable method for preparing aqueous solutions of the hypohalous acids owing to the unfavorable equilibria. A useful method is the following general reaction, which is carried out by passing the halogen into a well agitated suspension of mercuric oxide:

$$2X_2 + 2HgO + H_2O = HgO \cdot HgX_2 + 2HOX$$

All of the hypohalous acids are rather unstable, HOI being the most unstable, and none can be obtained in the pure state. They are all good oxidizing agents, especially in acid solution, as the potentials in Table 22-4 show.

The hypohalite ions can all be produced in principle by dissolving the halogens in base according to the general reaction

$$X_2 + 2OH^- = X^- + XO^- + H_2O$$

For these reactions the equilibrium constants are all quite favorable— 7.5×10^{15} for Cl_2, 2×10^8 for Br_2, and 30 for I_2—and the reactions are rapid.

However, the situation is complicated by the tendency of the hypohalite ions to disproportionate further in basic solution to produce the halate ions:

$$3XO^- = 2X^- + XO_3^-$$

For this reaction, the equilibrium constant is in each case very favorable, that is, 10^{27} for ClO^-, 10^{15} for BrO^-, and 10^{20} for IO^-. Thus the actual products obtained on dissolving the halogens in base depend on the rates at which the hypohalite ions initially produced undergo disproportionation, and these rates vary from one to the other and with temperature.

The disproportion of ClO^- is slow at and below room temperature. Thus when chlorine reacts with base "in the cold," reasonably pure solutions of Cl^- and ClO^- are obtained. In hot solutions, $\sim 75°C$., the rate of disproportionation is fairly rapid and, by using proper conditions, good yields of ClO_3^- can be secured.

The disproportionation of BrO^- is moderately fast even at room temperature. Consequently solutions of BrO^- can only be made and/or kept at around $0°C$. At temperatures above room temperature—say, 50–$80°C$.,—quantitative yields of BrO_3^- are obtained according to equation 22-3.

$$3Br_2 + 6OH^- = 5Br^- + BrO_3^- + 4H_2O \qquad (22\text{-}3)$$

The rate of disproportionation of IO^- is very fast at all temperatures, so that it is unknown in solution. Reaction of iodine with base gives IO_3^- quantitatively according to an equation analogous to equation 22-3 for bromine.

It remains now to consider the equilibria and kinetic relations of the other oxy anions not yet mentioned to those we have discussed. Halite ions and halous acids do not arise in the hydrolysis of the halogens. First, the only halous acid known definitely is $HClO_2$. HIO_2 apparently does not exist and $HBrO_2$ is doubtful. $HClO_2$ does not form by disproportionation of $HClO$ if for no other reason than that the equilibrium constant is quite unfavorable:

$$2HClO = Cl^- + H^+ + HClO_2 \qquad K \sim 10^{-5}$$

Finally, we must consider the possibility of production of perhalate ions by disproportionation of the halate ions. Since the acids HXO_3 and HXO_4 are all strong, these equilibria are independent of pH. The reaction

$$4ClO_3^- = Cl^- + 3ClO_4^-$$

has an equilibrium constant of 10^{29}, but takes place only very slowly in solution even near $100°C$.; hence perchlorates are not readily produced. Since perbromic acid and perbromates apparently do not exist, bromate is quite stable. The equilibrium constant for disproportionation of iodate is 10^{-53} so that, irrespective of the question of rate, no disproportionation of IO_3^- occurs.

In addition to the reactions already noted, the following additional facts are of importance.

The only definitely known halous acid is chlorous acid. We have seen that it does not arise in the disproportionation of $HClO$. It may be obtained in aqueous solution by treating a suspension of barium chlorite with sulfuric acid and filtering off the precipitate of barium sulfate. It is a relatively weak acid ($K_a \approx 10^{-2}$) and cannot be isolated in the free state. Chlorites themselves are obtained by reaction of ClO_2 with solutions of bases,

$$2ClO_2 + 2OH^- = ClO_2^- + ClO_3^- + H_2O$$

Chlorites are used as bleaching agents. Alkaline solutions are fairly stable, whereas in acid solutions the weak acid is formed and this decomposes rather rapidly, probably according to the equation

$$4HClO_2 = 2ClO_2 + ClO_3^- + Cl^- + 2H^+ + H_2O$$

Of the halic acids only iodic acid is known in the free state. This is a stable white solid obtained by oxidizing iodine with concentrated nitric acid, hydrogen peroxide, ozone, and various other strong oxidizing agents. It can be dehydrated to its anhydride, I_2O_5, as already noted. Chloric and bromic acids are best obtained in solution by treating the barium halates with sulfuric acid. All the halic acids are strong and are powerful oxidizing agents. The halate ions, XO_3^-, are all pyramidal as is to be expected from the presence of an octet, with one unshared pair, in the halogen valence shell.

Iodates of certain +4 metal ions—notably those of Ce, Zr, Hf, and Th— are insoluble in, and can be precipitated from, $6N$ nitric acid to provide a useful means of separation.

Of the peracids, perbromic and perbromate ion are unknown. Perchloric and periodic acids are rather different from one another. Both are of considerable importance.

Perchloric Acid and Perchlorates. Although disproportionation of ClO_3^- to ClO_4^- and Cl^- is thermodynamically very favorable, the reaction occurs only very slowly in solution and does not constitute a useful preparative procedure. Perchlorates are most commonly prepared by electrolytic oxidation of chlorates. Also, if solid potassium chlorate is carefully heated, it disproportionates in the following way

$$4KClO_3 = 3KClO_4 + KCl$$

Perchlorates of practically all electropositive metals are known. Except for a few with large cations of low charge, such as $CsClO_4$, $RbClO_4$, $KClO_4$, and NH_4ClO_4, they are readily soluble in water. Solid perchlorates containing the tetrahedral perchlorate ion are often isomorphous with permanganates, sulfates, fluoroborates and other salts of tetrahedral anions. A particularly important property of the perchlorate ion is its very slight tendency to serve as a ligand in complexes. No perchlorate complex has yet been isolated, and estimates of the stability of perchlorate complexes in solution indicate that they are virtually nonexistent. Thus perchlorates are widely used in studies of complex ion formation, since no appreciable correction for the concentration of perchlorate complexes need be considered.

Perchloric acid can be obtained by vacuum distillation of aqueous solutions and is a colorless liquid freezing at $-112°C$. Commercial, concentrated perchloric acid is 72% by weight. It is a very strong acid in aqueous solution. As the potential in Table 22-4 shows, perchlorates and perchloric acid are strong oxidizing agents. Nonetheless, both the acid and its salts tend to be unreactive at room temperature; however, when hot and concentrated, solutions of the acid or its salts react vigorously and even violently. Perchloric acid can react explosively with organic matter.

Periodic Acid and Periodates. Periodic acid exists in solution in several forms. In strongly acid solutions it exists as *paraperiodic acid*, H_5IO_6. This is a fairly weak acid.

$$H_5IO_6 = H^+ + H_4IO_6^- \qquad K_a = 5.1 \times 10^{-4}$$

The $H_4IO_6^-$ ion is in equilibrium with $H_3IO_6^{2-}$

$$H_4IO_6^- = H^+ + H_3IO_6^{2-} \qquad K = 2 \times 10^{-7}$$

and also with the *metaperiodate* ion, IO_4^-,

$$H_4IO_6^- = IO_4^- + 2H_2O \qquad K = 40$$

These equilibria are apparently established rapidly and are pH dependent.

The chief characteristic of periodic acids and periodates is that they are powerful oxidizing agents which usually react smoothly and rapidly. They are thus quite useful for analytical purposes, for example, to oxidize manganous ion to permanganate. Ozone may be liberated in the reactions, but not hydrogen peroxide.

Salts of periodic acid are of several types. The commonest are the acid paraperiodates such as $Na_2H_3IO_6$ and $Na_3H_2IO_6$. Metaperiodates with tetrahedral IO_4^- ions are also known in the solid state. Although other salts such as $K_4I_2O_9$ are known, there is no evidence for an $I_2O_9^{4-}$ ion in solution, rather, the major components in solutions appear to be hydrated ions such as $H_4IO_6^-$ or $H_5IO_5^-$. The IO_6 group in periodates has been shown to be octahedral; the free acid can be dehydrated to $H_4I_2O_9$ at 80°C. and to HIO_4 at 100°C. The complexity of the periodates is similar to that found for the oxy acids of antimony and tellurium, and periodates resemble tellurates in many respects.

HALIDES AND HALIDE COMPLEXES

With the exception of the inert gases, all the elements in the periodic table form halides, often in several oxidation states, and halides generally are among the most important and common compounds. The radii of halides are shown in Table 22-6.

TABLE 22-6

The Radii of the Halides

Element	Crystal radius, X^-, A.	Covalent radius, A.
Fluorine	1.34	0.72
Chlorine	1.80	0.99
Bromine	1.90	1.14
Iodine	2.23	1.33

There are almost as many ways of classifying halides as there are types of halides—and this is many. There are not only binary halides which can range from simple molecules, ionic or molecular lattices to complicated polymers but also oxyhalides, hydroxy halides, and other complex halides of varied structural types.

22-8. Binary Ionic Halides

Metal halides are substances of predominantly ionic character, although partial covalence is important in some. Actually of course there is a uniform gradation from halides which are for all practical purposes purely ionic through those of intermediate character to those which are essentially covalent. As a rough guide we can consider those halides in which the lattice consists of discrete ions rather than definite molecular units to be basically ionic, although there may still be considerable covalence in the metal–halogen interaction.

The halides of the alkali metals, except perhaps lithium, of the alkaline earths, with the definite exception of beryllium, and of most of the lanthanides and a few halides of the actinides can be considered as mainly ionic materials. As the charge/radius ratio of the metal ions increases however, covalence increases. Consider for instance the sequence KCl, $CaCl_2$, $ScCl_3$, $TiCl_4$. KCl is completely ionic, whereas $TiCl_4$ is essentially covalent. Similarly, for a metal with variable oxidation state, the lower halides will tend to be ionic, whereas the higher ones will tend to be covalent. As examples we can cite $SnCl_2$ and $SnCl_4$ and again UF_4, which is an ionic solid while UF_6 is a gaseous covalent compound.

The size and polarizability of the halide ion is also important in determining the character of the halide. Thus we have the rather classic case of the aluminum halides, where AlF_3 is basically ionic, whereas $AlCl_3$, $AlBr_3$, and AlI_3 exist as covalent dimers.

Most ionic halides dissolve in water to give hydrated metal ions and halide ions, although some, such as the chlorides, bromides, and iodides of Ag^I, Cu^I, Hg^I, and Pb^{II}, are quite insoluble. The reverse however is not necessarily so, since the hydrogen halides are covalent, but, excepting HF, are essentially completely dissociated in aqueous solution. Solubility through a series of mainly ionic halides of a given element, MF_n, MCl_n, MBr_n, MI_n, may vary in either order. In cases where all four halides are essentially ionic, the solubility order will be iodide > bromide > chloride > fluoride, since the governing factor will be the lattice energies which increase as the ionic radii decrease. This order is found among the alkali, alkaline earth, and lanthanide halides. In the last two cases, the fluorides are quite insoluble. On the other hand, if covalence is fairly important, it can invert the trend making the fluoride most and the iodide least soluble, as in the familiar cases of silver and mercurous halides.

It should be clear that no broad simple generalizations are possible, and the properties of metal halides are determined by the interplay of a number of factors.

22-9. Covalent Halides

Just as we considered halides which in the crystalline state consisted of separate metal and halide ions to be essentially ionic with perhaps some covalent character, so we can roughly define a covalent halide as one in which there are discrete molecules which persist even in the crystalline state. A solid consisting of separate molecules held together by van der Waals forces and perhaps dipole–dipole and dipole–induced dipole forces will have a low lattice energy; therefore covalent halides are generally quite volatile compared to ionic halides.

Most of the electronegative elements and the metals in very high oxidation states form covalent halides. Among the most important covalent halides are the hydrogen halides. The main properties of these substances should already be familiar and will be reviewed only briefly and in part here; also, HF has already been discussed at some length (Chapter 14, page 290). HCl, HBr, and HI are all gases at room temperature, readily soluble in water with essentially complete dissociation to H^+ and X^- ions. Actually the acid strengths increase in the order $HCl < HBr < HI$. The reasons for this, as well as the weakness of HF have been considered in detail already (Chapter 5, page 138). The H—X bond energies and the thermal stabilities decrease markedly in the order $HF > HCl > HBr > HI$, that is with increasing atomic number of the halogen. This same trend is found, in varying degrees, among the halides of all elements giving a set of covalent halides, such as those of carbon and boron already noted, and those of P, As, Sb, Si, Ge, Sn, S, Se, Te, etc.

A fairly general property of covalent halides is their easy hydrolysis to produce the hydrohalic acid and an acid of the other element. Typical examples are:

$$BCl_3 + 3H_2O = B(OH)_3 + 3H^+ + 3Cl^-$$
$$PBr_3 + 3H_2O = HPO(OH)_2 + 3H^+ + 3Br^-$$
$$SiCl_4 + 4H_2O = Si(OH)_4 + 4H^+ + 4Cl^-$$

However, the detailed properties of a given covalent halide depend intimately on the particular element concerned, and further discussion of covalent halides will be found in chapters dealing with the other elements.

The formation of *halogen bridges* between two other atoms—usually, but not exclusively, metallic—is a common occurrence. Although such bridges are often written as involving donation from lone pair electrons on the halogen atom, as in 22-I and 22-II, the bond distances in the bridge are

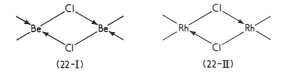

(22-I)   (22-II)

usually the same and the bonds are equivalent. Both simple molecular or ionic species, for example Al_2Cl_6, $Tl_2Cl_9^{3-}$, and $Mo_6Cl_8^{4+}$, and highly polymeric bridged halides are known; it must also be noted that the formation of labile intermediates in which halogen bridges are present has been demonstrated in a variety of systems.

22-10. Preparation of Anhydrous Halides

Although preparations of individual halogen compounds are mentioned throughout the text, anhydrous halides are of such great importance in chemistry that a few of the more important general methods of preparation can be noted.

1. *Direct interaction.* This method is perhaps the most important preparative method for all halides, and the halogens or their acids where appropriate are employed. Elevated temperatures are usually required with transition metals although rapid reaction can often occur with Cl_2 or Br_2 when tetrahydrofuran or other ethers are used as the reaction medium, the halide being obtained as a solvate; where different oxidation states are possible, chlorine, at elevated temperatures, usually gives a higher state than bromine or iodine. Nonmetals, such as phosphorus, usually react readily without heating.

2. *Halogen exchange.* Many halogen compounds will undergo rapid halogen exchange with either the elements or their acids. An excess of reagent is usually required since the reactions are normally equilibrium ones.

3. *Halogenation by halogen compounds.* This is an important method, particularly for metal halides, notably chlorides. The reactions can involve treatment of anhydrous compounds, principally oxides, with halogen compounds such as CCl_4, hexachlorobutadiene, hexachloropropene at elevated temperatures or dehydration of hydrated halides with compounds such as $SOCl_2$, S_2Cl_2, etc.:

$$[Cr(H_2O)_6]Cl_3 + SOCl_2 \xrightarrow{\text{reflux}} CrCl_3$$
$$UO_3 + CCl_2=CCl-CCl=CCl_2 \xrightarrow{\text{reflux}} UCl_4$$
$$Pr_2O_3 + 6NH_4Cl(s) \xrightarrow{300°C.} PrCl_3 + 3H_2O + 6NH_3$$
$$Sc_2O_3 + CCl_4 \xrightarrow{600°C.} 2ScCl_3$$

22-11. Halide Complexes

All of the halide ions including fluorine have the ability to function as ligands and form, with various metal ions or covalent halides, complexes such as $FeCl_4^-$, SiF_6^{2-}, HgI_4^{2-}, etc., as well as mixed complexes along with other ligands, for example, $[Co(NH_3)_4Cl_2]^+$. We merely make some general remarks and cite some typical characteristics of such complexes, reserving detailed discussions for other places in connection with the chemistries of the complexed elements.

One of the important general questions which arise concerns the relative affinities of the several halide ions for a given metal ion. There is no simple answer to this however. For crystalline materials it is obvious that lattice energies play an important role and there are cases, such as BF_4^-, BCl_4^-, BBr_4^- in which the latter two are known only in the form of crystalline salts with large cations where lattice energies are governing. In considering the stability of the complex ions in solution it is important to recognize that (*a*) the stability of a complex involves not only the absolute stability of the $M—X \leftrightarrow M^+\cdots X^-$ bond but also its stability relative to the stability of ion-solvent bonds, and (b) in general an entire series of complexes will exist, $M^{n+}(aq)$, $MX^{(n-1)+}(aq)$, $MX_2^{(n-2)+}(aq)$, ..., $MX_x^{(n-x)+}(aq)$, where x is the maximum coordination number of the metal ion. Of course, these two points are of importance in all types of complexes in solution.

It has been found from a survey of all of the available data on the stability of halide complexes that generally the stability decreases in the series $F > Cl > Br > I$, but with some metal ions the order is the opposite, namely, $F < Cl < Br < I$. No rigorous theoretical explanation for either sequence or for the existence of the two classes of acceptors relative to the halide ions has been given. It is likely that charge/radius ratio, polarizability, and the ability to use empty outer d orbitals for back bonding are significant factors, but their relative importance remains a subject for investigation. From the few available results it appears that for complexes where the replacement stability order is $Cl < Br < I$, the actual order of $M—X$ bond strengths is $Cl > Br > I$ so that ionic size and polarizability appear to be the critical factors.

The literature contains many references to the effect of steric factors in accounting for such facts as the existence of $FeCl_4^-(aq)$ as the highest ferric complex with Cl^- whereas FeF_6^{3-} is rather stable, and similar cases such as $CoCl_4^{2-}$, SCl_4, $SiCl_4$, as the highest chloro species compared to the fluoro species CoF_6^{3-}, SF_6, SiF_6^{2-}. Recently, however, it has been pointed out that in many such cases thorough steric analysis, considering the probable bond lengths and van der Waals radii of the halide ions, shows that this steric factor alone cannot account for the differences in maximum coordination number. This point is also one requiring further study.

Finally, it may be mentioned that in effecting the separation of metal ions for analytical or radiochemical purposes, halide complex formation equilibria may be taken advantage of in conjunction with anion exchange resins. In fact the objective of metal ion separation has stimulated a great deal of the postwar research on metal–halide complex equilibria. To take an admittedly extreme example, Co^{2+} and Ni^{2+}, which are not easily separated by classical methods, can be efficiently separated by passing a strong hydrochloric acid solution through an anion exchange column. Co^{2+} forms the anionic complexes $CoCl_3^-$ and $CoCl_4^{2-}$ rather readily, whereas it does not seem that any anionic chloro complexes of nickel form in aqueous solution even at the highest attainable activities of Cl^-; however, tetrachloronickelates can be obtained in fused salt systems or in nonaqueous media. More commonly, effective separation depends on properly exploiting the *difference* in complexation between two cations *both* of which have some tendency to form anionic halide complexes.

POSITIVE OXIDATION STATES OF THE HALOGENS

22-12. General Evidence of Electropositive Character

In groups IV, V, and VI we have seen that metallic and electropositive character increases markedly in going down the groups. The results of this trend in these groups is actually to make the heaviest members decidedly metallic (Pb, Bi, and Po) and the next heaviest members either decidedly metallic (Sn) or at least partially so (Sb, Te) even though the first members of these groups are quite distinctly nonmetals (C, N, O). We shall now consider the trend toward increasingly metallic character with increasing atomic number in the halogens. For two reasons we might expect to find less evidence of distinctly metallic character in the heavier members of this group than in the preceding ones. First, we have practically no conclusive knowledge about At which should be the most metallic. Second, because of the trend to less metallic character *across* each *period* of the table, we expect iodine to be less metallic than tellurium (just as Te is less so than Sb which is less so than Sn). In fact, elemental iodine is not metallic at all. The only evidence we have of a *tendency*, which is never actually realized, toward metallic character in the series F, Cl, Br, I is the increasing stability of positive oxidation states. It is this evidence which will now be considered.

For fluorine there are no known compounds in which the fluorine atom appears to be appreciably positive. In ClF evidence from chlorine nuclear quadrupole coupling (see page 440) shows that the bonding is best represented in terms of the resonance:

$$Cl—F \leftrightarrow Cl^+F^-$$

In the oxygen fluorides there is no direct physical evidence, but it is likely that the fluorine is at least neutral and probably somewhat negative with respect to oxygen. It is also to be recalled that no oxyfluoric acids or anions exist.

With Cl, Br, and I there is evidence for electropositive behavior. We may, for convenience, divide this evidence into two classes. The first class, which is for the most part only loosely defined, concerns polarities of bonds. In ClF as we have already noted, the nuclear quadrupole spectrum of Cl indicates with certainty that the canonical structure Cl^+F^- makes a substantial contribution to the electronic state of the molecule. Nuclear quadrupole spectroscopy has also given evidence of the importance of I^+CN^- in ICN, and I^+Cl^- in ICl. In general, we expect that when a halogen atom forms a bond with another atom which is more electronegative than itself, the bond will be polar, the halogen having a partial positive charge. However, we can scarcely say that the halogen atom is in a positive oxidation *state*, although we may assign positive oxidation *numbers* (e.g., $+7$ to Cl in ClO_4^-) in an essentially arbitrary way for convenience in balancing oxidation-reduction equations.

22-13. Cationic Compounds

The second type of evidence for electropositive character of the halogens Cl, Br, and I consists in the isolation of compounds in which atoms of these elements are positive in the sense of being physically cationic. Cationic iodine compounds are most numerous, most stable, and have been most thoroughly studied. Hence we shall describe these first and then refer to such Cl and Br analogs as exist later.

There are several compounds which appear to contain more or less ionic I^{III}. It may be said immediately that no comparable compounds of bromine or chlorine are known, so that the existence of these iodine compounds shows that iodine has the greatest tendency to electropositive behavior. Fuming nitric acid in the presence of acetic anhydride oxidizes iodine producing the compound $I(OCOCH_3)_3$. Analogous compounds have been obtained with chloro-, dichloro-, and trichloroacetic acids. $I(OCOCH_3)_3$ reacts with methyl sulfonic acid to give $(CH_3SO_3)_3I$. On oxidation of iodine with concentrated nitric acid in the presence of acetic anhydride and phosphoric acid, the compound IPO_4 is obtained. Unfortunately no direct structural information is available for these compounds, but electrolytic studies seem to leave no choice but to believe that I^{3+} ions, stabilized by coordination, are present. When a saturated solution of $I(OCOCH_3)_3$ in acetic anhydride is electrolyzed, the quantity of silver iodide formed at a silvered platinum gauze *cathode* is in good agreement with Faraday's law calculations assuming the presence of I^{3+}:

$$I^{3+} + Ag + 3e \rightarrow AgI$$

These compounds are quite sensitive to moisture and are not stable much above room temperature. They are hydrolyzed with disproportionation of the I^{III} as illustrated with IPO_4

$$5IPO_4 + 9H_2O = I_2 + 3HIO_3 + 5H_3PO_4$$

The iodine oxide, I_4O_9, produced on treatment of iodine with ozonized oxygen can be formulated as $I^{3+}(IO_3^-)_3$ by analogy with the above-mentioned compounds. It may also be noted that covalent I^{III} is known in the compounds triphenyl iodine, $(C_6H_5)_3I$, and a large number of diaryl iodonium salts, such as $(C_6H_5)_2I^+X^-$, where X may be one of a number of common anions. The so-called iodosyl sulfate, $(IO)_2SO_4$, which is a yellow solid obtained by treating I_2O_5 with I_2 in sulfuric acid, and some similar compounds have been shown not to contain IO^+ ions as such. They have polymeric IO chains linked together by the anions.

There is a large number of well-characterized compounds of unipositive iodine, and some of these have bromine and also chlorine analogs. It appears, as would be expected, that the iodine compounds are most stable and the chlorine compounds least stable. The best-known unipositive iodine compounds contain the ions $(Ipy)^+$ and $(Ipy_2)^+$ (py = pyridine). These compounds are generally prepared by treatment of a silver salt with the stoichiometric amount of iodine and an excess of pyridine in chloroform according to the typical equation

$$AgNO_3 + I_2 + 2py = Ipy_2NO_3 + AgI$$

The silver iodide is immediately precipitated and the complex can then be precipitated from the filtered supernatant liquid by addition of ether or petroleum. The compound $IpyNO_3$ can also be prepared. It appears that the iodonium ion, I^+, has a strong tendency to be two coordinate, so that Ipy_2NO_3 should be formulated $[pyIpy]^+NO_3^-$ and $IpyNO_3$ as $[pyIONO_2]$. The former gives a much more highly conducting solution in acetone than does the latter. When the anion is perchlorate, only Ipy_2ClO_4 can be obtained, in agreement with the requirement of bicoordination for the I^+ since ClO_4^- is well known to have little or no capacity to function as a ligand. With carboxylate anions, the compounds are generally of the type $[pyIOCOR]$, and give only very weakly conducting solutions in acetone. Evidence that the iodine in these compounds is unipositive is of several kinds. All compounds release iodine when they are dissolved in a sodium hydroxide solution containing iodide and the solution acidified:

$$I^+ + I^- = I_2$$

This reaction is quantitative. Electrolysis of $[pyIpy]^+NO_3^-$ in anhydrous chloroform yields iodine at the *cathode* only. Bases other than pyridine may be used, in particular various methyl-substituted pyridines.

In the compound "py_2I_2," obtained by direct interaction of pyridine with iodine, X-ray studies show the presence of the essentially planar cation $[pyIpy]^+$ along with I_3^- and I_2 molecules.

Similar complexes of unipositive bromine, for example, $[pyBrpy]^+NO_3^-$ (ClO_4^-), have been prepared by methods similar to those used in preparing the iodine compounds. The chlorine compound $[pyClpy]^+NO_3$ has also been reported.

To conclude, it should be mentioned that cationic iodine species also appear to exist in sulfuric acid media. I_2 and ICl dissolve in 100% sulfuric acid and in oleum. In dilute oleums the brown solutions are believed to contain I^{3+}, but in more concentrated oleums blue solutions are obtained which appear to contain I^+. An ion with a $5s^2 5p^4$ configuration should have two unpaired electrons and the species is paramagnetic but μ_{eff} is only 1.5 B.M. This is probably due to strong spin-orbit coupling effects such as are often observed in heavy elements. The ion is presumably stabilized by the solvation.

INTERHALOGEN COMPOUNDS

22-14. General Survey

The halogens form various compounds which are binary and ternary combinations of the halogens among themselves. Table 22-7 shows the

TABLE 22-7

The Known Interhalogen Compounds

	Cl	Br	I
F	ClF	BrF	
	ClF_3	BrF_3	$IF_3(?)$
		BrF_5	IF_5
			IF_7
Cl		BrCl	ICl
			ICl_3
Br			IBr

known binary interhalogen compounds. Ternary compounds occur only as polyhalide ions, and the principal types of binary and ternary polyhalide salts are listed in Table 22-9 (page 464).

It will be noted that all of the interhalogen compounds are of the type XX'_n where n is an odd number and X' is always the lighter halogen when n is greater than 1. Because n is always odd it follows that all interhalogen compounds are diamagnetic having all valence electrons present either as shared (bonding) or unshared pairs. The general scarcity and instability of odd molecules makes this seem reasonable, and it is to be expected that any further interhalogens, if discovered, will also contain an even number of atoms. No ternary interhalogen compounds are known, although attempts have been made to prepare them. This is probably because any ternary molecules formed can readily redistribute to form a mixture of the (presumably) more stable binary compounds and/or elemental halogens. Another general observation which may be made is that stability of the compounds with higher n increases as X becomes larger and X′ smaller.

The structures of the interhalogen compounds are all known with varying degrees of certainty. For the diatomic compounds there is no question. For the XX′$_3$ species, ClF$_3$ and BrF$_3$ are T-shaped, whereas ICl$_3$ is T-shaped but dimerized. IF$_5$ contains a square pyramidal IF$_4$ grouping with the fifth fluorine along the four-fold axis on the *same* side as the other four. The structure of BrF$_5$ has not been firmly established, but presumably is analogous to that of IF$_5$. IF$_7$ has been shown to be a pentagonal bipyramid, perhaps somewhat distorted in the solid state. These structures and the reasons for them in terms of the electronic configuration of the molecules have already been discussed in Chapter 15.

In their physical properties, the diatomic interhalogens XX′ are usually intermediate between the constituent halogens X$_2$ and X′$_2$. They are of course polar, whereas the halogen molecules are not. ClF is colorless, BrF, BrCl, ICl, and IBr are red or red-brown.

Chemically, the interhalogens are all quite reactive. They behave as oxidizing agents. They attack most other elements producing mixtures of the halides. They are all more or less readily hydrolyzed (some such as BrF$_3$ being dangerously explosive in this respect), in some cases according to the equation

$$XX' + H_2O = H^+ + X'^- + HOX$$

The diatomic compounds often add to ethylenic double bonds and may react with the heavier alkali and alkaline earth metals to give polyhalide salts.

The diatomic compounds are ClF, BrF, BrCl, IBr, and ICl. IF is unknown except in minute amounts observed spectroscopically. It is apparently too unstable with respect to disproportionation to IF$_5$ and I$_2$ to permit its isolation. The other isolable diatomic compounds have varying degrees of stability with respect to disproportionation and fall in the following stability order where the numbers in parentheses represent the disproportionation constants for the gaseous compounds and the elements in their standard states at 25°C.: ClF (2.9×10^{-11}) > ICl (1.8×10^{-3}) > IBr (4.9×10^{-2}) > BrCl (0.34). BrF is omitted since it is extremely unstable and its characteristic disproportionation is to Br$_2$ and BrF$_3$. This is due not to any particular weakness of the BrF bond (50 kcal./mole) but to the even greater stabilities of the products of disproportionation.

ClF may be prepared by direct reaction of the elements in a copper vessel at 250°C. It is best prepared free of ClF_3, however, by mixing Cl_2 and ClF_3 in equimolar quantities. BrF also results on direct reaction of Br_2 and F_2, but has never been obtained in high purity because of its ready disproportionation. Iodine monochloride is obtained as brownish red tablets (β form) by treating liquid chlorine with solid iodine in stoichiometric amount, and cooling to solidify the liquid product. It readily transforms to the α form, ruby red needles. BrCl has never been isolated in a pure state, but there is much evidence for its existence in equilibrium with Br_2 and Cl_2 under various conditions. IBr as a solid results from direct combination of the elements. It is endothermic and extensively dissociated in the vapor.

ICl_3 is also formed (like ICl) by treatment of liquid chlorine with the stoichiometric quantity of iodine or with a deficiency of iodine followed by evaporation of the excess chlorine. It forms as a fluffy orange powder, unstable much above room temperature.

The remaining molecular interhalogen compounds are all halogen fluorides.

22-15. The Halogen Fluorides

As with fluorine chemistry in general, much of our knowledge of the halogen fluorides has developed since the war when reliable fluorine generators and even tanks of compressed fluorine became available. The known

TABLE 22-8

Some Physical Properties of Halogen Fluorides

	Melting point, °C.	Boiling point, °C.	Specific conductivity[a] at 25°C., ohm^{-1} $cm.^{-1}$	Dielectric constant of liquid at 25°C.	Trouton's constant
ClF	−154	−101	—	—	28.0
ClF_3	−76	12	3.9×10^{-9}	4.304	23.1
BrF	−33	20	—	—	20.5
BrF_3	9	126	8.0×10^{-3}	—	25.7
BrF_5	−60	41	9.1×10^{-8}	7.76	23.2
IF_5	10	101	5.4×10^{-6}	36.14	26.3
IF_7	5	277 (subl.)	—	—	—

[a] The literature values may not be too accurate in view of the possibility of hydrolysis by traces of water.

halogen fluorides and some of their important physical properties are listed in Table 22-8.*

The preparations of ClF and BrF have already been mentioned. ClF_3 may be prepared by direct combination of the elements and is also available commercially. BrF_3 is also conveniently obtainable in the laboratory by direct combination of the elements at 200°C. or higher or by action of ClF_3 on Br_2 at 10°C. IF_5 is prepared by reaction of iodine in excess with fluorine at ordinary and slightly elevated temperatures, whereas IF_7 is obtained if the reaction occurs at temperatures of 250–270°C. using excess fluorine.

There are two principal features of the chemistry of halogen fluorides. The first is their activity as fluorinating agents. Although in most cases only qualitative data on the rates and products of the reactions are available, all are moderately to vigorously reactive, the approximate order of reactivity being $ClF_3 > BrF_5 > IF_7 > ClF > BrF_3 > IF_5 > BrF$.

The second feature, and one which has been studied rather actively in the past few years, is the functioning of several halogen fluorides as solvent systems. Inspection of the data in Table 22-8 will indicate their potentialities in this respect. First let us consider the Trouton constants.† With the exception of IF_7, for which this datum is unavailable and BrF, the Trouton constants indicate varying but appreciable degrees of association of the liquids. This is believed to occur through fluorine bridging, which in BrF_3, for example, may be indicated as in formula 22-III, which is comparable to the dimeric structure of ICl_3.

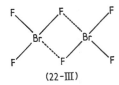

(22-III)

In addition to association, reasonably common to all, it will be seen that in BrF_3 and IF_5 the conductivity indicates appreciable self-ionization; moreover, the dielectric constant of IF_5 is extremely high, which would enable it to function as a good ionizing solvent. Unfortunately BrF_3 is so

---

* IF_3 is alleged to be a yellow powder, obtained by fluorination of I_2 in freon at −78°C., and to decompose to I_2 and IF_5 above −35°C.

† The Trouton constant is the heat of vaporization in cal./mole at the normal boiling point divided by the normal boiling point in °K. It is thus the entropy of vaporization at the boiling point and gives a measure of association in the liquid as compared to the gas phase. For "normal" liquids, for example, those not appreciably associated in either phase, it averages 17–21. Higher values indicate association in the liquid phase. Thus the Trouton constant of methane is 17.5, whereas those of NH_3 and H_2O are 23.3 and 28.3, respectively.

reactive that no reliable measurement of its dielectric constant has been reported, although it is probably high. Thus it might be expected that these two liquids would be useful reaction media and would give rise to systems of acids and bases. These expectations have been confirmed especially for BrF_3 which has been extensively studied and will now be discussed in some detail.

The reported conductivity of BrF_3 suggests appreciable self-ionization, and this might be expected to be

$$2BrF_3 = BrF_2^+ + BrF_4^-$$

In this system the acid is then BrF_2^+ and the base BrF_4^- (compare H_3O^+, OH^- and NH_4^+, NH_2^- in the H_2O and NH_3 systems). In order to provide chemical confirmation that this is in fact the correct dissociation reaction, three kinds of evidence have been adduced.

1. Compounds which can be considered as acids and bases have been isolated and shown to give highly conducting solutions when dissolved in BrF_3. Typical are $BrF_2^+SbF_6^-$ and $BrF_2^+AuF_4^-$. It is possible that these compounds are not entirely ionic as solids, there being some fluorine bridging, but they do ionize when dissolved in BrF_3. Among the bases isolated are $KBrF_4$ (shown by X-ray studies definitely to contain discrete planar BrF_4^- ions), $AgBrF_4$ and $Ba(BrF_4)_2$.

2. Neutralization reactions have been carried out producing salts. For example:

$$\underset{\text{Base}}{AgBrF_4} + \underset{\text{Acid}}{BrF_2SbF_6} = \underset{\text{Salt}}{AgSbF_6} + \underset{\text{Solvent}}{2BrF_3}$$

3. It has also been shown that acids may be titrated with bases and vice versa, and that when these titrations are followed conductimetrically they show sharp end points (minimum in conductivity) at a 1:1 mole ratio of reactants.

Although chemical evidence for the dissociation of IF_5 according to

$$2IF_5 = IF_4^+ + IF_6^-$$

is much less complete than for BrF_3, it is likely that this ionization reaction is the correct one and that it is of importance. Thus the acid IF_4^+ SbF_6^- and the base $K^+IF_6^-$ have been isolated and on mixing their solutions in IF_5 and removing excess solvent the salt $KSbF_6$ is isolated.

22-16. Polyhalide Anions

Table 22-9 indicates the general types of such ions. A few, such as I_3^-, are stable in solution, but most of them, especially the larger ones, exist only in crystalline salts with large cations. The salts are simply made by

TABLE 22-9

Principal Types of Binary and Ternary Polyhalide Salts
(M represents a large univalent cation, e.g., Cs^+, $(CH_3)_4N^+$, etc.)

Type X_n^-	Type XX'_n	Type $XX'X''_n$
MBr_3	$MIBr_2$	$MIBrF$
MI_3	$MICl_2$	$MIFCl_3$
MI_5	$MBrCl_2$	$MIClBr$
MI_7	$MClBr_2$	
MI_9	$MICl_4$	
	$MClF_4$	
	$MBrF_4$	
	MIF_4	
	MIF_6	

crystallizing the halide salt in presence of excess of the halogen. For triiodide only, spectral studies have shown that in CCl_4 at 25°C. there is the
equilibrium:

$$HI + I_2 = HI_3 \qquad K \sim 100$$

The action of IF_5 on alkali iodides and of fluorine on alkali chlorides gives
white powders such as KIF_4 and $CsClF_4$.

So far as is known, all those with three atoms are linear with the heaviest
atom in the middle. In the case of $ClBr_2^-$, however, it is not known whether
the structure is Br—Cl—Br or Br—Br—Cl. The ICl_4^- ion is square planar.
The structure of IF_6^- is unknown. According to the theory outlined in
Chapter 15 this would be expected to have an irregular structure because
of the unshared pair of electrons on iodine rather than a regular octahedral
structure. The I_5^-, I_7^-, and I_9^- ions are rather loose aggregates. In the
tetramethylammonium salt I_5^- has been shown to have the structure depicted in Figure 22-1. The short I—I distance is greater than in the I_2

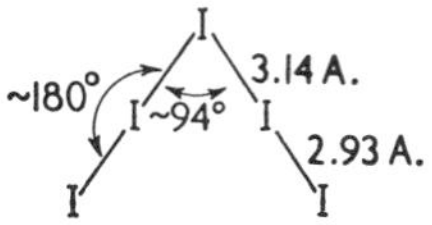

Fig. 22-1.   Structure of the pentaiodide ion, I_5^-, as it occurs in $[(CH_3)_4N]I_5$.

molecule, that is, 2.67 A., but the long I—I distance indicates very weak
bonding, and the ion can be considered to consist of two I_2 molecules fairly
weakly coordinated to I^-.

PSEUDOHALOGENS OR HALOGENOIDS

22-17. Definition

A pseudohalogen or halogenoid is defined as a molecule consisting of more than two electronegative atoms which, in the free state, resembles the halogens; these pseudohalogens give rise to anions which resemble the halide ions in their behavior. The most important pseudohalogens are $(CN)_2$, cyanogen; $(OCN)_2$, oxycyanogen (existence in free state uncertain); $(SCN)_2$, thiocyanogen; $(SeCN)_2$, selenocyanogen; and $(SCSN_3)_2$, azidocarbon disulfide. The pseudohalide ions corresponding to these are CN^-, cyanide; OCN^-, cyanate; SCN^-, thiocyanate; $SeCN^-$, selenocyanate, and $SCSN_3^-$, azidodithiocarbonate. In addition, there are the following pseudohalide ions which have no known pseudohalogen parents: N_3^-, azide, and $TeCN^-$, tellurocyanide. The question of whether there exists a full or partial series of isomeric ions—CNO^-, CNS^-, etc.—will not be discussed here. It is a complicated matter, not admitting, on the basis of available information, of any certain answer.

Let us now state more explicitly those physical and chemical properties of the halogens and halide ions which should characterize substances to be classified as pseudohalogens or pseudohalide ions.

1. The halogenoid should be a volatile substance consisting of a symmetrical combination of two radicals, X—X.

2. The halogenoids should combine with various metals to give salts containing X$^-$ anions.

3. The salts of silver, mercury(I), and lead(II) should be insoluble in water.

4. There should exist acids HX.

5. The pseudohalogen radicals should form compounds among themselves, X—X′, and with the halogens, for example, Cl—X.

6. The halogenoid ions should form complexes with metals as do the halide ions, complexes like $HgCl_4^{2-}$, $CoCl_4^{2-}$, etc.

7. The halogenoid should form covalent compounds analogous to covalent halides.

8. The X$^-$ ion should be oxidized to X$_2$ by suitable oxidizing agents.

22-18. Properties of Particular Compounds

We may now consider the extent to which the various pseudohalogens mentioned above fulfill these requirements.

Cyanogen, $(CN)_2$. This is probably the best known and most important halogenoid, and it fulfills the above requirements quite well. Thus, like iodine, it can be obtained by the reaction

$$2CN^- + Cu^{2+} = CuCN + \tfrac{1}{2}(CN)_2$$

$(CN)_2$ is a poisonous gas (b.p. $= -21°C.$), consisting of two identical radicals, $N\equiv C—C\equiv N$. Salts containing CN^- anions are numerous, and those of Ag^I, Hg^I, and Pb^{II} are very insoluble. The acid HCN is a colorless liquid (b.p. 25.6°C.) of high dielectric constant which can explosively polymerize in the absence of stabilizers. It is hydrogen bonded and it is a weak acid in water (even weaker than HF), so that soluble cyanides hydrolyze,

$$CN^- + H_2O = HCN + OH^-$$

In the crystalline alkali cyanides at normal temperatures the CN^- ion is freely rotating and is thus effectively spherical with a radius of 1.92 A. These cyanides therefore have the same cubic structures as the corresponding halides. Compounds between CN and other halogenoid radicals are known, such as NCN_3 formed by the reaction

$$BrCN + NaN_3 = NaBr + NCN_3$$

and others.

Compounds of CN with the halogens (called both halogen cyanides and cyanogen halides) are well known, except for FCN, which has only recently been shown definitely to exist in equilibrium with F_2 and $(CN)_2$. The cracking of cyanuric fluoride, $(FCN)_3$, produces FCN. ClCN and BrCN are prepared by treating aqueous solutions of CN^- with chlorine or bromine, while ICN is obtained by treating a dry cyanide usually $Hg(CN)_2$, with iodine. ClCN, BrCN, and ICN are all rather volatile compounds which behave like the halogens and like other halogenoids. The molecules are linear, and the important canonical forms, in a valence bond view of the electronic structures are 22-IV, with 22-IVb becoming more important as the electropositive nature

$$:\overset{..}{X}:C:::N: \quad \leftrightarrow \quad :\overset{+}{X}::C::\overset{-}{N}:$$

$$(22\text{-}IVa) \qquad\qquad (22\text{-}IVb)$$

of the halogen increases. The halogen cyanides tend to polymerize forming the trimeric cyanuric halides, which have cyclic structures similar to 22-V. Hydrogen cyanide can polymerize similarly; one product has been shown to be $N\equiv C—CH=NH$.

(22-V)

Cyanide ion not only forms many complexes analogous to halide complexes, but a host of others peculiar to itself. It usually brings out the highest coordination number of the metal ion, resembling F^- somewhat in this respect. Thus there are $[Ag(CN)_2]^-$, analogous to but much more stable than corresponding halide complexes, and $Hg(CN)_4{}^{2-}$, analogous to the tetrahalide complexes of Hg^{II}. With Fe^{III} chloride ion gives $FeCl_4{}^-$, but CN^- gives $[Fe(CN)_6]^{3-}$. Also $[Fe(CN)_6]^{4-}$ exists, whereas no halide complexes of Fe^{II} are known. In general, it can be said that CN^- has an extraordinary ability to function as a ligand and far outclasses all other halide and pseudohalide ions in this respect.

One respect in which cyanogen apparently fails to resemble the halogens closely is in the formation of covalent cyanides of the nonmetals. Only a few such compounds are known. However, it may be that this is due more to lack of efforts to prepare them than to their inherent instability.

The CN^- ion can be oxidized to cyanogen, for instance by Cu^{2+} or Pb^{4+} just as is I^-. Another point of resemblance of $(CN)_2$ to the halogens is its disproportionation in basic solution,

$$(CN)_2 + 2OH^- = CN^- + OCN^- + H_2O$$

Thiocyanogen, $(SCN)_2$. This pseudohalogen is much less well known than its ion, SCN^-, and is more or less a laboratory curiosity. It can be prepared by oxidation of SCN^- by, for instance, lead tetraacetate or MnO_2. It apparently exists in the dimeric state in certain solvents, but in the free state it rapidly and irreversibly polymerizes to brick red parathiocyanogen, $(SCN)_n$, the structure of which is unknown. Chemical evidence, of a rather inconclusive sort, suggests that the dimer has structure 22-VIa rather than 22-VIb.

$$\begin{array}{cc} & \overset{\displaystyle S}{\overset{\displaystyle \|}{}} \\ N\equiv C-S-S-C\equiv N & N\equiv C-S-C\equiv N \\ (22\text{-VIa}) & (22\text{-VIb}) \end{array}$$

The thiocyanate ion, SCN^-, is far more important than its parent pseudohalogen. It has been shown definitely to have the structure SCN, but the question of its linearity is not definitely settled. It is a good ligand, numerous thiocyanate complexes being known, which are usually stoichiometrically analogous to halide complexes, for example, $CoCl_4{}^{2-}$ and $Co(NCS)_4{}^{2-}$. Present information suggests that SCN^- can coordinate either through sulfur or through nitrogen. It tends to coordinate through nitrogen to metal ions of the first transition series and through sulfur to ions of the second and third transition series. Numerous covalent thiocyanates are known, such as $SiCl_3(NCS)$ and $P(NCS)_3$, in which it is believed, although conclusive evidence is lacking, that bonding is to the nitrogen atom.

Cyanate, OCN^-. Evidence for the existence of $(OCN)_2$ is marginal.

However, the OCN⁻ ion and covalent compounds and complexes containing OCN⁻ groups are well known.

(SeCN)₂ and SeCN⁻. Selenocyanogen is obtained as a yellow powder by oxidation of SeNC⁻ with iodine or $Pb(OCOCH_3)_4$. It is fairly stable when dry and in vacuum, but otherwise changes rather rapidly, presumably by polymerization, to a red material of unknown structure. Solutions of the yellow material in benzene contain $(SeCN)_2$ according to molecular weight determinations. Ionic and covalent selenocyanates as well as selenocyanate complexes are known, but are not commonly encountered.

TeCN⁻. The free halogenoid, $(TeCN)_2$ or $(TeCN)_n$, is not known. Tellurocyanides are at present only laboratory curiosities.

Azido carbon disulfide, (SCSN₃)₂. This rather bizarre compound is a white crystalline substance, obtained by oxidizing $KSCSN_3$ with H_2O_2, KIO_3, and various other oxidizing agents. $KSCSN_3$ is obtained by reaction of KN_3 with CS_2 at 40°C. $(SCSN_3)_2$ is not very stable and may decompose violently, according to

$$(SCSN_3)_2 = 2N_2 + 2S + (SCN)_2$$

The structure of $(SCSN_3)_2$ is unknown. It may be either 22-VIIa or 22-VIIb, with 22-VIIa perhaps the more likely.

$$N\!\equiv\!N\!=\!N\!-\!\underset{\underset{S}{\|}}{C}\!-\!S\!-\!S\!-\!\underset{\underset{S}{\|}}{C}\!-\!N\!=\!N\!\equiv\!N \qquad N\!\equiv\!N\!=\!N\!-\!\overset{\overset{S}{\|}}{\underset{\underset{S}{\|}}{C}}\!-\!S\!-\!\overset{\overset{S}{\|}}{C}\!-\!N\!=\!N\!\equiv\!N$$

$$\text{(22-VIIa)} \qquad\qquad\qquad\qquad \text{(22-VIIb)}$$

Azide ion, N₃⁻. The chemistry of azides has been discussed previously (Chapter 12, page 253). The free pseudohalogen N_6 is unknown.

References

Anders, E., *Ann. Rev. Nuclear Sci.*, **9**, 203 (1959). A good review of the nuclear and chemical properties of the element astatine.

Andrews, L. J., and R. M. Keefer, in H. J. Eméleus and A. G. Sharpe, eds., *Advances in Inorganic Chemistry and Radiochemistry*, Vol. 3, Academic Press, New York, 1961, p. 91. A review of complexes of halogen and interhalogen molecules with organic molecules.

Das, T. P., and E. L. Hahn, *Nuclear Quadrupole Resonance Spectroscopy*, Academic Press, New York, 1958. Detailed discussion of theory and experimental results for many halogen compounds.

Hassel, O., *Mol. Phys.*, **1**, 241 (1958). Electron transfer and related molecular complexes of halogens in the solid state.

Havinga, E. E., and E. H. Wiebenga, *Rec. trav. chim.*, **78**, 72 (1959). A review of the interhalogen compounds and polyhalides.

Hyde, E. K., *J. Chem. Educ.*, **36**, 15 (1959). Review on astatine.

Mellor, J. W., *Comprehensive Treatise on Inorganic Chemistry*, Suppl. II, Pt. I, Longmans, Green, New York–London, 1956. Contains all the group VII elements.

Schumaker, J. C., ed., *Perchlorates* (*American Chemical Society Monograph*, No. 146), Reinhold, New York, 1960. An extensive review of perchloric acid and perchlorates.

Sharpe, A. G., *Quart. Revs.* (*London*), **4**, 115 (1950). Interhalogen compounds and polyhalides.

Wiebenga, E. H., E. E. Havinga, and K. H. Boswijk, in H. J. Emeléus and A. G. Sharpe, eds., *Advances in Inorganic Chemistry and Radiochemistry*, Vol. 3, Academic Press, New York, 1961, p. 133. A survey of structures, properties, and bonding in interhalogen compounds.

23

Zinc, Cadmium, and Mercury

GENERAL REMARKS

23-1. Electronic Structures

These three elements follow copper, silver, and gold and have two s electrons outside filled d shells. Their configurations and ionization potentials are given in Table 23-1. Whereas in the elements Cu, Ag, and Au the filled

TABLE 23-1

Some Properties of the Zn, Cd, and Hg Atoms

Element	Outer electronic configuration	Ionization potentials, e.v.		
		1st	2nd	3rd
Zn	$3d^{10}4s^2$	9.39	17.89	40.0
Cd	$4d^{10}5s^2$	8.99	16.84	38.0
Hg	$5d^{10}6s^2$	10.43	18.65	34.3

d shells lose one or two d electrons to give ions or complexes in the II and III oxidation states, this is no longer possible for the group II elements and there is no evidence for oxidation states higher than II. This follows from the fact that the third ionization potentials are extremely high for Zn, Cd, and Hg, and energies of solvation or lattice formation cannot suffice to render the III oxidation states chemically stable.

The primary divergence from the group valence lies in the rather special case of mercurous mercury, where the unique ion Hg_2^{2+} is formed. There have been some unconfirmed reports of monovalent zinc, but Cd^I appears definitely to have been obtained in melts; there is no evidence for Zn^I or Cd^I in aqueous solution, however.

Thus since these elements do not show multiple valence and form no compounds in which the d shell is other than full, they are regarded as nontransition elements, whereas by the same criteria Cu, Ag, and Au are considered as transition elements. Zinc, cadmium, and mercury differ in other ways from the transition metals. Thus, although they are metals, they are softer and lower melting, and Zn and Cd are considerably more electropositive, than their near neighbors in the transition groups. However, there is some resemblance to the transition elements, as well as a considerable difference from the strictly nontransition elements which follow them—Ga, In, and Tl, respectively—in their ability to form complexes, particularly with ammonia, amines, halide ions, and cyanide.

23-2. Trends in the Group

Although the chemistry of cadmium is essentially homologous to that of zinc, mercury is more different from than similar to Zn and Cd both in the properties of the element and in its compounds.

As would be expected, $Cd(OH)_2$ is more basic than $Zn(OH)_2$, which is amphoteric, whereas $Hg(OH)_2$ is an extremely weak base. Zinc and cadmium form halides which are essentially ionic, crystallizing in layer lattices, but the mercuric halides are covalent; thus discrete $HgCl_2$ molecules may be discerned in the crystal lattice and mercuric halides are almost undissociated in aqueous solution.

Although Zn and Cd are electropositive metals, mercury has unusually high ionization potentials, a very negative electrode potential, and is generally rather inert chemically. These properties of mercury may be regarded as a manifestation of the "inert pair" effect which has been noted also in the chemical properties of Tl, Pb, and Bi and to a lesser extent in In and Sn.

The Zn^{2+} and Cd^{2+} ions are rather similar in many respects to Mg^{2+} and have numerous isomorphous salts. While all of the ions Zn^{2+}, Cd^{2+}, and Hg^{2+} have a pronounced tendency to form complexes, the Hg^{2+} complexes are usually orders of magnitude more stable than those of Zn^{2+} and Cd^{2+} as can be seen from Table 23-2. All three elements form a variety of covalently bound compounds, and the polarizing ability of the M^{2+} ions appears to be larger than might have been expected by comparing their radii with those of the Mg, Ca, Sr, Ba group, a fact that can be associated with the greater ease of distortion of the filled d shell compared to the inert-gas-like ions of the latter elements.

In line with its superior tendency to form covalent bonds, mercury forms a large number of organometallic compounds, generally R_2Hg and $RHgX$,

TABLE 23-2

Equilibrium Constants for Some Typical Complexes
of Zn, Cd, and Hg
$(M^{2+} + 4X = [MX_4]; K = [MX_4]/[M^{2+}][X]^4)$

X	K		
	Zn^{2+}	Cd^{2+}	Hg^{2+}
Cl^-	1	10^3	10^{16}
Br^-	10^{-1}	10^4	10^{22}
I^-	10^{-2}	10^6	10^{30}
NH_3	10^9	10^7	10^{19}
CN^-	10^{16}	10^{18}	10^{41}

which are stable to air and water. The corresponding zinc and cadmium compounds are unstable to air and water and more generally reactive. The unusual stability of the mercury compounds is not indicative of high bond strengths—on the contrary, these are not high—but must be attributed to the very low affinity of mercury for oxygen.

THE ELEMENTS

23-3. Occurrence and Isolation

The elements are of relatively low abundance in nature but have long been well known because they occur in localized deposits and are rather easily won from their ores. Zinc occurs in a number of minerals—zinc blende, ZnS; smithsonite or calamine, $ZnCO_3$; willemite, Zn_2SiO_4; zincite, ZnO; and several others. Cadmium is most commonly found associated with zinc in such ores, but in small amounts. The commercially important zinc ores are mainly the carbonate and the sulfide. On roasting either in air, the oxide is obtained. This may then be reduced, commonly with coke, and the metal distilled out. Any cadmium present can be separated by fractional distillation since the boiling points differ appreciably (Zn, 907°C.; Cd, 767°C.). Alternatively, the ZnO may be dissolved in acid and the metal electrodeposited. This is possible because the high overvoltage of hydrogen on zinc (a phenomenon not well understood) allows zinc to deposit in the presence of H^+ despite the fact that *equilibrium* electrode potentials would require hydrogen to be reduced preferentially to zinc.

Cadmium may be obtained by treating the solution, prior to electrolysis, with zinc dust which reduces the Cd^{2+}:

$$Zn + Cd^{2+} = Zn^{2+} + Cd \qquad E^0 = 0.36 \text{ v.}$$

The only important ore of mercury is cinnabar, HgS, which is found mostly on the Iberian peninsula. Roasting HgS converts it to the oxide, and this, upon heating to about 500°C., decomposes without need of any reducing agent, so that free mercury distills out.

23-4. Physical and Chemical Properties

The main properties of the elements are listed in Table 23-3. Zinc and

TABLE 23-3

Some Characteristic Properties of the Group IIB Elements

	Zinc	Cadmium	Mercury
Melting point, °C.	419	321	−39
Boiling point, °C.	907	767	357
Heat of vaporization, kcal./mole	31.2	26.8	14.7
E^0 for $M = M^{2+} + 2e$, v.	0.762	0.402	−0.854
Radii of divalent ions, A.	0.69	0.92	0.93

cadmium are white, lustrous, but tarnishable metals. Like Be and Mg, with which they are isostructural, their structures deviate from perfect hexagonal close packing by elongation along the six-fold axis. Mercury is a shiny liquid at ordinary temperatures. All are remarkably volatile for heavy metals, mercury, of course uniquely so. Mercury gives a monatomic vapor and has an appreciable vapor pressure (1.3×10^{-7} mm.) at 20°C. It is also surprisingly soluble in both polar and nonpolar liquids; for example, a saturated solution in water at room temperature is about $10^{-7}M$. Because of its high volatility and toxic nature, mercury should always be kept in stoppered containers and handled in well-ventilated areas.

As may be seen from the oxidation potentials, Zn and Cd are fairly electropositive whereas mercury is "noble." Both Zn and Cd react readily with nonoxidizing acids releasing hydrogen and giving the divalent ions, whereas Hg is inert to nonoxidizing acids. Zinc also dissolves in strong bases because of its ability to form zincate ions, commonly written ZnO_2^{2-}, but certainly better represented as $[Zn(OH)_3(H_2O)]^-$, $[Zn(OH)_3(H_2O)_3]^-$, or $[Zn(OH)_4]^{2-}$. Although the structure of the species in solution is not definitely known, solid zincates such as $NaZn(OH)_3$ and $Na_2Zn(OH)_4$ can be obtained from concentrated solutions. Using the simpler formula, the reaction can be written

$$Zn + 2OH^- = ZnO_2^{2-} + H_2$$

Cadmium does not react with base since cadmiate ions are of negligible stability.

Zinc and cadmium react readily with oxygen on heating to give the oxides. Although mercury and oxygen are unstable with respect to HgO at room temperature, their rate of combination is exceedingly slow; the reaction proceeds at a useful rate at 300–350°C., but, around 400°C. and above, the stability relation reverses and HgO decomposes rapidly into the elements. This ability of mercury to absorb oxygen from air and regenerate it again in pure form was of considerable importance in the earliest studies of oxygen by Lavoisier and Priestley.

All of the elements react directly with halogens and with sulfur and other nonmetals such as phosphorus, selenium, etc.

Zinc and cadmium form very many alloys, some, such as brass, being of technical importance. Mercury combines with many other metals, sometimes with difficulty but sometimes, as with sodium or potassium, very vigorously; these alloys are called *amalgams*. Some amalgams are known to have definite compositions; that is, they are compounds, such as Hg_2Na. Some of the transition metals do not form amalgams, and iron is commonly used for containers of mercury. Sodium amalgams and amalgamated zinc are commonly used as reducing agents for aqueous solutions.

ZINC AND CADMIUM COMPOUNDS

23-5. Oxides and Hydroxides

The oxides, ZnO and CdO, are formed on burning the metals in air or by pyrolysis of the carbonates or nitrates; oxide smokes can be obtained by combustion of the alkyls, cadmium oxide smokes being exceedingly toxic. Zinc oxide is normally white but turns yellow on heating; cadmium oxide varies in color from greenish yellow through brown to nearly black, depending on its thermal history. These colors are the result of various kinds of lattice defects. Both oxides sublime without decomposition at very high temperatures.

The hydroxides are precipitated from solutions of salts by addition of bases. The solubility products of $Zn(OH)_2$ and $Cd(OH)_2$ are about 10^{-11}

and 10^{-14}, respectively, but $Zn(OH)_2$ is more soluble than would be expected from this constant owing to the equilibrium

$$Zn(OH)_2(s) = Zn(OH)_2(aq) \quad K = 10^{-6}$$

Further, $Zn(OH)_2$ readily dissolves in excess alkali bases to give zincate ions; $Cd(OH)_2$ is insoluble in bases. Both hydroxides readily dissolve in excess of strong ammonia to form ammine complexes, for example, $[Zn(NH_3)_4]^{2+}$.

23-6. Sulfides, Selenides, Tellurides

These are all crystalline substances insoluble in water; several of them (e.g., ZnS and CdS) occur in nature. The structures as well as those of the oxides are of interest. Three structures are represented among the eight compounds as shown in Table 23-4. The rock salt and zinc blende struc-

TABLE 23-4

Structures[a] of Zn and Cd Oxides and Chalconides[b]

Metal	O	S	Se	Te
Zn	W, Z	Z, W	Z	Z, W
Cd	NaCl	W, Z	W, Z	Z

[a] W = wurtzite structure; Z = zinc blende structure; NaCl = rock salt structure.
[b] Where two polymorphs occur, the one stable at lower temperatures is listed first.

tures have been described earlier (pages 37 and 44). In the former, the cation is octahedrally surrounded by six anions, whereas in the latter the cation is tetrahedrally surrounded by anions. The wurtzite structure (from the mineral wurtzite, which is the stable high temperature modifica-

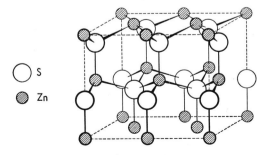

Fig. 23-1. The wurtzite structure.

tion of ZnS) also gives the cations tetrahedral coordination and is shown in Figure 23-1. It will be seen from Table 23-4 that, with the exception of CdO, zinc and cadmium prefer tetrahedral coordination in their chalconides.

23-7. Halides and Halide Complexes

All four halides of both zinc and cadmium are known. Some of their relevant properties are given in Table 23-5.

TABLE 23-5

Some Properties of the Zinc and Cadmium Halides

	Solubility in water, mole/liter	Melting point, °C.	Boiling point, °C.	Structure
ZnF_2	1.57 (20°C.)	872	1502	Unknown
$ZnCl_2$	31.8 (25°C.)	275	756	Three forms; see text
$ZnBr_2$	20.9 (25°C.)	394	697	CCP anions with Zn in
ZnI_2	13 (25°C.)	446	(Sublimes)	tetrahedral interstices
CdF_2	0.29 (25°C.)	1110	1747	Unknown
$CdCl_2$	7.7 (20°C.)	868	980	Close-packed anions
$CdBr_2$	4.2 (20°C.)	568	1136	with Cd in octahedral
CdI_2	2.3 (20°C.)	387	(Sublimes)	interstices

Both ZnF_2 and CdF_2 show distinct evidence of being considerably more ionic than the other halides of the same element. Thus they have higher melting points and boiling points, and they are considerably less soluble in water. The latter fact is attributable not only to the high lattice energies of the fluorides but also to the fact that the formation of halo complexes in solution, which enhances the solubility of the other halides, does not occur for the fluoride.

The structures of the chlorides, bromides, and iodides may be viewed as close-packed arrays of halide ions, but there is a characteristic difference in that zinc ions occupy tetrahedral interstices whereas cadmium ions occupy octahedral ones. Actually, there are at least three polymorphs of $ZnCl_2$ known, two of which are similar and in which the presence of zinc ions in tetrahedral holes has been demonstrated. It is curious that until quite recently it was erroneously believed that all zinc halides had the same structure as CdI_2.

Complex anions are formed by both metals, but the equilibrium constants vary rather widely as the data in Table 23-6 show. The exact values are not

TABLE 23-6

Some Formation Constants of Zinc and Cadmium Halide Complexes
(At 25°C.)

	Halogen	Log K_1	Log K_2	Log K_3	Log K_4	Medium
Zn	F	0.75	Not obs.	Not obs.	Not obs.	0.5–1.0M NaClO$_4$
	Cl	−1.0 to +1.0	−1.0 to +1.0	−1.0 to +1.0	−1.0 to +1.0	Variable
	Br	−0.60	−0.37	−0.73	0.44	Ionic str. = 4.5
	I	−2.93	1.25	−0.07	−0.59	Ionic str. = 4.5
Cd	F	0.46	0.07	Not obs.	Not obs.	1.0M NaClO$_4$
	Cl	1.77	1.45	−0.25	−0.05	2.1M KNO$_3$
	Br	1.97	1.25	0.24	0.15	1M KNO$_3$
	I	2.96	1.33	1.07	1.00	1.6M KNO$_3$

important since ionic strength effects are rather large, but certain qualitative features can be discerned. The formation of fluoro complexes is quite restricted, and none have been isolated as solids. There is evidence for the attainment of all four stages of complexation by both zinc and cadmium for Cl^-, Br^-, and I^-, with the cadmium complexes being moderately stable while those of zinc are of rather low stability. The ZnX_4^{2-} complexes can be isolated as salts of large cations.

It has long been known that aqueous solutions of cadmium halides appear, superficially, to be incompletely dissociated, that is, to be weak electrolytes. Although there are significant amounts of the undissociated halides, CdX_2, present in moderately concentrated solutions, there are other species also present as shown in Table 23-7. Thus the solutions are

TABLE 23-7

Approximate Concentrations of Dissociated and Undissociated Species
(In 0.5M CdBr$_2$ solution at 25°C.)

	Concentration, M		Concentration, M
Cd^{2+}	0.013	Br^-	0.200
$CdBr^+$	0.259	$CdBr_2$	0.174
$CdBr_3^-$	0.043	$CdBr_4^{2-}$	0.021

best regarded as systems containing all possible species in equilibrium rather than simply as solutions of a weak electrolyte; of course, the ratios of the species vary with conditions of concentration and pH.

The zinc halides are dissociated to a greater extent than the cadmium halides but are also more hydrolyzed in water; the aquo ion $[Zn(H_2O)_6]^{2+}$ is quite a strong acid. The major hydrolysis product of $CdCl_2$ appears to be $Cd(OH)Cl$.

Both zinc and cadmium halides are quite soluble in alcohol, acetone, and similar solvents.

23-8. Other Salts

These call for little comment. Oxy salts such as the nitrate, sulfate, sulfite, perchlorate, and acetate are known and are soluble in water. The Zn^{2+} and Cd^{2+} ions are rather similar to Mg^{2+}, and many of their salts are isomorphous with magnesium salts, for example, $Zn(Mg)SO_4 \cdot 7H_2O$ and $M^I_2SO_4 \cdot Zn(Cd, Mg, Hg)SO_4 \cdot 6H_2O$. Zinc forms a basic acetate isomorphous with the oxyacetate of beryllium, $Zn_4O(OCOCH_3)_6$, on distillation of the normal acetate in vacuum. It is a crystalline solid rapidly hydrolyzed by water, unlike the beryllium compound, the difference being due to the possibility of coordination numbers exceeding four for zinc.

Simple cyanides, $M(CN)_2$, and complex cyanides, such as $[M(CN)_4]^{2-}$, are also well characterized; carbonates and hydroxy carbonates are also known.

23-9. Organometallic Compounds

The organozinc compounds are historically important since they were the first organometallic compounds to be prepared; their discovery by Frankland in 1849 played a decisive part in the development of modern ideas of chemical bonding. The zinc and cadmium compounds are also of interest since their mild reactivities toward certain organic functional groups give them unique synthetic potentialities.

Organozinc compounds of the types "RZnX" and R_2Zn are known, whereas only R_2Cd compounds have been isolated. Quotation marks are required on "RZnX" since molecular weight and isotopic exchange studies show that no such species actually exist. The species $R_2Zn \cdot ZnX_2$ and $R_2Cd \cdot CdX_2$ apparently do exist, but the lack of exchange of radioactive zinc between R_2Zn and ZnX_2 when solutions of these components are mixed indicates that RZnX species never form. Similar remarks apply to "RMgX" and "RBeX," although RHgX species are quite genuine.

The zinc alkyls can be obtained by thermal decomposition of "RZnI," which is prepared by the reaction of alkyl iodides with a zinc–copper couple.

$$C_2H_5I + Zn(Cu) = C_2H_5ZnI \xrightarrow{heat} \tfrac{1}{2}(C_2H_5)_2Zn + \tfrac{1}{2}ZnI_2$$

The alkyls may also be prepared and the diaryls most conveniently obtained by the reaction of zinc metal with an organomercury compound

$$R_2Hg + Zn = R_2Zn + Hg$$

or by reaction of zinc chloride with organolithium or Grignard reagents.

The only satisfactory preparation of R_2Cd compounds is by treatment of the anhydrous cadmium halide with RLi or RMgX, the reaction of cadmium metal with a dialkyl or diaryl mercury gives an equilibrium mixture which is difficult to separate

$$Cd + R_2Hg = R_2Cd + Hg$$

The R_2Zn and R_2Cd compounds are nonpolar liquids or low-melting solids soluble in most organic liquids. The lower alkyl zinc compounds are spontaneously flammable, and all react vigorously with oxygen and with water. The cadmium compounds are less sensitive to oxygen but are less stable thermally.

Both zinc and cadmium compounds react readily with compounds containing active hydrogen, such as alcohols,

$$R_2M + R'OH = RMOR' + RH$$

and are generally similar to RLi or RMgX, although their lower reactivity allows selective alkylations not possible with the more standard reagents. An important example is the use of the cadmium compounds in the synthesis of ketones from acyl chlorides:

$$2RCOCl + R_2'Cd = 2RCOR' + CdCl_2$$

Diphenylzinc and diphenylcadmium react with excess phenyllithium to form complexes such as $Li[Zn(C_6H_5)_3]$.

23-10. Complex Compounds: Stereochemistry

It must be noted first of all that there are no ligand field stabilization effects in the Zn^{2+} and Cd^{2+} ions because of their completed d shells. Thus the stereochemistry of their compounds is determined solely by considerations of size, electrostatic forces, and covalent bonding forces. The effect of size is to make Cd^{2+} more likely than Zn^{2+} to assume a coordination number of six. For example, ZnO crystallizes in lattices where the Zn^{2+} ion is in tetrahedral holes surrounded by four oxide ions, whereas CdO has the rock-salt structure. Similarly $ZnCl_2$ crystallizes in at least three polymorphs, two or more of which have tetrahedrally coordinated zinc atoms; $CdCl_2$, on the other hand, has only one form, involving octahedral coordination.

In their complexes, zinc and cadmium often have coordination numbers of six, but four is more common; some examples are given in Table 23-8.

TABLE 23-8

Stereochemistry of Zinc and Cadmium

Coordination number	Bonding	Geometry	Examples
2	sp	Linear	$Zn(CH_3)_2$, $Cd(C_6H_5)_2$
4	sp^3	Tetrahedral	$[Zn(CN)_4]^{2-}$, $[CdBr_4]^{2-}$, $[Cd(NH_3)_4]^{2+}$, $Zn(NH_3)_2Cl_2$
5	sp^3d	Distorted trigonal bipyramidal	Terpyridyl $ZnCl_2$, $Zn(Acac)_2 \cdot H_2O$
6	sp^3d^2	Octahedral	$[Zn(NH_3)_6]^{2+}$ (in crystals only)

A few cases of square-planar four-coordinate zinc are known, for example, bis(glycinyl)zinc.

23-11. Univalent Cadmium

When cadmium is dissolved in molten cadmium halides, very dark red-black melts are obtained. The high color may be due to the existence of both Cd^I and Cd^{II} joined by halide bridges, since mixed valence states in complexes are known to give intense colorations in many other cases. If aluminum chloride is added to the $Cd–CdCl_2$ melt, for example, only a green-yellow melt is obtained and phase studies here and for the bromide have shown the presence of Cd^I. Yellow solids such as $CdAlCl_4$ can be isolated, and their spectra show the presence of the tetrahaloaluminate. Since they are diamagnetic, the solids can be formulated $(Cd_2)^{2+}(AlCl_4^-)_2$. When they are added to donor solvents or to water, cadmium metal is at once formed, together with Cd^{2+}, so that it is not surprising that there is no evidence for Cd^I in aqueous solution. The stabilization by the tetrahaloaluminate ions is presumably due to the lowering of the difference between the lattice energies of the two oxidation states and a lowering of the tendency to disproportionate. A similar case of this type of stabilization has been noted for Ga^I, as in $Ga^+AlCl_4^-$.

MERCURY COMPOUNDS

23-12. The Mercurous Ion and Mercurous-Mercuric Equilibria

As noted in Section 23-2, the chemistry of mercury differs from that of zinc and cadmium not only because of inherent peculiarities of the element and of mercuric compounds but also because of the existence of the unique mercurous ion, ^{+}Hg—Hg^{+}, which is readily obtained by reduction of mercuric salts and is also easily oxidized to them.

There have been many lines of evidence showing the binuclear nature of Hg_2^{2+}. A few of these may be noted:

1. Mercurous compounds are diamagnetic both as solids and in solution, whereas Hg^{+} would have an unpaired electron.

2. X-ray determination of the structures of several mercurous salts shows the existence of individual Hg_2^{2+} ions. We may note that the Hg—Hg distances are far from constant (Table 23-9).

TABLE 23-9

Mercury-Mercury Bond Lengths
in Mercurous Compounds

Salt	Hg—Hg, A.
Hg_2F_2	2.43
Hg_2Cl_2	2.53
Hg_2Br_2	2.58
Hg_2I_2	2.69
$Hg_2(NO_3)_2 \cdot 2H_2O$	2.54

3. The Raman spectrum of an aqueous solution of mercurous nitrate contains a strong line which can only be attributed to an Hg—Hg stretching vibration.

4. There are various kinds of equilibria for which constant equilibrium quotients can be obtained only by considering the mercurous ion to be Hg_2^{2+}. For example, suppose we add an excess of mercury to a solution initially X molar in mercuric nitrate. An equilibrium between Hg, Hg^{2+}, and mercurous ion will be reached (see below); depending on the assumed nature of mercurous ion the following equilibrium quotients can be written:

$$Hg(l) + Hg^{2+} = Hg_2^{2+} \qquad K = [Hg_2^{2+}]/[Hg^{2+}] = f/(1-f)$$
$$Hg(l) + Hg^{2+} = 2Hg^{+} \qquad K' = [Hg^{+}]^2/[Hg^{2+}] = (2fX)^2/(1-f)X = 4f^2X/(1-f)$$

where f represents the fraction of the initial Hg^{2+} found by analysis or otherwise to have disappeared when equilibrium is reached. It is found that when values of K and K' are calculated from experimental data at different values of X, the former are substantially constant while the latter are not.

5. The electrical conductances of solutions of mercurous salts resemble closely in magnitude and variation with concentration the conductances of uni-divalent rather than uni-univalent electrolytes.

Hg^I–Hg^{II} Equilibria. An understanding of the thermodynamics of these equilibria is essential to an understanding of the chemistry of the mercurous state. The important thermodynamic values are the potentials:

$$2Hg(l) = Hg_2^{2+} + 2e \qquad E^0 = -0.789 \text{ v.} \qquad (23\text{-}1)$$
$$Hg_2^{2+} = 2Hg^{2+} + 2e \qquad E^0 = -0.920 \text{ v.} \qquad (23\text{-}2)$$
$$Hg(l) = Hg^{2+} + 2e \qquad E^0 = -0.854 \text{ v.} \qquad (23\text{-}3)$$

For the disproportionation equilibrium

$$Hg_2^{2+} = Hg(l) + Hg^{2+} \qquad E^0 = -0.131 \text{ v.} \qquad (23\text{-}4)$$

we then have

$$K = [Hg^{2+}]/[Hg_2^{2+}] = 6.0 \times 10^{-3}$$
$$\frac{1}{K} = 166$$

The implication of the oxidation potentials is clearly that only oxidizing agents with potentials in the range 0.8–0.9 v. can oxidize mercury to Hg^I but not to Hg^{II}. Since no common oxidizing agents meet this requirement, it is found that when mercury is treated with an excess of oxidizing agent it is entirely converted to Hg^{II}. However, when mercury is in at least 50% excess only Hg^I is obtained since according to equation 23-4, $Hg(l)$ readily reduces Hg^{2+} to Hg_2^{2+}.

The equilibrium constant for reaction 23-4 shows that, although Hg_2^{2+} is stable with respect to disproportionation, it is only so by a small margin. Thus any reagents which reduce the activity (by precipitation or complexation) of Hg^{2+} to a significantly greater extent than they lower the activity of Hg_2^{2+} will cause disproportionation of Hg_2^{2+}. There are many such reagents, so that the number of stable Hg^I compounds is rather restricted.

Thus on adding OH^- to a solution of Hg_2^{2+}, a dark precipitate consisting of Hg and HgO is formed; evidently mercurous hydroxide if it could be isolated would be a stronger base than HgO. Similarly, addition of sulfide ions to a solution of Hg_2^{2+} gives a mixture of Hg and the extremely insoluble HgS. Mercurous cyanide does not exist because $Hg(CN)_2$ is so slightly dissociated though soluble. The reactions in these cited cases are:

$$Hg_2^{2+} + 2OH^- = Hg(l) + HgO(s) + H_2O$$
$$Hg_2^{2+} + S^- = Hg(l) + HgS$$
$$Hg_2^{2+} + 2CN^- = Hg(l) + Hg(CN)_2(aq)$$

23-13. Mercurous Compounds

As indicated above, no hydroxide, oxide, or sulfide can be obtained by addition of the appropriate anion to aqueous Hg_2^{2+}, nor have these compounds been otherwise made.

Among the best known of the few mercurous compounds are the *halides*. The fluoride is unstable toward water, being hydrolyzed to hydrofluoric acid and unisolable mercurous hydroxide which disproportionates as above. The other halides are highly insoluble, which thus precludes the possibilities of hydrolysis or disproportionation to give Hg^{II} halide complexes. Mercurous *nitrate* is known only as the dihydrate $Hg_2(NO_3)_2 \cdot 2H_2O$, which X-ray studies have shown to contain the ion $[H_2O—Hg—Hg—OH_2]^{2+}$; a *perchlorate*, $Hg_2(ClO_4)_2 \cdot 4H_2O$, is also known. Both are very soluble in water, and the halides and other relatively insoluble salts of Hg_2^{2+} may conveniently be prepared by adding the appropriate anions to their solutions. Other known mercurous salts are the sparingly soluble sulfate, chlorate, bromate, iodate, and acetate.

Mercurous ion forms few *complexes;* this may in part be due to a low tendency for Hg_2^{2+} to form coordinate bonds, but is probably due mainly to the fact that mercuric ion will form even more stable complexes with most ligands, for example, CN^-, I^-, amines and alkyl sulfides, so that the Hg_2^{2+} disproportionates. There is evidence that mercury(I) complexes can be obtained in solution with ligands which form essentially ionic metal–ligand bonds and hence no strong complexes with mercury(II). Such ligands are oxalate, succinate, pyrophosphate, and tripolyphosphate. Pyrophosphate gives the species $[Hg_2(P_2O_7)_2]^{6-}$ (pH range 6.5–9) and $[Hg_2(P_2O_7)OH]^{3-}$ for which stability constants have been measured.

23-14. Mercuric Oxide and Sulfide

Red mercuric oxide is formed on gentle pyrolysis of mercurous or mercuric nitrate or by direct interaction of mercury and oxygen at 300–350°C. Addition of OH^- to aqueous Hg^{2+} gives a yellow precipitate of HgO; the yellow form differs from the red only in particle size. The oxide has the zinc blende structure.

No hydroxide has been obtained, but the oxide is soluble (10^{-3} to 10^{-4} moles/liter) in water, the exact solubility depending on particle size, to give a solution of what is commonly assumed to be the hydroxide, although there is no proof for such a species. This "hydroxide" is an extremely weak base,

$$K = [Hg^{2+}][OH^-]^2/[Hg(OH)_2] = 1.8 \times 10^{-22}$$

and is somewhat amphoteric, though more basic than acidic. The equilibria involved in red HgO dissolved in $HClO_4$ have been interpreted in terms of the species Hg^{2+}, $HgOH^+$, and $Hg(OH)_2$. There is no evidence for any hydroxy complexes even in $2M$ NaOH, however.

Mercuric *sulfide*, HgS, is precipitated from aqueous solutions as a black, highly insoluble compound. The solubility product is 10^{-54}, but the sulfide is somewhat more soluble than this figure would imply because of some hydrolysis of Hg^{2+} and S^{2-} ions. The black sulfide is unstable with respect to a red form identical with the mineral cinnabar and changes into it on heating or digesting with alkali polysulfides or mercurous chloride. The red form has a distorted sodium chloride lattice. Another form, occurring as the mineral metacinnabarite, has a zinc blende structure.

The selenide and telluride have the zinc blende structure.

23-15. Mercuric Halides

All four halides are known. The *fluoride* is essentially ionic and crystallizes in the fluorite structure; it is almost completely decomposed, even by cold water, as would be expected for an ionic compound which is the salt of a weak acid and an extremely weak base. Not only does mercury(II) show no tendency to form covalent Hg—F bonds, but no fluoro complexes are known.

In sharp contrast to the fluoride, the other halides show marked covalent character, and indeed for $HgCl_2$ the covalent character is extreme. Mercuric *chloride* crystallizes in an essentially molecular lattice, the two short Hg—Cl distances being about the same length as the Hg—Cl bonds in gaseous $HgCl_2$ while the next shortest distances are much longer (see Table 23-10). The *bromide* and *iodide* both crystallize in layer lattices; in HgBr₂

TABLE 23-10

Hg—X Distances in Mercuric Halides
(In Angstrom units)

Compound	Solid			Gas
	Two at	Two at	Two at	
HgF_2		Eight at 2.40		—
$HgCl_2$	2.25	3.34	3.63	2.28 ± 0.04
$HgBr_2$	2.48	3.23	3.23	2.40 ± 0.04
HgI_2		Four at 2.78		2.57 ± 0.04

each mercury atom is surrounded by six bromine atoms, but two are so much closer than the other four that one can consider that perturbed molecules are present. The lattice of HgI_2 is not in any sense molecular; regular HgI_4 tetrahedra are found with an Hg—I distance appreciably in excess of the Hg—I distance in the free molecules. In the gas phase all three halides are distinctly molecular as they are also in solutions. Relative to ionic HgF_2 the other halides have very low melting and boiling points (Table 23-11). They also show marked solubility in many organic solvents.

TABLE 23-11

Some Properties of Mercuric Halides

Halide	Melting point, °C.	Boiling point, °C.	Solubility, moles/100 moles at 25°C.			
			In H_2O	In C_2H_5OH	In $C_2H_5OCOCH_3$	In C_6H_6
HgF_2	645	650	Hydrolyzes	Insol.	Insol.	Insol.
$HgCl_2$	280	303	0.48	8.14	9.42	0.152
$HgBr_2$	238	318	0.031	3.83	—	—
HgI_2	257	351	0.00023	0.396	0.566	0.067

In aqueous solution they exist almost exclusively ($\sim$99%) as HgX_2 molecules.

23-16. Other Mercuric Salts

Among the mercuric salts which are quite ionic and hence highly dissociated in aqueous solution are the nitrate, sulfate, and perchlorate. Because of the great weakness of mercuric hydroxide, aqueous solutions of these salts tend to hydrolyze extensively and must be acidified in order to be stable.

There are also salts which, like the halides and chalconides, are partly or wholly undissociated or insoluble in water and hence stable toward it. Among these are the cyanide, oxalate, phosphate, and thiocyanate as well as carboxylates which partly dissociate. The *cyanide* has been found to

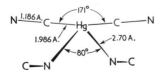

Fig. 23-2.   Details of the coordination of the Hg^{2+} ion in mercury(II) cyanide.

have a rather unexpected structure where almost linear $Hg(CN)_2$ molecules are linked together in endless zig-zig chains through a long $Hg—N$ (2.70 A.) bond (see Fig. 23-2).

23-17. Novel Compounds of Mercury(II) with Nitrogen

It has been known since the days of alchemy that when Hg_2Cl_2 is treated with aqueous ammonia a black residue is formed, and this reaction is still used in qualitative analysis to identify Hg_2Cl_2. Only relatively recently has the nature of the reaction been clarified. These residues contain nitrogen compounds of Hg^{II} plus metallic mercury, and the Hg^{II} compounds can be obtained directly from Hg^{II} salts.

There are three known products of the reaction of $HgCl_2$ with ammonia, the proportion of any one of them depending on the conditions. The possible products are $Hg(NH_3)_2Cl_2$, $HgNH_2Cl$ and $Hg_2NCl \cdot H_2O$ and they are formed according to the following equations:

$$HgCl_2 + 2NH_3 = Hg(NH_3)_2Cl_2(s)$$
$$HgCl_2 + 2NH_3 = HgNH_2Cl(s) + NH_4^+ + Cl^-$$
$$2HgCl_2 + 4NH_3 + H_2O = Hg_2NCl \cdot H_2O + 3NH_4^+ + 3Cl^-$$

The equilibria represented here seem to be labile so that the product obtained can be controlled by varying the concentrations of NH_3 and NH_4^+. In concentrated NH_4Cl solution, the diammine $Hg(NH_3)_2Cl_2$ is precipitated, whereas, with dilute ammonia and no excess NH_4^+, the amide $HgNH_2Cl$ is formed. The compound $Hg_2NCl \cdot H_2O$ is probably not produced in a pure state by the above reaction, but it can be obtained by treating the compound $Hg_2NOH \cdot 2H_2O$ (Millon's base) with hydrochloric acid. Millon's base itself is made by the action of aqueous ammonia on yellow mercuric oxide.

The diammine has been shown to consist of discrete tetrahedral molecules. The amide has infinite chains $—Hg—NH_2—Hg—NH_2—$, where the $N—Hg—N$ segments are linear while the bonds about nitrogen are tetrahedral; the chloride ions lie between the chains. The analogous bromide has the same structure.

Millon's base has a three dimensional framework of composition Hg_2N with the OH^- ions and water molecules occupying rather spacious cavities and channels. Many salts of Millon's base are known, for example, $Hg_2NX \cdot nH_2O$ ($X = NO_3^-$, ClO_4^-, Cl^-, Br^-, I^-; $n = 0–2$). In these the framework appears to remain essentially unaltered, and thus it is an ion exchanger similar to a zeolite.

Returning to the dark residues given by mercurous chloride, one or both of $HgNH_2Cl$ and $H_2NCl \cdot H_2O$ are present together with free metal. The insolubility of these compounds causes the disproportionation of the Hg_2^{2+}, for example,

$$Hg_2Cl_2(s) + 2NH_3 = Hg(l) + HgNH_2Cl(s) + NH_4^+ + Cl^-$$

There is no evidence for any intermediate ammonobasic or ammine compounds of mercury(I).

23-18. Organomercury Compounds

A vast number of organomercury compounds, some of which have useful physiological properties, are known. They are of the types RHgX, and R_2Hg, and are obtained from mercuric chloride and Grignard reagents in the appropriate mole ratios.

In the case of arylmercury compounds, many other reactions may be used. Notable among these is the fairly general "mercuration" reaction of aromatic hydrocarbons by mercuric acetate shown in equation 23-5. The

$$X\text{—}\langle\bigcirc\rangle \; + \; Hg(OCOCH_3)_2 \; = \; o\text{- or } p\text{-}(\langle\bigcirc\rangle)Hg(OCOCH_3) \; + \; CH_3COOH \tag{23-5}$$

variation in rates of reactivities with varying X suggests that attack upon the aromatic ring is by a positive species, but the mechanism is not well understood.

The *RHgX compounds* are crystalline solids whose properties depend on the nature of X. When X is an atom or group which can form covalent bonds to mercury, for example, Cl, Br, I, CN, SCN, OH, the compound is a covalent nonpolar substance more soluble in organic liquids than in water. When X is SO_4^- or NO_3^-, the substance is salt-like and presumably quite ionic, for instance, $[RHg]^+NO_3^-$. Acetates behave as weak electrolytes.

The dialkyls and diaryls are nonpolar, volatile, dangerously toxic liquids or low-melting solids. All are thermally rather unstable and light sensitive, but can be kept for months without great loss. Their principal use, and a valuable one, is in the preparation of other organometallic compounds by direct interchange, for example,

$$\frac{n}{2} R_2Hg + M = R_nM + \frac{n}{2} Hg$$

This reaction proceeds essentially to completion with alkali metals, alkaline earths, zinc, aluminum, gallium, tin, lead, antimony, bismuth, selenium, and tellurium, but with indium, thallium, and cadmium reversible equilibria are established.

The R_2Hg compounds have very low reactivity toward oxygen, water, active hydrogen, and organic functional groups in general. They are quite useful for partial alkylations of reactive halides, for instance,

$$(C_2H_5)_2Hg + AsCl_3 = C_2H_5HgCl + C_2H_5AsCl_2$$

There are also numerous compounds formed by the addition of mercuric salts to *olefins*. While it has been considered that some of these have olefin–metal μ bonds (see page 642), there is no good evidence for such bonding, and the present evidence favors the view that addition of HgX_2 occurs across the double bond, followed in many cases by hydrolysis in aqueous solution, for example,

$$CH_2{=}CH_2 + Hg(NO_3)_2 + OH^- = HO{-}CH_2{-}CH_2{-}Hg^+NO_3^- + NO_3^-$$

The catalytic action of mercuric salts in sulfuric acid solutions in converting acetylene to acetaldehyde probably proceeds in a similar way.

No organomercury(I) compounds have been prepared.

23-19. Mercuric Complexes

A number of these have been mentioned above. The Hg^{2+} ion has indeed a strong tendency to complex formation, and the characteristic coordination numbers and stereochemical arrangements are two-coordinate, linear, and four-coordinate, tetrahedral; octahedral coordination is rare but occurs in $[Hg\ en_3]^{2+}$ and $[Hg(pyO)_6]^{2+}$. There appears to be considerable covalent character in the mercury-ligand bonds, especially in the two-coordinate complexes. The most stable complexes are those with halogen, carbon, nitrogen, phosphorus and sulfur as ligand atoms.

For the halogens, there are the species $[HgX]^+$, HgX_2, $[HgX_3]^-$, and $[HgX_4]^{2-}$. Mercuric cyanide is soluble in excess cyanide to give the tetrahedral $[Hg(CN)_4]^{2-}$ ion; the thiocyanate $[Hg(SCN)_4]^{2-}$ is similar. Dialkyl sulfides give complexes of the type $R_2S \cdot HgX_2$ ($X = Cl$, Br, I), which are dimeric (23-I), and also monomeric $(R_2S)_2HgX_2$ complexes. Phosphines

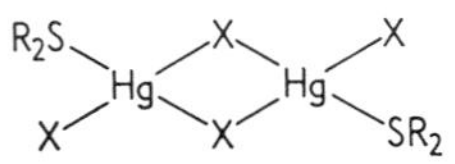

(23–I) 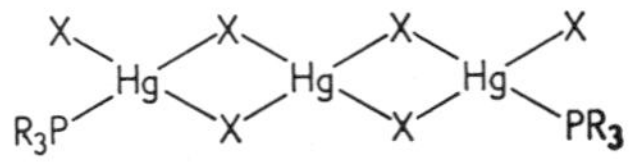   (23–II)

and arsines form complexes with the halides similarly and also give more highly bridged structures such as 23-II. There are rather few well characterized amine complexes owing to the tendency to form the ammonobasic compounds noted earlier, but in addition to the ammonia and amine complexes of the type $Hg(NH_3)_2X_2$, tetramines such as $[Hg(NH_3)_4](NO_3)_2$ can be prepared in saturated aqueous ammonium nitrate; some similar complexes with organic amines are known.

Reference

Lipscomb, W. N., *Anal. Chem.*, **25**, 737 (1953). Structures of mercury-nitrogen compounds.

PART THREE

Chemistry of the Transition Elements

24

Introductory Survey of Transition Elements

ELECTRONIC STRUCTURES

24-1. Definition and General Characteristics of Transition Elements

The transition elements may be strictly defined as those which, *as elements*, have partly filled d or f shells. Here we shall adopt a slightly broader definition and include also elements which have partly filled d or f shells in any of their commonly occurring oxidation states. This means that we treat the coinage metals, Cu, Ag, and Au as transition metals, since Cu^{II} has a $3d^9$ configuration, Ag^{II} a $4d^9$ configuration, and Au^{III} a $5d^8$ configuration. From a purely chemical point of view it is also appropriate to consider these elements as transition elements since their chemical behavior is, on the whole, quite similar to that of other transition elements.

With the above broad definition in mind, one finds that there are at present some 54 transition elements, counting the heaviest elements out through the one of atomic number 102. Clearly, the majority of all known elements are transition elements. All of these transition elements have certain general properties in common:

1. They are all metals.

2. They are practically all hard, strong, high-melting, high-boiling metals which conduct heat and electricity well. In short, they are "typical" metals of the sort we meet in ordinary circumstances.

3. They form alloys with one another and with other metallic elements.

4. Many of them are sufficiently electropositive to dissolve in mineral acids, although a few are "noble"—that is, they have such low electrode potentials as to be unaffected by simple acids.

493

5. With very few exceptions, they exhibit variable valence, and their ions and compounds are colored in one if not all oxidation states.

6. Because of partially filled shells they form at least some paramagnetic compounds.

This large number of transition elements is subdivided into three main groups: (a) the main transition elements or d-block elements, (b) the lanthanide elements, and (c) the actinide elements.

The main transition group or d-block includes those elements which have partially filled d shells only. Thus, the element scandium, with the outer electron configuration $4s^23d$, is the lightest member. The eight succeeding elements, Ti, V, Cr, Mn, Fe, Co, Ni, and Cu, all have partly filled 3d shells either in the ground state of the free atom (all except Cu) or in one or more of their chemically important ions (all except Sc). This group of elements is called the *first transition series*. At zinc the configuration is $3d^{10}4s^2$, and this element forms no compounds in which the 3d shell is ionized, nor does this ionization occur in any of the next nine elements. It is not until we come to yttrium, with ground state outer electron configuration $5s^24d$, that we meet the next transition element. The following eight elements, Zr, Nb, Mo, Tc, Ru, Rh, Pd, and Ag, all have partially filled 4d shells either in the free element (all but Ag) or in one or more of the chemically important ions (all but Y). This group of nine elements constitutes the *second transition series*.

Again there follows a sequence of elements in which there are never d-shell vacancies under chemically significant conditions until we reach the element lanthanum, with an outer electron configuration in the ground state of $6s^25d$. Now, if the pattern we have observed twice before were to be followed, there would follow eight elements with enlarged but not complete sets of 5d electrons. This does not happen, however. The 4f shell now becomes slightly more stable than the 5d shell, and, through the next fourteen elements, electrons enter the 4f shell until at lutetium it becomes filled. Lutetium thus has the outer electron configuration $4f^{14}5d6s^2$. Since both La and Lu have partially filled d shells and no other partially filled shells, it might be argued that both of these should be considered as d-block elements. However, for chemical reasons, it would be unwise to classify them in this way, since all of the fifteen elements La $(Z = 57)$ through Lu $(Z = 71)$ have very similar chemical and physical properties, those of lanthanum being in a sense prototypal; hence, these elements are called the *lanthanides*, and their chemistry will be considered separately in Chapter 31. Since the properties of Y are extremely similar, and those of Sc mainly like those of the lanthanide elements proper and quite different from those of the regular d-block elements, we will treat them also in Chapter 31.

For practical purposes, then, the *third transition series* begins with hafnium, having the ground state outer electron configuration $6s^2 5d^2$, and embraces the elements Ta, W, Re, Os, Ir, Pt, and Au, all of which have partly filled $5d$ shells in one or more chemically important oxidation states as well as (excepting Au) in the neutral atom.

Continuing on from mercury, which follows gold, we come via the inert gas radon and the radioelements Fr and Ra to actinium, with the outer electron configuration $7s^2 6d$. Here we might expect, by analogy to what happened at lanthanum, that in the following elements electrons would enter the $5f$ orbitals, producing a lanthanide-like series of fifteen elements. What actually occurs is, unfortunately, not so simple. Although, immediately following lanthanum, the $4f$ orbitals become decisively more favorable than the $5d$ orbitals for the electrons entering in the succeeding elements, there is apparently not so great a difference between the $5f$ and $6d$ orbitals until later. Thus, for the elements immediately following Ac, and their ions, there may be electrons in the $5f$ or $6d$ orbitals or both. Since it does appear (Section 24-3) that later on, after four or five more electrons have been added to the Ac configuration, the $5f$ orbitals do become definitely the more stable, and since the elements from about americium on do show moderately homologous chemical behavior, it has become accepted practice to call the fifteen elements beginning with Ac (not all of which are known as yet) the *actinide elements*.

There is an important distinction, based upon electronic structures, between the three classes of transition elements. For the d-block elements the partially filled shells are d shells, $3d$, $4d$, or $5d$. These d orbitals project well out to the periphery of the atoms and ions so that the electrons occupying them are strongly influenced by the surroundings of the ion and, in turn, are able to influence the environments very significantly. Thus, many of the properties of an ion with a partly filled d shell are quite sensitive to the number and arrangment of the d electrons present. In marked contrast to this, the $4f$ orbitals in the lanthanide elements are rather deeply buried in the atoms and ions. The electrons which occupy them are largely screened from the surroundings by the overlying shell of $4d$ electrons, and therefore reciprocal interactions between the $4f$ electrons and the surroundings of the atom or the ion are of relatively little chemical significance. This is why the chemistry of all the lanthanides is so homologous, whereas there are seemingly erratic and irregular variations in chemical properties as one passes through the series of d-block elements. The behavior of the actinide elements lies between the two types described above because the $5f$ orbitals are not so well shielded as are the $4f$ orbitals, although not so exposed as are the d orbitals in the d-block elements.

24-2. Position in the Periodic Table

We now consider the question of why the various transition series occur where they do in the periodic table. Figure 24-1 shows in a qualitative way the variations, especially the relative variations, in the energies of the

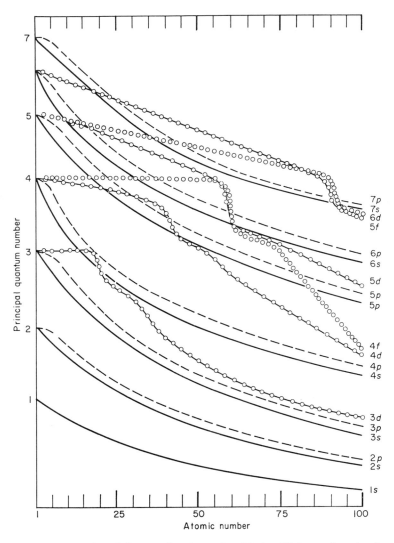

Fig. 24-1. The variation of the energies of atomic orbitals with increasing atomic number in neutral atoms (energies not strictly to scale).

atomic orbitals as a function of atomic number in neutral atoms. The first observation one might make about this diagram is that it is rather complicated. This observation is not without value, since it is well to realize that in a multielectron atom, one with say twenty or more electrons, the energies of all of the levels are more or less dependent on the populations of all of the other levels.

Turning now to the details of the diagram, we see that in hydrogen all of the subshells of each principal shell are equi-energic. As we proceed to more complex atoms, these various subshells, s, p, d, f, g, etc., split apart and at the same time drop to lower energies. This descent in energy occurs because the degree to which an electron in a particular orbital is shielded from the nuclear charge by all of the other electrons in the atom is insufficient to prevent a steady increase in the *effective nuclear charge* felt by that electron with increasing atomic number. In other words, each electron is imperfectly shielded from the nuclear charge by the other electrons. According to the equation for the energy of an electron in an atom,

$$E = -\frac{2\pi^2 \mu e^4 (Z^*)^2}{n^2 \mathbf{h}^2} \qquad (24\text{-}1)$$

where Z^* is the effective nuclear charge, the energy of the electron falls as Z^* increases.

The reason why the diagram is so complicated, however, is that all subshells do not drop in parallel fashion, but rather in varying and somewhat irregular ways. This is because the several subshells of the same principal shell are shielded to different degrees by the core of electrons beneath. This point has been mentioned briefly before (Section 1-11), but will be considered in more detail here.

From Figure 24-1 we see that the 1s, 2s, 2p, 3s, and 3p levels occur in that sequence in all known atoms. Thus through those atoms (H–Ar) in which this sequence of orbitals is being filled, they are filled in that order. While the filling of this set of orbitals is taking place, the energies of the higher and as yet unfilled orbitals are being variously affected by the screening power of these first eighteen electrons. In particular, the 3d levels, which penetrate the argon core rather little, have scarcely dropped in energy when we reach argon, whereas the 4s and 4p levels, especially the former, which penetrate the argon core quite a bit, have dropped rather steeply. Thus, when two more electrons are added to the argon configuration to give the potassium and calcium atoms, they enter the 4s orbital, which has fallen below the 3d orbitals. As these two electrons are added, the nuclear charge is also increased by two units. Since the 3d orbitals penetrate the electron density in the 4s orbitals very considerably, the net result is that the effective nuclear charge for the $3d$ orbitals increases rather abruptly, and they now drop well below the $4p$ orbitals to about the level of the $4s$ orbital. The next electron therefore enters the $3d$ shell, and scandium has the configuration $[\text{Ar}]4s^2 3d$. This $3d$ electron screens the $4p$ levels more effectively than it screens the remaining $3d$ orbitals so the latter remain the lowest available orbitals and the next electron is also added to the $3d$ shell to give Ti with the configuration $[\text{Ar}]4s^2 3d^2$. This process continues in a similar way until the entire $3d$ shell is filled. Thus at Zn we have the configuration $[\text{Ar}]4s^2 3d^{10}$, and the $4p$ orbitals, now the lowest available ones, become filled in the six succeeding elements.

This same sequence of events is repeated again in the elements following krypton, which has the electron configuration $[\text{Ar}]3d^{10}4s^2 4p^6$. Because of the way in which the shielding varies, the $4d$ levels, which in a one-electron atom would be next in order of stability, are higher in energy than the $5s$ and $5p$ orbitals, so that the next two electrons added go into the $5s$ orbitals, giving the alkali and alkaline earth elements Rb and Sr. But the shielding of the $4d$ orbitals by these $5s$ electrons is very poor so that the $4d$ orbitals feel strongly the increase of two units of nuclear charge and take a sharp drop, becoming appreciably more stable than the $5p$ orbitals, and the next electron added becomes a $4d$ electron. Thus the next element, Y, is the first member of the second transition series. This series is completed at Ag, configuration $[\text{Kr}]4d^{10}5s^2$, and then six $5p$ electrons are added to make Xe, the next inert gas.

At Xe ($Z = 54$) the next available orbitals are the $6s$ and $6p$ orbitals. The $4f$ orbitals are so slightly penetrating with respect to the Xe core that they have scarcely gained any stability, while the more penetrating $6s$ and $6p$ levels have dropped a good deal. Hence the next two electrons added are $6s$ electrons, giving again an alkali and an alkaline earth element, Cs and Ba, respectively. However, the $6s$ shell scarcely shields the $4f$ orbitals, so the latter abruptly feel an increase in effective nuclear charge and thus suffer a steep drop in energy. At the same time, however, the $5d$ levels also drop abruptly, just as $(n-1)d$ levels have done previously as electrons are added to the ns level, and the final situation is one in which, at Ba, the $6s$, $5d$, and $4f$ levels are all of about the same energy. The next entering electron, in the element lanthanum, enters a $5d$ orbital, but the following element, cerium, has the configuration $6s^2 4f^2$. Through the next twelve elements electrons continue to enter the $4f$ orbitals, and it is likely that even at cerium they are intrinsically more stable than the $5d$'s. Certainly they are so by the time we reach ytterbium, with the configuration $6s^2 4f^{14}$. Now, with the $6s$ and $4f$ shells full, the next lowest levels are unequivocally the $5d$'s, and from lutetium, with the configuration $6s^2 4f^{14}5d$, through mercury, with the configuration $[Xe]6s^24f^25d^{10}$, the ten $5d$ electrons are added. Chemically, lanthanum and lutetium, each of which has a single $5d$ electron, are very similar to one another, and all of the elements in between, with configurations $[Xe]4f^n6s^2$, have chemical properties intermediate between those of lanthanum and lutetium. Consequently these fifteen elements are all considered as members of one class, the lanthanides. Hafnium, $[Xe]4f^{14}5d^26s^2$, through gold are the eight elements which we regard as the members of the third transition series.

Following mercury there are six elements in which electrons enter the $6p$ orbitals until the next inert gas, radon, is reached. Its configuration is $[Xe]4f^{14}5d^{10}6s^26p^6$. The $5f$ orbitals have dropped so much more slowly, because of their relatively nonpenetrating character, than have the $7s$ and $7p$ orbitals that the next two electrons beyond the radon core are added to the $7s$ level, and again an alkali and an alkaline earth element are formed, namely, Fr, $[Rn]7s$, and Ra, $[Rn]7s^2$. But, again in analogy to the situation one row up in the periodic table, both the $5f$ and $6d$ orbitals penetrate the $7s$ orbitals very considerably; they are thus abruptly stabilized relative to the $7p$ orbitals, and the next electrons added enter them. It appears that as we proceed through actinium and the following elements, the energies of the $6d$ and $5f$ orbitals remain for a while so similar that the exact configuration is determined by interelectronic forces of the sort discussed in Section 24-3. In the case of protactinium it is not certain whether the ground state is $[Rn]7s^26d^3$, $[Rn]7s^26d^25f$, $[Rn]7s^26d5f^2$, or $[Rn]7s^25f^3$. These four configurations doubtless differ very little in energy, and for chemical purposes the question of which is actually the lowest is not of great importance. The next element, uranium, appears definitely to have the configuration $[Rn]7s^25f^36d$, and the elements thereafter are all believed to have the configurations $[Rn]7s^25f^n6d$. The important point is that, from actinium on, the $6d$ and $5f$ levels are of practically the same energy, with the $5f$'s probably becoming slowly more stable.

24-3. Electron Configurations of the Atoms and Ions

In this section we shall look a little more closely at the factors determining the electron configurations of transition metal atoms and ions. The discussion in the preceding section is not entirely adequate or accurate because it takes account only of the shielding of a given electron from the nuclear charge by other electrons in the atom. One electron may help to determine the orbital occupied by another electron not only in this indirect way but also by the direct effects of interelectronic repulsion and by the effect known as "exchange energy." Thus, in a case where two orbitals differ little in what we might loosely call their "intrinsic" energies, the effects of repulsions and exchange energies are such that an additional electron may not necessarily enter the lower of the two.

One very striking and general example of this is the usual superior stability of half-filled and filled subshells. This is exemplified in the first transition series by the "anomalous" configurations of the atoms of chromium and copper,

	Sc	Ti	V	Cr	Mn	Fe	Co	Ni	Cu	Zn
$4s$	2	2	2	1	2	2	2	2	1	2
$3d$	1	2	3	5	5	6	7	8	10	10

and in the lanthanides by the configuration of gadolinium:

	Sm	Eu	Gd	Tb
$6s$	2	2	2	2
$5d$	0	0	1	0
$4f$	6	7	7	9

In the first two cases an electron is "borrowed out of turn," so to speak, from an orbital of similar energy in order to achieve the exchange-energy-stabilized half-filled or filled shell, whereas in the case of gadolinium an electron is turned away into another shell of similar energy in order to preserve intact a half-filled arrangement.

In the second transition series the irregularities become more complex, as shown in the following order:

	Y	Zr	Nb	Mo	Tc	Ru	Rh	Pd	Ag	Cd
$5s$	2	2	1	1	1	1	1	0	1	2
$4d$	1	2	4	5	6	7	8	10	10	10

No simple analysis is possible here; both nuclear-electronic and electron-electron forces play their roles in determining these configurations. Although a preference for the filled $4d$ shell is evident at the end of the series and the elements Nb and Mo show a preference for the half-filled shell, the configuration of Tc shows that this preference is not controlling throughout this series.

It is also well to point out that the interelectronic forces and variations in total nuclear charge play à large part in determining the configurations of ions. We cannot say that because $4s$ orbitals became occupied before $3d$ orbitals, they are always more stable. If this were so, then we would expect the elements of the first transition series to ionize by loss of $3d$ electrons, whereas, in fact, they ionize by loss of $4s$ electrons first. Thus it is the net effect of all of the forces—nuclear-electronic attraction, shielding of one electron by others, interelectronic repulsions, and the exchange forces—which determines the stability of an electron configuration; and, unfortunately, there are many cases in which the interplay of these forces and their sensitivity to changes in nuclear charge and the number of electrons present cannot be simply described.

24-4. Russell-Saunders or LS Coupling

The purpose of this section is to explain how we describe the electronic state of an atom or ion containing a partly filled shell. We shall prefer to use as examples partly filled d shells because the occurrence of partly filled p shells is very rare in chemical compounds and partly filled f shells are merely more complex but not different in principle. The reader is already familiar with the idea of an electronic *configuration*. This is merely a statement of how many electrons are occupying each of the hydrogen-like orbitals which the atom possesses and is given synoptically by notation of the following kind: Fe^{III}: $1s^2 2s^2 2p^6 3s^2 3p^6 4s^2 3d^5$. In this case seven subshells are occupied. Six of these are fully occupied and require no further description, for there is only one possible state for a fully occupied shell. The $3d$ shell, however, is only partially occupied—that is, it contains but five electrons, as the notation tells us. For many purposes we need to have more information about this shell because there are many different *electronic states* of the $3d^5$ electronic configuration which differ considerably in their properties, such as energy, magnetic moment, spectrum, effect upon ionic radius, etc.

As explained previously (page 16), the small letters s, p, d, f, g, h . . . are used to indicate that an individual electron has orbital angular momentum, given by its quantum number l, of, respectively, 0, 1, 2, 3, 4, 5 . . . in units of $h/2\pi$. Partly filled shells also have a net orbital angular momentum which results from the combined angular momenta of the individual electrons. In a filled shell, the orbital momenta of the individual electrons always combine so as to give a net momentum of exactly zero. In order to indicate the orbital angular momentum, L, of an entire set of electrons in a partly occupied shell, we use the same set of letters as above, but in the upper case. That is, the state of a d^2 configuration in which the net orbital angular momentum $L = 1$ is called a P state, that in which $L = 4$ is a G state, and so forth.

Since the spin, s, of a single electron is always $\frac{1}{2}$, no explicit notation for this is necessary. However, the net spin, S, of a group of electrons may take any integral or half-integral value, and we require a simple notation to indicate that value. Spectroscopists have developed the following system for this purpose. The spin multiplicity of a state is defined as $(2S + 1)$, where S is the spin quantum number. Thus when $S = \frac{1}{2}$, which includes a one-electron configuration as a special case, the spin multiplicity equals 2; when $S = 1$, the spin multiplicity equals 3, and so forth. A state with a spin multiplicity of 2 is called a doublet; those with spin multiplicities of 3, 4, 5, 6, 7, . . . are called triplets, quartets, quintets, sextets, septets, ... There is a very simple relation between the spin multiplicity and the number of unpaired electrons. If a shell contains $(x + y)$ electrons, x having $s = \frac{1}{2}$ and y having $s = -\frac{1}{2}$, the spin quantum number for the whole group, S, will be equal to $|x - y|$; that is, $S =$ one-half of the number of unpaired electrons, n. Thus, the spin multiplicity is given by

$$2S + 1 = 2\left(\frac{n}{2}\right) + 1 = n + 1$$

The reader may naturally wonder why we do not simply denote the number of unpaired spins by n instead of by the spin multiplicity, which is $(n + 1)$. The only answer we can give here is that the spin multiplicity does have a meaning of its own and is a well-established convention which must be learned.

The complete symbol for any state of a partly filled shell thus includes a capital letter, S, P, D, F, G, H, . . . , representing the L value, and a number representing the spin multiplicity, $2S + 1$, or, equally, the number of unpaired electrons plus one. This number is written as a left superscript to the letter. Thus we get symbols such as ^4F, ^1D, ^3P, etc. A closed shell, of course, has no unpaired electrons and no orbital angular momentum and is thus always in the state represented by ^1S.

A d electron is defined as one having orbital angular momentum, l, equal to 2 (in units of $h/2\pi$), and of course every electron has spin angular momentum equal to $\frac{1}{2}$. Thus the simplest incomplete d shell configuration, d^1, must be characterized by a total orbital angular momentum, L, of 2 and a total spin angular momentum, S, of $\frac{1}{2}$. Thus there is only one possible state for the d^1 configuration, namely, ^2D. If, now, we have two d electrons, several states are possible. First of all, their spins may be parallel ($S = 1$), giving rise to triplet states, or opposed ($S = 0$), giving rise to singlet states. Second, their orbital angular momenta may add vectorially to give L values of 0, 1, 2, 3, or 4, meaning that there will be S, P, D, F, and G states possible. Now, not all five of these orbital states may be both singlet and triplet because of the Pauli exclusion principle. For instance, the G state can only result when both electrons have their m quantum numbers equal to 2. Since both electrons will then have the same principal quantum number because they are in the same d shell and the same quantum numbers l and m, they must have different values of s. Therefore, the only possible G state has S equal to zero and is thus ^1G. The rigorous application of the exclusion principle is more complicated than implied above, and we shall not offer a detailed explanation here. The final result for the d^2 case is that only the following states of this configuration are possible: ^3F, ^3P, ^1D, ^1G, and ^1S.

A similar analysis of each of the other d^n configurations can be made, and results of similar character are obtained. This entire approach to the problem of determining the states of a configuration is the method of Russell-Saunders or LS coupling. The former name honors those who devised the system; the latter emphasizes our assumption that electron spins couple only with other spins to give S, and orbital momenta couple only with other orbital momenta to give L, with little interaction between the spin and orbital momenta of individual electrons. The coupling which actually occurs in real atoms does approximate fairly closely to this scheme for light atoms, including the d^n configurations in atoms and ions of the first transition series. It is a somewhat poorer approximation for the $4d^n$ and $5d^n$ configurations of the second and third transition series.

In each of these states the configuration has a different energy, because each state involves different interelectronic repulsion energies and exchange energies. For instance, for the d^2 configuration in the V^{III} ion, spectroscopic studies have shown that the five states have the following relative energies, in wave numbers, the energy of the lowest state being taken as zero: ^3F, 0; ^1D, 10,960; ^3P, 13,100; ^1G, 18,400; and ^1S, not yet known but $> {}^1G$. For most of the d-block elements the energies of the various Russell-Saunders states are known from spectroscopic studies. This information is of great value in transition metal chemistry because these states and their energies form the starting point in treating certain properties, especially the spectra, of metal ions in crystals and in complexes by the methods of the crystal field and ligand field theories. This application will be described in the next chapter and results for particular ions will be mentioned throughout Chapters 29 and 30.

24-5. Hund's Rules

In the preceding section we have shown that, for any electron configuration involving a partly filled shell containing more than one but less than $(n - 1)$ electrons, where n is the total number the shell will hold, several states differing in their net spin and net orbital angular momentum may arise. Only by experiment can we determine the energies of these states. However, theories alone can tell us their relative energies, and, in particular, there are some very simple rules to tell us which state will be the ground state. These rules, known as Hund's rules, are as valid as the LS coupling scheme itself. When the latter is a good approximation, Hund's rules can always be trusted, and this is true for all of the lighter elements. The rules are:

1. The ground state will have the highest spin multiplicity, that is, the maximum number of unpaired electrons.

2. Of several states each having the highest spin multiplicity, the ground state will be the one with the highest L value.

Thus for the d^2 configuration, the ground state is ^3F.

MAGNETIC PROPERTIES OF CHEMICAL SUBSTANCES

24-6. The Importance of Magnetism in Transition Element Chemistry

Many—indeed, most—compounds of the transition elements are paramagnetic, and much of our understanding of transition metal chemistry has been derived from magnetic data. Consequently, it is necessary to explain the salient facts and principles of magnetism, from a chemical viewpoint, before proceeding with detailed discussion of transition metal chemistry.

All of the magnetic properties of substances in bulk are ultimately determined by the electrical properties of the subatomic particles, electrons, and nucleons. Because the magnetic effects due to nucleons and nuclei are some 10^{-3} times those due to electrons, they ordinarily have no detectable effect on magnetic phenomena of direct chemical significance. This is not to say that chemical phenomena do not have significant effects upon nuclear magnetism; it is just such effects that make nuclear magnetic resonance spectroscopy an extremely useful tool for the chemist. Thus we shall concentrate our attention entirely on the properties of the electron and on the magnetic properties of matter which result therefrom. We shall see that there are very often direct and sensitive relationships between the magnetic properties of matter in bulk and the number and distribution of unpaired electrons in its various constituent atoms or ions.

There are several kinds of magnetism, qualitatively speaking. In the following sections we shall consider first *paramagnetism*. A substance which is paramagnetic is attracted into a magnetic field with a force proportional to the field strength times the field gradient. Paramagnetism is generally caused by the presence in the substance of ions, atoms, or molecules which have unpaired electrons. Each of these has a definite paramagnetic moment which exists in the absence of any external magnetic field. A *diamagnetic* substance is repelled by a magnetic field. All matter has this property to some extent. Diamagnetic behavior is due to small magnetic moments which are induced by the magnetic field but do not exist in the absence of the field. Moments so induced are in opposition to the inducing field, thus causing repulsion. Finally, there are the more complex forms of magnetic behavior known as ferromagnetism and antiferromagnetism, and still others, which will not be discussed here.

24-7. Origin of Paramagnetic Moments

Electrons determine the magnetic properties of matter in two ways. First, each electron is, in effect, a magnet in itself. From a pre-wave mechanical viewpoint, the electron may be regarded as a small sphere of negative charge spinning on its axis. Then, from completely classical considerations, the spinning of charge produces a magnetic moment. Second, an electron which is traveling in a closed path around a nucleus, again according to the pre-wave mechanical picture of an atom, will also produce a magnetic moment, just as does an electric current traveling in a loop of wire. The magnetic properties of any individual atom or ion will result from some combination of these two properties, that is, the inherent *spin moment* of the electron and the *orbital moment* resulting from the motion of the electron around the nucleus. These physical images should not, of course, be taken too literally, for they have no place in wave mechanics, nor do they provide a basis for quantitatively correct predictions. They are qualitatively useful conceptual aids, however.

The magnetic moments of atoms, ions, and molecules are usually expressed in units called *Bohr magnetons*, abbreviated B.M. The Bohr magneton is defined in terms of fundamental constants as

$$1 \text{ B.M.} = \frac{e\mathbf{h}}{4\pi mc} \qquad (24\text{-}2)$$

where e is the electronic charge, $\mathbf{h}$ is Planck's constant, m is the electron mass, and c is the speed of light. This is *not*, however, the moment of a single electron. Because of certain features of quantum theory, the relationship is a little more complicated.

The magnetic moment, μ_s, of a single electron is given, according to wave mechanics, by the equation

$$\mu_s \text{ (in B.M.)} = g\sqrt{s(s+1)} \qquad (24\text{-}3)$$

in which s is simply the absolute value of the spin quantum number and g is the gyromagnetic ratio more familiarly known as the "g factor." The quantity $\sqrt{s(s+1)}$ is the value of the angular momentum of the electron, and thus g is the ratio of the magnetic moment to the angular momentum, as its name is intended to suggest. For the free electron, g has the value 2.00023, which may be taken as 2.00 for most purposes. From equation 24-3 we can calculate the spin magnetic moment of one electron as:

$$\mu_s = 2\sqrt{\tfrac{1}{2}(\tfrac{1}{2}+1)} = \sqrt{3} = 1.73 \text{ B.M.}$$

Thus any atom, ion, or molecule having one unpaired electron (e.g., H, Cu^{2+}, ClO_2) should have a magnetic moment of 1.73 B.M. from the electron spin alone. This may be augmented or diminished by an orbital contribution as will be seen later.

There are transition metal ions having one, two, three . . . up to seven unpaired electrons. As indicated in Section 24-4, the spin quantum number for the ion as a whole, S, is the sum of the spin quantum numbers, $s = \tfrac{1}{2}$, for the individual electrons. For example, in the manganese(II) ion with five unpaired electrons, $S = 5(\tfrac{1}{2}) = \tfrac{5}{2}$ and in the gadolinium ion with seven unpaired electrons, $S = 7(\tfrac{1}{2}) = \tfrac{7}{2}$. Thus we can use equation 24-3 to calculate the magnetic moment due to the electron spins alone, the so-called "spin-only" moment, for any atom or ion providing we know the total spin quantum number, S. The results are summarized in Table 24-1 for all possible real cases.

TABLE 24-1

"Spin-Only" Magnetic Moments for Various Numbers
of Unpaired Electrons

No. of unpaired electrons	S	μ_S, B.M.
1	$\tfrac{1}{2}$	1.73
2	1	2.83
3	$\tfrac{3}{2}$	3.87
4	2	4.90
5	$\tfrac{5}{2}$	5.92
6	3	6.93
7	$\tfrac{7}{2}$	7.94

In the two examples chosen above, namely, Mn^{II} and Gd^{III}, the observed values of their magnetic moments agree very well with the spin-only values in Table 24-1. Generally, however, experimental values differ from the spin-only ones, usually being somewhat greater. This is because the orbital motion of the electrons also makes a contribution to the moment.

The theory by which the exact magnitudes of these orbital contributions may be calculated is by no means simple and, indeed, still presents problems for theoretical study. We shall give here only a superficial and pragmatic account of the subject.

For Mn^{II}, Fe^{III}, Gd^{III}, and other ions whose ground states are S states, as shown in Section 24-5, there is no orbital angular momentum even in the free ion. Hence there cannot be any orbital contribution to the magnetic moment, and the spin-only formula applies exactly. In general, however, the transition metal ions in their ground states, D or F being most common, do possess orbital angular momentum. Wave mechanics shows that for such ions, if the orbital motion makes its full contribution to the magnetic moments, they will be given by:

$$\mu_{S+L} = \sqrt{4S(S+1) + L(L+1)} \qquad (24\text{-}4)$$

in which L represents the orbital angular momentum quantum number for the ion.

In Table 24-2 are listed magnetic moments actually observed for the

TABLE 24-2

Theoretical and Experimental Magnetic Moments for Various Transition Metal Ions
(In Bohr magnetons)

Ion	Ground state quantum numbers		Spectroscopic symbol	μ_S	μ_{S+L}	Observed moments
	S	L				
V^{4+}	$\frac{1}{2}$	2	^2D	1.73	3.00	1.7–1.8
Cu^{2+}	$\frac{1}{2}$	2	^2D	1.73	3.00	1.7–2.2
V^{3+}	1	3	^3F	2.83	4.47	2.6–2.8
Ni^{2+}	1	3	^3F	2.83	4.47	2.8–4.0
Cr^{3+}	$\frac{3}{2}$	3	^4F	3.87	5.20	~3.8
Co^{2+}	$\frac{3}{2}$	3	^4F	3.87	5.20	4.1–5.2
Fe^{2+}	2	2	^5D	4.90	5.48	5.1–5.5
Co^{3+}	2	2	^5D	4.90	5.48	~5.4
Mn^{2+}	$\frac{5}{2}$	0	^6S	5.92	5.92	~5.9
Fe^{3+}	$\frac{5}{2}$	0	^6S	5.92	5.92	~5.9

common ions of the first transition series together with the calculated values of μ_S and μ_{S+L}. It will be seen that observed values of μ frequently exceed μ_S, but seldom are as high as μ_{S+L}. This is because the electric fields of other atoms, ions, and molecules surrounding the metal ion in its compounds interfere with the orbital motion of the electrons so that the orbital angular momentum and hence the orbital moment are wholly or partially *"quenched."* In some cases the moments lie slightly below the value of μ_S. This effect, which never exceeds about 0.1 B.M. in the first transition series, is also caused by orbital angular momentum, but its explanation is beyond the level of this book.

24-8. Diamagnetism

As noted previously, only substances with unpaired electrons exhibit paramagnetism. There are certain exceptions to this which can safely be ignored here. Diamagnetism, however, is a property of all forms of matter. All substances contain at least some if not all electrons in closed shells. In closed shells the electron spin moments and orbital moments of individual electrons balance one another out so that there is no net magnetic moment. However, when an atom or molecule is placed in a magnetic field, a small magnetic moment directly proportional to the strength of the field is induced. The electron spins have nothing to do with this induced moment; they remain tightly coupled together in antiparallel pairs. However, the planes of the orbitals are tipped slightly so that a small net orbital moment is set up in opposition to the applied field. It is because of this opposition that diamagnetic substances are repelled from magnetic fields.

Even an atom with a permanent magnetic moment will have diamagnetic behavior working in opposition to the paramagnetism when placed in a magnetic field, providing only that the atom has one or more closed shells of electrons. Thus, the net paramagnetism measured is slightly less than the true paramagnetism because some of the latter is "canceled out" by the diamagnetism.

Diamagnetism is usually several orders of magnitude weaker than paramagnetism so that substances with unpaired electrons almost always have a net paramagnetism. Of course, a very dilute solution of a paramagnetic ion in a diamagnetic solvent such as water may be diamagnetic because of the large ratio of diamagnetic to paramagnetic species in it. Another important feature of diamagnetism is that its magnitude does not vary with temperature. This is because the moment induced depends only on the sizes and shapes of the orbitals in the closed shells and these are not temperature dependent.

24-9. Magnetic Susceptibility

Chemically useful information is obtained by proper interpretation of measured values of magnetic moments. However, magnetic moments are not measured directly. Instead, one measures the magnetic susceptibility of a material from which it is possible to calculate the magnetic moment of the paramagnetic ion or atom therein.

Magnetic susceptibility is defined in the following way. If a substance is placed in a magnetic field of magnitude H, the flux, B, within the substance is given by

$$B = H + 4\pi I \tag{24-5}$$

I is called the intensity of magnetization. The ratio B/H, called the magnetic permeability of the material, is given by

$$B/H = 1 + 4\pi(I/H) = 1 + 4\pi\kappa \tag{24-6}$$

κ is called the magnetic susceptibility per unit volume, or simply the volume susceptibility. The physical significance of equation 24-6 is easily seen. The permeability, B/H, is just the ratio of the density of lines of force within the substance to the density of such lines in the same region in the absence of the specimen. Thus, the volume susceptibility of a vacuum is by definition zero, since in a vacuum it must be that $B/H = 1$. The susceptibility of a diamagnetic substance is negative because lines of force from induced dipoles cancel out some lines of force due to the applied field. For paramagnetic substances the flux is greater within the substance than it would be in a vacuum, and thus paramagnetic substances have positive susceptibilities.

There are numerous methods for measuring magnetic susceptibilities, all of which depend on measuring the force exerted upon a body when it is placed in an inhomogeneous magnetic field. The more paramagnetic the body is, the more strongly will it be drawn toward the more intense part of the field. One of the commonest methods used by chemists for quantitative susceptibility measurements is the Gouy method, which is described in Appendix D.

24-10. Magnetic Moments from Magnetic Susceptibilities

In his classic studies, Pierre Curie showed that paramagnetic susceptibilities depend inversely on temperature and often follow or closely approximate the behavior required by the simple equation

$$\chi_M{}^{corr} = C/T \tag{24-7}$$

Here $\chi_M{}^{corr}$ is the paramagnetic susceptibility per mole, corrected for the diamagnetism due to closed shells; T represents the absolute temperature, and C is a constant which is characteristic of the substance and known as its Curie constant. Equation 24-7 expresses what is known as *Curie's law*.

Now, on theoretical grounds, just such an equation is to be expected.

The magnetic field in which the sample is placed tends to align the moments of the paramagnetic atoms or ions; at the same time, thermal agitation tends to randomize the orientations of these individual moments. The situation is entirely analogous to that encountered in the electric polarization of matter containing electric dipoles, with which the student is probably already familiar from a standard physical chemistry course. Applying a straightforward statistical treatment, one obtains the following equation showing how the molar susceptibility of a substance containing independent atoms, ions, or molecules, each of magnetic moment μ (in B.M.) will vary with temperature:

$$\chi_M{}^{corr} = \frac{N\mu^2/3k}{T} \tag{24-8}$$

where N is Avogadro's number, and k is the Boltzmann constant. Obviously, by comparison of equations 24-7 and 24-8

$$C = N\mu^2/3k \tag{24-9}$$

and at any given temperature

$$\mu = \sqrt{3k/N} \cdot \sqrt{\chi_M{}^{corr}T} \tag{24-10}$$

which, on evaluating $\sqrt{3k/N}$ numerically, becomes

$$\mu = 2.84\sqrt{\chi_M{}^{corr}T} \tag{24-11}$$

Thus, to recapitulate, one first makes a direct measurement of the volume susceptibility of a substance from which χ_M is calculated, and, in accurate work, corrected for diamagnetism. From this molar susceptibility and the temperature of the measurement, equation 24-11 enables one to calculate the magnetic moment of the ion, atom, or molecule responsible for the paramagnetism.

From equation 24-11 we should expect that if we measure χ_M for a substance at several temperatures and plot the reciprocals of the $\chi_M{}^{corr}$ values against T, we shall obtain a straight line of slope C which intersects the origin. Although there are many substances which, within the limits of experimental error, do show this behavior, there are also many others for which the line does not go through the origin, but instead looks somewhat like one of those shown in Figure 24-2, cutting the T axis at a temperature below 0°K. as in (a) or above 0°K. as in (b). Obviously, such a line can be represented by a slight modification of the Curie equation,

$$\chi_M{}^{corr} = \frac{C}{T - \theta} \tag{24-12}$$

Here θ is the temperature at which the line cuts the T axis. This equation expresses what is known as the *Curie-Weiss law*, and θ is known as the

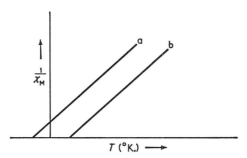

Fig. 24-2. Some curves showing deviations from the Curie law which may be fitted to the Curie-Weiss law.

Weiss constant. Actually, just such an equation can be derived if one assumes, not that the dipoles in the various ions, atoms, or molecules of a solid are completely independent—as was assumed in deriving equation 24-8—but that instead the orientation of each one is influenced by the orientations of its neighbors as well as by the field to which it is subjected. Thus the Weiss constant can be thought of as taking account of the interionic or intermolecular interactions, thereby enabling us to eliminate this extraneous effect by computing the magnetic moment from the equation

$$\mu = 2.84\sqrt{\chi_M{}^{corr}(T - \theta)} \tag{24-13}$$

instead of from equation 24-11. Unfortunately, there are also cases in which magnetic behavior appears to follow the Curie-Weiss equation without the Weiss constant having this simple interpretation. In such cases, it is often quite wrong to use equation 24-13. The whole matter is, however, too complex to go into further in this text.

24-11. Ferromagnetism and Antiferromagnetism

In addition to the simple paramagnetism we have discussed, where the Curie or Curie-Weiss law is followed and the susceptibility shows no dependence on field strength, there are other forms of paramagnetism in which the dependence on both temperature and field strength is complicated. Two of the most important of these are ferromagnetism and antiferromagnetism. No attempt will be made to explain either of these in detail, either phenomenologically or theoretically, but it is important for the student to recognize their salient features. Figure 24-3 compares the qualitative temperature dependence of the susceptibility for (a) simple paramagnetism, (b) ferromagnetism, and (c) antiferromagnetism. Of course (a) is just a rough graph of Curie's law. In (b) it should be noted

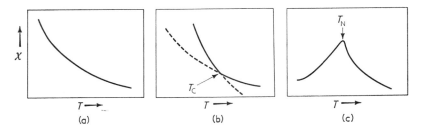

Fig. 24-3. Diagrams indicating the qualitative temperature dependence of magnetic susceptibility for (a) simple paramagnetism, (b) ferromagnetism, and (c) antiferromagnetism.

that there is a discontinuity at some temperature, T_C called the Curie temperature. Above the Curie temperature the substance follows the Curie or the Curie-Weiss law; that is, it is a simple paramagnetic. Below the Curie temperature, however, it varies in a different way with temperature and is also field-strength dependent. For antiferromagnetism there is again a characteristic temperature, T_N, called the Néel temperature. Above T_N the substance has the behavior of a simple paramagnetic, but below the Néel temperature the susceptibility *drops* with decreasing temperature.

These peculiarities in the behavior of ferromagnetic and antiferromagnetic substances below their Curie or Néel points are due to interionic interactions which have magnitudes comparable to the thermal energies at the Curie or Néel temperature and thus become progressively greater than thermal energies as the temperature is further lowered. In the case of antiferromagnetism, the moments of the ions in the lattice tend to align themselves so as to cancel one another out. Above the Néel temperature thermal agitation prevents very effective alignment, and the interactions are manifested only in the form of a Weiss constant which is of the same general magnitude as the Néel temperature itself. However, below the Néel temperature this antiparallel aligning becomes effective and the susceptibility is diminished. In ferromagnetic substances the moments of the separate ions tend to align themselves parallel and thus to reinforce one another. Above the Curie temperature, thermal energies are more or less able to randomize the orientations; below T_C, however, the tendency to alignment becomes controlling, and the susceptibility increases much more rapidly with decreasing temperature than it would if the ion moments behaved independently of one another.

Presumably, even in those substances we ordinarily regard as simple paramagnetics there are some interionic interactions, however weak, and therefore there must be some temperature, however low, below which they will show ferromagnetic or antiferromagnetic behavior, depending on the sign of the interaction. The question of why such interactions are so large in some substances that they have Curie or Néel temperature near and even above room temperature is still something of an unsolved problem. Suffice it to say here that in many cases it is certain that the magnetic interactions cannot be direct dipole-dipole interactions but instead the dipoles are coupled through the electrons of intervening atoms in oxides, sulfides, halides, and similar compounds.

24-12. Electron Spin Resonance, ESR

This relatively newly observed phenomenon opens new dimensions in the inference of chemically important features of molecular electronic structure by magnetic measurements. Because its proper understanding requires an extensive knowledge of wave mechanics, beyond the scope of this text, we shall present here only a brief and heuristic account, intended to draw attention to the kinds of useful results which may be obtained.

Electron spin resonance may be observed when molecules or ions containing one or more unpaired electrons are placed in a magnetic field. In a molecule containing a single unpaired electron in an S state ($l = 0$), the effect of the magnetic field is to lift the spin degeneracy, that is, to make the energy of the electron different in its two spin states, $+\frac{1}{2}$ and $-\frac{1}{2}$. This effect is easily understood by thinking of the electron classically as a small magnet in the field of a larger one. When its field is lined up with that of the larger one (Fig. 24-4a), there is an increase in potential energy, whereas

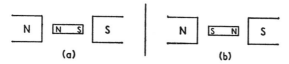

Fig. 24-4. Diagram indicating (a) favorable and (b) unfavorable alignments of a small magnet (e.g., an electron) in the field of a larger one.

the opposite alignment (Fig. 24-4b), decreases the potential energy. A quantitative treatment shows that the energy difference between these two electron spin alignments is equal to $g\beta H$, where g is the same gyromagnetic ratio discussed earlier, β is the Bohr magneton, and H is the strength of the magnetic field. The lower state is slightly more populated than the upper one at thermal equilibrium. Thus, when radiation of frequency ν such that $h\nu = g\beta H$ is applied to the system, there is a net absorption because absorptive transitions upward are more numerous than radiative transitions downward. By sweeping the frequency of an oscillator (in the microwave region) through the appropriate frequency range, ν is observed as the frequency of maximum absorption. From this the g value may be calculated. In this simple case, it would be 2.00, but in other cases, more complex behavior is observed. It is the added complexities from which detailed information on electronic structure can often be obtained. The three main types of more complex behavior and their significance will now be mentioned briefly.

1. It will often happen that the observed g value will differ from 2.00. This deviation can be attributed to orbital contributions to the magnetism, and, from the very precise data afforded by ESR measurements, these orbital contributions can be evaluated quite precisely. With such information, fairly detailed knowledge of orbital populations, degrees of hybridization, etc., may often be obtained.

In some substances there are two (or more) identical ions in different chemical environments or differently oriented with respect to the crystallographic axes. In a bulk susceptibility measurement, only the average magnetic properties of both ions could be determined, but even slight differences between them will result in their resonance frequencies being detectably different in an ESR measurement.

2. Magnetic anisotropy can often be observed by making measurements on small, oriented, single crystals. The anisotropy means that the g value and hence the resonance frequency vary according to the orientation of the crystal with respect to the direction of the external magnetic field, H. The g value in any particular, arbitrary direction can be expressed as the tensor resultant of three basic tensors, g_x, g_y, g_z, in mutually perpendicular directions. There are many cases in which two of these tensors are equal, and the two separate g values are called $g_\parallel$ and $g_\perp$; $g_\parallel$ is the value in the unique direction, while $g_\perp$ is the value in any direction in the plane perpendicular to this direction. From the properties of tensors, it follows that the g value averaged over all directions, g_{av}, is given by

$$g_{av}^2 = \tfrac{1}{3}(g_x^2 + g_y^2 + g_z^2) = \tfrac{1}{3}(g_\parallel^2 + 2g_\perp^2) \qquad (24\text{-}14)$$

Thus, although a bulk susceptibility measurement made in the usual way on a powdered sample could provide only a value of g_{av}, and give no hint about the individual g_x, g_y, g_z, or $g_\parallel$ and $g_\perp$ values, a relatively simple ESR measurement using a small single crystal can provide detailed knowledge of anisotropy. Anisotropy measurements can be and have been made by making bulk susceptibility measurements on quite large single crystals, but the experimental problems are formidable and the results of relatively low accuracy. Anisotropy data can usually be interpreted to give quite detailed information on metal-ligand bonding in complexes.

3. It often happens that the small magnetic fields of atomic nuclei cause splittings (fine structure) of ESR resonance lines. From the magnitudes of such splittings, semiquantitative information as to "electron densities" of the unpaired electrons in particular orbitals of particular atoms can be obtained.

In conclusion, one other great advantage and one disadvantage of ESR measurements relative to bulk susceptibility measurements should be recorded. ESR is extremely sensitive, responding, under optimum conditions (of line width, instrumental sensitivity, and signal-to-noise ratio), to $\sim 10^{-12}$ paramagnetic species per liter, whereas bulk susceptibility measurements can be accurate, as a rule, only when the net paramagnetism is greatly in excess of the diamagnetism in the sample and when the available quantity is relatively large (≥ 100 mg.). Thus, ESR can be used to study minute samples or larger samples containing the paramagnetic species at very low concentrations. A frequent disadvantage of the ESR method is that very low temperatures, for example, liquid nitrogen or even liquid helium temperatures, are often required in order to reduce spin-lattice relaxation effects sufficiently to make lines observable. In many instances, especially with paramagnetic ions having even numbers of electrons, there has been only slight success at observing resonance under any experimental conditions. Bulk susceptibility measurements do have the advantage that they can always be made and used to obtain some idea of the magnetic moment of the paramagnetic ion if it is present in sufficient concentration. ESR measurements have by no means supplanted bulk susceptibility measurements except for special cases and special purposes. The bulk susceptibility measurement still remains one of the chemist's most valuable and frequently used tools in his efforts to understand the electronic structures of transition metal compounds.

References

Carrington, A., and H. C. Longuet-Higgins, *Quart. Revs. (London)*, **14**, 427 (1960). Electron resonance in crystalline transition metal compounds.

Figgis, B. N., and J. Lewis, in J. Lewis and R. G. Wilkins, eds., *Modern Coordination Chemistry*, Interscience, New York–London, 1960. A review of magnetic properties.

Herzberg, G., *Atomic Spectra and Atomic Structure*, Dover, New York, 1944.

Ingram, D. J. E., *Spectroscopy at Radio and Microwave Frequencies*, Butterworths, London, 1955. An excellent introductory text dealing in part with electron spin resonance.

Selwood, P. W., *Magnetochemistry*, Interscience, New York–London, 1956.

25

Complexes of Transition Metals

INTRODUCTION

25-1. Early Development of Coordination Chemistry

Early in the development of chemical science, substances were prepared which appeared to consist of stoichiometric mixtures of two or more compounds, each of which is capable of independent existence. Some of these were the so-called double salts, of which $AlF_3 \cdot 3KF$, $KCl \cdot MgCl_2 \cdot 6H_2O$, $Fe(CN)_2 \cdot 4KCN$, $ZnCl_2 \cdot 3CsCl$, $Al_2(SO_4)_3 \cdot K_2SO_4 \cdot 12H_2O$, and many others are well-known examples. The other general class of these substances included the molecular compounds or addition compounds, in which one metal salt was combined with one or more neutral molecules, rather than another salt. Of these, the ones containing ammonia, which came to be called *ammines*, were among the earliest and best known. For example, over 140 years ago, it was found that the addition of aqueous NH_3 to a green solution of $NiCl_2$ caused an instant change in color to purple, and that from this solution purple crystals of the composition $NiCl_2 \cdot 6NH_3$ could be obtained. In a similar way, Cu^{II} afforded the ammine $CuSO_4 \cdot 4NH_3$. Of special importance, however, were the ammines of Co^{III}, Pt^{IV}, and Pt^{II}; whereas the ammines of most metal ions, such as Ni^{II} and Cu^{II}, are both limited in number and very labile with respect to acids and bases, those of Co^{III}, Pt^{IV}, and Pt^{II} (and also those of Cr^{III}, Pd^{II}, and several other metal ions) are numerous and varied and exhibit considerable stability. Thus, research directed at the understanding of the nature of addition compounds centered around the Co^{III}, Pt^{IV}, and Pt^{II} compounds and, toward the end of the nineteenth century, came to be dominated by the Danish chemist S. M. Jørgensen and the Swiss Alfred Werner. These two men, as well as others, prepared scores of addition compounds, mainly ammines, of these ions and examined their transformations, the occurrence of isomers, their degrees of ionization, etc. It was Werner, however, who had the imagination to deduce from these results his *coordination theory* for which he received the Nobel Prize in chemistry. In the following paragraphs, a few of the salient facts and Werner's deductions from them will be summarized. The intention is to be didactic rather than historically scrupulous.

Experiments showed that five ammines of Pt^{IV} (Table 25-1) could be

TABLE 25-1

Some Pt^{IV} Ammines and Their Degrees of Ionization

	Λ, ohm^{-1}	No. of ions	No. of Cl$^-$ ions
(1) $PtCl_4 \cdot 6NH_3$	523	5	4
(2) $PtCl_4 \cdot 5NH_3$	404	4	3
(3) $PtCl_4 \cdot 4NH_3$	299	3	2
(4) $PtCl_4 \cdot 3NH_3$	97	2	1
(5) $PtCl_4 \cdot 2NH_3$	0	0	0

isolated and that their electrolytic conductances had the values listed. These conductances, when compared with values for simpler electrolytes, indicate the number of ions produced by electrolytic dissociation, and these numbers are given in the table for convenience. In addition to the conductance data, it was also known that on addition of Ag^+ ion to solutions of the tabulated compounds no immediate precipitate was obtained with (5), whereas in each of the others the number of chloride ions immediately precipitated per molecule of the ammine addition compound are those listed in the last column of the table. This means that in (1) all chlorine is present in solution as chloride ions, which are immediately precipitated as AgCl, whereas in compounds (2), (3), and (4) only three, two, and one, respectively, of the chlorine atoms are present in solution as Cl^- ions. Werner proposed the following explanation for these facts. He assumed that for Pt^{IV}, in addition to its electrovalence of $+4$, which determines the total number of negative charges which may be carried by the anions present, there is another property of the Pt^{IV} ion called its *coordination number*, which is the total number of anions or molecules which may be directly associated with the cation. For Pt^{IV} this coordination number must be assumed to be 6. The five compounds of Table 25-1 can then be formulated

$$[Pt(NH_3)_6]Cl_4 = [Pt(NH_3)_6]^{4+} + 4Cl^-$$
$$[Pt(NH_3)_5Cl]Cl_3 = [Pt(NH_3)_5Cl]^{3+} + 3Cl^-$$
$$[Pt(NH_3)_4Cl_2]Cl_2 = [Pt(NH_3)_4Cl_2]^{2+} + 2Cl^-$$
$$[Pt(NH_3)_3Cl_3]Cl = [Pt(NH_3)_3Cl_3]^+ + Cl^-$$
$$[Pt(NH_3)_2Cl_4] \text{ (not dissociated)}$$

where all *coordinated* groups are written inside of the square bracket. It will be seen that this simple postulate—that Pt^{IV} always has six groups in its *coordination shell*—nicely explains the conductances and chloride ion numbers in all of the compounds. These formulations imply that two additional members of the series, the anions $[Pt(NH_3)Cl_5]^-$ and $[PtCl_6]^{2-}$, might be capable of existence and, indeed, both are now known. Their potassium salts are found to be 1:1 and 2:1 electrolytes, respectively, on the basis of conductance measurements. On the basis of similar data, Co^{III} and Cr^{III} were also shown to have a coordination number of 6, and Pt^{II} and Pd^{II} were shown to have a coordination number of 4.

Once coordination numbers are established, the next question that naturally arises concerns the geometrical arrangement of the coordinated groups around the cation. Werner was able to postulate the correct arrangements on the basis of the numbers of isomers and optical activity, especially for the Co^{III} compounds. For example, there are just two

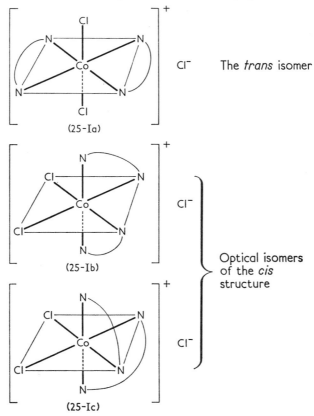

The *trans* isomer

(25-Ia)

(25-Ib)

(25-Ic)

Optical isomers of the *cis* structure

known isomers of $[Co(NH_3)_4Cl_2]Cl$, one lavender, the other green. There are also two known isomers of the analogous complex in which two molecules of ethylenediamine, $H_2NCH_2CH_2NH_2$ (abbreviated en), are substituted for the four NH_3 molecules, namely, $[Co(en)_2Cl_2]Cl$, and one of them can be resolved into optical isomers. These and many other facts led Werner to propose that the geometrical arrangement of the coordinated groups for the coordination number 6 is that of an octahedron. On this basis the isomers of $[Co(en)_2Cl_2]Cl$ would be formulated as 25-I. Similarly, on the basis of such facts as the occurrence of $[Pt(NH_3)_2Cl_2]$ in two isomeric forms, Werner proposed that the four-fold coordination sphere of Pt^{II} must be square. The two isomers mentioned are then formulated as *cis* (25-IIa) and *trans* (25-IIb).

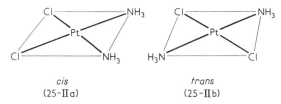

cis
(25-IIa)

trans
(25-IIb)

Once Werner's views about coordination numbers and the geometrical arrangements in the coordination shells became accepted, there still remained the intriguing question of the nature of the bonds which held the coordinated groups—*ligands*, as they are now called—to the metal ions. This is a question which even today is not settled in a definitive way. Werner simply attributed them to "secondary valences" of the metals. With the advent of the electronic theories of Lewis, Langmuir, and Sidgwick, emphasizing the importance of electron pairs in binding atoms together, the notion developed that ligands are of necessity ions or molecules which contain unshared pairs of electrons, as in $[:\overset{..}{Cl}:]^-$ or $H_3N:$, which could be used to form *dative* (i.e., donating) bonds, also called coordinate bonds, to the metal ions.

We shall now consider in detail the various aspects of the behavior of coordination compounds which have been touched on in this short introduction, but from a contemporary point of view.

25-2. Coordination Numbers and Symmetries

As outlined in the preceding section, the assumption that certain metal ions have characteristic coordination numbers and their coordination spheres certain definite shapes or symmetries provided Werner and those of his contemporaries who followed his lead with an extremely fruitful basis for the interpretation of many otherwise puzzling facts. As we shall see, the assumptions that the coordination spheres of Cr^{III}, Co^{III}, and Pt^{IV} are consistently octahedral and those of Pt^{II} and Pd^{II} consistently square planar were confirmed by a wealth of experimental data. In this section we will discuss the subject of coordination numbers and the shapes of coordination shells in a more general and comprehensive way. We shall discuss coordination numbers of 2 to 9, describing for each the various geometrical structures known and citing examples of their occurrence. It should be noted that we now possess an enormous amount of direct evidence via X-ray diffraction studies and indirect evidence via dipole moments, magnetic properties, and electronic spectra concerning coordination numbers and geometries, so that these ideas are no longer mere hypotheses but well-established facts.

It is also important to realize that a given metal ion does not necessarily have *one* characteristic coordination number and geometry. Some, such as Co^{III}, apparently do. There does not appear to be any complex of Co^{III} in which its coordination sphere is other than octahedral. Of course, the Co^{III} ion can be forced into other environments, a tetrahedral one, for instance, in certain solid compounds with extended, rigid structures, but few coordination chemists would quarrel with the statement that six octahedrally arranged ligand atoms constitute *the* characteristic coordination shell of Co^{III}. If we turn to Ni^{II}, however, we have quite the opposite situation. There are many well-established Ni^{II} complexes in each of the following classes: octahedral, six coordinate; planar, four coordinate; and tetrahedral, four coordinate. Zinc(II) and cobalt(II) also adopt all three of these coordination shells, and many other ions adopt at least two different coordination shells, depending on the conditions, types of ligands, etc.

Two Coordination. Coordination number 2 is not very common. It is best exemplified by some complexes of Cu^I, Ag^I, Au^I, and Hg^{II}. Such complexes have linear arrangements of the metal ion and the two ligand atoms, and typical ones are $[ClCuCl]^-$, $[NH_3AgNH_3]^+$, $[ClAuCl]^-$, and $[NCHgCN]$. The metal atoms in cations such as $[UO_2]^{2+}$, $[UO_2]^+$, $[MoO_2]^{2+}$, and $[PuO_2]^{2+}$ which are linear may also be said to have coordination number 2, but these oxy cations interact fairly strongly with additional ligands and their true coordination numbers are much higher. It is true, however, that they have a specially strong affinity for the two oxygen atoms.

Three Coordination. This coordination number is of little importance. In recent years a few complexes of copper and silver have been reported in which the metal atoms may have coordination number 3, but definitive proof is lacking for most of these. It is well to point out that one of the reasons why rather thorough evidence is necessary to document the occurrence of three-fold coordination is that so many compounds for which stoichiometry alone might suggest three-fold coordination turn out, on closer scrutiny, to be four or six coordinated. Thus, most of the halides of the trivalent metals crystallize in lattices containing metal ions in octahedral interstices, while $FeCl_3$, which is relatively volatile for a transition metal halide, vaporizes to Fe_2Cl_6 molecules consisting of two $FeCl_4$ tetrahedra sharing an edge, and $AuCl_3$ is a dimer consisting of two planar $AuCl_4$ units sharing an edge. Many complexes of the type $M^IM^{II}X_3$, for example, $CsCuCl_3$, contain not discrete MX_3^- anions but infinite chains —(MX_2)—X—(MX_2)—X— in which each M^{II} ion is surrounded by four X atoms; and others of the stoichiometry LMX_2, such as $(C_2H_5)_3PPtCl_2$ (25-III), are dimeric with X atom bridges. Of course, complexes in solu-

(25-III)

tion, which we may for simplicity write as ML_3, are almost certainly further coordinated by solvent molecules, for example, $M(H_2O)_3L_3$ or $M(H_2O)L_3$.

Tetrahedral Four Coordination. It is well established that there are many complexes with this geometry, but it is by no means as common as octahedral coordination among the transition elements. It occurs fairly commonly for complexes of nontransition ions where its stability can be attributed partly to the covalence in the bonds, achieved by the use of metal sp^3 hybrid orbitals, and partly to the fact that the tetrahedral configuration is the most stable one for four coordination from an electrostatic point of view. Thus, there are such tetrahedral complexes as BeF_4^{2-}, BF_4^-, BCl_4^-, BBr_4^-, $ZnCl_4^{2-}$, $ZnBr_4^{2-}$, $Zn(CN)_4^{2-}$, $Cd(CN)_4^{2-}$, and $Hg(CN)_4^{2-}$, all of which have been discussed earlier.

Among the genuine transition metal ions (i.e., those with d shell vacancies) tetrahedral complexes are usually stable only under certain conditions. Notable exceptions to this are the ions $FeCl_4^-$, $CoCl_4^{2-}$, $CoBr_4^{2-}$, CoI_4^{2-}, $Co(NCS)_4^{2-}$, and a few other CoX_4^{2-} species.* All of these form in aqueous solution despite the fact that water molecules are present in abundance which could serve to increase the coordination number to 6. The factors governing the stability of the tetrahedral configuration relative to the

---

* Evidence recently obtained shows that the main species in the aqueous Co systems are tetrahedral $[CoX_3(H_2O)]^-$ rather than $[CoX_4]^{2-}$.

planar one and the octahedral one which could be obtained by addition of two solvent molecules are not well understood.

Other transition metal ions have been shown to form tetrahedral complexes under special conditions, for example, in crystalline form where the tetrahedral anions are combined with large cations or in solvents of low coordinating power. Thus with cations such as $[C_nH_{2n+1})_4N]^+$, $[(C_6H_5)_4N]^+$, $[(C_6H_5)_3(CH_3)As]^+$, etc., the tetrahedral complex anions $[VX_4]^-$, $[MnX_4]^{2-}$, $[NiX_4]^{2-}$, and $[CuX_4]^{2-}$ (where X is Cl, Br, or I) have been obtained. None of them persist in solution in coordinating solvents such as water or alcohols, but many can be kept in solvents such as nitrobenzene, acetone, or dichloromethane.

Most of the known tetrahedral complexes are anionic, either $[M^{II}X_4]^{2-}$ or $[M^{II}LX_3]^-$ (where L is a neutral ligand), or neutral, $[ML_2X_2]$. Among the latter are, for example, those of Mn^{II}, Co^{II}, and Ni^{II} on which L is a phosphine oxide or an arsine oxide. There are very few known cationic tetrahedral complexes, such as $[ML_4]^{2+}$ or $[ML_3X]^+$. Some cations such as Cr^{III} and Co^{III} have never been found with tetrahedral coordination in simple complexes.

Planar Four Coordination.   This form of coordination is especially characteristic of certain elements and otherwise uncommon. For Rh^I, Ir^I, Pt^{II}, Pd^{II}, and Au^{III} it is the form of coordination usually found, and for Ni^{II} and Cu^{II} it is very common and important. For most other ions it is seldom or never observed.

With Pt^{II} and, to a lesser extent, Pd^{II} extensive investigations beginning in the late nineteenth century have led to the preparation of an enormous number of complexes illustrating essentially all of the possible types and their isomers. The latter will be discussed on page 533. With regard to charge types, all five possibilities are known, and are represented by the following:

2+ cation	$[Pt(NH_3)_4]^{2+}$
1+ cation	$[Pt(NH_3)_3Cl]^+$
Neutral	$[Pt(Ph_3P)_2Cl_2]$
1 − anion	$[Pt(py)Cl_3]^-$
2 − anion	$[PtCl_4]^{2-}$

Both cationic and anionic complexes of Ni^{II} and Cu^{II} are known, though not of all of the above five types.

Five Coordination.   Like coordination number 3, this one is relatively rare, and in various instances where stoichiometry might suggest its occurrence, the true coordination number is different, being either higher or lower. For instance, the crystalline compound Cs_3CoCl_5 contains tetrahedral $CoCl_4^{2-}$ ions and separate Cl^- ions in its lattice, whereas the crystalline compounds $NbCl_5$, $NbBr_5$, $TaCl_5$, and $MoCl_5$ all contain dimeric

M_2X_{10} molecules consisting of two octahedral MX_6 groups sharing an edge.

There are, however, a not insignificant number of definite, well-defined cases of five-fold coordination. For instance, those pentahalides mentioned above vaporize to pentacoordinate monomers which are trigonal bipyramids. Iron carbonyl, $Fe(CO)_5$, and the isoelectronic ions such as $Mn(CO)_5^-$ and $[Co(C{\equiv}NR)_5]^+$ also have trigonal bipyramidal configurations and so also do substituted iron carbonyls such as $R_3PFe(CO)_4$ and $(R_3P)_2Fe(CO)_3$. Bis(acetylacetonato)zinc(II) monohydrate has recently been shown to contain zinc surrounded by five trigonal bipyramidally disposed oxygen atoms, the one from water being in the equatorial set. There are then a number of five-coordinate derivatives of Ni, Co, Pd, and several other metals toward the right side of the transition block which are believed to have a square pyramid configuration, although only a little conclusive evidence for this has yet been produced. These compounds are exemplified by $NiBr_3[(C_2H_5)_3P]_2$, $CoI_2 \cdot$ triarsine and $NiI_2 \cdot$ triarsine (triarsine represents a tridentate ligand of the type $R_2As(CH_2)_2As(R)(CH_2)_2AsR_2$), and $[Pd(diarsine)_2Cl]ClO_4$. X-ray study has shown recently that the square pyramidal configuration exists in bis(salicylaldehydeethylenediimine)zinc monohydrate (25-IV) and in 25-V, a complex of Ni^{II} with the triarsine

(25-IV)

(25-V)

noted above having R equal to CH_3. One bromide ion is appreciably ($\sim 20°$) out of the basal plane, presumably because of steric pressure by the two methyl groups.

Six Coordination. This is the commonest one and is found in only one geometrical arrangement, the octahedron, although large distortions are often found. Some of the reasons for such distortions are discussed in Section 26-6.

The octahedron is a figure of very high symmetry. It is important to note that although we often draw an octahedral complex, for example,

$PtCl_6^{2-}$, as in 25-VI, so that two of the chloride ions might *look* different from the other four, all six are completely equivalent in an undistorted octahedron.

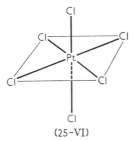

(25-VI)

Two forms of distortion commonly occur in complexes we might loosely call octahedral. The first is a *trigonal distortion,* in which the octahedron is extended or compressed along one of its three-fold axes. A trigonally distorted octahedron is, of course, a trigonal antiprism (25-VII). The second

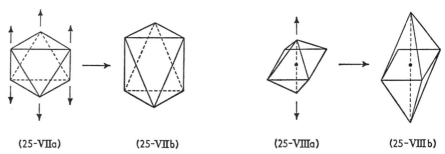

(25-VIIa)   (25-VIIb)   (25-VIIIa)   (25-VIIIb)

important form of distortion is the *tetragonal distortion,* in which the octahedron is elongated or flattened along a four-fold axis as in 25-VIII. Obviously, in the limit, a tetragonally distorted octahedron complex (by elongation) completely loses two *trans* ligands and becomes a four-coordinated, square complex. There is no definite answer to the question of how long the two metal-ligand bonds must become, relative to the other four, before we cease to regard these two ligands as truly coordinated. Thus, we must take the view that the octahedral and square planar forms of coordination merge into one another.

Coordination Numbers Greater Than Six. Coordination numbers 7, 8, and 9 are known to occur, but they are relatively rare and, with only few exceptions, confined to compounds of the elements in the second and third transition series, the lanthanides and the actinides. This is attributable in part to the larger size of these ions and also to the availability of orbitals.

Seven coordination is known to occur with at least two different geometrical arrangements. In the $[UO_2F_5]^{3-}$ ion there is a pentagonal bipyramid configuration with the oxygen atoms at the apices as shown in 25-IX. The ions UF_7^{3-}, ZrF_7^{3-}, and HfF_7^{3-} also have the shape of a pentagonal bipyramid. A second well-established type of heptacoordinated structure is found in the ions NbF_7^{2-} and TaF_7^{2-}, despite the fact that they

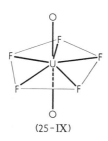

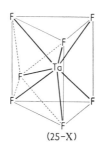

(25-IX)

(25-X)

are isoelectronic with the ZrF_7^{3-} and HfF_7^{3-} ions. This second structure is derived from a distorted trigonal prism by addition of a seventh ligand atom along the normal to one face (25-X). There is also a report that the ion $[NbOF_6]^{3-}$ has still a different structure in which the six fluorine atoms form a distorted octahedron with the oxygen atom outside the center of one triangular face.

Eight coordination is known in three geometrical forms. One of these is the square, or Archimedian, antiprism (25-XI). This structure has been found in the TaF_8^{3-} and $[Sr(H_2O)_8]^{2+}$ ions and also in the tetrakis(acetyl-

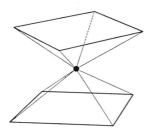

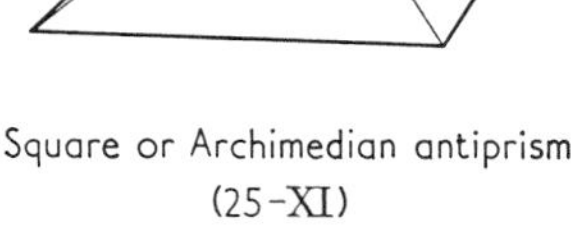

Square or Archimedian antiprism

(25-XI)

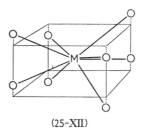

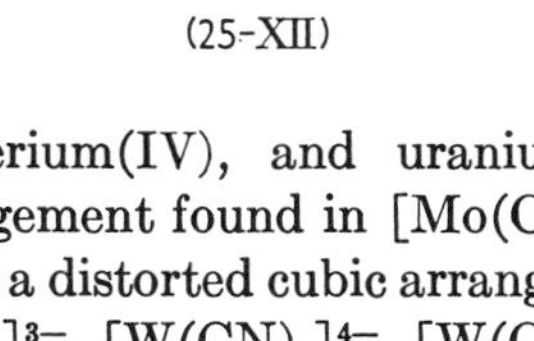

(25-XII)

acetonato) complexes of thorium(IV), cerium(IV), and uranium(IV). The second form is the dodecahedral arrangement found in $[Mo(CN)_8]^{4-}$. This, as shown in 25-XII, can be regarded as a distorted cubic arrangement. It is likely that the structures of $[Mo(CN)_8]^{3-}$, $[W(CN)_8]^{4-}$, $[W(CN)_8]^{3-}$, and $[Re(CN)_8]^{4-}$ ions are similar. Still another eight-coordinate structure is found in the $[UO_2(O_2CCH_3)_3]^-$ ion and is shown in Figure 32-4.

Nine coordination has been shown to occur in the cation in $[Nd(H_2O)_9](BrO_3)_3$ with the geometry illustrated in 25-XIII. Other nona-

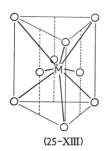

(25-XIII)

hydrates of rare earth salts probably contain similar aquo ions, and the same type of coordination shell geometry is found in lanthanide chlorides and, by sharing of anions, in some salts of UF_6^-, ThF_6^{2-}, and LaF_4^-.

25-3. Types of Ligands

The most general definition of a ligand might be that it is any atom, ion, or molecule capable of functioning as the donor partner in one or more coordinate bonds. There may be cases—for example, among the metal carbonyls—where the partner we call the ligand, namely CO, does as much accepting as donating, but in general the above definition will serve our purposes here.

At present there is no evidence that any single uncharged atom functions as a ligand. However, monatomic ions, especially the halogens, do so. Thus, there are numerous complexes containing only halide ions as ligands, such as $[CoF_6]^{3-}$, $[FeCl_4]^-$, $[CoBr_4]^{2-}$, and $[PtI_4]^{2-}$, as well as many containing halide ions along with other ligands, such as $[Co(NH_3)_5Cl]^{2+}$, $[Pt(Et_3P)_2Br_2]$, $[CoPyCl_3]^-$, and $[Cr(H_2O)_4Cl_2]^+$.

Monatomic ions necessarily belong to the general class of ligands known as *monodentate* (literally, one-toothed) ligands. Monodentate ligands use only one atom at a time as a donor atom, and hence they fill only one coordination position of a given cation. Of course, many polyatomic ions and molecules are also monodentate ligands. Some representative and important ones are: halide ions—F^-, Cl^-, Br^-, I^-; other ions—H^-, CN^-, SCN^-, NO_3^-, NO_2^-, N_3^-, $RCOO^-$, SO_4^{2-}; molecules—R_3N, R_3P, CO, R_2S, R_3PO, R_2SO, pyridine, H_2O. It should be noted that a monodentate ligand may simultaneously fill coordination positions in two or even three *different* metal ions; that is, they may function as bridges. The kinds of bridging illustrated in 25-XIV through 25-XX are well known and illustrative. In 25-XIV through 25-XVII the bridging ligand is still strictly monodentate

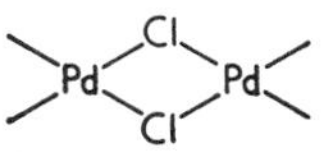

(25-XIV)

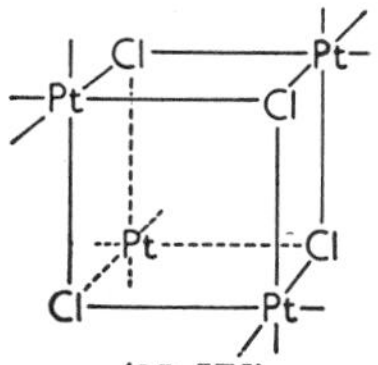

(25-XV)

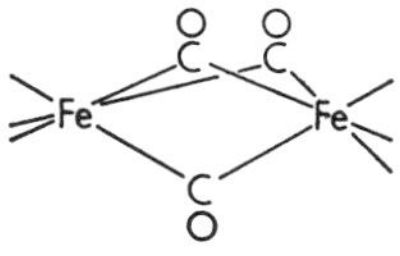

(25-XVI)

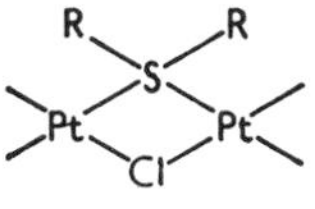

(25-XVII)

(25-XVIII)

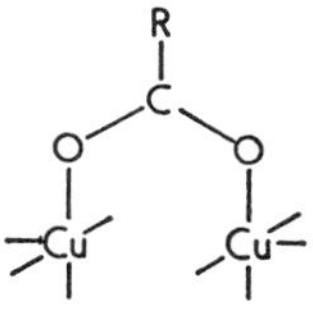

(25-XIX)

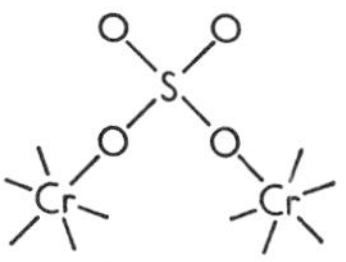

(25-XX)

in the sense that only one atom in it is functioning as a donor atom. In 25-XVIII, 25-XIX, and 25-XX different metal ions are coordinated by different atoms of the ligand. In the thiocyanate ion only one of the two potential donor atoms, S and N, can be bonded to one metal ion for geometric reasons, but both ends may be simultaneously bound to different cations. In the carboxylate anions and in the sulfate, carbonate, and nitrate ions, two atoms could be coordinated to the same metal ion, and there are cases known in which this happens with all of them.

Ligands having two or more atoms which can simultaneously serve as donors are called *polydentate* ligands. Those with two donor sites are called bidentate, those with three, four, five, and six donor sites are called tri(or ter)-, tetra(or quadri)-, penta-, and hexa(or sexi)dentate ligands, respectively. Polydentate ligands whose structures permit the attachment of two or more donor sites to the same metal ion simultaneously, thus closing one or more rings, are called *chelate* (from the Greek for claw) ligands, and are the more important class of polydentate ligands. Thus, both of the

$$\begin{array}{c}
\ce{CH2 - CH2}\\
\ce{:N-CH2-CH2-N:}\\
\ce{H2C - CH2}
\end{array}$$
(25-XXI)

$$\begin{array}{c}
\ce{CH2 - CH2}\\
\ce{H2N} \qquad \ce{NH2}
\end{array}$$
(25-XXII).

diamines 25-XXI and 25-XXII are bidentate ligands, but only ethylene-diamine is a chelate. Examples of various polydentate chelate ligands are given in Table 25-2.

STRUCTURE, ISOMERISM, AND NOMENCLATURE OF COMPLEX COMPOUNDS

25-4. Elements of Nomenclature

Coordination compounds can be sufficiently complicated and intricate structurally that a certain minimum discussion of formal rules of nomenclature is necessary in even an elementary account of their chemistry. Therefore, before discussing isomerism, we shall state and illustrate some of the more important and indispensable rules selected from a considerably larger body of rules proposed by the International Union of Chemistry.

1. Naming of ligands

a. Negative (anionic) ligands have names ending in *o*, derived, usually, by adding *o* to the stem name of the group. For example, Cl^- (chloro), Br^- (bromo), SCN^- (thiocyanato), CN^- (cyano), SO_4^{2-} (sulfato), OH^- (hydroxo), O^{2-} (oxo), O_2H^- (perhydroxo), O_2^{2-} (peroxo), NH_2^- (amido), and NH^{2-} (imido). Note the following special points. Since SCN^- may coordinate through either S or N, the distinction, when known, is made using the terms thiocyanato-*S* and thiocyanato-*N*. The ion NO_2 may coordinate via nitrogen, and is then called nitro, or through oxygen, when it is called nitrito.

b. For neutral ligands, the names are not systematic. For less common ones, the name of the free molecule is used as such. For some of the common ones, special names are used. The more important ones are H_2O (aquo), NH_3 (ammine), CO (carbonyl), and NO (nitrosyl).

2. Naming of mononuclear complex ions

a. If the compound is ionic, the cation(s) are mentioned first (whether complex or not).

b. In naming the complex, whether it is cationic or neutral, the ligands are listed beginning with the negative ones, then the central metal is mentioned, followed by a roman numeral in parentheses giving its oxidation number. (0) is used for an oxidation state of zero.

TABLE 25-2

Polydentate Chelate Ligands

Name	Formula
Some Bidentate Ligands	
S-Methylmercaptoacetic acid	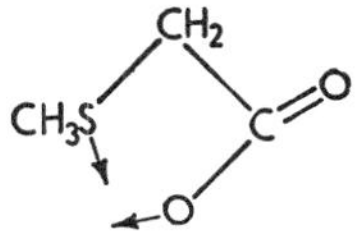
Acetylacetonato ion (AcAc⁻)	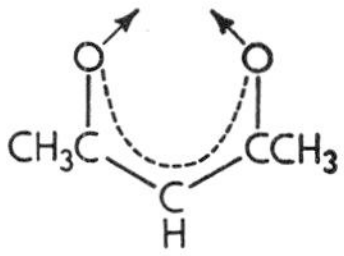
N,N-Diethylthiocarbamate ion	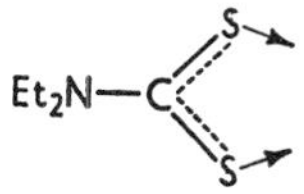
Oxalate ion	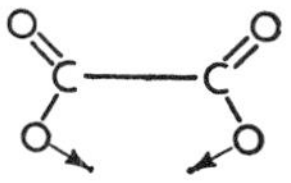
Anion of salicylaldehyde	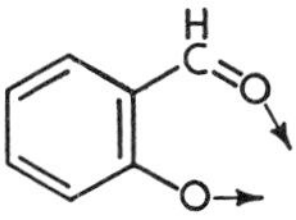
2,2'-Dipyridyl (dipy)	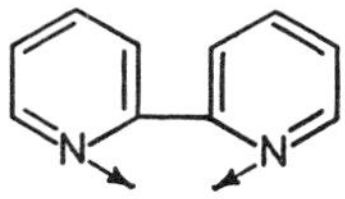
1,10-Phenanthroline (o-phen)	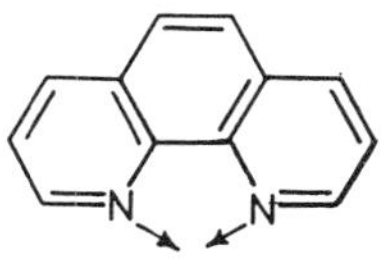
Dimethylglyoxime anion	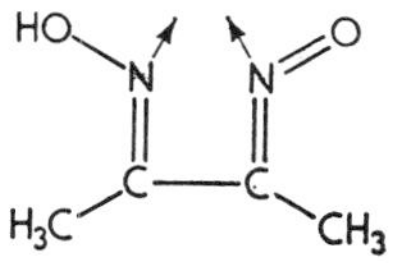
o-Phenylenebisdimethylarsine (diars)	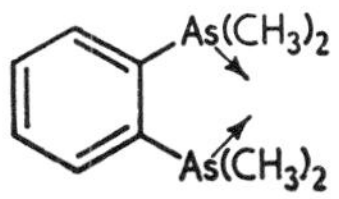

(*continued*)

TABLE 25-2 (*continued*)

Name	Formula

Some Tridentate Ligands

Diethylenetriamine

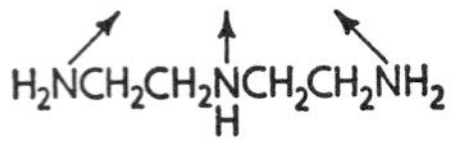

$$H_2NCH_2CH_2NCH_2CH_2NH_2$$
$$H$$

Iminodiacetic acid anion

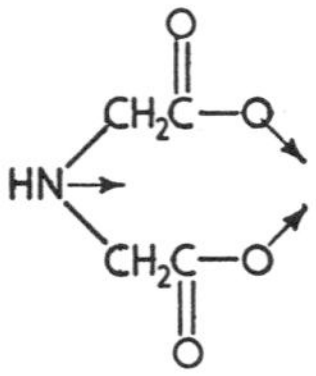

o-Azophenoxide ion

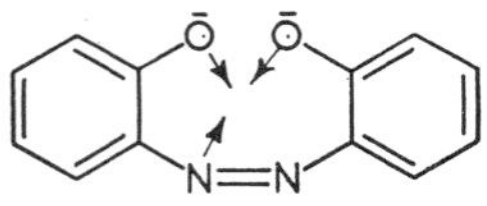

Some Tetradentate Ligands

Triethylenetetramine (trien)

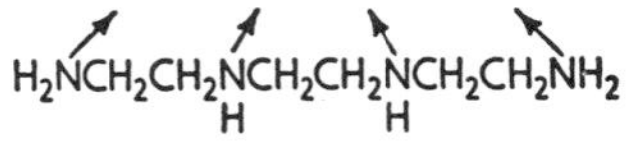

$$H_2NCH_2CH_2NCH_2CH_2NCH_2CH_2NH_2$$
$$HH$$

β,β',β''-Triaminotriethylamine (tren)

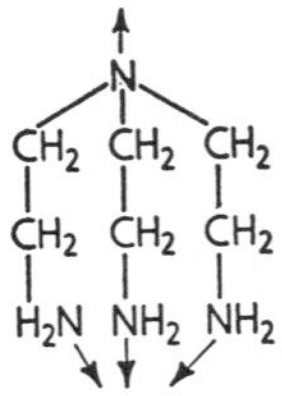

Anion of nitrilotriacetic acid

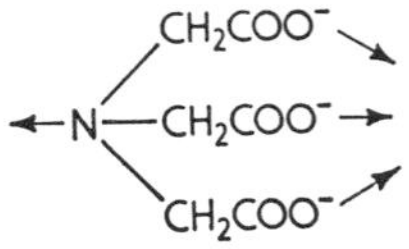

Bisacetylacetoneethylenediimine

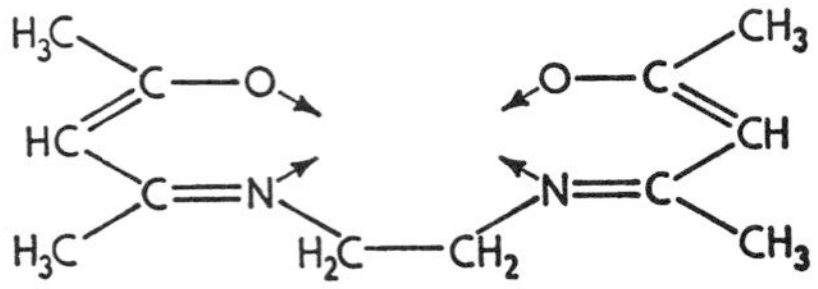

TABLE 25-2 (*continued*)

Name	Formula

Pentadentate Ligand

Anion of ethylenediaminetriacetic acid

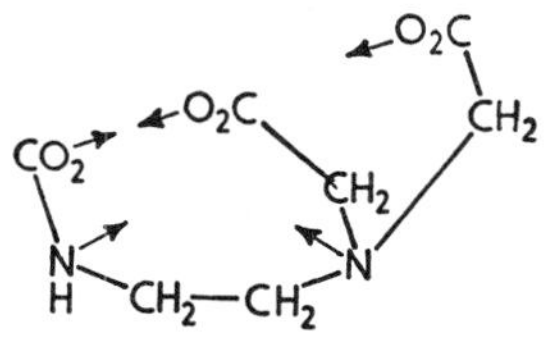

Some Hexadentate Ligands

1,8-Bis(salicylideneamino)-3,6-dithiaoctane

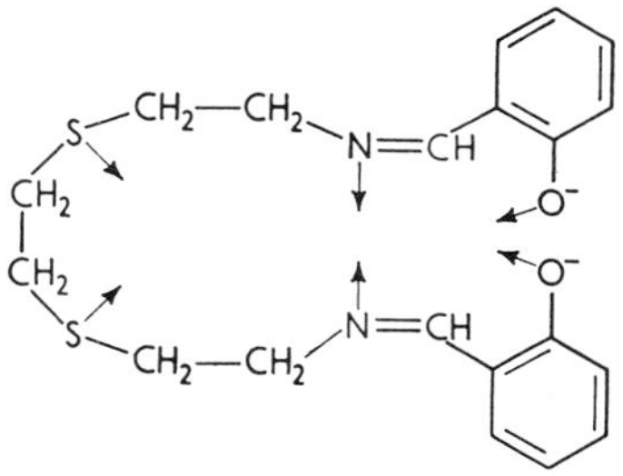

Trissalicylidene derivative of
2-aminomethyl-1,3-diaminopropane

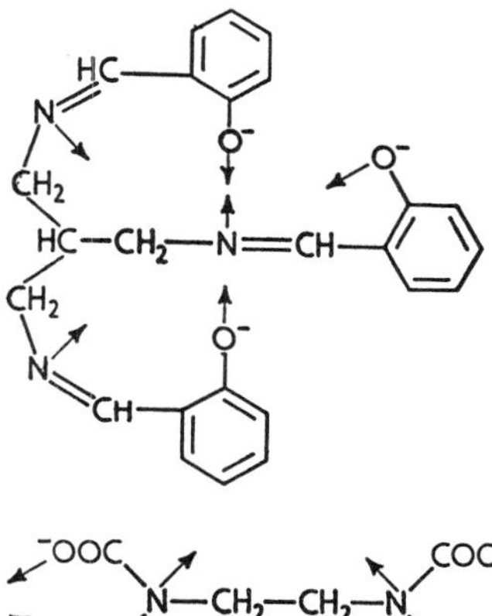

Anion of ethylenediaminetetraacetic acid
(EDTA)

531

c. If the complex is an anion, the suffix -*ate* is attached to the name of the central metal, and this suffix is followed by the oxidation number.

d. The number of each kind of ligand is specified using the Greek prefixes di-, tri-, tetra-, penta-, and hexa-. The examples below illustrate these rules.

$[Co(NH_3)_6]Cl_3$	Hexaamminecobalt(III) chloride
$K_3[Fe(C_2O_4)_3]$	Potassium trioxalatoferrate(III) or -iron(III)
$[Cr(H_2O)_4Cl_2]Cl$	Dichlorotetraaquochromium(III) chloride
$[Co(NH_3)_4(NO_2)Cl]NO_3$	Chloronitrotetraamminecobalt(III) nitrate
$K_3[Co(CN)_5NO]$	Potassium pentacyanonitrosylcobaltate(III)
$K[PtCl_3(NH_3)]$	Potassium trichloroammineplatinate(II)
$[(CH_3)_4N]_2[Co(NCS)_4]$	Tetramethylammonium tetrathiocyanato-*N*-cobaltate(II)

2. Dealing with complicated ligands. When ligands themselves have polysyllabic names, perhaps containing numerical prefixes, they are closed in parentheses, and the number present is indicated by the prefixes bis, tris, tetrakis, pentakis, hexakis:

$[Coen_3]Cl_3$	Tris(ethylenediamine)cobalt(III) chloride
$[Co(H_2NCH_2CH_2NHCH_2CH_2HN_2)_2](NO_3)_3$	Bis(diethylenetriamine)cobalt(III) nitrate
$Ni(PF_3)_4$	Tetrakis(phosphorus(III) fluoride)nickel(0)
$[Fe(CNCH_2C_6H_5)_5CN]Cl$	Cyanopentakis(benzylisocyanide)iron(II) chloride

4. Bridged polynuclear complexes. A bridging ligand is indicated by placing μ- before its name. The μ should be repeated before the name of each different bridging group. Some examples are

Bis(ethylenediamine)cobalt(III)-μ-imido-μ-hydroxobis(ethylenediamine)cobalt(III)

Triamminecobalt(III)-μ-trihydroxotriamminecobalt(III)

Chlorotriphenylphosphinepalladium(II)-μ-dichlorochlorotriphenylphosphinepalladium(II)

5. Geometrical and optical isomerism. In several of the examples used above, the names given are not quite complete, since no specification is made regarding the particular structural isomer. The kinds of isomers which can occur will be described next, at which time the necessary nomenclature will be introduced.

25-5. Stereoisomerism

Both geometrical and optical isomerism are encountered among coordination complexes. In the following outline, we shall restrict our attention to tetrahedral, square, and octahedral complexes only.

Geometrical Isomers. Geometrical isomerism with respect to the metal has not been found among tetrahedral complexes, nor can it be expected except perhaps when some very complex and esoteric ligands might be involved.

In square complexes, several types of geometrical isomerism are of frequent occurrence.

1. Any complex of the type MA_2B_2 can exist in *cis* or *trans* forms:

$$
\begin{array}{ccc}
\text{A} & \quad & \text{A} \\
 & \text{M} & \\
\text{B} & \quad & \text{B} \\
\end{array}
\qquad
\begin{array}{ccc}
\text{B} & \quad & \text{A} \\
 & \text{M} & \\
\text{A} & \quad & \text{B} \\
\end{array}
$$

cis   trans

In a complex of the type MA_2BC, there are also *cis* and *trans* isomers. For a complex of the type MABCD, three isomers are possible, and all three have been isolated in several cases, such as in 25-XXIII.

$$
\begin{array}{ccc}
\text{H}_3\text{N} & & \text{Py} \\
 & \text{Pt} & \\
\text{Cl} & & \text{Br}
\end{array}
\qquad
\begin{array}{ccc}
\text{H}_3\text{N} & & \text{Py} \\
 & \text{Pt} & \\
\text{Br} & & \text{Cl}
\end{array}
\qquad
\begin{array}{ccc}
\text{H}_3\text{N} & & \text{Br} \\
 & \text{Pt} & \\
\text{Cl} & & \text{Py}
\end{array}
$$

(25-XXIIIa)   (25-XXIIIb)   (25-XXIIIc)

2. A chelate complex with substituents on the ring atoms can be expected

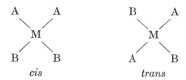

cis   trans
(25-XXIVa)   (25-XXIVb)

to afford geometrical isomers which are *cis* (25-XXIVa) and *trans* (25-XXIVb) with respect to the median plane of the molecule.

3. In bridged binuclear planar complexes *cis* (25-XXVa) and *trans* (25-XXVb) isomers as well as the "unsymmetrical" isomer (25-XXVc) are

(25-XXVa)   (25-XXVb)   (25-XXVc)

possible, although in the example cited, and in all other cases, only the first two have been found.

In octahedral complexes, two kinds of *cis-trans* isomerism are known:

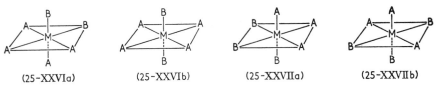

(25-XXVIa)   (25-XXVIb)   (25-XXVIIa)   (25-XXVIIb)

the *cis* (25-XXVIa) and *trans* (25-XXVIb) isomers in MA_4B_2 and the *cis* (25-XXVIIa) and *trans* (25-XXVIIb) isomers in MA_3B_3.

In naming compounds capable of existing in *cis* and *trans* isomers, the isomer intended is specified by placing the prefix with a hyphen before the name of the compound, for example, *cis*-dichlorotetraamminecobalt(III) chloride (25-XXVIII).

$$\left[\begin{array}{c} NH_3 \\ H_3N\underset{\underset{NH_3}{\overset{\displaystyle Co}{|}}}{\overset{\displaystyle |}{\diagdown}}Cl \\ H_3N \diagup Cl \end{array} \right]^{+} \quad Cl^{-}$$

(25-XXVIII)

Optical Isomers. Of various conceivable types of optical isomers obtainable with tetrahedral complexes, only the kind which occurs in bis chelates with unsymmetrical ligands have been detected. These are of the general type 25-XXIXa and 25-XXIXb. The bis(salicylato)boron(III) anion, mentioned earlier (Chapter 10, page 180), represents a case where resolution has been accomplished.

(25-XXIXa)   (25-XXIXb)   (25-XXX)

Optical isomers occur only rarely among square complexes, the known cases involving rather unusual chelate ligands which are unsymmetrical. For example, the Pt^{II} complex (25-XXX) was resolved, thus proving that the coordination is planar, for the tetrahedral form would have a plane of symmetry and therefore no optical isomerism.

More recently, it has been shown that EDTA forms an anionic complex with Pd^{II} which can be resolved into optical isomers. These must be the antimers of 25-XXXIa; the *cis* isomer, 25-XXXIb, was not detected.

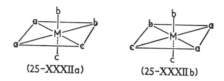

(25-XXXIa)   (25-XXXIb)

The most important cases of optical isomerism occur among octahedral complexes. Optical isomers can occur in nonchelate complexes with three or more different kinds of ligands and no more than two of any one kind, namely, in the cases $[Ma_2b_2c_2]$, $[Ma_2b_2cd]$, $[Ma_2bcde]$, and $[Mabcdef]$. For the $[Ma_2b_2c_2]$ case there are five geometrical isomers and 25-XXXII

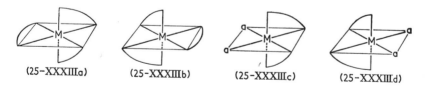

(25-XXXIIa)   (25-XXXIIb)

exists in optical isomers. No resolution of a complex containing only monodentate ligands has as yet been reported, however.

A great deal of work on optical isomerism has been done with octahedral complexes containing chelate ligands. The most common types are those containing three bidentate ligands or two bidentate and two monodentate ligands. The enantiomorphs in these cases are 25-XXXIIIa through

(25-XXXIIIa)   (25-XXXIIIb)   (25-XXXIIIc)   (25-XXXIIId)

25-XXXIIId. There are a vast number of complexes of these types, and many have been resolved. Resolution is usually achieved using cationic (e.g., $[Cr(en)_3]^{3+}$ or cis-$[Co(en)_2Cl_2]^+$) or anionic (e.g., $[Co(oxalato)_3]^{3+}$) species by fractional crystallization of the diastereoisomeric salts with optically active organic anions or cations. For example, a racemic mixture of cis-$[Coen_2Cl_2]Cl$ can be treated with ammonium d-α-bromocamphor-π-sulfonate to yield a mixture of diastereoisomers as indicated by equation 25-5. The diastereoisomers, once separated, may then be treated with

$$\left.\begin{matrix} \text{D-}[\text{Coen}_2\text{Cl}_2]\text{Cl} \\ \text{L-}[\text{Coen}_2\text{Cl}_2]\text{Cl} \end{matrix}\right\} + 2\text{NH}_4(d\text{-C}_{10}\text{H}_{14}\text{BrO}_4\text{S}) \rightarrow$$

$$\text{D-}[\text{Coen}_2\text{Cl}_2](d\text{-C}_{10}\text{H}_{14}\text{BrO}_4\text{S}) + \text{L-}[\text{Coen}_2\text{Cl}_2](d\text{-C}_{10}\text{H}_{14}\text{BrO}_4\text{S}) + 2\text{NH}_4\text{Cl} \quad (25\text{-}5)$$

hydrochloric acid and the acid of the organic anion removed to allow recovery of the two optical isomers of $[\text{Coen}_2\text{Cl}_2]\text{Cl}$. Of course, resolution is not always possible for kinetic reasons. For example, there is scarcely any doubt that $[\text{Znen}_3]^{2+}$ and $[\text{Nien}_3]^{2+}$ have octahedral structures and exist as DL mixtures even though their antimers have never been separated. It is well known that the rates of reaction and rearrangement, as judged from tracer exchange experiments, are extremely fast for Ni^{II} and Zn^{II} complexes in general, and thus, an isolated antimer would racemize so quickly that its initial presence would be undetectable. With Cr^{III} and Co^{III} complexes, reaction rates are in general slow, requiring hours and even days for rearrangements to occur, so that isolated optical antimers are stable for hours and even days, but they do, of course, eventually racemize. We may also note that by a special X-ray diffraction technique, whereby X-rays of the same wavelength as an X-ray absorption edge of the metal ion are used (the technique of "anomalous dispersion"), the absolute configurations of the $[\text{Coen}_3]^{3+}$ ions have been determined.

Optical activity in complexes with sexidentate ligands has also been rather extensively studied. For example, the first of the sexidentate ligands shown in Table 25-2, which we will here represent simply as O—N—S—S—N—O, can arrange itself in four geometrically different ways around an octahedral ion, and each of these geometrical isomers can exist in optical antimers (25-XXXIVa–d). Detailed steric considerations, best appreciated

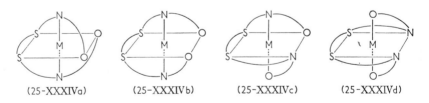

(25-XXXIVa)   (25-XXXIVb)   (25-XXXIVc)   (25-XXXIVd)

by inspection of models, indicate that 25-XXXIVa is much less strained than the others, and the green cation obtained with Co^{III} is assumed to have this structure. This cation has been resolved using an optically active anion, and the resulting optical antimers have the highest molecular rotations so far reported among complex compounds.

Complexes of ethylenediaminetetraacetic acid should also exist in optical antimers, and resolution of the cobalt(III) anions has been accomplished (25-XXXV).

(25-XXXVa)   (25-XXXVb) d-pn (25-XXXVIa) l-pn (25-XXXVIb)

When complexes in which the metal atoms themselves lie at centers of asymmetry (e.g., $[Co(en)_3]^{3+}$ and cis-$[Coen_2X_2]^+$ mentioned above) are made using ligands which contain centers of asymmetry, various diastereoisomers may be formed. For example, the ligand propylenediamine, pn, exists in optical antimers (25-XXXVI). In $[Copn_3]^{3+}$ these may be grouped in eight ways. If we use D and L to indicate the configuration of the entire octahedral unit, and d and l to indicate the configurations of the ligand molecules (this being the standard nomenclature), the eight diastereoisomers may be specified as:

1. D-$[Co(l$-$pn)_3]^{3+}$
2. D-$[Co(l$-$pn)_2(d$-$pn)]^{3+}$
3. D-$[Co(l$-$pn)(d$-$pn)_2]^{3+}$
4. D-$[Co(d$-$pn)_3]^{3+}$

5. L-$[Co(l$-$pn)_3]^{3+}$
6. L-$[Co(l$-$pn)_2(d$-$pn)]^{3+}$
7. L-$[Co(l$-$pn)(d$-$pn)_2]^{3+}$
8. L-$[Co(d$-$pn)_3]^{3+}$

It has long been known that in systems of this kind the various diastereoisomers are not formed in statistically expected proportions, but instead certain ones are distinctly favored. For example, in the $[Co(l$-$pn)_3]^{3+}$ system, the L complex is present in great excess over the D isomer, and when $[Co(l$-$pn)_2Cl_2]^+$ is treated with d-pn, there is obtained a mixture of L-$[Co(l$-$pn)_3]^{3+}$ and D-$[Co(d$-$pn)_3]^{3+}$ rather than either of the diastereoisomers of the mixed complex $[Co(l$-$pn)_2(d$-$pn)]^{3+}$. The stereospecificities observed here and in similar equilibria can be understood by detailed consideration of the configurations and conformations of the ligands and the relative amounts of steric hindrance resulting in the several diastereoisomers. In fact, the absolute configuration of D-$[Co(d$-$pn)_3]^{3+}$ has been deduced and shown to agree with that found for D-$[Coen_3]^{3+}$ by the anomalous dispersion X-ray method mentioned above.

25-6. Other Types of Isomerism

1. Ionization isomerism. Compounds which have the same composition but yield different ions in solution are called ionization isomers. Some representative examples are: $[Co(NH_3)_4Cl_2]NO_2$ and $[Co(NH_3)_4(Cl)(NO_2)]Cl$; $[Coen_2(NO_2)Cl]SCN$, $[Coen_2(NO_2)(SCN)]Cl$, and $[Coen_2(SCN)Cl]NO_2$; $[Pt(NH_3)_4Cl_2]Br_2$ and $[Pt(NH_3)_4Br_2]Cl_2$.

A special case of this, often called hydrate isomerism, is sometimes encountered, as in the three isomers of $CrCl_3 \cdot 6H_2O$, which are correctly formulated as (1) $[Cr(H_2O)_6]Cl_3$—violet; does not lose water over H_2SO_4; all Cl^- immediately precipitated by Ag^+. (2) $[Cr(H_2O)_5Cl]Cl_2 \cdot H_2O$—green; loses one H_2O over H_2SO_4; two Cl^- immediately precipitated by Ag^+. (3) $[Cr(H_2O)_4Cl_2]Cl \cdot 2H_2O$—green; loses two H_2O over H_2SO_4; one Cl^- immediately precipitated by Ag^+. Additional evidence for these formulations is obtained from molar conductances which show them to be uni-tri-, uni-di-, and uni-univalent electrolytes in the above order. An example involving both ionization and hydrate isomerism is provided by the compounds $[Co(NH_3)_4(H_2O)Cl]Br_2$ and $[Co(NH_3)_4Br_2]Cl \cdot H_2O$.

2. Ligand isomerism. Some ligands themselves can exist as isomers and be so incorporated into complexes. Thus there are both 1,2-diaminopropane (pn) and 1,3-diaminopropane, also called trimethylenediamine (tmen) and the isomeric complexes $[Co(pn)_2Cl_2]Cl$ and $[Co(tmen)_2Cl_2]Cl$.

2. Linkage isomerism. This occurs with ligands capable of coordinating in more than one way. The best-known simple cases are those involving nitro-nitrito isomerism, for example, the nitro isomer $[Co(NH_3)_5NO_2]^{2+}$ and the nitrito isomer $[Co(NH_3)_5ONO]^{2+}$. The thiocyanate ion coordinates through sulfur in some complexes and through nitrogen in others, but no isomeric pair has as yet been bound. Similarly, sulfoxides, R_2SO, can coordinate through either S or O, but no isomeric pair of complexes is known.

4. Coordination Isomerism. In compounds where both anion and cation are complex, the distribution of ligands between the two coordination spheres can vary, giving rise to isomers. This is illustrated by $[Co(NH_3)_6]$ $[Cr(CN)_6]$ and $[Cr(NH_3)_6][Co(CN)_6]$; $[Co(NH_3)_6][Cr(C_2O_4)_3]$ and $[Cr(NH_3)_6][Co(C_2O_4)_3]$; $[Cu(NH_3)_4][PtCl_4]$ and $[Pt(NH_3)_4][CuCl_4]$; $[Co(en)_3][Cr(C_2O_4)_3]$, $[Co(en)_2(C_2O_4)][Cr(en)(C_2O_4)_2]$, $[Co(en)(C_2O_4)_2][Cr(en)_2(C_2O_4)]$ and $[Co(C_2O_4)_3][Cr(en)_3]$. Such isomerism may also occur even when the same metal atom occurs in cation and anion, for example, $[Cr(NH_3)_6][Cr(SCN)_6]$ and $[Cr(NH_3)_4(SCN)_2][Cr(NH_3)_2(SCN)_4]$; $[Pt^{II}(NH_3)_4][Pt^{IV}Cl_6]$ and $[Pt^{IV}(NH_3)_4Cl_2][PtCl_4]$.

5. Polymerization isomers. These are not truly isomers, but they have classically been considered so. They are not isomers because they differ in size of the smallest representative unit, but they do have the same empirical composition. Some examples are $[Pt(NH_3)_2Cl_2]$ and $[Pt(NH_3)_4][PtCl_4]$; $[Co(NH_3)_3(NO_2)_3]$, $[Co(NH_3)_6][Co(NO_2)_6]$, $[Co(NH_3)_4(NO_2)_2][Co(NH_3)_2(NO_2)_4]$, $[Co(NH_3)_5NO_2][Co(NH_3)_2(NO_2)_4]_2$, $[Co(NH_3)_6][Co(NH_3)_2(NO_2)_4]_3$, $[Co(NH_3)_4(NO_2)_2]_3[Co(NO_2)_6]$ and $[Co(NH_3)_5(NO_2)][Co(NO_2)_6]_2$.

STABILITY OF COMPLEX IONS IN SOLUTION

25-7. Introduction

When we speak of the stability of a compound, we should be careful to specify what kind of stability we mean. In studying the formation of co-ordination complexes in solution, two kinds of stability come into question, namely, thermodynamic stability and kinetic stability. The thermo-dynamic stability of a species is a measure of the extent to which this species will form from or be transformed into other species under certain conditions *when the system has reached equilibrium.* The kinetic stability of a species refers to the speed with which transformations leading to the attainment of equilibrium will occur. In this and the next several sections we will consider problems of thermodynamic stability, that is, the nature of equilibria once they are established. Kinetic problems are discussed on page 548.

Suppose we put a metal ion, M, and some monodentate ligand, L, together in solution. Assuming that no insoluble products are formed, nor any species containing more than one metal ion, equilibrium expressions of the following sort will describe the system:

$$M + L = ML \qquad K_1 = \frac{[ML]}{[M][L]}$$

$$ML + L = ML_2 \qquad K_2 = \frac{[ML_2]}{[ML][L]}$$

$$ML_2 + L = ML_3 \qquad K_3 = \frac{[ML_3]}{[ML_2][L]}$$

$$\cdot \qquad \cdot \qquad \cdot \qquad \cdot$$
$$\cdot \qquad \cdot \qquad \cdot \qquad \cdot$$
$$\cdot \qquad \cdot \qquad \cdot \qquad \cdot$$

$$ML_{N-1} + L = ML_N \qquad K_N = \frac{[ML_N]}{[ML_{N-1}][L]}$$

There will be N such equilibria, where N represents the maximum co-ordination number of the metal ion M for the ligand L. N may vary from one ligand to another. For instance, Fe^{3+} forms $FeCl_4^-$ and $Fe(CN)_6^{3-}$, and Co^{2+} forms $CoCl_4^-$ and $Co(NH_3)_6^{2+}$, as the highest complexes with the ligands indicated.

Another way of expressing the equilibrium relations is the following:

$$M + L = ML \qquad \beta_1 = \frac{[ML]}{[M][L]}$$

$$M + 2L = ML_2 \qquad \beta_2 = \frac{[ML_2]}{[M][L]^2}$$

$$M + 3L = ML_3 \qquad \beta_3 = \frac{[ML_3]}{[M][L]^3}$$

$$\cdot \qquad\qquad \cdot \qquad \cdot \qquad \cdot$$
$$\cdot \qquad\qquad \cdot \qquad \cdot \qquad \cdot$$
$$\cdot \qquad\qquad \cdot \qquad \cdot \qquad \cdot$$

$$M + NL = ML_N \qquad \beta_N = \frac{[ML_N]}{[M][L]^N}$$

Since there can be only N independent equilibria in such a system, it is clear that the K_i's and the β_i's must be related. The relationship is indeed rather obvious. Consider, for example, the expression for β_3. Let us multiply both numerator and denominator by $[ML][ML_2]$ and then rearrange slightly:

$$\beta_3 = \frac{[ML_3]}{[M][L]^3} \cdot \frac{[ML][ML_2]}{[ML][ML_2]}$$

$$= \frac{[ML]}{[M][L]} \cdot \frac{[ML_2]}{[ML][L]} \cdot \frac{[ML_3]}{[ML_2][L]}$$

$$= K_1 K_2 K_3$$

It is not difficult to see that this kind of relationship is perfectly general, namely:

$$\beta_k = K_1 K_2 K_3 \ldots K_k = \prod_{i=1}^{i=k} K_i$$

The K_i's are called the *stepwise formation constants* (or stepwise stability constants), and the β_i's are called the *over-all formation constants* (or over-all stability constants); each type has its special convenience in certain cases. A brief treatment of experimental methods for determining stability constants is given in Appendix F.

In all of the above equilibria we have written the metal ion without specifying charge or degree of solvation. The former omission is obviously of no importance, for the equilibria may be expressed as above whatever the charges. It is also true that the equilibria may be treated as written without taking any explicit account of solvation of the ions, but the latter point is of current interest, and we shall therefore digress briefly to summarize some basic facts about aquo ions.

25-8. Condition of Ions in Aqueous Solution

We know that ions in solution interact with and in some sense bind the solvent molecules. From thermodynamic cycles the enthalpies of plunging gaseous metal ions into water can be estimated and the results, 10^2–10^3 kcal./mole, show that these interactions are very strong indeed. It is of importance in understanding the behavior of transition metal ions—and, indeed, all ions in solution—to know how many water molecules each of these ions binds by direct metal-oxygen bonds. To put it another way, if we regard the ion as being an aquo complex, $[M(H_2O)_x]^{n+}$, which is then further and more loosely solvated, we wish to know the coordination number x and also the manner in which the x water molecules are arranged around the metal ion. Classical measurements of various types—for example, ion mobilities, apparent hydrated radii, entropies of hydration, etc. —fail to give such detailed information because they cannot make any explicit distinction between those water molecules directly bonded to the metal—the x water molecules in the inner coordination sphere—and additional molecules which are held less strongly by hydrogen bonds to the water molecules of the inner coordination sphere. There are, however, ways of answering the question in many instances, ways depending, for the most part, on modern physical and theoretical developments. A few illustrative examples will be considered here.

For the transition metal ions, the spectral and, to a lesser degree, magnetic properties depend upon the constitution and symmetry of their surroundings. As a favorable but not essentially atypical example, the Co^{II} ion is known to form both octahedral and tetrahedral complexes. Thus, we might suppose that the aquo ion could be either $[Co(H_2O)_6]^{2+}$ with octahedral symmetry, or $[Co(H_2O)_4]^{2+}$ with tetrahedral symmetry. It is found that the spectrum and magnetism of Co^{II} in pink aqueous solutions of its salts with noncoordinating anions such as ClO_4^- or NO_3^- are very similar to the corresponding properties of octahedrally coordinated Co^{II} in general, and virtually identical with those of Co^{II} in such hydrated salts as $Co(ClO_4)_2 \cdot 6H_2O$ or $CoSO_4 \cdot 7H_2O$ where octahedral $[Co(H_2O)_6]^{2+}$ ions are known from X-ray studies definitely to exist. Complementing this, we have the fact that the spectral and magnetic properties of the many known tetrahedral Co^{II} complexes, such as $[CoCl_4]^{2-}$, $[CoBr_4]^{2-}$, $[Co(NCS)_4]^{2-}$, and $[(pyridine)_2 CoCl_2]$, which have intense blue or purple colors, are completely different from those of Co^{II} in aqueous solution. Thus, there can scarcely be any doubt that aqueous solutions of otherwise uncomplexed Co^{II} contain well-defined, octahedral $[Co(H_2O)_6]^{2+}$ ions, further hydrated, of course. Evidence of similar character can be adduced for many of the other transition metal ions. For all of the di- and tripositive ions of the first transition series, it is certain that the aquo ions are octahedral $[M(H_2O)_6]^{2(\text{or }3)+}$ species, although in those of Mn^{III} and Cu^{II} there are definite distortions of the octahedra because of the Jahn-Teller effect (see Section 26-6).

Information on ions of the second and third transition series is not so certain. It is probable that the coordination is octahedral in many, but higher coordination numbers may occur.

For ions which do not have partly filled d shells, evidence of the kind mentioned is lacking, since such ions do not have spectral or magnetic properties related in a straightforward way to the nature of their coordination spheres. We are therefore not entirely sure about the state of aquation of many such ions, although kinetic and other techniques can sometimes supply such information. It should be noted that even when the existence of a well-defined aquo ion is certain, there are vast differences in the average length of time which a water molecule spends in the coordination sphere, the so-called mean residence time. For Cr^{III} this time is so long that on mixing a solution of $[Cr(H_2O)_6]^{3+}$ in ordinary water with water enriched in ^{18}O, many hours are required for complete equilibration of the enriched solvent water with the coordinated water. From a measurement of how many molecules of H_2O in the Cr^{III} solution fail immediately to exchange with the enriched water added, the coordination number of Cr^{III} by water was shown to be 6. The chromium(III) case is exceptional, however. Most other aquo ions are far more labile, and a similar equilibration would occur too rapidly to permit the same type of measurement. This particular rate problem is only one of several which will be discussed more fully in Sections 25-11 and 25-12.

Aquo ions are all more or less acidic; that is, they dissociate in a manner represented by the equation:

$$M(H_2O)_x{}^{n+} = [M(H_2O)_{x-1}(OH)]^{(n-1)+} + H^+ \qquad K_A = \frac{[H^+][M(H_2O)_{x-1}(OH)]}{[M(H_2O)_x]}$$

The acidities vary widely, as the following K_A values show.

M in $[M(H_2O)_6]^{n+}$	K_A
Al^{III}	1.12×10^{-5}
Cr^{III}	1.26×10^{-4}
Fe^{III}	$6.3 \ \times 10^{-3}$

Coordinated water molecules in other complexes also dissociate in the same way, for example,

$$[Co(NH_3)_5(H_2O)]^{3+} = [Co(NH_3)_5(OH)]^{2+} + H^+ \qquad K \approx 10^{-5.7}$$
$$[Pt(NH_3)_4(H_2O)_2]^{4+} = [Pt(NH_3)_4(H_2O)(OH)]^{3+} + H^+ \qquad K \approx 10^{-2}$$

25-9. The "Stepwise" Formation of Complexes

The series of stepwise formation constants, K_i's, have been described. These imply that all complexes in the series ML . . . ML$_N$ can exist in the system; their proportions will depend, of course, on the concentrations [M] and [L] and on the relative values of the K_i's. With only a few exceptions, there is generally a slowly descending progression in the values of the K_i's in any particular system. This is illustrated by the data* for the Cd^{II}–NH_3 system where the ligands are uncharged and by the Cd^{II}–CN^- system where the ligands are charged.

$$Cd^{2+} + NH_3 = [Cd(NH_3)]^{2+} \qquad K = 10^{2.65}$$
$$[Cd(NH_3)]^{2+} + NH_3 = [Cd(NH_3)_2]^{2+} \qquad K = 10^{2.10}$$
$$[Cd(NH_3)_2]^{2+} + NH_3 = [Cd(NH_3)_3]^{2+} \qquad K = 10^{1.44}$$
$$[Cd(NH_3)_3]^{2+} + NH_3 = [Cd(NH_3)_4]^{2+} \qquad K = 10^{0.93} \; (\beta_4 = 10^{7.12})$$

$$Cd^{2+} + CN^- = [Cd(CN)]^+ \qquad K = 10^{5.48}$$
$$[Cd(CN)]^+ + CN^- = [Cd(CN)_2] \qquad K = 10^{5.12}$$
$$[Cd(CN)_2] + CN^- = [Cd(CN)_3]^- \qquad K = 10^{4.63}$$
$$[Cd(CN)_3]^- + CN^- = [Cd(CN)_4]^{2-} \qquad K = 10^{3.55} \; (\beta_4 = 10^{18.8})$$

Thus, typically, as ligand is added to the solution of metal ion, ML first forms more rapidly than any other complexes in the series. As addition of ligand is continued, the ML_2 concentration rises rapidly, while the ML concentration drops, then ML_3 becomes dominant, ML and ML_2 becoming unimportant, and so forth until the highest complex, ML_N is formed to the nearly complete exclusion of all others at very high ligand concentrations.

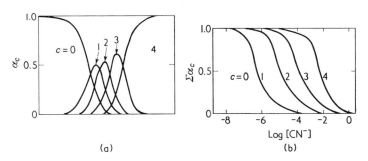

Fig. 25-1. Plots of the proportions of the various complexes $[Cd(CN)_c]^{(2-c)+}$ as a function of the ligand concentration:

$$\alpha_c = [Cd(CN)_c]/\text{total Cd} \qquad \Sigma \, \alpha_c = \sum_{c=0}^{4} [Cd(CN)_c]$$

(Reproduced by permission from F. J. C. Rossotti in J. Lewis and R. G. Wilkins, eds., *Modern Coordination Chemistry*, Interscience, New York–London, 1960, p. 10.)

From the formation constants given above for the Cd–CN system, graphical pictures of these relations may be drawn, as shown in Figure 25-1.

* Cd–NH_3 constants determined in $2M$ NH_4NO_3; Cd–CN constants determined in $3M$ $NaClO_4$.

A steady decrease in K_i values with increasing i is to be expected provided there are only slight changes in the metal-ligand bond energies as a function of i, which is usually the case. For example, in the Ni^{2+}–NH_3 system to be discussed below, the enthalpies of the successive reactions $Ni(NH_3)_{i-1} + NH_3 = Ni(NH_3)_i$ are all within the range of 4.0–4.3 kcal./mole.

There are several reasons for a steady decrease in K_i values as the number of ligands increases: (1) statistical factors; (2) increased steric hindrance as the number of ligands increases; (3) coulombic factors, mainly in complexes with charged ligands. The statistical factors may be treated in the following way. Suppose, as is almost certainly the case for Ni^{2+}, that the coordination number remains the same throughout the series $[M(H_2O)_N]$ . . . $[M(H_2O)_{N-n}L_n]$ . . . $[ML_N]$. The $[M(H_2O)_{N-n}L_n]$ species has n sites from which to lose a ligand, whereas the species $[M(H_2O)_{N-n+1}L_{n-1}]$ has $(N - n + l)$ sites at which to gain a ligand. Thus the relative probability of passing from $[M(H_2O)_{N-n+1}L_{n-1}]$ to $[M(H_2O)_{N-n}L_n]$ is proportional to $(N - n + l)/n$. Similarly, the relative probability of passing from $[M(H_2O)_{N-n}L_n]$ to $[M(H_2O)_{N-n-1}L_{n+1}]$ is proportional to $(N - n)/(n + 1)$. Hence, on the basis of these statistical considerations alone, we expect

$$K_{n+1}/K_n = \frac{(N - n)}{n + 1} \div \frac{N - n + 1}{n} = \frac{n(N - n)}{(n + 1)(N - n + 1)}$$

In the Ni^{2+}–NH_3 system $(N = 6)$, we find the comparison between experimental ratios of successive constants and those calculated from the above formula to be as shown in Table 25-3. The experimental ratios are

TABLE 25-3

	Experimental	Statistical
K_2/K_1	0.28	0.417
K_3/K_2	0.31	0.533
K_4/K_3	0.29	0.562
K_5/K_4	0.36	0.533
K_6/K_5	0.2	0.417

consistently smaller than the statistically expected ones, which is typical and shows that other factors are also of importance.

There are cases where the experimental ratios of the constants do not remain constant or change monotonically; instead, one of them is singularly large or small. There are several reasons for this: (1) an abrupt change in coordination number and hybridization at some stage of the sequence of complexes, (2) special steric effects which become operative only at a certain stage of coordination, and (3) an abrupt change in electronic structure of the metal ion at a certain stage of complexation. A few illustrations of each of these will now be given.

Values of K_3/K_2 are anomalously low for the halogeno complexes of mercury(II); HgX_2 species are linear, whereas $[HgX_4]^{2-}$ species are tetrahedral. Presumably the change from sp to sp^3 hybridization occurs on going from HgX_2 to $[HgX_3]^-$. K_3/K_2 is anomalously small for the ethylenediamine complexes of Zn^{II}, and this is believed to be due to the change from sp^3 to sp^3d^2 hybridization if it is assumed that $[Znen_2]^{2+}$ is tetrahedral. For the Ag^+–NH_3 system $K_2 > K_1$, indicating that the linear, sp-hybridized structure probably is attained with $[Ag(NH_3)_2]^+$ but not with $[Ag(NH_3)(H_2O)_{3(or\ 5)}]^+$.

H$_3$C   CH$_3$

(25-XXXVII)

With 6,6'-dimethyl-2,2'-dipyridyl (25-XXXVII), many metal ions which form tris-2,2'-dipyridyl complexes form only bis or mono complexes, or, in some cases, no isolable complexes at all, because of the steric hindrance between the methyl groups and other ligands attached to the ion.

In the series of complexes of Fe^{II} with 1,10-phenanthroline (and also with 2,2'-dipyridyl), K_3 is greater than K_2. This is because the tris complex is diamagnetic (i.e., the ferrous ion has the low-spin state* t_{2g}^6), whereas in the mono and bis complexes, as in the aquo ion, there are four unpaired electrons. This change from the $t_{2g}^4e_g^2$ to the t_{2g}^6 causes the enthalpy change for addition of the third ligand to be anomalously large.

25-10. The Chelate Effect

This term refers to the enhanced stability of a complex system containing one or more chelate rings as compared to the stability of a system which is as similar as possible without containing the rings. As an example, consider the equilibrium constants for the Ni^{II}–NH_3 and Ni^{II}–en (en = $H_2NCH_2CH_2NH_2$) systems:

$$Ni^{2+} + 2NH_3 = [Ni(NH_3)_2]^{2+} \quad \log \beta = 5.00$$
$$Ni^{2+} + 4NH_3 = [Ni(NH_3)_4]^{2+} \quad \log \beta = 7.87$$
$$Ni^{2+} + 6NH_3 = [Ni(NH_3)_6]^{2+} \quad \log \beta = 8.61$$
$$Ni^{2+} + en = [Nien]^{2+} \quad \log \beta = 7.51$$
$$Ni^{2+} + 2en = [Nien_2]^{2+} \quad \log \beta = 13.86$$
$$Ni^{2+} + 3en = [Nien_3]^{2+} \quad \log \beta = 18.28$$

* The nomenclature t_{2g}, $t_{2g}e_g$ is described in Chapter 26.

Thus it is clear that the chelate effect can, and often does, amount to many orders of magnitude in the stability constants. It has also been established that five-membered rings are more stable than comparable six-membered rings, providing no special resonance effects are involved, as shown, for example, by data for Cu^{II} complexes of en, $H_2N(CH_2)_2NH_2$, and tn, $H_2N(CH_2)_3NH_2$.

$$
\begin{array}{lll}
Cu^{2+} + en = [Cuen]^{2+} & \log \beta = 10.72 \\
Cu^{2+} + 2en = [Cuen_2]^{2+} & \log \beta = 20.03 \\
Cu^{2+} + tn = [Cutn]^{2+} & \log \beta = 9.98 \\
Cu^{2+} + 2tn = [Cutn_2]^{2+} & \log \beta = 17.17
\end{array}
$$

This decreasing stability with increasing ring size continues so that there are few complexes known with seven-membered rings and none with larger rings. Finally, experiments also show that the more rings are formed, other things being more or less equal, the higher the stability constant. As an example of this, reaction 25-6 and its equilibrium constant may be com-

$$K = 10^{17.5}$$

(25-6)

pared with the data given above for nickel–ammonia and nickel–ethylene-diamine complexes. The constant for a reaction similar to 25-6, but using a ligand in which the COO^- groups would be replaced by $-CH_2NH_2$ groups, would certainly be larger than $10^{18.3}$. This is because (a) nitrogen generally forms stronger bonds to nickel than does oxygen and (b) with a neutral ligand there would be no electrostatic effect—i.e., repulsion of negative charges—opposing the formation of the complex ion.

In order properly to understand the chelate effect, we must consider in more detail the thermodynamic significance of the stability constants. First of all, we note that an equilibrium constant is a measure of the standard free energy of the reaction, that is,

$$\Delta F^0 = -RT \ln K$$

There is also the following relation between the free energy change and the enthalpy and entropy changes:

$$\Delta F^0 = \Delta H^0 - T\Delta S^0$$

Thus an increase in an equilibrium constant may arise because ΔH^0 becomes more negative, because ΔS^0 becomes more positive, or both.

In the formation of a complex, ΔH^0 is attributable mainly to the difference in bond energies of the metal-oxygen bonds broken and the new metal ligand bonds formed. Experimental studies of the enthalpy changes for the various reactions mentioned above, as well as for a number of others, have shown that enthalpy differences between chelated and nonchelated systems cannot in general account for the chelate effect. Hence, the chelate effect must be mainly an entropy effect, and, from the measured values of the equilibrium constants and enthalpies, the ΔS^0 values may be calculated. The general result is, as it must be, that increasing chelation corresponds to increasingly positive values of ΔS^0 in the formation of the complexes.

The physical reason for the favorable entropies of chelation reactions is not difficult to appreciate in a qualitative way. To do so, we must recognize that when atoms of the ligand enter the coordination sphere, water molecules are necessarily displaced. Now, one contribution to an increase in the entropy or disorder of the system is an increase in the number of free molecules. Thus, in a nonchelate system, each water molecule is displaced by one ligand molecule, and the total number of molecules in the system remains constant. In chelation reactions, one ligand molecule displaces two or more water molecules, so that the net number of more or less independent molecules increases. Another more pictorial way to look at the problem is to visualize a chelate ligand with one end attached to the metal ion. The other end cannot then get very far away, and the probability of it, too, becoming attached to the metal atom is greater than if this other end were instead another independent molecule which would then have access to a much larger volume of the solution. This latter view provides an explanation for the decreasing magnitude of the chelate effect with increasing ring size. If the ring which must be formed becomes sufficiently large (seven-membered or more), it becomes more probable that the other end of the chelate molecule will contact another metal ion than that it will come around to the first one and complete the ring.

An interesting but easily understood exception to the considerations outlined above is the Ag^I ion, which has a characteristic coordination number of 2, with the two Ag-ligand bonds lying colinearly. For five- and six-membered rings, the requirement that one angle be 180° prevents closure, and, for rings sufficiently large to close despite the 180° angle, the probability of ring closure irrespective of the angles becomes negligible. Thus, bicoordinate Ag^I forms no chelated complexes. There are some ligands such as diphosphines which form tetrahedral complexes with Ag^I, and in this case of course chelate rings can be stable.

KINETICS AND MECHANISMS IN REACTIONS OF COMPLEX IONS

25-11. Ligand Replacement Reactions

There are many reactions of complexes in which the composition of the coordination sphere changes. Included in this category are those in which complexes are formed from the metal ions and the ligands, since the "uncomplexed" metal ions are actually aquo complexes. The ability of a particular complex ion to engage in reactions which result in replacing one or more ligands in its coordination sphere by others is called its *lability*. Those complexes for which reactions of this type are very rapid are called labile, whereas those for which such reactions proceed only slowly or not at all are called *inert*. It is important to emphasize that these two terms refer to rates of reactions and should not be confused with the terms stable and unstable which refer to the thermodynamic tendency of species to exist under equilibrium conditions. A simple example of this distinction is provided by the $[Co(NH_3)_6]^{3+}$ ion which will persist for weeks in an acid medium because of its kinetic inertness or lack of lability despite the fact that it is thermodynamically unstable, as the following equilibrium constant shows:

$$[Co(NH_3)_6]^{3+} + 6H_3O^+ = [Co(H_2O)_6]^{3+} + 6NH_4^+ \qquad K \sim 10^{25}$$

In contrast, the stability of $Ni(CN)_4^{2-}$ is extremely high,

$$Ni(CN)_4^{2-} = Ni^{2+} + 4CN^- \qquad K \sim 10^{-22}$$

but the rate of exchange of CN^- ions with isotopically labeled CN^- added to the solution is immeasurably fast by ordinary techniques. Of course this lack of any necessary relation between thermodynamic stability and kinetic lability is to be found generally in chemistry, but its appreciation here is especially important.

In the first transition series, virtually all octahedral complexes save those of Cr^{III} and Co^{III} are normally quite labile; that is, ordinary complexes come to equilibrium with additional ligands, including H_2O, so rapidly that the reactions appear instantaneous by ordinary techniques of kinetic measurement. Complexes of Cr^{III} and Co^{III} ordinarily undergo ligand replacement reactions with half-times of the order of hours or days, thus making them convenient systems for detailed kinetic and mechanistic study. No fully satisfactory theoretical explanation for the observed relative labilities of octahedral complexes of the first transition series has yet been given.

Both qualitative valence bond theory and semiquantitative ligand field theory have been applied to the problem, each with partial success, but neither has explained all of the observed facts. The interested student is directed to several summaries of the theoretical position noted in the reading list on page 558.

Among complexes of the second and third transition series elements there are more inert complexes known. Some of the more important ones are those of Mo^{III}, W^{III}, Re^{IV}, Rh^{III}, and Ir^{III}, which are analogs of Cr^{III} or Co^{III}, as well as others such as Ru^{II}, Os^{II}, and Re^{II}, whose congeners in the first transition series are labile, and those of Pd^{IV} and Pt^{IV}, which have no parallels in the chemistry of their congener, Ni.

In recent years increasing attention has been devoted to detailed kinetic studies of ligand replacement reactions with the objective of learning details of the mechanisms by which such reactions take place. Although a great deal remains to be done, some important advances have been made. Two extreme mechanistic possibilities may be considered for such reactions. First, there is the S_N1 mechanism, in which the complex dissociates, losing the ligand to be replaced, the vacancy in the coordination shell then being taken by the new ligand. This path may be represented as follows

$$[L_6MX]^{n+} \xrightarrow{\text{slow}} X^- + \underset{\substack{\text{Five-coordinated} \\ \text{intermediate}}}{[L_5M]^{(n+1)+}} \xrightarrow[\text{fast}]{+Y^-} [L_5MY]^{n+}$$

The important feature here is that the first step, in which X^- is lost, proceeds *relatively* slowly and thus determines the rate at which the complete process can proceed. In other words, once it is formed, the intermediate complex, which is only five coordinated, will react with the new ligand, Y^-, almost instantly. When this mechanism is operative, the rate of the reaction necessarily is directly proportional to the concentration of $[L_5MX]^{n+}$ but independent of the concentration of the new ligand, Y^-. The symbol S_N1 stands for *substitution, nucleophilic, unimolecular*. The other extreme pathway for a ligand exchange is the S_N2 mechanism. In this case the new ligand attacks the original complex directly to form a seven-coordinated activated complex which then ejects the displaced ligand, as indicated in the following scheme:

$$[L_5MX]^{n+} + Y^- \xrightarrow{\text{slow}} \left\{ \begin{bmatrix} & X \\ L_5M \Big\langle & \\ & Y \end{bmatrix}^{(n-1)+} \right\} \xrightarrow{\text{fast}} [L_5MY]^{n+} + X^-$$

When this mechanism is operative, the rate of the reaction will be proportional to the concentration of $[L_5MX]^{n+}$ times that of Y^-. The symbol S_N2 stands for *substitution, nucleophilic, bimolecular*.

Between these extremes are all degrees of "concerted" mechanisms, in which loss of X does not become complete before Y becomes at least partially bonded. A special case, which will be considered below, is formation of an "ion pair" between the complex $[ML_5X]^{n+}$ and Y^- prior to loss of X^- and the entrance of Y into the coordination sphere of M.

Aquation Reactions.   Although other solvents are occasionally used, complexes are normally studied in aqueous solution. Our major interest, therefore, is in their reactions and kinetic behavior in aqueous solution, which means in the presence of an approximately $55M$ concentration of a potential ligand, H_2O. It is therefore important to consider, first, the action of water molecules of the solvent in displacing various ligand molecules from the coordination sphere and, second, the possibility of exchange of hydrogen in the solvent water with hydrogen attached to coordinated ligand atoms, such as oxygen in H_2O and the nitrogen atoms in ammonia and amines. We have already (Section 25-8) noted that coordinated H_2O has a tendency to lose protons, making aquo ions more or less acidic, in the sense:

$$[ML_5H_2O]^{n+} = [ML_5OH]^{(n-1)+} + H^+$$

It has been found that the *rate* of this type of reaction, irrespective of the equilibrium constant for it, is, in all cases examined, very fast. Thus, whenever an aquo complex is placed in D_2O it may be assumed that it becomes the corresponding D_2O complex essentially instantaneously. For example:

$$[Co(NH_3)_4(H_2O)_2]^{3+} \xrightarrow[\text{instantaneous}]{D_2O} [Co(NH_3)_4(D_2O)_2]^{3+}$$

It has also been found that hydrogen atoms attached to coordinated amine nitrogen atoms, although considerably less acidic, nevertheless exchange with solvent water. The rates of these exchanges are generally slow enough to be measurable. For example:

$$[Co(NH_3)_6]^{3+} \xrightarrow{D_2O} [Co(ND_3)_6]^{3+}$$

The rates of aquation reactions are often sharply dependent upon pH. For example, the reaction

$$[Co(NH_3)_4(H_2O)(NO_3)]^{2+} + H_2O \xrightarrow{k_1} [Co(NH_3)_4(H_2O)_2]^{3+} + NO_3^-$$

has been shown to proceed by two paths. One is that indicated by the equation given, but the second path involves the preliminary acid ionization of the complex,

$$[Co(NH_3)_4(H_2O)(NO_3)]^{2+} = [Co(NH_3)_4(OH)(NO_3)]^+ + H^+$$
$$[Co(NH_3)_4(OH)(NO_3)]^+ + H_2O \xrightarrow{k_2} [Co(NH_3)_4(OH)(H_2O)]^{2+} + NO_3^-$$
$$[Co(NH_3)_4(OH)(H_2O)]^{2+} + H^+ = [Co(NH_3)_4(H_2O)_2]^{3+}$$

Although the equilibrium for this ionization lies far to the left so that little of the hydroxo complex is present and available to react, k_2 is about 10^4 times greater than k_1, and this path does make an important contribution to the over-all rate even in fairly acid solutions. At least part of the reason why the hydroxo complex reacts more rapidly than the aquo one is that the over-all positive charge is lower, thus making it easier electrostatically for the negative ion to move away, although there are indications that changes in bonding are also important. For complexes containing no H_2O but only the much more weakly acidic amine ligands, the aquation rate is not very sensitive to pH until the solution becomes quite basic. Some researchers believe that at high OH^- concentrations direct attack by OH^- occurs, for example,

$$[Co(NH_3)_5Cl]^{2+} + OH^- \rightarrow \{[HO\cdots Co(NH_3)_5\cdots Cl]^+\} \rightarrow [Co(NH_3)_5OH]^{2+} + Cl^-$$
$$\text{Transition state}$$

while others believe that a conjugate base process is operative, the lower sensitivity to pH being attributed to the greater difficulty of dissociation of N—H protons,

$$[Co(NH_3)_5Cl]^{2+} + OH^- = [Co(NH_3)_4(NH_2)Cl]^+ + H_2O$$
$$[Co(NH_3)_4(NH_2)Cl]^+ \rightarrow [Co(NH_3)_4(NH_2)]^{2+} + Cl^-$$
$$[Co(NH_3)_4(NH_2)]^{2+} + H_2O \rightarrow [Co(NH_3)_5(OH)]^{2+}$$

Other Ligand Exchange Reactions. There are many reactions in which one ligand is replaced by another one which is not H_2O. It now appears that in every case, or nearly so, aquation occurs first, followed by replacement of the coordinated H_2O by the new ligand. For example, the net over-all reaction

$$[Coen_2(NO_2)Cl]^+ + NO_2^- \rightarrow [Coen_2(NO_2)_2]^+ + Cl^-$$

involves preliminary aquation,

$$[Coen_2(NO_2)Cl]^+ + H_2O \rightarrow [Coen_2(NO_2)(H_2O)]^{2+} + Cl^-$$

It appears that the rate of the reaction of the second ligand with the intermediate aquo complex is generally proportional to the concentrations of both the aquo complex and the ligand, when the ligand is an anion. This does not, however, necessarily mean that the reaction proceeds by a true S_N2 mechanism with a seven-coordinated intermediate. If an ion pair equilibrium is established prior to reaction,

$$\{[Co(NH_3)_5X]^{2+}\cdots Y\} = [Co(NH_3)_5X]^{2+} + Y^-$$

and it is only, or mainly, the ion pair which splits out X^-, immediately or perhaps simultaneously drawing Y^- into the coordination sphere, the reaction rate will depend on the concentration of Y^-. This is because the rate will be proportional to the concentration of ion pairs, and this concentration is in turn proportional to the Y^- concentration. Experimentally it is very difficult to distinguish between the *bona fide* S_N2 mechanism and the ion pair process, and the question of mechanism remains controversial in such reactions.

There are some reactions known where ligand exchange does not involve the breaking of metal-ligand bonds, but instead bonds within the ligands themselves are broken and re-formed. One well-known case is the aquation of carbonato complexes. When isotopically labeled water, H_2O^*, is used, it is found that no O^* gets into the coordination sphere of the ion during aquation,

$$[Co(NH_3)_5OCO_2]^+ + 2H_3^*O^+ \rightarrow [Co(NH_3)_5(H_2O)]^{3+} + 2H_2^*O + CO_2$$

The most likely path for this reaction involves proton attack on the oxygen atom bonded to Co followed by expulsion of CO_2 and then protonation of the hydroxo complex (eq. 25-7). Similarly, in the reaction of NO_2^- with

$$\left\{ \begin{array}{c} Co(NH_3)_5-O\cdots C \overset{\displaystyle O}{\underset{\displaystyle O}{\diagdown}} \\ \overset{\cdot\cdot}{H^+} \\ | \\ O \\ \diagup \ \diagdown \\ H \quad H \end{array} \right\} \longrightarrow [Co(NH_3)_5-O]^{2+}\underset{H}{\overset{+H^+}{\longrightarrow}} [Co(NH_3)_5(H_2O)]^{3+} \quad (25\text{-}7)$$

Transition state

pentaamminoaquocobalt(III) ion, isotopic labeling studies show that the oxygen originally in the bound H_2O turns up in the bound NO_2^-. This remarkable result is explained by the reaction sequence 25-8.

$$2NO_2^- + 2H^+ \overset{fast}{=} N_2O_3 + H_2O \qquad (25\text{-}8a)$$

$$[Co(NH_3)_5^*OH]^{2+} + N_2O_3 \longrightarrow \left\{ \begin{array}{c} (NH_3)_5Co\overset{*}{-}O\cdots H \\ \vdots \\ ON\cdots ONO \end{array} \right\} \overset{fast}{\longrightarrow}$$

Transition state

$$HNO_2 + [Co(NH_3)_5^*ONO]^{2+} \overset{slow}{\longrightarrow} [Co(NH_3)_5(NO^*O)]^{2+} \quad (25\text{-}8b)$$

The *trans* Effect. Ligand replacement reactions in square complexes have certain special features. Most work has been done with Pt^{II} complexes, which are numerous and varied and have fairly convenient rates of reaction. Consider the general reaction 25-9.

$$[PtLX_3]^- + Y^- \rightarrow [PtLX_2Y]^- + X^- \qquad (25\text{-}9)$$

Sterically, there are two possible reaction products, with *cis* and *trans* orientation of Y with respect to L. It has been observed that the relative proportions of the *cis* and *trans* products varies appreciably with the ligand L. Moreover, in reactions of the type 25-10, either or both of the indicated

$$\begin{bmatrix} L & X \\ & Pt & \\ L' & X \end{bmatrix} + Y^- \rightarrow X^- + \begin{bmatrix} L & X \\ & Pt & \\ L' & Y \end{bmatrix} \ or \ \begin{bmatrix} L & Y \\ & Pt & \\ L' & X \end{bmatrix} \qquad (25\text{-}10)$$

isomers may be produced. It is found that in both these types of reaction and in others a fairly extensive series of ligands may be arranged in the same order with respect to their ability to facilitate substitution in the position *trans* to themselves. This phenomenon is known as the *trans effect*, and the order of ligands is, in part: $H_2O < OH^- < NH_3 < Cl^- < Br^- < I^- \sim NO_2^- \sim PR_3 \ll CO \sim C_2H_4 \sim CN^-$.

The *trans* effect series has proved very useful in rationalizing known synthetic procedures and in devising new ones. As an example we may consider the synthesis of the *cis* and *trans* isomers of $[Pt(NH_3)_2Cl_2]$. The synthesis of the *cis* isomer is accomplished by treatment of the $[PtCl_4]^{2-}$ ion with ammonia (eq. 25-11). Since Cl has a greater *trans*-directing in-

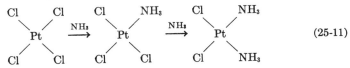

fluence than does NH_3, substitution of NH_3 into $[Pt(NH_3)Cl_3]^-$ is least likely to occur in the position *trans* to the NH_3 already present and thus the *cis* isomer is favored. The *trans* isomer is made by treating $[Pt(NH_3)_4]^{2+}$ with Cl^- (eq. 25-12). Here the superior *trans*-directing influence of Cl^-

$$\begin{matrix} H_3N & NH_3 \\ & Pt & \\ H_3N & NH_3 \end{matrix} \xrightarrow{Cl^-} \begin{matrix} H_3N & NH_3 \\ & Pt & \\ H_3N & Cl \end{matrix} \xrightarrow{Cl^-} \begin{matrix} Cl & NH_3 \\ & Pt & \\ H_3N & Cl \end{matrix} \qquad (25\text{-}12)$$

causes the second Cl^- to enter *trans* to the first one, producing *trans*-$[Pt(NH_3)_2Cl_2]$.

As is the case with ligand replacement reactions in octahedral complexes, much remains to be learned about mechanistic details of such reactions in square planar complexes. Such knowledge must precede the development of a final theory of the *trans* effect. At present two different but not mutually exclusive theoretical approaches to the problem are being considered.

There is, first, the "bond weakening" theory, according to which the *trans* effect series arranges the ligands in order of their tendency to weaken preferentially, by electrostatic and polarization effects, the bonds to ligands *trans* to themselves. This theory could account for the experimental facts regardless of whether the reaction mechanism is S_N1 or S_N2. In the former case, bond weakening would naturally favor the rate-controlling dissociative act; in the latter, if the entering ligand is assumed to descend upon the metal ion directly down the axis perpendicular to the molecular plane, using the vacant p_z orbital for incipient bond formation, it might then be expected to push out that ligand which is least strongly bonded.

The second theory presupposes that the mechanism is S_N2 and begins by noting that the order of increasing *trans* effect is very similar to the order of increasing capacity of the ligands to function as acceptors of electrons from metal $d\pi$ orbitals. If a particular ligand in a square complex has a strong tendency to accept electrons originally occupying a d_{xz} or d_{yz} orbital on the metal atom into a π orbital of its own, then the electron density above and below the bond between the metal ion and the ligand *trans* to the particular ligand is lessened. This in turn makes this region of space more attractive to an attacking nucleophilic ligand. This is illustrated in Figure 25-2.

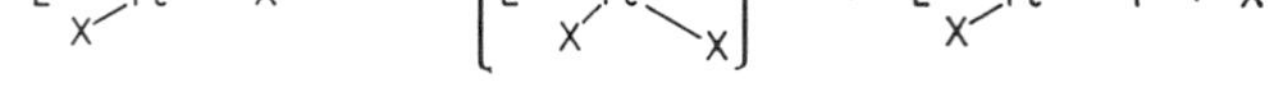

Fig. 25-2. Diagram showing how the presence of a strongly accepting π orbital on L withdraws electron density in the $d\pi$ orbital which it has in common with the ligand *trans* to it, thus making the region near this *trans* ligand more accessible to the nucleophilic group.

Unfortunately, there is a dearth of the necessary experimental data (it is not always easy to get), and for the most part it is not known whether reactions governed by the *trans* effect are uni- or bimolecular. It is very possible that both bond-weakening and π-bonding effects play a significant part in determining the complete *trans* effect series.

25-12. Electron Transfer Reactions

Electron transfer reactions are of two types from a stoichiometric point of view. Those in which an electron is transferred from one metal ion to another of different atomic number are called oxidation-reduction reactions. An example is

$$[Co(NH_3)_5(H_2O)]^{3+} + Cr^{2+}(aq) + 5H^+ = Co^{2+}(aq) + Cr^{3+}(aq) + 5NH_4^+ + H_2O$$

When both metal ions are of the same atomic number, the process is called electron exchange. In many cases electron exchange is not accompanied by any net chemical change; in such cases, isotopic labeling is necessary in order to show that electron exchange does in fact occur. For example, the ferrous–ferric electron exchange can be followed by using radioactive Fe^{III} denoted $*Fe^{3+}$, and ordinary Fe^{II}:

$$*Fe^{3+} + Fe^{2+} = Fe^{3+} + *Fe^{2+}$$

The reason these electron exchange reactions are of interest is just because there is no net chemical change so that, outside of entirely negligible isotope effects, the thermodynamic properties of reactants and products are iden-

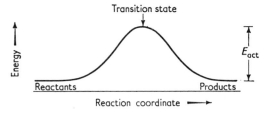

Fig. 25-3. Graph of the energy versus reaction coordinate for an electron exchange reaction in which reactants and products are identical.

tical. A graph of the energy versus the reaction coordinate (Fig. 25-3) is then symmetrical and more amenable to theoretical treatment.

The study of several dozen electron transfer reactions, especially electron exchange reactions, has shown that there are at least three mechanisms by which these reactions occur, namely, (1) by direct electron tunneling, (2) by way of a ligand-bridged transition state, and (3) by way of a hydrogen-bridged transition state.

Direct electron tunneling is believed to occur in a number of systems in which both cations are fully coordinated. Some examples, with their rates of reactions, are shown in Table 25-4. It is possible to account for the qualitative order of these rates by considering the electronic structures and dimensions of the reacting species in relation to the activation energy, that is, to the energy of the transition state in which the electron jump actually

TABLE 25-4

Rates of Some Electron Exchange Reactions

Reactants	Rates
$[Fe(dipy)_3]^{2+}$, $[Fe(dipy)_3]^{3+}$ $[Mn(CN)_6]^{3-}$, $[Mn(CN)_6]^{4-}$ $[Mo(CN)_8]^{3-}$, $[Mo(CN)_8]^{4-}$ $[W(CN)_8]^{3-}$, $[W(CN)_8]^{4-}$ $[IrCl_6]^{2-}$, $[IrCl_6]^{3-}$ $[Os(dipy)_3]^{2+}$, $[Os(dipy)_3]^{3+}$	Immeasurably fast (too fast to measure rate by techniques so far used)
$[Fe(CN)_6]^{3-}$, $[Fe(CN)_6]^{4-}$ $[MnO_4]^{-}$, $[MnO_4]^{2-}$	Very fast but measurable by special methods
$[Coen_3]^{2+}$, $[Coen_3]^{3+}$ $[Co(NH_3)_6]^{2+}$, $[Co(NH_3)_6]^{3+}$ $[Co(C_2O_4)_3]^{3-}$, $[Co(C_2O_4)_3]^{4-}$	Slow (second-order rate constants $\sim 10^{-4}$)

takes place. In the following explanation of this we shall discuss only the reactions between octahedral complexes.

The slowness of the electron exchanges between the cobalt-containing species is due to the high activation energies required. Because the anti-bonding e_g electrons* tend greatly to increase metal–ligand distances, whereas the nonbonding t_{2g} electrons have only a slight effect, the Co^{II} complexes, in which the cobalt has the configuration $t_{2g}^5 e_g^2$, are much larger (Co^{II}—N, 2.5 A.) than the corresponding Co^{III} complexes (Co^{III}—N, 2.05 A.), which have one more t_{2g} electron but no e_g electrons The transition state for electron exchange will be one in which each species has the same dimensions,** so that the more the two reacting species differ in their sizes the higher will be the activation energy, which will be just the energy required to equalize the bond distances in the two complex ions.

All of the cases in which the electron exchange is fast involve pairs in which both members have only t_2 electrons. They are therefore nearly the same size, and only a little energy need be expended to reach a transition state in which they are exactly the same size. Thus, to summarize, it is

* For explanation of the symbols e_g and t_{2g}, see Chapter 26.

** This is so because a transition state for a process in which there is no adjustment of bond lengths prior to the electron jump would necessarily have a much higher energy. Suppose the electron jumped while both ions were in their normal configurations. This would produce a Co^{II} complex with bonds compressed *all the way* to the length appropriate to a Co^{III} complex and a Co^{III} complex with the bonds lengthened *all the way* to the length of those in the Co^{II} complex. This would be the zenith of energy, and, as the bonds readjusted, the energy of the exchanging pair would drop to the initial energy of the systems. However, this zenith of energy is obviously higher than it would be if the reacting ions first adjusted their configurations so that each met the other one *only halfway* and then exchanged the electron.

believed that in these cases the two exchanging species approach one another closely, perhaps with their coordination shells in contact, and adjust their coordination shells to the same size (intermediate between the dimensions of those of the separate ions), after which an electron leaks from one to the other.

Ligand-bridged transition states have been shown to occur in a number of reactions, mainly through the elegant experiments devised and executed by H. Taube and his school. He has demonstrated that the following general reaction occurs:

$$[Co(NH_3)_5X]^{2+} + Cr^{2+}(aq) + 5H^+ = [Cr(H_2O)_5X]^{2+} + Co^{2+}(aq) + 5NH_4^+$$
$$(X = F^-, Cl^-, Br^-, I^-, SO_4{}^{2-}, NCS^-, N_3{}^-, PO_4{}^{3-}, P_2O_7{}^{4-}, CH_3COO^-,$$
$$C_3H_7COO^-, \text{crotonate, succinate, oxalate, maleate})$$

The significance and success of these experiments rest on the following facts. The Co^{III} complex is not labile while the Cr^{II} aquo ion is, whereas, in the products, the $[Cr(H_2O)_5X]$ ion is not labile while the Co^{II} aquo ion is. It is found that the transfer of X from $[Co(NH_3)_5X]^{2+}$ to $[Cr(H_2O)_5X]^{2+}$ is quantitative. The only reasonable explanation for these facts is the postulation of the transition state $(H_3N)_5Co—X—Cr(H_2O)_5$ and the assumption that when the electron is transferred from Cr^{II} to Co^{III} the Co—X bond becomes labile (the Co now being Co^{II}) while the Cr—X bond becomes nonlabile (the Cr now being Cr^{III}). It is also significant that, of the organic anions in the above list of X groups, the two (oxalate and male-

Oxalate   Maleate

ate) which provide a continuous pathway of conjugated π bonds between the metal ions allow electron exchange to occur about 100 times faster than do the others.

Reactions 25-13, which are catalyzed by a trace of Cr^{2+}, must occur as

$$[Cr(NH_3)_5X]^{2+} + 5H^+ = [Cr(H_2O)_5X]^{2+} + 5NH_4^+ \qquad (25\text{-}13)$$
$$(X = F, Cl, Br, I)$$

shown in equation 25-14, in view of the complete retention of X by Cr^{III} while the NH_3's are completely lost.

$$[Cr(NH_3)_5X]^{2+} + {}^*Cr^{2+}(aq) \rightarrow$$

$$\{[(H_3N)_5Cr—X—{}^*Cr(H_2O)_5]^{4+}\} \rightarrow [{}^*Cr(H_2O)_5X]^{2+} + \{Cr(NH_3)_5{}^{2+}\} \qquad (25\text{-}14)$$
Transition state

rapidly
$+5H^+$

$$5NH_4^+ + Cr^{2+}(aq)$$

There are various other cases, especially the $[Cr(H_2O)_5X]^{2+}$–$[Cr(H_2O)_6]^{2+}$ exchanges, in which retention of the X groups shows that they must be bridges in the activated complex. Also when Fe^{3+} is reduced by Cr^{2+} in the presence of halide ions, the chromium(III) is produced as $[Cr(H_2O)_5X]^{2+}$.

The Fe^{II}–Fe^{III} exchange has been extensively studied and found to be sensitive to the presence of various anions in the solution. In perchlorate solutions the reaction is presumably between the hexaquo ions, and the activated complex is believed to be 25-XXXVIII. The hydrogen *atom*,

$$\left[(H_2O)_5Fe^{III}\!\!-\!\!O\!\!\underset{\overset{|}{H}}{\overset{\overset{H}{\diagup}}{\cdots\cdots}}\!H^*\cdots O\!\!-\!\!Fe^{II}(H_2O)_5 \right]^{5+}$$
(25-XXXVIII)

H^*, is then thought to transfer from Fe^{II} to Fe^{III} giving:

$$[(H_2O)_5Fe^{II}OH_3]^{3+} \qquad and \qquad [Fe^{III}(H_2O)_5(OH)]^{2+}$$

$-H^+$ | rapidly $\qquad\qquad\qquad$ $+H^+$ | rapidly

$$[Fe^{II}(H_2O)_6]^{2+} + H^+ \qquad\qquad [Fe^{III}(H_2O)_6]^{3+}$$

In support of this it is found that the $[Fe^{II}(H_2O)_6]^{2+}$–$[Fe^{III}(H_2O)_5(OH)]^{2+}$ exchange is over 1000 times faster than that between the two aquo ions, which may be attributed to the unusually favorable conditions for hydrogen atom transfer in the symmetrical transition state (25-XXXIX). $[Cr(H_2O)_5$

$$\left[(H_2O)_5Fe\!\!-\!\!O\!\!\underset{\overset{|}{H}}{\cdots}\!H\cdots O\!\!-\!\!Fe(H_2O)_5 \right]^{4+}$$
(25-XXXIX)

$(OH)]^{2+}$ exchanges about 10^5 times more rapidly with $[Cr(H_2O)_6]^{2+}$ than does $[Cr(H_2O)_6]^{3+}$. It should be noted, however, that there is as yet no direct proof that hydrogen transfer from M^{II} to M^{III} occurs rather than electron transfer from M^{II} to M^{III}. The net result is the same and only very sophisticated experiments might provide a definitive answer.

References

Bailar, J. C., Jr., ed., *The Chemistry of Coordination Compounds*, Reinhold, New York, 1956. A good source book with many references.

Basolo, F., and R. G. Pearson, *Mechanisms of Inorganic Reactions*, Wiley, New York, 1958. An excellent review of mechanisms and the theory; strongly recommended.

————, in H. J. Emeléus and A. G. Sharpe, eds., *Advances in Inorganic and Nuclear Chemistry*, Vol. III, Academic Press, New York, 1961. A review on recent aspects of substitution reactions.

Davidson, N., *J. Am. Chem. Soc.*, **71**, 3089 (1949); **73**, 1946 (1951). Colors due to mixed oxidation states in complexes.

Halpern, J., *Quart. Revs. (London)*, **15**, 207 (1961). Mechanisms of electron transfer and related processes in solution.

Lewis, J., and R. G. Wilkins, eds., *Modern Coordination Chemistry, Principles and Methods*, Interscience, New York–London, 1960. A collection of authoritative reviews on stability constants, stereochemistry, spectra, reaction mechanisms, and magnetic properties of complexes.

Martell, A. E., and M. Calvin, *Chemistry of the Metal Chelate Compounds*, Prentice-Hall, New York, 1952. A general survey with many references.

Rossotti, F. J. C., and H. Rossotti, *The Determination of Stability Constants and Other Equilibrium Constants in Solution*, McGraw-Hill, London, 1961.

Wells, A. F., *Structural Inorganic Chemistry*, 3rd ed., Oxford University Press, London–New York, 1962. An excellent book on structural aspects of inorganic compounds, including complexes.

26

The Theory of Metal-Ligand Bonding

INTRODUCTION

26-1. Brief Genealogy of the Several Theories

We noted in Section 25-1 that the studies of Werner and his contemporaries followed by the ideas of Lewis and Sidgwick on electron pair bonding led to the idea that ligands are groups which can in some way donate electron pairs to metal ions or other acceptors, thus forming the so-called coordinate link. This approach to bonding in complexes was extended by Pauling and developed into the *valence bond theory* of metal-ligand bonding. This theory enjoyed great and almost exclusive popularity among chemists through the 1930's and 1940's, but during the 1950's it was supplemented by the *ligand field theory*. This was developed between 1930 and 1940 by physicists, mainly J. H. Van Vleck and his students, and rediscovered in the early 1950's by several theoretical chemists. The ligand field theory as we have it today evolved out of a purely electrostatic theory called the *crystal field theory* which was first expounded in 1929 by H. Bethe.

In addition to his work on the ligand field theory, Van Vleck also laid the basis of a *molecular orbital theory* of the bonding in complexes. This theory, which is particularly useful for highly covalent complexes such as metal carbonyls, complex cyanides, etc., is also, in principle, the most complete and comprehensive theory in every case. It has the disadvantage that quantitative calculations are not easily made.

Thus, altogether, there are four major theoretical approaches to the bonding in complexes:

1. The fundamentally correct and complete molecular orbital theory.

2. The electrostatic crystal field theory, which, although approximate and quite unsuited for some classes of complexes, is very useful for calculations on a great many of the common ones.

3. The ligand field theory, which is a modified form of crystal field theory in which computational advantages are largely preserved but allowance is made for orbital overlap.

4. The valence bond theory, which in its usual form is nonquantitative.

In this chapter we shall first give a fairly detailed treatment of the electrostatic crystal field theory and then show how this may be modified to give the ligand field theory. We shall then outline the molecular orbital theory and finally give a resume of the valence bond formalism.

THE ELECTROSTATIC CRYSTAL FIELD THEORY

26-2. The Splitting of d Orbitals by Electrostatic Fields

Let us consider a metal ion, M^{m+}, lying at the center of an octahedral set of anions, X^-, as shown in Figure 26-1. Let us suppose that this metal

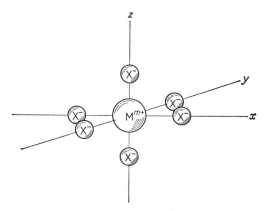

Fig. 26-1.   Sketch showing six X^- ions arranged octahedrally around a central M^{m+} ion with a set of Cartesian axes for reference.

ion has a single d electron outside of closed shells; such an ion might be Ti^{III}, V^{IV}, etc. In the free ion, this d electron would have had equal probability of being in any one of the five d orbitals, since all are equivalent. Now, however, the d orbitals are not all equivalent. Some are concentrated in regions of space closer to the negative ions than are others, and the electron will obviously prefer to occupy the orbital(s) in which it can get as far as possible from the negative charges on the ligands. Recalling the shapes of the d orbitals (Fig. 1-7) and comparing them with Figure 26-1, we see that both the d_{z^2} and $d_{x^2-y^2}$ orbitals have lobes which are heavily concentrated in the vicinity of the ligands, whereas the d_{xy}, d_{yz}, and d_{zx} orbitals have lobes which project between the ligand atoms. This is illustrated in Figure 26-2. It can also be seen that each of the three orbitals in

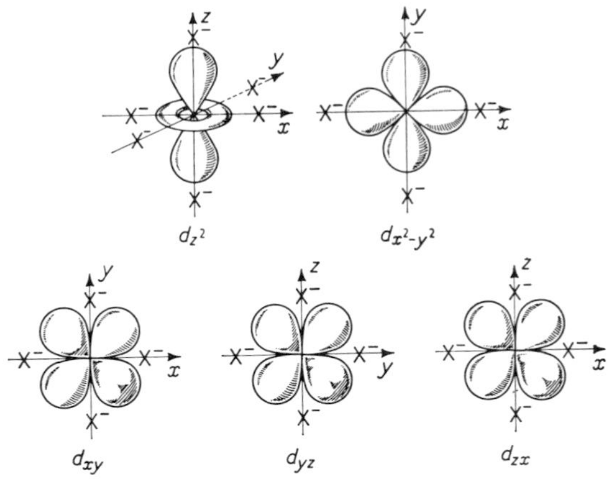

Fig. 26-2. Sketches showing the distribution of electron density in the five d orbitals with respect to a set of six octahedrally arranged X^- ions (cf. Fig. 26-1).

the later group, namely, d_{xy}, d_{yz}, d_{zx}, is equally favorable for the electron; these three orbitals have entirely equivalent environments in the octahedral complex. The two relatively unfavorable orbitals, d_{z^2} and $d_{x^2-y^2}$, are also equivalent; this is not obvious from inspection of Figure 26-2, but a proof is given in Appendix E. Thus, in the octahedral environment of the six X^- ions, the metal ion now has two kinds of d orbitals: three of one kind, equivalent to one another and conventionally labeled t_{2g} (sometimes $d\epsilon$ or γ_5), and two of another kind, equivalent to each other, conventionally labeled e_g (sometimes $d\gamma$ or γ_3); furthermore, the e_g orbitals are of higher energy than the t_{2g} orbitals. These results may be expressed in an energy level diagram as shown in Figure 26-3a.

In Figure 26-3a it will be seen that we have designated the energy difference between the e_g and the t_{2g} orbitals as Δ_o, where the subscript o stands for octahedral. The additional feature of Figure 26-3a—the indication that the e_g levels lie $\frac{3}{5}\Delta_o$ above and the t_{2g} levels lie $\frac{2}{5}\Delta_o$ below the energy of the unperturbed d orbitals—will now be explained. Let us suppose that a cation containing ten d electrons, two in each of the d orbitals, is first placed at the center of a hollow sphere whose radius is equal to the M—X internuclear distance, and that charge of total quantity $6e$ is spread uniformly over the sphere. In this spherically symmetric environment the d

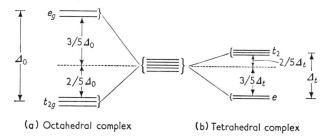

(a) Octahedral complex   (b) Tetrahedral complex

Fig. 26-3.   Energy level diagrams showing the splitting of a set of d orbitals by octahedral and tetrahedral electrostatic crystal fields.

orbitals are still five-fold degenerate. The entire energy of the system, that is the metal ion and the charged sphere, has a definite value. Now suppose the total charge on the sphere is caused to collect into six discrete point charges, each of magnitude e, and each lying at an apex of an octahedron but still on the surface of the sphere. Merely redistributing the negative charge over the surface of the sphere in this manner cannot alter the total energy of the system when the metal ion consists entirely of spherically symmetrical electron shells, and yet we have already seen that as a result of this redistribution electrons in e_g orbitals now have higher energies than those in t_{2g} orbitals. It must therefore be that the total increase in energy of the four e_g electrons equals the total decrease in energy of the six t_{2g} electrons. This then implies that the rise in the energy of the e_g orbitals is $\frac{6}{4}$ times the drop in energy of the t_{2g} orbitals, which is equivalent to the $\frac{3}{5}:\frac{2}{5}$ ratio shown.

This pattern of splitting, in which the algebraic sum of all energy shifts of all orbitals is zero, is said to "preserve the center of gravity" of the set of levels. This center of gravity rule is quite general for any splitting pattern when the forces are purely electrostatic and where the set of levels being split is well removed in energy from all other sets with which they might be able to interact.

By an analogous line of reasoning it can be shown that the electrostatic field of four charges surrounding an ion at the apices of a tetrahedron causes the d shell to split up as shown in Figure 26-3b. In this case the d_{xy}, d_{yz}, and d_{zz} orbitals are less stable than the d_{z^2} and $d_{x^2-y^2}$ orbitals. This may be appreciated qualitatively if the spatial properties of the d orbitals are considered with regard to the tetrahedral array of four X^- ions as depicted in Figure 26-4. If the cation, the anions, and the cation–anion distance are the same in both the octahedral and tetrahedral cases, it can be shown that

$$\Delta_t = \tfrac{4}{9}\Delta_o$$

In other words, other things being about equal, the crystal field splitting in a tetrahedral complex will be about half the magnitude of that in an octahedral complex.

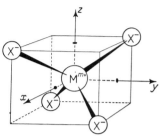

Fig. 26-4. Sketch showing the tetrahedral arrangement of four anions, X^-, around a cation, M^{m+}, with respect to coordinate axes which may be used in identifying the d orbitals.

The above results have been derived on the assumption of ionic ligands, such as F^-, Cl^-, or CN^-. Ligands which are neutral, however, are dipolar (e.g., 26-I and 26-II), and they approach the metal ion with their negative

(26-I)   (26-II)

poles. Actually, in the field of the positive metal ion such ligands are further polarized. Thus, in a complex such as a hexammine, the metal ion is surrounded by six dipoles with their negative ends closest; this array has the same general effects upon the d orbitals as an array of six anions, so that all of the above results are valid for complexes containing neutral, dipolar ligands.

We next consider the pattern of splitting of the d orbitals in tetragonally distorted octahedral complexes and in planar complexes. We begin with an octahedral complex, MX_6, from which we slowly withdraw two *trans* ligands. Let these be the two on the z axis. As soon as the distance from M^{m+} to these two ligands becomes greater than the distance to the other four, new energy differences among the d orbitals arise. First of all, the degeneracy of the e_g orbitals is lifted, the z^2 orbital becoming more stable than the $(x^2 - y^2)$ orbital. This happens because the ligands on the z axis exert a much more direct repulsive effect on a d_{z^2} electron than upon a $d_{x^2-y^2}$ electron. At the same time the three-fold degeneracy of the t_{2g} orbitals is also lifted. As the ligands on the z axis move away, the yz and zx orbitals remain equivalent to one another, but they become more stable than the

xy orbital because their spatial distribution makes them more sensitive to the charges along the z axis than is the xy orbital. Thus for a small tetragonal distortion of the type considered, we may draw the energy level diagram shown in Figure 26-5. It should be obvious that for the opposite type of

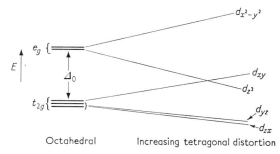

Octahedral   Increasing tetragonal distortion

Fig. 26-5. Energy level diagram showing the further splitting of the d orbitals as an octahedral array of ligands becomes progressively distorted by the withdrawal of two *trans* ligands, specifically those lying on the z axis.

tetragonal distortion, that is, one in which two *trans* ligands lie closer to the metal ion than do the other four, the relative energies of the split components will be inverted.

As Figure 26-5 shows, it is in general *possible* for the tetragonal distortion to become so large that the z^2 orbital eventually drops below the xy orbital. Whether this will *actually happen* for any particular case, even when the two *trans* ligands are completely removed so that we have the limiting case of a square, four-coordinated complex, depends upon quantitative properties of the metal ion and the ligands concerned. Semiquantitative calculations with parameters appropriate for square complexes of Co^{II}, Ni^{II}, and Cu^{II} lead to the energy level diagram shown in Figure 26-6, in which the

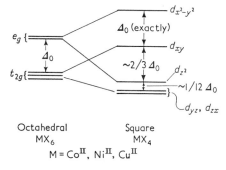

Octahedral   Square
MX_6 MX_4
M = Co^{II}, Ni^{II}, Cu^{II}

Fig. 26-6. Approximate energy level diagram for corresponding octahedral and square complexes of some metal ions in the first transition series.

z^2 orbital has dropped so far below the xy orbital that it is nearly as stable as the (yz, zx) pair.

26-3. Magnetic Properties from Crystal Field Theory

In a study of the magnetic properties of a transition metal complex, our first concern will be to know how many unpaired electrons are present. We shall now see how this property may be understood in terms of the orbital splittings described in the preceding section. We have already noted in several places* that it is a general rule that if a group of n or less electrons occupy a set of n degenerate orbitals, they will spread themselves out among the orbitals and give n unpaired spins. This is Hund's first rule, or the rule of maximum multiplicity. It means that pairing of electrons is an unfavorable process; energy must be expended in order to make it occur. If two electrons are not only to have their spins paired but also to be placed in the same orbital, there is a further unfavorable energy contribution because of the increased electrostatic repulsion between electrons which are compelled to occupy the same regions of space. Let us suppose now that in some hypothetical molecule we have two orbitals separated by an energy ΔE and that two electrons are to occupy these orbitals. Referring to Figure 26-7, we see that when we place one electron in each orbital, their spins will

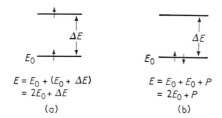

$$E = E_0 + (E_0 + \Delta E)$$
$$= 2E_0 + \Delta E$$
(a)

$$E = E_0 + E_0 + P$$
$$= 2E_0 + P$$
(b)

Fig. 26-7. A hypothetical two-orbital system in which the two important distributions of two electrons and the resulting total energies are as shown.

remain uncoupled and their combined energy will be $(2E_0 + \Delta E)$. If we place both of them in the lower orbital, their spins will have to be coupled to satisfy the exclusion principle, and the total energy will be $(2E_0 + P)$, where P stands for the energy required to cause pairing of two electrons in the same orbital. Thus, whether this system will have distribution (a) or (b) for its ground state depends on whether ΔE is greater or less than P. If $\Delta E < P$, the triplet state (a) will be the more stable; if $\Delta E > P$, the singlet state (b) will be the more stable.

* See, for example, pages 22 and 503.

This sort of analysis may be applied to complexes. Let us first consider octahedral complexes. As indicated in Figure 26-8, we may place one, two,

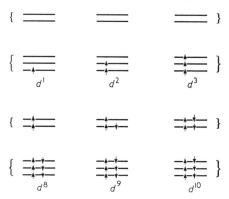

Fig. 26-8. Sketches showing the unique ground state occupancy schemes for d orbitals in octahedral complexes with d configurations d^1, d^2, d^3, d^8, d^9, d^{10}.

and three electrons in the d orbitals without any possible uncertainty about how they will occupy the orbitals. They will naturally enter the more stable t_{2g} orbitals with their spins all parallel, and this will be true irrespective of the strength of the crystal field as measured by the magnitude of Δ. Further, for ions with eight, nine, and ten d electrons, there is only one possible way in which the orbitals may be occupied to give the lowest energy (see Fig. 26-8). For the remaining configurations, d^4, d^5, d^6, and d^7, two possibilities exist, and the question of which one represents the ground state can only be answered by comparing the values of Δ_0 and P, an average pairing energy. The two configurations for each case, together with simple expressions for their energies, are set out in Figure 26-9. The configurations with the maximum possible number of unpaired electrons are called the *high-spin* configurations, and those with the minimum number of unpaired spins are called the *low-spin* or *spin-paired* configurations. These configurations can be written out in a notation similar to that used for electron configurations of free atoms, whereby we list each occupied orbital or set of orbitals, using a right superscript to show the number of electrons present. For example, the ground state for a d^3 ion in an octahedral field is t_{2g}^3; the two possible states for a d^5 ion in an octahedral field are t_{2g}^5 and $t_{2g}^3 e_g^2$. This notation is further illustrated in Figure 26-9. The energies are referred to the energy of the unsplit configuration (the energy of the ion in a spherical shell of the same total charge) and are simply the sums of $-\frac{2}{5}\Delta_0$ for each t_{2g} electron, $+\frac{3}{5}\Delta_0$ for each e_g electron, and P for every pair of electrons occupying the same orbital.

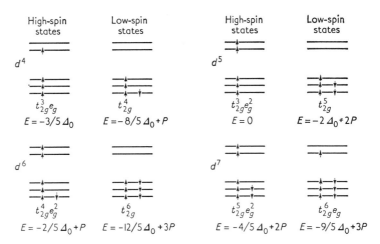

Fig. 26-9. Diagrams showing the possible high-spin and low-spin ground states for d^4, d^5, d^6, and d^7 ions in octahedral crystal fields including the notation for writing out the configurations and expressions for their energies, derived as explained in the text.

For each of the four cases where high- and low-spin states are possible, we may obtain from the equations for the energies which are given in Figure 26-9 the following expression for the relation between Δ_0 and P at which the high- and low-spin states have equal energies:

$$\Delta_0 = P$$

The relationship is the same in all cases, and means that the spin state of any ion in an octahedral electrostatic field depends simply upon whether the magnitude of the field as measured by the splitting energy Δ_0 is greater or less than the mean pairing energy, P, for the particular ion. For a particular ion, of the d^4, d^5, d^6, or d^7 type, the stronger the crystal field, the more likely it is that the electrons will crowd as much as possible into the more stable t_{2g} orbitals, whereas in the weaker crystal fields, where $P > \Delta_0$, the electrons will remain spread out over the entire set of d orbitals as they do in the free ion. For ions of the other types, d^1, d^2, d^3, d^8, d^9, and d^{10}, the number of unpaired electrons is fixed at the same number as in the free ion irrespective of how strong the crystal field may become.

Approximate theoretical estimates of the mean pairing energies for the relevant ions of the first transition series have been made from spectroscopic data. In Table 26-1 these energies, along with Δ_0 values for some complexes (derived by methods to be described in the next section), are listed. It will be seen that the theory developed above affords correct predictions in all cases. It will further be noted that the mean pairing

TABLE 26-1

Crystal Field Splittings, Δ_0, and Mean Electron Pairing Energies, P,
for Several Transition Metal Ions
(Energies in cm.$^{-1}$)

Config-uration	Ion	P^a	Ligands	Δ	Spin state	
					Predicted	Observed
d^4	Cr^{2+}	23,500	$6H_2O$	13,900	High	High
	Mn^{3+}	28,000	$6H_2O$	21,000	High	High
d^5	Mn^{2+}	25,500	$6H_2O$	7,800	High	High
	Fe^{3+}	30,000	$6H_2O$	13,700	High	High
d^6	Fe^{2+}	17,600	$6H_2O$	10,400	High	High
			$6CN^-$	33,000	Low	Low
	Co^{3+}	21,000	$6F^-$	13,000	High	High
			$6NH_3$	23,000	Low	Low
d^7	Co^{2+}	22,500	$6H_2O$	9,300	High	High

[a] These energies may be generally 10–20% too high, since they are all calculated from interelectronic interaction parameters of the free gaseous ions, and it is known (Section 26-9) that these parameters decrease somewhat when the ions are surrounded by ligands.

energies vary irregularly from one metal ion to another as do the values of Δ_0 for a given set of ligands. Thus, as Table 26-1 shows, the d^5 systems should be exceptionally stable in their high-spin states, whereas the d^6 systems should be exceptionally stable in their low-spin states. These expectations are in excellent agreement with the experimental facts.

Finer details of magnetic properties such as orbital contributions, unusual temperature dependencies of magnetic moments, and magnetic anisotropies can also be calculated using the electrostatic crystal field theory and the results are generally good approximations. They are not perfect because the basic premise in the theory—namely, that the interaction between the metal ion and its surroundings is a purely electrostatic perturbation by nearest neighbors—is not perfect. It is the consideration of this point which will lead us into ligand field theory in Section 26-8.

Metal ions in tetrahedral electrostatic fields may be treated by the same procedure outlined above for the octahedral cases. For tetrahedral fields it is found that for the d^1, d^2, d^7, d^8, and d^9 cases, only high-spin states are possible as shown in Figure 26-10. For d^3, d^4, d^5, and d^6 configurations both high-spin and low-spin states are in principle possible as shown in Figure 26-11. Once again the existence of low-spin states requires that $\Delta_t > P$. Since Δ_t values are only about half as great as Δ_0 values, it is to be expected that low-spin tetrahedral complexes of first transition series ions with d^3,

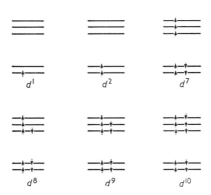

Fig. 26-10.   Sketches showing the unique ground state occupancy schemes for d orbitals in tetrahedral complexes with d configurations d^1, d^2, d^7, d^8, d^9, d^{10}.

d^4, d^5, and d^6 configurations would be scarce or even unknown. None have so far been definitely shown to exist.

We must also consider the effect of distortions of the coordination polyhedron upon the magnetic properties. Even when the strictly octahedral environment does not permit the existence of a low-spin state, as in the d^8 case, distortions of the octahedron will cause further splitting of degenerate orbitals which may become great enough to overcome pairing energies and cause electron pairing. Let us consider as an example the d^8 system in an octahedral environment which is then subjected to a tetragonal distortion. We have already seen (Figure 26-5) how a decrease in the electrostatic

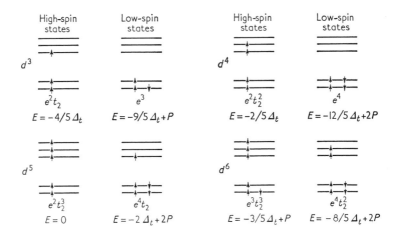

Fig. 26-11.   Diagrams showing the possible high-spin and low-spin ground states for d^3, d^4, d^5, and d^6 ions in tetrahedral crystal fields.

field along the z axis, which may arise either by moving the two z-axis
ligands out to a greater distance than are their otherwise identical neighbors in the xy plane or by having two different ligands on the z axis which
make an intrinsically smaller contribution to the electrostatic potential
than do the four in the xy plane. Irrespective of its origin, the result of a
tetragonal distortion of an initially octahedral field is to split apart the
$(x^2 - y^2)$ and z^2 orbitals. We have also seen that if the tetragonal distortion, that is, the disparity between the contributions to the electrostatic
potential of the two z-axis ligands and the other four, becomes sufficiently
great, the z^2 orbital may fall below the xy orbital. In either case, the two
least stable d orbitals are now no longer degenerate but are separated by
some energy, Q. Now the question of whether the tetragonally distorted
d^8 complex will have high or low spin depends on whether the pairing
energy, P, is greater or less than the energy Q. Figure 26-12 shows the

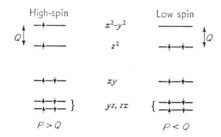

Fig. 26-12. Energy level diagrams showing the possible high-spin and low-spin ground
states for a d^8 system (e.g., Ni^{2+}) in a tetragonally distorted octahedral field.

situation for the case of a "weak" tetragonal distortion, that is, for one in
which the second highest d orbital is still d_{z^2}.

The simple theory just outlined enables us to predict, or at least to understand, the number of unpaired electrons possessed by the transition metal
ions in various environments. As we shall see later, the valence bond theory
can also do this, although there are certain d^n configurations for which its
predictions are misleading. The great advantage of crystal field theory
(and also ligand field theory) is that the prediction of actual magnetic
moments is also possible. Such predictions require the use of some fairly
sophisticated quantum mechanics, and are thus not the sort that an experimental inorganic chemist will carry out for himself; however, it is of
considerable importance that they can be made, for they often provide
extremely useful chemical information. For example, we have seen that
the simple theory predicts that for $Co^{2+}(d^7)$ all tetrahedral complexes and
those octahedral ones in which the crystal field is relatively weak will have

three unpaired electrons. Refined calculations, however, show that it is possible in many cases to distinguish between octahedral and tetrahedral coordination because for the former the moments should (and do, with very few exceptions) have large orbital contributions, putting them in the range 4.8–5.2 B.M. ($\mu_S = 3.89$). For the tetrahedral complexes, however, the orbital contributions are generally smaller (moments run 4.2–4.8 B.M.) and are inversely proportional to the strength of the crystal field. Thus the moments of the Co^{II} ions in the tetrahedral complexes $[CoX_4]^{2-}$ are, for X = NCS$^-$, Cl$^-$, Br$^-$, and I$^-$, $\sim$4.4, $\sim$4.6, $\sim$4.7, and $\sim$4.8 B.M., respectively, while the Δ_t values are, in the same order of ligands, $\sim$4500, $\sim$3100, $\sim$2800, and $\sim$2600 cm.$^{-1}$. It is one of the very great virtues of the crystal (and ligand) field theory that it supplies a theoretical basis for quantitative correlations of this sort. It also supplies the theoretical basis for understanding the variation of magnetic moments with temperature which is quite important, since many complexes deviate from the Curie and Curie-Weiss laws governing temperature dependence of the moment.

26-4. Absorption Spectra

Let us first consider the simplest possible case, the d^1 configuration. If such an ion lies at the center of an octahedral field due to ions or dipoles, for example, the Ti^{III} ion in $[Ti(H_2O)_6]^{3+}$, the d electron will occupy a t_{2g} orbital. Upon irradiation with light of frequency ν, equal to $\Delta_0/\mathbf{h}$, where $\mathbf{h}$ is Planck's constant and Δ_0 is the energy difference between the t_{2g} and the e_g orbitals, it should be possible for such an ion to capture a quantum of radiation and convert that energy into energy of excitation of the electron from the t_{2g} to the e_g orbitals. The absorption band which results from this process is found in the visible spectrum of the hexaquotitanium(III) ion, shown in Figure 26-13, and is responsible for its violet color. Three features of this absorption band are of importance here: its position, its intensity, and its breadth.

In discussing the positions of absorption bands in relation to the splittings of the d orbitals, it is convenient and common practice to use the same unit, the reciprocal centimeter or wave number, abbreviated cm.$^{-1}$, for both the unit of frequency in the spectra and the unit of energy for the orbitals. With this convention, we see that the spectrum of Figure 26-13 tells us that Δ_0 in $[Ti(H_2O)_6]^{3+}$ is 20,000 cm.$^{-1}$. Since there are 350 cm.$^{-1}$ per kilocalorie, this means that the splitting energy is $\sim$57 kcal./mole, which is quite comparable with the usual values of chemical bond energies. In general, we shall see that the crystal field theory enables us to calculate the energy separations between various states of the d electrons from the

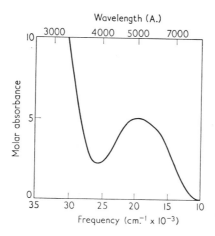

Fig. 26-13.   The visible absorption spectrum of $[Ti(H_2O)_6]^{3+}$.

frequencies of the absorption bands in the visible spectra. In the present case the relationship is the simplest possible one, namely, the observed frequency is identical with the d orbital splitting.

Turning now to the intensity of this absorption band in the $[Ti(H_2O)_6]^{3+}$ ion, we note that it is extremely weak by comparison with absorption bands found in many other systems. The reason for this is that the electron is jumping from one orbital which is centrosymmetric to another which is also centrosymmetric, and that all transitions of this type are nominally "forbidden" by the rules of quantum mechanics. One-electron transitions which are "allowed" have intensities which give molar absorbance values at the absorption peaks of $\sim 10^4$. If the postulate of the crystal field theory, that in both the ground and excited states the electrons of the metal ion occupy completely pure d orbitals which have no other interaction than a purely coulombic one with the environment of the ion, were precisely correct, the intensity of this band would be precisely zero. It gains a little intensity because the postulate is not perfectly valid in ways which will be discussed in Section 26-8. Suffice it to say here that low intensities, indicative of essentially "forbidden" character, are observed in the d–d transitions of all of the metal ions of the first transition series.

Finally, we note that the observed absorption is not an infinitely thin line lying at precisely the frequency equivalent to Δ_0. The breadth of the absorption is caused by the fact that the electronic excitation is accompanied by a host of vibrational excitations, spread over a range of several thousand wave numbers. This, too, is a general phenomenon found in the spectra of all d^n systems in crystal fields, although there are certain cases, for example, Mn^{II} and Cr^{III} spectra, in which relatively narrow lines are found. Further discussion of line breadths will be found in Section 29-19.

It is also possible to interpret the d–d spectrum of a d^9 ion as simply as we have done with the spectrum of a d^1 ion. This is a special case of a general idea called the *hole formalism* according to which a d^{10-n} configuration will have the same behavior in a crystal field, except for certain changes in the signs of energy terms, as a d^n configuration. The former has as many holes in its d shell as the latter has electrons. According to the hole formalism, which is perfectly rigorous within the limits of the electrostatic crystal field theory, n holes in the d shell may be treated like n positrons. Now all of the d level splittings which we have deduced for the levels of one electron in various electrostatic fields will be quantitatively the same for one positron, *except* that the patterns will be inverted because a positron will be most electrostatically stable in just those regions where an electron is least electrostatically stable, and vice versa. We can thus look upon a Cu^{II} ion in an octahedral environment as a one-positron ion in an octahedral field and deduce that in the ground state the positron will occupy an e_g orbital from which it may be excited by radiation providing energy Δ_0 to a t_{2g} orbital.

Experimentally it is found, however, that the absorption band of the Cu^{II} ion in aqueous solution is not a simple, symmetrically shaped band but instead appears to consist of two (or three) nearly superposed bands. The observant reader may have noticed that the absorption band of the $[Ti(H_2O)_6]^{3+}$ ion is not quite a simple, symmetrical band either. In each case these complications are traceable to distortions of the octahedral environment which are required by the Jahn-Teller theorem. We shall discuss this theorem a little later (page 582).

In order to interpret the spectra of complexes in which the metal ions have more than one but less than nine d electrons, we must introduce the device of the energy level diagram based upon the Russell-Saunders states of the relevant d^n configuration in the free (uncomplexed) ion. It can be shown that just as the set of five d orbitals is split apart by the electrostatic field of surrounding ligands to give two or more sets of lower degeneracy, so also are the various Russell-Saunders states of a d^n configuration. The number and types of the components into which an octahedral or tetrahedral field will split a state of given L is the same regardless of the d^n configuration from which it arises, and these facts are summarized in Table 26-2. The designations of the states of the ion in the crystal field are the *Mulliken* symbols; their origin is in group theory, but they may be regarded simply as labels.

Although the states into which a given free ion state splits are the same

TABLE 26-2

Splitting of Russell-Saunders States in Octahedral
and Tetrahedral Electrostatic Fields

State of free ion	States in the crystal field
S	A_1
P	T_1
D	$E + T_2$
F	$A_2 + T_1 + T_2$
G	$A_1 + E + T_1 + T_2$
H	$E + 2T_1 + T_2$

in number and type in both octahedral and tetrahedral fields, the pattern of energies is inverted in one case relative to the other. This is quite analogous to the results in the d^1 case as we have already seen (Fig. 26-3).

A discussion of the way in which the energies of the crystal field states are calculated would be beyond the scope of this book. For the inorganic chemist it is not essential to know how the energy level diagrams are obtained in order to use them; it is, of course, necessary to know how to interpret them properly. At this point we shall examine several of them in some detail in order to explain their interpretation. Others will be introduced subsequently in discussing the chemistry of particular transition elements.

We shall look first at the energy level diagram for a d^2 system in an octahedral field, as shown in Figure 26-14. The ordinate is in energy units, usually cm.$^{-1}$, and the abscissa is in units of crystal field splitting energy as measured by Δ_0, the splitting of the one-electron orbitals. At the extreme left are the Russell-Saunders states of the free ion. It may be seen that each of these splits up in the crystal field into the components specified in Table 26-2. Three features of this energy level diagram which are particularly to be noted because they will be found in all such diagrams are:

1. States with identical designations never cross.

2. The crystal field states have the same spin multiplicity as the free ion states from which they originate.

3. States which are the only ones of their type have energies which depend linearly on the crystal field strength, whereas, when there are two or more states of identical designation, their lines will in general show curvature. This is because such states interact with one another as well as with the crystal field.

It is interesting to note in this diagram that a triplet state lies lowest at all field strengths shown, and, since its slope is as steep as the slope of

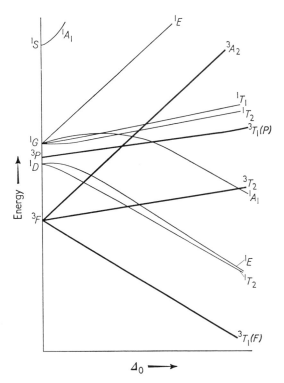

Fig. 26-14. The complete energy level diagram for the d^2 configuration in an octahedral crystal field. The heavier lines are those for the triplet states.

any other state, it will continue to be the lowest state no matter how intense the crystal field may become. This is in complete agreement with our previous conclusion, based on the simple splitting diagram for the d orbitals, which showed that the two d electrons would have their spins parallel in an octahedral field irrespective of how strong the field might be.

In order to use this energy level diagram to predict or interpret the spectra of octahedral complexes of d^2 ions, for example, the spectrum of the $[V(H_2O)_6]^{3+}$ ion, we first note that there is a quantum mechanical selection rule which forbids transition between states of different spin multiplicity. This means that in the present case only three transitions, those from the $^3T_1$ ground state to the three triplet excited states, $^3T_2$, $^3A_2$, and $^3T_1(P)$, will occur. Actually, spin-forbidden transitions, that is, those between levels of different spin multiplicity, do occur very weakly because of weak spin-orbit interactions, but they are several orders of magnitude weaker than the spin-allowed ones and are ordinarily not observed.

Experimental study of the $[V(H_2O)_6]^{3+}$ ion reveals just three absorption bands in the appropriate energy range, at 17,200, 25,000, and ~38,000 cm.$^{-1}$. Using an energy level diagram like that in Figure 26-14, in which the separations of the free ion states are adjusted to match exactly those appropriate for V^{III}, one finds that, at a Δ_0 of 21,500 cm.$^{-1}$, the three transitions are expected at 17,300, 25,500, and 38,600 cm.$^{-1}$, in excellent agreement with observation. For high-spin complexes of the first transition series metals in their normal oxidation states, quantitative agreement of this sort, or nearly as good, is generally attained.

We shall look next at the energy level diagram for a d^8 ion in an octahedral field (Fig. 26-15), restricting our attention to the triplet states

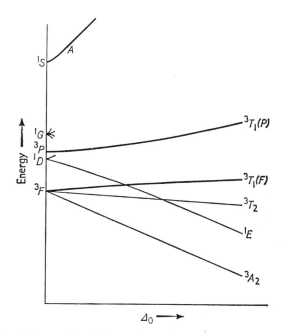

Fig. 26-15.   Partial energy level diagram for a d^8 ion in an octahedral field, showing the triplet states and only the lowest singlet state.

except for the lowest energy singlet state which comes from the ^1D state of the free ion. This has been included to show that for this system the ground state will always be a spin triplet no matter how strong the crystal field, a result in agreement with the conclusion previously drawn from consideration of the distribution of eight electrons among a set of five d orbitals. On comparing the arrangements of the three components derived from the

^3F ground state for the d^2 and the d^8 cases, we note that one pattern is the inverse of the other. This is a manifestation of the "hole formalism" for the d^2–d^{10-2} configurations which is fundamentally quite analogous to the d^1–d^{10-1} example we previously examined.

Similar energy level diagrams may be drawn for d^n systems in tetrahedral crystal fields. There is an interesting relationship between these and the ones for certain systems in octahedral fields. We have already seen that the splitting pattern for the d orbitals in a tetrahedral field is just the inverse of that for the d orbitals in an octahedral field. A similar inverse relationship exists between the energy level diagrams of d^n systems in tetrahedral and octahedral fields. The components into which each Russell-Saunders state is split are reversed in their energy order in the tetrahedral compared to the octahedral cases. Furthermore, as in the one-electron case, a purely electrostatic interaction between metal ion and ligands will produce only $\frac{4}{9}$ the splittings in the tetrahedral case as in the octahedral case, all other factors such as metal–ligand distance being kept constant.

Finally, there are rather extensive qualitative similarities between the energy level diagrams of groups of the d^n systems because of the combined effects of reversals in the splitting patterns by changing from an octahedral to a tetrahedral field and by changing from a d^n to a d^{10-n} configuration. When we go from d^n in an octahedral field to d^n in a tetrahedral field, all splittings of the Russell-Saunders states are inverted. But the same inversions occur on changing from the d^n configuration in an octahedral (tetrahedral) field to the d^{10-n} configuration in an octahedral (tetrahedral) field. These relations, combined with the fact that, for the free ions, the Russell-Saunders states of the pairs of d^n and d^{10-n} systems are identical in number, type, and relative (though certainly not absolute) energies, mean that various pairs of configuration–environment combinations have qualitatively identical energy level diagrams in crystal fields, and that these differ from others only in the reversal of the splittings of the individual free ion states. These relations are set out in Table 26-3.

It will be evident from the foregoing description and illustrations of energy level diagrams that they may be used to determine from observed spectral bands the magnitudes of Δ_0 and Δ_t in complexes. It may be noted in the diagrams for the d^2 and d^8 systems that there are three spin-allowed absorption bands whose positions are all determined by the one* parame-

---

* This is only approximately true because the separation between the ^3F and ^3P states is not the same in the complexed ion as it is in the free ion, and this separation therefore becomes a second parameter, in addition to Δ, to be determined from experiment. We shall return to this point on page 596.

TABLE 26-3

Relations between Energy Level Diagrams for Various d^n Configurations
in Octahedral and Tetrahedral Crystal Fields

Octahedral d^1 and tetrahedral d^9	Reverse[a] of	Octahedral d^9 and tetrahedral d^1
Octahedral d^2 and tetrahedral d^8	Reverse of	Octahedral d^8 and tetrahedral d^2
Octahedral d^3 and tetrahedral d^7	Reverse of	Octahedral d^7 and tetrahedral d^3
Octahedral d^4 and tetrahedral d^6	Reverse of	Octahedral d^6 and tetrahedral d^4
Octahedral d^5	Identical with	Tetrahedral d^5

[a] "Reverse" means that the order of levels coming from each free ion state is reversed;
it does *not* mean that the diagram as a whole is reversed.

ter, Δ_0 or Δ_t. Thus in these cases the internal consistency of the theory may be checked.

Certain generalizations may be made about the dependence of the magnitudes of Δ values on the valence and atomic number of the metal ion, the symmetry of the coordination shell and the nature of the ligands. For octahedral complexes containing high-spin metal ions, it may be inferred from the accumulated data for a large number of systems that:

1. Δ_0 values for complexes of the first transition series are 7,500–12,500 cm.$^{-1}$ for divalent ions and 14,000–21,000 cm.$^{-1}$ for trivalent ions.

2. Δ_0 values for corresponding complexes of metal ions in the same group and with the same valence increase by about 30% on going from the first transition series to the second and by about this amount again from the second to the third.

3. Δ_t values do seem to be about 40–50% of Δ_0 values for complexes differing as little as possible except in the geometry of the coordination shell, in agreement with theoretical expectation.

4. The dependence of Δ values on the identity of the ligands follows a regular order known as the spectrochemical series which will now be explained.

26-5. The Spectrochemical Series

It has been found by experimental study of the spectra of a large number of complexes containing various metal ions and various ligands, that ligands may be arranged in a series according to their capacity to cause d-orbital splittings. This series, for the more common ligands, is: $I^- < Br^- < Cl^- < F^- < OH^- < C_2O_4^{2-} \sim H_2O < -NCS^- < py \sim NH_3 < en < dipy < o\text{-phen} < NO_2^- < CN^-$. The idea of this series is that the d-orbital splittings and hence the relative frequencies of visible absorption bands for two complexes containing the same metal ion but different ligands can be predicted from the above series whatever the particular metal ion may be. Naturally, one cannot expect such a simple and useful rule to be universally applicable. The following qualifications must be remembered in applying it.

1. The series is based upon data for metal ions in common oxidation states. Because the nature of the metal–ligand interaction in an unusually high or unusually low oxidation state of the metal may be in certain respects qualitatively different from that for the metal in a normal oxidation state, striking violations of the order shown often occur for complexes in unusual oxidation states.

2. Even for metal ions in their normal oxidation states inversions of the order of adjacent or nearly adjacent members of the series are sometimes found.

26-6. Structural Effects of Crystal Field Splittings

We have so far considered how the electrostatic effects of ligands cause the d electrons to prefer certain regions of space (i.e., certain orbitals) to others. We shall now look briefly at some ways in which the nonspherical distribution of the d electrons, caused by the environment, reacts back upon the environment.

Ionic Radii. We consider first the effect of d orbital splittings on the variation of ionic radii with atomic number in a series of ions of the same charge. We shall use as an example the octahedral radii of the divalent ions of the first transition series. Figure 26-16 shows a plot of the experimental values. The points for Cr^{2+} and Cu^{2+} are indicated with open circles

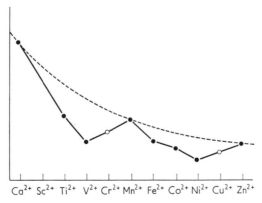

Ca^{2+} Sc^{2+} Ti^{2+} V^{2+} Cr^{2+} Mn^{2+} Fe^{2+} Co^{2+} Ni^{2+} Cu^{2+} Zn^{2+}

Fig. 26-16. The relative ionic radii of divalent ions of the first transition series. The dashed line is a theoretical curve explained in the text.

because the Jahn-Teller effect, to be discussed shortly, makes it impossible to obtain these ions in truly octahedral environments, thus rendering the assessment of their "octahedral" radii somewhat uncertain. A smooth curve has also been drawn through the points for Ca^{2+}, Mn^{2+}, and Zn^{2+} ions which have the electron configurations $t_{2g}^0 e_g^0$, $t_{2g}^3 e_g^2$, and $t_{2g}^6 e_g^4$, respectively. In these three cases the distribution of d electron density around the metal ion is spherical because all d orbitals are either unoccupied or equally occupied. Because the shielding of one d electron by another from the nuclear charge is imperfect, there is a steady contraction in the ionic radii. It is seen that the radii of the other ions are all below the values expected from the curve passing through Ca^{2+}, Mn^{2+}, and Zn^{2+}. This is because the d electrons in these ions are not distributed uniformly (i.e., spherically) about the nuclei as we shall now explain.

The Ti^{2+} ion has the configuration t_{2g}^2. This means that the negative charge of two d electrons is concentrated in those regions of space away from the metal-ligand bond axes. Thus, compared to the effect that they would have if distributed spherically around the metal nucleus, these two electrons provide abnormally little shielding between the positive metal ion and the negative ligands; therefore the ligand atoms are drawn in closer than they would be if the d electrons were spherically distributed. Thus, in effect, the radius of the metal ion is smaller than that for the hypothetical, isoelectronic spherical ion. In V^{2+} this same effect is found in even greater degree because there are now three t_{2g} electrons providing much less shielding between metal ion and ligands than would three spherically distributed d electrons. For Cr^{2+} and Mn^{2+}, however, we have the configurations $t_{2g}^3 e_g$ and $t_{2g}^3 e_g^2$, in which the electrons added to the t_{2g}^3 configuration of V^{2+} go into orbitals which concentrate them mainly between the metal ion and the ligands. These e_g electrons thus provide a great deal more screening than would be provided by spherically distributed electrons, and indeed the effect is so great that the radii actually increase. The same sequence of events is repeated in the second half of the series. The first three electrons added to the spherical $t_{2g}^3 e_g^2$ configuration of Mn^{2+} go into the t_{2g} orbitals where the screening power is abnormally low, and the radii therefore decrease abnormally rapidly. On going from Ni^{2+}, with the configuration $t_{2g}^6 e_g^2$, to Cu^{2+} and Zn^{2+}, electrons are added to the e_g orbitals where their screening power is abnormally high, and the radii again cease to decrease and actually show small increases. Similar effects may be expected with trivalent ions, with ions of other transition series, and in tetrahedral environments as well, although in these other circumstances fewer experimental data are available to verify the predictions which may be made by reasoning similar to that used above.

Jahn-Teller Effects. In 1937 Jahn and Teller proved a rather remarkable theorem which states that any nonlinear molecular system in a degenerate electronic state will be unstable and will undergo some kind of distortion which will lower its symmetry and split the degenerate state. Although it may sound somewhat abstract, this simple theorem has great practical importance in understanding the structural chemistry of certain transition metal ions. In order to illustrate this, we shall begin with the Cu^{2+} ion. Suppose this ion finds itself in the center of an octahedron of ligands. As shown on page 574, this ion may be thought of as possessing one hole in the e_g orbitals and the electronic state of the ion is hence a degenerate, E_g, state. According to the Jahn-Teller theorem then, the octahedron cannot remain perfect at equilibrium but must become distorted in some way.

The dynamic reason for the distortion is actually rather easy to appreciate in terms of simple physical reasoning. Let us suppose that, of the two e_g orbitals, it is the $(x^2 - y^2)$ orbital which is doubly occupied while the z^2 orbital is only singly occupied. This must mean that the four anions or the negative ends of ligand dipoles in the xy plane will be more screened from the electrostatic attraction of the Cu^{2+} ion than will the two ligands on the z axis. Naturally, then, the later two ligands will be drawn in somewhat more closely than the other four. If, conversely, the z^2 orbital is doubly occupied and the $(x^2 - y^2)$ orbital only singly occupied, the four ligands in the xy plane will be drawn more closely to the cation than will the other two on the z axis. It is also possible that the unpaired electron could be in an orbital which is some linear combination of $(x^2 - y^2)$ and z^2 in which case the resulting distortion would be some related combination of the simple ones considered above. These simple considerations call attention to several important facts relating to the operation of the Jahn-Teller theorem:

1. The theorem only predicts that for degenerate states a distortion must occur. It does not give any indication of what the geometrical nature of the distortion will be nor how great it will be.

2. In order to make a prediction of the nature and magnitude of the distortion, detailed calculations must be made of the energy of the entire complex as a function of all possible types and degrees of distortion. The configuration having the lowest over-all energy may then be predicted to be the equilibrium one. Such calculations, however, are extremely laborious and few have been attempted.

3. It may be noted that there is one general restriction on the nature of the distortions, namely, that if the undistorted configuration has a center of symmetry, so also must the distorted equilibrium configuration.

In order to give a little more insight into the energy problem noted under paragraph 2 above, let us consider what happens to the d orbital energies when there occurs a small distortion of the type in which the octahedron becomes stretched along its z axis. The effects are shown in Figure 26-17.

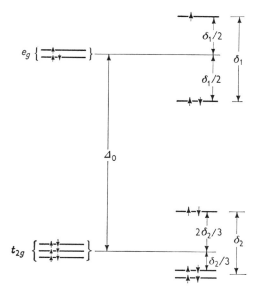

Fig. 26-17. Schematic diagram of the splittings caused by an elongation of an octahedron along one axis. The various splittings are not to the same scale, δ_1 and δ_2 being much smaller relative to Δ than indicated.

In this diagram the various splittings are not drawn to scale in the interest of clarity. Both of the splittings due to the distortion are much smaller than Δ_0 and, as noted below, δ_2 is much smaller than δ_1. It should also be noted that each of the splittings obeys a center of gravity rule. The two e_g orbitals separate so that one goes up as much as the other goes down; the t_{2g} orbitals separate so that the doubly degenerate pair goes down only half as far as the single orbital goes up. It can be seen that, for the d^9 case, there is no net energy change for the t_{2g} electrons, since four are destabilized by $\delta_2/3$ while two are stabilized by $2\delta_2/3$. For the e_g electrons, however, a net stabilization occurs, since the energy of one electron is raised by $\delta_1/2$, but two electrons have their energies lowered by this same amount; the net lowering of the electronic energy is thus $\delta_1/2$. It is this stabilization which provides the driving force for the distortion.

It is easy to see from Figure 26-17 that, for both the configurations $t_{2g}{}^6 e_g$ and $t_{2g}{}^6 e_g{}^3$, distortion of the octahedron will cause stabilization; thus we predict, as could also be done directly from the Jahn-Teller theorem, that distortions are to be expected in the octahedral complexes of ions with these configurations, but not for ions having t_{2g}^6, $t_{2g}^6 e_g^2$, or $t_{2g}^6 e_g^4$ configurations. In addition it should also be obvious from the foregoing considerations that a high-spin d^4 ion, having the configuration $t_{2g}^3 e_g$, will also be subject to distortion. Some real ions having these configurations which are subject to distortion are:

$t_{2g}^3 e_g$:   high-spin Cr^{II} and Mn^{III}
$t_{2g}^6 e_g$:   low-spin Co^{II} and Ni^{III}
$t_{2g}^6 e_g^3$: Cu^{II}

For low-spin Co^{II} no structural data are available, but in the other four cases there are ample data to show that distortions do occur and that they take the form of elongation of the octahedron along one axis. Indeed, in a number of Cu^{II} compounds the distortions of the octahedra around the cupric ion are so extreme that the coordination is best regarded as virtually square and, of course, Cu^{II} forms many square complexes. Specific illustrations of distortions in the compounds of these several ions will be mentioned when the chemistry of the elements is described in Chapter 29.

It may also be noted that the Jahn-Teller theorem applies to excited states as well as to ground states, although in such cases the effect is a complicated dynamic one because the short lifetime of an electronically excited state does not permit the attainment of a stable equilibrium configuration of the complex. To illustrate the effect on excited states, we may consider the $[Ti(H_2O)_6]^{3+}$, $[Fe(H_2O)_6]^{2+}$, and $[CoF_6]^{3-}$ ions. The first of these has an excited state configuration e_g. The presence of the single e_g electron causes the excited state to be split, and it is this which accounts for the broad, flat contour of the absorption band of $[Ti(H_2O)_6]^{3+}$ as seen in Figure 26-13. In both $[Fe(H_2O)_6]^{2+}$ and $[CoF_6]^{3-}$, the ground state has the configuration $t_{2g}^4 e_g^2$, and the excited state with the same number of unpaired electrons has the configuration $t_{2g}^3 e_g^3$. Thus, the excited states of these ions are subject to Jahn-Teller splitting into two components, and this shows up very markedly in their absorption spectra, as Figure 26-18 shows for $[CoF_6]^{3-}$.

Jahn-Teller distortions can also be caused by the presence of 1, 2, 4, or 5 electrons in the t_{2g} orbitals of an octahedrally coordinated ion. This can easily be seen by referring to the lower part of Figure 26-17. If one t_{2g} electron is present, distortion by elongation on one axis will cause stabilization by $\delta_2/3$. Distortion by flattening along one axis would produce a splitting of the t_{2g} orbitals which is just the reverse of that shown in Figure 26-17 for elongation, and thus would cause stabilization by twice as much, namely, $2\delta_2/3$. The same predictions can obviously be made for the

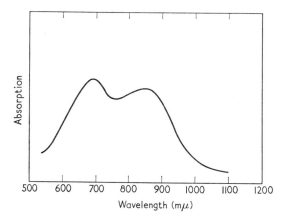

Fig. 26-18. The absorption spectrum of the $[CoF_6]^{3-}$ ion in $K_2Na[CoF_6]$ showing the splitting due to a Jahn-Teller distortion of the excited state with the configuration $t_{2g}^3 e_g^3$.

t_{2g}^4 case. For a t_{2g}^2 configuration (assuming, with good reason since δ_2 will be much less than the electron pairing energy, that pairing of electrons will not occur) the elongation distortion would be favored, since it will provide a total stabilization of

$$2 \times \delta_2/3 = 2\delta_2/3$$

whereas the flattening would give a net stabilization energy of only

$$2\delta_2/3 - \delta_2/3 = \delta_2/3$$

For the t_{2g}^5 case, flattening is again predicted to cause the greater stabilization.

There is, however, little experimental confirmation of these predictions of Jahn-Teller effects for partially filled t_{2g} shells. This is mainly due to the fact that the effects are expected, theoretically, to be much smaller than those for partially filled e_g orbitals. In terms of Figure 26-17, theory shows that for a given amount of distortion δ_2 is much smaller than δ_1. Thus the stabilization energies, which are the driving forces for the distortions, are evidently not great enough to cause well-defined, clearly observable distortions in cases of partially occupied t_{2g} orbitals. From a qualitative point of view the relation $\delta_2 \ll \delta_1$ is easily understood. Since the e_g orbitals are directed right at the ligands, the presence of an electron in one e_g orbital but not in the other will cause a much larger disparity in the metal–ligand distances than will nonuniform occupancy of t_{2g} orbitals which concentrate their electrons between the metal–ligand bonds where their effects on metal–ligand distances is much less (cf. the discussion of ionic radii at the beginning of this section).

26-7. Thermodynamic Effects of Crystal Field Splittings

We have seen in Section 26-2 that the d orbitals of an ion in an octahedral field are split so that three of them become more stable (by $2\Delta_0/5$) and two of them less stable (by $3\Delta_0/5$) than they would be in the absence of the splitting. Thus, for example, a d^2 ion will have each of its two d electrons stabilized by $2\Delta_0/5$, giving a total stabilization of $4\Delta_0/5$. Recalling from Section 26-4 that Δ_0 values run about 10,000 and 20,000 cm.$^{-1}$ for di- and trivalent ions of the first transition series, we can see that these "extra" stabilization energies—extra in the sense that they would not exist if the d shells of the metal ions were symmetrical as are the other electron shells of the ions—will amount to $\sim$25 and $\sim$50 kcal./mole, respectively, for di- and trivalent d^2 ions. Such energies are of course of the same order of magnitude as the energies of most chemical changes, and they will therefore play an important role in the thermodynamic properties of transition metal compounds.

Let us first of all consider high-spin octahedral complexes. Every t_{2g} electron represents a stability increase (i.e., energy lowering) of $2\Delta_0/5$, whereas every e_g electron represents a stability decrease of $3\Delta_0/5$. Thus, for any configuration $t_{2g}^p e_g^q$, the net stabilization will be given by $(2p/5 - 3q/5)\Delta_0$. The results obtained for all of the ions, that is, d^0 to d^{10}, using this formula are collected in Table 26-4. Since the magnitude of Δ_0 for any particular complex can be obtained from the spectrum, it is pos-

TABLE 26-4

Ligand-Field Stabilization Energies for Octahedrally
Coordinated High-Spin Ions

Number of d electrons	Stabilization energy
1, 6	$2\Delta_0/5$
2, 7[a]	$4\Delta_0/5$
3, 8	$6\Delta_0/5$
4, 9	$3\Delta_0/5$
0, 5, 10	0

[a] For the d^2 and d^7 ions, the figure obtained in this way and given above is not exactly correct because of the effect of configuration interaction.

sible to determine the magnitudes of these crystal field stabilization energies independently of thermodynamic measurements and thus to see what part they play in the thermodynamics of the transition metal compounds.

As an example of this, let us consider the heats of hydration of the divalent ions of the first transition series. These are the energies of the processes:

$$M^{2+}(gas) + \infty H_2O = [M(H_2O)_6]^{2+}(aq)$$

and they can be estimated using thermodynamic cycles. The energies calculated are shown by the filled circles in Figure 26-19. It will be seen

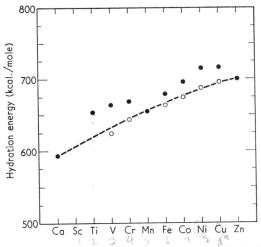

Fig. 26-19. Hydration energies of some divalent ions. Solid circles are the experimentally derived hydration energies. Open circles are energies corrected for crystal field stabilization.

that a smooth curve, which is nearly a straight line, passes through the points for the three ions, Ca^{2+} (d^0), Mn^{2+} (d^5), and Zn^{2+} (d^{10}), which have no crystal field stabilization energy while the points for all other ions lie above this line. On subtracting the crystal field stabilization energy from each of the actual hydration energies, the values shown by open circles are obtained, and these fall on the smooth curve. It may be noted that, alternatively, crystal field stabilization energies could have been estimated from Figure 26-19 and used to calculate Δ_0 values. Either way, the excellent agreement between the spectrally and thermodynamically assessed Δ_0 values provides convincing evidence for the fundamental correctness of the orbital splitting picture provided by the crystal field theory.

Two more examples of these thermodynamic consequences of crystal

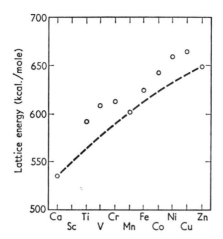

Fig. 26-20. The lattice energies of the dichlorides of the elements from Ca to Zn.

field splittings are shown in Figures 26-20 and 26-21. In Figure 26-20 the lattice energies of the dichlorides of the metals from calcium to zinc are plotted versus atomic number. Once again they define a curve with two maxima and a minimum at Mn^{2+}. As before, the energies for all the ions having crystal field stabilization energies lie above the curve passing through the energies of the three ions which do not have any crystal field stabilization energy. Similar plots are obtained for the lattice energies of other halides and of the chalconides of di- and trivalent metals. In Figure 26-21 are plotted the gas phase dissociation energies, estimated by means

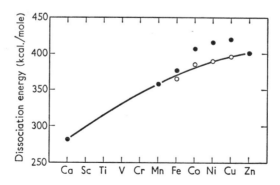

Fig. 26-21. Dissociation energies of the hexammines of some divalent metal ions; ● represents the total energies; O represents the total energies minus the crystal field stabilization energies estimated from spectroscopically derived Δ_0 values.

of thermodynamic cycles, for the hexammine ions of some divalent metals. These energies are for the process:

$$[M(NH_3)_6]^{2+}(g) = M^{2+}(g) + 6NH_3(g)$$

and thus are equal to six times the mean M—NH_3 bond energy. The hydration energies discussed above do not have quite this simple interpretation because they include the energy of further hydration of the hexaquo ions in addition to the energy of the process:

$$M^{2+}(g) + 6H_2O(g) = [M(H_2O)_6]^{2+}(g)$$

decreased by the heat of vaporization of six moles of water. Although the data for the dissociation of the hexammines are limited, they show the same trend as do the hydration and lattice energies and, as shown by the open circles of Figure 26-21, the deviations from the smooth curve are equal within experimental error to the spectroscopically estimated crystal field stabilization energies.

It will be noted in all three of the Figures, 26-19 to 26-21, that the smooth curves from Ca^{2+} through Mn^{2+} to Zn^{2+}, on which the corrected energies do, or presumably would, fall, rise with increasing atomic number. This is to be expected, since the smooth curve on which the radii of (real or hypothetical) spherical ions lie, as shown in Figure 26-16, falls from Ca^{2+} to Zn^{2+}. A steady decrease in ionic radius naturally leads to a steady increase in the electrostatic interaction energy between the cation and the ligand anions or dipoles. A feature of particular importance, which is most directly evident in Figure 26-21, is that the crystal field stabilization energies, critical as they may be in explaining the *differences* in energies between various ions in the series, make up only a small fraction, 5–10%, of the *total* energies of combination of the metal ions with the ligands. In other words, the crystal field stabilization energies, though crucially important in many ways, are not by any means the main sources of the binding energies in complexes.

It is a fairly general observation that the equilibrium constants for the formation of analogous complexes of the divalent metal ions of Mn through Zn with ligands which contain nitrogen as the donor atom fall in the following order of the metal ions: $Mn^{2+} < Fe^{2+} < Co^{2+} < Ni^{2+} < Cu^{2+} > Zn^{2+}$. There are occasional exceptions to this order, sometimes called the Irving-Williams order, which may be attributed to the occurrence of spin-pairing in strong crystal fields. Spin-pairing, naturally, affects the relative energies in a different way. The great generality of the above order of stability constants receives quite a natural explanation in terms of crystal field stabilization energies. It must first be noted that the magnitudes of stability constants are proportional to the antilogarithms of standard free energy changes so that the above order is also that of the $-\Delta F^0$ values for the formation reactions. Now the standard free energies of formation are related to the enthalpies by the relation:

$$-\Delta F^0 = -\Delta H^0 + T\Delta S^0$$

and since there are good reasons to believe that entropies of complex formation are substantially constant in the above series of ions, we come finally to the conclusion that the above order of formation constants is also the order of $-\Delta H^0$ values for the formation reactions. Indeed, in a few cases direct measurements of the ΔH^0 values have shown this to be true.

Let us now remember that the formation of the complex involves the displacement of water molecules by ligands. If the metal ion concerned is subject to crystal field stabilization, as is, for example, Fe^{2+}, this stabilization will be greater in the complex than that in the aquo ion, since the nitrogen-containing ligand will be further along in the spectrochemical series than is H_2O (see Section 26-5). For Mn^{2+}, however, there is no crystal field stabilization energy in the hexaquo ion or in the complex so that complexation cannot cause any increased stabilization. Thus the Fe^{2+} ion has more to gain by combining with the ligands than does Mn^{2+}, and it accordingly shows a greater affinity for them. Similarly, of two ions, both of which experience crystal field stabilization, the one which experiences the greater amount from both the ligand and from H_2O will also experience the larger increase on replacement of H_2O by the ligand. Thus the order of the ions in the stability series follows their order in regard to crystal field stabilization energies with only the exception of the position of Cu^{2+} relative to Ni^{2+}. There are several possible reasons for this discrepancy, but further work is needed to provide a completely unambiguous explanation.

THE LIGAND FIELD THEORY

26-8. Experimental Evidence for Orbital Overlap in Metal Ligand Bonds

All of the theory so far presented in Sections 26-2 through 26-7, and called crystal field theory, is developed from the assumption that the interactions between metal ions and the surrounding anions or dipolar molecules are strictly electrostatic in the sense that the metal ion orbitals do not in any way mix with ligand atom orbitals. Now we might certainly expect that this assumption will never be literally true in real chemical compounds, and indeed there is sufficient experimental evidence to give us a fair picture of how far many real complexes do deviate from this idealization. We shall consider some of this evidence presently. Before doing so, we shall antic-ipate the remaining contents of this and the immediately following sections by stating that we use the term *ligand field theory* to mean the theory which uses the basic electrostatic viewpoint and the methods of calculation of the crystal field theory, but which contains certain modifications to take ac-count of deviations from the electrostatic idealization which are not so great as fundamentally to undermine the usefulness of the basic approach. When the electrostatic approach of the crystal field theory is so very far from the truth that it does not offer an adequate *formal* starting point, it is then best to go to the other extreme and assume extensive mixing of ligand and metal orbitals and treat the problem in terms of molecular orbitals. We shall first consider the experimental evidence that *some* mixing of ligand and metal ion orbitals always occurs even in those cases where the crystal field approximation should be at its best.

One source of such evidence, probably the most direct one we possess, is electron spin resonance data. The nature of electron spin resonance (here-after ESR) has been briefly described in Section 24-12. In many cases it has been found that instead of the single absorption band expected for a group of d electrons localized on a particular metal atom, there is observed a complex pattern of sub-bands, as shown in Figure 26-22 for the now classic case of the $[IrCl_6]^{2-}$ ion. The pattern of sub-bands, called the hyperfine structure, has been satisfactorily explained by assuming that

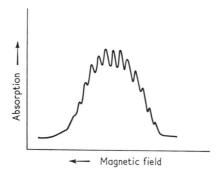

Fig. 26-22. The ESR spectrum of the $[IrCl_6]^{2-}$ ion, obtained with the applied mag-netic field aligned along one of the Cl—Ir—Cl axes of the complex ion in a single crystal of $Na_2PtCl_6 \cdot 6H_2O$ containing about 0.5% Ir^{IV} substitutionally replacing Pt^{IV}.

certain of the iridium d orbitals and certain orbitals of the surrounding chloride ions overlap to such an extent that the single unpaired electron is not localized entirely on the metal ion but instead is about 5% localized on each Cl^- ion. The hyperfine structure is caused by the nuclear magnetic moments of the chloride ions, and the hyperfine splittings are proportional to the fraction of its time which the electron spends in the orbitals of these chloride ions. The electron is thus only 70% an "iridium(IV) $4d$ electron," instead of the 100% that is assumed in the purely electrostatic crystal field theory. Another similar example is that of the $[Mo(CN)_8]^{3-}$ ion. The ESR spectrum of this ion when it is enriched in ^{13}C, which has a nuclear spin (^{12}C does not), exhibits marked hyperfine structure showing that the unpaired electron is significantly delocalized onto the carbon atoms of the CN^- ions.

Closely related to ESR experiments of the sort just mentioned are nuclear magnetic resonance experiments in which the nuclear resonances of atoms in ligands are found to be affected by unpaired electrons in a manner which can only be explained by assuming that electron spin density is transferred from metal orbitals into orbitals of ligand atoms. Thus, for example, the resonance frequency of the ring protons, H_α, in tris(acetylacetonato)vanadium(III) (Fig. 26-23) is considerably shifted from its position

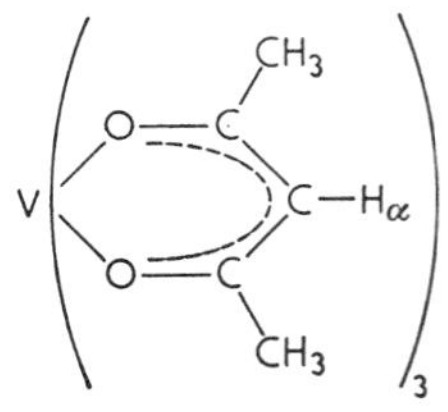

Fig. 26-23. Tris(acetylacetonato)vanadium(III) indicating the ring hydrogen, H_α, whose nuclear resonance frequency is strongly affected by the unpaired electrons on the V^{III} ion.

in a comparable diamagnetic compound, say its Al^{III} analog. In order to account for the magnitude of the shift, it is necessary to assume that the spin density of unpaired electrons, *formally* restricted to t_{2g} metal orbitals in the crystal field treatment, actually moves out into the π electron system of the ligand to a significant extent and eventually into the $1s$ orbitals of the hydrogen atoms. Even in MF_6^{2-} octahedra, where we should certainly expect the metal–ligand bonding to be as electrostatic as anywhere, fluorine nuclear resonance spectra have shown that delocalization of the spin density of metal ion d electrons takes place to the extent of 2–5%.

Another indication that metal ion and ligand orbitals overlap with the result that the d orbitals of the metal ions are not pure metal ion d orbitals is given by the intensities of the optical absorption bands due to "d–d" transitions. If the crystal field approximation were perfect, the only mechanisms by which these absorptions could gain intensity would be by interactions of the d orbital wave functions with vibrational wave functions of the complex ion and by mixing of d orbitals with other *metal ion* orbitals in those complexes (e.g., tetrahedral ones) where there is no center of symmetry. There are, however, cases in which it is fairly certain that these two processes are insufficient to account for the intensities observed, and it must be assumed then that the additional process of overlap and mixing of the metal d orbitals with various ligand atom orbitals, which is a powerful mechanism for enhancing the intensities, occurs to a significant degree.

It was noted on page 578, that if the energy level diagrams for transition metal ions with two to eight d electrons are calculated assuming that the separations between the various Russell-Saunders states are exactly the same in the complexed ion as they are in the free, gaseous ion (which leaves Δ as the only variable parameter) the fitting of experimental data is not exact. In some cases the discrepancies are quite marked. It is invariably found that the fit can be improved by assuming that the separations between the Russell-Saunders states are smaller in the complexed ion than in the free ion. Now the separations between these states are attributable to the repulsions between the d electrons in the d^n configuration, so that the decrease in the energy separations between the states suggests that the d electron cloud has expanded in the complex, thus increasing the mean distance between d electrons and decreasing the interelectronic repulsions. It is now generally believed that this expansion of the d electron cloud occurs at least partly because the metal ion d orbitals overlap with ligand atom orbitals thus providing paths by which d electrons can, and do, escape to some extent from the metal ion. This effect of ligands in expanding the d electron clouds has been named the *nephelauxetic* (from the Greek, meaning "cloud expanding") effect, and it has been found that the common ligands can be arranged in order of their ability to cause cloud expansion. This order, which is more or less independent of the metal ion, similarly to the spectrochemical series, is in part: $F^- < H_2O < NH_3 <$ oxalate $\sim$ ethylenediamine $< \text{—NCS}^- < Cl^- \sim CN^- < Br^- < I^-$.

Still another evidence of some overlap between metal ion d orbitals and ligand orbitals in compounds which are usually described as "ionic" comes from detailed consideration of antiferromagnetism as it is observed in, for example, the oxides MnO, FeO, CoO, and NiO. As we have already noted (Section 24-11), an antiferromagnetic substance is one which follows a

Curie or Curie-Weiss law at high temperatures but below a certain temperature (the Néel temperature) shows decreasing rather than increasing magnetic susceptibility as the temperature is lowered further. It has been conclusively shown by neutron diffraction studies that this effect is not due to pairing of electron spins within individual ions but is due rather to a tendency of half of the ions to have their magnetic moments lined up in the opposite direction to those of the other half of the ions. Such anti-parallel aligning, in which nearest neighbor metal ions separated by an oxide ion colinear with them have opposed moments, cannot be explained merely by the direct effect, over the intervening distance, of one magnetic dipole on another; their separation is too great to permit an effect of the observed magnitude. Instead, the oxide ions are assumed to participate in the following way. Let us consider an M^{2+}—O^{2-}—M^{2+} set in which each metal ion possesses an unpaired electron. The oxide ion also has pairs of electrons occupying π orbitals. If there is overlap between that d orbital of one metal ion which contains its unpaired electron and a π orbital of the oxide ion, an electron from the oxide ion will move so as to occupy partially the d orbital. In so doing, however, it must have its spin opposed to that of the d electron because of the exclusion principle. The other π electron then has its spin aligned parallel to that of the d electron on the first metal ion. If it moves to some extent into the d orbital of the second metal ion which already contains that metal ion's unpaired d electron, the spin of that d electron will have to be aligned opposite to that of the entering π electron and, hence, opposite to that of the d electron on the first metal ion. The net result is that by this intervention of the oxide ion, which can only occur because there is some finite though not necessarily large degree of overlap between metal d and oxygen π orbitals, we obtain from a system in which the two metal ion d electrons were free to orient their spins independently one in which they are coupled together with their spins antiparallel. If this latter state has slightly lower energy at low temperatures than does the former, then as the temperature is lowered the entire metal oxide lattice will tend to drop into it, and antiferromagnetism will be exhibited. This, in somewhat simplified form, is the currently accepted explanation of antiferromagnetic behavior in most "ionic" salts, oxides, and chalconides, and its key assumption is that these substances are not in fact completely ionic but instead involve some significant degree of overlap between metal ion d orbitals and anion orbitals.

26-9. Effects of Orbital Overlap on the Methods of Crystal Field Theory

We have now recognized that the central assumption of crystal field theory, namely, that the metal ion and the surrounding ligand atoms interact with one another in a purely electrostatic way and do not mix their orbitals or share electrons, is never strictly true. The question then is whether we may still use the crystal field theory, perhaps with certain modifications and adjustments, as a *formalism* to make predictions and calculations even though we do not take its assumptions literally. The answer to this question is in the affirmative provided the degree of orbital overlap is not too great, and experience has now shown that, for most complexes of metals in their normal oxidation states, the amount of overlap is small enough to be manageable in such a way. The crystal field theory so modified to take account of the existence of moderate amounts of orbital overlap is called the ligand field theory. When the amount of orbital overlap is excessive—and this is likely to happen for complexes which contain the metals in unusual oxidation states—we must have recourse to the molecular orbital theory which is outlined in the next section.

The most straightforward modifications of simple crystal field theory which make allowance for orbital overlap involve using all parameters of interelectronic interactions as variables rather than taking them equal to the values found for the free ions. Of these parameters, three are of decisive importance, namely, the spin-orbit coupling constant, λ, and the two Racah parameters, B and C.

The spin-orbit coupling constant plays a considerable role in determining the detailed magnetic properties of many ions in their complexes, for example, the deviations of some actual magnetic moments from spin-only values and inherent temperature dependence of some moments. All studies to date show that in ordinary complexes the values of λ are 70–85% of those for the free ions. It is possible to get excellent agreement between crystal field theory predictions and experimental observations simply by using these smaller λ values.

The Racah parameters are measures of the energy separations of the various Russell-Saunders states of an atom. The energy differences between states of the same spin multiplicity are multiples of B only, whereas the differences between states of different multiplicity are expressed as sums of multiples of both B and C. The basic theoretical treatment from which the expressions for energy differences between Russell-Saunders states of a particular configuration are derived was first given by J. C.

Slater, and the results were expressed in terms of some parameters now known as Slater integrals. The Racah parameters are particular sums and differences of the Slater integrals, chosen in such a way as to make energy differences between states of the same spin explicitly dependent on one parameter only. To illustrate their use, let us take the d^8 (2 positron) system as it occurs in some tetrahedral nickel(II) complexes. As a 2-positron system in a tetrahedral field, it has, qualitatively, the same energy level diagram as a 2-electron system in an octahedral field which we have already shown in Figure 26-14. Now an exact calculation of the energy of the transition, ν_3, from the $^3T_1(F)$ ground state to the $^3T_1(P)$ state gives the result:

$$\nu_3 = (E_P - E_F) + \tfrac{6}{5}\Delta_t$$

In the $[NiX_4]^{2-}$ complexes $(X = Cl^-, Br^-, I^-)$, this transition is observed at $\sim 14,000$ cm.$^{-1}$. It is completely impossible to account for this result if we assume that the energy difference $(E_P - E_F)$ has the same value in these complexes as it has in the free ion, for in the free ion it is about 16,000 cm.$^{-1}$, which is greater than ν_3. The only way out of this paradox is to assume that $(E_P - E_F)$ shrinks to $\sim 70\%$ of the free ion value. Now theory expresses $(E_P - E_F)$ as $15B$, so that this is equivalent to saying that B', the value of this Racah parameter for the Ni^{2+} ion in the complexes is $\sim 70\%$ of B, the value in the free ion. Similarly, it is found that the observed energies of several transitions from the $^3T_1(F)$ ground state to excited singlet states require that their separations from the ground state be reduced to about 70% of the free ion values. This implies that the Racah parameter C is also diminished and by about the same amount as B. Indeed it is a general rule that

$$B'/B \approx C'/C \approx 0.7$$

Moreover, for a series of analogous complexes with different ligands, the B'/B ratios will be in the order required by the nephelauxetic series.

Thus in order to calculate an energy level diagram and/or details of magnetic behavior in ligand field theory, one proceeds in the same manner as in crystal field theory except that, instead of assuming the free ion values for λ, B, and C, one either assumes somewhat smaller ones or leaves them as parameters to be evaluated from the experimental observations. In this way all the computational and conceptual advantages of the simple electrostatic theory are preserved while allowance is made—in an indirect and admittedly artificial way—for the consequences of finite orbital overlap. One also bears in mind that there are other consequences, for example, electron delocalization, of the overlap. This, in essence, is the ligand field theory.

THE MOLECULAR ORBITAL THEORY

26-10. Molecular Orbital Theory for Octahedral Complexes

The molecular orbital theory starts with the premise that overlap of orbitals will occur, to some degree, whenever symmetry permits. It thus includes the electrostatic situation (no overlap) as one extreme, maximal overlapping of orbitals as the other extreme, and all intermediate degrees of overlap in its scope. The first task in working out the MO treatment for a particular type of complex is to find out which orbital overlaps are and are not possible because of the inherent symmetry requirements of the problem. This can be done quite elegantly and systematically using some principles of group theory, but such an approach is outside the scope of this discussion. Instead we shall simply present the results that are obtained for octahedral complexes, illustrating them pictorially. It may be noted that, ultimately, for the experimental inorganic chemist, this pictorial representation is much more important than mathematical details, for it provides a basis for visualizing the bonding and thinking concretely about it.

The molecular orbitals we shall use here will once again be of the LCAO (see page 74) type. Our method for constructing them, which we shall apply specifically to octahedral complexes, will take the following steps.

1. We note that there are nine valence shell orbitals of the metal ion to be considered. Six of these—d_{z^2}, $d_{x^2-y^2}$, s, p_x, p_y, and p_z—have lobes lying along the metal-ligand bond directions (i.e., are suitable for σ bonding), whereas three, namely, d_{xy}, d_{yz}, d_{zx}, are so oriented as to be suitable only for π bonding. Figures 1-7 and 26-1 should be consulted to verify these statements.

2. We shall assume that each of the six ligands possesses one σ orbital; the exact nature of this orbital need not be specified further, unless it is intended to perform a quantitative treatment. These individual σ orbitals must then be combined into six "symmetry" orbitals, each constructed so as to overlap effectively with a particular one of the six metal ion orbitals which are suitable for σ bonding. Each of the metal orbitals must then be combined with its matching symmetry orbital of the ligand system to give a bonding and an antibonding molecular orbital.

3. If the ligands also possess π orbitals, these too must be combined into "symmetry" orbitals constructed so as to overlap effectively with the metal ion π orbitals, and the bonding and antibonding MO's then formed by overlap.

Complexes with No π Bonding. The six σ symmetry orbitals are indicated in Figure 26-24, in which they are illustrated pictorially, expressed algebraically as normalized linear combinations of the individual ligand σ orbitals, and juxtaposed with the metal ion orbitals with which they are matched by symmetry. On the left side of Figure 26-24 are the symmetry symbols, A_{1g}, E_g, and T_{1u}, for these orbitals. These symbols are of group theoretical origin, and they stand for the symmetry class to which belong the metal orbital, the matching symmetry orbital of the ligand system, and the molecular orbitals which will result from the overlap of these two. They are very commonly used simply as convenient labels, but they also carry information. The symbol A_{1g} always represents a single orbital which has the full symmetry of the molecular system. The symbol

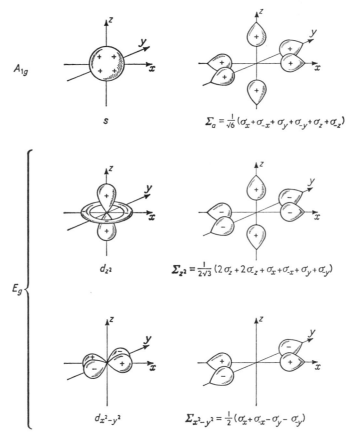

$$A_{1g}$$

s

$$\Sigma_a = \frac{1}{\sqrt{6}}(\sigma_x + \sigma_{-x} + \sigma_y + \sigma_{-y} + \sigma_z + \sigma_{-z})$$

$$E_g$$

d_{z^2}

$$\Sigma_{z^2} = \frac{1}{2\sqrt{3}}(2\sigma_z + 2\sigma_{-z} + \sigma_x + \sigma_{-x} + \sigma_y + \sigma_{-y})$$

$d_{x^2-y^2}$

$$\Sigma_{x^2-y^2} = \frac{1}{2}(\sigma_x + \sigma_{-x} - \sigma_y - \sigma_y)$$

Fig. 26-24.　The six metal ion σ orbitals and their matching ligand symmetry orbitals.

E_g represents a pair of orbitals which are equivalent except for their orientations in space, whereas T_{1u} represents a set of three orbitals which are equivalent except for their orientations in space. The subscripts g and u are used to indicate whether the orbital(s) is centrosymmetric (g from the German *gerade* meaning even) or anticentrosymmetric (u from the German *ungerade* meaning uneven).

The final step now to obtain the molecular orbitals themselves is to allow each metal orbital to overlap with its matching symmetry orbital of the ligand system. As before (page 74), two combinations are to be considered: one in which the matched orbitals unite with maximum positive overlap, thus giving a bonding MO, and the other in which they unite with maximum negative overlap to give the corresponding antibonding MO. Let us illustrate this process for the pair p_z and Σ_z. The results are shown pictorially in Figure 26-25. From the energy point of view, these results may be expressed in the usual type of MO energy level diagram (see page 75), and this is done at the right side of Figure 26-25. It will be noted there

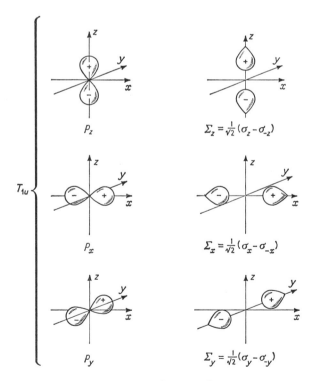

Fig. 26-24 (*continued*)

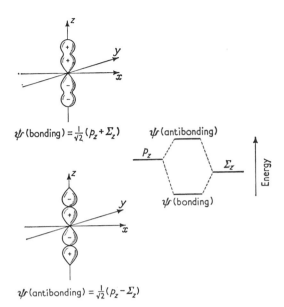

Fig. 26-25. To the left are orbital pictures showing the bonding and antibonding molecular orbitals which are the z components of the T_{1u} sets. To the right is an energy level diagram showing how the energies of the various orbitals are related.

that the p_z and Σ_z orbitals are not assumed to have the same energies, for in general they do not. To a first approximation, the energies of the bonding and antibonding MO's lie equal distances below and above, respectively, the mean of the energies of the combining orbitals.

In just the same way, the other metal ion orbitals combine with the matching symmetry orbitals of the ligand system to form bonding and anti-bonding MO's. The MO's of the same symmetry class—which are equivalent except for their spacial orientations—have the same energies, but orbitals of different symmetry classes do not in general have the same energies, since they are not equivalent. The energy level diagram which results when all of the interactions are considered is shown in Figure 26-26. Here we name the orbitals only by their symmetry designations, using the asterisk to signify that a molecular orbital is antibonding. It should be noted in Figure 26-26 that the three metal ion d orbitals which are suitable for forming π bonds but not σ bonds are given their appropriate symmetry label, T_{2g}, and shown as remaining unchanged in energy, since we are considering ligands which have no π orbitals with which they might interact.

There are certain implications of this energy level diagram deserving of special attention. In general, in molecular orbital diagrams of this type, it

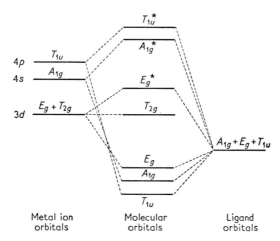

Fig. 26-26. The molecular orbital energy level diagram, qualitative, for an octahedral complex between a metal ion of the first transition series and six ligands which do not possess π orbitals.

may be assumed that, if a molecular orbital is much nearer in energy to one of the atomic orbitals used to construct it than to the other one, it has much more the character of the first one than of the second. On this basis then, Figure 26-26 implies that the six bonding σ MO's, three T_{1u}'s, the A_{1g}, and the two E_g's, have more the character of ligand orbitals than they do of metal orbitals. It can then be said that electrons occupying these orbitals will be mainly "ligand electrons" rather than "metal electrons," though they will partake of metal ion character to some significant extent. Conversely, electrons occupying any of the antibonding MO's are to be considered as predominantly metal electrons. Any electrons in the T_{2g} orbitals will be *purely* metal electrons when there are no ligand π orbitals as in the case being considered.

Let us now look at the center of the MO diagram, where we see the T_{2g} orbitals and, somewhat higher in energy, the $E_g{}^*$ orbitals. The latter, as noted, are predominantly of metal ion d orbital character though with some ligand orbital character mixed in. Is this not the same situation, qualitatively speaking, as we obtained from the electrostatic arguments of crystal field theory? Indeed it is, and, moreover, it is the same result we get from ligand field theory, where we allow for the occurrence of orbital overlap which destroys to some extent the "purity" of the metal ion d orbitals.

To make the comparison of the ligand field and molecular orbital treatments more concrete, let us consider, for example, the particular case of the ferrous ion, Fe^{2+}, which is a d^6 system, in the hexammine ion, $[Fe(NH_3)_6]^{2+}$.

The MO treatment tells us that the $3d_{z^2}$, $3d_{x^2-y^2}$, $4s$, $4p_x$, $4p_y$, and $4p_z$ orbitals of the ferrous ion combine with the appropriate symmetry orbitals made up from the σ orbitals of the six ammonia molecules. The six electron pairs which occupied the σ orbitals of the individual ammonia molecules before they entered into the $[Fe(NH_3)_6]^{2+}$ ion now occupy the six bonding σ MO'S. But, as noted, these will be mainly ligand orbitals in character. The six d electrons of the ferrous ion now find that the lowest unoccupied molecular orbitals are, in order of increasing energy, T_{2g}, $E_g{}^*$, $A_{1g}{}^*$, $T_{1u}{}^*$. As indicated in Figure 26-26, the last two types are of very high energy relative to the T_{2g} and $E_g{}^*$ orbitals and, so far as we know, are never occupied in the ground states of real complexes. Thus the six d electrons must arrange themselves in the T_{2g} and $E_g{}^*$ orbitals. Thus we finally arrive at the same problem as the one treated in connection with crystal field and ligand field theory, namely, how will the d electrons be distributed among the d orbitals (or nearly pure d orbitals) of the metal ion when it is surrounded by six ligands at the apices of an octahedron?

In summary, we may say that the crystal field and ligand field theories focus attention entirely on the metal ion d orbitals, saying nothing at all as to the behavior of the other metal orbitals and the ligand orbitals. It will be clear that so long as we deal with complexes where the metal-ligand interactions are not so extensive as seriously to mix metal and ligand orbitals, this procedure will not be unreasonable. Moreover, we need not be too concerned that the splitting of the d orbitals is attributed exclusively to electrostatic interactions in the crystal field theory, whereas the molecular orbital theory shows that the origin of the splitting is more complex. After all, we do not attempt to calculate Δ from first principles in using the crystal field or ligand field theories: we only consider how its magnitude will influence the properties of the system. Thus the use of the ligand field theory as a *formalism* is quite justified so long as orbital overlaps do not become excessively large.

Complexes with π Bonding. If the ligands have π orbitals, filled or unfilled, it is necessary to consider their interactions with the T_{2g} d orbitals, that is, the d_{xy}, d_{yz}, and d_{zx} orbitals. The most general case is the one where each ligand has a pair of π orbitals mutually perpendicular, making $6 \times 2 = 12$ altogether. From group theory it is found that these may be combined into four triply degenerate sets belonging to the symmetry classes T_{1g}, T_{2g}, T_{1u}, and T_{2u}. Those in the classes T_{1g} and T_{2u} will remain rigorously nonbonding. (We use the terms bonding, nonbonding, and antibonding with reference to the metal-ligand interactions regardless of the character of the orbitals in respect to bonding between atoms within polyatomic ligands.) This is for the simple reason that the metal ion does not possess any orbitals of these symmetries with which they might interact. The T_{1u} set can interact with the metal ion p orbitals, which are themselves a set with T_{1u} symmetry, and in a quantitative discussion it would be necessary to make allowance for this. However, there is reason to believe that this is not too important qualitatively, since the p orbitals are already required for the σ bonding; we shall not consider π bonding by means of T_{1u} orbitals. This then leaves us with only the T_{2g} set of symmetry orbitals to overlap with the metal ion T_{2g} d orbitals.

The ligand π orbitals may be simple $p\pi$ orbitals, as in the Cl^- ion, simple $d\pi$ orbitals as in phosphines or arsines, or molecular orbitals of a polyatomic ligand as in CO, CN^-, or pyridine. When they are simple $p\pi$ or $d\pi$ orbitals, it is quite easy to visualize how they combine to form the proper symmetry orbitals for overlapping with the metal ion orbitals. This is illustrated for $p\pi$ orbitals in Figure 26-27.

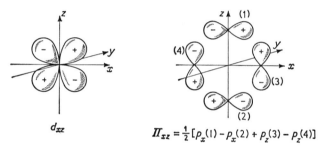

$$\Pi_{xz} = \tfrac{1}{2}[p_x(1) - p_x(2) + p_z(3) - p_z(4)]$$

Fig. 26-27. At the right is the symmetry orbital made up of ligand p orbitals which has the proper symmetry to give optimum interaction with the metal ion d_{xz} orbital shown at the left. There are quite analogous symmetry orbitals, π_{xy} and π_{yz} which are similarly related to the metal ion d_{xy} and d_{yz} orbitals.

The effects of π bonding via molecular orbitals of the T_{2g} type upon the energy levels must now be considered. These effects will vary depending on the energy of the ligand π orbitals relative to the energy of the metal T_{2g} orbitals and on whether the ligand π orbitals are filled or empty. Let us consider first the case where there are empty π orbitals of higher energy than the metal T_{2g} orbitals. This situation is found in complexes where the ligands are phosphines or arsines, for example. As shown in Figure 26-28a, the net result of the π interaction is to stabilize the metal T_{2g} orbitals (they actually also acquire some ligand orbital character in the process) relative to the metal E_g^* orbitals. In effect, the π interaction causes the Δ value for the complex to be greater than it would be if there were only σ interactions.

A second important case is the one in which the ligands possess only filled π orbitals of lower energy than the metal T_{2g} orbitals. As shown in Figure 26-28b, the interaction here destabilizes the T_{2g} orbitals relative to the E_g^* orbitals and thus diminishes the value of Δ. This is probably the situation in complexes of metal ions in their normal oxidation states, especially the lower ones, with the ligands atoms oxygen and fluorine.

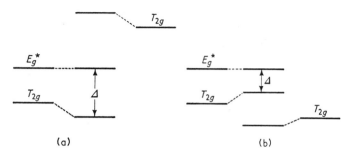

Fig. 26-28.   Energy level diagrams showing how π interactions can affect the value of Δ. (a) Ligands have π orbitals of higher energy than the metal T_{2g} orbitals; (b) ligands have π orbitals of lower energy than the metal T_{2g} orbitals.

There are also important cases in which the ligands have both empty and filled π orbitals. In some, such as the Cl^-, Br^-, and I^- ions, these two types are not directly interrelated, the former being outer d orbitals and the latter valence shell p orbitals. In others, such as CO, CN^-, and pyridine, the empty and filled π orbitals are the antibonding and bonding $p\pi$ orbitals. In such cases the net effect is the result of competition between the interaction of the two types of ligand π orbitals with the metal T_{2g} orbitals, and simple predictions are not easily made. Moreover, the outcome of this competition can be strongly affected, even reversed, by large changes in the metal orbital energies, as, for example, on going from a normal oxidation state of the metal to an unusually low or high one. The following general observations are fairly certain, however. In relation to metal ions of the first transition series in their normal oxidation states, the dominant interaction for the halide ions appears to be with the stable filled $p\pi$ orbitals, thus accounting for the position of these ions at the weak end of the spectrochemical series. With some of the heavier metal ions, such as Pd^{II}, Pt^{II}, Hg^{II}, and Au^{III}, on the other hand, there is reason to believe that the stabilizing action of the unfilled $d\pi$ orbitals becomes dominant. For CO and CN^- in their normal and common complexes, the stabilizing effect of the unfilled antibonding π orbitals is definitely dominant. This leads, in effect, to electron drift from the metal atom to the ligands as will be discussed more fully in Chapter 27.

26-11. MO Theory for Nonoctahedral Complexes

The molecular orbital treatment can be applied to other classes of complexes—planar, tetrahedral, linear, etc.—but the simplicity of the energy level diagrams is rapidly lost as we proceed to the less symmetric situations. The same loss of simplicity also occurs in ligand field theory.

Even for tetrahedral complexes, the analysis becomes more complicated because there is no center of symmetry to keep various kinds of orbitals symmetrically distinct from one another. For instance, the three p orbitals and the three d orbitals, d_{xy}, d_{yz}, and d_{zx}, are in the same symmetry class in a tetrahedral complex and thus they mix with one another. Obviously, this makes it harder to produce simple predictions from simple considerations.

Suffice it to say that it would be beyond the scope of our objectives in this book to treat any other types of complex in detail. In Table 26-5,

TABLE 26-5

Bonding Capabilities of Metal Atom Orbitals
in Some Relatively Symmetrical Complexes

Stereochemistry	σ orbitals	π orbitals	Notes
Linear, LML	s, p_z	p_x, p_y	z axis is molecular axis
	s, d_{z^2}	d_{xz}, d_{yz}	
Tetrahedral, ML_4	s, p_x, p_y, p_z	d_{z^2}, $d_{x^2-y^2}$; d_{xy}, d_{xz}, d_{yz}	Axes as in Figure 26-4
	s, d_{xy}, d_{xz}, d_{yz}	d_{z^2}, $d_{x^2-y^2}$; p_x, p_y, p_z	
Square, ML_4	$d_{x^2-y^2}$, s, p_x, p_y	p_z, d_{xz}, d_{yz}	z axis is perpendicular to plane
	$d_{x^2-y^2}$, d_{z^2}, p_x, p_y		
Trigonal bipyramid, ML_5	s, p_x, p_y, p_z, d_{z^2}	p_x, p_y, p_z; $d_{x^2-y^2}$, d_{xy};	z axis is the three-fold axis
		d_{xz}, d_{yz}	

however, are summarized some useful facts about the bonding capabilities of various metal orbitals in several types of complex.

26-12. Charge Transfer Spectra

When the absorption of radiation causes an electronic transition between two orbitals such that one is more heavily concentrated on one atom while the other is more heavily concentrated on a different atom, we speak of this as a charge transfer transition and the plot of absorption versus wavelength of light as a charge transfer band or spectrum. The actual degree of charge transfer can, of course, vary from the almost negligible to the almost complete, and transitions so classified are found in many classes of compound. We wish here only to note very briefly that for metal complexes there are often charge transfer bands occurring in the ultraviolet region. They are generally far more intense than the d–d bands considered previously, and often even the low energy wing of a strong charge transfer band in the ultraviolet will extend far enough into the visible region to obscure d–d transitions.

At present the exact nature of charge transfer transitions of complexes is known in only a very few cases. The general types which are known to occur in the near ultraviolet part of the spectrum (from about 1800 to 4000 A.) are:

1. Those in which electrons from σ bonding orbitals are excited to empty T_{2g} or E_g^* orbitals. Since the former are predominantly ligand orbitals and the latter mainly metal orbitals, these transitions transfer charge from ligand to metal.

2. Those in which electrons from filled π orbitals localized mainly on the ligands are excited to the E_g^*, A_{1g}^*, or T_{1u}^* orbitals. Again transfer of charge is from ligand to metal.

3. Those in which electrons from bonding σ orbitals are excited to vacant π orbitals localized very greatly on the ligands. In these the charge transfer is modest and from metal to ligand.

A great deal more study will be required before a comprehensive understanding of these spectra is attained.

26-13. The Valence Bond Method

This approach, which was widely used by chemists until the advent of ligand field theory, originated shortly after the formulation of wave mechanics, largely through the efforts of L. Pauling. It may be considered as a direct attempt to invest the Lewis-Langmuir-Sidgwick ideas of the coordinate bond with quantum mechanical validity. Today it is still useful for qualitative explanations of stereochemistry, magnetic properties, etc., and since so much of the literature on coordination chemistry from about 1935 until the late 1950's uses its concepts and terminology, it is necessary that a brief summary be given and that its relationship to the more useful theories already described be indicated.

In its application to an octahedral complex it takes the following form. Each of the ligands is considered as the donor of an electron pair to the metal ion. In order to accept these six electron pairs, the metal ion must have available a set of six, equivalent σ orbitals with their lobes directed toward the apices of an octahedron. As we have already seen (page 70), such a set of orbitals may be constructed out of s, p, and d atomic orbitals in only one way, namely, by hybridizing the following group of orbitals: s, p_x, p_y, p_z, $d_{x^2-y^2}$, d_{z^2}.

For a complex such as $[Cr(NH_3)_6]^{3+}$, the following sort of diagram is then drawn:

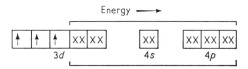

This is intended to convey the following information:

1. It shows, in an entirely qualitative manner, that the order of the energies of the valence shell orbitals is $4p > 4s > 3d$, which is quite correct.

2. It indicates that a set of d^2sp^3 hybrid orbitals has been formed and that these are occupied by electron pairs (xx) donated by the six NH_3 ligands.

3. It shows that three of the d orbitals remain to be occupied by the three $3d$ electrons and that this occurs in accordance with Hund's first rule (maximum number of unpaired spins). It thus predicts that there will be paramagnetism due to three unpaired electrons—which is, of course, correct.

Suppose that we now apply this treatment to $[Co(NH_3)_6]^{3+}$. Since the Co^{3+} ion has six $3d$ electrons, which, following Hund's rule, occupy the orbitals in the following way:

It is evident that the required d^2sp^3 hybrid orbitals cannot be constructed until the necessary two d orbitals are cleared. What is to become of the two electrons removed from them? One possibility is that they be promoted to the next lowest orbitals above the $4p$ orbitals, these being either the $4d$ or $5s$ orbitals, probably the latter. The other alternative is to put them into two of the other $3d$ orbitals; the energy opposing this is twice the average pairing energy for this configuration. Enough was known years ago of the approximate values of the energies required to dispose of the two electrons in each of these two ways to indicate quite surely that the latter way would be the more likely. Accordingly, the following diagram of the electron distribution is obtained:

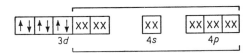

Thus the prediction is made that the $[Co(NH_3)_6]^{3+}$ ion should have no unpaired electrons, and this is correct.

It is evident, however, that it will also be predicted that *all* octahedral complexes of Co^{III} must be diamagnetic. Although virtually every known cobalt(III) complex is diamagnetic, there is at least one indubitable exception, namely, the $[CoF_6]^{3-}$ ion. In this, the Co^{III} has four unpaired electrons just as it does in the free state. In order to account for this, it was proposed that here the metal-ligand bonds are ionic, not covalent as in other cases, and that the d orbitals need not, therefore, be disturbed.

Although this ionic bond postulate might be considered acceptable in the case of $[CoF_6]^{3-}$, there are other cases where its credibility becomes strained. The octahedral complexes of Ni^{II}, which has eight d electrons, provide a good illustration here. With only one definite exception, all of these are paramagnetic (two unpaired electrons) as is the free Ni^{II} ion:

Now, aside from the energetically unacceptable assumption that two $3d$ electrons are promoted to the $4d$ orbitals, the only apparent explanation for the paramagnetism is to assume that all of the octahedral complexes of nickel(II), for example, $[Ni(H_2O)_6]^{2+}$, $[Ni(NH_3)_6]^{2+}$, $[Ni(o\text{-phen})_3]^{2+}$, $[Ni(en)_3]^{2+}$, are ionic. This hardly seems believable, and in the early 1950's another alternative was proposed, namely, that the d^2sp^3 set was made up, using $4d$ (so-called "outer" d) orbitals, thus leaving the $3d$ electrons unaffected. It then became fashionable to speak of high-spin complexes as "outer orbital complexes" rather than "ionic complexes" and low-spin complexes as "inner orbital complexes" rather than "covalent complexes."

Let us now compare this theory with the molecular orbital theory. It is evident that the VB method considers only those orbitals which are identified in MO theory as the bonding σ MO's and the metal d orbitals of the T_{2g} set; it ignores the existence of all of the antibonding orbitals. Therefore, whenever there are more electrons present than can be accommodated in the bonding σ MO's and the T_{2g} d orbitals, it becomes necessary either to introduce the *ad hoc* assumption of ionic bonding or the unsupported postulate of "outer orbital" hybridization.

In addition to its *ad hoc* and artificial prescriptions as to the nature of the bonds, there are various other grounds for regarding the VB treatment of transition metal complexes as unsatisfactory. The major ones are:

1. Because, in its usual form, it pays no attention to the existence of excited states, let alone their energies, it offers no explanation at all for the spectra of complexes.

2. It offers no possibility of predicting or explaining magnetic behavior beyond the level of specifying numbers of unpaired electrons.

3. Its predictive value even for the number of unpaired electrons, and the correlation of this datum with stereochemistry, is often poor or even seriously misleading. For example, it was long assumed that a square nickel(II) complex would be formed by the use of a dsp^2 set of hybrid orbitals, thus leading to the following diagram:

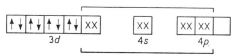

which implies that all square nickel(II) complexes must be diamagnetic. This, in turn, led to the assignment of a tetrahedral configuration (sp^3 hybridization assumed) for all complexes which appeared to be four coordinate and paramagnetic, with the following diagram:

It is now recognized that this so-called "magnetic criterion of stereochemistry" is unreliable because a square nickel(II) complex can be paramagnetic, as shown earlier (page 571). Of course, the VB treatment can be further modified, as for instance by introducing the outer-orbital or ionic-bond postulates for square complexes, or by assuming that a d electron is promoted to the vacant p orbital. Actually, the latter assumption is energetically unlikely and can be positively disproved by detailed magnetic studies, and the assumption of ionic bonding is hardly consistent with the square configuration, since electrostatics would favor the tetrahedral one for an ionic complex.

A related situation occurs with square Cu^{II} complexes, where the VB theory was used to predict that the unpaired electron would occupy a $4p$ orbital. It is now known from details of the electron spin resonance spectra of several square Cu^{II} complexes that the orbital occupied does not have p_z character.

References

Dunitz, J. D., and L. E. Orgel, in H. J. Emeléus and A. G. Sharpe, eds., *Advances in Inorganic Chemistry and Radiochemistry*, Vol. II, Academic Press, New York, 1960, p. 1.

Dunn, T. M., in J. Lewis and R. G. Wilkins, eds., *Modern Coordination Chemistry*, Interscience, New York–London, 1960, p. 229.

George, P., and D. S. McClure, in F. A. Cotton, ed., *Progress in Inorganic Chemistry*, Vol. I, Interscience, New York–London, 1959, p. 38. Effects of crystal field splittings on thermodynamic properties of compounds.

Griffith, J. S., *The Theory of Transition Metal Ions*, Cambridge University Press, 1961. A comprehensive mathematical treatise.

Griffith, J. S., and L. E. Orgel, *Quart. Revs. (London)*, 11, 381 (1957). Ligand field theory.

International Conference on Coordination Chemistry, Proceedings, Chem. Soc. (London), Spec. Publ. No. 13 (1959). A collection of papers.

Ions of the Transition Elements, Discussions Faraday Soc., No. 26 (1958). A collection of papers and discussions.

Jørgensen, C. K. *Absorption Spectra and Chemical Bonding in Complexes*, Pergamon, London, 1961.

Kirschner, S., ed., *Advances in the Chemistry of the Coordination Compounds*, Macmillan, New York, 1961. A collection of papers.

Liehr, A. D., in F. A. Cotton, ed., *Progress in Inorganic Chemistry*, Vol. III, Interscience, New York–London, 1962, p. 281.

McClure, D. S., *Solid State Phys.*, 9, 399 (1959).

Moffitt, W., and C. J. Ballhausen, *Ann. Rev. Phys. Chem.*, 7, 107 (1956).

Nyholm, R. S., *Proc. Chem. Soc. (London)*, 1961, 273. Electron configurations of transition metal elements.

Orgel, L. E., *Quart. Revs. (London)*, 8, 422 (1954). Charge transfer spectra and some related phenomena.

27

Complexes of π-Bonding Ligands: CO, CNR, PR$_3$, NO, etc.

A characteristic feature of the d-group transition metals is their ability to form complexes with a variety of neutral molecules such as carbon monoxide, isocyanides, substituted phosphines, arsines, stibines, or sulfides; and nitric oxide. Very diverse types of complex exist, ranging from binary molecular compounds such as $Cr(CO)_6$ or $Ni(PF_3)_4$ through mixed species such as $Co(CO)_3NO$ and $(C_6H_5)_3PFe(CO)_4$, to complex ions like $[Fe(CN)_5CO]^{3-}$, $[Mo(CO)_5I]^-$, or $[Mn(CNR)_6]^+$.

In many of these complexes, the metal atoms are in low-positive, zero, or low-negative oxidation states. It is a characteristic of the ligands now under discussion that they can stabilize low oxidation states; this property is associated with the fact that the donor atoms of these ligands possess vacant orbitals in addition to lone pairs. These vacant orbitals accept electron density from filled metal orbitals to form a type of π bonding which supplements the σ bonding arising from lone pair donation; high electron density on the metal atom—of necessity in low oxidation states—can thus be delocalized onto the ligands.

We can note at this point that the stoichiometries of many, though not all, of the complexes can be predicted by use of the *inert-gas formalism*. This requires that the number of valence electrons possessed by the metal atom plus the number of lone pair electrons contributed by the ligands equals the number of electrons in the succeeding inert-gas atom. This formalism is of considerable utility in the design of new compounds.

CARBON MONOXIDE COMPLEXES

The most important π-bonding ligand is carbon monoxide. Many of its complexes are of considerable structural interest as well as of importance

TABLE 27-1

The More Important Binary Carbonyls[a]

Compound	Color and form	Melting point, °C.	Comments
$V(CO)_6$	Black crystals	Decomposes at 70; sublimes in vacuo	Paramagnetic (1e); appears to dimerize to $V_2(CO)_{10}$, yellow-orange in solution; Na gives $V(CO)_6^-$
$Cr(CO)_6$ $Mo(CO)_6$ $W(CO)_6$	Colorless crystals	Sublime in vacuo	Octahedral; stable in air, soluble in organic solvents; decompose at 180–200°C.
$Mn_2(CO)_{10}$	Golden crystals	154–155; sublimes in vacuo	Slowly oxidized in air, especially in solution. Metal-metal bond cleaved by Na in THF giving green $Mn(CO)_5^-$; halogens give $Mn(CO)_5X$.
$Re_2(CO)_{10}$	Colorless crystals	177; sublimes in vacuo	Stable in air, otherwise similar to $Mn_2(CO)_{10}$. $Tc_2(CO)_{10}$ is similar.
$Fe(CO)_5$	Yellow liquid	−20; b.p. 103	Ultraviolet on petrol solution gives $Fe_2(CO)_9$
$Fe_2(CO)_9$	Bronze mica-like platelets	Decomposes at 100	Nonvolatile; almost insoluble in organic solvents
$Fe_3(CO)_{12}$	Dark green crystals	Decomposes at ∼140; sublimes in vacuo slowly	Soluble in organic solvents; more chemically reactive than $Fe(CO)_5$
$Co_2(CO)_8$	Orange crystals	51; sublimes in vacuo	Air sensitive, particularly in solution; decomposes at m.p. to $Co_4(CO)_{12}$ (black crystals; decompose at 60°)
$Ni(CO)_4$	Colorless liquid	−25; b.p. 43	Toxic with musty smell; burns readily and decomposes to metal readily

[a] Other less well studied carbonyls are $Ru(CO)_5$, $Ru_2(CO)_9$, $Ru_3(CO)_{12}$, $Os(CO)_5$, $Os_2(CO)_9$, $Os_3(CO)_{12}$, $Rh_2(CO)_8$, $Rh_2(CO)_9$, $[Rh(CO)_3]_n$, $[Rh_4(CO)_{11}]_n$, $Ir_2(CO)_8$, and $[Ir(CO)_3]_n$. Recent X-ray evidence indicates that the $Os_2(CO)_9$ and $Ru_2(CO)_9$ reported in the literature are in fact trinuclear species with probable formula $[M(CO)_4]_3$; there are no bridging carbonyl frequencies in the infrared, and the existence of metal-metal bonds is thus indicated.

industrially and in catalytic and other reactions. Carbonyl derivatives of at least one type are known for all of the transition metals with the exception of Zr and Hf, and it is possible that carbonyls of these elements will be made in due course.

27-1. Binary Molecular Metal Carbonyls

The important binary carbonyls, together with some of their properties, are listed in Table 27-1; the carbonyls of the platinum metals are not especially well characterized. The compounds are all hydrophobic and are inflammable liquids or readily combustible solids; with some exceptions they are soluble in nonpolar organic solvents. Vanadium carbonyl is rather air sensitive and so are the cobalt carbonyls, but the other carbonyls are fairly stable in air, especially the group VI and rhenium carbonyls. The liquids $Fe(CO)_5$ and $Ni(CO)_4$ must be handled with caution since they are highly toxic and their vapors can form explosive mixtures with air; they can be readily destroyed by bromine in an organic solvent.

Preparation. The preparative methods for carbonyls are numerous and varied. Only nickel tetracarbonyl and iron pentacarbonyl can be prepared by direct interaction of the metal, in finely divided reactive form, with carbon monoxide. Nickel carbonyl can be obtained at normal temperature and pressure. Since the reaction

$$Ni + 4CO = Ni(CO)_4$$

is reversible, the carbonyl decomposing readily on warming, it provides a method for obtaining very pure nickel. This method, which was developed by Mond, the discoverer of this first carbonyl, is now operated only at Clydach in South Wales. Iron pentacarbonyl is obtained only by using elevated temperatures and pressures. Both $Ni(CO)_4$ and $Fe(CO)_5$ are commercially available in cylinders.

Cobalt octacarbonyl is readily prepared by treating cobaltous carbonate with carbon monoxide and hydrogen at 250–300 atm. pressure and 120–200°C.:

$$2CoCO_3 + 2H_2 + 8CO = Co_2(CO)_8 + 2CO_2 + 2H_2O$$

Other binary carbonyls are made from the metal halides. The general method is to treat them, usually in suspension in an organic solvent, often tetrahydrofuran, with carbon monoxide at 200–300 atm. pressure and temperatures up to 300°C. in presence of some powerful reducing agent. A variety of reducing agents have been employed—electropositive metals like Na, Al or Mg, trialkyl aluminums, copper, or the sodium ketyl of benzophenone (Ph_2CONa). The detailed course of the reactions is not well known, but when organometallic reducing agents are employed it is likely that unstable organo derivatives of the transition metal are formed as intermediates. Vanadium carbonyl is most easily obtained by the method shown in the equation.

$$VCl_3 + CO + Na \text{ (excess) } \xrightarrow[\text{120°C.; 5000 p.s.i.}]{\text{diglyme}}$$

$$[Na \text{ diglyme}_2][V(CO)_6] \xrightarrow[\text{then sublime 50°C.}]{H_3PO_4} V(CO)_6$$

Rhenium and technetium carbonyls can be obtained by the direct reaction under very high pressure of CO and the heptoxides or the potassium salt of the oxyanion. Since the carbon monoxide in $Fe(CO)_5$ is labile, exchange reactions can occur and Russian workers have shown that the group VI carbonyls can be obtained from interaction of $Fe(CO)_5$ and their halides.

The secondary carbonyls of Fe, Ru, Os, Co, Rh, and Ir are obtained from the primary carbonyls by photodecomposition in solvents or by thermal decomposition. The green $Fe_3(CO)_{12}$ is best obtained by oxidation of the ion $[HFe(CO)_4]^-$ (see page 620) by manganese dioxide in aqueous solution.

The reactions of the binary carbonyls are very numerous and the important ones are mentioned at various places in this chapter. However, Figure 27-1 gives some idea of the types of chemical reaction of two of the more common carbonyls.

Structure and Bonding in Binary Carbonyls. The structures of several of the binary carbonyls are known. Only for $Ni(CO)_4$ is there definite X-ray evidence that the metal atom is bound to carbon, but it is commonly assumed and seems likely that this is quite generally the case. For the binary compounds which have been studied so far the M—C—O grouping appears to be linear or close to linear in *terminal* carbon monoxide groups. In certain polynuclear carbonyls, *bridging* carbon monoxide groups

$$\begin{array}{c} O \\ \| \\ M-C-M \end{array}$$

have been established.

The C—O distances in terminal CO groups are close to 1.16 A., versus 1.13 A. for CO itself, indicating that the C—O bonds have an order very little different from the bond order in carbon monoxide. This conclusion is also supported by the C—O bond stretching force constants which are in the range 15.5–16.5 in dynes/A. versus 19.0 dynes/A. for CO. At the same time, the M—C bonds appear to be somewhat shorter than might be estimated for metal to carbon single bonds, which would imply an M—C bond order greater than unity. Older literature suggests that the M—C bond

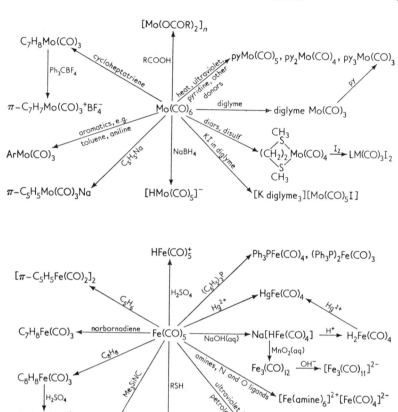

Fig. 27-1. Some reactions of molybdenum and iron carbonyls.

orders are considerably greater than unity, but these estimates are unreliable since the "single bond radii of zero-valent metal atoms" employed are hardly more than guesses and the bond radius for carbon was taken as 0.77 A., which is appropriate for sp^3 hybridized carbon, rather than about 0.70 which would be approximately correct for sp hybridized carbon. Stretching force constants for the M—C bond also indicate that these bonds are about the same strength as single bonds, and estimates of the bond energies from thermal data are also in accord with this view. Now carbon monoxide is an exceedingly weak Lewis base indeed and does not

form complexes with Lewis acids such as aluminum or boron compounds*
or with nontransition metal ions, although a donor such as NH_3 or pyridine
gives complexes with these species as well as transition metals; the lone
pair electrons on carbon could not be expected to give more than a weak
σ bond probably with the electron density remaining close to the carbon
atom. Since transition metal–to–carbon monoxide bonds are so readily
formed, some additional bonding mechanism specific for such metal atoms
must be invoked, and the accepted view now is that the weak M—C
σ bond is supplemented by an M—C π bond.

This situation can be conceived to arise as follows. There is first a dative
overlap of the filled carbon σ orbital with an empty metal σ orbital (Fig.
27-2a) and second a dative overlap of a filled $d\pi$ or hybrid $dp\pi$ metal orbital
with an empty antibonding $p\pi$ orbital of the carbon monoxide (Fig. 27-2b).

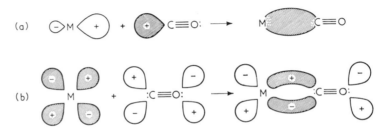

Fig. 27-2.   (a) The formation of the metal←carbon σ bond using an unshared pair
on C atom. (b) The formation of the metal→carbon π bond. The other orbitals on
the CO are omitted for clarity.

It should be noted that this bonding mechanism is *synergic*, since the
drift of metal electrons into CO orbitals will tend to make the CO as a
whole negative and hence to increase its basicity via the σ orbital of carbon;
at the same time the drift of electrons to the metal in the σ bond tends to
make the CO positive, thus enhancing the acceptor strength of the π
orbitals. Thus, up to a point, the effects of σ bond formation strengthen
the π bonding and vice versa. It may be noted here that dipole moment
studies indicate that the moment of an M—C bond is only very low, about
0.5 D., suggesting a close approach to electroneutrality. In valence bond

---

* CO gives no adduct with BF_3 but does form borine carbonyl $H_3\overset{-}{B}—\overset{+}{C}O$. Although
this difference has been attributed to the special nature of borine in being able to enter
into "hyperconjugation," it is just as valid to regard H_3B as being a more powerful
Lewis acid than BF_3 since in the latter the acceptor p_z orbital can be already partially
involved in B—F multiple bonding.

TABLE 27-2

Structures of Mononuclear Carbonyls

Compound	Determined structure	M—C length, A.	Metal σ bonds	Metal π-bonding electron pairs
Ni(CO)$_4$	Tetrahedral	1.84	sp^3	$d_{xy}, d_{yz}, d_{zz}, d_{x^2-y^2}, d_{z^2}$
Fe(CO)$_5$[a]	Trigonal bipyramidal	1.84	dsp^3	$d_{xy}, d_{yz}, d_{zz}, d_{x^2-y^2}$
Cr(CO)$_6$	Octahedral	1.92	d^2sp^3	d_{xy}, d_{yz}, d_{zz}
Mo(CO)$_6$	Octahedral	2.08	d^2sp^3	d_{xy}, d_{yz}, d_{zz}
W(CO)$_6$	Octahedral	2.06	d^2sp^3	d_{xy}, d_{yz}, d_{zz}

[a] Fe(CO)$_5$ behaves as a weak base and can be protonated in concentrated sulfuric acid to give HFe(CO)$_5{}^+$.

formalism the bond can be represented by

$$\overset{-}{M}-\overset{+}{C}{\equiv}O \leftrightarrow M{=}C{=}O$$

From either the MO or the VB viewpoint, back-donation is seen to lower the C—O bond order which should cause the C—O stretching frequencies to be *lower* in metal carbonyls than in free CO. This is observed in all cases,* since the frequencies of terminal C—O groups are, with some exceptions (where they are lower still) noted later, in the range 2100–1850 cm.$^{-1}$, whereas carbon monoxide itself has a stretching frequency of 2146 cm.$^{-1}$. For the mononuclear carbonyls we can summarize the structure and bonding in Table 27-2.

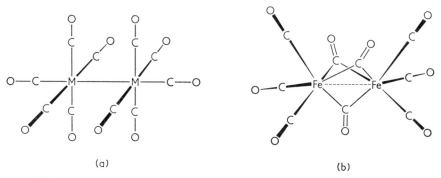

(a)   (b)

Fig. 27-3. Structures of (a) Mn$_2$(CO)$_{10}$ and Re$_2$(CO)$_{10}$ and (b) Fe$_2$(CO)$_9$.

For the *polynuclear carbonyls*, the structures are known in detail only for Mn$_2$(CO)$_{10}$, Re$_2$(CO)$_{10}$ and Fe$_2$(CO)$_9$ (Fig. 27-3), and Co$_2$(CO)$_8$ (Fig. 27-5).

* The positions of absorption lines of carbonyls in solution depend to some extent on the nature of the solvent used.

In manganese carbonyl, the metal–metal bond is of length 2.93 A. and of estimated strength about 34 kcal./mole. Each metal atom can be considered to use d^2sp^3 hybrid orbitals for forming σ bonds to the terminal CO groups and to the other metal atom. Similar metal–metal bonds are known in some other carbonyl complexes, notably in $[\pi\text{-}C_5H_5Mo(CO)_3]_2$ and its tungsten analog; it is a characteristic of these bonds that they can be cleaved by alkali metals or by halogens:

$$Mn_2(CO)_{10} + 2Na \xrightarrow{\text{THF}} Na[Mn(CO)_5]$$
$$Re_2(CO)_{10} + I_2 \xrightarrow{\text{heat}} 2Re(CO)_5I$$

In di-iron enneacarbonyl, $Fe_2(CO)_9$, there are bridging carbon monoxide groups. Such a group has a C—O bond which is of order about two and resembles a ketonic carbonyl group, at least superficially, although there is no evidence to show that bridging carbonyls can react with the chemical reagents that form derivatives with ketones. Each iron atom can be considered to use a set of approximately d^2sp^3 orbitals to bind the three terminal CO's and to form electron pair bonds with the carbon atoms of the bridging CO's. This leaves three d orbitals and five electrons on each iron atom to be accounted for. Two of the d orbitals will be occupied by electron pairs, while the remaining d orbital, so chosen as to have a lobe directed toward the other iron atom, and the remaining electron are used to form an Fe—Fe bond (2.5 A.). This bond need not be very strong; it need only be strong enough to keep the electrons paired at ordinary temperatures in order that the observed diamagnetism of the substance be explained. It is somewhat surprising that $Fe_2(CO)_9$ is highly insoluble in organic solvents, but the crystal structure shows no evidence for polymerization through intermolecular bonding.

Infrared spectra of metal carbonyls have become increasingly useful for gaining some idea of the kinds of CO groups present in a molecule, and the development of criteria for doing this originated with the study of di-iron enneacarbonyl. Its infrared spectrum is shown in Figure 27-4. It will be seen that in addition to the bands around 2000 cm.$^{-1}$, which are characteristic of terminal CO groups, there is a band at 1830 cm.$^{-1}$. This is the region where strong C—O double bonds would be expected to absorb, and the band is thus logically assigned to the bridging CO groups. There is additional evidence which shows that strong absorption bands in the region 1750–1875 cm.$^{-1}$ is generally diagnostic of the presence of bridging CO groups in neutral metal carbonyls provided that they do not contain substituents incapable of π bonding (see page 627).

The structure of $Co_2(CO)_8$ has only recently been determined definitively by X-ray crystallography, and is shown schematically in Figure 27-5. The

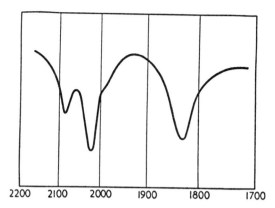

Fig. 27-4.   The infrared spectrum of iron enneacarbonyl in the carbonyl stretching region (ordinate gives the percentage transmission). (F. A. Cotton in J. Lewis and R. G. Wilkins, eds., *Modern Coordination Chemistry*, Interscience, New York–London, 1960, p. 345.)

infrared spectrum of this compound is in good accord with this structure and adumbrated its principal features. The presence of bridging CO groups and the rather low symmetry were inferred from study of the CO stretching frequencies under high resolution. The question of why the cobalt carbonyl uses CO bridges while the dinuclear carbonyls of Mn, Tc, and Re use only metal–metal bonds is an interesting one but as yet unanswered. It will be noticed in Figure 27-5 that there is a vacant bridging position where overlap of two metal orbitals occurs giving what may be regarded as a "bent" Co—Co bond. At very high pressures of CO, $Co_2(CO)_8$ takes up another

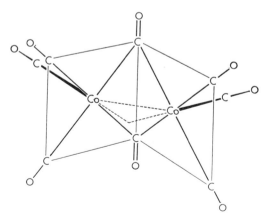

Fig. 27-5.   Proposed structure of $Co_2(CO)_8$.

molecule of CO, perhaps using these metal orbitals and electrons to form a third CO bridge, which would give $Co_2(CO)_9$ a structure similar to that of $Fe_2(CO)_9$ (Fig. 27-3).

The structure of tetracobalt dodecacarbonyl has recently been elucidated with fair certainty by X-ray diffraction study; it contains all three of the structural units so far found in metal carbonyls, namely, terminal carbonyls, metal–metal bonds, and bridging carbonyls. The structure of triiron dodecacarbonyl is only partially known because orientational disorder in the lattice has so far frustrated efforts to locate the CO's relative to the iron atoms. It is known, however, that the iron atoms are situated at the corners of an equilateral triangle. The infrared spectrum shows weak absorption in the bridging region, but it is not certain whether bridging CO groups are present or not.

27-2. Carbonylate Ions and Their Salts

It was first shown by Hieber, who has made many notable contributions to carbonyl chemistry, that if iron pentacarbonyl is treated with aqueous alkali it dissolves to give an initially yellow solution containing the ion $HFe(CO)_4^-$, which on acidification gives a thermally unstable gas $H_2Fe(CO)_4$. Carbonylate anions have now been obtained from most of the carbonyls. Some do not give hydrides on acidification; however, the carbonylate ions of Mn, Re, Fe, and Co certainly do. These and other related hydrides are considered later (page 631).

The carbonylate anions can be obtained in a number of ways—by treating carbonyls with aqueous or alcoholic alkali hydroxide or with amines, sulfoxides or other Lewis bases, by cleaving metal–metal bonds with sodium, or in special cases by refluxing carbonyls with salts in an ether medium. Illustrative examples are:

$$Fe(CO)_5 + 3NaOH(aq) = Na[HFe(CO)_4](aq) + Na_2CO_3(aq) + H_2O$$

$$Co_2(CO)_8 + 2Na/Hg \xrightarrow{THF} 2Na[Co(CO)_4]$$

$$\tfrac{3}{2}Mn_2(CO)_{10} + 6C_5H_5N = [Mnpy_6]^{2+}[Mn(CO)_5]_2^- + 5CO$$

$$Mo(CO)_6 + KI \xrightarrow{diglyme} [K(diglyme)_3]^+[Mo(CO)_5I]^- + CO$$

$$2Co^{2+}(aq) + 11CO + 12OH^- \xrightarrow{KCN(aq)} 2[Co(CO)_4]^- + 3CO_3^{2-} + 6H_2O$$

$$TaCl_5 + CO + Na(excess) \xrightarrow[3000-5000 \text{ p.s.i.}]{diglyme, \sim100°C.} [Na(diglyme)_2][Ta(CO)_6]^-$$

The carbonylate ions, like the binary carbonyls, can be said to obey the inert-gas formalism, and their stoichiometries can be readily predicted.

The ions are usually fairly readily oxidized by air; the alkali metal salts are soluble in water, from which they can be precipitated by large cations such as $[Co(NH_3)_6]^{3+}$ or $[Ph_4As]^+$. The precipitates formed with Zn^{2+}, Cd^{2+}, Hg^{2+}, In^+, Tl^+, Sn^{2+}, Pb^{2+}, and Bi^{3+} ions are insoluble in water and appear to be covalent compounds, being sublimable in some cases and soluble in organic solvents. Little is known of their structures.

The effect of the negative charge of a carbonylate anion on the C—O stretching frequencies is significant. If the values for a series of isostructural species—for example, $Ni(CO)_4$, $Co(CO)_4^-$, $Fe(CO)_4^{2-}$; or $Fe(CO)_5$, $Mn(CO)_5^-$; or $Cr(CO)_6$, $V(CO)_6^-$—are compared, the frequencies *decrease* with *increasing* charge. This indicates that the negative charge on an ion increases the amount of metal–carbon π bonding through which mechanism the negative charge on the metal atom is delocalized onto the carbonyl groups causing the lowering of the C—O stretching frequencies. Although only a few *carbonylate cations* are known, here the opposite effect is observed and the C—O frequencies are *higher* than for a corresponding neutral species; carbonylate cations can be prepared by reactions such as

$$Mn(CO)_5Cl + AlCl_3 \xrightarrow{CO} [Mn(CO)_6]^+[AlCl_4]^-$$

$$\pi\text{-}C_5H_5Fe(CO)_2Cl + NaBPh_4 \xrightarrow{CO} [\pi\text{-}C_5H_5Fe(CO)_3]^+[BPh_4]^-$$

In addition to mononuclear carbonylate anions, a variety of polynuclear species have been obtained, though in several cases these are not fully established. These ions are obtained by the action of aqueous alkali or Lewis bases on binary carbonyls or in other ways, for example,

$$Fe_2(CO)_9 + 4OH^- = [Fe_2(CO)_8]^{2-} + CO_3^{2-} + 2H_2O$$
$$Fe_3(CO)_{12} + 4OH^- = [Fe_3(CO)_{11}]^{2-} + CO_3^{2-} + 2H_2O$$

$$Ni(CO)_4 \xrightarrow[NH_3(l)]{Na\ in} Na_2[Ni_4(CO)_9]$$

$$3Ni(CO)_4 + 3(o\text{-phen}) \rightarrow [Ni^{II}(o\text{-phen})_3]^{2+}[Ni_2(CO)_6]^{2-} + 6CO$$

$$5Fe(CO)_5 + 6HN\text{(}O\text{)} \xrightarrow{100°C} [Fe(HN\text{(}O\text{)}_6]^{2+}[Fe_4(CO)_{13}]^{2-} + 12CO$$

$$Cr(CO)_6 + 3KOH = K[HCr(CO)_5] + K_2CO_3 + H_2O$$
$$2K[HCr(CO)_5] + 4KOH + 3H_2O = K_2[Cr_2(CO)_6(OH)_3H] + 2H_2 + 4HCOOK$$

The structures are probably related to those of the polynuclear carbonyls themselves but are so far little known. The ion $[Fe_2(CO)_8]^{2-}$ has been shown to have a structure with terminal CO groups and a metal–metal bond (cf. $Mn_2(CO)_{10}$).

27-3. Carbonyl Halides

Carbonyl halides, $M_x(CO)_yX_z$, are known for most of the elements forming binary carbonyls but also for Pd, Pt, and Au which do not form binary carbonyls; cuprous and argentous complexes of carbon monoxide also exist (see page 752).

The carbonyl halides are obtained either by the direct interaction of metal halides with carbon monoxide, usually at high pressure, or in a few cases by the cleavage by halogens of polynuclear carbonyls, for example,

$$Mn_2(CO)_{10} + Br_2(l) \overset{40°C.}{=} 2Mn(CO)_5Br \underset{CO,\ 150\ atm.}{\overset{in\ petrol\ at\ 120°C.}{\rightleftarrows}} [Mn(CO)_4Br]_2 + 2CO$$

$$RuI_3 + 2CO \overset{200°C.}{=} [Ru(CO)_2I_2]_n + \tfrac{1}{2}I_2$$
$$2PtCl_2 + 2CO = [Pt(CO)Cl_2]_2$$

A few examples of the halides and some of their properties are listed in Table 27-3. The structures of the carbonyl halides present little problem;

TABLE 27-3

Some Examples of Carbonyl Halides, Isocyanide Complexes,
and Substituted Phosphine and Arsine Complexes

Compound	Form	Melting point, °C.	Comment
$Mn(CO)_5Cl$	Pale yellow crystals	Sublimes	Loses CO at 120°C. in organic solvents; can be substituted by pyridine, etc.
$[Re(CO)_4Cl]_2$	White crystals	Decomposes >250	Halogen bridge cleavable by donor ligands or by CO (pressure)
$[Ru(CO)_2I_2]_n$	Black powder	Stable 200	Halide bridges cleavable by ligands
$[Pt(CO)Cl_2]_2$	Yellow crystals	195; sublimes	Hydrolyzed H_2O; PCl_3 replaces CO
$Cr(CNPh)_6$	Red crystals	156	
$[Mn(CNCH_3)_6]I$	White needles	263	Stable to air; soluble in benzene
$Co(CO)NO(CNC_7H_7)_2$	Orange-red crystals	156	
$RuCl_2(CNCH_3)_4$	Yellow-green crystals		
$Ni(PCl_3)_4$	Yellow crystals	Decomposes >200	Soluble in benzene; stable in dry air
$Ni(PF_3)_4$	Colorless liquid	−55; b.p. 70.7	Resembles $Ni(CO)_4$; stable to H_2O
$Fe(CO)_3(PPh_3)_2$	Yellow crystals	Decomposes >265	Protonates in conc.H_2SO_4
$Mn(CO)_3Cl(AsPh_3)_2$	Yellow crystals	Decomposes >200	Octahedral; stable to air
$Mo[o-C_6H_4(PEt_2)_2]_3$	Red-black needles	236	Very soluble in petrol and oxidized in air

where they are dimeric or polymeric they are invariably bridged through the halogen atoms and *not* by carbonyl bridges, for example, in 27-I and 27-II. The halogen bridges can be broken by numerous donor ligands such as pyridine, substituted phosphines, isocyanides, etc. The breaking of halogen bridges by other donor ligands is not of course confined to the

(27-I)　　　　　　　　　　　　(27-II)

carbonyl halides, and other bridged halides such as those given by olefins (see page 641) can be cleaved. As an example we can use the reaction

$$[\text{Mn(CO)}_4\text{I}]_2 + 4\text{py} = 2\text{Mn(CO)}_3\text{Ipy}_2 + 2\text{CO} \qquad (27\text{-}1)$$

Although the initial product of the cleavage in reaction 27-1 would have been expected to be 27-III, the reaction cannot be stopped without dis-

(27-III)　　　　　　　　　　　　(27-IV)

placement of carbon monoxide and the product 27-IV is isolated. This occurs because in 27-III two of the CO groups are *trans* to each other and thus will be competing across the metal atom for the same metal π-bonding orbitals. Hence in the presence of any ligand like a nitrogen, phosphorus, or arsenic donor, of *lower* π-bonding requirement or capacity compared to CO, one of the *trans* CO groups will be displaced. It follows that the two pyridine (or other) ligands inserted must appear in the *cis* position to each other. This type of labilization of groups in certain stereochemical situations has been discussed elsewhere under the *trans effect* (see page 552). We can also note that in 27-IV, which is resistant to further displacement of CO, three of the octahedral positions are occupied by essentially non-π-bonding ligands, so that the remaining three CO groups must be responsible for the delocalization of the negative charge on the metal atom; they will, however, now have the exclusive use of the electrons in the d_{xy}, d_{yz}, and d_{zx} metal orbitals for π bonding, and hence the metal–carbon bonding is about at a maximum in 27-IV and similar derivatives.

Although carbonyl chlorides, bromides, and iodides have long been known, only recently have carbonyl fluorides, $\text{Pt(CO)}_2\text{F}_8$ and $\text{Rh(CO)}_2\text{F}_3$, been obtained by the action of high pressure CO on the metal fluorides. Although these are sublimable compounds, they are readily hydrolyzed by water and attack organic solvents. Their structures are unknown.

We may finally note that, although Ni(CO)_4 exists, there are no corresponding palladium and platinum carbonyls, while, on the other hand, carbonyl halides of Pd^{II} and Pt^{II} exist but there is no carbonyl halide of Ni^{II} (substituted phosphine halides of Ni^{II} do exist, however). The reasons for these differences probably lie in the electronic structures (Ni, d^8s^2; Pd, d^{10}; Pt, d^9s) and promotional energies involved in forming the complexes in the zero and II oxidation states; it would appear that Ni^0 can form π bonds more readily than Pd^0 or Pt^0, but Pd^{II} and Pt^{II} can form π bonds more readily than Ni^{II}.

27-4. Isocyanide Complexes

Isocyanides are electronically quite similar to carbon monoxide since the —NR group is isoelectronic with the oxygen atom. Thus an isocyanide can enter into the same type of synergic σ–π bonding as does CO:

$$\overset{-}{M}—\overset{+}{C}\equiv NR \leftrightarrow M=C=\overset{..}{N}R$$

However, they do not appear to be capable of back-accepting as extensively as CO, in accord with the lower electronegativity of RN compared to O. As with the carbonyls, there is infrared evidence that some M—C π bonding does occur causing the C—N stretching frequencies to be lowered by 100–200 cm.$^{-1}$ compared to the free isocyanides.

Isocyanide complexes can be obtained by direct substitution reactions of the metal carbonyls and in other ways. Some examples are given in Table 27-3.

Isocyanides generally appear to be stronger σ donors than CO, and various complexes such as $[Ag(CNR)_4]^+$, $[Fe(CNR)_6]^{2+}$, and $[Mn(CNR)_6]^{2+}$ are known where π bonding is of relatively little importance; derivatives of this type are not known for CO. There is no evidence for isocyanides acting as bridging groups.

27-5. Phosphorus and Arsenic Donor Complexes

A variety of trivalent phosphorus, arsenic, and, to a lesser extent, antimony and bismuth, compounds can also give complexes with transition metals; we can include thio derivatives R_2S in this category. Some examples are given in Table 27-3. These donor molecules are of course quite strong Lewis bases and will give complexes with acceptors such as BR_3 compounds where d orbitals are not involved. However, the donor atoms do have empty $d\pi$ orbitals and back-acceptance into these orbitals is conceivable as shown in Figure 27-6. The availability of the d orbitals on the donor atom is very much influenced by the electronegativity of the groups attached to the donor atom. Only phosphorus trifluoride, PF_3, seems to

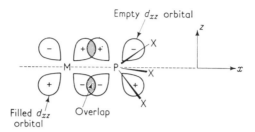

Fig. 27-6. Diagram showing the back bonding from a filled metal d orbital to an empty phosphorus $3d$ orbital in the PX_3 logand taking the internuclear axis as the x axis. An exactly similar overlay occurs in the xy plane using the d_{xy} orbitals.

behave like CO in respect to its donor-acceptor properties; the highly electronegative fluorine atoms would remove electron density from the P atom, reducing the σ donor character but increasing the acceptor character of the $3d$ orbitals. (As for the Ni—C bond in $Ni(CO)_4$, the force constant of the Ni—P bond in $Ni(PF_3)_4$ has been shown to be essentially that of a single bond.) With trialkylphosphines such as $P(C_2H_5)_3$ the opposite effect applies. Thus if we consider nickel, we can obtain $Ni(PF_3)_4$ but only mono- or disubstituted trialkylphosphine nickel carbonyls can be obtained.

Although it has not so far been possible to detect the σ–π synergic bonding in complexes with P, As, or S donors by infrared spectra, as can be done for CO or CNR using C—O or C—N stretching frequencies, it is generally *assumed* that *some* π bonding occurs; however, it is quite small except where the attached groups are highly electronegative. It has been possible, however, in substituted carbonyls such as $Mo(CO)_3L_3$ to study the effect of PR_3 or AsR_3 donors on the C—O stretching frequencies; these show that there is very little difference between the donor or multiple bonding capacities of P or As in similar compounds. Although these ligands are as a class undoubtedly much poorer π bonders than CO, the ability to form stable complexes can be substantially increased by utilizing the chelate effect with ligands such as 27-V through 27-VIII. However, even with ligands

$$
\begin{array}{cccc}
\text{As}(CH_3)_2 & PCl_2 & P(CH_3)_2 & SCH_3 \\
& & (CH_2)_2 & (CH_2)_2 \\
\text{As}(CH_3)_2 & PCl_2 & P(CH_3)_2 & SCH_3 \\
(27\text{-}V) & (27\text{-}VI) & (27\text{-}VII) & (27\text{-}VIII)
\end{array}
$$

of this type it is not too easy to disperse onto the ligand the negative charge built up on the metal atom by donation, so that complete substitution of carbon monoxide in carbonyls is rare. For transition metal atoms in the higher oxidation states these chelating ligands can be readily bound, however, as has been noted elsewhere (see Chapter 25); for higher oxidation states especially, the dialkyldithiocarbamates, for example, $Na[R_2NCS_2]$, are effective complexing agents giving complexes involving the grouping shown in 27-IX.

(27-IX)

It is pertinent here, in discussing P, As, and S donors which have only weak π bonding tendencies, to discuss the effects of substitution in metal carbonyls by nitrogen and oxygen donors such as amines and ethers. Such ligands cannot engage in synergic σ–π bonding because they lack the necessary vacant orbitals for back-acceptance of electron density from filled metal $d\pi$ orbitals. Exceptions to this statement are a few compounds of which pyridine, 1,10-phenanthroline and 2,2'-dipyridyl are typical examples. In these cases the nitrogen atom is in an aromatic ring system with delocalized π orbitals so that there is a possibility of transmission through the donor atom to the π system of some electron density. For aliphatic amines and similar compounds there can be only a pure σ donor function, and complete substitution of CO in carbonyls cannot of course occur. As was noted briefly above, partial substitution can occur, in which case the remaining CO groups must back-accept more negative charge per CO than in the unsubstituted carbonyl. This results in a considerable lowering of the C—O stretching frequencies, and, indeed, comparison of the C—O frequencies in a series of substituted carbonyls provides an excellent method of determining the relative ability of ligands to engage in synergic σ-π bonding. Some representative data are shown in Figure 27-7. It is to be noted that with the nitrogen donors the C—O frequencies can drop well below the so-called "bridging carbonyl" region although no such bridging groups could be present. It is also interesting to note that, if the isoelectronic species 27-X and 27-XI are compared, the positive charge on

(27-X)   (27-XI)

the manganese reverses the flow of negative charge into the M—C—O system to some extent, and there is a rise in the C—O stretching frequencies of about 150 cm.$^{-1}$.

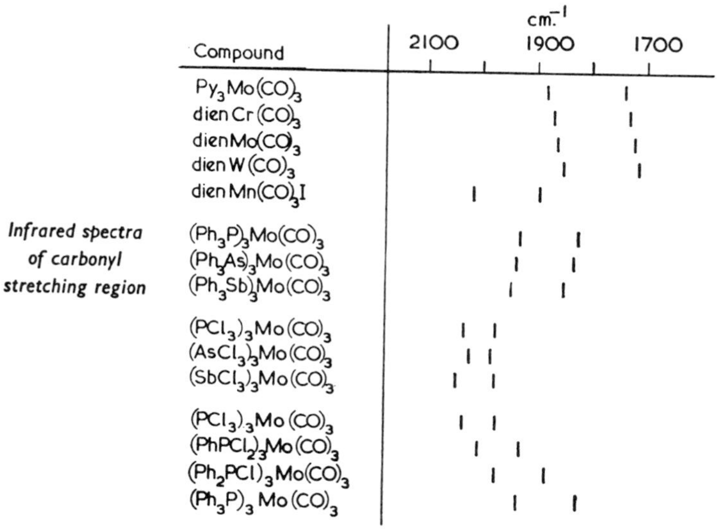

		cm.$^{-1}$	
Compound	2100	1900	1700
Py$_3$Mo(CO)$_3$			
dien Cr (CO)$_3$			
dien Mo(CO)$_3$			
dien W (CO)$_3$			
dien Mn(CO)$_3$I			
(Ph$_3$P)$_3$Mo(CO)$_3$			
(Ph$_3$As)$_3$Mo(CO)$_3$			
(Ph$_3$Sb)$_3$Mo(CO)$_3$			
(PCl$_3$)$_3$Mo(CO)$_3$			
(AsCl$_3$)$_3$Mo(CO)$_3$			
(SbCl$_3$)$_3$Mo(CO)$_3$			
(PCl$_3$)$_3$Mo (CO)$_3$			
(PhPCl$_2$)$_3$Mo (CO)$_3$			
(Ph$_2$PCl)$_3$Mo(CO)$_3$			
(Ph$_3$P)$_3$ Mo (CO)$_3$			

Infrared spectra of carbonyl stretching region

Fig. 27-7. Chart of infrared spectra of various substituted carbonyls. (Reprinted with permission from Abel, Bennett, and Wilkinson, *J. Chem. Soc.* (*London*), **1959**, 2325.)

We may note finally with regard to P, As (Sb, Bi), and S ligands that halide complexes similar to the carbonyl halides are known, for example [PtCl$_2$(PCl$_3$)$_2$]$_2$, and also that in many of the carbonyl complexes with hydrocarbons (Chapter 28, page 647) or complexes with hydrogen as a ligand (page 635), types of complex similar in stoichiometry to the carbonyls can be made either by substitution or by direct methods.

27-6. Nitric Oxide Complexes

The nitric oxide molecule is very similar to the carbon monoxide molecule in forming complexes with transition metals but not with simple acceptors or nontransition metal atoms. However, NO has an additional electron in an antibonding π-MO which is readily lost to give the nitrosonium ion, NO$^+$ (Chapter 12, page 257); the increased strength of the N—O bond caused by loss of this antibonding electron is shown by the increase in the N—O stretching frequency from 1878 cm.$^{-1}$ in free NO to 2200–2300 cm.$^{-1}$ in nitrosonium salts.

1. Complexes regarded as derived from the nitrosonium ion. The majority of NO complexes are best regarded as being formed by donation from the nitrosonium ion (NO$^+$) to the metal atom with M—N back-bonding in a manner entirely analogous to that in the M—C bond in carbonyls. However, since we have initially neutral NO, it is first necessary formally to transfer one electron to the metal atom, reducing its valency by one unit,* for example,

$$M + NO \rightarrow M^- + NO^+ \rightarrow M^{2-}—N^+{\equiv}O^+ \leftrightarrow M^-{=}N{=}O^+$$

Thus if we regard CO, PR_3, etc., as two-electron donors, NO must be considered as a three-electron donor; with this assumption, the formulas of NO compounds can often be predicted using the inert-gas rule, namely, $Fe(CO)_2$ $(NO)_2$, $Co(CO)_3NO$, $Mn(CO)(NO)_3$, etc. Since the formation of an M—NO bond according to the above view would lead to a very polar structure $M^{2-}—N^+{\equiv}O^+$, it would be expected that back-donation from filled metal $d\pi$ orbitals to empty antibonding orbitals on NO would be quite extensive. As for carbonyls, infrared spectra show evidence for this behavior, and, in those complexes in which NO can be considered as donating as NO^+, the frequencies lie in the range 1600–1940 cm.$^{-1}$; the relatively greater lowering of the N—O stretching frequencies compared to C—O frequencies in carbonyls is indicative of more extensive back-donation as expected. The range 1600–1900 cm.$^{-1}$ brackets the free N—O value, suggesting that the average number of back-donated electrons is about one per NO group. The series of ions $[Fe(CN)_5NO]^{2-}$, $[Mn(CN)_5NO]^{3-}$, $[V(CN)_5$ $NO]^{5-}$ illustrates a trend, similar to the one found in carbonylate anions, in which increasing negative charge causes a marked increase in back-donation with a resultant decrease in the N—O stretching frequency. The frequencies are in the same order: 1944, 1730, and 1575 cm.$^{-1}$.

Structural studies of carbonyl nitrosyls show that the M—N—O groups are very nearly, and probably exactly, linear. In π-C_5H_5NiNO, the linearity of the Ni—N—O group is rigorous according to sensitive microwave spectral studies. Whether M—N—O groups are generally linear, however, is still not established, and some deviations from linearity are known. Thus in the dithiocarbamate complex, $[(CH_3)_2NCS_2]_2CoNO$, where the N—O stretching frequency is 1626 cm.$^{-1}$, the Co—N—O chain is far from linear. Substantial deviations from linearity can be attributed to some contri-

$$M—\overset{\displaystyle O}{\underset{\displaystyle N}{|||}}$$

(27-XII)

bution of the type of which 27-XII is the extreme; the latter structure can be compared to the ethylene–metal bond (page 642).

---

* Support for the view that electron transfer to the metal occurs comes from electron spin resonance studies on $K_3[Cr(CN)_5NO]$ where it is found that the unpaired electron spends most of its time in an orbital of the Cr atom. Further, the chromium atom is now formally Cr^I, and the absorption spectra can be interpreted on ligand field theory on this basis.

There are a very large number of complexes which can be formulated as NO^+ complexes, and only a few examples are listed in Table 27-4. Nitric

TABLE 27-4

Some Nitric Oxide (NO^+) Complexes

Compound	Form	Melting point, °C.	Comment
$Mn(NO)_3CO$	Green solid or liquid	27	Unstable in air; soluble in organic solvents
$Co(CO)_3NO$	Red-brown liquid	-1; b.p. 49	N—O str. 1832
π-C_5H_5NiNO	Red liquid	-41; b.p. 144/715 mm.	N—O str. 1820 cm.$^{-1}$
$[Rh(NO)_2Cl]_2$ (or 4)	Black solid		N—O str. 1703, 1605 cm.$^{-1}$; insoluble in H_2O and solvents; halide bridges
$K_2[Fe(CN)_5NO]\cdot H_2O$	Red crystals		So-called nitroprusside; soluble in water; N—O str. 1944 cm.$^{-1}$; OH^- converts NO to NO_2
$K_5[V(CN)_5NO]\cdot H_2O$	Orange crystals		Soluble in water; N—O str. 1575 cm.$^{-1}$
$\left[\begin{array}{c} \overset{\displaystyle Et}{\underset{\diagdown\;\diagup}{\overset{\displaystyle S}{}}} \\ (NO)_2Fe \\ \diagdown \end{array}\right]_2$	Red crystals		Roussin's red salt as ethyl ester

oxide complexes can be prepared in many ways, the simplest being the direct replacement of CO or other ligands by NO gas. Nitrosyl halides, like carbonyl halides, can be obtained by direct interaction of the halide and the gas. In a few instances, special methods are available using nitrite, hydroxylamine, or NOCl as the source of NO. Some preparative examples are:

$$Co_2(CO)_8 + 2NO \xrightarrow{\text{petrol}} 2Co(CO)_3NO + 2CO$$

$$(Ph_3P)_2Ni(CO)_2 + 2NO = (Ph_3P)_2Ni(NO)_2 + 2CO$$

$$K_2CrO_4 + NH_2OH + OH^- + CN^- \rightarrow K_3[Cr^I(CN)_5NO]\cdot H_2O$$

A few nitric oxide compounds merit further discussion.

Brown-ring compounds. The nature of these classical nitrosyl complexes, which were discovered in 1790 by Priestley and have long been used as a test for nitrates, has remained a problem until recently. The compounds can be obtained by direct interaction of aqueous solutions of ferrous salts with nitric oxide; the reaction

$$Fe^{2+}(aq) + NO = FeNO^{2+}(aq)$$

is reversible, and the equilibrium constant has been measured. The NO can be readily swept out of the solution by nitrogen. Infrared studies confirm the presence of a coordinated NO^+ group, since there is a band at 1745 cm.$^{-1}$ and susceptibility measurements give a value of 3.90 B.M. for the complex. The only formulation in keeping with these facts is that of a spin-free d^7 octahedral complex with NO donating three electrons to give, formally, a complex of Fe^I, that is, $[Fe^INO(H_2O)_5]^{2+}$. The brown color is attributable to charge-transfer bands associated with the Fe—N—O system.

Ruthenium forms a large number of NO complexes of exceptional stability; they are discussed later (Section 30-22).

2. Other types of NO complex. We have considered in the last section complexes where NO donates formally as NO^+. It is conceivable that instead of the electron in the antibonding orbital being transferred to the metal, it could stay on the NO which would then donate M←N—O; since NO is paramagnetic, there should be an unpaired spin on the NO in such a complex. In paramagnetic ions such as $[Mn(CN)_5NO]^{2-}$ and $[Cr(CN)_5NO]^{3-}$, it is more realistic to consider the unpaired electron as localized mainly on the metal atom, and electron spin resonance data have been obtained which support this view. In one case, however, that of the NO complex of heme, such data have indicated that the unpaired spin resides mainly on the NO.

Although carbon monoxide bridging groups are well characterized, there is so far only one compound in which NO bridges may be present; they are obviously of very rare occurrence at best.

It remains to discuss the well established group of complexes in which NO is bound to the metal atom in such a manner that we *assume* transfer of an electron *from* the metal to NO and donation from NO^-. The classic case of such complexes is that of the red pentammine or pentacyanocobaltate ions, $[Co(NH_3)_5NO]^{2+}$ and $[Co(CN)_5NO]^{3-}$, which are obtained by the action of nitric oxide on cobaltous solutions containing either ammonia or cyanide. According to their charges and magnetic properties, these must be regarded as analogous to such ions as $[Co(NH_3)_5Cl]^{2+}$ and $[Co(CN)_5Br]^{3-}$ which contain low-spin Co^{III} with $(t_{2g})^6$ $3d$ configurations and, hence, NO^- ions as ligands. Since NO^- is derived from NO by adding an electron to the half-filled π antibonding orbital, it is to be expected that the NO^- stretching frequency would be several hundred wave numbers lower than that of NO itself. Although the compound NaNO has been reported and some evidence presented that it is an NO^- salt rather than a hyponitrite (i.e., $Na_2N_2O_2$), the N—O frequency is not known. In the cobalt complexes the N—O stretching frequencies have been unequivocally shown, using isotopic substitution, to lie in the region 1100–1200 cm.$^{-1}$. Although we have considered NO as donating through the nitrogen atom, some recent studies of the ultraviolet and visible absorption spectra of single crystals of $[Co(NH_3)_5NO]^{2+}$ salts have indicated a close similarity to the spectra of the nitrito complex, $[Co(NH_3)_5ONO]^{2+}$. On this basis it was suggested that the bonding in these cases is M—O—N, which would fit equally well with the stoichiometries and infrared data; however, the matter is not yet definitely settled. There are two cases known in which NO^+ and NO^- groups apparently are present in the same compound. The action of NO on $Fe(CO)_5$ gives black unstable crystals of $Fe(NO)_4$. This compound has been shown to be $(NO^+)_3Fe(NO^-)$, comparable to $(NO)_3FeCl$, since it shows N—O stretching frequencies in both the high- and low-frequency ranges, indicating the presence of both types of nitrosyl grouping. The action of NO on $(Ph_3P)_2Ni(CO)_2$ gives purple crystals of the dinitrosyl $(Ph_3P)_2Ni(NO)_2$, which also must be formulated with both NO^+ and NO^- groups.

27-7. Hydride Complexes

The thermally unstable gaseous carbonyl hydrides, $H_2Fe(CO)_4$ and $HCo(CO)_4$, were the first molecular hydrogen compounds of transition metals to be characterized and, with the exception of some vaguely characterized Ru, Rh, and Ir analogs, remained the only ones for 20 years. In 1955 it was shown that the π-bonding ligand π-C_5H_5 (see page 6 14) can give the thermally stable, yellow, crystalline hydride, $(\pi$-$C_5H_5)_2ReH$. This molecule has proved to have an important pivotal position in hydride chemistry. First, it was in this molecule that high-resolution proton magnetic resonance studies detected a resonance line at extremely high fields; such high-field lines are now known to be diagnostic for transition metal–hydrogen bonds and have enabled M—H bonds to be detected in quite low concentrations in solutions of unstable or air-sensitive unisolable species. Second, in $(\pi$-$C_5H_5)_2ReH$, the region for transition metal–hydrogen stretching frequencies, about 2000 cm.$^{-1}$, was recognized. Hydride complexes have now also been made using substituted phosphine, arsine, and sulfide ligands and with CN^- as ligand; the preparation of complexes with isonitriles may reasonably be expected. It is now recognized in fact that many compounds which were previously thought to be complexes with metals in low oxidation states are actually hydride complexes. For example, the yellow solution obtained by the action of sodium amalgam on aqueous cobalt(II) cyanide has been shown to contain the ion $[HCo^{III}(CN)_5]^{3-}$, and a compound made in 1941 by the reduction of $RhCl_3$ in presence of Ph_2MeAs with hypophosphorous acid, and regarded as a dimeric Rh^{II} complex on account of its diamagnetism, is now known to be $HRhCl_2(AsMePh_2)_3$.

Some examples of hydrides and their properties are listed in Table 27-5.

TABLE 27-5

Some Complexes with Transition Metal to Hydrogen Bonds

Compound	Form	Melting point, °C.	M—H stretch, cm.$^{-1}$	τ value[a]	Comment
$HMn(CO)_5$	Colorless liquid	−25	1783	17.5	Stable liquid at 25°C.; weakly acidic
$H_2Fe(CO)_4$	Yellow liquid, colorless gas	−70	?	21.1	Decomposes at −10°C. giving H_2 + red $H_2Fe_2(CO)_8$
$H_2Fe_3(CO)_{11}$	Dark red liquid		?	25	
$HCo(CO)_4$	Yellow liquid, colorless gas	−26	~1934	20	Decomp. above m.p. giving H_2 + $Co_2(CO)_8$
$HW(CO)_3(\pi\text{-}C_5H_5)$	Yellow crystals	69	1854	17.5	Stable short time in air
$HRe(\pi\text{-}C_5H_5)_2$	Yellow crystals	161	2030	22.8	Stable to 200°C.; acid gives $H_2Re(\pi\text{-}C_5H_5)_2{}^+$
$HPtCl(PEt_3)_2$	Colorless crystals	82	2183	26.5	
$HFe(CO)_3(PPh_3)_2{}^+$	Yellow	—	?	17.6	Formed by protonation in H_2SO_4
$[HCo(CN)_5]^{3-}$	Colorless or pale yellow	—	?	22	Made in aqueous solution

[a] τ value is position of high-resolution proton magnetic resonance line in parts per million referred to tetramethylsilane reference as 10.00.

It is pertinent to note at this point that the characterization of alkyls of transition metals where π-bonding ligands are present (see page 658), has rather closely followed the line of development of hydrides, and, in many respects, the cases, for example, L_nM—CH_3 and L_nM—H, are very similar. Thus many compounds have obviously similar stoichiometries, namely, $CH_3Mn(CO)_5$ and $HMn(CO)_5$, $(R_3P)_2Pt(CH_3)_2$ and $(R_3P)_2PtHCl$, $\pi\text{-}C_5H_5$ $Fe(CO)_2CH_3$ and $\pi\text{-}C_5H_5Fe(CO)_2H$, etc. The thermal and air resistance of like derivatives similarly increase with the atomic number of the metal atom, for example, the order is Cr < Mo < W for $\pi\text{-}C_5H_5M(CO)_3R$ where R is H or CH_3. Although metal species with metal–hydrogen or metal–alkyl group bonds are known in absence of π-bonding ligands, such derivatives are usually thermally unstable with respect to the metal, very air sensitive, or both. Although there is probably very little difference in the *strength* of M—H or M—R bonds in the two cases—an indication being the fact that both gaseous binary transition metal hydrides stable only under spectroscopic conditions and stable hydrides, L_nMH, have infrared bands in the 2000 cm.$^{-1}$ region—the presence of π-bonding ligands (a) tends to deny positions in the coordination sphere to attacking ligands or reagents, (b) causes spin-pairing with the removal of unpaired electrons which would be chemically susceptible to attack, and (c) in contrast to non-π-

bonding ligands, minimizes charge separations in M—L bonds which would be positions of attack by certain reagents.

The term "stability" is a much misused one and requires more careful usage than it is usually given. The failure of a compound to decompose thermally under certain conditions, or to interact with a reagent, does not necessarily tell us anything about the bond strengths; for the hydrides and alkyls such data are as yet nonexistent.

1. *The carbonyl hydrides.* These compounds can be obtained by acidification of the appropriate alkali carbonylates or in other ways. Examples of the preparations are:

$$NaCo(CO)_4 + H^+(aq) = HCo(CO)_4 + Na^+(aq)$$

$$Fe(CO)_4I_2 \xrightarrow{\text{NaBH}_4 \text{ in THF}} H_2Fe(CO)_4$$

$$Mn_2(CO)_{10} + H_2 \xrightarrow[200°C.]{200 \text{ atm.}} 2HMn(CO)_5$$

$$Co + 4CO + \tfrac{1}{2}H_2 \xrightarrow[150°C.]{50 \text{ atm.}} HCo(CO)_4$$

$$2RhS + H_2O + 9CO + 4Cu \xrightarrow[150°C.]{200 \text{ atm.}} 2HRh(CO)_4 + CO_2 + 2Cu_2S$$

The iron and cobalt carbonyl hydrides form pale yellow solids or liquids at low temperatures and in the liquid state begin to decompose above about -10 and $-20°C.$, respectively; they are relatively more stable in the gas phase, however, particularly when diluted with carbon monoxide. They both have revolting odors and are readily oxidized by air.

The hydrides are not very soluble in water but in water they behave as acids, ionizing to give the carbonylate ions:

$$\begin{array}{ll}
HMn(CO)_5 = H^+ + [Mn(CO)_5]^- & pK \sim 7.1 \\
H_2Fe(CO)_5 = H^+ + [HFe(CO)_5]^- & pK_1 \sim 4.4 \\
HFe(CO)_5^- = H^+ + [Fe(CO)_4]^{2-} & pK_2 \sim 14 \\
HCo(CO)_4 = H^+ + [Co(CO)_4]^- & \text{strong acid}
\end{array}$$

It was established some years ago by electron diffraction that for $H_2Fe(CO)_4$ and $HCo(CO)_4$ the $M(CO)_4$ skeletons are nearly tetrahedral and there is evidence that the $Mn(CO)_5$ skeleton is probably approximately the same as that of $Fe(CO)_5$, but in all three cases the skeletons are distorted. It does appear, however, that the hydrogen atom does not occupy a definite bonding position as do, for example, halogen atoms in stoichiometrically analogous carbonyl halides; that is, $HMn(CO)_5$ and $H_2Fe(CO)_4$ are not octahedral. The question of where and how the hydrogen atoms are bound in view of the fact that they cause only slight distortion of the skeletal symmetry was a vexed one until quite recently. It is now known that the earlier suggestions that the hydrogen atom was bound to oxygen or carbon are incorrect and that there is definitely direct metal–hydrogen bonding. Thus broad-line proton magnetic resonance studies on solid $H_2Fe(CO)_4$ have shown that the Fe—H distance is only about 1.1–1.2 A. Since the radius of the metal atom itself is also of this order of magnitude, the hydrogen atom can certainly be regarded as bound to the iron atom. The carbonyl hydrides in high-resolution nuclear magnetic resonance also show the high-field resonance characteristic of M—H bonds, so that in view of the short M—H distance it could be argued that the hydrogen atom is buried in the electron density of the metal atom. The large shift to the high field here and also in other complex hydrides could, however, well be due to indirect effects attributable to counter magnetic fields induced in the metal atoms by the external field. These are matters which are not yet settled.

Although evidence for an M—H bond should also be obtainable from infrared spectra, only in $HMn(CO)_5$ and $HRe(CO)_5$ has such a frequency been detected with complete certainty (at 1783 and 1832 cm.$^{-1}$, respectively). Quite recently evidence has been presented indicating that the Co—H stretching frequency is probably at or near 1934 cm.$^{-1}$. Since all other hydride species for which spectra are available have bands between 1720 and 2200 cm.$^{-1}$, the failure to detect stretching frequencies in $H_2Fe(CO)_4$ may be due to experimental difficulties, since the compound is not only thermally unstable but can exchange its acidic hydrogen atoms quite rapidly with water adsorbed on apparatus. For $H_2Fe(CO)_4$, the direct M—H bonding is quite consistent with the great difference (10^9) between k_1 and k_2; such large separations are found only where both dissociable protons are bound to the same atom (as in H_2S, k_1/k_2 is about 10^7; cf. page 138).

The carbonyl hydrides can act as hydrogen transfer reagents in non-aqueous media, for example,

$$\pi\text{-}C_5H_5Fe(CO)_2H + CCl_4 = CHCl_3 + \pi\text{-}C_5H_5Fe(CO)_2Cl$$

and many such hydrogen transfer reactions are known. Cobalt carbonyl hydride is considered to be the main catalytic species in hydroformylation reactions where monoolefins are converted to aldehydes and subsequently to alcohols by the action of hydrogen and carbon monoxide at high temperature and pressure in the presence of cobalt carbonyl (page 659).

Polynuclear carbonyl hydrides corresponding to the polynuclear carbonylate ions are also known, of which $H_2Fe_3(CO)_{11}$ is an example.

2. Other hydrides. The important di-π-cyclopentadienylmetal hydrides are mentioned later (page 650). Other hydride complexes in which there are also π-bonding ligands attached to the metals Re, Fe, Ru, Os, Rh, Ir, Pd,

Pt, Ni, and Co can be made by the action of reducing agents such as hydrazine, hypophosphorous acid, lithium aluminum hydride, etc., on the appropriate halides or in other ways. Some examples are:

$$trans\text{-}(Et_3P)_2PtCl_2 \xrightarrow{\text{KOH, } C_2H_5OH} (Et_3P)_2PtClH$$

$$RhCl_3 + 3Ph_2MeAs \xrightarrow{H_2P(OH)_2} (Ph_2MeAs)_3RhCl_2H$$

$$\pi\text{-}C_5H_5Fe(CO)_2Cl \xrightarrow[\text{in THF}]{NaBH_4} \pi\text{-}C_5H_5Fe(CO)_2H$$

$$Co^{2+}(aq) + CN^-(aq) \xrightarrow{Na/Hg} [HCo(CN)_5]^{3-}$$

$$Fe + 2o\text{-}C_6H_4(PEt_2)_2 + H_2 \xrightarrow{200°C.} [o\text{-}C_6H_4(PEt_2)_2]_2FeH_2$$

Some of the phosphine and arsine complexes are thermally stable as well as being stable to oxidation by air; the stability is highest with the heaviest metals. It has been possible with the platinum compounds, $trans\text{-}L_2PtXH$, to study the effects on the Pt—H stretching frequency of different phosphines, L, and different anions, X. For a given phosphine, the frequencies decrease in the order $NO_3 > Cl > Br > I > NO_2 > CN$. This order, which is the order of increasing *trans* effect, is consistent with the view that increasing *trans* effect of a ligand is associated with increased weakening of the bond in a *trans* position to it.

Unlike the case of the carbonyl hydrides, where the hydrogen atom appears to have a rather small effect on the geometry, in the di-π-cyclopentadienylmetal derivatives this does not appear to be the case, nor is it apparently so in the only hydride complex so far studied by X-rays, namely, $trans\text{-}(Et_3P)_2PtBrH$ (Fig. 27-8). Here the H atom has replaced a bromide

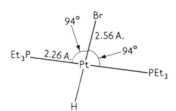

Fig. 27-8. Structure of $trans\text{-}(Et_3P)_2PtBrH$; the hydrogen atom is not detected by X-rays. (P. G. Owston, J. M. Partridge, and J. M. Rowe, *Acta Cryst.*, **13**, 246 (1960).)

ion in the normal planar complex; the Pt—Br bond appears to be rather long, implying some ionic character consistent with its lability.

It has also been shown that borohydride in aqueous solution can displace other ions in normal octahedral complexes and in suitable cases this can lead to hydride complexes with non-π-bonding ligands,

$$trans\text{-}[Rhen_2Cl_2]^+ \xrightarrow{\quad BH_4^-(aq) \quad} = trans\text{-}[Rhen_2ClH]^+$$

The borohydride ion here acts as a source of the highly nucleophilic hydride ion in aqueous solution.

Transition metal–hydrogen bonds can also be obtained by protonation of suitable complexes dissolved in very strong acids such as sulfuric, trifluoroacetic, or boron trifluoride aquate. The complexes must have lone pairs or at least nonbonding electrons present. The protonated species can be detected by the characteristic high-field proton resonance line. The protonation of $(\pi\text{-}C_5H_5)_2M$ compounds is noted later (page 650), but other examples are:

$$(Ph_3P)_2Fe(CO)_3 + H^+ = (Ph_3P)_2Fe(CO)_3H^+$$

$$[\pi\text{-}C_5H_5Mo(CO)_3]_2 + H^+ = (\pi\text{-}C_5H_5)_2Mo_2(CO)_6H^+$$

A final comment seems appropriate. Although spectroscopic data indicate little difference in the M—H bond in the various hydride complexes, some of these compounds behave as acids, for example $HCo(CO)_4$, whereas some, like $(\pi\text{-}C_5H_5)_2WH_2$, behave as bases. It might thus appear that hydrogen could be bound as H^+ or H^-, and this would affect the formal oxidation state of the metal. Thus if we regarded $HCo(CO)_4$ as having bound H^+, then Co is in the -1 oxidation state as in $[Co(CO)_4]^-$. Applying the same reasoning to $[HCo(CN)_5]^{3-}$ would give Co^I, but since this ion can be obtained by hydride displacement on $[Co^{III}(CN)_5Br]^{3-}$ it is more realistic to regard the hydride as also containing Co^{III}. The acid, neutral, or base character of the species with M—H bonds undoubtedly depends on the same sort of factors that govern the acid, neutral, or base character of nontransition metal hydrides which also have covalent bonds such as SiH_4, CH_4, NH_3, H_2O, or HCl. The electronegativity of the grouping to which hydrogen is attached and the presence or absence of nonbonding electrons will govern the acid-base character, whereas the ease of electron transfer from the hydrogen to the metal atom will determine the thermal stability.

References

Cable, J. W., and R. K. Sheline, *Chem. Revs.*, **56**, 1 (1956). Bond hybridization and structure in the metal carbonyls.

Chatt, J., P. L. Pauson, and L. M. Venanzi, "Metal Carbonyls and Related Compounds," in H. Zeiss, ed., *Organometallic Chemistry* (*American Chemical Society Monograph*, No. 147), Reinhold, New York, 1960, p. 468.

Emeléus, H. J., and J. S. Anderson, "Carbonyls and Related Compounds," in *Modern Aspects of Inorganic Chemistry*, 3rd ed., Routledge and Kegan Paul, London, 1960.

Green, M. L. H., *Angew. Chem.*, **72**, 719 (1960). Review of transition metal hydride complexes.

Hieber, W., W. Beck, and G. Braun, *Angew. Chem.*, **72**, 795 (1960). A review of carbonylate anions.

Lewis, J., *Sci. Progr.*, **47**, No. 187, 506 (1959). Chemistry of NO complexes.

———, *Sci. Progr.*, **49**, No. 193, 67 (1961). A review of transition metal hydride complexes.

——— and C. C. Addison, *Quart. Revs. (London)*, **9**, 115 (1955). Chemistry of NO complexes.

Malatesta, L., "Chemistry of Isocyanide Complexes," in F. A. Cotton, ed., *Progress in Inorganic Chemistry*, Vol. I, Interscience, New York–London, 1959, p. 283.

Nyholm, R. S., *Proc. Chem. Soc. (London)*, **1961**, 273. Detailed discussion of electron configuration and structure of transition metal complexes with special reference to metal carbonyls.

Sternberg, H. W., and I. Wender., *International Conference on Coordination Chemistry*, *Chem. Soc. (London)*, *Spec. Publ.*, No. 13 (1959). Metal carbonyls as intermediates in organic reactions.

28

Organometallic Compounds of Transition Metals

Although a few compounds with transition metal–carbon bonds have been known for a long time, it is only comparatively recently, principally during the years of intense activity following the discovery of the compound di-π-cyclopentadienyliron, $(\pi\text{-}C_5H_5)_2Fe$, that it has become clearly recognized that the formation of bonds to carbon is a general and characteristic property of all of the d-group transition metals. The metals can form a variety of compounds in which there is a normal σ bond to carbon although the binary alkyls and aryls are usually much less stable thermally and chemically than those in which other ligands, notably π-bonding ligands, are in addition bound to the metal atom. The unique characteristics of d orbitals also allow certain types of unsaturated hydrocarbons and some of their derivatives to be bound to metals in a nonclassical manner to give molecules or ions with structures which have no counterpart elsewhere in chemistry. Not only are a wide range of organo compounds of different types isolable, but labile species play an important role in many metal-complex catalyzed reactions of olefins, acetylenes, and their derivatives. Many of these reactions also involve the incorporation of carbon monoxide and/or hydrogen into unsaturated molecules.

28-1. Olefin Complexes

About 1830, Zeise, a Danish pharmacist, characterized a compound of stoichiometry $PtCl_2 \cdot C_2H_4$ which is now known to be a dimer with chlorine bridges; he also isolated, from the reaction products of chloroplatinite with ethanol, salts of the ion $[C_2H_4PtCl_3]^-$. Although the structure of these ethylene complexes was not in fact settled until a few years ago, they were the first organometallic derivatives of transition metals to be prepared.

It was later found that certain metal halides or ions other than Pt^{II}, notably Cu^I, Ag^I, Hg^{II}, and Pd^{II}, formed complexes when treated with a variety of olefins. Thus cuprous chloride in aqueous suspension will absorb ethylene, both components dissolving well beyond their normal solubilities and in a 1:1 mole ratio. Solid cuprous halides also absorb some gaseous olefins, but the dissociation pressures of the complexes are quite high. The interaction of silver ions especially, with a variety of unsaturated substances, has been studied by physical measurements such as distribution equilibria between an aqueous and an organic solvent phase. The results can be accounted for in terms of equilibria of the type:

$$Ag^+(aq) + \text{olefin} = [Ag\ \text{olefin}]^+(aq)$$

Certain trends were observed, for a series of olefins, which could be correlated with steric and inductive factors. In some cases, the interaction of hydrocarbons with Ag$^+$ ions gives crystalline precipitates which are often useful for purification of the olefins. Thus cyclooctatetraene or bicyclohepta-2,5-diene on shaking with aqueous silver perchlorate (or nitrate) give white crystals of stoichiometry olefin·AgClO$_4$ or 2olefin·AgClO$_4$, depending on the conditions. Benzene with AgNO$_3$, AgClO$_4$, or AgBF$_4$ also gives crystalline complexes and the structure of C$_6$H$_6$·AgNO$_3$ is shown in Figure 28-1, from which it will be noted that the metal ion is asymmetrically located with respect to the ring.

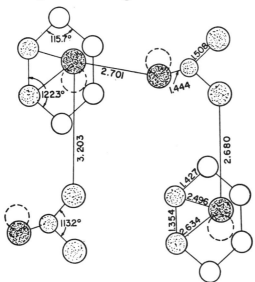

Fig. 28-1. The structure of benzene silver nitrate. (Reprinted with permission from H. G. Smith and R. E. Rundle, *J. Am. Chem. Soc.*, **80**, 5075 (1958).)

Although until quite recently it was believed that olefin complexes were confined to the elements at the heavy end of the transition series as well as Cu^I and Ag^I, there is now an array of well-characterized olefin complexes of the elements of groups VI–VIII, while evidence for rather thermally unstable complexes of titanium and vanadium has also been obtained. Some examples of olefin complexes are given in Table 28-1.

TABLE 28-1

Some Representative Olefin Complexes of Transition Metals

Olefin	Complex	Properties
Ethylene	$K[C_2H_4PtCl_3]$	Pale yellow, water-soluble salt
Cyclopentene	$\pi\text{-}C_5H_5Re(CO)_2C_5H_8$	Colorless crystals soluble in organic solvents; quite stable in air
Bicyclohepta-2,5-diene (norbornadiene)	$C_7H_8Fe(CO)_3$	Yellow distillable liquid
Cycloocta-1,5-diene	$[C_8H_{10}RhCl]_2$	Orange crystalline solid; halide bridge cleavable by p-toluidine, etc.
Cyclopentadiene	$\pi\text{-}C_5H_5CoC_5H_6$	Red crystals; gives $(\pi\text{-}C_5H_5)_2Co^+$ ion with acids
Octafluorocyclohex-1,3-diene	$C_6F_8Fe(CO)_3$	Colorless, air-stable, and volatile crystalline solid
Cycloheptatriene	$C_7H_8Mo(CO)_3$	Red crystals; loses H^- with $(C_6H_5)_3C^+BF_4^-$ to give $C_7H_7Mo(CO)_3^+$

Olefin complexes are generally prepared by direct interaction of the olefin with a metal halide or complex, usually a carbonyl. Only a few isolable compounds of monoolefins are known, and the most stable complexes are those given by chelating diolefins such as bicyclohepta-2,5-diene, which is the strongest complexing olefin known, conjugated olefins, and cyclic olefins, as in equations 28-1, 28-2, and 28-3. Some olefin complexes can be

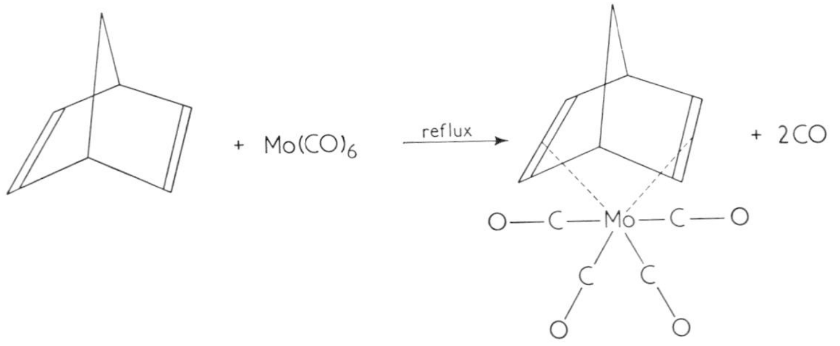

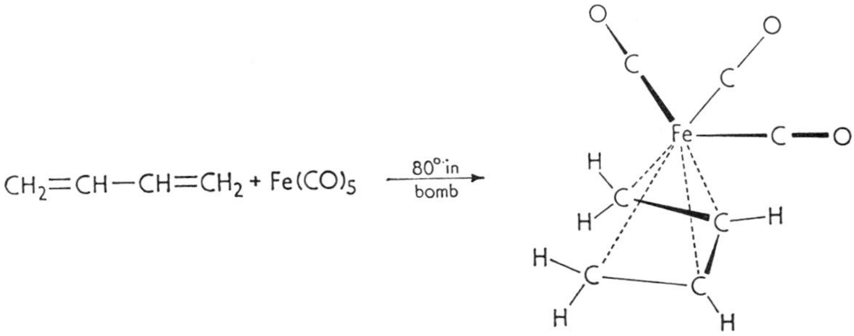

$$CH_2{=}CH{-}CH{=}CH_2 + Fe(CO)_5 \xrightarrow[\text{bomb}]{80° \text{ in}} \qquad (28\text{-}2)$$

$$+ RhCl_3 \cdot 3H_2O \xrightarrow[\text{ethanol}]{\text{reflux in}} \qquad (28\text{-}3)$$

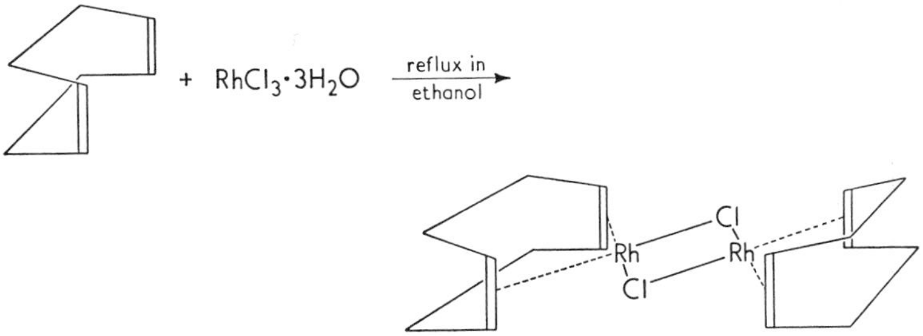

obtained indirectly, notably by hydride ion attack (eq. 28-4) on the "sandwich" or delocalized bonded complexes to be discussed later. The cyclo-

$$(\pi\text{-}C_5H_5)_2Co^+ + H^- \xrightarrow[\text{in THF}]{NaBH_4} \pi\text{-}C_5H_5CoC_5H_6 \qquad (28\text{-}4)$$

pentadiene derivatives obtained in this way are noteworthy in that it has been shown that one of the hydrogen atoms (H_α on the metal side of the ring) gives an intense and unusually low ($\sim$2750 cm.$^{-1}$) C—H stretching frequency. In addition, this particular hydrogen atom is the one that is placed on the ring by hydride ion attack, as well as being the one that is removed by chemical agents which can remove hydride ion, for example, acids, $(C_6H_5)_3C^+BF_4^-$, N-bromosuccinimide, etc. Thus we have reversible hydride ion transfer reactions such as that shown in equation 28-5.

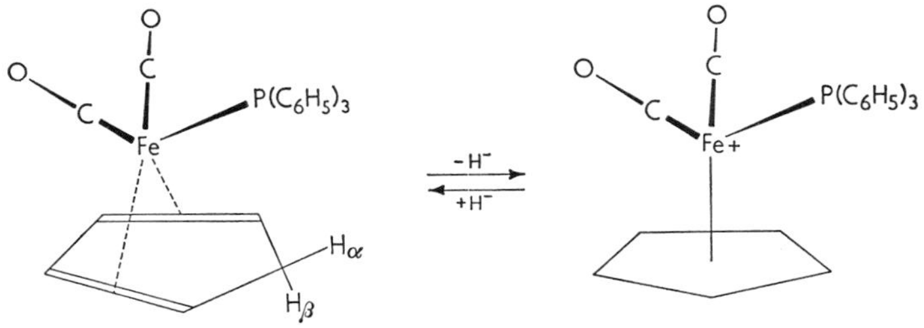

$$(28\text{-}5)$$

It now appears that reversible hydride ion additions or abstractions are quite general reactions of cyclic systems which contain, respectively, an odd or even number of π electrons involved in bonding to the metal.

Structure and Bonding in Olefin Complexes. The nature of the bonding of olefins to metal atoms is still not fully understood, but it does seem quite clear that localized σ bonds between the metal atom and a particular carbon atom do not exist. The bonding is generally attributed to interaction between π electrons in the unsaturated molecule and hybrid orbitals of the metal, but the extent to which electron density is localized between the metal atom and the double bond is not clear. Comparatively few olefin complexes have yet been studied by X-ray diffraction; two of the known structures are given in Figures 28-2 and 28-3.

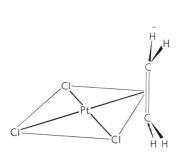

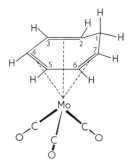

Fig. 28-2. The structure of the ion of Zeise's salt, $[C_2H_4PtCl_3]^-$.

Fig. 28-3. The structure of cycloheptatrienemolybdenum carbonyl, $C_7H_8Mo(CO)_3$. The bond distances are as follows: C_1—C_2 = C_7—C_1 = 1.53 A.; C_2—C_3 = C_6—C_7 = 1.34 A.; C_3—C_4 = C_5—C_6 = 1.42 A.; C_4—C_5 = 1.38 A.; Mo—C_{2-7} = 2.32 A.

During their studies on silver–olefin complexes, Winstein and Lucas proposed, in the framework of valence bond theory, that the olefin–metal bond could be represented by resonance among canonical forms such as 28-I.

$$
\begin{array}{ccc}
\underset{C}{\overset{H_2}{}} & \underset{C}{\overset{H_2}{}} & \underset{C^+}{\overset{H_2}{}} \\[2pt]
\| \quad Ag^+ \leftrightarrow & \Big\backslash \quad Ag \leftrightarrow & \Big/ \quad Ag \\[2pt]
\underset{H_2}{\overset{C}{}} & \underset{H_2}{\overset{C^+}{}} & \underset{H_2}{\overset{C}{}} \\[4pt]
(28\text{-Ia}) & (28\text{-Ib}) & (28\text{-Ic})
\end{array}
$$

Specific interaction involving metal d orbitals was not invoked. An alternative molecular orbital treatment, first used by Dewar, is now more

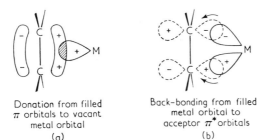

Donation from filled
π orbitals to vacant
metal orbital
(a)

Back-bonding from filled
metal orbital to
acceptor π* orbitals
(b)

Fig. 28-4. Diagrams showing the molecular orbital view of olefin–metal bonding according to Dewar. The donor part of the bond is shown in (a), and the back-bonding part in (b).

fashionable. This view, illustrated in Figure 28-4, is that the metal to olefin bond consists of two parts: (a) overlap of the π-electron density of the olefin with a σ type acceptor orbital on the metal atom; (b) a "back-bond" resulting from flow of electron density from filled metal d_{xy} or other $d\pi–p\pi$ hybrid orbitals into *antibonding* orbitals on the carbon atoms. This view is thus similar to that discussed for the bonding of carbon monoxide and similar weakly basic ligands and involves some "double bond" character in the metal–olefin bond—though how much is uncertain. The polarity of the donor bond (μ bond) is thus $(C_2H_4)^+$—M^-, whereas in the "back-bond" it is in the opposite direction so that these two modes of dative bonding mutually reinforce each other electrostatically and can lead to electroneutrality. The C—C distance in ethyleneplatinum compounds is ~1.47 A., showing the reduction in the C—C bond order of the olefin on coordination. It may be noted that olefin complexes are like the carbonyls in being almost exclusively diamagnetic, and, if each double bond is considered to contribute two electrons, the inert-gas rule holds and provides a useful guide to the prediction of stoichiometries.

It appeared at one time that conjugated and unconjugated olefins behaved differently toward metals, but there now seems to be little difference

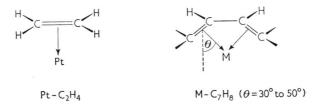

Pt–C_2H_4 M–C_7H_8 ($\theta = 30°$ to $50°$)

Fig. 28-5. Diagrams showing the different angles between the metal atom and the double bond in olefin complexes.

in the types of compounds they can form. It also seems that it is not necessary to have the metal atom lying exactly along the direction of maximum
π-electron density of the olefin, as in the ethyleneplatinum compounds,
since the angles of overlap of metal and hydrocarbon orbitals can be quite
different as shown in Figure 28-5, but the criteria for bonding of olefins with
different geometries is not fully established.

28-2. "Sandwich"-Bonded Compounds

The first compound of this class, reported in 1951, is di-π-cyclopenta-
dienyliron, $(\pi$-$C_5H_5)_2$Fe, now called *ferrocene*. Although it was at first
supposed that this exceedingly thermally stable compound had a structure
with σ bonds to iron (28-II), it was shown by a combination of chemical and

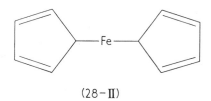

(28 – II)

physical studies, culminating with X-ray confirmation, that the correct
structure is that shown in Figure 28-6. Although in the crystal of ferrocene

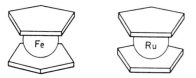

Fig. 28-6. Staggered and eclipsed configurations found for ferrocene and rutheno-
cene, respectively, in their crystals. (G. Wilkinson and F. A. Cotton in F. A. Cotton, ed.,
Progress in Inorganic Chemistry, Vol. I, Interscience, New York–London, 1959, p. 22.)

the two symmetrical five-membered rings are staggered, in the corresponding ruthenium compound (Fig. 28-6) they are eclipsed. From various
lines of physical and chemical evidence, it seems certain that the barrier to
rotation of the rings about the metal to ring axis is very small. The relative orientations of the rings in crystals are probably mainly a reflection
of packing forces in the lattice.

The recognition of the "sandwich" concept of bonding has stimulated a
vast amount of work not only on cyclopentadienyl derivatives but also on
similar systems with four-, six-, seven-, and eight-membered carbon rings.

We discuss first the cyclopentadienyl system since this is by far the most important and forms a greater variety of isolable compounds than the other systems.

π-Cyclopentadienyl Metal Complexes. The hydrocarbon cyclopentadiene is a weak acid ($pK_a \sim 20$) and with a variety of bases can give salts of the symmetrical cyclopentadienide ion, $C_5H_5^-$; like other ring systems which give "sandwich" compounds, this ion has the "aromatic" sextet of π electrons. The most general and useful method for the preparation of all cyclopentadienyl compounds is the reaction of sodium cyclopentadienide with a metal halide in tetrahydrofuran, ethylene glycol dimethyl ether, dimethylformamide, or similar solvent. The sodium salt is obtained by treating dispersed sodium with the hydrocarbon in tetrahydrofuran (in which it is quite soluble). Thus we have

$$C_5H_6 + Na \xrightarrow{\text{THF}} C_5H_5^- + Na^+ + \tfrac{1}{2}H_2$$
$$C_5H_5^- + MR^+ = C_5H_5MR$$

Although the reaction of sodium with cyclopentadiene is approximately that of the above equation, about 10% of the olefin is reduced by the hydrogen, and in liquid ammonia the reaction is

$$3C_5H_6 + 2Na = 2C_5H_5^-Na^+ + C_5H_8$$

An alternative method useful in some cases employs a strong base, preferably diethylamine, for example,

$$2C_5H_6 + 2(C_5H_5)_2NH + FeCl_2 \xrightarrow[\text{amine}]{\text{in excess}} (\pi\text{-}C_5H_5)_2Fe + 2(C_5H_5)_2NH_2Cl$$

Since the $C_5H_5^-$ anion functions as a uninegative ligand, the di-π-cyclopentadienyl metal complexes are of the type $[(\pi\text{-}C_5H_5)_2M^{n+}]X_{n-2}$, where $n+$ is the oxidation state of the metal M and X is a uninegative ion. Hence in the $+2$ oxidation state we obtain neutral, sublimable, and organic-solvent-soluble molecules like $(\pi\text{-}C_5H_5)_2Fe$ and $(\pi\text{-}C_5H_5)_2Cr$ and in $+3$, $+4$, and $+5$ oxidation states species such as $(\pi\text{-}C_5H_5)_2Co^+$, $(\pi\text{-}C_5H_5)_2TiCl_2$, and $(\pi\text{-}C_5H_5)_2NbBr_3$, respectively.

All of the $3d$ elements have been obtained in neutral molecules, and, with the exception of the manganese compound discussed below, they appear to have the same structure and essentially the same bonding as in ferrocene; however, only ferrocene is air stable, the others being sensitive to destruction or oxidation by air; the stability order is Ni > Co > V ≫ Cr $\sim$ Ti.

The cationic species, several of which can exist in aqueous solutions provided these are acidic, behave like large unipositive ions such as Cs^+ and can be precipitated by silicotungstate, chloroplatinate, tetraphenylborate, and other large anions. The $(\pi\text{-}C_5H_5)_2Co^+$ ion is remarkably stable and is unaffected by concentrated sulfuric and nitric acids, even on heating.

Some typical π-cyclopentadienyl compounds are given in Table 28-2.

TABLE 28-2

Some Di-π-cyclopentadienyl Metal Compounds

Compound	Appearance; melting point, °C.	Unpaired electrons	Other properties
$(\pi\text{-}C_5H_5)_2Fe$	Orange crystals; 174; monoclinic	dia.	Oxidized by Ag^+(aq), dil. HNO_3; $\pi\text{-}Cp_2Fe = \pi\text{-}Cp_2Fe^+$, $E^0 = +0.3$ V. (vs. SCE); stable thermally to $\sim$500°C.
$(\pi\text{-}C_5H_5)_2Cr$	Scarlet crystals; 173; monoclinic	2	Very air sensitive; soluble acids giving C_5H_6 and blue cation, probably $[\pi\text{-}C_5H_5CrCl(H_2O)_n]^+$
$(\pi\text{-}C_5H_5)_2Ni$	Bright green; 173 (d.); monoclinic	2	Fairly air stable as solid; oxidized to Cp_2Ni^+; NO gives $\pi\text{-}CpNiNO$; Na/Hg in C_2H_5OH gives $\pi\text{-}CpNiC_5H_7$
$(\pi\text{-}C_5H_5)_2Co^+$	Yellow ion in aqueous solution	dia.	Forms numerous salts and a stable strong base (absorbs CO_2 from air); thermally stable to *ca.* 400°C.
$(\pi\text{-}C_5H_5)_2TiCl_2$	Bright red crystals; 230	dia.	Sl. sol. H_2O giving $\pi\text{-}Cp_2TiOH^+$; C_6H_5Li gives $\pi\text{-}Cp_2Ti(C_6H_5)_2$; reducible to $\pi\text{-}Cp_2TiCl$; Al alkyls give polymerization catalyst
$(\pi\text{-}C_5H_5)_2WH_2$	Yellow crystals; 163	dia.	Moderately stable in air, soluble benzene, etc.; soluble in acids giving $\pi\text{-}Cp_2WH_3^+$ ion

In addition to the true "sandwich" compounds, many other sandwich-bonded compounds exist in which only one $\pi\text{-}C_5H_5$ ring is present, together with other ligands such as CO, PR_3, NO, C_5H_6, C_6H_7, etc. A few of these compounds, their methods of production and reactions are shown below and in Figure 28-7.

$$Co_2(CO)_8 \xrightarrow{C_5H_6} \begin{cases} \xrightarrow{200°} \pi\text{-}Cp_2Co \xrightarrow{H^+} \pi\text{-}Cp_2Co^+ \xrightarrow[\substack{90\% \\ \text{ethanol}}]{NaBH_4} \pi\text{-}CpCo(C_5H_6) \\ \xrightarrow{25°} \pi\text{-}CpCo(CO)_2 \end{cases}$$

$$\pi\text{-}Cp_2V + CO \xrightarrow[200°]{100\text{--}200 \text{ atm.}} \pi\text{-}CpV(CO)_4 \xrightarrow{HCl + O_2} \pi\text{-}CpVOCl_2$$

$$\pi\text{-}Cp_2Ni + NO \xrightarrow{\text{hexane}} \pi\text{-}CpNiNO$$

$$CrCl_3 + NaC_5H_5 \xrightarrow[NO]{THF} \pi\text{-}CpCr(NO)_2Cl \xrightarrow{RMgBr} \pi\text{-}CpCr(NO)_2R$$

Since the $\pi\text{-}C_5H_5$ ring has a resemblance to benzene in its C—C bond order, it was anticipated that the ring would have aromatic character. For compounds whose properties allow them to survive the reaction conditions, this possibility has been amply realized. The most extensive study has been made with ferrocene, which has been shown to undergo a large number of

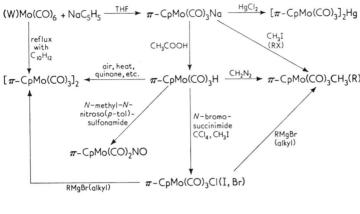

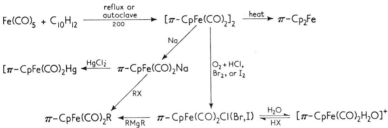

Fig. 28-7.   Some reactions of mono-π-cyclopentadienyl compounds.

reactions such as Friedel-Crafts acylation, metalation by butyllithium, sulfonation, etc.; there is now an exceedingly extensive organic chemistry of ferrocene, and hundreds of derivatives of all types are known. A mono-cyclopentadienyl compound, π-$C_5H_5Mn(CO)_3$, has also been shown to undergo aromatic substitution reactions.

Bonding in π-Cyclopentadienylmetal Compounds. A detailed theoretical account of the bonding between the metal atoms and the C_5H_5 rings is beyond the scope of this text; although numerous different approaches have been made, there are still unsettled problems. However, the essential feature of the bonding is fairly easy to grasp. We can consider the ferrocene molecule to result from a combination of a ferrous ion with two $C_5H_5^-$ anions or from a combination of an iron atom with two C_5H_5 radicals. There are advantages for the former, and it is more realistic in view of the methods of preparation. Each $C_5H_5^-$ anion is planar and is a symmetrical pentagon in shape. Each carbon atom of the ring has a p_z orbital perpendicular to the plane of the ring and these p_z (or $p\pi$) orbitals combine into π molecular orbitals. Five MO's are formed, and the lower three of these are occupied by three electron pairs. It is the overlap of these filled MO's with empty orbitals on the iron atom which gives rise to the bonding. There may also be some back-bonding between filled orbitals on the iron atom and the unfilled MO's of the $C_5H_5^-$ anion in a manner analogous to the bonding in ethylene or CO complexes. "Back-bonding" is not required, however, since in compounds such as $(\pi\text{-}C_5H_5)_2TaH_3$ there are no filled orbitals on the tantalum atom; but, where filled nonbonding orbitals exist, the "back-bonding" effect can enhance the metal to ring bonding.

As an example of the overlap of a filled π MO of the $C_5H_5^-$ ring with an empty d orbital of the iron atom—and in fact the one believed to be of major importance in the bonding—consider the diagrams in Figure 28-8.

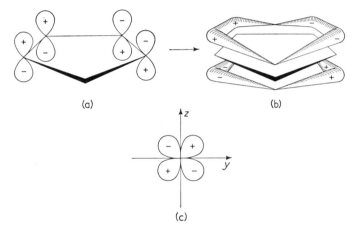

Fig. 28-8.   Diagrams showing the molecular orbital view of the bonding in di-π-cyclopentadienyl compounds of the ferrocene type (see text).

In Figure 28-8a the p_z orbitals of four of the carbon atoms of a C_5H_5 ring are shown. In Figure 28-8b the general nature of the MO formed by overlap of these orbitals is sketched. This is one of the three π MO's which contains a pair of electrons. Figure 28-8c shows the d_{yz} orbital of the ferrous ion which is empty and which also has the xz plane as a nodal plane. The ring MO and the iron d_{yz} orbital are thus symmetrically compatible and can overlap to give a bond. The primary metal to ring bond is thus a two-electron covalent bond. The empty d_{zx} orbital of iron can overlap with a filled π MO similar to Figure 28-8b on another $C_5H_5^-$ ring, thus producing $(\pi\text{-}C_5H_5)_2Fe$ with the "sandwich" geometry. In order to account in detail for all features of the structure, all of the possible overlaps must be considered. In a very crude way we can envisage the existence of a circularly

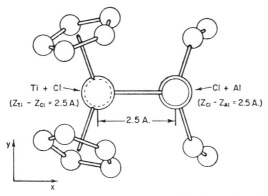

Ti + Cl →
$(Z_{Ti} - Z_{Cl} = 2.5 A.)$

← Cl + Al
$(Z_{Cl} - Z_{Al} = 2.5 A.)$

← 2.5 A. →

Fig. 28-9. The structure of $(\pi\text{-}C_5H_5)_2TiCl_2Al(C_2H_5)_2$. (Reprinted with permission from Natta, Corradini, and Bassi, *J. Am. Chem. Soc.*, **80**, 755 (1958).)

symmetric tube of π-electron density on the $C_5H_5^-$ anion overlapping with a circularly symmetric set of orbitals on the metal atom. Although it was originally believed that there was some special feature of the bonding that gave the parallel ring sandwich configuration as in ferrocene, this view had to be modified to account for monocyclopentadienyl metal compounds, and recently further modification has been required by the realization that even in di-π-cyclopentadienyl compounds the two rings need not be parallel. Effective bonding can still be obtained when the metal to ring axes are at an angle; in the compound $(\pi\text{-}C_5H_5)_2TiCl_2Al(C_2H_5)_2$ the rings have been shown to be distinctly nonparallel (Fig. 28-9). For an angular ring sym-

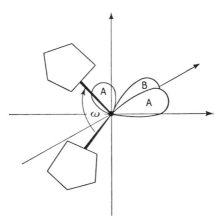

Fig. 28-10. Proposed structure of di-π-cyclopentadienyl metal compounds of the type $(\pi\text{-}C_5H_5)_2MX_n$ where the metal to ring axes are not colinear and are at some angle ω where $150 < \omega < 180°$.

metry it can be shown that three essentially nonbonding orbitals on the metal atom remain; these can either form bonds, as in $(\pi\text{-}C_5H_5)_2TaH_3$, can be occupied by stereochemically important "lone pair" electrons, or can be vacant as in $(\pi\text{-}C_5H_5)_2Ti(C_6H_5)_2$. This view resulted mainly from the observations that the compounds $(\pi\text{-}C_5H_5)_2ReH$ and $(\pi\text{-}C_5H_5)_2WH_2$ behave as *bases* and can be protonated by aqueous acids to give the ions $(\pi\text{-}C_5H_5)_2$ ReH_2^+ and $(\pi\text{-}C_5H_5)_2WH_3^+$, respectively, and that in a very strong acid— boron trifluoride hydrate—even ferrocene can be protonated to give the ion $(\pi\text{-}C_5H_5)_2FeH^+$. Nuclear resonance studies show that in $(\pi\text{-}C_5H_5)_2TaH_3$ and $(\pi\text{-}C_5H_5)_2WH_3^+$ two of the hydrogen atoms are equivalent and the third different. The structures of the species can be represented as in Figure 28-10, where the orbitals A and B can hold either hydrogen atoms or lone pairs which can be protonated (cf. NH_3).

Ionic Cyclopentadienides. It was noted above that the alkali metals give ionic derivatives such as $C_5H_5^-Na^+$. On electrostatic grounds, we could expect that for a dipositive metal, M^{2+}, in which there is no possibility of covalent bonding due to d overlap, the two $C_5H_5^-$ rings would align themselves on opposite sides of the metal atom to give the same sandwich structure as in ferrocene. In two cases, $Mg(C_5H_5)_2$ and Mn $(C_5H_5)_2$, this appears to be so. The manganese compound is anomalous among the other neutral $(C_5H_5)_2M$ compounds; it reacts with water like C_5H_5Na, for example, and with ferrous chloride in tetrahydrofuran gives ferrocene quantitatively. Also the free molecule has five unpaired electrons like the Mn^{2+} ion; in addition the pure crystals show anomalous antiferromagnetic behavior like other manganous ionic salts such as MnF_2.

It is convenient to note here that the lanthanide elements also form crystalline ionic derivatives, $M(C_5H_5)_3$, which are extremely thermally stable, although they are sensitive to air and to water. They also undergo quantitative ionic reactions, for example,

$$2Pr^{3+}(C_5H_5^-)_3 + 3Fe^{2+} \overset{THF}{=} 3(\pi\text{-}C_5H_5)_2Fe + 2Pr^{3+}$$

Other Symmetrically Delocalized Hydrocarbon Metal Complexes. It has been noted that the $C_5H_5^-$ ion has a sextet of π electrons. Other ring systems with this sextet could be expected to give "sandwich" compounds

Cyclobutadienyl (hypothetical) $(28\text{-}IIIa)$ Cyclopentadienyl $(28\text{-}IIIb)$ Arene $(28\text{-}IIIc)$ Cycloheptatrienyl (tropylium) $(28\text{-}IIId)$

similar to the π-cyclopentadienyl compounds. We have thus the iso-π-electronic series shown in 28-III. All four ring systems have been bound to metal atoms, although only $C_5H_5^-$ and arenes give L_2M type compounds.

Cyclobutadienylmetal Compounds. Although there has been much speculation on the existence of four-membered ring complexes, particularly since they have been postulated to act as intermediates in reactions of acetylenes with metal carbonyl complexes, only a few established cases are known.

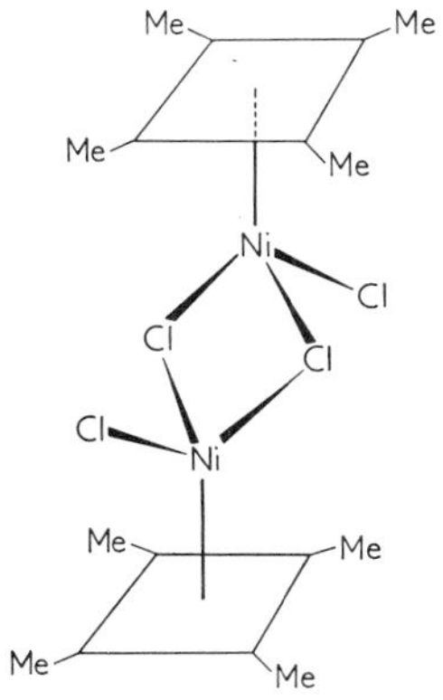

Fig. 28-11.   The structure of the compound $[(CH_3C)_4NiCl_2]_2$.

The first of these was the methyl-substituted nickel compound (Fig. 28-11), which was obtained by the reaction of nickel carbonyl with the compound 28-IV.

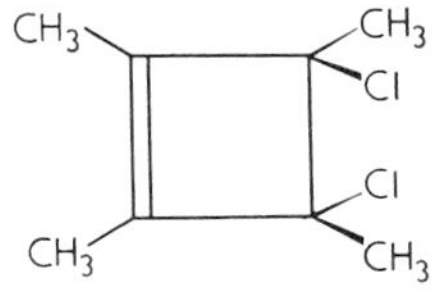

(28–IV)

It has also been shown that the compound $(C_6H_5CCC_6H_5)_2Fe(CO)_3$, obtained by reaction of diphenylacetylene with $Fe_3(CO)_{12}$ under appropriate conditions, contains the tetraphenylcyclobutadiene system, with an essentially square ring, bound to the iron atom.

Arene Metal Compounds. The arene compounds have had a curious history. They were prepared for chromium by Hein over 30 years ago by the reaction of chromic chloride with phenylmagnesium bromide; acid hydrolysis of the reaction mixture gave yellow solutions which were believed to contain σ-bonded phenyl cationic derivatives such as $(C_6H_5)_3Cr^+$. It has now been shown that these "polyphenylchromium" compounds are in fact diarene chromium cations with benzene, di- or triphenyl units "sandwich" bonded to the metal, such as 28-V.

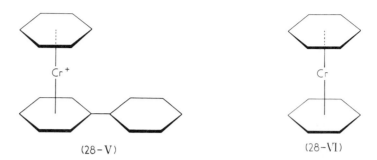

(28–V)   (28–VI)

The prototype neutral compound, dibenzenechromium, $(C_6H_6)_2Cr$ (28-VI), has been obtained from the Grignard reaction of chromic chloride, but a more effective method of wider applicability to other metals is the direct interaction of an aromatic hydrocarbon with a transition metal halide in presence of aluminum powder as a reducing agent and halogen acceptor and aluminum chloride as a Friedel-Crafts type activator. Although the neutral species are formed directly in the case of chromium, the usual procedure is to hydrolyze the reaction mixture with dilute acid which gives the cations $(C_6H_6)_2Cr^+$, $(mesitylene)_2Ru^{2+}$, etc. In several cases these cations can be reduced to the neutral molecules by reducing agents such as hypophosphorous acid.

Dibenzenechromium, which forms dark brown crystals, is much more sensitive to air than ferrocene, with which it is isoelectronic; it does not survive the reaction conditions of aromatic substitution reactions. As with the π-C_5H_5 compounds, a variety of complexes with only one arene ring have been prepared, for example,

$$C_6H_5CH_3 + Mo(CO)_6 \overset{\text{reflux}}{=} C_6H_5CH_3Mo(CO)_3 + 3CO$$

$$C_6H_6 + Mn(CO)_5Cl + AlCl_3 = C_6H_6Mn(CO)_3{}^+AlCl_4{}^-$$

Some X-ray measurements on dibenzenechromium have indicated that the carbon–carbon bond lengths are not equivalent. However, this conclusion is still not entirely certain since there appears to be some doubt as to the adequacy of the experimental data for detecting relatively small differences in bond lengths.

π-*Cycloheptatrienyl or Tropylium Compounds.* The seven-membered ring complexes are few and not too stable; they have not been prepared directly from the $C_7H_7^+$ ion itself, but only indirectly, for example,

$$C_7H_8Mo(CO)_3 + (C_6H_5)_3C^+BF_4^- \overset{\text{in petrol}}{=} \pi\text{-}C_7H_7Mo(CO)_3^+BF_4^- + (C_6H_5)_3CH$$

$$\pi\text{-}C_5H_5V(CO)_4 + C_7H_8 \xrightarrow{\text{reflux}} \pi\text{-}C_5H_5V\pi\text{-}C_7H_7$$

Although no X-ray studies are available, nuclear magnetic resonance studies show the equivalence of the seven hydrogen atoms in $[C_7H_7Mo(CO)_3]^+$ and the probable structure of this ion is shown in 28-VII.

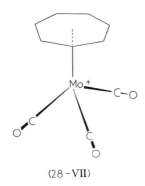

(28-VII)

Cyclooctatetraene Compounds. Although some cyclooctatetraene complexes appear to have the olefin bound in the boat form with only two of the double bonds utilized in metal bonding—thus being chelate olefin complexes—the reaction of the olefin with $Fe_3(CO)_{12}$ or $Fe(CO)_5$ gives a red crystalline product $C_8H_8Fe(CO)_3$ (28-VIIIa). This compound, like C_8H_8

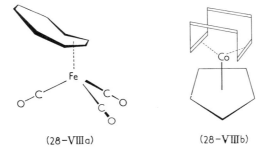

(28-VIIIa)   (28-VIIIb)

itself, has only one proton resonance line unlike other complexes, for example, $\pi\text{-}C_5H_5CoC_8H_8$ (28-VIIIb), which have two lines, for the "bound" and "free" olefinic protons. However, X-ray study has shown that the iron atom is not bound symmetrically to all of the carbon atoms but rather to four, coplanar adjacent ones, much as though these are acting like a 1,3-butadiene unit. It is not at present clear why all eight protons appear equivalent in the proton resonance spectrum of the molecule since they are not equivalent structurally. Although $C_8H_8Fe(CO)_3$ does not undergo aromatic substitution reactions, it cannot be hydrogenated to a cycloocta-diene complex as is possible for the other olefinic cyclooctatetraene complexes. However, the presence of unused π-electron density in $C_8H_8Fe(CO)_3$ is shown by the fact that it can be protonated in concentrated sulfuric acid to give the ion $C_8H_9Fe(CO)_3^+$ and by its reaction with tetracyano-ethylene, a good acceptor reagent for conjugated dienes, to give a 1:1 adduct.

In the compound $(OC)_3Fe(C_8H_8)Fe(CO)_3$ it has been found that C_8H_8 behaves like two $C{=}C{-}C{=}C$ units, one such unit binding each $Fe(CO)_3$ moiety.

28-3. Unsymmetrically Delocalized π-Bonded Hydrocarbon Metal Complexes

In the compounds described in the last section, except those of C_8H_8, there is symmetrical overlap between metal and ring orbitals to give a "sandwich" bond. Although delocalization of electron density probably occurs to some extent in olefin complexes of conjugated hydrocarbons, there has recently been characterized a class of compounds which are in a sense intermediate between the olefin and sandwich complexes.

π-Allyl and Related Metal Compounds. A number of compounds have been prepared in which there is conclusive evidence that a three-carbon delocalized allyl or allylic system $CH_2{-}CH{-}CH_2$ can act as a sort of "half sandwich"; these systems can be regarded, like NO, as formal three-electron donors.

The methods of preparation of the allyl complexes have been of the type:

$$CH_2{=}CH{-}CH{=}CH_2 + HCo(CO)_4 \rightarrow \pi\text{-}CH_3 \cdot CHCHCH_2Co(CO)_3 + CO$$
Butadiene

$$CH_2{=}CH{-}CH_2Cl + NaMn(CO)_5 \rightarrow CH_2{=}CH{-}CH_2{-}Mn(CO)_5 \xrightarrow{\text{heat}}$$
Allyl chloride $\qquad\qquad\qquad$ σ-Allyl compound
$$\pi\text{-}CH_2CHCH_2Mn(CO)_4 + CO$$
$\qquad\qquad\qquad\qquad$ π-Allyl compound

$$CH_2{=}CH{-}CH_2Cl + Ni(CO)_4 \rightarrow (\pi\text{-}CH_2CHCH_2NiCl)_2 + 4CO$$

The action of allyl alcohol on platinous or palladous halides also gives π-allyl, halide-bridged complexes. Concerning the latter it appears that the allyl derivative is an intermediate in the catalytic conversion of allyl alcohol into diallyl ether by acidified platinous solutions. It will be noted that for π-bonded, terminally substituted allyl compounds there are two isomers possible, as shown in Figure 28-12, where the stereochemistry is related to

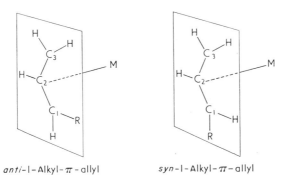

anti-l-Alkyl-π-allyl   syn-l-Alkyl-π-allyl

Fig. 28-12. The structure and stereochemistry of π-allyl compounds.

the middle hydrogen atom on C_2. Such isomers of π-$CH_3CHCHCH_2Co$ $(CO)_3$ have been characterized.

A similar allylic three-electron donor system can be expected to be obtained for cyclic systems, and π-cyclopentenyl and π-cyclohexenyl metal derivatives have been prepared, for example,

$$(\pi\text{-}C_5H_5)_2Ni \quad \xrightarrow{\text{Na/Hg in ethanol}} \quad \pi\text{-}C_5H_5Ni \; \pi\text{-}C_5H_7$$

$$\begin{array}{cc} \pi\text{-}C_6F_8Fe(CO)_3 & + \; CsF \rightarrow & Cs[\pi\text{-}C_6F_9Fe(CO)_3] \\ \text{Perfluorocyclohexa-1,3-diene} & & \pi\text{-Perfluorocyclohexenyl} \end{array}$$

π-Cyclohexadienyl and Related Metal Compounds. Although the organic groups in the above complexes function as three-electron donors, another partially delocalized system derived from 1,3-cyclic dienes can act as a ligand formally analogous to π-C_5H_5. It has been shown that hydride ion attack on suitable arene metal cations, or hydride ion abstraction from cyclohexa-1,3-diene olefin complexes, leads to π-cyclohexadienyl compounds. Thus arene manganese tricarbonyl cations can be readily converted by sodium borohydride in tetrahydrofuran into the π-cyclohexadienyls, the added hydride ion going to the H_α position on the metal side of the ring (eq. 28-6). This H_α atom is readily removed chemically. The action of triphenylmethyl tetrafluoroborate on cyclohexa-1,3-dieneiron tricarbonyl gives the corresponding iron compound:

$$C_6H_8Fe(CO)_3 + (C_6H_5)_3C^+BF_4^- = C_6H_7Fe(CO)_3^+BF_4^- + (C_6H_5)_3CH$$

Similar derivatives have been obtained for the seven-membered ring system; thus the ion $C_7H_9Fe(CO)_3^+$, for example, can be obtained by protonation of cycloheptatrieneiron tricarbonyl, $C_7H_8Fe(CO)_3$, which has one double bond not utilized in bonding to the metal atom.

28-4. Acetylene and Acetylene-Derived Complexes

We have seen that the π-electron density of a double bond in olefins can be utilized in bonding to a transition metal atom. In acetylene there are two π bonds at right angles to each other, and it might be expected that a metal atom could be bound to each. This possibility has been realized, for example, in the reaction of cobalt carbonyl with acetylenes of various types;

$$Co_2(CO)_8 + CF_3C\equiv CCF_3 = Co_2(CO)_6(CF_3C\equiv CCF_3)$$

The diphenylacetylene derivative has been studied by X-ray diffraction and it is indeed found, as shown in 28-IX, that two cobalt atoms (which

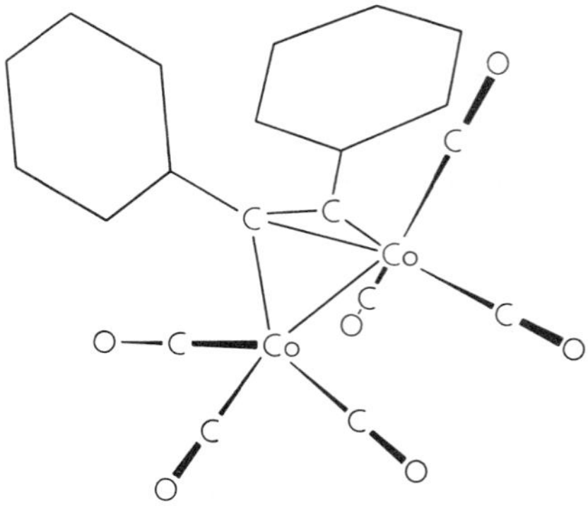

(28–IX)

also are bound to each other by a metal–metal bond) are linked to the acetylene; the angle between the cobalt atoms and the C—C axis of the acetylene is about 90° as expected. With platinum and rhenium, complexes of a different type have been obtained where the acetylene is bound only to one metal atom; in these compounds, the C—C bond appears to have considerable residual multiple bond character judging from infrared spectra and the most reasonable structure is probably one involving σ bonds (28-X). Still another type is the product from the reaction of acetylene with the cyanide complex $K_4[Co_2(CN)_{10}]$, where it appears that σ bonds

(28-X)   (28-XI)

are formed to give what is in effect a substituted olefin, probably in the *trans* form (28-XI).

The majority of complexes derived from acetylenes (other than acetylides of monoacetylenes which have the grouping M—C≡CR and which are closely related to cyanide complexes, though they are often explosively unstable) are more complex products in which the identity of the acetylene has been lost.

The reaction of acetylenes with metal carbonyls has been studied for many years following the original work of Reppe in the early 1940's. An array of metal complexes of unusual stoichiometry as well as a variety of organic ketones and other products can be obtained, the exact nature depending on the conditions of the reaction such as temperature and pressure. Some of the metal products formed in the reactions and their structures are 28-XII through 28-XIV. Although the bonding of carbonylated derivatives

(28-XII)   (28-XIII)

(28–XIV)   (28–XV)

such as quinone or cyclopentadienone can be considered as involving delocalized systems in which conjugation of the CO group is involved, they
are perhaps best regarded as olefin complexes; for example, the nuclear
magnetic resonance spectra of cyclopentadienoneiron tricarbonyl is very
similar to that of cyclopentadieneiron tricarbonyl where the $>CH_2$ cannot
of course be involved in bonding to the metal.

28-5. Transition Metal to Carbon σ Bonds

Although some metal alkyl derivatives have long been known, notably
the platinum methyl compounds such as $(Me_3PtI)_4$, it has generally been
held until fairly recently that normal σ-bonded compounds of transition
metals were unstable. This view now needs qualification. It is true that for
most of the elements, binary alkyls or aryls (that is, R_nM) are indeed unstable or at least unisolable; however, it is possible through chemical
reactions to obtain evidence even for very labile species such as $(C_2H_5)_2Ni$,
and, indeed, such species are quite useful reagents for various organic
syntheses using acetylenes. However, if halogen atoms, and especially π-
bonding ligands such as CO, π-C_5H_5, PR_3, etc., are present also, quite stable
σ-bonded complexes can be obtained. The first extensive series to be prepared were the π-cyclopentadienyl metal carbonyl alkyls and aryls, but
other types are now well known. The methods of preparation are fairly
standard—the action of metal complex halides with Grignard reagents or
of sodium salts with organic halides,

$$\pi\text{-}C_5H_5Fe(CO)_2Br + CH_3MgBr = \pi\text{-}C_5H_5Fe(CO)_2CH_3 + MgBr_2$$

$$Mn(CO)_5Na + RX = RMn(CO)_5 + NaX$$

$$TiCl_4 + LiCH_3 \xrightarrow{\text{cold}} (CH_3)_4Ti \xrightarrow{TiCl_4} CH_3TiCl_3$$

$$(R_3P)_2PtCl_2 + 2CH_3MgBr \longrightarrow (R_3P)_2Pt(CH_3)_2$$

Generally, for any given series of compounds the stability increases with increasing atomic number of the metal and with increasing electronegativity of the alkyl or aryl substituent, but in some cases steric factors can also be of importance in stabilizing the alkyl complexes. Although iron and cobalt carbonyl alkyls decompose below room temperature, the perfluorinated alkyls are quite stable, and, from the reaction of metal carbonyls with tetrafluoroethylene, compounds such as $(CO)_3Co(CF_2)_2Co(CO)_3$ and

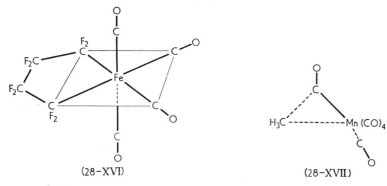

(28–XVI)   (28–XVII)

28-XVI have been isolated. Perfluoroalkyl metal carbonyls can also be obtained by decarbonylation of the acyls such as $CF_3COMn(CO)_5$.

There is also little doubt that σ-bonded species are intermediates in many reactions involving metal carbonyls with unsaturated hydrocarbons and in some cases these have been isolated. It has also been shown that carbon monoxide insertion reactions can proceed:

$$CH_3Mn(CO)_5 + CO = CH_3COMn(CO)_5$$
$$(CH_3)_2Pt(PR_3)_2 + 2CO = (CH_3CO)_2Pt(PR_3)_2$$

Tracer studies on the manganese compound have shown that the entering CO does not become the one in the acetyl group, however. Thus the transition state of the reaction probably has somewhat the structure 28-XVII. It is likely that a similar step occurs in the important "oxo reaction," the over-all stoichiometry of which is the following:

$$RCH{=}CH_2 + CO + H_2 \xrightarrow{Co_2(CO)_8} RCH_2CH_2CHO$$

A mechanism which seems to fit all of the available kinetic and stoichiometric data for the oxo reaction is:

$$Co_2(CO)_8 + H_2 = 2HCo(CO)_4$$
$$RCH{=}CH_2 + HCo(CO)_4 = RCH_2CH_2Co(CO)_4$$
$$RCH_2CH_2Co(CO)_4 + CO = RCH_2CH_2COCo(CO)_4$$
$$RCH_2CH_2COCo(CO)_4 + H_2 \text{ [or } HCo(CO)_4]$$
$$= RCH_2CH_2CHO + HCo(CO)_4 \text{ [or } Co_2(CO)_8]$$

Metal alkyl bonds are also involved in the low-temperature and low-pressure polymerization processes for ethylene, propylene, butadiene, etc., in which a metal halide or complex metal halide together with an alkyl of an electropositive metal (usually Al) functions as a catalyst (Ziegler-Natta process).

References

Chatt, J., in P. L. Plesch, ed., *Cationic Polymerization*, Academic Press, New York, 1953. Chemistry of unsaturated hydrocarbon complexes.

Coates, G. E., *Organometallic Compounds*, 2nd ed., Methuen, London, 1960.

Eisch, J., and H. Gilman, in H. J. Emeléus and A. G. Sharpe, eds., *Advances in Inorganic Chemistry and Radiochemistry*, Vol. 2, Academic Press, New York, 1960, p. 61. New developments in organometallic compounds.

Fischer, E. O., *International Conference on Coordination Chemistry, Proceedings, Chem. Soc. (London), Spec. Publ.*, No. 13, 73 (1959). Chemistry of unsaturated hydrocarbon complexes.

Fritz, H. P., and E. O. Fischer, in H. J. Emeléus and A. G. Sharpe, eds., *Advances in Inorganic Chemistry and Radiochemistry*, Vol. 1, Academic Press, New York, 1959, p. 55. General chemistry of sandwich compounds.

Nast, R., *International Conference on Coordination Chemistry, Proceedings, Chem. Soc. (London), Spec. Publ.*, No. 13, 103 (1959). Chemistry of complex acetylides.

Pauson, P. L., *Quart. Revs. (London)*, 9, 391 (1955). Organic chemistry of ferrocene and related compounds.

——, in D. Ginsburg, ed., *Non-Benzenoid Aromatic Compounds*, Interscience, New York–London, 1959, p. 107. Organic chemistry of ferrocene and related topics.

——, *Proc. Chem. Soc. (London)*, 1960, 297. Hydrocarbon derivatives of metal carbonyls.

Sternberg, H. W., and I. Wender, *International Conference on Coordination Chemistry, Proceedings, Chem. Soc. (London), Spec. Publ.*, No. 13, 35 (1959). Metal complexes in organic syntheses.

Wilkinson, G., and F. A. Cotton, "Cyclopentadienyl and Arene Metal Compounds," in F. A. Cotton, ed., *Progress in Inorganic Chemistry*, Vol. I, Interscience, New York–London, 1959, p. 1.

Zeiss, H., ed., *Organometallic Chemistry (American Chemical Society Monograph, No. 147)*, Reinhold, New York, 1960. Several sections on transition metal compounds.

29

The Elements of the First Transition Series

GENERAL REMARKS

The main features of the transition elements and a considerable amount of their complex chemistry have been presented both explicitly and implicitly in the preceding chapters. In describing in more detail the individual elements and their chemistries, frequent use will be made of this material.

We discuss in this chapter the elements of the first transition series, titanium through copper. There are two main reasons for considering these elements apart from their heavier congeners of the second and third transition series: (1) in each group, for example, V, Nb, Ta, the first series element always differs appreciably from the heavier elements, and there is little to be gained by comparisons; and (2) the aqueous chemistry of the first series elements is much simpler, and accordingly the use of ligand-field theory in explaining both the spectra and magnetic properties of compounds has been far more extensive. The ionization potentials for the first series atoms are listed in Table 29-1. Under the sections for each element the oxidation states and stereochemistries are summarized; we do not specify except in special cases of interest distortions from perfect geometries which can be expected in octahedral d^1 and d^2 (slight), octahedral d^4 spin-free (two long coaxial bonds), octahedral d^4 spin-paired (slight), octahedral d^6, d^7 spin-free (slight), or octahedral d^7, d^8 spin-paired (two long coaxial bonds). Although some general features of the elements have been noted previously, a few other points can be mentioned here.

The energies of the $3d$ and $4s$ orbitals in the neutral atoms are quite similar, and their structures are $3d^n4s^2$ with the exception of Cr, $3d^54s^1$, and Cu, $3d^{10}4s^1$, which are attributable to the stabilities of the half-filled and

TABLE 29-1

Some Properties of the Elements of the First Transition Series

	Sc	Ti	V	Cr	Mn	Fe	Co	Ni	Cu	Zn
Electronic structure	$3d^14s^2$	$3d^24s^2$	$3d^34s^2$	$3d^54s^1$	$3d^54s^2$	$3d^64s^2$	$3d^74s^2$	$3d^84s^2$	$3d^{10}4s^1$	$3d^{10}4s^2$
Ionization potential, e.v.										
1st	6.56	6.83	6 74	6.76	7.43	7.90	7.86	7.63	7.72	9.39
2nd	12.80	13.57	14 65	14.49	15.64	16.18	17.05	18.15	20.29	17.96
3rd	24.75	29.47	29.31	30.95	33.69	30.64	33.49	35.16	36.83	39.7
4th	73.9	43.24	48	50	52					
5th	92	99.8	65.2	73	76					
6th	111	120	128.9							
Crystal radii, A.[a]										
M+									0.96	
M2+		0.90	0.88	0.84	0.80	0.76	0.74	0.72	~0.72	0.74
M3+	0.81	0.76	0.74	0.69	0.66	0.64	0.63	0.62		
M4+		0.68	0.60	0.56	0.34					
M5+			0.59	0.52						
M6+										
M7+					0.46					

[a] Pauling's values.

662

filled d shells, respectively. Since the d orbitals become stabilized relative to the s orbital when the atoms are charged, the predominant oxidation states in ionic compounds and complexes of non-π-bonding ligands are II or greater. Owing to its electronic structure, copper has a higher second ionization potential than the other elements and the univalent state is important for copper. The high values of third ionization potentials also indicate why it is difficult to obtain oxidation states for nickel and copper greater than II. Although ionization potentials give some guidance concerning the relative stabilities of oxidation states, this problem is a very complex one and not amenable to facile generalization. Indeed it is often futile to discuss relative stabilities of oxidation states as some oxidation states may be perfectly stable under certain conditions, for example, in solid compounds, in fused melts, in the vapor at high temperatures, in absence of air, etc., and non-existent in aqueous solutions or in air. Thus there is no aqueous chemistry of Ti^{2+}, yet crystalline $TiCl_2$ is stable up to about 400°C. in absence of air; also in fused potassium chloride, titanium and titanium trichloride give Ti^{II} as the main species and Ti^{IV} is in vanishingly small concentrations. On the other hand, in aqueous solutions in air only Ti^{IV} species are stable.

However, it is sometimes profitable to compare the relative stabilities of ions differing by unit charge when surrounded by similar ligands with similar stereochemistry, as in the case of the Fe^{2+}–Fe^{3+} potentials (page 707) or with different anions. In these cases, as elsewhere, many factors are usually involved; some of these have already been discussed, but they include (a) ionization potentials of the metal atoms, (b) ionic radii of the metal ions, (c) electronic structure of the metal ions, (d) the nature of the anions or ligands involved with respect to their polarizability, donor $p\pi$-, or acceptor $d\pi$-bonding capacities, (e) the stereochemistry either in a complex ion or a crystalline lattice, and (f) nature of solvents or other media. In spite of the complexities there are a few trends which can be found, namely:

1. From Ti to Mn the highest valence, which is usually found only in oxy compounds or fluorides or chlorides, corresponds to the total number of d and s electrons in the atom. The stability of the highest state decreases from Ti^{IV} to Mn^{VII}. After Mn, that is, for Fe, Co, and Ni, the higher oxidation states are difficult to obtain.

2. In the characteristic oxy anions of the valence states IV to VII, the metal atom is tetrahedrally surrounded by oxygen atoms, whereas in the oxides of valences up to IV the atoms are usually octahedrally coordinated.

3. The oxides of a given element become more acidic with increasing

oxidation state and the halides more covalent and susceptible to hydrolysis by water.

4. In the II and III states, complexes in aqueous solution or in crystals are usually either in four or six coordination and, across the first series, generally of a similar nature in respect of stoichiometry and chemical properties.

5. The oxidation states less than II are found only with π-bonding ligands with the exception of Cu^I.

Finally we re-emphasize that the occurrence of a given oxidation state as well as its stereochemistry depends very much on the experimental conditions and that species which cannot have independent existence under ordinary conditions of temperature and pressure in air may be the dominant species under others. As a final point in this connection we may note that transition metal ions may be obtained in a particular configuration difficult to produce by other means through incorporation by isomorphous substitution in a crystalline host lattice, for example, tetrahedral Co^{3+} in other oxides, V^{3+} tetrahedral in the $NaAlCl_4$ lattice, as well as by ligands of fixed geometry such as phthalocyanins.

Although some discussion of the relationships between the first, second, and third transition series is useful, we defer this until the next chapter on the latter elements.

TITANIUM

Titanium is the first member of the d-block transition elements and has four valence electrons, $3d^24s^2$. Titanium(IV) is the most stable and common oxidation state; compounds in lower oxidation states, $-I$, 0, II, and III, are quite readily oxidized to Ti^{IV} by air, water, or other reagents. The energy for removal of four electrons is high so that the Ti^{4+} ion does not have a real existence and Ti^{IV} compounds are generally covalent in nature. In this IV state, there are some resemblances to the elements Si, Ge, Sn, and Pb, especially Sn. The estimated radii ($Sn^{4+} = 0.71$, $Ti^{4+} = 0.68$ A.) and octahedral covalent radii ($Sn^{IV} = 1.45$, $Ti^{IV} = 1.36$ A.) are similar; thus TiO_2 (rutile) is isomorphous with SnO_2 (cassiterite) and is similarly yellow when hot. Titanium tetrachloride, like $SnCl_4$, is a distillable liquid readily hydrolyzed by water and behaving as a Lewis acid, giving adducts with donor molecules; $SiCl_4$ and $GeCl_4$ do not give stable, solid, molecular addition compounds with ethers although $TiCl_4$ and $SnCl_4$ do so, a difference which may be attributed to ability of the halogen atoms to fill the coordination sphere of the smaller Si and Ge atoms. There are also similar halogeno anions such as TiF_6^{2-}, GeF_6^{2-}, $TiCl_6^{2-}$, $SnCl_6^{2-}$, $PbCl_6^{2-}$, some of whose salts are isomorphous. There are other similarities such as the behavior of the tetrachlorides on ammonolysis to give amido species. It is a characteristic of Ti^{IV} compounds to undergo hydrolysis to give species with Ti—O bonds, most of which are octahedrally coordinated by oxygen; Ti—O—C bonds are well known, and examples of compounds with Ti—O—Si and Ti—O—Sn bonds are known.

The stereochemistry of titanium compounds is summarized in Table 29-2.

TABLE 29-2

Oxidation States and Stereochemistry of Titanium

Oxidation state	Coordination number	Geometry	Examples
Ti^{-I}	6	Octahedral	Ti dipy$_3^-$
Ti^0	6	Octahedral	Ti dipy$_3$
Ti^{II}, d^2			$(\pi\text{-}C_5H_5)_2Ti$, $(\pi\text{-}C_5H_5)_2Ti(CO)_2$
	6	Octahedral	$TiCl_2$
Ti^{III}, d^1	6	Octahedral	TiF_6^{3-}, $[Ti(H_2O)_6]^{3+}$
Ti^{IV}, d^0	4[a]	Tetrahedral	$TiCl_4$
		Distorted tetrahedral	$(\pi\text{-}C_5H_5)_2TiCl_2$
	5	Distorted trigonal bipyramid	$K_2Ti_2O_5$ (only example)
	6[a]	Octahedral	TiF_6^{2-}, $Ti(AcAc)_2Cl_2$, $[(Cl_3PO)TiCl_4]_2$, $[Ti(OC_2H_5)_4]_3$,[b] TiO_2[c]
	8	Duodecahedral	$TiCl_4(diars)_2$[d]

[a] Most common states.

[b] Could also be a cyclic polymer with trigonal bipyramidal coordination.

[c] Distortions occur in some forms of TiO_2 and in $BaTiO_3$.

[d] diars = o-phenylenebis(dimethylarsine). Structure is that of $Mo(CN)_6^{4-}$ ion but with four equivalent Ti—As and four equivalent Ti—Cl bonds.

29-1. The Element

Titanium is relatively abundant in the earth's crust (0.6%), but has remained a rarity in the metallic state until very recently because of difficulties in separating it from its ores. The main ores are ilmenite, $FeTiO_3$, and rutile, one of the several crystalline varieties of TiO_2. It is not possible to obtain the metal by the common method of reduction with carbon because a very stable carbide is produced and, moreover, the metal is rather reactive toward oxygen and nitrogen at elevated temperatures. However, because the metal appears to have certain uniquely useful metallurgical properties, the following rather expensive process (Kroll process) has been developed commercially. Ilmenite or rutile is treated at red heat with carbon and chlorine to give $TiCl_4$, which is fractionated to free it from impurities such as $FeCl_3$. The $TiCl_4$ is then reduced with molten magnesium at $\sim 800°C$. in an atmosphere of argon. This gives metallic titanium as a spongy mass from which excess Mg and $MgCl_2$ are removed by volatilization at $\sim 1000°C$. The sponge may then be fused in an atmosphere of argon or helium, using an electric arc, and cast into ingots.

Extremely pure titanium can be made on the laboratory scale by the van Arkel–de Boer method (also used for other metals) in which TiI_4, which has been carefully purified, is vaporized and decomposed on a hot wire in vacuum.

The metal has a hexagonal close-packed lattice and resembles other transition metals such as iron, nickel, etc., in being hard, refractory (m.p. $1680 \pm 10°C$., b.p. $3260°C$.), and a good conductor of heat and electricity. It is, however, quite light in comparison to other metals of similar mechanical and thermal properties and unusually resistant to certain kinds of corrosion and has therefore come into demand for special applications in turbine engines and industrial chemical and marine equipment.

Although rather unreactive at ordinary temperatures, titanium combines directly with most nonmetals, for example, hydrogen, the halogens, oxygen, nitrogen, carbon, boron, silicon, and sulfur, at elevated temperatures. The resulting nitride, TiN, carbide, TiC, and the borides, TiB and TiB_2, are interstitial compounds which are very stable, hard, and refractory.

As noted, corrosion resistance is one of the technologically desirable properties of titanium. The metal is not attacked by mineral acids at room temperature or even by hot aqueous alkali. It dissolves in hot HCl giving Ti^{III} species, whereas hot nitric acid converts it to a hydrous oxide which is rather insoluble in acid or base. The best solvents are HF or acids to which fluoride ions have been added. Such media dissolve titanium and hold it in solution as fluoro complexes.

29-2. Compounds of Tetravalent Titanium

Titanium(IV) Halides. The most important one is titanium tetrachloride which is normally prepared in the laboratory by passing chlorine over a hot mixture of the dioxide and carbon:

$$TiO_2 + C + 2Cl_2 = TiCl_4 + CO_2$$

$TiCl_4$ is a colorless liquid freezing at $-23°C$. and boiling at $137°C$. It has a pungent odor and fumes strongly in moist air. It is vigorously hydrolyzed by water:

$$TiCl_4 + 2H_2O = TiO_2 + 4HCl$$

With some HCl present or a deficit of H_2O, partial hydrolysis occurs giving oxychlorides, whereas in concentrated HCl the titanium remains in solution due to formation of chloro complexes, namely, $[TiCl_5(H_2O)]^-$ and $[TiCl_6]^{2-}$. Salts of the latter may be precipitated on addition of cations such as NH_4^+ or Cs^+. $TiCl_4$ is a strong Lewis acid and forms addition compounds of the types R_2OTiCl_4 and $(R_2O)_2TiCl_4$ with various oxygen donors such as ethers, alcohols, and esters. Although most of the structures of the adducts are not known, the crystalline adduct $TiCl_4 \cdot POCl_3$ has been shown to be dimeric with a double chlorine bridge between the octahedral titanium atoms and with oxygen bound to titanium.

$TiBr_4$ and TiI_4 are generally similar to the chloride, but they are solids at room temperature. Their crystals are isomorphous with those of SiI_4, GeI_4, and SnI_4; that is, they have molecular, not ionic, lattices.

TiF_4, which may be obtained by treatment of $TiCl_4$ with HF, is a white, powdery solid. It is presumably an ionic substance, although this is not known with certainty. However, it does function as a Lewis acid, forming complexes similar to those given by $TiCl_4$, and it readily adds F^- ions to give the hexafluorotitanate ion, $[TiF_6]^{2-}$, of which various salts are known. The TiF_6^{2-} ion is not stable in aqueous solution, being rapidly hydrolyzed, initially to $TiOF_4^{2-}$ and more slowly to other less fluorinated species.

Titanium Oxide; Complex Oxides. The dioxide, TiO_2, is known in three crystal modifications, rutile, anatase, and brookite, all of which occur in nature. In rutile, the commonest, the titanium is octahedrally coordinated, and this structure has been illustrated and discussed earlier (page 46), as it is a common one for MX_2 compounds. In anatase and brookite there are very distorted octahedra of oxygen atoms about each titanium, two being relatively close.

Under the name *titania*, the dioxide finds some commercial use as a white pigment. Naturally occurring forms are usually colored, sometimes even black, owing to the presence of impurities such as iron. Pigment grade material is generally made by hydrolysis of $TiOSO_4$ or vapor phase oxidation of $TiCl_4$. The solubility of TiO_2 depends a good deal on its chemical and thermal history. Strongly roasted specimens are quite inert.

No definite hydroxide, $Ti(OH)_4$, appears to exist, and the precipitates obtained on adding base to Ti^{IV} solutions are best regarded as hydrous TiO_2. This substance dissolves in concentrated alkali hydroxide to give solutions from which hydrated "titanates" having formulas such as

$M^I_2TiO_3 \cdot nH_2O$ and $M^I_2Ti_2O_5 \cdot nH_2O$ but of unknown structure may be obtained.

A number of materials often called "titanates" are of special importance. With only one exception, to be mentioned below, the structures of these materials show that there are no complex titanate ions, for example, TiO_3^{2-} in ilmenite, $FeTiO_3$, and that they are properly regarded as mixed metal oxides. The structure of ilmenite can be described as a hexagonally close-packed array of oxide ions in which one third of the octahedral holes are occupied by Fe^{2+} ions and another third by Ti^{4+} ions. The arrangement of the metal ions is orderly, not random, but the exact ordering need not concern us here. In speaking of oxide ions and metal ions we do not, of course, mean that the substance is believed to be strictly ionic; this is merely a convenient way to speak of it.

The main point, however, is that this substance does not have a structure which depends upon any property peculiar to Ti^{IV} or indeed to Fe^{II} and a similar structure might well be expected for other oxides, ABO_3, where the sum of the valences of A and B is equal to $+6$. In fact, it is the same structure as that of α-Al_2O_3 (page 335) and α-Fe_2O_3, and is also adopted by $MgTiO_3$, $MnTiO_3$, $CoTiO_3$, and $NiTiO_3$. It is stable whenever the two metal ions are of about the same size and is referred to as the *ilmenite structure*.

Another so-called "titanate," with the same stoichiometry as ilmenite is *perovskite*, $CaTiO_3$, but this has a different structure. There are a number of other ABO_3 compounds which have the same structure, which is called the *perovskite structure*. It is found often in ABO_3 systems when one cation is much larger than the other. It may be described as a cubic close-packed arrangement of the oxide ions and the larger cations, with the smaller cations occupying octahedral interstices in an ordered pattern. The resulting structure has a cubic unit cell which is shown in Figure 29-1. This

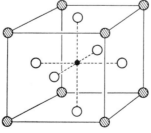

Fig. 29-1. The perovskite structure. Large open circles are O^{2-} ions, and large shaded circles are the large cations. Together they form a cubic close-packed (i.e., face-centered cubic) array. The small filled circle represents the small cation which lies at the center of an octahedron of oxide ions.

perovskite structure is adopted by many other ABO_3-type oxides (excluding those where A = B in view of the requirement that one cation be much larger than the other), including the other "titanates," $SrTiO_3$ and $BaTiO_3$, a number of compounds where the ion valences are +3 and +3, for example, $YAlO_3$ and $LaGaO_3$, some where they are +1 and +5, for example, $NaNbO_3$ and $KNbO_3$, and also by some mixed fluorides, namely, $KMgF_3$, $KNiF_3$, and $KZnF_3$. Barium titanate is of particular interest, since it shows remarkable ferroelectric behavior. The reason for this is understood in terms of the structure. Here the large ion, Ba^{2+}, is so large relative to the small ion, Ti^{4+}, that the latter can literally "rattle around" in its octahedral hole. When an electric field is applied to a crystal of this material, it can be highly polarized because the Ti^{4+} ions are drawn over to one side of their octahedra, thus causing an enormous electrical polarization of the crystal as a whole.

There are also a number of "titanates" such as Mg_2TiO_4, Zn_2TiO_4, and Co_2TiO_4, which have the *spinel structure* (page 336) where the cations occupy both octahedral and tetrahedral interstices in a close-packed array of oxide ions.

The only compound in which there is evidence for discrete titanate ions is Ba_2TiO_4. This compound has a structure of the β-K_2SO_4 type to which that of β-Ca_2SiO_4 is closely related. It contains discrete TiO_4 groups which are moderately distorted tetrahedra. Sr_2TiO_4 has quite a different structure (but not the spinel structure) in which there are layers of TiO_6 octahedra sharing oxygen atoms.

Aqueous Chemistry; Oxy Salts. There is no simple aquated Ti^{4+} ion because of the extremely high charge to radius ratio, and in aqueous solutions hydrolyzed species occur and basic oxy salts or hydrated oxides may precipitate. Although there have been claims for a titanyl ion TiO^{2+}, this ion does not appear to exist in either solutions or in crystalline salts such as $TiOSO_4 \cdot H_2O$.* The latter has been shown to have $(TiO)_n^{2n+}$ chains

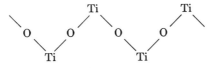

which are joined together in the crystal by sulfate groups, each of which is in contact with three metal ions; the water molecule is associated with the

---

* The only established compound with a Ti=O bond appears to be $TiO(AcAc)_2$. It has been observed that metal compounds with true metal–oxygen double bonds have a band in the infrared spectrum from about 850–1100 cm.$^{-1}$; other compounds with such bonds will be noted later, but some examples are VO_2Cl_2, CrO_2Cl_2, ReO_3Cl, and OsO_4.

titanium atoms so that the latter are approximately octahedrally coordinated by oxygen.

In dilute perchloric acid solutions, there appears to be an equilibrium between the main species

$$Ti(OH)_3{}^+ + H^+ = Ti(OH)_2{}^{2+} + H_2O$$

each of which is almost certainly octahedrally coordinated, as, for example, $[Ti(OH)_2(H_2O)_4]^{2+}$. In sulfuric acid, these and other species such as $Ti(OH)_3HSO_4$ and $Ti(OH)_2HSO_4{}^+$ have been invoked. On increasing the pH, polymerization and further hydrolysis eventually give colloidal or precipitated hydrous TiO_2.

When halide or other coordinating anions are present in solution, various complex species exist; in HF solutions the ion containing most fluorine is $TiOF_4{}^{2-}$, but $TiOF^+$, $TiOF_2$, and $TiOF_3{}^-$ are also present.

A characteristic reaction of acidified titanium solutions is the development of an intense yellow-orange color on addition of hydrogen peroxide. This reaction can be used as a colorimetric method of analysis for either Ti^{IV} or hydrogen peroxide. The colored species, which is destroyed by fluoride ion, appears to be the peroxytitanyl group $TiO_2{}^{2+}$(aq). Peroxy complexes such as $(NH_4)_3[TiF_5O_2]$ and $K_2[TiO_2(SO_4)_2]\cdot 3H_2O$ have been isolated.

A normal Ti^{IV} sulfate has been made by the reaction

$$TiCl_4 + 6SO_3 = Ti(SO_4)_2 + 2S_2O_5Cl_2$$

and N_2O_4 at $-17°C.$ converts TiI_4 to $Ti(NO_3)_4$. The latter decomposes above $10°C.$ to give $TiO(NO_3)_2$. The interaction of $TiCl_4$ with acetic anhydride gives a basic acetate $[Ti(OAc)_3]_2O$.

Alkoxides. Many metal chlorides undergo solvation and/or partial solvolysis with alcohols, but replacement of chloride is incomplete in absence of a base such as the ethoxide ion, ammonia, pyridine, etc. The titanium alkoxides have been much studied and are generally typical of many other transition metal alkoxides, such as those of Hf, Ce, V, Nb, Fe, U, which will not be discussed elsewhere. The compounds can be obtained by reactions such as:

$$TiCl_4 + 4ROH + 4NH_3 = Ti(OR)_4 + 4NH_4Cl$$
$$TiCl_4 + 3EtOH = 2HCl + TiCl_2(OEt)_2\cdot EtOH$$

The titanium alkoxides are liquids or solids which can be distilled or sublimed and are soluble in organic solvents such as benzene. They are exceedingly readily hydrolyzed by even traces of water, the ease decreasing with increasing chain length of the alkyl group. The initial hydrolytic step probably involves coordination of water to the metal; a proton on H_2O

could then interact with the oxygen of an —OR group through hydrogen bonding, leading to hydrolysis as in equation 29-1.

$$M(OH)(OR)_{x-1} + ROH \quad (29\text{-}1)$$

Probably the most important structural feature of the titanium and other alkoxides is that, although monomeric species can in certain cases exist, especially in very dilute solution, most alkoxides are polymeric, for example, $Ti(OC_2H_5)_4$, $Ti(OC_3H_7)_4$, and $Ti(OC_4H_9)_4$ being trimeric, $Ti_3(OR)_{12}$. There are several possible modes of polymerization with linear or cyclic forms, and it is not certain which is correct. However it would appear that the Ti atom is coordinated by six oxygens either octahedrally (linear polymer) or trigonal bipyramidally (cyclic polymer) with bridging alkoxy groups of the type

Partially hydrolyzed polymer species could have OH or O bridges.

It is convenient to note here when dealing with oxygen ligands that titanium gives an acetylacetonate $Ti(AcAc)_2Cl_2$ which is a normal six-coordinate, monomeric nonelectrolyte.

Nitrogen Compounds. Nitrogen ligands appear to react with titanium halides initially to give an adduct from which hydrogen halide is eliminated by base catalysis. Thus the action of diluted gaseous ammonia on $TiCl_4$ gives addition, but with excess ammonia, ammonolysis occurs and up to three Ti—Cl bonds are converted to $TiNH_2$ bonds. With increasing substitution, the remaining Ti—Cl bonds become more ionic and even liquid ammonia ammonolyzes only three bonds. Primary and secondary amines react in a similar way to give orange or red solids such as $TiCl_2$ $(NHR)_2$ and $TiCl_3NR_2$ which can be further solvated by the amine.

The action of lithium alkylamides, $LiNR_2$, on $TiCl_4$ leads to liquid or solid compounds of the type $Ti[N(C_2H_5)_2]_4$, which, like the alkoxides, are readily hydrolyzed by water with liberation of amine.

Other covalent halides such as $NbCl_5$ or VCl_4 react in similar ways, but we shall not discuss these reactions further.

29-3. Lower Valent Titanium Compounds

Valence states of -1 and 0 are known only in the special case of the 2,2'-dipyridyl complexes, $Li[Ti(dipy)_3]\cdot3.5C_4H_8O$ and $[Ti(dipy)_3]$, which are formed as black plates or purple needles, respectively, by the lithium reduction of $TiCl_4$ in presence of dipyridyl in tetrahydrofuran. These compounds, which are presumably stabilized by delocalization of electron density over the aromatic rings, are readily oxidized by air.

Divalent compounds are few in number and Ti^{II} has no aqueous chemistry, which may be attributed to its oxidation by water, although it has been reported that ice-cold solutions of TiO in dilute HCl contain Ti^{II} ions which persist for some time. The well defined compounds are $TiCl_2$, $TiBr_2$, TiI_2, TiO, and $(\pi\text{-}C_5H_5)_2Ti$. The halides are best obtained by reduction of the tetrahalides with titanium:

$$TiX_4 + Ti = 2TiX_2$$

or by disproportionation of the trihalides,

$$2TiX_3 = TiX_2 + TiX_4$$

the volatile tetrahalides being removed by distillation.

TiO is obtained by heating TiO_2 with Ti. It has a rock salt structure, but it has a marked tendency to have lattice vacancies so that the precise stoichiometry TiO is seldom found.

$(\pi\text{-}C_5H_5)_2Ti$, a dark-green sublimable solid, is, unexpectedly, diamagnetic, but this can be accounted for by molecular orbital treatments of the bonding in such compounds.

Titanium(III) has a fairly extensive chemistry. On reduction of aqueous titanium(IV) either electrolytically or chemically (e.g., with zinc and acid), violet solutions containing the $[Ti(H_2O)_6]^{3+}$ ion are obtained. These solutions are fairly rapid, mild reducing agents and are used in certain quantitative analyses.

$$Ti^{3+} + H_2O = \text{``}TiO^{2+}\text{''}(aq) + 2H^+ + e \qquad E^0 = ca. - 0.1 \text{ v.}$$

The solutions reduce atmospheric oxygen and must therefore be stored in sealed containers and handled in hydrogen or nitrogen atmosphere.

From aqueous solutions of Ti^{III} and chloride ions, the violet hexahydrate, which should presumably be formulated $[Ti(H_2O)_6]Cl_3$, may be crystallized. If, however, the aqueous solution is covered with a layer of ether and saturated with HCl, a green hexahydrate is obtained. It is probable that this is a hydration isomer similar to one of those known for $CrCl_3 \cdot 6H_2O$ (see page 538). Anhydrous $TiCl_3$, as a violet powder, is prepared by passing the vapors of $TiCl_4$ together with excess of hydrogen through a red-hot tube ($\sim$650°C.) and rapidly quenching the hot gases. When heated to above 500°C., $TiCl_3$ disproportionates into $TiCl_2$ and $TiCl_4$.

The other titanium(III) halides, including TiF_3, are also known.

Ti^{III} is decidedly more basic than Ti^{IV}, as would be expected, and the purple precipitate obtained on addition of base to Ti^{III} solutions shows no amphoteric behavior. It is usually written as $Ti(OH)_3$, but is probably the hydrous oxide, $Ti_2O_3 \cdot nH_2O$. The anhydrous oxide, Ti_2O_3, can be obtained by heating TiO_2 to 1000°C. in a stream of hydrogen and $TiCl_4$. It has the corundum (α-Al_2O_3) structure as does Fe_2O_3 also. It is quite stable and is attacked only by oxidizing acids.

Ti^{III} forms a number of double or complex sulfate salts such as $NH_4Ti_3(SO_4)_5 \cdot 9H_2O$, $RbTi_3(SO_4)_5 \cdot 12H_2O$, and $NaTi(SO_4)_2 \cdot 2.5H_2O$ of unknown structure, as well as two alums (page 339), $RbTi(SO_4)_2 \cdot 12H_2O$ and $CsTi(SO_4)_2 \cdot 12H_2O$, which contain $[Ti(H_2O)_6]^{3+}$ ions. It also forms a green, anhydrous sulfate, $Ti_2(SO_4)_3$, of unknown structure.

The best-known complexes of Ti^{III} are the pentachloroaquotitanium(III), $[TiCl_5(H_2O)]^{2-}$, and hexafluorotitanium(III), $[TiF_6]^{3-}$, both found in crystals with alkali metal cations. There are also the $M^I_2TiF_5$ compounds whose structures are unknown. It seems likely that they contain octahedral TiF_6 units as a result of sharing F^- ions.

The Ti^{III} ion is a d^1 system, and in an octahedral ligand field the configuration must be t_{2g}. One absorption band is expected ($t_{2g} \rightarrow e_g$ transition), and this has been observed in several compounds. The spectrum of the $[Ti(H_2O)_6]^{3+}$ ion is shown in Figure 26-13 and discussed on pages 572 and 584. The violet color of the hexaquo ion is attributable to this band which is so placed as to permit some blue and most red light to be transmitted. Magnetic measurements on Ti^{III} compounds show the ion to have a moment of $\sim$1.7 B.M., very close to the spin-only value for one electron.

VANADIUM

The maximum valence shown by vanadium is $+5$. There is little similarity in this state to the chemistries of the phosphorus group elements. Although V^V does indeed form vanadates, these have little in common chemically or structurally with phosphates; the oxychlorides, $VOCl_3$ and $POCl_3$, are both readily hydrolyzed liquids, however.

The oxidation states and stereochemistries for vanadium are summarized in Table 29-3.

29-4. The Element

Vanadium occurs in the earth's crust to the extent of about 0.02%. It is widely spread—over sixty vanadium minerals being known—but there are few concentrated deposits. The more important minerals are a complex

TABLE 29-3

Oxidation States and Stereochemistry of Vanadium

Oxidation state	Coordi- nation number	Geometry	Examples
V^{-1}	6	Octahedral	K$_5$[V(CN)$_5$NO], V(CO)$_6^-$, Li[V(dipy)$_3$]·4C$_4$H$_8$O
V^0	6	Octahedral	V(CO)$_6$, Vdipy$_3$, V[C$_2$H$_4$(PMe$_2$)$_2$]$_3$
V^I, d^4	6	Octahedral	[V(dipy)$_3$]$^+$
V^{II}, d^3	6	Octahedral	[V(H$_2$O)$_6$]$^{2+}$, [V(CN)$_6$]$^{4-}$
V^{III}, d^2	4	Tetrahedral	[VCl$_4$]$^-$
	6^a	Octahedral	[V(NH$_3$)$_6$]$^{3+}$, [V(C$_2$O$_4$)$_3$]$^{3-}$
V^{IV}, d^1	4	Tetrahedral	VCl$_4$
	5	Tetragonal pyramidal	VO(AcAc)$_2$
	?		VCl$_3$(OPR$_3$)$_2$, [VO(SCN)$_4$]$^{2-}$
	6^a	Octahedral	VO$_2$ (rutile), K$_2$VCl$_6$, VO(AcAc)$_2$py
	8	Duodecahedral	VCl$_4$ (diars)$_2$
V^V, d^0	4	Tetrahedral	VOCl$_3$
	5	Trigonal bipyramidal	VF$_5$
	6^a	Octahedral	VF$_6^{2-}$; V$_2$O$_3$ (very distorted; almost trigonal bipyramidal with one distant O)

^{a} Most important states.

sulfide called *patronite*, *vanadinite* (Pb$_5$(VO$_4$)$_3$Cl), and *carnotite* (K(UO$_2$) VO$_4$·$\frac{3}{2}$H$_2$O). The last-named is more important as a uranium ore, but the vanadium is usually recovered as well.

Very pure vanadium is rather rare because, like titanium, it is quite reactive toward oxygen, nitrogen, and carbon at the elevated temperatures used in conventional thermometallurgical processes. Since its chief commercial use is in alloy steels and cast iron, to which it lends ductility and shock resistance, commercial production is mainly as an iron alloy called *ferrovanadium*. The very pure metal can be prepared by the de Boer–van Arkel process (page 666).

The pure metal is reported to melt at ~1700°C., but addition of small percentages of carbon (interstitially) raises the melting point markedly: vanadium containing 10% carbon melts at ~2700°C. The pure, or nearly pure, metal resembles titanium in being corrosion resistant, hard, and steel grey in color. In the massive state it is not attacked by air, water, alkalies, or nonoxidizing acids other than HF at room temperature. It does dissolve in nitric acid, concentrated sulfuric acid, and in aqua regia.

At elevated temperatures it combines with most nonmetals. With oxygen it gives V_2O_5 contaminated with lower oxides, and with nitrogen the interstitial nitride, VN. Arsenides, silicides, carbides, and other such compounds, many of which are definitely interstitial and nonstoichiometric, are also obtained by direct reaction of the elements.

29-5. The Chemistry of Vanadium(V)

Vanadium(V) Oxide and the Vanadates. Vanadium(V) oxide is obtained on burning the finely divided metal in excess of oxygen, although some quantities of lower oxides are also formed. The usual method of preparation is by heating so-called ammonium meta-vanadate:

$$2NH_4VO_3 = V_2O_5 + 2NH_3 + H_2O$$

It is thus obtained as an orange powder which melts at about 650°C. and solidifies on cooling to orange, rhombic needle crystals. It has a slight solubility in water (~ 0.007 g./liter) to give pale yellow acidic solutions. Although mainly acidic in character and hence readily soluble in bases V_2O_5 also dissolves in acids. That the V^V species so formed are moderately strong oxidizing agents is indicated by the fact that chlorine is evolved when V_2O_5 is dissolved in hydrochloric acid, V^{IV} being produced. The following standard potential has been estimated:

$$VO^{2+} + H_2O = VO_2^+ + 2H^+ + e \qquad E^0 = -1.0 \text{ v.}$$

Solutions of V_2O_5 in base have been extensively studied to determine the species present and the pH-dependent equilibria among them. The available data are satisfied by the following equilibrium expressions and constants:

$$VO_4^{3-} + H^+ = [VO_3(OH)]^{2-} \qquad K = 10^{12.6}$$
$$2[VO_3(OH)]^{2-} + H^+ = [V_2O_6(OH)]^{3-} + H_2O \qquad K = 10^{10.6}$$
$$[VO_3(OH)]^{2-} + H^+ = [VO_2(OH)_2]^- \qquad K = 10^{7.7}$$
$$3[VO_3(OH)]^{2-} + 3H^+ = V_3O_9^{3-} + 3H_2O \qquad K = 10^{30.7}$$

Before discussing these equilibria, it must be noted—and this comment will apply to all similar equilibria discussed later—that equilibrium measurements in dilute aqueous solutions cannot establish the extent of hydration of the various species so that the formulas given are arbitary in this regard. In general, though not always, we write the simplest possible formula, that is, the one containing no water. Thus $[VO_3(OH)]^{2-}$ probably is $[VO_2(OH)_3]^{2-}$ or $[VO_2(OH)_3(H_2O)]^{2-}$, etc.

The above equilibria show that in the most basic solutions, mononuclear vanadate ions, VO_4^{3-}, or a hydration isomer thereof, are formed and that, as the basicity is reduced, these aggregate into dinuclear and trinuclear species, written above as $[V_2O_6(OH)]^{3-}$ and $[V_3O_9]^{3-}$. It has been suggested that these several anions may be built up from linear VO_2^+, pervanadyl ions (which are discussed further below), and OH^- ions as indicated in 29-I, 29-II, and 29-III, but this is only speculative at present.

(29-I) $\approx [VO_3OH]^{2-}$

(29-II) $\approx [V_2O_6(OH)]^{3-}$

(29-III) $\approx [V_3O_9]^{3-}$

At very high pH the solutions are essentially colorless, but they become yellow and then orange as the pH is lowered. When the pH is lowered below about 6.8, hydrous V_2O_5 precipitates. Even at the higher pH's solid "vanadates" can be crystallized from the solutions. These solids have a great variety of compositions, such as, $M^I_3V_5O_{14}$, $M^I_4HV_5O_{15}$, etc., and their structures are almost entirely unknown. It is very important to bear in mind that from the compositions of these precipitates *nothing* can be inferred as to the polyvandate ions which are present in the solutions from which they were obtained. Failure to recognize that an equilibrium can exist between such solids and the solutions without the same species being present in both phases is responsible for a great deal of confusion in the older literature in this field.

When V_2O_5 is dissolved in acid, complex solutions are again obtained. The most recent data can be accounted for by the following equilibria:

$$10VO_2^+ + 8H_2O = [H_2V_{10}O_{28}]^{4-} + 14H^+ \qquad K = 10^{-6.75}$$
$$[H_2V_{10}O_{28}]^{4-} = [HV_{10}O_{28}]^{5-} + H^+ \qquad K = 10^{-3.6}$$
$$[HV_{10}O_{28}]^{5-} = [V_{10}H_{28}]^{6-} + H^+ \qquad K = 10^{-5.8}$$

Again, simplest formulas are used; the actual species may contain more water. It is also possible that other species may exist in small amounts, but the data can be fitted within experimental error by these equilibria so that such other species are, in effect, undetectable. The data are sufficiently accurate to make the V_{10} species rather certain; equilibria with V_9, V_{11}, or V_{12} species cannot be devised so as to be in as good accord with the experimental measurements over the entire ranges of pH and total V concentration as are those given above. These equilibrium expressions show that from the lowest pH's studied ($\sim$1) up to pH's of 1.3–2.0, depending on total V concentrations, the pervanadyl ion, VO_2^+ is the main species, with the decanuclear species, $[H_n V_{10}O_{28}]^{(6+n)-}$, arising as the pH is raised. In the pH region 4–7 there is little known of the species present at equilibrium, mainly because in this region attainment of equilibrium is extremely slow and reliable measurements thus very difficult to obtain.

The pervanadyl group occurs in some complex vanadium(V) salts, for example, $M^I[VO_2(C_2O_4)_2]$ and $M^I[VO_2(SO_4)]$.

Vanadium(V) Halides and Oxyhalides. The only pentahalide of V is VF_5, a volatile white solid, m.p. 19.5°C., obtained by direct fluorination of the metal at 300°C. Similarly, the only hexahalovanadate(V) ion known is $[VF_6]^-$. It is not stable toward water, however, and its salts are made by combined oxidation and fluorination of alkali metal chlorides and VCl_3 in liquid BrF_3.

A number of oxyhalides and oxyhalo complex anions of V^V are known. Vanadium oxytrichloride, $VOCl_3$, and oxytribromide, $VOBr_3$, can be prepared by halogenation of V_2O_3,

$$V_2O_3 + 3X_2 = 2VOX_3 + \tfrac{1}{2}O_2$$

and the chloride also by chlorination of V_2O_5. Both are rather volatile substances, suggesting that they are simple molecular compounds, at least in the vapor state, and for $VOCl_3$ this is confirmed by electron diffraction study which has shown the molecule to be essentially tetrahedral. Vanadium oxytrifluoride is also known, being obtained by treatment of the oxytrichloride with cold concentrated hydrofluoric acid or by oxidation of VF_3 with molecular oxygen at 500–600°C. All three oxytrihalides are rapidly hydrolyzed by water.

Several salts containing fluorovanadate(V) anionic complexes have been reported, although their exact structures are not known. They are obtained by reactions between vanadium pentoxide and an alkali metal fluoride, usually in hydrofluoric acid solution. They are of the types $M^I[VOF_4]$, $M^I_2[VOF_5]$, and $M^I_2[VO_2F_3]$.

With pyridinium chloride, (pyH)Cl, in alcoholic solution, $VOCl_3$ forms the salt (pyH)[$VOCl_4$], which is hydrolyzed by water.

Other Vanadium(V) Compounds. A sulfide, V_2S_5, has been claimed, but its existence seems doubtful at present. The metal reacts with N_2O_4 in acetonitrile to give a brick-red solid, VO_2NO_3, which is very soluble in water and on heating gives V_2O_5 and N_2O_5.

There is a series of peroxy compounds of V^V of which the solid salts $KH_2[VO_2(O_2)_2] \cdot H_2O$, $(NH_4)_2H[VO_2(O_2)_2] \cdot nH_2O$, and $M^I_3[V(O_2)_4] \cdot nH_2O$

are insolable. In these, two or all of the oxygen atoms of $[VO_4]^{3-}$ are replaced by peroxy groups, O_2.

29-6. The Chemistry of Vanadium(IV)

This important oxidation state of vanadium is the most stable one under ordinary conditions. V^{III} is oxidized to V^{IV} by molecular oxygen, and V^V is reduced to V^{IV} by fairly mild reducing agents. The dark blue oxide, VO_2, can be obtained by mild reduction of V_2O_5, a classic method being by fusion of the latter with oxalic acid; it is amphoteric, being about equally readily soluble in both acids and bases. In strongly basic solutions vanadate(IV) ions, VO_4^{4-}, probably not of this simple nature, exist and from these solutions, and less basic ones, various vanadate(IV) compounds, also called *hypovanadates* are obtainable. They are of the type $M^I_2V_4O_9 \cdot 7H_2O$. By fusion of VO_2 with alkaline earth oxides, other vanadate(IV) compounds, for example, $M^{II}VO_3$, $M^{II}_2VO_4$, and $M^{II}_3VO_5$, have been obtained. Virtually nothing is known of their structures.

In acid solutions, vanadium(IV) exists as VO^{2+}, the bright blue *vanadyl* ion, and this species dominates the chemistry of vanadium(IV). With virtually no significant exceptions all V^{IV} complexes are vanadyl complexes. Thus there are numerous compounds containing fluoro- and chlorovanadyl anions, for example, $M^I_2VOF_4 \cdot 2H_2O$, $(pyH)_2[VOCl_4] \cdot nH_2O$, and $(pyH)_4$ $[VOCl_6]$. The structure of the last-mentioned is unknown, but seven-coordinated V^{IV} seems unlikely. There are also thiocyanato complexes, such as $M^I_2[VO(CNS)_4] \cdot nH_2O$, oxalato complexes, for example, $M^I_2[VO(C_2O_4)_2]$ and $M^I_2[(VO)_2(C_2O_3)_3]$, and sulfato salts, $M^I_2[VO(SO_4)_2]$ and $M^I_2[(VO)_2(SO_4)_3]$. Again, the structures are not known and the use of square brackets to imply complex anions is only speculative.

The vanadyl ion also forms neutral complexes with the enol anions of β-diketones. The acetylacetonate (29-IV) has a square pyramidal structure

(29-IV)

with the V atom above the center of the base square of oxygens. The V—O bond length is 1.56 A. These complexes further coordinate with amines to give octahedral complexes.

The best-known vanadyl salts are the sulfate, $VOSO_4$, and the several vanadyl halides, also called vanadium oxydihalides, all of which are known except the iodide. The chloride, $VOCl_2$, is best made by reduction of $VOCl_3$ with hydrogen at high temperatures. It is a bright green, deliquescent substance, soluble in water. Its structure, particularly whether it is molecular, ionic (VO^{2+}, $2Cl^-$), or intermediate is unknown. The bromide, $VOBr_2$, is obtained by thermal decomposition of $VOBr_3$ and in other ways. The fluoride can be prepared from the bromide by heating it with hydrogen fluoride.

Compounds of vanadium(IV) which are not of the vanadyl type include the two tetrahalides, VF_4 and VCl_4, and a complex salt, K_2VCl_6, formed by reaction of VCl_4 with KCl in iodine monochloride. The tetrachloride itself may be prepared in various ways, useful ones being by passing carbon tetrachloride vapors over V_2O_5 at red heat and by chlorination of vanadium metal, vanadium nitride, ferrovanadium (followed by fractional distillation to separate the VCl_4 from ferric chloride), etc. The tetrachloride is a dark, oily, red-brown liquid, b.p. 154°C., which is immediately hydrolyzed by water to give vanadyl chloride. The chlorine decomposition pressure for the liquid going to $VCl_3(s)$ is almost 1 atm. at 25°C., but the heat of decomposition is almost zero and the chlorine pressure hardly changes up to the boiling point. VBr_4, on the other hand, is quite unstable at room temperature and exists only in the gas phase above $\sim$260°C. Vanadium tetrafluoride is prepared by treating the tetrachloride with hydrogen fluoride at room temperature. It is a hygroscopic brown powder which disproportionates into VF_3 and VF_5 at about 325°C.

29-7. The Chemistry of Vanadium(III)

This oxidation state is of moderate importance in vanadium chemistry. The parent oxide, V_2O_3, is a black, refractory substance made by reduction of V_2O_5 with moderately powerful reducing agents such as hydrogen or carbon monoxide. It has the α-alumina structure, but it is difficult to obtain in an exactly stoichiometric condition since it has a marked tendency to become oxygen deficient without change in structure. Compositions as low in oxygen as $VO_{1.35}$ are reported to retain the α-alumina structure.

V_2O_3 is entirely basic in nature and dissolves in acids to give solutions of the V^{III} aquo ion or its complexes. The same solutions may also be obtained by electrolytic reduction of acid solutions containing vanadium in the IV or V state. In solutions free of complexing agents, V^{III} exists as the green hexaquo ion, $[V(H_2O)_6]^{3+}$. Such solutions, and also others, of V^{III} are subject to air oxidation in view of the potential:

$$V^{3+} + H_2O = VO^{2+} + 2H^+ + e \qquad E^0 = -0.36 \text{ v.}$$

Hydrous V_2O_3 can be precipitated by addition of hydroxide to these solutions; it is very easily oxidized.

All of the halides of vanadium(III) are known. The trifluoride and trichloride can both be obtained by thermal decomposition of the respective tetrahalides, and VF_3 can also be obtained by treating VCl_3 with hydrogen fluoride at 600°C. The tribromide and triiodide are both formed by direct reaction of the elements at high temperatures. The trihalides vary irregularly in their thermal stabilities. The trifluoride is thermally stable, but VBr_3 and VI_3 decompose above 280°C. to give the dihalides. The chloride has more complex behavior as indicated by the equations:

$$2VCl_3 = VCl_2 + VCl_4$$
$$VCl_4 = VCl_3 + \tfrac{1}{2}Cl_2$$

Thus, in excess chlorine VCl_3 is converted to VCl_4, but, on heating at 450–500°C. under pumping to remove chlorine, it can be converted entirely to the dichloride.

The hydrates $VF_3 \cdot 3H_2O$, $VCl_3 \cdot 6H_2O$, $VBr_3 \cdot 6H_2O$, and $VI_3 \cdot 6H_2O$ can be crystallized from acidic aqueous solutions. $VF_3 \cdot 3H_2O$ seems probably to consist of octahedral $[VF_3(H_2O)_3]$ units and $VCl_3 \cdot 6H_2O$ to contain $[V(H_2O)_6]^{3+}$ ions.

Vanadium(III) forms a fair number of complexes, mostly anionic. The only halo complexes are those with fluoride of which three types, $M^I_3[VF_6]$, $M^I_2[VF_5(H_2O)]$, and $M^I[VF_4(H_2O)_2]$, are known. Salts of the trioxalato ion, $[V(C_2O_4)_3]^{3-}$, the hexacyano ion, $[V(CN)_6]^{3-}$, and the hexathiocyanato ion, $[V(NCS)_6]^{3-}$, are also known. In addition to its occurrence in aqueous solutions, where partial hydrolysis to $V(OH)^{2+}$ and VO^+ occurs, and its probable occurrence in hexaquovanadium(III) chloride, the $[V(H_2O)_6]^{3+}$ ion occurs in the vanadium alums, $M^IV(SO_4)_2 \cdot 12H_2O$. It is also noteworthy that, although Ti^{III} does not appear to form ammine complexes, the moderately stable $[V(NH_3)_6]Cl_3$ is known. Vanadium(III) also forms neutral, "inner salt" complexes with β-diketones.

29-8. The Chemistry of Vanadium(II)

This is decidedly the least stable or important of the oxidation states of vanadium. The black oxide, VO, has a crystal lattice of the rock salt type, but it shows a marked tendency to nonstoichiometry, being obtainable with anywhere from ~45 to ~55 atom % oxygen. It has a metallic luster and rather good electrical conductivity of a metallic nature. There is doubtless a good deal of direct metal–metal bonding. It is an entirely basic substance, dissolving in acids to give V^{II} solutions.

Violet aqueous solutions of V^{II} may also be obtained by reduction of acidic solutions of V^{IV} electrolytically or using zinc. V^{II} is isoelectronic with Cr^{III} and therefore has an analogous energy level diagram (see page 689 for the Cr^{III} diagram). From the spectrum of V^{II} solutions of non-complexing anions, it can be deduced that they contain octahedral $[V(H_2O)_6]^{2+}$ ions, as might be expected. Solutions of V^{II} are strongly reducing, even attacking the solvent water with the evolution of hydrogen. It may be noted that this attack on neutral water ought to require an oxidation potential of $\geqslant 0.414$ v. (see page 114), although the reported standard potential for the V^{2+}–V^{3+} couple is only 0.25 v.

Few crystalline V^{II} salts are known. The Tutton salts, $M^I_2SO_4 \cdot VSO_4 \cdot 6H_2O$, containing $[V(H_2O)_6]^{2+}$ ions, and the sulfate, $VSO_4 \cdot 7H_2O$, isomorphous with the corresponding Cr^{II} and Fe^{II} compounds, are known. The dihalides VF_2, VCl_2, VBr_2, and VI_2 are also known. The fluoride is made by treating VCl_2 with HF gas. The chloride and iodide are obtained by thermal decomposition of the V^{III} halides, and VBr_2 is prepared by reduction of VBr_3 with hydrogen at high temperatures. A complex cyanide, $K_4[V(CN)_6] \cdot 3H_2O$, is also known.

CHROMIUM

The highest oxidation state of chromium continues, as for Ti and V, to be the one corresponding to the total number of $3d$ and $4s$ electrons. Although Ti^{IV} is the most stable state for titanium and V^V is only mildly oxidizing, chromium(VI), which exists only in oxy species such as CrO_3, CrO_4^{2-}, and CrO_2F_2, is rather strongly oxidizing. Apart from stoichiometric similarities, chromium resembles the group VI elements of the sulfur group only in the acidity of the trioxide and the covalent nature and ready hydrolysis of CrO_2Cl_2.

Although Cr^V and Cr^{IV} are formed as transient intermediates in the reduction of Cr^{VI} solutions, these oxidation states have no stable solution chemistry because of their ready disproportionation to Cr^{III} and Cr^{VI}. A few solid compounds do exist, however.

The most stable and important state is Cr^{III}, d^3, which in an octahedral complex has each t_{2g} level singly occupied giving a sort of half-filled shell stability. The lower oxidation states are strongly reducing; in aqueous solution only the divalent state, Cr^{2+}, is known. Since for Cr and also for the following elements of the first transition series the more important oxidation states are the lower ones, we discuss them first.

The oxidation states and stereochemistry are summarized in Table 29-4.

TABLE 29-4

Oxidation States and Stereochemistry of Chromium

Oxidation state	Coordination number	Geometry	Examples
Cr^{-II}		?	$Na_2[Cr(CO)_5]$
Cr^{-I}		?	$Na_2[Cr_2(CO)_{10}]$
Cr^0	6	Octahedral	$Cr(CO)_6$, $[Cr(CO)_5I]^-$, $Cr(dipy)_3$
Cr^I, d^5	6	Octahedral	$K_3[Cr(CN)_5NO]$, $[Cr(dipy)_3]^+$
Cr^{II}, d^4	6	Distorted[b] octahedral	$[Cr(H_2O)_6]^{2+}$, CrF_2, $KCrF_3$
Cr^{III}, d^3	6[a]	Octahedral	$[Cr(NH_3)_6]^{3+}$, $Cr(AcAc)_3$, $K_3[Cr(CN)_6]$
Cr^{IV}, d^2	4 (in vapor?)		CrF_4, $Cr(OC_4H_9)_4$, Ba_2CrO_4
	6	Octahedral	K_2CrF_6
Cr^V, d^1	4	Tetrahedral	CrO_4^{3-}
	6	Octahedral	$K_2[CrOCl_5]$
	8	—	K_3CrO_8 (see text)
Cr^{VI}, d^0	4	Tetrahedral	CrO_4^{2-}, CrO_2Cl_2, CrO_3 (two more distant O)

[a] Most stable state.

[b] Four long and two short bonds.

29-9. The Element

Chromium is produced in large quantities for industrial purposes. The chief ore is chromite, $FeCr_2O_4$, which is a spinel with Cr^{III} on octahedral sites and Fe^{II} on the tetrahedral ones. If pure chromium is not required—as for use in ferrous alloys—the chromite is simply reduced with carbon in a furnace affording the carbon-containing alloy ferrochromium:

$$FeCr_2O_4 + 4C = Fe + 2Cr + 4CO$$

When pure chromium is required, the chromite is first treated with molten alkali and oxygen to convert the Cr^{III} to chromate(VI) which is dissolved in water and eventually precipitated as sodium dichromate. This is then reduced with carbon to Cr^{III} oxide:

$$Na_2Cr_2O_7 + 2C = Cr_2O_3 + Na_2CO_3 + CO$$

This oxide is then reduced with aluminum:

$$Cr_2O_3 + 2Al = Al_2O_3 + 2Cr$$

Chromium is a white, hard, lustrous, and brittle metal, melting at $1890 \pm 10°C$. It is extremely resistant to ordinary corrosive agents, which accounts for its extensive use as an electroplated protective coating. The metal dissolves fairly readily in nonoxidizing mineral acids, for example, hydrochloric and sulfuric, but not in cold aqua regia or nitric acid, either concentrated or dilute. These latter reagents passivate the metal in a manner which is not well understood. The electrode potentials of the metal are:

$$Cr = Cr^{2+} + 2e \qquad E^0 = 0.91 \text{ v.}$$
$$Cr = Cr^{3+} + 3e \qquad E^0 = 0.74 \text{ v.}$$

so that it is rather active when not passivated. Thus it readily displaces copper, tin, and nickel from aqueous solutions of their salts.

At elevated temperatures, chromium unites directly with the halogens, sulfur, silicon, boron, nitrogen, carbon, and oxygen.

29-10. The Chemistry of Chromium (II)

A fair number of Cr^{II} compounds are known, all of them strong and rapid reducing agents. The chromous ion in aqueous solution has a sky-blue color and is very easily oxidized:

$$Cr^{2+} = Cr^{3+} + e \qquad E^0 = 0.41 \text{ v.}$$

Thus it is easily oxidized by molecular oxygen, and solutions can only be preserved by exclusion of air, as for example by placing a layer of oil on the surface. Even then they decompose, at rates varying with the acidity and the anions present, by reducing the water with liberation of hydrogen. The solutions are best obtained by reducing Cr^{III} solutions with zinc in acid or electrolytically at a lead cathode. Various hydrated salts can be crystallized from the aqueous solutions, for example, $CrSO_4 \cdot 7H_2O$, $CrCl_2 \cdot 4H_2O$, and $[Cr(OCOCH_3)_2]_2 \cdot 2H_2O$. The sulfate is reported to be isomorphous with the analogous V^{II} and Fe^{II} compounds.

The acetate of Cr^{II} is one of the commonest, most stable, and most easily prepared chromous compounds. It comes down as a sparingly soluble, red crystalline precipitate when a solution of Cr^{II} chloride is run into a fairly concentrated solution of sodium acetate. It is also the most curious of Cr^{II} compounds. It has the dimeric structure shown in Figure 29-2; only Cu^{II} acetate of all other M^{II} acetates examined also has such a structure. The very short Cr—Cr distance would imply that the interaction between the two metal ions is strong, and, indeed, it is so great that the four d electrons of each metal ion become fully paired and the substance is diamagnetic at room temperature.

Anhydrous Cr^{II} compounds are best obtained by dry procedures. The four halides are known and can be prepared by reaction of HF, HCl, or HBr on the metal at 600–700°C. or by reduction of the anhydrous tri-

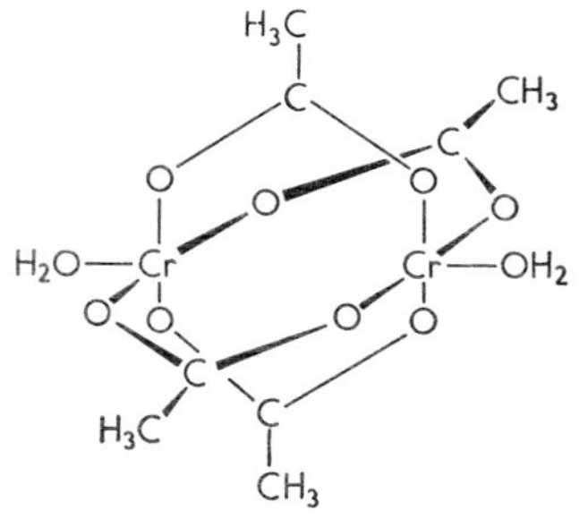

Cr—O (acetate) = 1.97 A.
Cr—OH$_2$ = 2.20 A.
Cr—Cr   = 2.46 A

Fig. 29-2.   The structure of Cr^{II} acetate hydrate.

halides with hydrogen at 500–600°C. The iodide and the sulfide, CrS, are prepared by direct combination of the elements at elevated temperatures. The halides rather readily take up gaseous ammonia to form addition compounds, $CrX_2 \cdot nNH_3$ (n = 6, 5, 3, 2, 1). The hexammoniate of CrCl$_2$ has been reported to contain octahedral $[Cr(NH_3)_6]^{2+}$ ions.

Cr^{II} also forms other complexes, such as those of hydrazine and dipyridyl. The hydrazine complexes, of the type $CrCl_2 \cdot 2N_2H_4$ and $CrI_2 \cdot 2N_2H_4$, are unusually stable toward oxidation and rather insoluble in water. The dipyridyl complex, as the perchlorate, is black-violet; it forms a wine-red solution which can be fairly easily oxidized, reduced, or caused to disproportionate:

$$2[Cr(dipy)_3]^{2+} = [Cr(dipy)_3]^+ + [Cr(dipy)_3]^{3+}$$

There are also complexes known with ethylenediamine, thiocyanate (e.g., $M^I_4[Cr(NCS)_6]$), and cyanide (e.g., $K_4[Cr(CN)_6]$).

The only coordination number reported for Cr^{II} is 6, the geometry being that of a distorted octahedron (see next paragraph). In an octahedral environment two electron distributions, $t_{2g}^3 e_g$ and t_{2g}^4, are possible. The magnetic data available for chromium(II) complexes are very meager, but it appears that most are of high spin (i.e., four unpaired electrons and magnetic moments of ~5.0 B.M.). The $[Cr(CN)_6]^{4-}$ ion, however, has a moment of only ~3.2 B.M. and is thus a low-spin complex. For the high-spin complexes only one spin-allowed absorption band is to be expected. The blue color of the aquo Cr^{II} ion is attributable to the existence of this band, which is rather broad, at about 700 mμ.

As noted earlier (page 582), an ion with a d^4 high-spin configuration should cause Jahn-Teller distortion of an octahedral environment. The exceptional breadth of the absorption band of $[Cr(H_2O)_6]^{2+}$ may be due to distortion, and, in the several instances mentioned above where the Cr^{II} ion is reported to have an "octahedral" environment, it is possible that there are distortions not detected in the X-ray studies, which were not all of a highly precise nature. In a few instances precise X-ray studies have shown marked distortions, of the type found so commonly in Cu^{II} compounds (page 747), where two ligands are much farther from the metal ion than are the other four. Thus in CrF_2 there are four F^- at 1.98–2.01 and two *trans* ones at 2.43 A.; in CrS there are four S at 2.43 A. and two S at 2.88 A.; and in $CrCl_2$ there are four Cl^- at 2.39 A. and two at 2.90 A.

29-11. The Chemistry of Chromium(III)

This is the most stable and important oxidation state of the element in general and particularly in its aqueous chemistry. The foremost characteristic of this state is the formation of a large number of relatively kinetically inert complexes. It is largely because of this kinetic inertness that so many complex species can be isolated as solids and that they persist for relatively long periods of time in solution, even under conditions where they are thermodynamically quite unstable.

Chromium(III) Oxide. The parent oxide is green Cr_2O_3 which has the corundum (α-Al_2O_3) structure. It is formed on burning the metal in oxygen, on thermal decomposition of Cr^{VI} oxide or ammonium dichromate or on roasting the hydrous oxide, $Cr_2O_3 \cdot nH_2O$. The latter, commonly called chromic hydroxide, although its water content is variable, is precipitated on addition of hydroxide to solutions of Cr^{III} salts. The oxide, if ignited too strongly, becomes inert toward both acid and base, but otherwise it and its hydrous form are amphoteric, dissolving readily in acid to give aquo ions, $[Cr(H_2O)_6]^{3+}$, and in concentrated alkali to form chromites.

The species present in these chromite solutions have not been identified with certainty, but they are most probably $[Cr(OH)_6]^{3-}$ and perhaps $[Cr(OH)_5(H_2O)]^{2-}$. From such solutions crystalline compounds such as $M^I_nCr(OH)_{3+n}$ ($n = 3$–5) and similar alkaline earth salts can be obtained. Although no X-ray structural data are available, it seems doubtful if any such species as $[Cr(OH)_8]^{5-}$ or $[Cr(OH)_7]^{4-}$ are present; compounds with more than six OH^- per chromium ion more likely contain uncoordinated OH^- ions.

On fusing Cr_2O_3 with the oxides of a number of bivalent metals, well-crystallized compounds of the composition $M^{II}O \cdot Cr_2O_3$ are obtained. These are often given the trivial name chromites, but this is a misnomer (page 336). These compounds are true mixed metal oxides having the spinel structure. In all of those examined structurally thus far, Cr^{III} ions occupy the octahedral interstices.

Chromium(III) Sulfide. Like aluminum sulfide, chromium(III) sulfide cannot be precipitated from aqueous solution because of its instability toward hydrolysis to $Cr_2O_3 \cdot nH_2O$ and H_2S. It can be made by treatment of $CrCl_3$ with H_2S at red heat or directly from the elements. It is a black solid which is quite stable toward nonoxidizing acids.

Chromium(III) Halides. The fluoride, chloride, and bromide are known in the anhydrous state, and all four halides are known in one or more hydrated forms. The chlorides are by far the commonest and most important chromium halides. The anhydrous chloride can be prepared by each of the following methods, all of which represent fairly general preparative methods for anhydrous metal chlorides:

$$2Cr + 3Cl_2 \overset{500\text{–}600°C.}{=} 2CrCl_3$$

$$Cr_2O_3 + 3C + 3Cl_2 \overset{500\text{–}600°C.}{=} 2CrCl_3 + 3CO$$

$$Cr_2O_3 + 3CCl_4 \overset{400\text{–}500°C.}{=} 2CrCl_3 + 3COCl_2$$

$$[Cr(H_2O)_6]Cl_3 + SOCl_2 \xrightarrow{\text{reflux}} CrCl_3 + SO_2 + HCl$$

This red-violet substance can be sublimed in a stream of chlorine at about 600°C., but if heated to such a temperature in the absence of chlorine it decomposes to Cr^{II} chloride and chlorine. The flaky or leaflet form of $CrCl_3$ is a consequence of its crystal structure, which is of an unusual type. It consists of a cubic close-packed array of chlorine atoms in which two thirds of the octahedral holes between *every other* pair of Cl planes are occupied by metal atoms. Those alternate layers of chlorine atoms with no metal atoms between them are held together only by van der Waals' forces and thus the crystal has pronounced cleavage parallel to the layers. $CrCl_3$ is the only substance known to have this exact structure, but $CrBr_3$, as well as $FeCl_3$ and triiodides of As, Sb, and Bi have one which differs only in that the halogen layers are stacked ABABAB, that is, in hexagonal close packing, rather than cubic (ABCABCABC).

Chromic chloride does not dissolve at a significant rate in pure water, but in presence of Cr^{II} ion or reducing agents such as $SnCl_2$ which can generate some Cr^{II} from the $CrCl_3$ it dissolves readily. This is because the process of solution can then take place by electron transfer from Cr^{II} in solution via a Cl bridge to the Cr^{III} in the crystal. This Cr^{II} can then leave the crystal and act upon a Cr^{III} ion elsewhere on the crystal surface, or perhaps it can act without moving. At any rate, the "solubilizing" effect of reducing agents must be related in this or some similar way to the mechanism by which chromous ions cause decomposition of otherwise inert Cr^{III} complexes in solution (page 557). From aqueous solution, Cr^{III} chloride may be crystallized as one or another of the three hydration isomers of $CrCl_3 \cdot 6H_2O$ already discussed (page 538).

The other halides of Cr^{III} are generally similar to the chloride. The fluoride occurs in various hydrated forms, $CrF_3 \cdot 3H_2O$ and $CrF_3 \cdot 6H_2O$ being best known; the bromide forms two hydration isomers, a violet one which is most probably $[Cr(H_2O)_6]Br_3$ and a green one thought to be $[Cr(H_2O)_4Br_2]Br \cdot 2H_2O$. The iodide is known only as a nonahydrate of unknown structure.

Other Simple and Hydrated Chromium(III) Salts. Only a few of these are of much importance. Chromium(III) sulfate is known as $Cr_2(SO_4)_3 \cdot 18H_2O$ and with a variety of lower degrees of hydration including the anhydrous substance obtained only by prolonged heating at low pressure. The nitrate can be crystallized from water with various amounts of water of hydration. The anhydrous nitrate cannot be obtained by dehydration because of decomposition to the Cr^{III} oxide and oxides of nitrogen. Hydrated forms of the oxalate, acetate, and other salts are also known.

29-12. Complexes of Chromium(III)

Literally thousands of these are known, and only a brief outline of them can be given here. There are no known exceptions to the rule that Cr^{III} is always hexacoordinate.

Chromium(III) Ammines. These are perhaps the most numerous and most extensively studied. They include the pure ammines, $[CrAm_6]^{3+}$, the mixed amine-aquo types, that is, $[CrAm_{6-n}(H_2O)_n]^{3+}$ ($n = 0\text{--}4, 6$), the mixed amine-acido types, that is, $[CrAm_{6-n}R_n]^{(3-n)+}$ ($n = 1\text{--}4, 6$), and mixed amine-aquo-acido types, for example, $[CrAm_{6-n-m}(H_2O)_nR_m]^{(3-m)+}$. In these general formulas, Am represents the monodentate ligand NH_3 or half of a polydentate amine such as ethylenediamine, and R represents an acido ligand such as a halide, nitro, or sulfate ion. These ammine complexes, in their profusion, provide examples of virtually all of the kinds of isomerism possible in octahedral complexes (see pages 533–538).

They react, in general, more sluggishly than Co^{III} complexes and are therefore not as convenient for kinetic studies as the latter.

Aquo Chromium(III) Ions. The hexaquo ion occurs in aqueous solution under many circumstances as well as in various crystalline compounds. Among these are the violet hexahydrates of the chloride and bromide and an extensive series of alums, $M^I Cr(SO_4)_2 \cdot 12H_2O$. The kinetic inertness of Cr^{III} complexes is dramatically illustrated by the fact that the rate of exchange of the coordinated water in $[Cr(H_2O)_6]^{3+}$ is so slow that it has been possible in effect to "count" these coordinated water molecules separately from the rest in exchange experiments on aqueous solutions of Cr^{III} as described on page 542.

Acido Chromium(III) Complexes. Many complex anions of the type $[CrX_6]^{3-}$, where X is a monodentate acido ligand such as Cl^-, NCS^-, and CN^-, or part of a polydentate anion such as oxalate, are known. There are, of course, many mixed amine-acido and aquo-acido complexes. A particularly common one is Reinecke's salt, $NH_4[Cr(NCS)_4(NH_3)_2]\cdot H_2O$. The anion in this salt is widely used to precipitate large cations, both organic and inorganic.

Polynuclear Complexes. A large number of these are also known. In fact, the formation of the hydroxo- and oxo-bridged polynuclear complexes frequently causes difficulties in carrying out reactions in basic or neutral solutions. There are also amino- and thiocyanato-bridged polynuclear complexes. Some representative polynuclear complexes whose structures are fairly certain are shown in equation 29-2.

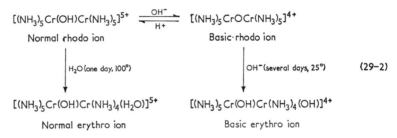

$$\text{(29-2)}$$

Electronic Structures of Chromium(III) Complexes. The magnetic properties of the octahedral Cr^{III} complexes are quite uncomplicated. From the simple orbital splitting diagram it follows (page 567) that all such complexes must have three unpaired electrons irrespective of the strength of the ligand field, and, in all known mononuclear complexes, this has been confirmed. More sophisticated theory further predicts that the magnetic moments should be very close to, but slightly below, the spin-only value of 3.88 B.M.; this, too, is observed experimentally.

The spectra of Cr^{III} complexes are also well understood in their main features. A partial energy level diagram is shown in Figure 29-3. It is seen that three spin-allowed transitions are expected, and these have been observed in a considerable number of complexes. Indeed, the spectrochemical series was originally established by Tsuchida using data for Cr^{III} and Co^{III} complexes. In the aquo ion, the bands are found at 17,400, 24,700, and 37,000 cm.$^{-1}$.

Ruby, natural or synthetic, is α-Al_2O_3 containing occasional Cr^{III} ions in place of Al^{III} ions. The environment of the Cr^{III} in ruby is thus a slightly distorted octahedron of oxide ions. The frequencies of the spin-allowed bands of Cr^{III} in ruby indicate that the Cr^{III} ions are under considerable

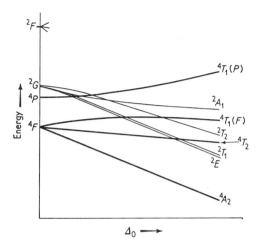

Fig. 29-3. Partial energy level diagram for a d^3 ion in an octahedral field (also for a d^7 ion in a tetrahedral field). The quartet states are drawn with heavier lines.

compression, since the value of Δ_0 calculated is significantly higher than it is in the $[Cr(H_2O)_6]^{3+}$ ion or in other oxide lattices and glasses. Also, in ruby, spin-forbidden transitions from the $^4A_2$ ground state to the doublet states arising from the ^2G state of the free ion are observed. The transitions to the ^2E and $^2T_1$ states give rise to extremely sharp lines because the slopes of the energy lines for these states are the same as that for the ground state (except in extremely weak fields). This relationship is explained more fully on page 703 in connection with Mn^{II} complexes.

These same doublet states play a key role in the operation of the ruby LASAR. In this device a large single crystal of ruby is irradiated with light of the proper frequency to cause excitation to the $^4T_2(F)$ state. The exact magnitudes of certain energy differences and relaxation times are such, in the ruby, that the system rapidly makes a radiationless transition (i.e., by loss of energy to the crystal lattice in the form of vibrations) to the ^2E and $^2T_1$ states, instead of decaying directly back to the ground state. The systems then return from these doublet states to the ground state by emission of very sharp lines which are also coherent and offer considerable opportunity for use in communications.

29-13. The Chemistry of Chromium(VI)

In this, its highest oxidation state, chromium forms compounds which are exclusively oxy compounds and all potent oxidizing agents. The parent oxide, chromic oxide, CrO_3, can be obtained as an orange-red precipitate on adding sulfuric acid to aqueous solutions of sodium or potassium dichromates. Chromium(VI) oxide is readily soluble in water. It is not thermally stable above its melting point (197°C.), losing oxygen to give, after a series of intermediate stages, Cr_2O_3. It oxidizes most forms of organic matter vigorously or even violently and is highly poisonous.

It is the aqueous chemistry of Cr^{VI} which is most important. In basic solution it exists as the yellow tetrahedral chromate ion, CrO_4^{2-}. Insoluble chromates such as those of Ba^{2+}, Pb^{2+}, and Ag^+ can be precipitated from these solutions. As the pH is lowered, solutions of chromate ions turn orange because of the formation of dichromate ions according to the equilibrium:

$$2CrO_4^{2-} + 2H^+ = Cr_2O_7^{2-} + H_2O \qquad K = 4.2 \times 10^{14}$$

This equilibrium is quite labile and, on adding cations which form insoluble chromates to moderately acid solutions, the chromates can be immediately precipitated. There is an additional equilibrium:

$$Cr_2O_7^{2-} + H_2O = 2HCrO_4^- \qquad K = 3.0 \times 10^{-2}$$

Acid solutions of dichromate are powerful oxidizing agents:

$$2Cr^{3+} + 7H_2O = Cr_2O_7^{2-} + 14H^+ + 6e \qquad E^0 = -1.33 \text{ v.}$$

The chromate ion in basic solution is much less oxidizing, however:

$$Cr(OH)_3(s) + 5OH^- = CrO_4^{2-} + 4H_2O + 3e \qquad E^0 = 0.13 \text{ v.}$$

Chromium(VI) does not give rise to the extensive and complex series of poly acids and anions characteristic of the somewhat less acidic oxides of V^V, Mo^{VI}, and W^{VI}. Other than the chromate and dichromate ions there are no oxy acids or anions of major importance, although trichromates, $M^I_2Cr_3O_{10}$, and tetrachromates, $M^I_2Cr_4O_{13}$, have been reported. The dichromate ion in the ammonium salt has the structure shown in Figure 29-4.

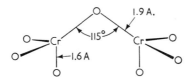

Fig. 29-4.   The structure of the dichromate ion as found in $(NH_4)_2Cr_2O_7$.

Chromium(VI) also exists in a series of halochromate anions, CrO_3X^-, formed with all of the halogens. When potassium dichromate solution containing excess HCl is boiled and then cooled, orange crystals of potassium chlorochromate, $K[CrO_3Cl]$, separate. It can be recrystallized from hydrochloric acid, but is hydrolyzed by pure water:

$$2CrO_3Cl^- + H_2O = Cr_2O_7^{2-} + 2H^+ + 2Cl^-$$

The potassium salts of CrO_3F^-, CrO_3Br^-, and CrO_3I^- are obtained in a similar manner. They owe their existence to the fact that dichromate, though a powerful oxidizing agent, is kinetically slow in its oxidizing action toward the halide ions.

One more type of chromium(VI) compound of note is exemplified by chromyl chloride, CrO_2Cl_2, a deep red liquid boiling at 117°C. It is formed by the action of hydrogen chloride on chromium(VI) oxide

$$CrO_3 + 2HCl = CrO_2Cl_2 + H_2O$$

by warming dichromate with alkali metal chloride in concentrated sulfuric acid:

$$K_2Cr_2O_7 + 4KCl + 3H_2SO_4 = 2CrO_2Cl_2 + 3K_2SO_4 + 3H_2O$$

and in other ways. It is photosensitive but otherwise rather stable, although it vigorously oxidizes organic matter. It is hydrolyzed by water to chromate ion and hydrochloric acid.

Chromyl fluoride, CrO_2F_2, obtained by the action of fluorine on chromyl chloride or by treatment of CrO_3 with anhydrous HF, is a red-brown gas condensing to a deep red-violet solid at 30°C. Some other chromyl compounds such as the acetate have also been reported.

Finally, it must be mentioned that a considerable number of peroxychromates are known. These compounds are all more or less unstable, both in and out of solution, decomposing slowly with the evolution of oxygen, and some of them are explosive or flammable in air. For these and other reasons they are not fully understood structurally. The main ones are deep blue chromium peroxide, CrO_5, the blue peroxychromates, $M^I_2[Cr_2O_{12}]$, the red peroxychromates, $M^I_3CrO_8$, and the addition compounds of CrO_4.

When acid dichromate solutions are treated with hydrogen peroxide, a deep blue color appears but does not persist long. The species responsible for it decomposes yielding Cr^{III} aquo ions. However, the blue species may be extracted into ether where it is more stable and, on addition of pyridine to the ether solution, the compound $pyCrO_5$, a monomer in benzene and essentially diamagnetic, is obtained. These facts lead to the formulation of the blue species as aquo, ether, or pyridine adducts of the molecule CrO_5 (29-V) containing Cr^{VI}. In aqueous solution, the main equilibrium is

$$HCrO_4^- + 2H_2O_2 + H^+ = CrO_5 + 3H_2O$$

When ice-cold solutions of ammonium dichromate are treated with 30% hydrogen peroxide and potassium or thallous ions added, the blue salts

$M^I_2[Cr_2O_{12}]$ crystallize. The thallous salt has been shown to be diamagnetic and to contain 2.5 peroxy groups per chromium atom. On the basis of these facts the $[Cr_2O_{12}]^{2-}$ ion is believed to have the constitution shown in 29-VI and thus contains Cr^{VI}.

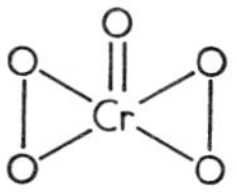

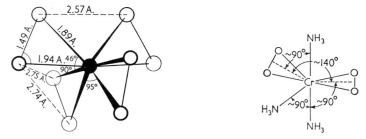

(29-V) 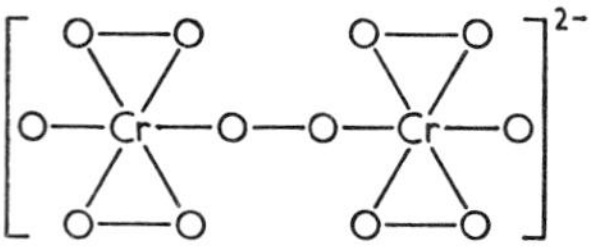   (29-VI)

On treatment of alkaline chromate solutions with 30% hydrogen peroxide—and after further manipulations—the red-brown peroxychromates, $M^I_3CrO_8$, can be isolated. They are paramagnetic with one unpaired electron per formula unit and K_3CrO_8 forms mixed crystals with K_3NbO_8 and K_3TaO_8, in both of which the heavy metals are pentavalent. On these facts, the $CrO_8{}^{3-}$ ion is formulated as a peroxy complex of Cr^V (Fig. 29-5).

Fig. 29-5.   The structure of the $CrO_8{}^{3-}$ ion. (Reprinted with permission from Stromberg and Brosset, *Acta Chem. Scand.*, **14,** 441 (1960).)

Fig. 29-6.   The structure of $(NH_3)_3CrO_4$.

When the reaction mixture used in preparing $(NH_4)_3CrO_8$ is heated to 50°C. and then cooled to 0°C., brown crystals of $(NH_3)_3CrO_4$ are obtained. From this, on gentle warming with KCN solutions, $K_3[CrO_4(CN)_3]$ is obtained. An X-ray study of the ammonia compound has revealed the structure shown in Figure 29-6. Thus, the chromium is in a lower valence state. It has been suggested that it be considered as Cr^{II} coordinated by two superoxide ions. In view of the magnetic susceptibility data which show the presence of two unpaired electrons, this would require the rather unlikely assumption that the Cr^{II} is here diamagnetic. It seems more natural to consider that the compound contains Cr^{IV}, with two unpaired electrons, coordinated by peroxide ions.

29-14. Chromium(IV) and Chromium(V) Compounds

Chromium(IV) compounds include the fluoride which is the major product of the action of fluorine on Cr^{III} fluoride or chloride. CrF_4 is a brown, volatile solid, which has a noticeable blue-grey vapor at 150°C. The complex salts $M^I_2CrF_6$ (M = K, Rb, Cs) can also be obtained by fluorination of a mixture of M^ICl and Cr^{III} chloride. It decomposes on standing. $CrBr_4$ appears to exist in the vapor when $CrBr_3$ is heated in bromine at temperatures in the range 400–800°C., but the solid compound cannot be isolated. There are data indicating that $CrCl_3$ in Cl_2 behaves similarly.

There are also some mixed oxides, $M^{II}_2CrO_4$, $M^{II}_3CrO_5$, and $M^{II}_4CrO_6$, with alkaline earths. Of these only blue-black Ba_2CrO_4 has been well characterized. It has a magnetic moment of 2.83 B.M., and an incomplete X-ray structure study indicates that discrete CrO_4^{4-} ions are present, although the structure is not the same as that of Ba_2TiO_4 (page 669) as had been claimed earlier.

It is also possible to prepare CrO_2 in several ways of which perhaps the best is by thermal decomposition of CrO_3 at 350°C. under 16 atm. of O_2. This black, ferromagnetic substance has the rutile structure and appears prone to exist in a defect condition.

When dibenzenechromium is treated with di-*tert*-butyl peroxide, a deep blue sublimable compound, sensitive to air and moisture, is obtained. This is tetra-*tert*-butoxychromium(IV). It has a magnetic moment of 2.88 B.M.

Compounds of Cr^V are somewhat more numerous. In the preparation of K_2CrF_6 (see above) small amounts of a substance which appears to be CrF_5 sublime out of the reaction mixture. The oxyfluorochromates(V) can be obtained by treating CrO_3 mixed with KCl or AgCl with bromine trifluoride. The products, $KCrOF_4$ and $AgCrOF_4$, are extremely sensitive to moisture. Oxychloro compounds are obtained by reduction of CrO_3 with concentrated hydrochloric acid in presence of alkali metal ions at 0°C. These have the general formula $M^I_2[CrOCl_5]$.

There are also mixed oxides of Cr^V with Ba^{II} and Sr^{II}, having the compositions $M^{II}_3(CrO_4)_2$ and $M^{II}_5(CrO_4)_3(OH)$. Magnetic and X-ray data support their formulation as authentic Cr^V compounds, but no structural details are known with certainty.

When K_2CrO_4 is heated in a KOH melt containing some water and in the absence of oxygen, a clear green solution is obtained which contains the hypochromate ion, CrO_4^{3-}.

MANGANESE

As with Ti, V, and Cr, the highest oxidation state of manganese corresponds to the total number of $3d$ and $4s$ electrons. This VII state occurs only in the oxy compounds MnO_4^-, Mn_2O_7, and MnO_3F, and these compounds show some similarity with corresponding compounds of the halogens, in the instability of the oxide, for example. Manganese(VII) is powerfully oxidizing, usually being reduced to Mn^{II}. The intermediate oxidation states are known, but only a few compounds of Mn^V have been characterized; nevertheless, Mn^V species are frequently postulated as intermediates in the reduction of permanganates.

Although Mn^{II} is the most stable state, partly because of the half-filled shell (page 580), it is quite readily oxidized in alkaline solution. The oxidation states and stereochemistry of manganese are summarized in Table 29-5.

TABLE 29-5

Oxidation States and Stereochemistry of Manganese

Oxidation state	Coordination number	Geometry	Examples
Mn^{-III}	4	Tetrahedral	$Mn(NO)_3CO$
Mn^{-I}	5	Trigonal bipyramid	$Mn(CO)_5^-$, $[Mn(CO)_4PR_3]^-$
	4	Tetrahedral	$Mn(CO)_3NO$
Mn^0	6	Octahedral	$Mn_2(CO)_{10}$[b]
Mn^I, d^6	6	Octahedral	$Mn(CO)_5Cl$, $K_5[Mn(CN)_6]$, $[Mn(NCR)_6]^+$
Mn^{II}, d^5	4	Tetrahedral	$MnCl_4^-$, $MnBr_2(OPR_3)_2$
	4	Planar	$[Mn(H_2O)_4]SO_4 \cdot H_2O$
	6[a]	Octahedral	$[Mn(H_2O)_6]^{2+}$, $[Mn(SCN)_6]^{4-}$
	7	NbF_7^{2-} structure	$[Mn(EDTA-H)(H_2O)]^-$
Mn^{III}, d^4	5	Square pyramidal?	$[Et_4N][MnCl_5]$
	6[a]	Octahedral	$Mn(AcAc)_3$, $[Mn(C_2O_4)_3]^{3-}$, MnF_3 (distorted)
Mn^{IV}, d^3	6	Octahedral	MnO_2, $Mn(SO_4)_2$
Mn^V, d^2	4	Tetrahedral	MnO_4^{3-}
Mn^{VI}, d^1	4	Tetrahedral	MnO_4^{2-}
Mn^{VII}, d^0	3	Planar	MnO_3^+
	4	Tetrahedral	MnO_4^-, MnO_3F

[a] Most common states.

[b] Can be regarded as Mn^I.

29-15. The Element

Manganese is relatively abundant, constituting about 0.085% of the earth's crust. Among the heavy metals, only iron is more abundant. Although widely distributed, it occurs in a number of substantial deposits of good ores, the most important being *pyrolusite*, MnO_2. The other ores are mainly oxides, hydrous oxides, or the carbonate, and from all these, or the Mn_3O_4 obtained by roasting them, the metal can be obtained by reduction with aluminum.

Manganese is roughly similar to iron in its physical and chemical properties, the chief difference being that manganese is harder and more brittle but less refractory (m.p. 1247°C.). It is fairly electropositive,

$$Mn = Mn^{2+} + 2e \qquad E^0 = 1.18 \text{ v.}$$

and readily dissolves in dilute, nonoxidizing acids. It is not particularly reactive toward nonmetals at ordinary temperatures, but at elevated temperatures it reacts vigorously with many. Thus it burns in chlorine to give $MnCl_2$, reacts with fluorine to give MnF_2 and MnF_3, burns in nitrogen above 1200°C. to give Mn_3N_2, and, of course, combines with oxygen, giving Mn_3O_4 at high temperatures. It also combines directly with boron, carbon, sulfur, silicon, and phosphorus, but not with hydrogen.

29-16. The Chemistry of Divalent Manganese

This is the most important and, generally speaking, the most stable oxidation state for the element. In neutral or acid aqueous solution it exists as the very pale pink hexaquo ion, $[Mn(H_2O)_6]^{2+}$, which is quite resistant to oxidation as shown by the potentials:

$$\overset{-1.5 \text{ v.}}{\underset{-1.51 \text{ v.}}{Mn^{2+} \rule{2cm}{0.4pt} Mn^{3+} \rule{3cm}{0.4pt} MnO_4^-}}$$

In basic media however, the hydroxide, $Mn(OH)_2$, is formed and this is more easily oxidized, by air for example, as shown by the potentials:

$$Mn(OH)_2 \overset{-0.1 \text{ v.}}{\rule{2cm}{0.4pt}} Mn_2O_3 \cdot xH_2O \overset{+0.2 \text{ v.}}{\rule{2cm}{0.4pt}} MnO_2 \cdot yH_2O$$

Manganese(II) oxide is a grey-green to dark green powder made by roasting the carbonate in hydrogen or nitrogen or by reduction of higher oxides with hydrazine. It has the rock salt structure and is insoluble in water. It is not a very common or important compound. Manganese(II) hydroxide is precipitated from Mn^{2+} solutions by alkali metal hydroxides as a gelatinous white solid which rapidly darkens because of oxidation by atmospheric oxygen. $Mn(OH)_2$ is a well-defined compound—not an indefinite hydrous oxide—having the same crystal structure as magnesium hydroxide. It is only very slightly amphoteric,

$$Mn(OH)_2 + OH^- = Mn(OH)_3^-   K \sim 10^{-5}$$

Manganous sulfide is a salmon-colored substance precipitated by alkaline sulfide solutions. It has a relatively high K_{SP} (10^{-14}) and redissolves easily in dilute acids. It is a hydrous form of MnS and turns brown on standing in air owing to oxidation. If air is excluded, the salmon-colored material changes on long standing, or more rapidly on boiling, into a green substance, which is crystalline, anhydrous MnS.

MnS, MnSe, and MnTe have the rock salt structure. They are all strongly antiferromagnetic as are also the anhydrous halides. The superexchange mechanism (page 594) is believed responsible for their antiferromagnetism.

Manganese(II) forms an extensive series of salts with all common anions. Most are soluble in water, although the phosphate and carbonate are only slightly so. Most of the salts crystallize from water as hydrates. The anhydrous salts must in general be obtained by dry reactions or using nonaqueous solvents. Thus $MnCl_2$ is made by reaction of chlorine with the metal or of HCl with the metal, the oxide, or the carbonate. The sulfate, $MnSO_4$, is obtained on fuming down sulfuric acid solutions. It is quite stable and may be used for manganese analysis provided no other cations giving nonvolatile sulfates are present.

Manganese(II) forms many complexes, but the equilibrium constants for their formation in aqueous solution are not high as compared to those for the divalent cations of succeeding elements (Fe^{II}–Cu^{II}) as noted earlier (page 589), because the Mn^{II} ion is the largest of these and it has no ligand field stabilization energy in its complexes (except in the few of low spin). Many hydrated salts, $Mn(ClO_4)_2 \cdot 6H_2O$, $MnSO_4 \cdot 7H_2O$, etc., contain the $[Mn(H_2O)_6]^{2+}$ ion, and the direct action of ammonia on anhydrous salts leads to the formation of ammoniates, some of which have been shown to contain the $[Mn(NH_3)_6]^{2+}$ ion. Chelating ligands such as ethylenediamine, EDTA, oxalate ions, etc., form complexes isolable from aqueous solution. No hexahalo complexes have been isolated but $M^I_4[Mn(SCN)_6]$ salts can be crystallized as hydrates from aqueous solutions.

Square complexes also occur, although not many have been positively characterized as such. The dihydrate of bis(acetylacetonato)manganese(II) has a planar structure with the water molecules completing a distorted octahedron, and the planar arrangement probably remains in the anhydrous compound. $MnSO_4 \cdot 5H_2O$ is isostructural with $CuSO_4 \cdot 5H_2O$ and thus contains planar $[Mn(H_2O)_4]^{2+}$ units with sulfate oxygens more distantly coordinated.

A number of tetrahedral complexes are also known. These are not stable in contact with water or other donor solvents, but they exist in crystals and in solvents of only low or moderate polarity such as $CHCl_3$, CH_3CN, $C_6H_5NO_2$, etc. They include salts of the tetrahalo anions, $[MnX_4]^{2-}$, with large cations such as R_4N^+, R_4P^+, or R_4As^+, as well as neutral complexes containing triphenylphosphine oxide or triphenylarsine oxide and halide ions, for example, $[Mn(Ph_3PO)_2Br_2]$. Manganese(II) ions are also known to occupy tetrahedral holes in certain glasses and to substitute for Zn^{II} in ZnO. In tetrahedral environments, Mn^{II} has a green-yellow color, far more intense than the pink of the octahedrally coordinated ion, and it very often exhibits intense yellow-green fluorescence. Indeed most commercially used phosphors are manganese-activated zinc compounds wherein Mn^{II} ions are substituted for some of the Zn^{II} ions in tetrahedral surroundings, as for example in Zn_2SiO_4.

All of the complexes so far mentioned have five unpaired electrons. There are also some, such as $[Mn(CN)_6]^{4-}$ and $[Mn(CN)_5NO]^{3-}$, and the isonitrile complexes, $[Mn(CNR)_6]^{2+}$, which have only one unpaired electron.

29-17. The Chemistry of Manganese(III)

The chemistry of Mn^{III} is not extensive. In aqueous solution it is quite unstable, being easily reduced to Mn^{II}, and even in the absence of reducing agents the Mn^{III} aquo ion is subject to disproportionation, as the following equilibrium constant shows:

$$2Mn^{3+} + 2H_2O = Mn^{2+} + MnO_2(s) + 4H^+ \qquad K = 10^9$$

Mn_2O_3 occurs in nature as the mineral braunite and can be prepared by heating MnO_2 in air at temperatures of about 550–900°C. The product of oxidation of precipitated manganous hydroxide is hydrous manganese(III) oxide, $Mn_2O_3 \cdot nH_2O$, which on drying at 100°C. gives a definite hydrate $Mn_2O_3 \cdot H_2O$. This is also found in nature as the mineral manganite, and its true structure is better described by the formula $Mn(OH)O$. Manganese(III) also occurs in the oxide Mn_3O_4, which is obtained on heating Mn_2O_3 above 950°C. in air or above 1100°C. in oxygen. This substance is correctly formulated as $Mn^{II}Mn^{III}_2O_4$ and has a distorted spinel structure, which will be discussed on page 706.

The only simple halide known is MnF_3, which is a red solid obtained by the action of fluorine on manganese(II) iodide. This dissolves in water to give a red-brown solution which may also be obtained by dissolving the oxide Mn_2O_3 in hydrofluoric acid; from this solution the hydrate $MnF_3 \cdot 2H_2O$ may be crystallized as ruby red crystals. Dark red complex salts of the types M^IMnF_4 and $M^I{}_2MnF_5$ may be crystallized on addition of alkali metal fluorides to the solution.

No simple chloride, bromide, or iodide of manganese(III) is known, but dark red salts of chloro complexes, of the formula $M^I{}_2MnCl_5$, are known. The absence even of complexes with Br^- and I^- may be attributed to their being able to reduce Mn^{III}.

Manganese(III) acetate, $Mn(C_2H_3O_2)_3 \cdot 2H_2O$, is one of the best-known manganese(III) compounds since it is easy to prepare, relatively stable, and serves as a good starting point for the preparation of other Mn^{III} compounds. It is obtained by oxidizing a solution of manganese(II) acetate in hot glacial acetic acid with permanganate or chlorine; it comes out rather easily in the form of red-brown crystals.

Several phosphates and an acid sulfate of Mn^{III} are also known. The $[Mn(H_2O)_6]^{3+}$ ion occurs in the alum $CsMn(SO_4)_2 \cdot 12H_2O$.

In addition to the fluoro and chloro complexes mentioned, Mn^{III} forms several others of fair stability. Tris(acetylacetonato)manganese(III) is best prepared by reaction of Mn^{II} with permanganate in the presence of excess acetylacetone; even air will oxidize Mn^{II} in the presence of this ligand, making the preparation of pure bis(acetylacetonato) manganese(II) tedious. The tris(oxalato)-and tris(malonato)manganese(III) complex anions are also known, but they are not very stable toward heat, light, or water.

The only low-spin manganese(III) compounds reported are the salts of the $[Mn(CN)_6]^{3-}$ ion. Manganese(II) in the presence of excess CN^- is readily oxidized, even by a current of air, with the production of this ion which is first isolated from the solution as the Mn^{II} salt, $Mn^{II}{}_3[Mn(CN)_6]_2$, from which other salts are obtained.

29-18. The Chemistry of Manganese(IV)

This is not extensive; aside from MnO_2 the only stable compounds are a few complexes.

MnO_2 is a grey to grey-black solid, usually nonstoichiometric. It occurs extensively in nature and is one of the chief manganese ores. It can be prepared by mild ignition ($\sim$530°C.) of $Mn(NO_3)_2$ in air, and it also arises in a hydrated form by reduction of permanganate in basic solution. Its stability is due primarily to its insolubility, but it is readily attacked by reducing agents in acid solution. It is rather inert to most acids except on heating and then it does not dissolve to give Mn^{IV} in solution but instead functions as an oxidizing agent, the exact manner of this depending on the acid. With HCl, chlorine is evolved:

$$MnO_2 + 4HCl = MnCl_2 + Cl_2 + 2H_2O$$

and this reaction is often used for small-scale generation of the gas in the laboratory. With sulfuric acid at 110°C., oxygen is evolved and a Mn^{III} acid sulfate formed. MnO_2 can be fused with other metal oxides to give substances called *manganites*. With alkaline earth oxides, MO, for instance, substances of the compositions $MO \cdot \frac{1}{2}MnO_2$, $MO \cdot MnO_2$, $MO \cdot 2MnO_2$, $MO \cdot 3MnO_2$ and $MO \cdot 5MnO_2$ have been reported. Little is known of their structures, and they are in general not well characterized. MnO_2 dissolves in concentrated KOH to give a blue solution which contains equimolar amounts of Mn^V and Mn^{III}; Mn^{IV} is thermodynamically unstable in such solutions.

If $MnSO_4$ in sulfuric acid is oxidized with permanganate, black crystals of $Mn(SO_4)_2$ may be obtained on cooling. This substance is quickly hydrolyzed by treatment with water or dilute sulfuric acid to deposit hydrous MnO_2.

Complex salts include the chloro and fluoro salts, $M^I_2[MnX_6]$, the iodates, $M^I_2[Mn(IO_3)_6]$, and some curious glyceryl complexes such as $Na_2[Mn(C_3H_5O_3)_2]$.

29-19. Chemistry of Manganese(VI) and -(VII)

Manganese(VI) is known in only one environment, namely, as the deep green *manganate* ion, $[MnO_4]^{2-}$. This ion is formed on oxidizing MnO_2 in fused KOH with potassium nitrate, air, or other oxidizing agents. Only two salts, K_2MnO_4 and several hydrated forms of Na_2MnO_4, have been isolated in completely pure condition. Both are very dark green, in fact nearly black, in color.

The manganate ion is stable only in very basic solutions. In acid, neutral, or only slightly basic solutions it readily disproportionates according to the equation:

$$3MnO_4^{2-} + 4H^+ = 2MnO_4^- + MnO_2(s) + 2H_2O \qquad K \sim 10^{58}$$

Manganese(VII) is best known in the form of salts of the permanganate ion, $[MnO_4]^-$, of which the potassium salt is by far the commonest, being widely used as a laboratory oxidizing agent. $KMnO_4$ is manufactured on a large scale by electrolytic oxidation of a basic solution of potassium manganate. Aqueous solutions of MnO_4^- may be prepared by oxidation of solutions of Mn^{II} ion with very powerful oxidizing agents such as PbO_2 or BiO_3^-. The ion has an intense purple color, and crystalline salts look almost black. Solutions of permanganate are intrinsically unstable, and decomposition according to the equation

$$4MnO_4^- + 4H^+ = 3O_2(g) + 2H_2O + 4MnO_2(s)$$

takes place slowly but observably in acid solution. In neutral or slightly alkaline solutions in the dark, decomposition is immeasurably slow. It is, however, catalyzed by light so that standard permanganate solutions should be stored in dark bottles.

In basic solution permanganate functions as a powerful oxidizing agent according to the equation

$$MnO_4^- + 2H_2O + 3e = MnO_2(s) + 4OH^- \qquad E^0 = +1.23 \text{ v.}$$

In very strong base and with excess MnO_4^-, however, manganate ion is produced:

$$MnO_4^- + e = MnO_4^{2-} \qquad E^0 = +0.6 \text{ v.}$$

In acid solution permanganate is reduced to Mn^{2+} by excess of reducing agent,

$$MnO_4^- + 8H^+ + 5e = Mn^{2+} + 4H_2O \qquad E^0 = +1.51 \text{ v.}$$

but because MnO_4^- oxidizes Mn^{2+},

$$2MnO_4^- + 3Mn^{2+} + 2H_2O = 5MnO_2(s) + 4H^+ \qquad E^0 = +0.46 \text{ v.}$$

the product in presence of excess permanganate is MnO_2.

The addition of small amounts of potassium permanganate to concentrated sulfuric acid gives a clear green solution. If a little water is added, or if a large amount of $KMnO_4$ is added, manganese heptoxide, Mn_2O_7, separates as an unstable oil which is red by transmitted and green by reflected light. The oxide decomposes explosively on heating into oxygen and MnO_2 and with water gives a solution of permanganic acid.

The green solutions of $KMnO_4$ in concentrated sulfuric acid are unstable, but cryoscopic measurements on dilute solutions are consistent with the ionization

$$KMnO_4 + 3H_2SO_4 = K^+ + MnO_3^+ + H_3O^+ + 3HSO_4^-$$

At higher concentrations, MnO_3HSO_4 or MnO_4SO_3H may be formed. The visible and ultraviolet absorption spectra are consistent with a planar trigonal ion, MnO_3^+.

The only other manganese(VII) compound which has been reported is the oxyfluoride, MnO_3F.

29-20. Electronic Structures of Manganese Compounds

The electronic structures of manganese compounds, especially the complexes of Mn^{II}, are of unusual interest since they exemplify some important fundamental principles very clearly.

High-Spin Manganese(II) Complexes. Figure 29-7 shows the visible spectrum of the $[Mn(H_2O)_6]^{2+}$ ion. Mn^{II} in other octahedral environments has a very similar spectrum. Its most striking features are (a) the weakness

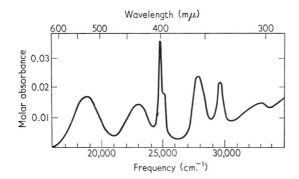

Fig. 29-7. The visible spectrum of the $[Mn(H_2O)_6]^{2+}$ ion obtained using an aqueous solution of the perchlorate.

of the bands, (b) the large number of bands, and (c) the great variation in the widths of the bands, with one being extremely narrow indeed. All of these main features of the spectrum are easily understood in terms of ligand field theory.

Let us consider first the weakness of the bands. It is because of their extreme weakness that the ion has such a pale color, and the many other salts and complexes of Mn^{II} in which the ion finds itself in octahedral surroundings are also very pale pink in color; finely ground solids often appear to be white. The reason for the weakness of the bands is very simple. The ground state of the d^5 system in a weak octahedral field has one electron in each d orbital, and their spins are parallel, making it a spin sextuplet. This same state is the ^6S ground state of the free ion, and it is not split by the ligand field. This, however, is the only sextuplet state possible, for every conceivable alteration of the electron distribution $t_{2g}^3 e_g^2$ with all spins parallel, results in the pairing of two or four spins thus making quartet or doublet states. Hence, all excited states of the d^5 system have different spin multiplicity from the ground state, and transitions to them are spin forbidden. Because of weak spin-orbit interactions, such transitions are not totally absent, but they give rise only to very weak absorption bands. As a rough rule such spin-forbidden transitions give absorption bands $\sim$100 times weaker than those for similar but spin-allowed transitions.

In order to understand the number and widths of the spin-forbidden bands, we must refer to an energy level diagram. Figure 29-8 shows a

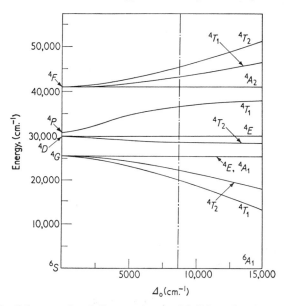

Fig. 29-8. Partial energy level diagram for the Mn^{II} ion, showing only the ^6S state and the quartet states. The separations of the Russell-Saunders states at $\Delta = 0$ are those appropriate for the $[Mn(H_2O)_6]^{2+}$ ion and the vertical line $(- \cdot - \cdot -)$ is at the Δ value (8600 cm.$^{-1}$) for this species.

simplified one for the d^5 system in which all spin-doublet states are omitted. Most of these are of very high energy, and transitions to them from the sextuplet ground state are doubly spin-forbidden and hence never observed. It is seen that there are four Russell-Saunders states of the free ion which are quartets, and their splittings as a function of ligand field strength are shown. It is found that the observed bands can be fitted by taking Δ equal to about 8600 cm.$^{-1}$. This is indicated by the vertical dashed line in the diagram. The diagram shows that to the approximation used to calculate it the ^4E and $^4A_1$ states arising from the ^4G term are degenerate. This is very nearly but not exactly so, as the slight shoulder on the sharp band at $\sim$25,000 cm.$^{-1}$ shows. It may also be pointed out that the energies of the Russell-Saunders states shown in this diagram are all lower than those for the free ion. This contraction in the separations of the free-ion states has been discussed more generally (page 595) as evidence for some degree of metal-ligand orbital overlap. It will also be noted that there are three states, the $^4A_2$ state from ^4F, the ^4E state from ^4D, and the ($^4E_1$, $^4A_1$) state from ^4G, whose energies are independent of the strength of the ligand field. Such a situation, which never occurs for upper states of the same spin multiplicity as the ground state, makes it unusually easy to measure accurately the decrease in the interelectronic repulsion parameters.

Theoretical considerations show that the widths of spectral bands due to d–d transitions should be proportional to the slope of the upper state relative to that of the ground state. In the present case, where the ground state energy is independent of the ligand field strength, this means that the band widths should be proportional to the slopes of the lines for the respective upper states as they are seen in Figure 29-8. Comparison of the spectrum of $[Mn(H_2O)_6]^{2+}$ with the energy level diagram shows that this expectation is very well fulfilled indeed. Thus the narrowest bands are those at $\sim$25,000 and $\sim$29,500 cm.$^{-1}$, which correspond to the transitions to upper states with zero slope. The widths of the other lines are also seen to be greater in proportion to the slopes of the upper state energy lines.

The reason why the band widths are proportional to the slopes is easy to grasp in a qualitative way. As the ligand atoms vibrate back and forth, the strength of the ligand field, Δ, also oscillates back and forth about a mean value corresponding to the mean position of the ligands. Now, if the separation between the ground and excited states is a sensitive function of Δ, then the energy difference will vary quite a bit over the range in Δ which corresponds to the range of metal–ligand distances covered in the course of the vibrational motion. If, on the other hand, the energy separation of the two states is rather insensitive to Δ, only a narrow range of energy will be encompassed over the range of the vibration. This argument is illustrated in Figure 29-9.

As we have already noted, tetrahedral complexes of Mn^{II} are yellow-green, and the coloration is more intense than that of the octahedral complexes. A typical spectrum is shown in Figure 29-10. First it will be noted that the molar absorbance values are in the range 1.0–4.0, whereas for octahedral Mn^{II} complexes (see Fig. 29-7), they are in the range 0.01–0.04. This factor of about 100 in the intensities of tetrahedral complexes over octahedral ones is entirely typical and will be seen again, especially for complexes of Ni^{II} and Co^{II}. The reasons for it are not known with complete certainty, but it is thought to be due in part to mixing of metal p and d orbitals in the tetrahedral environment which is facilitated by overlap of metal d orbitals with ligand orbitals in the tetrahedral complexes.

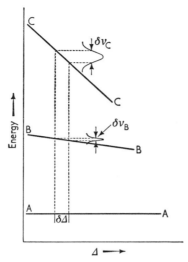

Fig. 29-9. Diagram showing how band width is related to the slope of the upper
state relative to that of the ground state. $A–A$ gives the energy of the ground state,
$B–B$ and $C–C$ the energies of two upper states as functions of the ligand field strength, Δ.
$\delta\Delta$ represents the range of variation of Δ due to ligand vibrations, and $\delta\nu_B$ and $\delta\nu_C$ are
the widths of the bands due to the transitions $A \rightarrow B$ and $A \rightarrow C$.

It may also be seen in Figure 29-10 that there are six absorption bands
in two groups of three, just as there are in $[\mathrm{Mn(H_2O)_6}]^{2+}$, but they are here
much closer together. This is to be expected since the Δ value for the tetrahedral complex, $[\mathrm{MnBr_4}]^{2-}$, should be less than that for $[\mathrm{Mn(H_2O)_6}]^{2+}$. From
the energy level diagram (Fig. 26-7) it can be seen that the uppermost band

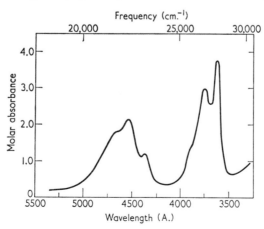

Fig. 29-10. The visible absorption spectrum of the tetrahedral manganese(II) complex,
$[\mathrm{MnBr_4}]^{2-}$.

in the group at lower energy should be due to the transition to the field-strength-independent ($^4E_1$, $^4A_1$) level, and this band does seem to be quite narrow, although it is partly overlapped by the other two in the group. The fact that this band occurs at $\sim$22,000 cm.$^{-1}$, whereas the corresponding band occurs at $\sim$25,000 cm.$^{-1}$ in $[\mathrm{Mn(H_2O)_6}]^{2+}$, provides evidence that there is greater orbital overlap leading to greater reduction of the Racah parameters in the tetrahedral than in the octahedral complexes. This is in accord with the suggestion made above that the greater intensity of the bands is due at least in part to greater orbital overlap.

Low-Spin Manganese(II) Complexes. Inspection of Figure 29-8 shows that a quartet state is destined to drop below the ^6S ground state. As noted above, however, we have omitted all of the doublet states from the diagram for clarity, and it turns out that one of these will cut the ^6S state first and will remain the ground state thereafter. Using a simple splitting diagram of the d orbitals we have already (page 568) reached the same conclusion, namely, that if Δ_0 becomes sufficiently large, the ground configuration will be t_{2g}^5, with one unpaired electron. It turns out that the pairing energy for Mn^{II} is quite high so that only a few of the strongest ligands, especially those which can increase Δ_0 by π-bonding are capable of causing spin pairing. Among the better-known low-spin complexes of Mn^{II} are $[\mathrm{Mn(CN)_6}]^{4-}$, $[\mathrm{Mn(CN)_5NO}]^{3-}$, and several isonitrile complexes of the type $[\mathrm{Mn(CNR)_6}]^{2+}$.

Manganese(III) Compounds. A simplified energy level diagram for d^4 systems is shown in Figure 29-11. It is consistent with the existence of

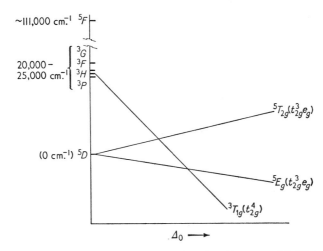

Fig. 29-11. Simplified energy level diagram for the d^4 system Mn^{III} in octahedral surroundings.

both high-spin and low-spin octahedral complexes. Because the next quintet state (^5F) above the ^5D ground state of the free ion is of such high energy, only one spin-allowed absorption band ($^5E_g \rightarrow {}^5T_{2g}$) is to be expected in the visible region. For $[Mn(H_2O)_6]^{3+}$ and tris(oxalato)- and tris(acetylacetonato)manganese(III) one rather broad band appears around 20,000 cm.$^{-1}$. The red or red-brown colors of high-spin Mn^{III} compounds may be attributed to such absorption bands. For the low-spin complex $[Mn(CN)_6]^{3-}$, there appear to be no transitions likely below frequencies where they would be obscured by strong ultraviolet bands, and none have been observed.

A most important feature of the high-spin ^5E_g ground state of Mn^{III} is that, according to the Jahn-Teller theorem, it must cause distortion in the surrounding octahedron and this distortion should be of appreciable magnitude because of the odd number of e_g electrons—one in this case. The underlying reasoning has been given on pages 582–586. In those cases where structural studies have been made, very significant distortions have been found. MnF_3 has the same basic structure as VF_3, in which each V^{3+} ion is surrounded by a regular octahedron of F^- ions, except that the octahedron in MnF_3 is quite irregular. Two Mn—F distances are 1.79 A., two more are 1.91 A., and the remaining two are 2.09 A. In Mn(OH)O, each Mn^{3+} has four near oxygens in a plane at distances of 1.85 and 1.92 A. and two more at 2.30 A. Finally, there is the distortion of the spinel structure (page 336) of Mn_3O_4. Here Mn^{2+} ions are in tetrahedral interstices and Mn^{3+} ions in octahedral interstices. Each of the latter tends to distort its own octahedron and the cumulative effect is that the entire lattice is distorted from cubic to elongated tetragonal.

Manganese(VI) and -(VII) Compounds. In the manganate ion there is one unpaired electron, but its behavior cannot be predicted by a ligand field treatment because the overlap of metal and oxygen orbitals is too great. Instead, a molecular orbital approach must be used. This is, of course, in no way surprising, for we surely could not expect to have an Mn^{6+} ion surrounded by O^{2-} ions without a great deal of electron density being drawn from the oxide ions to the Mn orbitals.

The permanganate ion has no unpaired electrons, but it does have a small paramagnetism which is temperature independent. Temperature-independent paramagnetism (TIP) of this sort occurs in other cases (e.g., CrO_4^- and many "diamagnetic" complexes of the heavier transition elements) and is due to interactions of diamagnetic ground states with excited states under the influence of a magnetic field.

IRON

With this element, the trends already noted in the relative stabilities of oxidation states continue, except that there are now no compounds or chemically important circumstances in which the oxidation state equal to the total number of valence shell electrons—eight in this case—is found. The highest oxidation state known is VI, and it is rare and of little importance. Even the trivalent state which rose to a peak of importance at chromium now loses ground to the divalent state. We shall see later that this trend continues, Co^{III} being stable only in complexes (of which, however, there are many) and Ni^{III} being found only in a few very special circumstances.

It is convenient to note here that the ferrous-ferric aqueous system provides a good example of the effect of complexing ligands on the relative stabilities of oxidation states,

$$[Fe(CN)_6]^{4-} = [Fe(CN)_6]^{3-} + e \qquad E^0 = -0.36 \text{ v.}$$
$$[Fe(H_2O)_6]^{2+} = [Fe(H_2O)_6]^{3+} + e \qquad E^0 = -0.77 \text{ v.}$$
$$[Fe(o\text{-phen})_3]^{2+} = [Fe(o\text{-phen})_3]^{3+} + e \qquad E^0 = -1.12 \text{ v.}$$

The oxidation states and stereochemistry of iron are summarized in Table 29-6.

TABLE 29-6

Oxidation States and Stereochemistry of Iron

Oxidation state	Coordination number	Geometry	Examples
Fe^{-II}	4	Tetrahedral	$Fe(CO)_4^{2-}$, $Fe(CO)_2(NO)_2$
Fe^0	5	Trigonal bipyramidal	$Fe(CO)_5$, $(Ph_3P)_2Fe(CO)_3$
	6	Octahedral(?)	$Fe(CO)_5H^+$, $Fe(CO)_4PPh_3H^+$
Fe^I, d^7	6	Octahedral	$[Fe(H_2O)_5NO]^{2+}$
Fe^{II}, d^6	4	Tetrahedral	$FeCl_4^{2-}$
	6[a]	Octahedral	$[Fe(H_2O)_6]^{2+}$, $[Fe(CN)_6]^{4-}$
Fe^{III}, d^5	4	Tetrahedral	$FeCl_4^-$, Fe^{III} in Fe_3O_4
	6[a]	Octahedral	Fe_2O_3, $[Fe(C_2O_4)_3]^{3-}$, $Fe(AcAc)_3$
	7	Approx. pentagonal bipyramidal	$[Fe EDTA(H_2O)]^-$
Fe^{IV}, d^4	6	Octahedral	$[Fe (diars)_2 Cl_2]^{2+}$
Fe^V, d^3	4	Tetrahedral	FeO_4^{3-}
Fe^{VI}, d^2	4	Tetrahedral	FeO_4^{2-}

[a] Most common states.

29-21. The Element

Iron is the second most abundant metal, after aluminum, and the fourth most abundant element in the earth's crust. The core of the earth is believed to consist mainly of iron and nickel, and the occurrence of many iron meteorites suggests that it is abundant throughout the solar system. The major iron ores are hematite, Fe_2O_3, magnetite, Fe_3O_4, limonite, $FeO(OH)$, and siderite, $FeCO_3$.

The technical production and metallurgy of iron constitute a vast subject which will not be discussed here. A good short summary will be found in H. Remy, *Treatise on Inorganic Chemistry*, Vol. II, Elsevier, 1956. Chemically pure iron can be prepared by reduction of pure iron oxide (which is obtained by thermal decomposition of ferrous oxalate, carbonate, or nitrate) with hydrogen, by electrodeposition from aqueous solutions of iron salts, or by thermal decomposition of iron carbonyl.

Pure iron is a white, lustrous metal melting at 1528°C. It is not particularly hard, and it is quite reactive. In moist air it is rather rapidly oxidized to give a hydrous oxide, $Fe_2O_3 \cdot nH_2O$, which affords no protection since it flakes off, exposing fresh metal surfaces. In a very finely divided state, metallic iron is pyrophoric. It combines vigorously with chlorine on mild heating and also with a variety of other nonmetals including the other halogens, sulfur, phosphorus, boron, carbon, and silicon. The carbide and silicide phases play a major role in the technical metallurgy of iron.

The metal dissolves readily in dilute mineral acids. With nonoxidizing acids and in the absence of air, Fe^{II} is obtained. With air present or when warm dilute nitric acid is used, some of the iron goes to Fe^{III}. Very strongly oxidizing media such as concentrated nitric acid or acids containing dichromate passivate iron. Air-free water and dilute air-free hydroxides have little effect on the metal, but hot concentrated sodium hydroxide attacks it.

At temperatures up to 906°C. the metal has a body-centered lattice. From 906 to 1401°C., it is cubic close-packed, but at the latter temperature it again becomes body-centered. It is ferromagnetic up to its Curie temperature of 768°C. where it becomes simply paramagnetic.

29-22. The Oxides of Iron

Because of the fundamental structural relationships between them, we discuss these compounds together, rather than separately under the different oxidation states. Three iron oxides are known. They all tend to be nonstoichiometric, but their ideal compositions are FeO, Fe_2O_3, and Fe_3O_4.

Iron(II) oxide can be obtained as a black pyrophoric powder when iron(II) oxalate is heated in vacuum. If heated to a higher temperature for a short time, it becomes less reactive. Crystalline FeO can only be obtained by preparing it under equilibrium conditions at quite high temperatures and quenching the system rapidly, for at lower temperatures it is unstable with respect to Fe and Fe_3O_4. If the high temperature FeO system is cooled slowly, disproportionation into these two substances takes place. FeO has the rock salt structure.

Iron(III) oxide, Fe_2O_3, is obtained as a red-brown powder on igniting $Fe_2O_3 \cdot nH_2O$ which is precipitated by ammonia from solutions of Fe^{III} ions; on stronger ignition it turns into a grey, crystalline mass and becomes insoluble in acids. As it occurs in nature, as the mineral hematite, it has the corundum (α-Al_2O_3) structure and is called α-Fe_2O_3. In this structure the oxide ions form a *hexagonally* close-packed array with Fe^{III} ions occupying octahedral interstices. However, by careful oxidation of Fe_3O_4 or by heating one of the modifications of FeO(OH) (lepidocrocite) one obtains another type of Fe_2O_3 called γ-Fe_2O_3. The structure of this phase may be regarded as a *cubic* close-packed array of oxide ions with the Fe^{III} ions distributed randomly over both the octahedral and tetrahedral interstices.

Finally, there is Fe_3O_4, a mixed Fe^{II}–Fe^{III} oxide which occurs in nature in the form of black, octahedral crystals of the mineral magnetite. It can be made by strong ignition of Fe_2O_3 (above 1400°C.) or by heating Fe_2O_3 to 250°C. *in vacuo*. It has the inverse spinel structure (page 336). Thus the Fe^{II} ions are all in octahedral interstices, whereas the Fe^{III} ions are half in tetrahedral and half in octahedral interstices of a cubic close-packed array of oxide ions.

The tendency of each of these oxides to be nonstoichiometric is due to the intimate relationship between their structures. In each case the structure may be visualized by starting with a cubic close-packed array of oxide ions and distributing a certain number of Fe^{II} and/or Fe^{III} ions among the octahedral and tetrahedral holes. Thus, when all of the octahedral holes are filled by Fe^{II} ions, we have the ideal FeO structure. If a small portion, x, of these Fe^{II} ions are replaced by two-thirds their number of Fe^{III} ions, we get the usual defect structure for ferrous oxide, for example, $Fe_{1-\frac{1}{3}x}O$, where x is commonly $\sim$0.15, giving $Fe_{0.95}O$. If this process is continued until two-thirds of the iron atoms are Fe^{III} and half of these migrate to tetrahedral sites, we have Fe_3O_4. Conversion of the remaining Fe^{II} to Fe^{III} gives γ-Fe_2O_3. The fact that each of these oxides can alter its composition in the direction of one or two of the others without there being any major structural change—only a redistribution of ions among the tetrahedral and octahedral interstices—accounts for their ready interconvertibility, their tendency to be nonstoichiometric, and, in general, the complexity of the Fe–O system.

29-23. The Chemistry of Iron(II)

Halides. All four are known in both anhydrous and hydrated forms. The iodide and bromide can be prepared by direct reaction of the elements, though when iron is burned in bromine there must be an excess of metal present to prevent formation of $FeBr_3$. The direct reaction of chlorine and fluorine with iron yields the iron(III) halides, but the action of hydrogen fluoride and hydrogen chloride on the metal affords FeF_2 and $FeCl_2$. Iron(II) chloride is also conveniently prepared by reduction of the heated trichloride with hydrogen or by reduction of a solution of the trichloride in tetrahydrofuran with excess iron filings.

The metal dissolves in the aqueous hydrohalic acids (and also slowly in water containing iodine), and from these solutions the hydrated iron(II) halides, $FeF_2 \cdot 8H_2O$, (colorless), $FeCl_2 \cdot 6H_2O$ (pale green), $FeBr_2 \cdot 6H_2O$ (pale green), and $FeI_2 \cdot 4H_2O$ (pale green), may be crystallized. The anhydrous fluoride and chloride may be obtained by heating the hydrates in a stream of the appropriate hydrogen halide. An X-ray structural study has shown that $FeCl_2 \cdot 6H_2O$ contains *trans* octahedral $[FeCl_2(H_2O)_4]$ units and not hexaquo ions.

Other Salts. Iron(II) forms salts with virtually every stable anion. These are almost invariably obtained as green hydrated substances by evaporating aqueous solutions of the appropriate composition. Typical ones are $Fe(NO_3)_2 \cdot 6H_2O$, $Fe(SO_4) \cdot 7H_2O$, $Fe(ClO_4)_2 \cdot 6H_2O$, $Fe(SCN)_2 \cdot 3H_2O$, and $FeC_2O_4 \cdot \frac{3}{2}H_2O$. It has been shown that the sulfate and perchlorate contain octahedral $[Fe(H_2O)_6]^{2+}$ ions. An important double salt is Mohr's salt, $(NH_4)_2SO_4 \cdot FeSO_4 \cdot 6H_2O$, which is quite stable toward both air oxidation and loss of water. It is commonly used in volumetric analysis to prepare standard solutions of iron(II) and as a calibration substance in magnetic measurements. Many other ferrous compounds are more or less susceptible to superficial oxidation by air and/or loss of water of crystallization, thus making them unsuitable as primary standards. This behavior is particularly marked for $FeSO_4 \cdot 7H_2O$, which slowly effloresces and turns yellow-brown on standing.

Iron(II) carbonate, hydroxide, and sulfide may be precipitated from aqueous solutions of ferrous salts. Both the carbonate and the hydroxide are white, but in presence of air they quickly darken due to oxidation. On long standing in contact with air, precipitated $Fe(OH)_2$ is eventually converted entirely into $Fe_2O_3 \cdot nH_2O$. The sulfide also undergoes slow oxidation.

$Fe(OH)_2$ is somewhat amphoteric. It readily redissolves in acids, but also in concentrated sodium hydroxide. On boiling 50% NaOH with finely divided iron and cooling, fine, blue-green crystals of $Na_4[Fe(OH)_6]$ are obtained. The strontium and barium salts may also be precipitated.

Iron(II) hydroxide can be obtained as a definite crystalline compound having the brucite $(Mg(OH)_2)$ structure.

Iron(II) sulfide has already been discussed along with FeS_2 with regard to their structures (page 414).

Aqueous Chemistry. Aqueous solutions of iron(II) not containing other complexing agents contain the hexaquoiron(II) ion, $[Fe(H_2O)_6]^{2+}$, which has a pale blue-green color. The oxidation potential of the reaction

$$Fe^{2+} = Fe^{3+} + e \qquad E^0 = -0.771 \text{ v.}$$

is such that molecular oxygen can convert ferrous to ferric ion in acid solution,

$$2Fe^{2+} + \tfrac{1}{2}O_2 + 2H^+ = 2Fe^{3+} + H_2O \qquad E^0 = 0.46 \text{ v.}$$

In basic solution, the oxidation potential is still more favorable,

$$Fe(OH)_2(s) + OH^- = \tfrac{1}{2}Fe_2O_3 \cdot 3H_2O + e \qquad E^0 = 0.56 \text{ v.}$$

Thus, ferrous hydroxide almost immediately turns dark when precipitated in presence of air. Neutral and acid solutions of ferrous ion oxidize *less* rapidly with increasing acidity (despite the fact that the potential of the oxidation reaction will become more positive). This is because Fe^{III} is actually present in the form of hydroxo complexes, except in extremely acid solutions, and there perhaps are also kinetic reasons.

Complexes. Iron(II) forms a number of complexes, most of them octahedral. The occurrence of the octahedral hexaquo ion in aqueous solution and in some crystalline hydrates has already been noted.

The ferrous halides combine with gaseous ammonia, forming several ammoniates of which the highest are the hexammoniates. X-ray studies have shown that these contain the hexammine ion, $[Fe(NH_3)_6]^{2+}$. Other anhydrous ferrous compounds also absorb ammonia. The ammine complexes are not stable in water, however, except in saturated aqueous ammonia. With chelating amine ligands, many complexes stable in aqueous solution are known. For example, ethylenediamine forms the entire series:

$$[Fe(H_2O)_6]^{2+} + en = [Fe\ en(H_2O)_4]^{2+} + 2H_2O \qquad K = 10^{4.3}$$
$$[Fe\ en(H_2O)_4]^{2+} + en = [Fe(en)_2(H_2O)_2]^{2+} + 2H_2O \qquad K = 10^{3.3}$$
$$[Fe(en)_2(H_2O)_2]^{2+} + en = [Fe(en)_3]^{2+} + 2H_2O \qquad K = 10^2$$

A considerable number of β-diketones (dike) form stable, inner-salt complexes, $[Fe(dike)_2]$, in which the ferrous ion is apparently four coordinated.

The famous brown ring test for nitrates and nitrites depends on the fact that, under the conditions of the test, nitric oxide is generated. This combines with ferrous ion to produce a brown complex. It appears that the formula of this complex in aqueous solution is $[Fe^I(H_2O)_5NO]^{2+}$. The iron is regarded as being formally in the $+1$ oxidation state, since the magnetic moment of 3.90 B.M. shows that only three unpaired electrons are present, and the stretching vibration of the NO is in the region characteristic of NO^+ (see page 627 for further discussion).

The hexacyanoferrate(II) ion, commonly called ferrocyanide, is an extremely stable and well-known complex of iron(II). It forms a vast number of salts with various cations. The free acid, $H_4[Fe(CN)_6]$, can be precipitated as an ether addition compound (probably containing oxonium ions, R_2OH^+) by adding ether to a solution of the ion in strongly acid solution. The ether can be removed to leave the acid as a white powder. It is a strong tetrabasic acid when dissolved in water; in the solid, the protons are bound to the nitrogen atoms of the CN groups with intermolecular hydrogen bonding.

Fe^{II} does not, so far as is known, normally form tetrahedral complexes. However, the tetrahalo complexes, $[FeX_4]^{2-}$, exist in salts with large cations such as $[(C_6H_5)_3(CH_3)As]^+$.

Finally, one of the most important and celebrated of all iron(II) complexes must be mentioned. This is the porphyrin complex called *heme* which exists associated with a globular protein in hemoglobin. The *heme* is an iron(II) complex of porphyrin, which is a substituted derivative of the porphin ring system (Fig. 29-12). Four of these units are present for each globin, and they appear to be attached to the protein by coordination

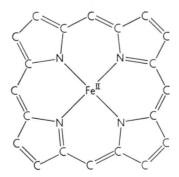

Fig. 29-12. The iron(II) complex of the porphin ring system. The actual molecule should be thought of as a resonance hybrid of this and other double bond arrangements. Heme itself has this nucleus with certain substituents on the periphery of the ring.

of imidazole nitrogen atoms in the globin to the iron atoms. In an aqueous medium the remaining coordination position is most likely occupied by a water molecule. The magnetic moment of each iron ion is 5.4 B.M., showing the presence of four unpaired electrons. When exposed to molecular oxygen, the iron combines with an oxygen molecule as indicated in 29-VII,

(29-VII)

simultaneously becoming diamagnetic. This process is one of *oxygenation*, not oxidation, for the oxygen can be pumped off again. It is by this mechanism that red blood cells "carry" oxygen from one part of the body to another. When the iron in heme is oxidized to give Fe^{III}, oxygen-carrying power is lost, and fairly powerful reducing agents are required to regenerate it. The iron can also combine with CN^-, CO, or PF_3 rather strongly, thus blocking the site for oxygenation. This is the reason for the poisonous nature of these and some other donor molecules.

Electronic Structures of Iron(II) Complexes. The ground state for a d^6 configuration is ^5D. This is the only quintet state, the higher states being triplets and singlets. Hence in weak octahedral ligand fields, the ground state is $^5T_{2g}$, and the only excited state of the same spin multiplicity is the ^5E_g state, also originating from ^5D. In sufficiently strong fields, however, it is possible for a singlet state arising from one of the excited free-ion states to drop far enough to become the ground state. These features of the energy level diagram (and a few others which will be of interest later in connection with the other well-known d^6 ion, Co^{III}) are indicated in Figure 29-13.

For iron(II) quite strong ligand fields are required to cause spin-pairing. Thus practically all iron(II) complexes are high spin, but some, such as the $[Fe(CN)_6]^{4-}$ and $[Fe(CNR)_6]^{2+}$ and $[Fe(o\text{-phen})_3]^{2+}$, are low spin (diamagnetic).

The spectra of the high-spin complexes consist of only the $^5T_{2g} \rightarrow {}^5E_g$ transition which in the aquo ion occurs around 1000 mμ. A tail of the absorption band runs into the visible at the red end, thus causing the characteristic, very pale, blue-green color of $[Fe(H_2O)_6]^{2+}$. This absorp-

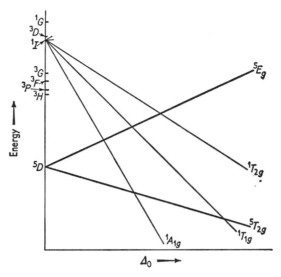

Fig. 29-13. Simplified energy level diagram for a d^6 ion in an octahedral ligand field.

tion band is actually split because of a Jahn-Teller effect in the ^5E_g state. The same thing happens with the isoelectronic high-spin Co^{III} complex $[CoF_6]^{3-}$, and this has already been discussed and illustrated on page 585.

29-24. The Chemistry of Iron(III)

Halides. The fluoride, chloride, and bromide are known, but the iodide does not exist in the pure state, although some of it may be formed in equilibrium with iron(II) iodide and iodine. In effect, iron(III) is too strong an oxidizing agent to coexist with a good reducing agent like I^-. In aqueous solution Fe^{3+} and I^- react quantitatively,

$$Fe^{3+} + I^- = Fe^{2+} + \tfrac{1}{2}I_2$$

The three stable iron(III) halides can be obtained by direct halogenation of the metal. The chloride and bromide are quite similar in their properties, both being red-brown, very hygroscopic (forming yellow-brown liquids), and volatile. If heated in vacuum, they both decompose with loss of halogen to give the iron(II) halides. In the gaseous state iron(III) chloride exists as dimers with a structure geometrically the same as those of the aluminum halide dimers up to about 700°C., where monomers begin to predominate. In contrast to $AlCl_3$, however, $FeCl_3$ does not exist in this form in the crystal. It has instead a semicovalent layer structure similar to that of $CrCl_3$ (see page 686 for a description). Ordinarily, iron(III) chloride is encountered as the hexahydrate, $FeCl_3 \cdot 6H_2O$, in the form of yellow lumps obtained by evaporating aqueous solutions on steam baths. The fluoride is obtained from aqueous solution as either the $4\frac{1}{2}$ or 3 hydrate, both pink. The anhydrous compound is green.

Other Salts. Iron(III) occurs in salts with most anions except those which are incompatible with it because of their character as reducing agents. The nitrate, perchlorate, and sulfate are obtained as pale pink to nearly white hydrates from aqueous solutions, namely, $Fe(ClO_4)_3 \cdot 10H_2O$, $Fe(NO_3)_3 \cdot 9(\text{or } 6)H_2O$, and $Fe_2(SO_4)_3 \cdot 10H_2O$. Other hydrates are also known.

Aqueous Chemistry. One of the most conspicuous features of ferric iron in aqueous solution is its tendency to hydrolysis and/or formation of complexes. It has been established that the hydrolysis (equivalent in the first stage to acid dissociation of the aquo ion) is governed in its initial stages by the following equilibrium constants:

$$[Fe(H_2O)_6]^{3+} = [Fe(H_2O)_5(OH)]^{2+} + H^+ \qquad\qquad K = 10^{-3.05}$$
$$[Fe(H_2O)_5(OH)]^{2+} = [Fe(H_2O)_4(OH)_2]^+ + H^+ \qquad\qquad K = 10^{-3.26}$$
$$2[Fe(H_2O)_6]^{3+} = [Fe(H_2O)_4(OH)_2Fe(H_2O)_4]^{4+} + 2H^+ \qquad K = 10^{-2.91}$$

In the last of these equations the binuclear species is written to imply the structure 29-VIII for the dimer, which, though it seems probable, is quite

(29-VIII)

unproved. From the constants for these equilibria it can be seen that even at the rather acid pH's of 2–3, the extent of hydrolysis is very great, and in order to have solutions containing Fe^{III} mainly (say $\sim99\%$) in the form of the pale purple hexaquo ion the pH's must be around zero. As the pH is raised above 2–3, more highly condensed species than the dinuclear one noted above are formed, attainment of equilibrium becomes sluggish, and soon colloidal gels are formed. Ultimately, as on addition of dilute aqueous ammonia to Fe^{III} solution, hydrous Fe_2O_3 is precipitated as a red-brown gelatinous mass.

There is no evidence that any definite hydroxide, $Fe(OH)_3$, exists, and most probably it does not. The red-brown precipitate commonly called ferric hydroxide should be described as hydrous ferric oxide, $Fe_2O_3 \cdot nH_2O$.

At least a part of such precipitates seems to be FeO(OH), which exists in at least two definite crystalline forms.

The various hydroxo species, such as $[Fe(OH)(H_2O)_5]^{2+}$, are yellow in color because of charge transfer bands in the ultraviolet which have tails coming into the visible. Thus aqueous solutions of ferric salts even with noncomplexing anions are yellow unless strongly acid.

Hydrous iron(III) oxide is readily soluble in acids but also to a slight extent in strong bases. On boiling concentrated solutions of strontium or barium hydroxide with ferric perchlorate, the hexahydroxoferrates(III), $M^{II}_3[Fe(OH)_6]_2$, are obtained as white crystalline powders. With alkali metal hydroxides, substances of composition M^IFeO_2 can be obtained. The latter can also be made by fusion of Fe_2O_3 with the alkali metal hydroxide or carbonate in the proper stoichiometric proportion. Moderate concentrations of what is presumably the $[Fe(OH)_6]^{3-}$ ion can be maintained in strongly basic solutions.

Just as the aquo ion readily loses protons to form the mono- and dihydroxy species, so also are halo complexes, also yellow in color, readily formed,

$$\begin{aligned} Fe^{3+} + Cl^- &= FeCl^{2+} & K &\sim 30 \\ FeCl^{2+} + Cl^- &= FeCl_2^+ & K &\sim 5 \\ FeCl_2^+ + Cl^- &= FeCl_3 & K &\sim 0.1 \\ Fe^{3+} + Br^- &= FeBr^{2+} & K &\sim 4 \end{aligned}$$

Perhaps the best-known reaction of aqueous Fe^{III} is with thiocyanate ion to form one or more thiocyanate complexes which have an intense red color and are therefore of use in the detection and quantitative estimation of trace quantities of Fe^{III}. The red color is destroyed by fluoride ion. Although salts of the FeF_6^{3-} ion can be prepared by dry methods, in aqueous solution the main equilibria appear to be

$$\begin{aligned} Fe^{3+} + F^- &= FeF^{2+} & K &\sim 10^5 \\ FeF^{2+} + F &= FeF_2^+ & K &\sim 10^4 \\ FeF_2^+ + F^- &= FeF_3 & K &\sim 10^3 \end{aligned}$$

Ferric iron in aqueous solution is rather readily reduced by many reducing agents, such as I^-, as already noted. It also oxidizes sulfide ion so that no ferric sulfide can be precipitated. On adding H_2S or a sulfide to Fe^{III} solution, a precipitate consisting of iron(II) sulfide and colloidal sulfur is obtained.

It may also be noted that ferric carbonate cannot be precipitated either; addition of carbonate or bicarbonate to an iron(III) solution precipitates the hydrous oxide.

Iron(III) Complexes. Iron(III) forms a large number of complexes, mostly octahedral ones, and the octahedron may be considered its characteristic coordination shell. It does also form a few tetrahedral complexes.

The hexaquo ion exists in very strongly acid solutions of ferric salts and presumably also in the highly hydrated crystalline ones. It is known to occur in the several ferric alums, $M^I Fe(SO_4)_2 \cdot 12H_2O$.

The affinity of iron(III) for amine ligands is very low. No simple ammine complexes exist in aqueous solution; addition of aqueous ammonia only precipitates the hydrous oxide. Chelating amines, for example, EDTA, do form some definite complexes. Also, those amines such as α,α-dipyridyl and o-phenanthroline which produce ligand fields strong enough to cause spin-pairing form fairly stable complexes, isolable in crystalline form with large anions such as perchlorate.

Iron(III) has its greatest affinity for ligands which coordinate via oxygen, especially monophosphate ions, $H_n PO_4^{(3-n)-}$, polyphosphates, and polyols such as glycerine, sugars, etc. With oxalate the trisoxalato complex, $[Fe(C_2O_4)_3]^{3-}$, and with β-diketones the neutral $[Fe(dike)_3]$ complexes are formed. Formation of complexes with β-diketones is the cause of the intense colors that develop when they are added to solutions of ferric ion, and this serves as a useful diagnostic test for them.

Important complexes are formed with halide and pseudohalide ions. The formation of FeX^{2+} and FeX_2^+ species in aqueous solution has already been noted. The hexachloro- and hexathiocyanatoferrate(III) complexes can be isolated; the more common halo complexes appear to be the penta species, for example, $[FeF_5H_2O]^{2-}$. With cyanide ion only the hexacyano-ferrate(III) ion, commonly called the ferricyanide ion, and some penta-cyano species are known. All of these are of low spin (one unpaired electron). The pentacyano species $[Fe(CN)_5X]$ ($X = H_2O$ and NO_2) are known. $[Fe(CN)_6]^{3-}$ is quite poisonous, in contrast to $[Fe(CN)_6]^{4-}$, which is not; this is a kinetic effect, the former dissociating or reacting rapidly and the latter only slowly. The free acid, $H_3[Fe(CN)_6]$, is known as well as many salts of which the potassium one is most common.

It has long been known that on treating a solution of Fe^{III} with hexa-cyanoferrate(II) a blue precipitate called *prussian blue* is formed, and that on treating a solution of Fe^{II} with hexacyanoferrate(III) a blue precipitate called *Turnbull's blue* is formed. It appears probable that these substances are actually identical, having the formulas $M^I FeFe(CN)_6$, where M^I is Na, K, Rb, but not Li or Cs. Their structure is closely related to those of brown ferric ferricyanide, $FeFe(CN)_6$, the white, insoluble potassium ferrous ferrocyanide, $K_2 FeFe(CN)_6$, and a number of similar compounds such as $KCu^{II}Fe(CN)_6$, and $Cu^{II}_2 Fe(CN)_6$. In all cases the basic structural feature seems to be a cubic array of iron ions with CN^- ions along cube edges between them. In $Fe^{III}Fe^{III}(CN)_6$ this is the complete structure, except for water molecules inside some of the cubes. In $M^IFe^{II}Fe^{III}(CN)_6$ every other cube contains an M^I ion at its center, and in $M^I_2Fe^{II}Fe^{II}(CN)_6$ every cube contains an M^I ion at its center. Other compounds such as the Cu^{II} salts appear to have the same sort of structure.

Iron(III) and also chromium(III) and aluminum(III) form basic acetates of the type $[M_3(OCOCH_3)_6(OH)_2]^+$, usually when the nitrates are treated with acetic anhydride. Although the structures are not proved, it appears that they may have a central oxygen coordinated by three planar metal atoms with bridging acetate groups.

Electronic Structures of Iron(III) Compounds. Iron(III) is isoelectronic with manganese(II), discussed in Section 29-16. Although the energy level diagrams of Fe^{III} and Mn^{II} are identical except for exact energies of the Russell-Saunders states of the free ions and for the somewhat stronger Δ values to be expected for the trivalent ion, much less is known of the details of Fe^{III} spectra. This is because of the very much greater tendency of the trivalent ion to have charge transfer bands in the near ultraviolet which have sufficiently strong low energy wings in the visible to obscure almost completely—or completely in many cases—the very weak, spin-forbidden d–d bands. Insofar as they are known, however, the spectral features of iron(III) ions in octahedral surroundings are in accord with theoretical expectations. Charge transfer absorption is so strong in tetrahedral $[FeCl_4]^-$ that nothing is known of its d–d bands.

Magnetically, iron(III), like manganese(II), is high spin in nearly all of its complexes except those with the strongest ligands, of which $[Fe(CN)_6]^{3-}$, $[Fe(dipy)_3]^{3+}$, and $[Fe(o\text{-}phen)_3]^{3+}$ are well-known examples. In the high-spin complexes, the magnetic moments are always very close to the spin-only value of 5.9 B.M. because the ground state has no orbital angular momentum (being to a high approximation just the same as the ^6S state of the free ion), and there is no effective mechanism for introducing any by coupling with excited states. The low-spin complexes, with t_{2g}^5 configurations, usually have considerable orbital contributions to their moments at around room temperature, values of $\sim$2.3 B.M. being obtained. The moments are, however, intrinsically temperature dependent, and at liquid nitrogen temperature (77°K.) they are down to $\sim$1.9 B.M.

29-25. Compounds of Iron(IV) and Iron(VI)

Iron(IV). The best-known compounds of iron in this oxidation state are Sr_2FeO_4 and Ba_2FeO_4. Both are made by oxidation of the hexahydroxoferrates(III) with molecular oxygen at elevated temperatures:

$$M^{II}_3[Fe(OH)_6]_2 + M^{II}(OH)_2 + \tfrac{1}{2}O_2 \xrightarrow{\text{800--900°C.}} 2M^{II}_2FeO_4 + 7H_2O$$

X-ray studies have shown that these do not contain any discrete ferrate(IV) ions, although the compounds are commonly called ferrates(IV), but that they are mixed metal oxides, the barium one having the spinel structure (page 336).

The compound $[Fe^{IV}(diars)_2Cl_2][Fe^{III}Cl_4]_2$ has been reported (diars is the bidentate diarsine shown on page 529); the cation here is the only discrete Fe^{IV} complex to be reported so far. It has only two unpaired electrons, which may be due to the over-all strength of the octahedral field or to the further splitting of the d orbitals caused by the dissimilarity of the six ligand atoms.

Iron(VI). The ferrate(VI) ion, FeO_4^{2-}, can be obtained by oxidizing suspensions of $Fe_2O_3 \cdot nH_2O$ in concentrated alkali with chlorine or by anodic oxidation of metallic iron in concentrated alkali. It is also reported that when iron filings are fused with potassium nitrate, the melt becomes incandescent and on cooling dissolves in water to give a violet solution of K_2FeO_4. The red-purple ferrate(VI) ion is most easily precipitated with barium ion, but the very soluble sodium and potassium salts are also known.

The ferrate(VI) ion is relatively stable in basic solution, but in neutral or acidic solution it decomposes according to the equation:

$$2FeO_4^{2-} + 10H^+ = 2Fe^{3+} + \tfrac{3}{2}O_2 + 5H_2O$$

It is an extremely potent oxidizing agent, even stronger than permanganate. Thus it oxidizes ammonia to nitrogen, Cr^{III} to chromate, and arsenite to arsenate.

The ferrate ion is tetrahedral; the potassium salt has been shown to be isomorphous with potassium sulfate and chromate. It has, as expected, two unpaired electrons, exhibiting a magnetic moment of 3.06 B.M. at room temperature.

COBALT

The trends toward decreased stability of the very high oxidation states and increased stability of the II state, relative to the III state, which have been noted through the series Ti, V, Cr, Mn, and Fe, persists with cobalt. Indeed, the former trend culminates in the complete absence of oxidation states higher than IV under chemically significant conditions. The III state is stable relative to the II state only in the form of complexes, of which, however, there are a great many. There are also some important complexes of Co^I; this oxidation state is better known for cobalt than for any other element of the first transition series.

The oxidation states and stereochemistry are summarized in Table 29-7.

TABLE 29-7

Oxidation States and Stereochemistry of Cobalt

Oxidation state	Coordination number	Geometry	Examples
Co^{-I}	4	Tetrahedral	Co(CO)$_4^-$, Co(CO)$_3$NO
Co^0	4	Tetrahedral(?)	K$_4$[Co(CN)$_4$]
Co^I, d^8	4	Tetrahedral	[Co(CN)$_3$CO]$^{2-}$
	5	Trigonal bipyramidal	[Co(NCR)$_5$]$^+$
		Tetragonal pyramidal	(R$_2$CS$_2$)$_2$CoNO
	6	Octahedral	[Co(dipy)$_3$]$^+$
Co^{II}, d^7	4[a]	Tetrahedral	[CoCl$_4$]$^{2-}$, CoBr$_2$(PR$_3$)$_2$, Co^{II} in Co$_3$O$_4$
	6[a]	Octahedral	CoCl$_2$, [Co(NH$_3$)$_6$]$^{2+}$, [Co(diars)$_3$]$^{2+}$
Co^{III}, d^6	4	Tetrahedral	In a 12-heteropolytungstate
	6[a]	Octahedral	[Co(en)$_2$Cl$_2$]$^+$, [Cr(CN)$_6$]$^{3-}$, ZnCo$_2$O$_4$, [CoF$_6$]$^{3-}$
Co^{IV}, d^5	6	Octahedral	[CoF$_6$]$^{2-}$

[a] Most common states.

29-26. The Element

Cobalt always occurs in nature in association with nickel and usually also with arsenic. The most important cobalt minerals are smaltite, CoAs$_2$, and cobaltite, CoAsS, but the chief technical sources of cobalt are residues called "speisses," which are obtained in the smelting of arsenical ores of nickel, copper, and lead. The separation of the pure metal is somewhat complicated and of no special relevance here.

Cobalt is a hard, bluish white metal. Its density is about 8.8, and it has high melting (1490°C.) and boiling (3100°C.) points. It is ferromagnetic with a Curie temperature of about 1150°C. It dissolves slowly in dilute mineral acids, the oxidation potential being:

$$Co = Co^{2+} + 2e \qquad E^0 = 0.277 \text{ v.}$$

Metallic cobalt is relatively unreactive. It does not combine directly with hydrogen or nitrogen, and, in fact, no hydride or nitride appears to exist. The metal will combine with carbon, phosphorus, and sulfur on heating. It also is attacked by atmospheric oxygen and by water vapor at elevated temperatures, giving CoO.

29-27. Simple Salts and Compounds of Cobalt(II) and Cobalt(III)

In its ordinary aqueous chemistry, cobalt has two important oxidation states, II and III. In aqueous solutions containing no complexing agents, the oxidation to Co^{III} is very unfavorable:

$$[Co(H_2O)_6]^{2+} = [Co(H_2O)_6]^{3+} + e \qquad E^0 = -1.84 \text{ v.}$$

although in the presence of complexing agents, such as NH_3, which form stable complexes with Co^{III} the stability of trivalent cobalt is greatly improved:

$$[Co(NH_3)_6]^{2+} = [Co(NH_3)_6]^{3+} + e \qquad E^0 = -0.1 \text{ v.}$$

Trivalent cobalt is also more stable in basic than in acid media:

$$Co(OH)_2(s) + OH^- = Co(OH)_3(s) + e \qquad E^0 = -0.17 \text{ v.}$$

It will be noted that the potential for the oxidation in acid solutions containing no complexing anion is so high that Co^{III} in appreciable concentrations rapidly oxidizes water. Hence aqueous solutions of free Co^{III} are of little importance.

The relative instability of uncomplexed Co^{III} is evidenced by the rarity of simple salts and binary compounds, whereas Co^{II} forms such compounds in abundance.

Cobalt(II) oxide, an olive-green substance, is easily prepared by reaction of the metal with oxygen at high temperature, by pyrolysis of the carbonate or nitrate, and in other ways. It has the rock salt structure and is antiferromagnetic at ordinary temperatures. On firing it at 400–500°C. in an atmosphere of oxygen, the oxide Co_3O_4 is obtained. The nature of this substance has been definitely elucidated by magnetic and X-ray studies. It is a normal spinel containing Co^{II} ions in tetrahedral interstices and diamagnetic Co^{III} ions in octahedral interstices. It does not contain any Co^{IV}, as had once been supposed. There is no evidence for the existence of the pure cobaltic oxide Co_2O_3, although the monohydrate $Co_2O_3 \cdot H_2O$, whose true structure is unknown, is a definite compound. On being heated to about 300°C., it loses both water and oxygen, giving Co_3O_4.

The only apparently simple Co^{III} salts known are the fluoride, CoF_3, a hydrate of the fluoride, $CoF_3 \cdot 3.5H_2O$, and the sulfate, $Co_2(SO_4)_3 \cdot 18H_2O$. The anhydrous fluoride is prepared by fluorination of the metal or of another Co^{II} halide at 300–400°C. It is a brown powder instantly reduced by water. The hydrate is of uncertain nature. It separates as a green powder on electrolysis of Co^{II} in 40% HF solution. The blue sulfate, which is stable when dry but decomposed by water, is precipitated when Co^{II} in 8N H$_2$SO$_4$ is oxidized either electrolytically or by ozone or fluorine. Co^{III} also occurs in the alums MCo(SO$_4$)$_2 \cdot$12H$_2$O (M = K, Rb, Cs, NH$_4$), which are also dark blue and reduced by water. Presumably there are [Co(H$_2$O)$_6$]$^{3+}$ ions in the sulfate as there are known to be in the alum. It is noteworthy that the alums are diamagnetic. Cobaltic acetate precipitates from a solution of cobaltous acetate in glacial acetic acid on electrolytic oxidation. Its constitution is not known, but it perhaps involves some relatively stable complex of Co^{III}, since it dissolves in water but is only slowly reduced.

Cobalt(II) forms an extensive group of simple and hydrated salts. The parent base, cobaltous hydroxide, may be precipitated by strong bases as either a blue or a pink solid, depending on conditions, but only the pink form is permanently stable. It is rather insoluble ($K_{SP} = 2.5 \times 10^{-16}$) but somewhat amphoteric, dissolving in very concentrated alkali to give a deep blue solution of [Co(OH)$_4$]$^{2-}$ ions, from which Na$_2$Cd(OH)$_4$ and Ba$_2$Co(OH)$_6$ may be precipitated. Addition of sulfide ions or H$_2$S to solutions of Co^{2+} ion causes precipitation of a black solid, usually taken to be CoS and assigned a K_{SP} of about 10^{-22}. However, after standing a short while, this substance becomes far less soluble in acid than the above K_{SP} would indicate. The suggestion has been made that the initial precipitate transforms into a less soluble polymorph, but polymorphs do not usually differ so greatly in solubility. Another proposed explanation is that, in the presence of air, sulfide ion is oxidized and the precipitate is transformed into Co$_2$S$_3$ or CoS$_2$, both of which are quite insoluble. In favor of this theory is the observation that CoS precipitated in the absence of air retains its solubility in acid indefinitely.

The anhydrous halides of Co^{II} are all known. They may be obtained by direct union of the elements at elevated temperatures, or from hydrates by dehydration procedures such as:

$$CoCl_2 \cdot 6H_2O + 6SOCl_2 \rightarrow CoCl_2 + 6SO_2 + 12HCl$$

All of the anhydrous halides have structures in which the Co^{II} ion is octahedrally coordinated.

Hydrated cobaltous salts with all common anions are known. They are easily obtained by reaction of Co(OH)$_2$ with the appropriate acid or by metathetical reactions. So far as is known, all such hydrated salts are red or pink in color and contain octahedrally coordinated Co^{II}. In many there are [Co(H$_2$O)$_6$]$^{2+}$ ions.

29-28. Complexes of Cobalt(II)

Divalent cobalt forms numerous complexes of both octahedral and tetrahedral types. They are all labile, and many of those with the more strongly π-bonding ligands have a strong tendency to be oxidized by molecular oxygen; they must therefore be prepared in an inert atmosphere.

Addition of ammonia to aqueous solutions of cobalt(II) leads to the formation of the hexammine ion, $[Co(NH_3)_6]^{2+}$, and several crystalline compounds containing this ion may be isolated, for example, $[Co(NH_3)_6]Cl_2$. Similarly, chelate amines such as ethylenediamine and EDTA form octahedral complexes. With halide ions and NCS^-, aqueous Co^{II} forms deep blue tetrahedral complexes, and these may be isolated from solution as salts of large cations such as quinolinium ion, quaternary ammonium, phosphonium, and arsonium ions, and the K^+ and Cs^+ ions. Another fairly broad class comprises the neutral tetrahedral Co^{II} complexes of general formula $[CoL_2X_2]$, where L is a neutral ligand such as an amine, phosphine, arsine oxide, etc., and X is a halide or pseudohalide ion.

(29-IX)
Salicylaldehyde ethylenediiminocobalt (II)

(29-X)
Bis(iminooxalato) cobalt(II)

(29-XI)
Bis(o-aminophenol)cobalt(II)

(29-XII)
Bis(dimethylglyoximato)cobalt(II)

A third class of Co^{II} complexes is those of the inner salt type containing chelate ligands. One of these, with the ligand 29-XIII, is known to be

(29-XIII)

tetrahedral, but the structures of all others with three unpaired electrons are as yet unknown. Those with one unpaired electron are definitely planar as, for example, salicylaldehydeethylenediaminocobalt(II) (29-IX), bis(iminooxalato)cobalt(II) (29-X), bis(dimethylglyoximato)cobalt(II) (29-XI), and bis(o-aminophenol)cobalt(II) (29-XII).

The cobaltous cyanide system is most unusual. From the green solutions of Co^{II} in CN^- can be obtained purple crystals of $K_6[Co_2(CN)_{10}]$, which is believed to be dimeric with a Co—Co bond. The solution absorbs molecular hydrogen, with the formation of the colorless species $[Co^{III}(CN)_5H]^{3-}$, which can also be obtained by hydride ion displacement on $[Co(CN)_5Br]^{3-}$.

29-29. Electronic Structures, Colors, and Magnetism of Cobalt(II) Compounds

The Co^{II} ion has the electron configuration d^7, and its ground state configuration in an octahedral ligand field may be either $t_{2g}^5 e_g^2$ in weaker fields or $t_{2g}^6 e_g$ in stronger fields. Figure 29-14 shows a portion of the energy level

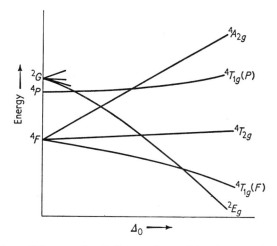

Fig. 29-14. A partial energy level diagram for a d^7 ion (e.g., Co^{II}) in an octahedral field. All of the quartet states are shown along with the $^2E_g(G)$ state which becomes the ground state in sufficiently high fields.

diagram for Co^{II} in an octahedral field. It is seen that at a sufficiently high value of the octahedral field a ^2E state originating in the ^2G state of the free ion will become the ground state. It turns out that this critical value is attained in reality with several of the stronger ligands. Thus, although octahedrally coordinated Co^{II} usually has three unpaired electrons, there are complexes such as $[Co(NO_2)_6]^{4-}$, $[Co(diarsine)_3]^{2+}$, and $[Co(tri-arsine)_3]^{2+}$ in which it has only one unpaired electron. The high-spin octahedral compounds have magnetic moments ranging from 4.7 to 5.2 B.M., that is, they have very high orbital contributions since the spin-only moment for three unpaired electrons is only 3.89 B.M. The reason for this high orbital contribution is given by detailed ligand field theory.

It will be seen from Figure 29-14 that an octahedrally coordinated Co^{II} ion should have three spin-allowed d–d transitions, those from the ground state, $^4T_1(F)$, to the states $^4T_2(\nu_1)$, $^4A_2(\nu_2)$, and $^4T_1(P)(\nu_3)$. The hexaquo cobalt(II) ion has the visible absorption shown as curve A in Figure 29-15.

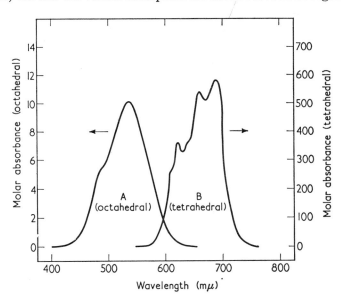

Fig. 29-15. The visible spectra of $[Co(H_2O)_6]^{2+}$ (curve A) and $[CoCl_4]^{2-}$ (curve B). The molar absorbance scale at the left applies to curve A, and the one at the right applies to curve B.

It has been shown by calculations that the shoulder on the higher frequency side is ν_3, whereas the main band is ν_2. From these assignments ν_1 would be expected to lie in the near infrared where it has indeed been observed. Note that the visible absorption is rather weak and placed in the blue part of the spectrum, thus accounting for the pale pink color of the aquo cobalt(II) ion.

Considerably less is known about the magnetic and spectral properties of low-spin octahedral cobaltous complexes, since they are relatively rare and, in the stronger ligand fields required to produce spin pairing, there is appreciable mixing of metal and ligand orbitals which makes a simple ligand field theory treatment of their electronic structures somewhat inadequate. The magnetic moments of these complexes are generally only a little above the spin-only value, that is, 1.8–2.0 B.M.

The energy level diagram for tetrahedral cobalt(II) is qualitatively the same as the one for octahedral Cr^{III} (see Table 26-3), and this has already been given (Fig. 29-3). From this it follows that tetrahedral Co^{II} complexes must have high spin regardless of the strength of the ligand field. This is, of course, the same conclusion which was reached by the simple orbital occupancy argument on page 569.

Figure 29-15, curve B, shows the visible absorption spectrum of the $[CoCl_4]^{2-}$ ion, which is a representative tetrahedral species. Note that this absorption is placed in the red part of the spectrum and is very intense compared to the absorption of the $[Co(H_2O)_6]^{2+}$ ion. This accounts for the deep blue color of this and most other tetrahedral Co^{II} complexes. This absorption band is due to the transition from the $^4A_2$ ground state to the $^4T_1(P)$ state. The fine structure is caused by spin-orbit coupling which both splits the $^4T_1(P)$ state itself and allows the transitions to the neighboring doublet states to gain some intensity. Like octahedral high-spin Co^{II} the tetrahedral ion has a magnetic moment appreciably in excess of the spin-only value, again because of an orbital contribution which is well understood theoretically. Moments of tetrahedrally coordinated Co^{II} run from about 4.1 to 4.9 B.M., and theory shows that in this case there is an inverse relationship between the magnitude of the orbital contribution and the strength of the ligand field (see page 572).

29-30. Complexes of Cobalt(III)

The complexes of cobalt(III) are exceedingly numerous. Because they generally undergo ligand exchange reactions slowly but not too slowly, they have, from the days of Werner and Jørgensen, been extensively studied and a large fraction of our knowledge of the isomerism, modes of reaction, and general properties of octahedral complexes as a class is based upon studies of Co^{III} complexes. All known Co^{III} complexes are octahedral, and a considerable number of representative ones have been mentioned in Chapter 25 as examples in general discussions. The Co^{III} and Cr^{III} complexes are very similar in most ways. Tetrahedral Co^{III} is known in a heteropolytungstate, however.

Co^{III} shows a particular affinity for nitrogen donors and the majority of its complexes contain ammonia, amines, such as ethylenediamine, nitro groups, nitrogen-bonded SCN groups, as well as halide ions and water molecules. In general, these complexes are synthesized in several steps beginning with one in which the aquo Co^{II} ion is oxidized in solution, typically using molecular oxygen or hydrogen peroxide and often a surface active catalyst such as activated charcoal, in the presence of the ligands. For example, on drawing a vigorous stream of air for several hours through a solution of a cobalt(II) salt, CoX_2 (X = Cl, Br, or NO_3), containing ammonia, the corresponding ammonium salt, and some activated charcoal, good yields of the hexammine salts are obtained:

$$4CoX_2 + 4NH_4X + 20NH_3 + O_2 = 4[Co(NH_3)_6]X_3 + 2H_2O$$

In the absence of charcoal, substitution usually occurs to give, for example, $[Co(NH_3)_5Cl]^+$ and $[Co(NH_3)_4(CO_3)]^+$. Similarly, on air oxidation of a solution of $CoCl_2$ ethylenediamine, and an equivalent quantity of its hydrochloride salt, tris(ethylenediamine)cobalt(III) chloride is obtained.

$$4CoCl_2 + 8en + 4en \cdot HCl + O_2 = 4[Co(en)_3]Cl_3 + 2H_2O$$

However, a similar reaction using entirely the ligand hydrochloride gives the green *trans*-dichlorobis(ethylenediamine)cobalt(III) chloride as the hydrochloride, which on heating loses HCl.

$$4CoCl_2 + 8en \cdot HCl + O_2 = 4 \ trans\text{-}[Co(en)_2Cl_2]Cl \cdot HCl + 2H_2O$$

This *trans* isomer may be isomerized to the red racemic *cis* isomer on evaporation of a neutral aqueous solution at 90–100°C. Both the *cis* and *trans* isomers are aquated on heating in water,

$$[Co(en)_2Cl_2]^+ + H_2O = [Co(en)_2Cl(H_2O)]^{2+} + Cl^-$$
$$[Co(en)_2Cl(H_2O)]^{2+} + H_2O = [Co(en)_2(H_2O)_2]^{3+} + Cl^-$$

and on treatment with solutions of other anions are converted into other $[Co(en)_2X_2]^+$ species, for example,

$$[Co(en)_2Cl_2]^+ + 2NCS^- = [Co(en)_2(NCS)_2]^+ + 2Cl^-$$

These few reactions are illustrative of the very extensive chemistry of Co^{III} complexes with nitrogen-coordinating ligands.

In addition to the numerous mononuclear ammine complexes of Co^{III}, there are a number of polynuclear ammine complexes in which hydroxo $(OH)^-$, peroxo (O_2^{2-}), amido (NH_2^-), and imido (NH^{2-}) groups function as bridges. Some typical complexes of this class are the following: $[(NH_3)_5Co\text{---}O\text{---}O\text{---}Co(NH_3)_5]^{4+}$, $[(NH_3)_3Co(OH)_3Co(OH)_3Co(NH_3)_3]^{3+}$, and $[(NH_3)_4Co(OH)(NH_2)Co(NH_3)_4]^{4+}$. The first of these may be further oxidized to give the binuclear cation $[(NH_3)_5CoO_2Co(NH_3)_5]^{5+}$, which formerly was thought to contain Co^{III}, O_2^{2-}, and Co^{IV}. It has more recently been shown by electron spin resonance and X-ray structural studies

(Fig. 29-16) that the two cobalt ions are entirely equivalent and that the single unpaired electron is distributed equally over both of them so that the above assignment of integral oxidation numbers is without meaning. It may be expected that this sort of delocalization of unpaired electrons will prevail in other polynuclear complexes with symmetrical structures.

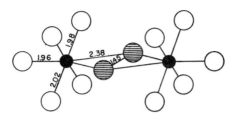

Fig. 29-16.   The structure of the ion $[(NH_3)_5CoO_2Co(NH_3)_5]^{5+}$. (Reprinted with permission from C. Brosset and N.-G. Vannerberg, *Nature*, **190**, 714 (1961).)

An important Co^{III} complex which occurs in nature is vitamin B_{12}. This enzyme contains the cobalt ion in a porphyrin-like ring coordinated by four nitrogen atoms, with the fifth position in the octahedron filled by an adenine nitrogen. The sixth position is often filled by a CN^- ion, but the ligand occupying this position, which seems to be the active site of the enzyme, is variable.

Some other Co^{III} complexes of significance are the hexacyano complex, $[Co(CN)_6]^{3-}$, the oxygen-coordinated complexes such as cobalt(III) acetylacetonate (29-XIV), and salts of the tris(oxalato)cobalt(III) anion

(29-XV). There is some evidence that the so-called cobaltinitrite, $[Co(NO_2)_6]^{3-}$, is a mixture of nitrito and nitro species in solution.

29-31. Electronic Structures of Cobalt(III) Complexes

The free Co^{III} ion has a d^6 configuration and thus has qualitatively the same energy level diagram as does Fe^{II} (see page 714). However, with Co^{III} the $^1A_{1g}$ state originating in one of the high energy singlet states of the free ion drops very rapidly and crosses the $^5T_{2g}$ state at a very low value of Δ. Thus all Co^{III} complexes known, including even $[Co(H_2O)_6]^{3+}$ and $[Co(NH_3)_6]^{3+}$, have diamagnetic ground states, with the one exception of $[CoF_6]^{3-}$, which is paramagnetic with four unpaired electrons.

The visible absorption spectra of Co^{III} complexes may thus be expected to consist of transitions from the $^1A_{1g}$ ground state to other singlet states. Although the entire energy level pattern for Co^{III} is not known in detail, the two absorption bands found in the visible spectra of regular octahedral Co^{III} complexes represent transitions to the upper states $^1T_{1g}$ and $^1T_{2g}$. In complexes of the type CoA_4B_2, which can exist in both *cis* and *trans* configurations, there are certain spectral features which are diagnostic of the *cis* or *trans* configurations, as shown in Figure 29-17. For a regular octa-

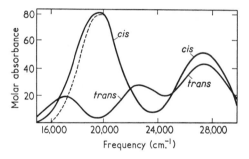

Fig. 29-17. The visible spectra of *cis*- and *trans*-$[Co(en)_2F_2]^+$. The dotted line shows where the low frequency side of the $^1A_{1g} \rightarrow {}^1T_{1g}$ band of the *cis* isomer would be if the band were completely symmetrical. The asymmetry is caused by slight splitting of the $^1T_{1g}$ state.

hedral Co^{III} complex, for example, $[Co(en)_3]^{3+}$, the energy level diagram will be as in Figure 29-18b, and two absorption bands will be found in the visible at $\sim$20,000 and $\sim$28,000 cm.$^{-1}$. When two of the six ligands are replaced by different ones, the lowering of the octahedral symmetry causes a splitting of the two upper states. Theory shows that the $^1T_{2g}$ state is not split observably, whereas the splitting of the $^1T_{1g}$ state should be at least twice as great for the *trans* compound as for the *cis*. These results are indicated in Figure 29-18a and Figure 29-18c. Moreover, because the *cis* isomer lacks a center of symmetry, it may be expected that if there is any difference in the intensities of absorption in the two isomers the greater intensity will be found in the *cis* isomer. It will be seen in Figure 29-18

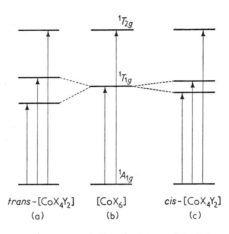

Fig. 29-18.   Diagrammatic representation (not to scale) of the energy levels involved in the transitions responsible for observed absorption bands of octahedral Co^{III} complexes. In the center, (b), are the levels for a regular octahedral complex, [CoX$_6$]. In (a) and (c) the splittings caused by the replacement of two ligands X by two ligands Y are indicated.

that qualitatively these predictions are nicely borne out by the spectra of *cis*- and *trans*-[Co(en)$_2$F$_2$]$^+$. More extensive studies have shown that so long as the two ligands, A and B, in complexes of the types [CoA$_4$B$_2$] and [CoA$_3$B$_3$], which also form *cis* and *trans* isomers, differ somewhat in their positions in the spectrochemical series, behavior of this kind is observed. Thus spectra provide a new and extremely useful criterion for identifying *cis* and *trans* isomers of Co^{III} complexes.

29-32. Tetravalent Cobalt

Compounds in this class are few and on the whole not well characterized. It has been reported that fluorination of Cs$_2$CoCl$_4$ gives Cs$_2$CoF$_6$, with a crystal structure isomorphous to that of Cs$_2$SiF$_6$ and a magnetic moment of 2.9 B.M. The latter value is difficult to explain, however, since the Co^{IV} ion would be expected to have either one or five unpaired electrons and the compound can be regarded as needing further characterization. The action of powerful oxidizing agents (e.g., Cl$_2$) on strongly alkaline Co^{II} solutions produces a material believed to be hydrous CoO$_2$, at least in part, but it is ill characterized. Ba_2CoO_4, a red-brown substance obtained by oxidation of $2Ba(OH)_2$ and $2Co(OH)_2$ at 1050°C., has been reported but not otherwise investigated. A heteropolymolybdate of Co^{IV}, namely, $3K_2O \cdot CoO_2 \cdot 9MoO_3 \cdot 6\frac{1}{2}H_2O$, has also been reported but not further investigated. It seems fairly certain that Co^{IV} is too unstable to have any very extensive chemistry.

29-33. Complexes of Cobalt(I)

Only a few of these are known, and all involve π-bonding ligands. Cobalt carbonyl reacts with isonitriles, disproportionating to Co^I and Co^{-I}:

$$Co_2(CO)_8 + 5RNC = [Co(CNR)_5]^+[Co(CO)_4]^- + 4CO$$

The ionic nature of the product, as indicated in this equation, is confirmed by the preparation of the same substance by the following reaction:

$$Na[Co(CO)_4] + [Co(CNR)_5]ClO_4 = [Co(CNR)_5][Co(CO)_4] + NaClO_4$$

Various salts of the $[Co(CNR)_5]^+$ cation, such as the perchlorate used above, can be prepared by the action of an excess of isonitrile on a Co^{II} salt or by first preparing the $Co(CNR)_4X_2$ compound and then reducing it with RNC or another reducing agent such as N_2H_4, $S_2O_4^{2-}$, or an active metal.

In polar solvents and at elevated temperatures triphenylphosphine reacts with cobalt carbonyl to give the cation $[Co(CO)_3(Ph_3P)_2]^+$ in the following disproportionation reaction:

$$Co_2(CO)_8 + 2Ph_3P = [Co(CO)_3(Ph_3P)_2]^+[Co(CO)_4]^- + CO$$

However, at a low temperature ($\sim$0°C.) in nonpolar solvents a genuine substituted cobalt carbonyl, $[Co_2(CO)_6(Ph_3P)_2]$, is produced. Both the $[Co(CNR)_5]^+$ and $[Co(CO)_3(Ph_3P)_2]^+$ ions are diamagnetic and have been shown by infrared study to have trigonal bipyramidal configurations. In the latter the phosphines occupy the apical positions. These Co^I complexes are rather similar to the various carbonyl and nitrosyl complexes in that the bonding involves a good deal of both σ and π orbital overlap.

It has also been reported that Co^{II} is reduced by CO in strongly alkaline solution containing CN^- to give $[Co(CN)_3CO]^{2-}$:

$$2Co^{2+} + 3CO + 6CN^- + 4OH^- = 2[Co(CN)_3CO]^{2-} + CO_3^{2-} + 2H_2O$$

NICKEL

The trend toward decreased stability of higher oxidation states continues with nickel so that only Ni^{II} occurs in the ordinary chemistry of the element, although Ni^{III} and Ni^{IV} occur in certain oxide systems and in a few complexes. Nickel(I) and Ni^0 compounds are scarcer still. Aside from nickel carbonyl and its derivatives (page 613) and organo derivatives (page 638), the only Ni^0 compounds reported are the copper-colored $K_4[Ni(CN)_4]$, which is obtained by treating $K_2[Ni(CN)_4]$ in liquid ammonia with excess potassium and is very unstable toward air and hydroxylic solvents, and the analogous acetylide complex, $K_4[Ni(C\equiv CH)_4]$, which is similarly prepared and is even less stable.

The oxidation states and stereochemistry of nickel are summarized in Table 29-8.

TABLE 29-8

Oxidation States and Stereochemistry of Nickel

Oxidation state	Coordination number	Geometry	Examples
Ni^{-I}	4?	?	$[Ni_2(CO)_6]^{2-}$
Ni^0	4	Tetrahedral	$Ni(PF_3)_4$, $[Ni(CN)_4]^{4-}$
Ni^I, d^9	4?	?	$K_4[Ni_2(CN)_6]$
Ni^{II}, d^8	4[a]	Square planar	$NiBr_2(PEt_3)_2$, $[Ni(CN)_4]^{2-}$
		Tetrahedral	$NiCl_4^{2-}$, $NiCl_2(PPh_3)_2$
	5?	?	$[Ni(CN)_5]^{2-}$
	6[a]	Octahedral	NiO, $[Ni(NCS)_6]^{4-}$, $KNiF_3$
			Ni $(dmg)_2$,[b] $[Ni(dipy)_3]^{2+}$
Ni^{III}, d^7	?	?	$Ni_2O_3 \cdot 2H_2O$
	5	Square pyramid	$NiBr_3(PEt_3)_2$
	6	Octahedral	$[NiCl_2(diars)_2]^+$
Ni^{IV}, d^6	6	Octahedral	K_2NiF_6, $[Ni(diars)_2 Cl_2]^{2+}$

[a] Most common state.

[b] Nitrogen atoms square planar about Ni with long Ni—Ni bonds.

29-34. The Element

Nickel occurs in nature mainly in combination with arsenic, antimony, and sulfur, for example, as *millerite*, NiS, red nickel ore which is mainly NiAs, as well as in deposits consisting chiefly of NiSb, $NiAs_2$, NiAsS, or NiSbS. The most important deposits commercially are *garnierite*, a magnesium-nickel silicate of variable composition, and certain varieties of the iron mineral *pyrrhotite* (Fe_nS_{n+1}) which contain 3–5% Ni. Elemental nickel is also found alloyed with iron in many meteors, and the central regions of the earth are believed to contain considerable quantities. The metallurgy of nickel is complicated in its details, many of which vary a good deal with the particular ore being processed. In general, the nickel ore is transformed to Ni_2S_3 which is roasted in air to give NiO, and this is then reduced with carbon to give the metal. Some high purity nickel is made by the *carbonyl process*. Carbon monoxide reacts with impure nickel at 50°C. and ordinary pressure or with nickel-copper matte under more strenuous conditions, giving volatile $Ni(CO)_4$, from which metal of 99.90–99.99% purity is obtained on thermal decomposition at 200°C.

Nickel is a silver-white metal with typically metallic properties. It has high electrical and thermal conductivities (both ~15% of those of silver), m.p. 1452°C., and it can be drawn, rolled, forged, and polished. It is quite resistant to attack by air or water at ordinary temperatures when compact and is therefore often electroplated as a protective coating. It is also ferromagnetic but not so much as iron. The finely divided metal is reactive to air, and it may be pyrophoric under some conditions.

The metal is moderately electropositive,

$$Ni = Ni^{2+} + 2e \qquad E^0 \approx 0.25 \text{ v.}$$

and dissolves readily in dilute mineral acids. Like iron, it does not dissolve in concentrated nitric acid because it is rendered passive by this reagent.

29-35. Chemistry of Divalent Nickel

In the divalent state nickel forms a very extensive series of compounds. This is the only oxidation state of importance in the aqueous chemistry of nickel, and, with the exception of a few special complexes of nickel in other oxidation states, Ni^{II} is also the only important oxidation level in its non-aqueous chemistry.

Nickel(II) Oxide. This green solid, which has the rock salt structure, is formed on heating the hydroxide, carbonate, oxalate, or nitrate of nickel(II). It is insoluble in water but dissolves readily in acids.

Nickel(II) Hydroxide. This may be precipitated from aqueous solutions of Ni^{II} salts on addition of alkali metal hydroxides as a voluminous green gel which becomes crystalline on prolonged standing. It is readily soluble in acid ($K_{SP} = 2 \times 10^{-16}$) and also in aqueous ammonia owing to the formation of ammine complexes. The crystalline substance is a definite hydroxide which, like the other hydroxides of divalent metals of the first transition series, has the $Mg(OH)_2$ structure. $Ni(OH)_2$ has little or no amphoteric tendency, and no nickelate(II) species of any kind have been reported.

Nickel(II) Sulfide. Addition of sulfide ions to aqueous solutions of nickel(II) ions precipitates black NiS. This is initially freely soluble in acid, but, like CoS, on exposure to air it soon becomes insoluble. Again this may be attributed to air oxidation of excess sulfide leading to the conversion of the simple sulfide to a much less soluble polysulfide.

Nickel(II) Halides.   All four are known in the anhydrous state. They can be prepared by direct reaction of the elements, except for the fluoride which is best made by heating the double salt $(NH_4)_2NiF_4$. All of the halides are soluble in water (the fluoride only moderately so), and from aqueous solutions they can be crystallized as the hexahydrates, except for the fluoride which gives $NiF_2 \cdot 3H_2O$. Lower hydrates are obtained from these on standing or on heating. The hydrates of $NiCl_2$ may be converted to the anhydrous chloride on heating in a stream of HCl.

Nickel(II) Cyanide.   This compound is precipitated in a green hydrated form on addition of CN^- ions to aqueous Ni^{II}. On heating at 180–200°C. the hydrate is converted to the yellow-brown, anhydrous $Ni(CN)_2$. The green precipitate readily redissolves in excess cyanide to form the yellow $[Ni(CN)_4]^{2-}$ ion, and many hydrated salts of this ion, for example, $Na_2[Ni(CN)_4] \cdot 3H_2O$, may be crystallized from such solutions. In strong cyanide solutions a further CN^- is taken up to give the $[Ni(CN)_5]^{3-}$ ion. Nickel(II) thiocyanate is also known as a yellow-brown (probably hydrated) precipitate obtained on concentrating the green solutions resulting from the reaction:

$$NiSO_4(aq) + Ba(SCN)_2(aq) = BaSO_4(s) + Ni(SCN)_2(aq)$$

It reacts with excess SCN^- to form complex ions, $[Ni(NCS)_4]^{2-}$ and $[Ni(NCS)_6]^{4-}$, which can be isolated in crystalline complexes.

Other Binary Nickel(II) Compounds.   A number of binary nickel compounds, probably all containing Ni^{II} but not all stoichiometric, may be obtained by direct reaction of nickel with various nonmetals such as P, As, Sb, S, Se, Te, C, and B. Nickel does not appear to form a nitride nor is the existence of a hydride certain, although the finely divided metal absorbs hydrogen in considerable amounts.

Salts of Oxy Acids.   A large number of these are known. They occur most commonly as hydrates, for example, $Ni(NO_3)_2 \cdot 6H_2O$, $NiSO_4 \cdot 7H_2O$, and most of them are soluble in water. Exceptions are the carbonate, $NiCO_3 \cdot 6H_2O$, which precipitates on addition of alkali bicarbonates to solutions of Ni^{II}, and the phosphate, $Ni_3(PO_4)_2 \cdot 7(?)H_2O$.

The Hexaquonickel(II) Ion.   Aqueous solutions of Ni^{II} not containing strong complexing agents contain the green hexaquonickel(II) ion, $[Ni(H_2O)_6]^{2+}$. This ion also occurs in a number of hydrated nickel(II) salts, for example in $Ni(NO_3)_2 \cdot 6H_2O$, $Ni(SO_4) \cdot 6H_2O$, $NiSO_4 \cdot 7H_2O$, $Ni(ClO_4)_2 \cdot 6H_2O$, but not in $NiCl_2 \cdot 6H_2O$ which contains instead *trans-*

[NiCl$_2$(H$_2$O)$_4$] units. It is quite labile as are nickel(II) complexes in general.

29-36. Stereochemistry and Electronic Structures of Nickel(II) Complexes

Nickel(II) forms a large number of complexes, almost all of which are of one or another of three structural types, namely, octahedral, tetrahedral, or square.

Octahedral Complexes. The maximum coordination number of nickel(II) is 6. A considerable number of neutral ligands, especially amines, displace some or all of the water molecules in the octahedral [Ni(H$_2$O)$_6$]$^{2+}$, ion to form complexes such as *trans*-[Ni(H$_2$O)$_2$(NH$_3$)$_4$](NO$_3$)$_2$, [Ni(NH$_3$)$_6$] (ClO$_4$)$_2$, [Ni(en)$_3$]SO$_4$, etc. Such ammine complexes characteristically have blue or purple colors in contrast to the bright green color of the hexaquonickel ion. This is because of shifts in the absorption bands when H$_2$O ligands are replaced by others lying toward the stronger end of the spectrochemical series. This can be seen in Figure 29-19, where the spectra of [Ni(H$_2$O)$_6$]$^{2+}$ and

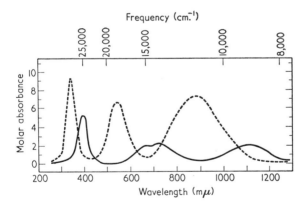

Fig. 29-19. Absorption spectra of [Ni(H$_2$O)$_6$]$^{2+}$ (———) and [Ni(en)$_3$]$^{2+}$ (– – – – – –).

[Ni(en)$_3$]$^{2+}$ are shown. These spectra can readily be interpreted by referring to the energy level diagram for d^8 ions (Fig. 26-15, page 577). It is seen that three spin-allowed transitions are expected, and the three observed bands in each spectrum may thus be assigned as shown in Table 29-9. It is a characteristic feature of the spectra of octahedral nickel(II) complexes, exemplified by those of [Ni(H$_2$O)$_6$]$^{2+}$ and [Ni(en)$_3$]$^{2+}$, that molar absorbances

TABLE 29-9

Spectra of Octahedral Nickel(II) Complexes
(Approximate band positions in cm.$^{-1}$)

Transition	$[Ni(H_2O)_6]^{2+}$	$[Ni(en)_3]^{2+}$
$^3A_{2g} \rightarrow {}^3T_{2g}$	9,000	11,000
$^3A_{2g} \rightarrow {}^3T_{1g}(F)$	14,000	18,500
$^3A_{2g} \rightarrow {}^3T_{1g}(P)$	25,000	30,000

of the bands are at the low end of the range (1–100) for octahedral complexes of the first transition series in general, namely, between 1 and 10. The splitting of the middle band in the $[Ni(H_2O)_6]^{2+}$ spectrum is due to spin-orbit coupling which mixes the $^3T_{2g}(F)$ and ^1E_g states which are very close in energy at the Δ_0 value given by $6H_2O$, whereas in the stronger field of the 3en they are so far apart that no significant mixing occurs.

Magnetically, octahedral nickel(II) complexes have relatively simple

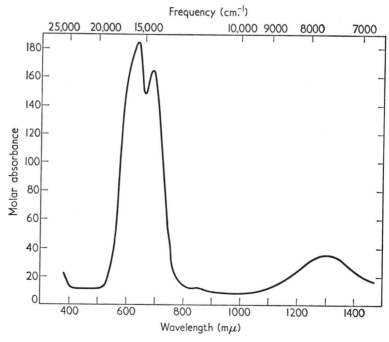

Fig. 29-20.   The visible and near-infrared absorption spectrum of a typical tetrahedral complex of nickel(II), $[Ni(Ph_3AsO)_2Br_2]$.

behavior. From both the simple d-orbital splitting diagram (page 568) and the energy level diagram (page 577), it follows that all of them should have two unpaired electrons, and this is found always to be the case, the magnetic moments ranging from 2.9 to 3.4 B.M. depending on the magnitude of the orbital contribution. One possible exception to the above rule is the diamagnetic $[Ni(diars)_3]^{2+}$, where diars represents o-phenylenebis(dimethylarsine). It is possible that in an extremely intense ligand field, such as this ligand might give, a singlet level originating in a Russell-Saunders state of a d^7s or d^7p configuration could drop down and become the ground state.

Tetrahedral Complexes. Although it was long believed that many seemingly four-coordinate nickel(II) complexes which are paramagnetic were tetrahedral, it is now known that most of them are actually octahedral. There are relatively few authentic tetrahedral complexes of nickel(II) known, and these are of recent preparation. Some representative ones are the blue $NiCl_2(OPPh_3)_2$, and $[Ph_4As][NiCl_4]$ and the brown $NiI_2(PPh_3)_2$. There are three identifying characteristics of tetrahedral nickel(II) complexes. First, there are two features of their spectra. Practically all tetrahedral complexes have a rather intense blue color due to the presence of an absorption band in the red part of the visible region. This may be seen in the spectrum of $[Ni(Ph_3AsO)_2Br_2]$ (Fig. 29-20). There is also a second absorption band around 7000–8000 cm.$^{-1}$. A simple energy level diagram for a d^8 ion in a tetrahedral field is given in Figure 29-21. The visible

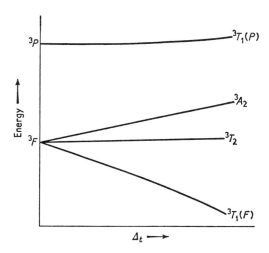

Fig. 29-21. Diagram showing the triplet levels of a d^8 ion (e.g., Ni^{II}) in a tetrahedral field.

absorption band, at $\sim$15,000 cm.$^{-1}$ is assigned to the $T_1(F) \rightarrow T_1(P)$ transition, the one at 7000–8000 cm.$^{-1}$ to the $T_1(F) \rightarrow A_2$ transition. The occasional appearance of a green or even red color in a tetrahedral nickel(II) complex is attributable to charge transfer absorption tailing into the visible region from the ultraviolet; it has been observed mainly in those complexes having coordinated iodide or bromide ions. The splitting of the visible band is caused by spin-orbit coupling which lifts the degeneracy of the $T_1(P)$ state.

The second feature of the spectra of tetrahedral nickel(II) complexes is the relatively high intensities of the absorption bands. We have already noted that for octahedral complexes the bands have molar absorbances at the peaks of only 1–10 and, as we shall see below, paramagnetic square complexes appear to have comparably weak bands. Tetrahedral complexes typically have molar absorbances of $\sim$200 at the peak of the visible band.

The final distinguishing characteristic of tetrahedral nickel(II) complexes is the common occurrence of very high orbital contributions to their magnetic moments. It has already been shown (page 570) that a d^8 system in a tetrahedral field must have two unpaired electrons, however strong the field. Although octahedral and high-spin square complexes have moments between 2.83 (the spin-only value) and $\sim$3.4 B.M., theory shows that a regular tetrahedral complex with four identical ligands should have a moment between 3.5 and 4.2 B.M. This is because in octahedral and planar complexes the ground state does not have orbital degeneracy, and the orbital contribution arises from a second-order process, whereas (Fig. 29-21) tetrahedral complexes have orbitally degenerate ground states and an orbital contribution to the magnetic moment is, as it were, built in. In agreement with this expectation, those tetrahedral complexes in which the ligands are all identical or come close together in the spectrochemical series (e.g., the halide ions and Ph_3PO or Ph_3AsO) have moments of 3.7–4.0 B.M. In those complexes containing ligands which are well separated in the spectrochemical series (e.g., Ph_3P and halide or NO^+ and OH^-), the degeneracy of the ground state is lost, and only second-order orbital contributions are possible. Such tetrahedral complexes thus have moments in the same lower range as those of octahedral ones.

Planar Complexes. As shown on page 571, a planar complex of nickel(II) may be diamagnetic or have two unpaired electrons depending on whether the energy separation of the two uppermost d orbitals is greater or less than the energy necessary to cause electron pairing. This separation in the energies of the uppermost d orbitals is determined by the nature of the four ligands and by the degree to which surrounding molecules—either solvent molecules or others in a crystal lattice—contribute to the ligand field by approaching the nickel atom along the two ends of the axis passing through the nickel atom and perpendicular to the plane of the other four ligand atoms. If planar complexes could be studied as strictly monomeric units *in vacuo*, such effects would not occur, but under actual conditions there are always some neighboring molecules. Of course, if these neighboring molecules should become identical to, or at least comparable to, those four in the plane in their ability to approach the nickel atom and contribute to the ligand field, then the ligand field would become exactly or approximately octahedral. In this case there would be little or no separation between the energies of the two highest *d* orbitals, and the nickel atom would have two unpaired electrons. Thus, as we have noted earlier, the two extremes of purely planar (i.e., no ligands or neighbors of any kind along the two ends of a particular axis) and regular octahedral merge into one another through a complete and conceivably continuous series of intermediate cases.

Under ordinary laboratory conditions, the most likely way of obtaining a situation approaching strict planar four coordination would seem to be to use two molecules of a bidentate, monoacid ligand and form a neutral, inner-salt complex, and then to dissolve this complex in a solvent such as benzene, chloroform, carbon disulfide, or, best of all, an aliphatic hydrocarbon; these solvents may be presumed to make a negligible contribution to the ligand field in comparison to the contribution by the four coordinated atoms in the plane of the complex. Some compounds which do exist in noncoordinating solvents as diamagnetic monomers—which are usually red because of an absorption band in the 400–450 mμ range—are bis(dimethylglyoximato)nickel(II) (29-XVI) and several *N*-alkyl salicylaldimine com-

(29-XVI)   (29-XVII)

plexes of the type 29-XVII where the R groups are ethyl, *n*-propyl, and *n*-butyl. Several other "normal" diamagnetic, planar complexes will be mentioned below as we discuss the many examples of "abnormal" planar complexes, that is, those which do not exhibit simple temperature-independent magnetic moments and spectra.

One cause of anomalous behavior of a supposedly planar nickel(II) complex can be molecular association. An example of this is the nickel dimethylglyoxime complex mentioned above, which, in the solid state, has octahedrally coordinated nickel; this arises because of the formation of a Ni—Ni bond between the metal atoms in the planar molecules. In the *trans*-ethylmethylglyoxime complex, however, there are no Ni—Ni bonds and the molecule is planar in the crystal.

A further striking example of association occurs with nickel(II) acetylacetonate, which associates into trimers by sharing of oxygen atoms as shown in Figure 29-22. In this trimeric unit, each nickel ion is surrounded

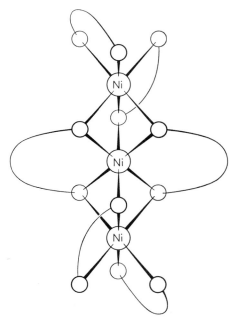

Fig. 29-22.   Sketch indicating the trimeric structure of nickel acetylacetonate. The unlabeled circles represent oxygen atoms, and the curved lines connecting them in pairs represent the remaining portions of the acetylacetonate rings.

by a distorted octahedron of oxygen atoms and the octahedra share triangular faces. This trimer, which is found in the crystal, persists up to very high temperatures in solution in noncoordinating solvents such as those mentioned in the preceding paragraph. In solvents such as alcohols, the trimers do break up but only to give essentially octahedral species in which two solvent molecules are coordinated; in the crystal of the dihydrate of nickel acetylacetonate, this essentially octahedral structure has been shown by X-ray study to exist. Thus under all ordinary circumstances, nickel acetylacetonate, which might naively have been expected to be square (or possibly tetrahedral) is not so at all.

If the trimeric structure of nickel acetylacetonate is examined in detail, it is found, however, that sufficiently large groups, for example, $(CH_3)_3C$— groups, in place of the methyl groups, should cause so much steric hindrance as to prevent association, and in fact, this has been observed. Thus the complex 29-XVIII remains monomeric in noncoordinating solvents such as

(29-XVIII)

toluene, as well as in its crystalline form. It is red and diamagnetic, unlike the trimeric and effectively octahedral acetylacetonate, which is bright green, and has two unpaired electrons per nickel atom. This molecule, although sterically prevented from associating with other molecules of the same kind, can admit small ligand molecules such as those of alcohols, amines, or water; the presence of these makes the ligand field approximately octahedral, and the complex becomes blue-green and paramagnetic.

When the ring substituents have steric requirements intermediate between those of CH_3 and $C(CH_3)_3$, as does $CH(CH_3)_2$ for example, more complicated behavior is observed. Thus the compound with isopropyl groups exists in a noncoordinating solvent such as toluene in a temperature-dependent and concentration-dependent equilibrium between red, diamagnetic monomers and green, paramagnetic trimers. At lower temperatures and higher concentrations the trimers are favored, whereas at higher temperatures and lower concentrations the monomers become predominant.

There is strong though not conclusive evidence that bis(salicylaldehydo) nickel(II) forms similar trimers. The dihydrate of this compound has the two water molecules coordinated to the nickel to complete an irregular octahedron.

Although, as noted earlier, some N-alkyl salicylaldimines form normal diamagnetic nickel(II) complexes, with certain R groups, for example, isopropyl, sec-butyl, and cyclopentyl, the complexes are partially associated in benzene solution and have average magnetic moments per nickel atom at 25°C. of 2.1–2.6 B.M. The manner in which they associate is not yet known.

Just as the extent of association of molecules can be partial and temperature dependent, so also can the process of coordination of solvent molecules when these are not too strongly coordinating. Thus there are a number of cases in which planar complexes, for example, the N-methylsalicylaldimine complex, dissolve in solvents such as methanol or dioxane to give solutions in which the average magnetic moments of the nickel atoms vary with temperature but not—so far as is known—with concentration. It is believed that in these cases the variation in the degree of coordination of solvent molecules with temperature is responsible for the intermediate (i.e., <2.86 but >0 B.M.) moments which vary with temperature.

Finally, there is the possibility that the energy separation of the two uppermost d orbitals can be such that the energy difference between the singlet and triplet states is comparable to thermal energies. Thus a temperature-dependent Boltzmann distribution of molecules between the singlet and triplet states will occur even if no temperature-dependent structural changes occur. The most definite example of this behavior is afforded by the N-methyl- and N-phenyltroponeimineates (29-XIX) in chloroform

(29-XIX)

solution, which have been studied by nuclear magnetic resonance techniques.

In most cases of anomalous temperature-dependent magnetic (and spectral) behavior in solution, it is probable that at least two and perhaps all three of the basic mechanisms we have mentioned will be operative. In such general cases detailed understanding of the various contributions to the over-all observed effects will be quite difficult to obtain.

In conclusion it should also be noted that molecular association and possibly Boltzmann distribution effects, though not solvation effects, might be expected in some pure solid or molten complexes, and they have been observed. For instance, most of the molten N-alkyl salicylaldimine complexes show intermediate, temperature-dependent magnetic moments and are simultaneously thermochromic. The N-methylsalicylaldimine complex actually occurs in two crystalline forms. In the one ordinarily obtained, the molecules are not associated and are red and diamagnetic, but when heated to ~170°C., this form is converted to a yellow-green paramagnetic form. The structure of the latter has not been determined, but it is doubtless such that by sharing of N or O ligand atoms, the nickel ions achieve some sort of distorted octahedral coordination.

Anomalous magnetic and spectral behavior among solid nickel(II) complexes is perhaps most spectacularly illustrated by the so-called Lifschitz salts (named after their discoverer) which are stilbenediamine complexes containing the planar complex cation 29-XX and various anions such as

(29-XX)

Cl⁻, Br⁻, I⁻, RCOO⁻, etc. Some of these are yellow and diamagnetic, others are blue and fully paramagnetic (i.e., the moments are 2.83 B.M. or greater), and still others change from the yellow to the blue form and back again upon heating and cooling, recrystallization from certain solvents, or removal and readdition of solvent of crystallization. The general explanation for these striking phenomena is that the variations in anion and in physical and chemical treatment of the compounds cause structural changes, and these in turn cause variations in the degree to which anions or solvent molecules present in the crystal approach and coordinate to the nickel atom and partially complete an octahedron about it. When this octahedron is not substantially completed, the splitting of the two uppermost d orbitals is so great that the yellow diamagnetic forms are stable, whereas when the anions or solvent molecules do cause the ligand field to become nearly octahedral, the blue paramagnetic forms occur.

29-37. Higher Oxidation States of Nickel

Oxides and Mixed Oxides. Both Ni^{III} and Ni^{IV} oxides are known, but neither type has been obtained in a pure state. When a suspension of $Ni(OH)_2$ in potassium hydroxide solution is treated with a fairly mild oxidizing agent such as bromine, a black solid is obtained which can be dried in vacuum to a composition of approximately $Ni_2O_3 \cdot 2H_2O$. Any attempt to dry it further by heating causes decomposition with loss of oxygen to give NiO, although a monohydrate has been claimed under special conditions. There is evidence that this substance contains Ni^{III} and not a mixture of Ni^{II} and Ni^{IV}. When the alkaline suspension of $Ni(OH)_2$ is treated with strong oxidizing agents, for example, chlorine, dark precipitates containing up to 1.9 atoms of oxygen per atom of nickel are obtained. These solids do not appear to contain peroxide and are thus thought to be impure, possibly hydrated, NiO_2. They are very unstable in presence of acid, rapidly oxidizing the water; they even convert Mn^{II} to permanganate in acid medium. It may be noted that the Edison or nickel-iron battery is based on the reaction:

$$Fe + Ni_2O_3 + 3H_2O \underset{\text{charge}}{\overset{\text{discharge}}{\rightleftarrows}} Fe(OH)_2 + 2Ni(OH)_2$$

using potassium hydroxide solution as the electrolyte; it produces $\sim$1.3 v.

Double oxides with nickel in higher oxidation states can be obtained by dry oxidations. It has been reported that when $Ni(OH)_2$ is fused with potassium nitrate and potassium hydroxide, the compound K_2NiO_4 is formed, but this has been questioned. On heating NiO with BaO or SrO in oxygen, the substances $BaNiO_3$, $BaNi_2O_5$, and $Sr_2Ni_2O_5$ are formed. The compounds $LiNiO_2$ and $NaNiO_2$ have been made by bubbling oxygen through the molten alkali metal hydroxides contained in nickel vessels at about 800°C. These mixed oxides, like the impure binary oxides, are quite unstable toward acids, dissolving therein with evolution of oxygen or the oxidation of the acid anion.

Complexes of Tetravalent Nickel. There are not a great number of these, but several of those known are quite well characterized and establish beyond doubt that this oxidation state can be stabilized by appropriate coordination. Complexes in which the high oxidation state is stabilized by coordination with ions derived from highly electronegative elements are the purple heteropoly salt $3BaO \cdot NiO_2 \cdot 9MoO_3 \cdot 12H_2O$, the dark purple periodate $Na(K)NiIO_6 \cdot nH_2O$, and the red complex fluoride K_2NiF_6. The first and the last of these are diamagnetic, but the periodate complex shows weak paramagnetism (leading to a calculated magnetic moment of only $\sim$1.2 B.M.), which is believed to be caused by impurities (e.g., Ni^{III}). Diamagnetism in these cases can be attributed to d orbital splitting by octahedral fields sufficient to produce t_{2g}^6 ground state configurations. That this can happen even with F^- ions as ligands is not too surprising when it is recalled that the d^6 configuration seems especially prone to spin pairing (cf. Co^{III} complexes) and that the magnitudes of Δ values increase sharply with increasing positive charge of the cation (page 579).

Other Ni^{IV} complexes are known in which the ligands are not derived from highly electronegative atoms. Instead these ligands may be presumed to stabilize the high oxidation state by forming stronger complexes with Ni^{IV} than with Ni^{II} or Ni^{III}, thus shifting the oxidation-reduction potentials in favor of Ni^{IV}. Such complexes are not obtained directly but rather by oxidation of the metal ion which has already been incorporated into the required coordination environment. Thus, oxidation of the o-phenylenebis-(dimethylarsine) complex of Ni^{III}, $[NiCl_2(diars)_2]Cl$, with nitric acid in presence of perchloric acid gives the deep blue Ni^{IV} species, $[NiCl_2(diars)_2]$ $(ClO_4)_2$. There are also binuclear Ni^{IV} complexes with sulfur ligands. Thus, the Ni^{II} complex of dithiobenzoic acid is oxidized by air in the presence of

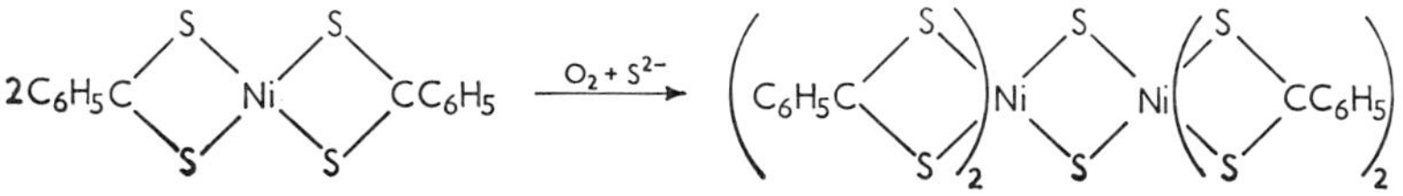

(29-3)

alkaline sulfide solution (eq. 29-3). Another complex in this same class is one obtained with o-aminothiophenol (29-XXI).

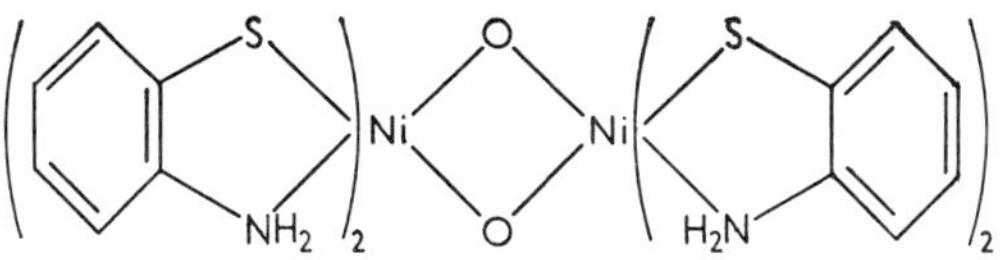

(29-XXI)

Complexes of Trivalent Nickel. There are many claims in the literature that oxidation of four-coordinate Ni^{II} complexes produces Ni^{III} complexes, but in many cases, particularly with amine or oxime ligands, the available experimental data do not adequately support the claims. However, there are at least four well-characterized Ni^{III} complexes. Oxidation of red, *trans*-planar dibromobis(triethylphosphine)nickel(II) with bromine yields a violet compound with the composition $NiBr_3(Et_3P)_2$. It is monomeric and has a dipole moment of 2.5 D. and a magnetic moment of ~1.8 B.M. On the basis of these facts the structure 29-XXII has

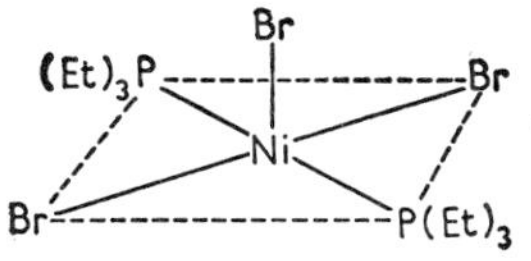

(29-XXII)

been proposed. Similarly, oxidation of $[Ni(diars)_2]Cl_2$ (where diars is o-phenylenebisdimethylarsine) by oxygen in presence of excess chloride ion gives a greenish yellow precipitate of $[NiCl_2(diars)_2]Cl$, which has been well characterized by various physical measurements, particularly, by magnetic measurements which show the presence of one unpaired electron (~1.9 B.M.). The analogous bromide and thiocyanate complexes are also known.

COPPER

Copper has a single s electron outside a completed d shell and accordingly has sometimes been classed in group I. There is little to be gained by this, since Cu has little in common with the alkalies except with regard to formal stoichiometries in the $+1$ oxidation state. The filled d shell is much less effective than is an inert-gas shell in shielding the s electron from the nuclear charge so that the first ionization potential of Cu is higher than those of the alkalies. Since the electrons of the d shell are also involved in metallic bonding, the heat of sublimation and the melting point of copper are also much higher than those of the alkalies. These factors are responsible for the more noble character of copper, and the effect is to make the compounds more covalent and to give them higher lattice energies, which are not offset by the somewhat smaller radii of the unipositive ion compared to the alkali ions in the same period—Cu^+, 0.93; Na^+, 0.95; and K^+, 1.33 A.

The second and third ionization potentials of Cu are lower than those of the alkalies and account in part for the transition metal character shown by the existence of colored paramagnetic ions and complexes in the II and III oxidation states. Even in the I oxidation state numerous transition metal-like complexes, for example, those with olefins, are formed.

There is only moderate similarity between copper and the heavier elements Ag and Au, but some points are noted in the later discussions of these elements (Chapter 30).

The oxidation states and stereochemistry of copper are summarized in Table 29-10.

TABLE 29-10

Oxidation States and Stereochemistry of Copper

Oxidation state	Coordination number	Geometry	Examples
Cu^I, d^{10}	2	Linear	Cu_2O, $[Cu(NH_3)_2]^+$
	3	Planar	$K[Cu(CN)_2]$
	4[a]	Tetrahedral	CuI, $[Cu(CN)_4]^{3-}$
Cu^{II}, d^9	4	Tetrahedral	$Cs_2[CuCl_4]$; distorted toward planar
	5	Trigonal bipyramid	$Cu(terpyridyl)Cl_2$
	4[a]	Square planar,	CuO, $[Cu(py)_4]^{2+}$
	6[a]	distorted octahedral	K_2CuF_4, $K_2[CuEDTA]$, $CuCl_2$
Cu^{III}, d^8	4?	Square planar	$KCuO_2$
	6	Octahedral	K_3CuF_6

[a] Most common states.

The stereochemistry of the d^9 ion Cu^{II} (also Ag^{II}) deserves special comment. It has already been shown (page 584) that according to the Jahn-Teller theorem d^9 ions will cause distortions in would-be octahedral surroundings. There is very little information on the actual effects for the Ag^{II} ion, but for Cu^{II} structural data are extensive and bear out the theory completely. Some data for discussion are summarized in Table 29-11. In

TABLE 29-11

Interatomic Distances in Some Cupric Coordination Polyhedra

Compound	Distances, A.
$CuCl_2$	4Cl at 2.30, 2Cl at 2.95
$CsCuCl_3$	4Cl at 2.30, 2Cl at 2.65
$CuCl_2 \cdot 2H_2O$	2O at 2.01, 2Cl at 2.31, 2Cl at 2.98
$CuBr_2$	4Br at 2.40, 2Br at 3.18
CuF_2	4F at 1.93, 2F at 2.27
$[Cu(H_2O)_2(NH_3)_4]$ in	
$\quad CuSO_4 \cdot 4NH_3 \cdot H_2O$	4N at 2.05, 1O at 2.59, 1O at 3.37
K_2CuF_4	2F at 1.95, 4F at 2.08

$CuCl_2$, $CuBr_2$, CuF_2, and $CsCuCl_3$ the structures are distorted cubic ones in which the Cu^{II} ions are found in distorted octahedra. In each case the distortion is such that two *trans* metal–ligand distances are greater than the other four. Analogous compounds containing metal ions (e.g., Ni^{II} or Zn^{II}) which are not subject to Jahn-Teller effects give cubic crystals with regular octahedra about the metal ions. It may be noted that in the two chlorine compounds the four short bonds are of the same length in both cases, whereas the long bonds are of quite different lengths. It is also true in other compounds that the short bonds are those to be expected for a fairly constant "radius" for the Cu^{II} ion in these directions, but the long bonds vary from only slightly longer than the short ones to much longer. Theoretically, this is to be expected since the degree of distortion will depend in detail on many forces within each particular compound. Thus, it may be argued that the case of square coordination as found in CuO and in many discrete complexes of Cu^{II} should be regarded as the extreme of Jahn-Teller distorted octahedral coordination rather than as a different type of coordination.

In the salt K_2CuF_4 each Cu^{II} ion is surrounded by six F^- ions in the form of an octahedron flattened along one axis. Although there are calculations to show that a distortion of this type might occur here solely because of the Jahn-Teller effect, the case is uncertain because the general nature of the crystal structure is such that perfectly regular octahedral coordination would not be possible even in the absence of a Jahn-Teller effect.

Finally, we note that the $[CuCl_4]^{2-}$ and $[CuBr_4]^{2-}$ ions, as they occur in their cesium salts, are approximately tetrahedral, but the tetrahedra are decidedly squashed as shown in Figure 29-23. Although tetrahedral sur-

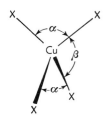

Fig. 29-23.   Squashed tetrahedral structures of $[CuX_4]^{2-}$ ions in Cs_2CuX_4 salts; $\alpha > \beta$.

roundings of a d^9 ion are also subject to Jahn-Teller distortion, and the irregularities in these tetrahedra might be so explained, it has also been pointed out that large spin-orbit coupling effects might be expected to supervene and nullify the Jahn-Teller effect. The question of the cause of the distortions here is certainly still quite an open one.

29-38. The Element

Copper is widely distributed in nature in the free state, in sulfides, arsenides, chlorides, and carbonates. Copper is extracted by oxidative roasting and smelting, followed by electrodeposition from sulfate solutions.

Copper is a tough, soft, and ductile reddish metal with a high thermal and electrical conductivity second only to silver. The metal is completely miscible with Au. It is only superficially oxidized in air, sometimes giving a green coating of hydroxy carbonate and hydroxy sulfate.

Copper reacts at red heat with oxygen to give CuO and, at higher temperatures, Cu_2O; with sulfur it gives Cu_2S or a nonstoichiometric form of this phase. It is attacked by halogens but is unaffected by nonoxidizing or noncomplexing dilute acids in absence of air. Copper readily dissolves in nitric acid and hot concentrated sulfuric acid. It is also soluble in ammonia or potassium cyanide solutions in the presence of oxygen, as indicated by the potentials

$$Cu + 2NH_3 \xrightarrow{\text{0.12 v.}} [Cu(NH_3)_2]^+ \xrightarrow[+2NH_3]{\text{0.01 v.}} [Cu(NH_3)_4]^{2+}$$

29-39. Copper(I) Compounds

The cuprous ion has the electronic structure $3d^{10}$ so that its compounds are diamagnetic and, except where color results from the anion or charge-transfer bands (page 605), colorless.

The relative stabilities of the cuprous and cupric states are indicated by the following potential data:

$$Cu = Cu^+ + e \quad E^0 = -0.52 \text{ v.}$$
$$Cu^+ = Cu^{2+} + e \quad E^0 = -0.153 \text{ v.}$$

whence

$$2Cu^+ = Cu + Cu^{2+} \quad E^0 = 0.367 \text{ v.}; K = [Cu^{2+}]/[Cu^+]^2 = \sim 10^6$$

The relative stabilities of Cu^I and Cu^{II} depend much more than do the relative stabilities of oxidation states of other elements differing by one unit on the nature of anions or other ligands present, on the dielectric constant of the solution, and on the nature of neighboring atoms in a crystal.

It is obvious that in aqueous solution the free Cu^+ ion can exist only in exceedingly low concentrations, and, indeed, the only cuprous compounds which are stable to water are the highly insoluble ones like CuCl or CuCN; cuprous salts of oxy anions can be obtained in nonaqueous media, but such salts as Cu_2SO_4 are at once decomposed by water to give copper and the cupric salt. This instability toward water is due partly to the greater lattice and solvation energies of the cupric ion so that cuprous ionic derivatives are unstable.

The equilibrium $2Cu^I = Cu + Cu^{II}$ can be displaced in either direction depending on the conditions. Thus with CN^-, I^-, and Me_2S, Cu^{II} reacts to give the Cu^I compound; with anions that cannot give covalent bonds or bridging groups, for example, ClO_4^- and SO_4^{2-}, or with complexing agents which have their greater affinity for Cu^{II}, the Cu^{II} state is favored—thus ethylenediamine reacts with cuprous chloride in aqueous potassium chloride solution:

$$2CuCl + 2en = [Cu(en)_2]^{2+} + 2Cl^- + Cu^0$$

That the latter reaction also depends on the geometry of the ligand, that is on its chelate nature, is shown by differences in the $[Cu^{2+}]/[Cu^+]^2$ equilibrium with chelating and nonchelating amines. Thus for ethylenediamine, K is $\sim 10^5$, for triethylenetriamine $\sim 10^4$, for pentamethylenediamine (which cannot chelate) 3×10^{-2}, and for ammonia 2×10^{-2}. Hence in the last case the reaction is

$$[Cu(NH_3)_4]^{2+} + Cu^0 = 2[Cu(NH_3)_2]^+$$

Cuprous Oxide and Sulfide. These solids are the most stable copper compounds at high temperatures, and the corresponding cupric compounds are thermally unstable toward them. The oxide is readily made as a yellow powder by controlled reduction of an alkaline solution of a cupric salt by hydrazine, or as red crystals by thermal decomposition of CuO. It is soluble in ammonia to give the ammine. The sulfide is a black crystalline solid obtained by heating copper and sulfur in absence of air.

Cuprous Halides. The fluoride is unknown. The chloride and bromide are made by boiling the cupric salt with excess copper in acid solution and, on addition of water to the CuX_2^- solutions so obtained, the white chloride and pale yellow bromide are precipitated. On addition of iodide ion to a cupric salt, a precipitate is formed which rapidly decomposes by a quantitative redox reaction to give cuprous iodide and iodine.

The three halides have the zinc blende structure with the metal atom tetrahedrally surrounded by halogen atoms. The chloride and bromide are associated in the vapor state, and for CuCl the principal species appears to be a cyclic trimer with alternating Cu and Cl atoms and a Cu—Cl distance of 2.16 A. The white CuCl becomes deep blue at 178°C. and gives a deep green liquid.

The halides are highly insoluble in water, the iodide being least soluble ($K_{SP} = 10^{-12}$). They are soluble to varying extents in complexing media such as CN^-, NH_3, $S_2O_3^{2-}$; excess of the halide ion gives species such as $CuCl_2^-$, $CuCl_3^{2-}$, $CuCl_4^{3-}$ depending on the conditions; in $1M$ KCl the main species is $CuCl_2^-$.

Cuprous Cyanide. This compound is similar to CuI and is made similarly in a redox reaction which also provides a convenient preparation of cyanogen:

$$2Cu^{2+}(aq) + 4CN^-(aq) = 2CuCN(s) + (CN)_2$$

The cyanide is soluble in solutions of complexing ions; cyanide gives $[Cu(CN_4]^{3-}$ as the main species. The latter has such a large formation constant that copper metal will dissolve in potassium cyanide solution with evolution of hydrogen.

Cuprous Sulfate. Although cuprous oxy salts are usually complex, there are a few simple salts, of which the sulfate is the best known. It is obtained as a greyish solid, stable in the absence of moisture, by the reaction

$$Cu_2O + (CH_3)_2SO_4 \xrightarrow{160°C.} Cu_2SO_4 + CH_3OCH_3$$

Cuprous Complexes. Cuprous complexes with non-π-bonding as well as $p\pi$ and $d\pi$ bonding ligands, olefins, and acetylenes are known.

With ammonia, halide ions, and monodentate ligands, the cuprous complexes usually have the highest stability for $n = 2$ (e.g., $[Cu(NH_3)_2]^+$). However, in general, the complexes from $n = 1$ to $n = 4$ can exist under appropriate conditions.

The cyanide complex $K[Cu(CN)_2]$ has been shown to have an unusual spiral polymeric structure where the copper atom has coordination number 3; the carbon and nitrogen atoms bound to copper are almost coplanar with the metal atom (Fig. 29-24). The corresponding silver and gold ions are discrete, $[NC—M—CN]^-$.

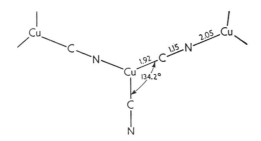

Fig. 29-24. A portion of the spiral chain in $K[Cu(CN)_2]$.

Acetylene complexes are readily formed. Thus cuprous chloride in concentrated hydrochloric acid absorbs acetylene to give colorless species such as $CuCl \cdot C_2H_2$ and $[CuCl_2C_2H_2]^-$. In neutral potassium chloride solution, sparingly soluble compounds like $K_2[Cu_2C_2(CuCl)_8]$ can be obtained. These halide solutions can also catalyze the conversion of acetylene to vinyl acetylene (in strong alkali chloride) or to vinyl chloride (high HCl), and the reaction of acetylene with hydrogen cyanide to give acrylonitrile is also catalyzed.

If cuprous ammine solutions are treated with acetylenes containing the $HC{\equiv}C—$ group, yellow or red precipitates, insoluble in solvents with which they do not react, are obtained. Acetylene itself gives $Cu_2C_2 \cdot H_2O$ quantitatively. The thermal stability and insolubility of these alkynyl complexes has been attributed to polymerization through π bonding (29-XXIII).

(29-XXIII)

Propynyl copper dissolves in triethylphosphine in toluene to give [Et₃PCuC≡CMe]₃, which is probably a cyclic polymer of similar type.

Olefins form cuprous complexes which are less stable than their silver analogs. Thus CuCl absorbs ethylene and other olefins under pressure, but the products have high dissociation pressures.

Carbon Monoxide and Related Complexes. Cuprous ammines or chloro-cuprates(I) absorb carbon monoxide giving colorless solutions. From the latter solutions the halogen-bridged dimer $[CuCOCl_2]_2$ can be obtained as crystals. The gas is absorbed quantitatively by $[Cu(NH_3)_2]^+$ and can be regenerated on acidification.

Substituted phosphines, arsines, and sulfides give stable complexes, notably with the iodide. The alkyl phosphine complexes are organic-soluble tetramers, $[R_3PCuI]_4$; the copper atoms lie at the corners of a tetrahedron and are tetrahedrally coordinated since the iodine atoms bridge two copper atoms. When the anion is noncomplexing, tetracoordinated cations can be obtained as in $[(Ph_3P)_4Cu]^+ClO_4^-$.

Rather unstable cuprous *alkyls* can be made by the action of Grignard reagents or lithium alkyls on cuprous halides. Methylcopper is a polymeric yellow solid which decomposes in boiling ether and explodes in the dry state. Phenylcopper is stable to about 80°C.

29-40. Copper(II) Compounds

The dipositive state is the most important one for copper. Most cuprous compounds are fairly readily oxidized to cupric compounds, but further oxidation to Cu^{III} is difficult. There is a well-defined aqueous chemistry of Cu^{2+}, and a large number of salts of various anions, many of which are water soluble, exist in addition to a wealth of complexes.

With the d^9 electronic configuration, cupric compounds are normally paramagnetic with a single unpaired electron. With the exception of an-hydrous CuF_2 and $CuSO_4$, which are white owing to the weakness of the ligand field, cupric salts are black or yellow-brown when anhydrous and blue or green when hydrated or complexed. The stereochemistry of Cu^{II} as it is influenced by the Jahn-Teller effect has been discussed earlier (page 747). The characteristic shape of the coordination shell of Cu^{II} is either an octahedron distorted by stretching along one axis or the limiting case of such a distortion, namely, a group of four ligand atoms at the corners of a square with the copper atom at its center.

As a result of the distorted octahedral or square coordination of Cu^{II}, a detailed interpretation of its electronic absorption spectrum is somewhat complicated. Virtually all complexes and compounds of Cu^{II} are blue or green. Exceptions are generally caused by strong ultraviolet bands—charge-transfer bands—tailing off into the blue end of the visible spectrum and thus causing the substances to appear red or brown. The blue or green colors are due to the presence of an absorption band in the 600–900 mμ region of the spectrum. However, close study of these somewhat asymmetric bands in a variety of complexes and salts has shown that they are made up of at least two, and very probably three, overlapping, symmetrical bands. Now we have already seen (page 565) that tetragonal distortion splits the e_g and t_{2g} levels so that more than one d–d transition, in fact three, are to be expected for Cu^{II} in its complexes. There is still some uncertainty as to whether all three bands are really under the envelop of the absorption observed in the visible, but if this is so, as some workers believe, then the splitting pattern must be similar to that shown in Figure 26-6 except that the d_{xy} level is even closer to the d_{z^2} level and the (d_{zx}, d_{yz}) pair. Then, since Cu^{II} is a one-positron case (see page 574), this diagram can be inverted and predicts that the following transitions of the positron

$$d_{x^2-y^2} \rightarrow d_{xy}$$
$$d_{x^2-y^2} \rightarrow d_{z^2}$$
$$d_{x^2-y^2} \rightarrow (d_{zx}, d_{yz})$$

will give absorption bands lying very close together. It is also possible, however, that the visible absorption consists only of the first and second of these with the $d_{x^2-y^2} \rightarrow (d_{zx}, d_{yz})$ transition being placed further out in the ultraviolet where it might escape detection.

Cupric Oxide and Hydroxide. On heating the nitrate or other oxy salt, the black crystalline *oxide* CuO is obtained. It is unstable above 800°C. toward cuprous oxide and oxygen and is readily reduced to the metal by hydrogen or carbon monoxide at about 250°C.

The *hydroxide*, Cu(OH)$_2$, is obtained as a blue bulky precipitate on addition of alkali hydroxide to cupric solutions; it can also be obtained as crystals. On warming in aqueous solution, the hydroxide is dehydrated to the oxide. It is soluble in moderately strong acids, but is also feebly acidic and dissolves in concentrated alkali hydroxide to give deep blue anions. These are believed to be of the type $[Cu_n(OH)_{2n-2}]^{2+}$. In ammoniacal solutions the deep blue ammine hydroxide is formed.

Cupric Halides. The *fluoride* is colorless and has a distorted rutile lattice. By contrast, the yellow *chloride* and the almost black *bromide* form layer lattices in which there are halogen-bridged chains with the coordination of the copper atom square planar. However, unlike some other similar polymeric halides, for example, PdCl$_2$, the packing of the copper chloride and bromide chains is such that two halogen atoms in one chain occupy the "long" octahedral positions to copper atoms in other chains. The chloride and bromide are readily soluble in water, hydrated salts being crystallizable, and also in donor organic solvents such as acetone, alcohol, or pyridine.

Cupric Oxy Acid Salts. Perhaps the commonest cupric salt is the hydrated sulfate, $CuSO_4 \cdot 5H_2O$. Here the cupric ion has its usual coordination with four oxygen atoms in a plane, and oxygen atoms from sulfate groups occupying each axial position. The additional water molecule is hydrogen bonded between a second sulfate oxygen and a bound water molecule in the plane as shown schematically (29-XXIV). The hydrated

(29-XXIV)

nitrate is a common salt, but of more interest is the unusual anhydrous nitrate. Copper metal is vigorously dissolved by a solution of N_2O_4 in ethyl acetate, and from this solution can be crystallized the salt $Cu(NO_3)_2 \cdot N_2O_4$, the infrared spectrum of which suggests that it is $[NO]^+[Cu(NO_3)_3]^-$. On heating at 90°C. this solvate gives the blue anhydrous $Cu(NO_3)_2$ which can be sublimed without decomposition in vacuum at 150–200°C. This was the first *anhydrous* transition metal nitrate to be isolated, and it disposed of the old idea that such nitrates decompose readily on heating. The crystal structure is rather complex (Fig. 29-25), each copper atom being eight coordinate with respect to oxygen, with two short Cu—O bonds (1.9 A.) linking the copper and nitrate groups in infinite chains parallel to one crystal axis. The other six bonds (2.5 A.) are to a distorted hexagon of oxygens at right angles to this axis, these oxygens being from nitrate groups holding the chains together. In the vapor, $Cu(NO_3)_2$ is monomeric and the structure (Fig. 29-26) indicates that there are nonequivalent nitrate groups, a fact which is consistent with the chemical properties which suggest that one nitrate group is more labile than the other.

Several *cupric carboxylates* are dimeric either in the crystalline state, in solution, or both. Thus the acetate, $[Cu_2(OCOCH_3)_4] \cdot 2H_2O$, is dimeric in the crystal, and the monochloroacetate is dimeric also in solution. Magnetic studies have shown that in these dimers there is extensive quenching

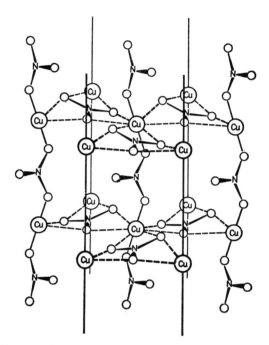

Fig. 29-25. The crystal structure of anhydrous copper nitrate. The full vertical lines represent nitrate chains. The nitrate groups are omitted for clarity. (Reprinted with permission from S. C. Wallwork, *Proc. Chem. Soc. (London)*, **1959**, 311.)

of the spin moment of the cupric ion. In the acetate shown (29-XXV), the metal atoms are surrounded in a square plane, or approximately so, by the four oxygens of the bridging acetato group. Each copper also has a water oxygen bound to it, and the Cu—Cu distance is only 2.64 A. Thus each copper atom has its usual distorted octahedral coordination. The metal

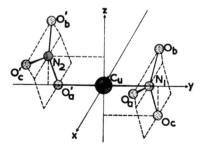

Fig. 29-26. Molecular structure of $Cu(NO_3)_2$ in the vapor phase. (Reprinted with permission from S. H. Bauer and C. C. Addison, *Proc. Chem. Soc. (London)*, **1960**, 251.)

atoms are sufficiently close to allow lateral overlap of the $3d_{x^2-y^2}$, orbitals; this type of metal–metal interaction is sometimes called δ bonding. Cr^{II} acetate has essentially this same structure (see page 684). It may be noted that the cupric salt of diazoaminobenzene, C_6H_5NH—N=N—C_6H_5 (29-XXVI), is also dimeric with bridging groups as indicated in the diagram. In this case the molecule is diamagnetic, the spins being completely coupled in the metal–metal bond.

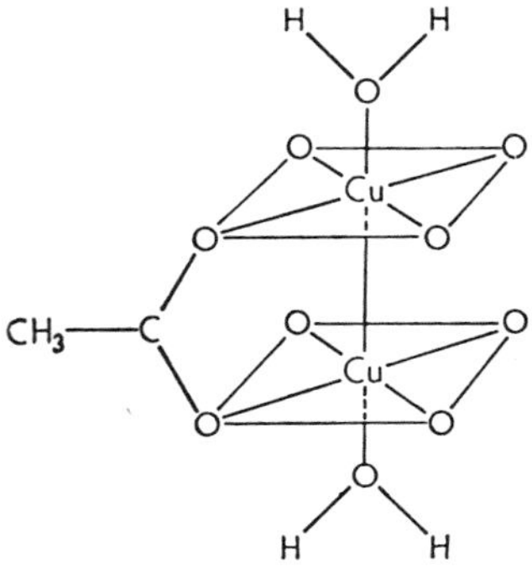

(29-XXV) 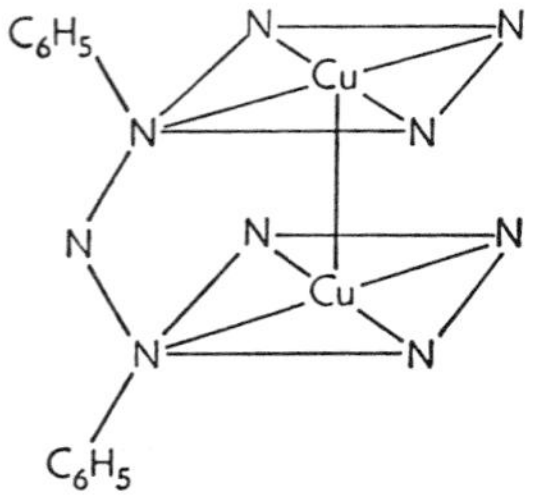   (29-XXVI)

Only one bridging group is shown

Aqueous Chemistry. Most cupric salts dissolve readily in water and give the cupric ion, which may be written $[Cu(H_2O)_6]^{2+}$, keeping in mind, however, that two of the water molecules are farther from the metal atom than the other four. Addition of ligands to such aqueous solutions leads to the formation of complexes by successive displacement of water molecules. With NH_3, for example, the species $[Cu(NH_3)(H_2O)_5]^{2+} \ldots [Cu(NH_3)_4 (H_2O)_2]^{2+}$ are formed in the normal way (page 543), but the addition of the fifth and sixth molecules of NH_3 is difficult. In fact, the sixth cannot be added to any significant extent in aqueous media; $[Cu(NH_3)_6]^{2+}$ can be obtained in liquid ammonia, however. The reason for this unusual behavior is connected with the Jahn-Teller effect. Because of it, the Cu^{II} ion does not bind the fifth and sixth ligands strongly (even the H_2O). When this intrinsic weak binding of the fifth and sixth ligands is added to the normally expected decrease in the stepwise formation constants (page 543) the formation constants, K_5 and K_6, are very small indeed. Similarly, it is found with ethylenediamine that $[Cuen(H_2O)_4]^{2+}$ and $[Cu(en)_2(H_2O)_2]^{2+}$ form readily, but $[Cu(en)_3]^{2+}$ forms only at extremely high concentrations of en. Many other amine complexes of Cu^{II} are known, and all are much more intensely blue than the aquo ion. This is because the amines produce a stronger ligand field which causes the absorption band to move from the far red to the middle of the red region of the spectrum. For example, in the aquo ion the absorption maximum is at ~800 mμ, whereas in $[Cu(NH_3)_4(H_2O)_2]^{2+}$ it is at ~600 mμ, as shown in Figure 29-27. The reversal of the

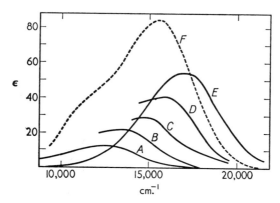

Fig. 29-27. Absorption spectra of $[Cu(H_2O)_6]^{2+}$ (A) and of the amines in $2M$ ammonium nitrate at 25°C., $[Cu(NH_3)(H_2O)_5]^{2+}$ (B), $[Cu(NH_3)_2(H_2O)_4]^{2+}$ (C), $[Cu(NH_3)_3(H_2O)_3]^{2+}$ (D), $[Cu(NH_3)_4(H_2O)_2]^{2+}$ (E), and $[Cu(NH_3)_5H_2O]^{2+}$ (F).

shifts with increasing take-up of ammonia for the fifth ammonia is to be noted, indicating again the weaker bonding of the fifth ammonia molecule.

Halide ion complexes are also formed in aqueous solution on addition of HCl, HBr, LiCl, or LiBr to the solutions. These range in color from green to brown, and on addition of large cations, for example, Cs$^+$ or $[(CH_3)_4N]^+$, the yellow and brown crystalline salts of $[CuCl_4]^{2-}$ and $[CuBr_4]^{2-}$ can be isolated. These have flattened tetrahedral structures as noted earlier (page 748).

Many other Cu^{II} complexes may be isolated by treating aqueous solutions with ligands. When the ligands are such as to form neutral, water-insoluble complexes, as in equation 29-4, the complexes precipitate and can

$$Cu^{2+}(aq) \ + \ 2 \quad \text{[structure]} \quad \longrightarrow \quad \text{[structure]} \tag{29-4}$$

be purified by recrystallization from organic solvents. The bis(acetylacetonato)copper(II) complex is another example of this type.

Some ligands which coordinate through oxygen form a large number of cupric complexes, often of considerable complexity. Thus the well-known blue solutions formed by addition of tartrate to Cu^{2+} solutions (Fehling's solution) are still far from understood, but it seems clear that polynuclear complexes must be present. Oxalate, glycerol, and various thio compounds also give cupric complexes; thus addition of potassium oxalate to cupric sulfate solutions gives stable crystalline $K_2(Cu(C_2O_4)_2] \cdot 2H_2O$ with the chelated oxalate oxygens in the plane and the two water oxygens normal to it.

29-41. Copper(III) Compounds

There is good evidence that Cu^{III} can occur in crystalline compounds and in complexes. It should be noted that Cu^{III}, with a d^8 shell, is isoelectronic with Ni^{II}.

If cupric hydroxide is treated with alkaline hypochlorite, it dissolves to give oxidizing solutions, which on acidification liberate oxygen. Some alkaline earth and alkali cuprates can be obtained, for example, by heating the mixed oxides in oxygen; $KCuO_2$ is steel blue in color and is diamagnetic, suggesting square planar coordination.

By treatment of a mixture of potassium and cupric chlorides with fluorine, a pale green crystalline solid, K_3CuF_6, is obtained. This is paramagnetic with $\mu = 2.8$ B.M.

The oxidation of alkaline cupric solutions containing periodate or tellurate by hypochlorite or other oxidizing agents leads to diamagnetic complex salts such as $K_7[Cu(IO_6)_2] \cdot 7H_2O$. These salts are strong oxidizing agents and liberate oxygen on acidification.

References

The following texts provide many general references to the chemistry of the first transition series elements. There are no recent reference books on the chemistry of these elements, and the *Annual Reports of the Chemical Society*, London, should be consulted.

Bailar, J. C., ed., *The Chemistry of Coordination Compounds* (*American Chemical Society Monograph*, No. 131), Reinhold, New York, 1956.

Latimer, W. M., *The Oxidation States of the Elements and their Potentials in Aqueous Solutions*, 2nd ed., Prentice-Hall, New York, 1952.

Lewis, J., and R. Wilkins, eds., *Modern Coordination Chemistry*, Interscience, New York–London, 1959.

Remy, H., *Treatise on Inorganic Chemistry* (translated and amended by J. S. Anderson), Vol. II, Elsevier, Amsterdam, 1956.

Sidgwick, N. V., *The Chemical Elements and their Compounds*, Vols. I and II, Oxford University Press, London, 1950.

Other more specialized references are:

Bénard, J., *Inst. intern. chim. Solvay, Conseil chim.*, **10**ᵉ *Conseil, Brussels*, **1956**. Interstitial compounds of transition metals and nonstoichiometric compounds such as sulfides.

Bradley, D. C., "Metal Alkoxides," in F. A. Cotton, ed., *Progress in Inorganic Chemistry*, Vol. II, Interscience, New York–London, 1960, p. 303.

Chemistry of the Ferrocyanides, American Cyanamid Co., New York, 1953.

Dunitz, J. D., and L. E. Orgel, "Stereochemistry of Ionic Solids," in H. J. Eméleus and A. G. Sharpe, eds., *Advances in Inorganic Chemistry and Radiochemistry*, Vol. II, Academic Press, 1960, p. 1.

Gray, J. J., and A. Carter, *Chemistry and Metallurgy of Titanium Production* (*Royal Institute of Chemistry Monograph*, No. 1), London, 1958.

Hartford, W. H., and M. Darrin, *Chem. Revs.*, **58**, 1 (1958). Review of chemistry of chromyl compounds.

Ives, D. J. G., *Principles of the Extraction of Metals* (*Royal Institute of Chemistry Monographs for Teachers*, No. 3), London, 1960. An excellent little monograph covering most of the metallic elements which stresses the thermodynamic principles of the extraction of metals from ores and their purification; can be strongly recommended.

James, B. R., and R. J. P. Williams, *J. Chem. Soc. (London)*, **1961**, 2007. Oxidation-reduction potentials of cupric compounds.

Krisnamurthy, K. K., and G. M. Harris, *Chem. Revs.*, **61**, 213 (1961). Metal oxalate complexes.

Martin, R. L., and G. Winter, *J. Chem. Soc. (London)*, **1961**, 2947. Structure of titanium alkoxides.

Pascal, P., *Nouveau traité de chimie minérale*, Vol. 14, Masson, Paris, 1959. Chromium chemistry.

Peacock, R. D., "Some Fluorine Compounds of the Transition Metals," in F. A. Cotton, ed., *Progress in Inorganic Chemistry*, Vol. II, Interscience, New York–London, 1960, p. 193.

Quill, L. L., ed., *The Chemistry and Metallurgy of Miscellaneous Materials*: *Thermodynamics*, National Nuclear Energy Series, Division IV, Vol. 19B, McGraw-Hill, New York, 1950. Contains many valuable thermodynamic data on elements and compounds such as the halides, oxides, nitrides, etc.

Selwood, P. W., *Magnetochemistry*, 2nd ed., Interscience, New York–London, 1956.

Sharpe, A. G., "Transition Metal Fluorides and their Complexes," in M. Stacey, J. C. Tatlow, and A. G. Sharpe, eds., *Advances in Fluorine Chemistry*, Vol. I, Butterworths, London, 1960, p. 29.

Shiihara, I., W. T. Schwartz, and H. W. Port, *Chem. Revs.*, **61**, 1 (1961). Chemistry of titanium alkoxides and organometallic compounds.

Ward, R., "Mixed Metal Oxides," in F. A. Cotton, ed., *Progress in Inorganic Chemistry*, Vol. I, Interscience, New York–London, 1959, p. 465.

30

The Elements of the Second and Third Transition Series

30-1. General Comparisons with the First Transition Series

In general, the second and third transition series elements of a given group have similar chemical properties but both show definite differences from their light congeners. A few examples which illustrate this generalization are the following. Although Co^{II} forms a considerable number of tetrahedral and octahedral complexes and is the characteristic species in ordinary aqueous chemistry, Rh^{II} and Ir^{II} are rare and relatively unimportant states for these elements. Similarly, for manganese, the Mn^{2+} ion is very stable, but for Tc and Re the II oxidation state is scarcely known save, perhaps, in a few complexes. Cr^{III} forms an enormous number of cationic ammine complexes which comprise one of the best known aspects of its chemistry, whereas Mo^{III} and W^{III} are not particularly stable states for these elements under any conditions and form only a few complexes, none of which are especially stable. Again, Cr^{VI} species are powerful oxidizing agents with no very extensive chemistry, whereas Mo^{VI} and W^{VI} are quite stable and give rise to an extensive series of polynuclear oxy anions.

This is not to say that there are no valid analogies between the chemistry of first transition elements and that of their heavier congeners. For example, the chemistry of Rh^{III} complexes is in general quite similar to that of Co^{III} complexes. On the whole, however, there are certain consistent differences of which the above-mentioned comparisons are particularly obvious manifestations.

The ionization potentials of the second and third series elements, with the exceptions of Zr and Nb, are not well known, but the available data are given in Table 30-1.

Some important features of the heavier transition elements and com-

TABLE 30-1

Ionization Potentials of the Elements of the Second and Third Transition Series
(In electron volts)

Element	1	2	3	4	5	6	7	8
Zr	6.84	13.13	22.98	34.33	—	99		
Nb	6.88	14.32	25.04	38.3	50	103	125	
Mo	7.10	16.15	27.13	46.4	61.2	68	126	153
Tc	7.28	15.26						
Ru	7.36	14.76	28.46					
Rh	7.46	18.07	31.05					
Pd	8.33	19.42	32.92					
Ag	7.57	21.48	34.82					
Hf	~7	14.9						
Ta	7.88	16.2						
W	7.98	17.7						
Re	7.87	16.6						
Os	8.7	17						
Ir	9							
Pt	9.0	18.56						
Au	9.22	20.5						

parison of these with the corresponding features of the light elements will now be mentioned.

1. Radii. The radii of the heavier transition atoms and ions are not very well known except in a few cases. An important general feature to be noted, however, is that the filling of the 4f orbitals through the lanthanide elements causes a steady contraction, called the *lanthanide contraction,* in atomic and ionic sizes. Thus the expected size increases of the third transition series elements relative to those of the second transition series, due to increased number of electrons and the higher principal quantum numbers of the outer ones, are almost exactly offset, and there is in general little difference in atomic and ionic sizes between the two heavy atoms of a group whereas the corresponding atom and ions of the first transition series are significantly smaller. (The lanthanide contraction is fully discussed on page 876.)

2. Oxidation states. For the heavier transition elements, higher oxidation states are in general much more stable than for the elements of the first transition series. Thus the elements Mo, W, Tc, and Re form oxy anions in high valence states which are not especially easily reduced, for example, MoO_4^{2-}, whereas the analogous compounds of the first transition series elements, when they exist, are strong oxidizing agents. Indeed, the heavier elements form many compounds such as RuO_4, OsO_4, WCl_6, RuF_6, PtF_6, etc., which have no analogs among the lighter ones. At the same time, the chemistry of complexes and aquo ions of the lower valence states, especially II and III, which plays such a large part in the chemistry of the lighter elements, is of relatively little importance for most of the heavier ones.

3. Aqueous chemistry. Aquo ions of the low and medium valence states are not in general well defined or important for any of the heavier transition elements, and some, such as Zr, Hf, and Re, do not seem to form cationic complexes of any kind. For most of them anionic oxy and halo complexes play a major role in their aqueous chemistry although some, such as Ru, Rh, Pd, and Pt, do form important cationic complexes as well.

4. Magnetic properties. Whereas the interpretation of magnetic susceptibilities of the compounds of first transition series elements can usually be made in a simple manner to obtain the number of unpaired electrons and hence the valence state and d orbital configuration, more complex behavior is often encountered in compounds of the heavier elements.

One important characteristic of the heavier elements is that they have a far greater tendency to give *low-spin* compounds, which means that in oxidation states where there is an odd number of d electrons there is frequently only one unpaired electron, and ions with an even number of d electrons are very often diamagnetic. There are two main reasons for this intrinsically greater tendency to spin-pairing in the heavier elements. First, the $4d$ and $5d$ orbitals are spatially larger than $3d$ orbitals so that double occupation of an orbital produces significantly less interelectronic repulsion. Second, a given set of ligand atoms produces larger splittings of $5d$ than of $4d$ orbitals and in both cases larger splittings than for $3d$ orbitals (see page 579).

In cases where there are unpaired electrons, the susceptibility data are often less easily interpreted. For instance, low-spin octahedral Mn^{III} and Cr^{II} complexes have t_{2g}^4 configurations and hence two unpaired electrons. They have magnetic moments in the neighborhood of 3.6 B.M. which can be correlated with the presence of the two unpaired spins, these alone being responsible for a moment of 2.83 B.M., plus a contribution from unquenched orbital angular momentum. Now, Os^{IV} also forms octahedral complexes with t_{2g}^4 configurations, but these commonly have moments of the order of 1.2 B.M. Such a moment taken at face value has little meaning and certainly does not give any simple indication of the presence of two unpaired electrons. Indeed, in older literature it was naively taken to imply that there was only one unpaired electron from which the erroneous conclusion was drawn that the osmium ion was in an odd oxidation state instead of the IV state.

Similar difficulties arise in other cases, and their cause lies in the *high spin-orbit coupling constants* of the heavier ions. Figure 30-1 shows how the effective magnetic moment of a t_{2g}^4 configuration depends on the ratio of the thermal energy, kT, to the spin-orbit coupling constant, λ. For Mn^{III} and Cr^{II}, λ is sufficiently small that at room temperature ($kT \approx 200$ cm.$^{-1}$) both of these ions fall on the plateau of the curve where their behavior is of the familiar sort. Os^{IV}, however, has a spin-orbit coupling constant

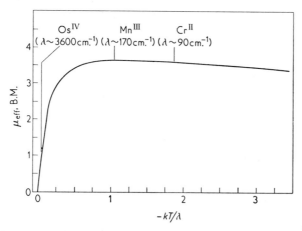

Fig. 30-1. Curve showing the dependence on temperature and on the spin-orbit coupling constant, λ, of the effective magnetic moment of a d^4 ion in octahedral coordination.

which is an order of magnitude higher, and at room temperature kT/λ is still quite small. Thus at ordinary temperatures, octahedral Os^{IV} compounds should (and do) have low, strongly temperature-dependent magnetic moments. Obviously, if measurements on Os^{IV} compounds could be made at sufficiently high temperatures—which is usually impossible—they would have "normal" moments, and, conversely, at very low temperatures Mn^{III} and Cr^{II} compounds would show "abnormally" low moments.

The curve shown in Figure 30-1 for the t_{2g}^4 case arises because of the following effects of spin-orbit coupling. First, the spin-orbit coupling splits the lowest triplet state in such a way that in the component of lowest energy the spin and orbital moments cancel one another completely. When λ and hence this splitting are large compared to the available thermal energy, the Boltzmann distribution of systems among the several spin-orbit split components is such that most of the systems are in the lowest one which makes no contribution at all to the average magnetic moment. At 0°K., of course, all systems would be in this nonmagnetic state and the substance would become entirely diamagnetic. Second, however, the spin-orbit coupling causes an interaction of this lowest, nonmagnetic state with certain high-lying excited states so that the lowest level is not actually entirely nonmagnetic at all temperatures, and in the temperature range where kT/λ is much less than 1 the effective magnetic moment varies with the square root of the temperature.

It is beyond the scope of this text to go more deeply into this subject, but it should be borne in mind, as the example given demonstrates, that the high spin-orbit coupling constants can cause metal ions of the second and third transition series to have magnetic moments at room temperature which cannot be simply interpreted in terms of the number of unpaired electrons present unless measurements are made over a considerable temperature range on magnetically dilute specimens and the results compared with theoretical calculations such as those represented by the curve in Figure 30-1 for the low-spin d^4 system. Other systems for which fairly complicated behavior is expected (only octahedral coordination being considered here) are d^1, d^2, d^7, d^8, and d^9. The d^6 systems have no paramagnetism (unless there is some of the temperature-independent type) since they have t_{2g}^6 configurations with no unpaired electrons. The d^3 systems have magnetic moments which are rigorously temperature independent regardless of the magnitude of λ. The d^5 systems have moments which vary with temperature only for very low values of kT/λ, and even then the temperature dependence is not severe; nevertheless, these systems can show complicated behavior because of intermolecular magnetic interactions in compounds which are not magnetically dilute.

ZIRCONIUM AND HAFNIUM

Because of the effects of the lanthanide contraction, both the atomic radii of Zr and Hf (1.45 and 1.44 A., respectively) and the radii of the Zr^{4+} and Hf^{4+} ions (0.74 and 0.75 A., respectively) are virtually identical. This has the effect of making the chemical behavior of the two elements extremely similar, more so than for any other pair of congeneric elements known.

The known oxidation states and stereochemistries are summarized in Table 30-2.

The chemistry of hafnium has been studied much less than that of

TABLE 30-2

Oxidation States and Stereochemistry of Zirconium and Hafnium

Oxidation state	Coordination number	Geometry	Examples
Zr^0	6	Octahedral(?)	$[Zr(dipyr)_3]$?
Zr^{II}, d^2	?	?	$ZrCl_2$
Zr^{III}, Hf^{III}, d^1	?	?	$ZrCl_3$, $HfBr_3$
Zr^{IV}, Hf^{IV}, d^0	4	Tetrahedral	$ZrCl_4(g)$
	6	Octahedral	Li_2ZrF_6, $ZrAcAc_2Cl_2$, $ZrCl_6^{3-}$, $ZrCl_4(s)$
	7	Pentagonal bipyramidal	Na_3ZrF_7, Na_3HfF_7
		See text, page 768	$(NH_4)_3ZrF_7$
		See text, Fig. 30-2	ZrO_2, HfO_2 (monoclinic)
	8	Square antiprism	$Zr(AcAc)_4$
		Dodecahedron	$[Zr(C_2O_4)_4]^{4-}$

zirconium, but so far as it has been examined it differs little from that of zirconium. We shall not, therefore, make many specific references to hafnium chemistry in this section, it being understood that it is generally comparable to that of zirconium, the small differences being in solubilities or volatilities of compounds.

With increasing atomic and ionic sizes of zirconium and hafnium over titanium, several important changes occur in the chemistry. The most important one is that lower oxidation states are of very minor chemical importance. There are few authenticated compounds of these elements except in their tetravalent states. They do, like titanium, form interstitial borides, carbides, nitrides, etc., but of course these are not to be regarded as having the metals in definite oxidation states. Increased size also makes the oxides more basic and the aqueous chemistry somewhat more extensive. Finally, the increased size permits the attainment of coordination numbers 7 and 8 in a number of compounds.

30-2. The Elements

Zirconium occurs widely over the earth's crust but not in very concentrated deposits. The major ores are the minerals baddeleyite, a form of ZrO_2, and zircon, $ZrSiO_4$. The chemical similarity of zirconium and hafnium is well exemplified in their geochemistry, for hafnium is found in nature in all zirconium minerals in the range of fractions of a per cent of the zirconium content. Again, because of their close chemical similarities, separation of the two elements is extremely difficult, even more so than for adjacent lanthanides, but the separation can now be accomplished satisfactorily by ion exchange or solvent extraction fractionation methods.

Zirconium metal, m.p. 1855 ± 15°C., like titanium, is hard and corrosion resistant, resembling stainless steel in appearance. It is made industrially by the Kroll process described (page 666) for titanium. Hafnium metal, m.p. 2222 ± 30°C., is similar. Like titanium, these metals are fairly resistant to acids, and they are best dissolved in HF where the formation of anionic fluoro complexes is important in the stabilization of the solutions.

30-3. Compounds of Zirconium and Hafnium

Halides. $ZrCl_4$ is a white solid, subliming at 331°C., and it has a molecular lattice of the SnI_4 type. It resembles $TiCl_4$ in its chemical properties. Thus, it may be prepared by chlorination of heated zirconium, zirconium carbide, or a mixture of ZrO_2 and charcoal; it fumes in moist air, and it is hydrolyzed vigorously by water. Hydrolysis proceeds only part way at room temperature, affording the very stable oxychloride,

$$ZrCl_4 + H_2O = ZrOCl_2 + 2HCl$$

This oxychloride crystallizes as the octahydrate, $ZrOCl_2 \cdot 8H_2O$, which contains $[Zr_4(OH)_8]^{8+}$ ions. $ZrCl_4$ also has a tendency to combine with additional ligands to form six-coordinated species. Thus it combines with donors such as ethers, esters, $POCl_3$, and CH_3CN and with Cl^- ions to form the hexachlorozirconate ion, $[ZrCl_6]^{2-}$, which has an octahedral structure. This ion exists in aqueous solution only in the presence of a high concentration of chloride ions.

The tetrabromide and tetraiodide of zirconium are physically and chemically similar to the tetrachloride.

Zirconium tetrafluoride is a white, insoluble crystalline material which seems to be ionic in nature, although this is not certain.

Zirconium Oxide and Mixed Oxides. Addition of hydroxide to zirconium(IV) solutions causes the precipitation of white gelatinous $ZrO_2 \cdot nH_2O$, where the water content is variable. Evidently no true hydroxide, $Zr(OH)_4$, exists. On strong heating this hydrous oxide loses its water to give hard, white, insoluble ZrO_2. This has an extremely high melting point (2700°C.), exceptional resistance to attack by both acids and alkalies, and good mechanical properties, and it therefore finds considerable use in the fabrication of high-temperature equipment such as crucibles and furnace cores. ZrO_2 in its monoclinic (baddeleyite) form and one form of HfO_2 are isomorphous and have a structure in which the metal atoms are seven coordinate, but in a very irregular way as shown in Figure 30-2.

A number of compounds called "zirconates" may be made by combining oxides, hydroxides, nitrates, etc., of other metals with similar zirconium compounds and firing the mixtures at high temperatures (1000–2500°C.). These, like their titanium analogs, are actually mixed metal oxides; there are no discrete zirconate ions known. They have structures of the types already discussed for titanates; thus, $CaZrO_3$ is isomorphous with perovskite, and there are a number of $M^{II}_2ZrO_4$ compounds having the spinel structure.

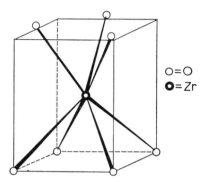

$O = O$
$\bullet = Zr$

Fig. 30-2. Diagram showing approximately the structure of baddeleyite, monoclinic ZrO_2. The Zr—O distances range from 2.04 to 2.26 A., and the O—Zr—O angles from 72 to 91°. The next nearest oxygen atoms are 3.77 A. from Zr.

Aqueous Chemistry. ZrO_2 is more basic than TiO_2. Hence it is virtually insoluble in excess base, but there is a more extensive aqueous chemistry of zirconium because of a lower tendency toward complete hydrolysis. The main species in aqueous solution is the zirconyl ion, ZrO^{2+}, and a number of crystalline salts of this are known. Some representative ones are the acetate, $ZrO(C_2H_3O_2)_2$; the nitrate, $ZrO(NO_3)_2 \cdot 2H_2O$; so-called zirconyl sulfuric acid, which most probably has the structure $H_2[ZrO(SO_4)_2] \cdot 3H_2O$, making it actually a sulfato complex of ZrO^{2+}; and the oxalate, $ZrO(C_2O_4)$. There are also more complex oxyzirconium species known both in solution and in crystals, such as the $[Zr_4(OH)_8]^{8+}$ ion mentioned earlier and possibly a $[Zr_2O_3^{2+}]_n$ species.

Although the larger Zr^{IV} ion should be less susceptible to hydrolysis than Ti^{IV}, it is doubtful if any significant amounts of the simple aquo zirconium(IV) cation exist, even in very acid solutions. Although there are compounds sometimes considered to be simple zirconium salts, these are probably best regarded either as essentially covalent molecules, for example, the acetate, $Zr(C_2H_3O_2)_4$, or as complexes, of which the sulfates are representative and will be discussed below.

Complexes. Although the crystal structures of compounds such as $(NH_4)_2[Zr(SO_4)_3]\cdot 3H_2O$ and $M^I_4[Zr(SO_4)_4]\cdot nH_2O$ are not known, it is generally believed that they contain the Zr^{IV} sulfato complex anions indicated. It has recently been shown that $Na_4[ZrC_2O_4)_4]\cdot 3H_2O$ and its Hf analog are isomorphous and contain eight-coordinate complex anions. The eight-coordinated oxygen atoms have the same configuration (dodecahedral) as do the cyanide ions in $[Mo(CN)_8]^{4-}$. Another octacoordinate Zr^{IV} complex is tetrakis(acetylacetonato)zirconium(IV), in which the coordination shell is a square antiprism.

Among the best-known complex salts of Zr^{IV} are the polyfluoro anions. A number of salts of the type $M^I_2ZrF_6$ have long been assumed to contain octahedral $[ZrF_6]^{2-}$ ions, analogous to the $[ZrCl_6]^{2-}$ ions which are definitely known to occur in $Rb_2[ZrCl_6]$ and $Cs_2[ZrCl_6]$. However, it has recently been reported that K_2ZrF_6 actually contains ZrF_8 units formed by sharing of F^- ions, although Li_2ZrF_6 does contain the octahedral ion. $[ZrF_7]^-$ ions apparently occur with two different structures, depending on the cations present. Na_3ZrF_7 and Na_3HfF_7 are reported to contain MF_7^{3-} ions which are pentagonal bipyramids (IF_7 structure), whereas, in $(NH_4)_3ZrF_7$, the ZrF_7^{3-} ion is reported to have the structure shown on page 525 for the TaF_7^{2-} ion. A number of compounds of the types $M^{II}_2ZrF_8$ ($M = Zn^{2+}$, Cd^{2+}, Cu^{2+}, Ni^{2+}) are known, but their structures have not been investigated. $[ZrF_8]^{4-}$ ions may be present, but this cannot necessarily be assumed.

Lower Oxidation States. The lower halides of zirconium such as $ZrBr_2$ and $ZrBr_3$, prepared by passing a mixture of $ZrBr_4$ and H_2 over aluminum wire at 450°C., and ZrI_2 and ZrI_3, made by reducing ZrI_4 with Zr, are known. $ZrCl_4$, but not $HfCl_4$, is reduced by Zr metal at about 450°C. so that the relatively involatile $ZrCl_3$ remains while $HfCl_4$ sublimes. ZrF_3 also seems authentic. These compounds have not been extensively studied. There is no evidence for lower oxidation states in solution. The only other compound in a low oxidation state is the violet tris-(2,2'-dipyridyl)-zirconium(0), $[Zr(dipy)_3]$, which is formed by reduction of $ZrCl_4$ with lithium in presence of 2,2'-dipyridyl in tetrahydrofuran solution.

NIOBIUM AND TANTALUM

These elements, though metallic in many respects, have chemistries in the V oxidation state which are very similar to those of typical nonmetals.

Thus the general features are quite reminiscent of the chemistry of phosphorus or arsenic, for example. They have virtually no cationic chemistry but form several kinds of anionic species; their halides and oxyhalides, which are perhaps their most important compounds, are quite covalent, volatile, and readily hydrolyzed.

The oxidation states and stereochemistries are summarized in Table 30-3.

TABLE 30-3

Oxidation States and Stereochemistries of Niobium and Tantalum

Oxidation state	Coordination number	Geometry	Examples
Nb^{-I}, Ta^{-I}	6	Octahedral(?)	$[Nb(CO)_6]^-$, $[Ta(CO)_6]^-$
Nb^{II}, Ta^{II}, d^3	?	?	$NbO(?)$, $TaCl_2(?)$
Nb^{III}, Ta^{III}, d^2	?	?	$NbCl_3$, $TaCl_3$
Nb^{IV}, Ta^{IV}, d^1		See text, Fig. 30-5	$Nb_6Cl_{12}^{2+}$, $Ta_6Cl_{12}^{2+}$
	6	Octahedral	NbO_2, TaO_2
			$NbCl_4$, $TaCl_4$
	6	Octahedral (distorted, see Fig. 30-6)	NbI_4 (Nb—Nb bond 3.2 A.), TiI_4
Nb^V, Ta^V, d^0	5	?	NbF_5, TaF_5
		Trigonal bipyramidal(?)	$NbCl_5(vapor)$, $TaCl_5(vapor)$, $(\pi\text{-}C_5H_5)_2TaH_3$
	6	Octahedral	$NaNbO_3(perovskite)$, TaF_6^- Nb_2Cl_{10}, Ta_2Cl_{10}, $K_2NbOF_5 \cdot H_2O$ $[Ta(OC_2H_5)_4]_2$, $NbOCl_3$ (Fig. 30-4)
	7	(See text, page 525)	K_2TaF_7, K_3NbOF_6
	8	Square antiprism	Na_3TaF_8

30-4. The Elements

Niobium and tantalum frequently occur together in nature, but not invariably. Their abundances in the earth's crust are of comparable magnitude, and they are often found in the form of $Fe(NbO_3)_2$, $Fe(TaO_3)_2$, or some composition intermediate between these two, which are isomorphous. In many deposits manganese replaces part of the iron.

Niobium and tantalum are separated by fractional crystallization of fluoro complexes, which are also used molten as electrolytes for the electrolytic reduction to the metals. Niobium and tantalum are bright, high-melting metals (Nb, 1950°C.; Ta, 3010°C.) which are very resistant to acid attack; the best solvent is a mixture of nitric and hydrofluoric acids. The elements are slowly attacked by fused alkalies and will react with various nonmetals at elevated temperatures.

30-5. Compounds of Pentavalent Niobium and Tantalum

Oxygen Compounds. The oxides, Nb_2O_5 and Ta_2O_5, are white powders obtained by dehydration of "niobic" or "tantalic" acids (see below), by roasting other compounds containing elements which can be driven off as oxides (e.g., sulfur, carbon) in excess of oxygen, or, in the case of Ta_2O_5, by heating the metal in oxygen.

They are dense, relatively inert substances. They can be brought into solution by fusing them with alkali hydrogen sulfate, alkali carbonate or hydroxide, or by treatment with concentrated hydrofluoric acid. They are not attacked by other acids.

The product of fusing Nb_2O_5 with excess sodium carbonate is the so-called orthoniobate,

$$Nb_2O_5 + 3Na_2CO_3 = 2Na_3NbO_4 + 3CO_2$$

The salt can be extracted with ethanol from $NaOH-Nb_2O_5$ melts. Tantalum(V) oxide reacts more sluggishly but in the same manner. The formulas of the niobate or tantalate are inferred from the amount of CO_2 displaced.

On leaching the carbonate melt with water, a residue is obtained which is not the orthoniobate, however, but the metaniobate, $NaNbO_3$, which has the perovskite structure (page 668). A number of other metaniobates, such as those of iron, manganese, and other divalent metals, $M(NbO_3)_2$, are also known. These also are not niobates in the sense of containing any discrete "niobate" ions but are mixed metal oxides.

There are also various other "niobates" and "tantalates" of more elaborate constitutions, for example, $M^I_4Nb_2O_7$, $M^I_7Nb_5O_{16} \cdot nH_2O$, $M^I_8Ta_6O_{19} \cdot nH_2O$, etc., which can be crystallized from strongly basic aqueous solutions. They are not well understood and almost completely uncharacterized structurally.

When Nb^V and Ta^V halides or the alkali hydrogen sulfate melts are treated with water, or when alkaline solutions of niobates and tantalates are neutralized with acid, white gelatinous precipitates of "niobic" and "tantalic" acids are obtained. These are actually the hydrous pentoxides, and they redissolve in strong base or in hydrofluoric acid.

Fluorides and Fluoride Complexes. The pentafluorides can be made either by the action of hydrogen fluoride on the pentachlorides, or, better, if elemental fluorine is readily available, by direct fluorination of the metals, the pentoxides, or the pentachlorides. They are both volatile white solids giving colorless liquids and vapors. Their melting and boiling points are 80 and 235°C. for NbF_5 and 95 and 229°C. for TaF_5. No structural studies of them have been reported.

Oxyfluorides have not been reported.

The solubility of the pentoxides in aqueous hydrofluoric acid is due to the formation of fluoro complexes. Although there is little definite information as to the constitutions of those existing in solution, quite a few crystalline complexes have been isolated and those existing in solution are undoubtedly related.

The M^INbF_6 and M^ITaF_6 salts can be obtained either by crystallization from aqueous solutions containing moderate concentrations of F^- or by fluorination of mixtures of the pentoxides with alkali metal chlorides using BrF_3,

$$Ta_2O_5 + 2KCl \xrightarrow{BrF_3} 2KTaF_6$$

X-ray studies have demonstrated the presence of MF_6^- octahedra, slightly distorted, in the potassium compounds of both elements.

From solutions containing larger excesses of F^-, the $M^I_2TaF_7$ compounds can be crystallized. The corresponding niobium complexes require the presence of still larger amounts of F^-, else salts of the $[NbOF_5]^{2-}$ ion, which has an octahedral structure, precipitate instead. The $[NbF_7]^{2-}$ and $[TaF_7]^{2-}$ ions exhibit true seven coordination and have structures already described on page 525.

From solutions containing very high concentrations of F^- are obtained salts of the $[NbOF_6]^{3-}$ and $[TaF_8]^{3-}$ complex ions. The $[NbF_8]^{3-}$ ion has not been isolated. The $[NbOF_6]^{3-}$ ion has a structure derived from an octahedron by spreading one triangular face and introducing the seventh ligand at its center. The $[TaF_8]^{3-}$ ion has, in $Na_3[TaF_8]$, the structure of a square (Archimedean) antiprism, slightly distorted.

The octahedral $[NbOF_5]^{2-}$ ion is found not only in the simple $M^I_2[NbOF_5]$ compounds but also in a compound with the formula K_3HNbOF_7 which actually consists of the following ions: $3K^+$, $[NbOF_5]^{2-}$, $[FHF]^-$.

Other Halides of Niobium(V) and Tantalum(V). All six of these are known. They are all yellow to brown or purple-red solids prepared by direct reaction of the metals with excess of the halogen, or in other ways, for example,

$$2Nb + 5I_2 \xrightarrow{280°C.} NbI_5$$

$$Ta_2O_5 + 5C + 5Cl_2 \xrightarrow{ca.\ 400°C.} 2TaCl_5 + 5CO$$

They melt and boil at rather low temperatures (200–300°C.) and are soluble in various organic liquids, such as ethers, CCl_4, etc. They are quickly hydrolyzed by water to "niobic" and "tantalic" acids and the hydrohalic acid, although the chlorides at least form clear solutions in concentrated hydrochloric acid, presumably by formation of anionic chloro complexes. The chlorides will react on heating with alcohols or alkali metal alkoxides to form niobium and tantalum alkoxides, $M(OR)_5$, and also with lithium amides, $LiNR_2$, to form amides and imides, such as $Ta(NMe_2)_5$ and $Ta(NMe)(NMe_2)_3$.

Molecular weight measurements on the vapors show that in this state the pentavalent halides are monomeric, and electron diffraction studies indicate, but do not conclusively establish, that the configurations are trigonal bipyramidal. X-ray studies of crystalline $NbCl_5$ have revealed a dimeric structure with shared chlorine atoms completing the octahedra about each niobium as shown in Figure 30-3, and it has also been shown

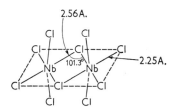

Fig. 30-3. The dinuclear structure of $NbCl_5$ in the solid. The octahedra are distorted as shown.

that $NbBr_5$, $TaCl_5$, and $TaBr_5$ are isomorphous and hence isostructural with $NbCl_5$. NbI_5 and TaI_5 are not isostructural with the others or with one another, and no details of their structures are known.

The processes of thermal decomposition of these halides will be described later in relation to the lower valent halides. All of the pentahalides can be sublimed without decomposition, providing this is done in an atmosphere of the appropriate elemental halogen.

Aside from their probable existence in solutions of the pentachlorides in concentrated hydrochloric acid, the $[MCl_6]^-$ ions appear also to exist in fused mixtures of the pentachlorides with all of the alkali metal chlorides except LiCl. There are compounds of the composition M^INbCl_6 or M^ITaCl_6, and it seems reasonable to suppose that they contain $[MCl_6]^-$ ions, but proof is lacking.

Oxyhalides. Four of these are known, namely, the chlorides, $NbOCl_3$ and $TaOCl_3$, and the bromides, $NbOBr_3$ and $TaOBr_3$. The chlorides are white, and the bromides yellow, volatile solids; they are, however, less volatile than the corresponding pentahalides, and small amounts of the oxyhalides which often arise in the preparation of the pentahalides in systems not scrupulously free of oxygen can be rather easily separated by fractional sublimation.

They can be prepared in various ways, but the most recent studies indicate that the best methods are by pyrolysis of the monoetherate of $TaCl_5$ for $TaOCl_3$ and by controlled reaction between the pentahalides and molecular oxygen for the others.

Like the pentahalides, they are all hydrolyzed to the hydrous pentoxides by water.

It has been reported that from their solutions in concentrated hydrohalic acids and alkali metal cations, complex oxyhalides such as M^INbOCl_4 and $M^I_2NbOCl_5$ can be crystallized.

There is evidence that the oxyhalides are monomeric in the vapor state. That they are less volatile than the corresponding pentahalides is under-

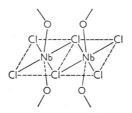

Fig. 30-4.   The structure of $NbOCl_3$ in the crystal. The oxygen atoms form bridges between the planar Nb_2Cl_6 groups. The structure is quite similar to that of $[NbCl_5]_2$, which is shown in Figure 30-3.

standable in view of the structure, which has been revealed by X-ray study for solid $NbOCl_3$. As seen in Figure 30-4, there are infinite chains of planar, chlorine-bridged Nb_2Cl_6 units linked together by oxygen atoms.

Other Compounds.   These are few in number and of minor importance. They include nitrides, sulfides, silicides, selenides, and phosphides as well as many alloys. Definite hydride phases also appear to exist.

There are no simple salts such as sulfates, nitrates, etc.

The volatile, white, crystalline compound $(\pi\text{-}C_5H_5)_2TaH_3$ is obtained by the action of $TaCl_5$ on a solution of sodium cyclopentadienide containing $NaBH_4$; its proton resonance spectrum shows that there are three hydrogen atoms bound to Ta, only two of which are equivalent. This has been explained on the basis of nonlinear $\pi\text{-}C_5H_5$—M axes (see page 649 for further discussion).

30-6. Lower Oxidation States

In recent years considerable work has been done on the lower halides, and this has revealed that there are quite a number of such compounds— or phases—and that there are some unusual structures to be found among them. Our knowledge in this area is still rather fragmentary, and more study will be needed to elucidate the relations between many of the compounds.

Niobium(IV) and Tantalum(IV) Oxides. These appear to be the only lower valent compounds, outside of the halides to be discussed below. Both of these oxides, NbO_2 and TaO_2, are dark grey to black powders; they are insoluble in water or acids, but they dissolve with oxidation in hot aqueous alkalies. NbO_2 is obtained on heating Nb_2O_5 to a white heat in a stream of hydrogen, TaO_2, by reduction of Ta_2O_5 with carbon at high temperature. NbO_2 has a rutile type lattice with NbO_6 octahedra.

The Lower Halides. These are, with two exceptions, trihalides, tetrahalides, or the $M_6X_{14}\cdot 7H_2O$ compounds. The only dihalides known are $TaCl_2$, which is formed on thermal disproportionation of $TaCl_3$ by allowing the $TaCl_5$ to distill off in vacuum, and $NbBr_2$, which is obtained by reducing $NbBr_5$ with hydrogen in an electric discharge. It is thus obtained in only very small quantities and is not well characterized. $TaCl_2$ is a greenish black solid, insoluble in water but slowly attacked by it to give Ta^{III} in solution. It has not been characterized structurally.

The compounds $Nb_6Cl_{14}\cdot 7H_2O$, $Nb_6Br_{14}\cdot 7H_2O$, $Ta_6Cl_{14}\cdot 7H_2O$, and $Ta_6Br_{14}\cdot 7H_2O$ are rather remarkable, especially from the structural point of view. Although they were first made by reduction of the pentahalides by sodium amalgam, they are best obtained in the following reactions:

$$NbX_5 + Cd \xrightarrow[\text{heat}]{\text{red}} Nb_6X_{14}(?) + CdX_2 \xrightarrow[\text{dil. HX}]{\text{diss. in warm } H_2S} CdS + Nb_6X_{14}\cdot 7H_2O$$

$$TaX_5 + Pb \xrightarrow[\text{heat}]{\text{red}} Ta_6X_{14}(?) + PbX_2 \xrightarrow[\text{dil. HX}]{\text{warm}} Ta_6X_{14}\cdot 7H_2O$$

$$(X = Cl \text{ or } Br)$$

These compounds are soluble in water and alcohols, and only two of the halogens are immediately precipitated by Ag^+. From an X-ray diffraction study of the alcohol solutions, it was shown that these substances ionize in solution to give the kinetically inert $[M_6X_{12}]^{2+}$ ions which have the structure shown for $[Ta_6Cl_{12}]^{2+}$ in Figure 30-5. This sort of structure is not entirely peculiar to these compounds; a rather similar one occurs in some lower halides of molybdenum and tungsten (see page 793).

Of the trihalides, all except TaI_3 are definitely known. The trichloride and tribromide of niobium are best made by reduction of the pentahalides with hydrogen at 500°C. They are black solids which vary greatly in reactivity depending on the manner in which they condense from the vapor phase. Niobium(III) iodide is made by heating NbI₅ or NbI₄ at ~430°C. for several days, allowing the iodine produced to sublime away. It is insoluble in and inert toward water. Tantalum(III) chloride is a green solid obtained by reduction of TaCl₅ with aluminum followed by

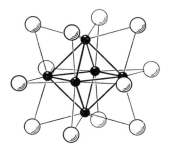

Fig. 30-5. The structure of the complex ion [Ta₆Cl₁₂]²⁺. (Reprinted with permission from L. Pauling, *The Nature of the Chemical Bond*, 3rd ed., Cornell University Press, Ithaca, N. Y., 1960, p. 440.)

strong heating to decompose TaCl₄ initially formed and to sublime out the aluminum(III) chloride. In contrast to its niobium analog, it dissolves in water to form a green solution which is fairly stable when cold, although on warming the tantalum(III) is oxidized with the precipitation of hydrous tantalum(V) oxide. TaBr₃ is obtained by reducing TaBr₅ with hydrogen at ~700°C. None of these trihalides are characterized structurally or indeed in any detail chemically.

Of the tetrahalides, the best characterized in many respects are the tetraiodides. NbI₄ is made by heating NbI₅ for two days at 270°C. while allowing the iodine produced to sublime away. TaI₄ is made by treating an excess of tantalum metal with iodine or by reducing TaI₅ with tantalum metal. These two tetraiodides are dark grey solids, volatile at 300°C. and—surprisingly, since one unpaired electron per metal(IV) atom would be expected—diamagnetic. The reason for the diamagnetism is found in their structure as shown in Figure 30-6. Infinite chains of octahedra of iodine atoms are found, but the metal atoms are not at their centers. Instead they are off-center to form pairs in which electron spins are coupled.

Niobium tetrachloride is obtained by reduction of NbCl₅ with aluminum, iron, or hydrogen. It rather easily disproportionates into NbCl₃ and NbCl₅. The preparation and disproportion of TaCl₄ are quite similar.

Only niobium(V) can be reduced in aqueous acidic solutions electrolyti-

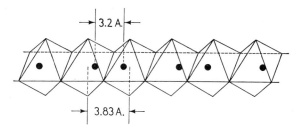

Fig. 30-6. The structure of NbI_4. The iodine atoms are at the apices of the octahedra, and the filled circles represent Nb atoms.

cally or by active metals and gives blue solutions, the nature of which is not fully settled; in sulfuric acid solutions reduction produces what is believed to be the $[Nb_6O_3(SO_4)_{12}]^{8-}$ ion, which may contain Nb^{III} and Nb^V in ratio 2:1.

MOLYBDENUM AND TUNGSTEN

Molybdenum and tungsten are quite similar elements chemically, although there are differences between them in various types of compounds which are not easy to explain. Some compounds of the same type, for example, the hexacarbonyls, also can differ quite noticeably in their reactivities toward various reagents and, again, no simple explanations are possible; for example, $Mo(CO)_6$ but not $W(CO)_6$ will react with acetic acid to give a polymeric diacetate.

Apart from compounds with π-bonding ligands, there is not a great deal of similarity between chromium and the two heavier elements; the divalent state, well defined for Cr, is not well known for Mo and W, and the high stability of Cr^{III} in its complexes has no counterpart in Mo or W chemistry. For the heavier elements, the higher oxidation states are more common and more stable to, for example, reduction.

Both Mo and W have a wide variety of stereochemistries in addition to the variety of oxidation states, and their chemistry is perhaps among the most complex of the transition elements. We may note that uranium has sometimes been classed with Mo and W in group VI, and indeed there are some valid, though often rather superficial, similarities; the three elements do form volatile hexafluorides, oxyhalides, and oxy anions which are similar in certain respects. There is little resemblance to the sulfur group except in regard to stoichiometric similarities, for example, SeF_6, WF_6, SO_4^{2-}, MoO_4^{2-}, and such comparisons are not profitable.

The oxidation states and stereochemistry are summarized in Table 30–4.

TABLE 30-4

Oxidation States and Stereochemistry of Molybdenum and Tungsten

Oxidation state	Coordination number	Geometry	Examples
Mo^{-II}, W^{-II}	5	?	$[Mo(CO)_5]^{2-}$
Mo^0, W^0	6	Octahedral	$W(CO)_6$, $Py_3Mo(CO)_3$, $Mo(diphosphine)_3$, $[Mo(CO)_5I]^-$
Mo^I, W^I, d^5		"Sandwich" bonding	$(C_6H_6)_2Mo^+$, $\pi\text{-}C_5H_5MoC_6H_6$, $[\pi\text{-}C_5H_5Mo(CO)_3]_2$
Mo^{II}, W^{II}, d^4	4	Tetrahedral(?)	$[Mo(OCOCH_3)_2]_n$
	5	?	$\pi\text{-}C_5H_5W(CO)_3Cl$
	7	?	$[Mo(diars)_2(CO)_2X]^+$
	8	Dodecahedral(?)	$[Mo(CN)_5(OH)_2NO]^{4-}$
	9	See text, page 793	Mo_6Cl_{12}
Mo^{III}, W^{III}, d^3	6	Octahedral	$[Mo(SCN)_6]^{3-}$, $[MoCl_6]^{3-}$
	8	Dodecahedral(?)	$[Mo(CN)_7(H_2O)]^{4-}$
Mo^{IV}, W^{IV}, d^2	4	Distorted tetrahedral(?)	$(\pi\text{-}C_5H_5)_2WH_2$, $(\pi\text{-}C_5H_5)_2MoH_2$
	5	Distorted trigonal bipyramid	$(\pi\text{-}C_5H_5)_2WH_3^+$
	6	Octahedral	$[Mo(SCN)_6]^{2-}$, $[Mo(diars)_2Br_2]^{2+}$
	6	Trigonal prism	MoS_2
	8	Dodecahedral[a]	$[Mo(CN)_8]^{4-}$, $[W(CN)_4(OH)_4]^{4-}$
Mo^V, W^V, d^1	5	Trigonal bipyramid	$MoCl_5(g)$
	6	Octahedral	$Mo_2Cl_{10}(s)$, $[MoOF_5]^{2-}$, WF_6^-
	8	Dodecahedral(?)	$[Mo(CN)_8]^{3-}$, $[W(CN)_8]^{3-}$
Mo^{VI}, W^{VI}, d^0	4	Tetrahedral	MoO_4^{2-}, MoO_2Cl_2, WO_4^{2-}, WO_2Cl_2
	5?	?	$WOCl_4$, $MoOF_4$
	6	Octahedral	MoO_6, WO_6 in poly acids WCl_6, MoF_6, $[MoO_2F_4]^{2-}$ MoO_3 (distorted), WO_3 (distorted)
	8?		MoF_8^{2-}, WF_8^{2-}, WF_7^-

[a] The Raman spectrum of $[Mo(CN)_8]^{4-}$ in water has been interpreted in terms of an Archimedean antiprism. The dodecahedral structures of salts of this ion and similar eight-coordinate ions are based on X-ray work on crystalline salts.

30-7. The Elements

In respect to occurrence, metallurgy, and properties of the elementary substances, molybdenum and tungsten are remarkably similar. Both are found in the earth's crust in an abundance of $\sim 10^{-4}\%$.

Molybdenum occurs chiefly as *molybdenite*, MoS_2, but also in the form of molybdates such as $PbMoO_4$ (*wulfenite*), $CaMoO_4$, $CoMoO_4$, and $MgMoO_4$. Tungsten is found almost exclusively in the form of various tungstates, the chief ones being wolframite (a solid solution and/or mixture of the isomorphous substances $FeWO_4$ and $MnWO_4$), scheelite, $CaWO_4$, and stolzite, $PbWO_4$. Both elements are occasionally found as the oxides, MoO_3 and WO_3.

Molybdenum ores contain relatively small amounts of MoS_2, but this can be concentrated by the foam flotation process; the concentrate is then converted, usually by roasting, to MoO_3. This is then extracted using aqueous ammonia, and ammonium molybdate, $(NH_4)_2MoO_4$, is isolated and roasted to yield relatively pure MoO_3 which is finally reduced with hydrogen to the metal. Reduction with carbon must be avoided because this will yield carbides rather than the metal.

Tungsten ores are concentrated by mechanical and magnetic processes and the concentrates attacked by fusion with NaOH. The cooled melts are leached with water giving solutions of sodium tungstate from which hydrous WO_3 is precipitated on acidification. The hydrous oxide is heated to dry it and then reduced to metal using hydrogen.

In the powder form in which they are first obtained by the above processes, both metals are dull grey, but when converted to the massive state by fusion both are lustrous, silver-white substances of typically metallic appearance and properties. They have electrical conductances approximately 30% that of silver. They are both extremely refractory; molybdenum melts at 2610°C. and boils at about 5560°C. (estimated) whereas tungsten melts at 3380°C. and has a boiling point estimated as about 5700°C.

Both metals are rather inert chemically at ordinary temperatures. They are not readily attacked by acids. Concentrated nitric acid initially attacks molybdenum, but the metal surface is soon passivated and the action ceases. Both metals can be dissolved—tungsten only slowly, however—by a mixture of concentrated nitric and hydrofluoric acids. Oxidizing alkaline melts such as fused KNO_3–NaOH or Na_2O_2 will attack them rapidly, but aqueous alkalies are without effect.

Both metals are inert to oxygen at ordinary temperatures, but at red heat they combine with it readily to give the trioxides. They both combine with chlorine when heated, but they are attacked by fluorine, yielding the hexafluorides, at room temperature. Other reactions of the metals which serve for preparation of compounds will be discussed at appropriate places later.

The chief commercial uses of both metals are in the production of alloy steels; even small amounts cause tremendous increases in hardness and strength. Tungsten and chromium alloyed together with iron produce the "high speed" steels which are used to make cutting tools which remain hard even at red heat. Tungsten is also extensively used for lamp filaments.

30-8. Oxides, Sulfides, and Simple Oxy Anions

Oxides. The following oxides are definitely established: MoO_3, WO_3; Mo_2O_5; MoO_2, WO_2. Although a large number of others, especially of tungsten, are described in the literature, it is likely that some are non-stoichiometric phases having the ideal structure of one of the oxides mentioned. Indeed, the WO_3 phase is well established to occur in an oxygen-defective condition. However, there are unquestionably various other stoichiometric oxides, and in the MoO_2–MoO_3 system seven intermediates such as Mo_8O_{23}, Mo_4O_{11} and $Mo_{17}O_{47}$ are known. The last of these has been shown to have MoO_6 octahedral and MoO_7 pentagonal bipyramidal units in the structure.

The most important of the oxides are MoO_3 and WO_3. These are the ultimate products of heating the metals or other compounds such as the sulfides in oxygen. They are not attacked by acids but dissolve in bases to form molybdate and tungstate solutions, which are discussed later.

MoO_3 is a white solid at room temperature but becomes yellow when hot and melts to a deep yellow liquid at 795°C. It boils at 1155°C. It is the anhydride of molybdic acid, but it does not form hydrates directly. The hydrates $MoO_3 \cdot 2H_2O$ and $MoO_3 \cdot H_2O$ can, however, be precipitated from approximately neutral solutions of molybdates. The crystal structure of MoO_3 is a very rare type of layer structure in which each molybdenum atom is surrounded by a distorted octahedron of oxygen atoms.

WO_3 is a lemon yellow solid melting at 1200°C. and boiling about 1430°C. Like CrO_3, it has a structure which is a slightly distorted form of the cubic rhenium trioxide structure shown in Figure 30-7.

Mo_2O_5 is a violet solid soluble in warm acids and is also a good conductor of electricity, better than MoO_2. It can be prepared by heating the required quantity of finely divided molybdenum with MoO_3 at 750°C. When ammonia is added to solutions containing Mo^V, $MoO(OH)_3$ is precipitated, and this can be dried by heating to give Mo_2O_5.

Molybdenum(IV) oxide, MoO_2, is obtained by reducing MoO_3 with hydrogen below 470°C. (above this temperature reduction proceeds to the metal) and by reaction of molybdenum with steam at 800°C. It is a brown-violet solid with a coppery luster, and it has fair electrical conductivity. It is insoluble in nonoxidizing mineral acids but dissolves in concentrated nitric acid with oxidation of the molybdenum to Mo^{VI}. Tungsten(IV) oxide is rather similar.

The Blue Oxides. These are also called *molybdenum blue* and *tungsten blue* and are obtained by mild reduction, for example, by Sn^{II}, SO_2, N_2H_4, H_2S, etc., of acidified solutions of molybdates and tungstates or of suspensions of MoO_3 and WO_3 in water. Moist tungsten(VI) oxide will acquire a blue tint merely on exposure to ultraviolet light.

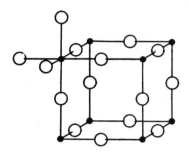

Fig. 30-7.   The ReO_3 structure. Small filled circles represent metal atoms; large open circles represent oxygen atoms. Each metal atom lies at the center of an octahedron of oxygen atoms. It may be seen that this structure is closely related to the perovskite structure since the latter (see Fig. 29-1) is obtained from this one on insertion of a large cation in the center of the cube shown.

The exact nature of these blue substances is not certain, but the following facts seem definite. The solid substances are not of uniform composition; they vary in formula within the limits $MoO_{2.5}$ (or $WO_{2.5}$) and MoO_3 (or WO_3). Thus the mean oxidation state of the metal atoms is between V and VI, and this is probably due to the presence of metal atoms in both of these oxidation states occupying metal sites in oxygen-defective MoO_3 and WO_3 lattices. The intense colors are then not surprising, since phases or compounds containing an element in two different oxidation states characteristically have intense colors due to electron transfer absorption bands. It seems very probable, though it is not conclusively proved, that the aqueous solutions of the blue oxides are colloidal.

Tungsten Bronzes. As long ago as 1824, Wöhler discovered that on reducing acid sodium tungstate at red heat with hydrogen a chemically inert substance with a bronze-like appearance was obtained. Subsequently various other methods have been found for preparing similar materials, the usual ones being by heating sodium, potassium, or alkaline earth tungstates or polytungstates in hydrogen, by electrolytic reduction of fused tungstates, and by reduction of sodium tungstate with sodium, tungsten, or zinc.

The products of these reactions are called tungsten bronzes. They are nonstoichiometric substances having the general formula Na_nWO_3 $(0 < n \leq 1)$ when sodium is present. The colors vary greatly with composition, as indicated in Table 30-5. All tungsten bronzes are extremely inert

TABLE 30-5

Variation of Color with Composition
of Sodium Tungsten Bronzes

n in Na_nWO_3	Color
~0.9	Golden-yellow
~0.6	Orange-red
~0.45	Red-violet
~0.3	Dark blue-violet

chemically and have semimetallic properties, especially metallic luster and good electrical conductivity. Their chemical inertness is manifested in their insolubility in water and resistance to all acids except hydrofluoric. They do, however, have reducing properties, reducing ammoniacal silver nitrate to metallic silver, and they can be oxidized by oxygen in presence of base to give tungstates(VI):

$$4NaWO_3 + 4NaOH + O_2 = 4Na_2WO_4 + 2H_2O$$

Structurally, the sodium tungsten bronzes may be regarded as defective $NaWO_3$ phases having the perovskite structure. It will be recalled (page 668) that for mixed oxides, ABO_3, where one cation is much larger than the other, a common structure is the perovskite structure in which the O^{2-} ions and large cations (Na^+ in $NaWO_3$) form a cubic close-packed array with the small cations occupying octahedral interstices. In the defective phase, Na_nWO_3, there are $(1 - n)$ W^{VI} atoms and $(1 - n)$ of the Na sites of the pure $NaWO_3$ phase are unoccupied. It appears that completely pure $NaWO_3$ has not been prepared, although heating phases with $n \sim 0.85$ with metallic sodium does result in sodium enrichment up to perhaps $n \sim 0.95$. In the other direction, it is found that the cubic structure collapses to rhombic and then triclinic for $n < \sim 0.3$. In the limit of $n = 0$ we have, of course, WO_3, which, as already noted, has a triclinically distorted ReO_3 structure. The cubic ReO_3 structure is just the same as the perovskite structure with all of the large cations removed. Thus the practical range (as opposed to the theoretical range) of composition of the tungsten bronzes is approximately $Na_{0.3}WO_3$–$Na_{0.9}WO_3$.

The semimetallic properties of the tungsten bronzes are associated with the fact that no distinction can be made between W^V and W^{VI} atoms in the lattice, all W atoms appearing equivalent. Thus the n "extra" electrons per mole (over the number for WO_3) are distributed throughout the lattice, delocalized in energy bands somewhat similar to those of genuine metals.

Sulfides. Five sulfides of molybdenum are known, namely Mo_2S_3, MoS_4, Mo_2S_5, MoS_3, and MoS_2. The last three are the most important and are the only ones which will be discussed here.

As already noted, MoS_2 occurs in nature. It can be prepared in the laboratory by direct combination of the elements, by heating molybdenum(VI) oxide in hydrogen sulfide, or by fusing molybdenum(VI) oxide with a mixture of sulfur and potassium carbonate. It is the most stable molybdenum sulfide at higher temperatures, and the others which are richer in sulfur revert to it upon heating in vacuum. It is quite inert chemically, dissolving only in strongly oxidizing acids such as aqua regia and boiling concentrated sulfuric acid. Chlorine and oxygen attack it at elevated temperatures giving $MoCl_5$ and MoO_3, respectively.

MoS_2 has an interesting layer structure in which the repeating unit is a sandwich consisting of a hexagonal sheet of molybdenum atoms between two hexagonal sheets of sulfur atoms. The stacking in this sandwich is such that the sulfur sheets are superposed and the molybdenum shifted so as to put each molybdenum at the center of a trigonal prism formed by six sulfur atoms. The forces between these sandwich-like layers are relatively weak ones between the sulfur atoms of adjacent layers, and MoS_2 therefore has lubricating properties similar to those of graphite, a substance it also resembles in general appearance.

MoS_3 is precipitated in hydrated form when hydrogen sulfide is passed into slightly acid solutions of molybdates. It can be dehydrated to give pure MoS_3. The hydrous precipitate dissolves in excess alkali sulfide solution to give thiomolybdates. On heating in vacuum, MoS_3 loses sulfur to form MoS_2.

Mo_2S_5 is precipitated in hydrated form when H_2S is passed into solutions containing Mo^V such as those obtained by reducing molybdate(VI) solutions with zinc and sulfuric acid. It can be dehydrated to give pure Mo_2S_5.

The tungsten sulfides, which are of little importance, are WS_2 and WS_3. They appear to be generally similar to their molybdenum analogs.

Simple Molybdates and Tungstates. As already noted, the trioxides of molybdenum and tungsten dissolve in alkali metal hydroxides, and from these solutions the simple or normal molybdates and tungstates can be crystallized. They have the general formulas $M^I_2MoO_4$ and $M^I_2WO_4$ and contain the discrete tetrahedral MoO_4^{2-} and WO_4^{2-} ions. The normal tungstates and molybdates of many other metals can be prepared by metathetical reactions. The alkali metal, ammonium, magnesium, and thallous salts are soluble in water, whereas those of other metals are nearly all insoluble.

The solutions of molybdates(VI) can be reduced to give molybdenum(V) species, for example, by using zinc and acid, and from these reduced solutions $MoO(OH)_3$ and Mo_2S_5 are precipitated on addition of ammonia and hydrogen sulfide, respectively. However, the VI oxidation state is remarkably stable for tungsten in the tungstates, and both the MoO_4^{2-} and WO_4^{2-} species lack the oxidizing power so characteristic of the Cr^{VI} species.

The dihydrate of molybdenum(VI) oxide, $MoO_3 \cdot 2H_2O$, is deposited as a yellow, crystalline precipitate when ammonium molybdate solutions containing nitric acid stand for long periods of time. This can be partially dehydrated to yield another definite compound, $MoO_3 \cdot H_2O$. The analogous tungsten compounds are obtained on acidification and boiling of tungstate solutions. These substances are often referred to as molybdic and tungstic acids, but there is definite evidence against their containing any discrete H_2MoO_4 or H_2WO_4 molecules. In fact, broad line proton magnetic resonance study of the molybdenum compounds indicates that all of the hydrogen is present in the form of water molecules; the same conclusion then follows for the tungsten compounds since they are isomorphous with those of molybdenum. A partial X-ray study of $MoO_3 \cdot 2H_2O$ shows the presence of sheets of MoO_6 octahedra sharing corners, but the complete structure has not been worked out.

30-9. Iso- and Heteropoly Acids and Their Salts

An important and characteristic feature of the chemistry of molybdenum and tungsten is the formation of a large number of polymolybdate(VI) and polytungstate(VI) acids and their salts in addition to the simple molybdates(VI) and tungstates(VI) already discussed. Although some analogies exist between these polymolybdates and polytungstates and the poly acids or anions of elements such as silicon, phosphorus, boron, etc., they are of only a very general nature and hence of little help in developing detailed knowledge of the molybdenum and tungsten compounds; indeed, these compounds must be regarded as practically unique. Of the other transition elements only vanadium(V) shows somewhat similar behavior, although so little is known of the vanadium compounds that the extent to which they may resemble the molybdenum and tungsten compounds in detail is not clear. There are also some fragmentary data suggesting that niobium and tantalum have some ability to form poly acids, but very little is known of them.

The poly acids of molybdenum and tungsten are of two types. There are (a) the *isopoly acids* and their related anions, which contain only molybdenum or tungsten along with oxygen and hydrogen, and (b) the *heteropoly acids* and anions, which contain one or two atoms of another element in addition to molybdenum or tungsten, oxygen, and hydrogen.

Isopolymolybdates. When a basic molybdate(VI) solution, containing only $[MoO_4]^{2-}$ and alkali metal or ammonium ions, is acidified, the molybdate ions condense in definite steps to form a series of polymolybdate ions. The over-all condensation process may be considered, formally at least, to begin with partial neutralization of $[MoO_4]^{2-}$ followed by elimination of H_2O to form an oxo bridge,

$$[MoO_4]^{2-} + H^+ = [MoO_3(OH)]^-$$
$$2[MoO_3(OH)]^- = [O_3Mo-O-MoO_3]^{2-} + H_2O$$

The subsequent condensation steps must be more complicated in detail. For example, it seems certain that the Mo (and W) atoms in both the iso- and heteropoly anions are always surrounded by an octahedron of six oxygen atoms, so that at some stage of the condensation process there are changes in coordination number (unless $[MoO_4]^{2-}$ in solution is actually $[MoO_4(H_2O)_2]^{2-}$, $[MoO_2(OH)_4]^{2-}$, or some similar species).

The molecular weights and certain other properties of the condensed species and their equilibria in solution have been studied by various methods including light scattering, acid-base titration, thermometric titrations, spectrophotometry, conductometric titration, cryoscopy, and diffusion measurements. It now appears that the conclusions drawn from diffusion measurements—and these figure importantly in the older literature—are very unreliable because certain assumptions made in the interpretation, especially assumptions about the relation between mobility and weight of the condensed anions, are not valid. However, the data obtained by the various other methods are for the most part reliable, internally consistent, and in general agreement with the results of X-ray studies of isolable crystalline compounds.

As the pH of a strongly basic molybdate solution is lowered to about pH 6, polymerization begins to be detectable. At this stage the main reaction appears to be

$$8H^+ + 7[MoO_4]^{2-} = [Mo_7O_{24}]^{6-} + 4H_2O$$

The $[Mo_7O_{24}]^{6-}$ ion, which may exist in protonated and hydrated forms, is called the *paramolybdate* ion. Salts of the paramolybdate ion, such as

$Na_6[Mo_7O_{24}] \cdot nH_2O$, can be crystallized from solutions at pH's of 4–5. No anionic species containing more than one but less than seven Mo atoms appears to exist in any significant concentration in the polymolybdate systems. The so-called dimolybdates, such as $Na_2O \cdot 2MoO_3 \cdot nH_2O$, which sometimes crystallize from solutions in the pH range of 5–6, are probably mixtures of normal molybdates and paramolybdates. Anhydrous dimolybdates, such as $Na_2Mo_2O_7$, can be obtained from molten alkali oxide–molybdenum oxide systems, but they contain no simple $Mo_2O_7^{2-}$ ion. They contain instead an infinite chain anion of rather complicated structure. Also, the various trimolybdates of general formula $M^I_2O \cdot 3MoO_3 \cdot nH_2O$ appear to contain acid paramolybdate ions or other ions with seven or more Mo atoms.

Tetramolybdates, of general formula $M^I_2O \cdot 4MoO_3 \cdot nH_2O$, are formed from concentrated solutions of alkali molybdates treated with 1.5 moles per mole of hydrochloric acid. They are also known as *metamolybdates*. *Octamolybdates* are obtained similarly from solutions containing 1.75 moles per mole of hydrochloric acid. It has been shown that both the tetra- and octamolybdates are derived from the acid $H_6[Mo_8O_{26}]$. There is evidence that species derived from $[Mo_8O_{26}]^{6-}$ exist in the more acid solutions in equilibrium with the heptamolybdate species. The existence of still more highly condensed anions is uncertain.

The structures of both the heptamolybdate and octamolybdate ions in crystals are known and are discussed on page 787 in relation to other hetero- and isopoly anion structures.

Isopolytungstates. The general behavior of the tungstate systems is quite similar to that of the molybdate systems. Again, the degree of aggregation in solution increases as the pH is lowered, and numerous tungstates, $M^I_2O \cdot nWO_3 \cdot mH_2O$, differing in the value of n have been crystallized from the solutions at different pH's. The two most important classes of these are the paratungstates and the metatungstates.

Analytical data for paratungstates do not in general provide conclusive evidence to choose between the formulas $5M^I_2O \cdot 12WO_3 \cdot nH_2O$ and $3M^I_2O \cdot 7WO_3 \cdot nH_2O$. The latter is analogous to that of the paramolybdates and was once considered the most likely one for the paratungstates. However, the paratungstates and paramolybdates are not crystallographically isomorphous; and, in fact, for the compound $5Na_2O \cdot 12WO_3 \cdot 28H_2O$ it has been shown conclusively that the 5:12 rather than the 3:7 ratio of M^I_2O to WO_3 is correct. The paratungstate ion has the formula $[W_{12}O_{46}]^{20-}$, and its structure is described later (Fig. 30-8).

The metatungstates have the general empirical formula $M^I_2O \cdot 4WO_3 \cdot nH_2O$. Since they have been shown to be isomorphous with 12-tungstophosphates and 12-tungstosilicates (see below) it follows that the true formula is $3M^I_2O \cdot 12WO_3 \cdot nH_2O$ and that they contain $[W_{12}O_{40}]^{8-}$ ions.

Heteropoly Acids and Their Salts. These are formed when molybdate and tungstate solutions containing other oxy anions (e.g., PO_4^{3-}, SiO_4^{4-}) or metal ions are acidified. An amazingly large number of other elements (at least 35) are known to be capable of functioning as the hetero atoms. The free acids and most salts of the heteropolymolybdates and heteropolytungstates are extremely soluble in water and very soluble in various oxygenated organic solvents, such as ethers, alcohols, and ketones, as well. When crystallized from water, the heteropoly acids and salts are always obtained in highly hydrated condition. Like the isopoly acids they are decomposed by strong base into simple molybdate or tungstate ions and either an oxy anion or a hydrous metal oxide of the hetero atom:

$$34OH^- + [P_2Mo_{18}O_{62}]^{6-} = 18MoO_4^{2-} + 2HPO_4^{2-} + 16H_2O$$
$$18OH^- + [Fe_2W_{12}O_{42}]^{6-} = 12WO_4^{2-} + Fe_2O_3 \cdot nH_2O + 6H_2O$$

In general, heteropolymolybdates and tungstates of small cations, including those of some heavy metals, are water soluble, but with larger cations insolubility is frequently found. Thus Cs^+, Pb^{2+}, and Ba^{2+} salts are usually insoluble, and NH_4^+, K^+, and Rb^+ salts are sometimes insoluble. Heteropoly salts with very large cations such as cationic coordination complexes, $[(\pi\text{-}C_5H_5)_2Fe]^+$, quaternary amines, phosphines, and alkaloids are invari-

TABLE 30-6

Principal Types of Heteropolymolybdates

Ratio of hetero atoms to Mo atoms	Principal hetero atoms occurring	Anion formulas
1:12	Series A: P^{5+}, As^{5+}, Si^{4+}, Ge^{4+}, $Sn^{4+}(?)$, Ti^{4+}, Zr^{4+}	$[X^{n+}Mo_{12}O_{40}]^{(8-n)-}$
	Series B: Ce^{4+}, Th^{4+}, $Sn^{4+}(?)$	$[X^{n+}Mo_{12}O_{42}]^{(12-n)-}$
1:11	P^{5+}, As^{5+}, Ge^{4+}	$[X^{n+}Mo_{11}O_{39}]^{(12-n)-}$ (possibly dimeric)
1:10	P^{5+}, As^{5+}, Pt^{4+}	$[X^{n+}Mo_{10}O_x]^{(2x-60-n)-}$ (possibly dimeric)
1:9	Mn^{4+}, Ni^{4+}	$[X^{n+}Mo_9O_{32}]^{(10-n)-}$
1:6	Te^{6+}, I^{7+}, Co^{3+}, Al^{3+}, Cr^{3+}, Fe^{3+}, Rh^{3+}	$[X^{n+}Mo_6O_{24}]^{(12-n)-}$
2:18	P^{5+}, As^{5+}	$[X_2^{n+}Mo_{18}O_{62}]^{(16-2n)-}$
2:17	P^{5+}, As^{5+}	$[X_2^{n+}Mo_{17}O_x]^{(2x-102-2n)-}$
$1m:6m$[a]	Ni^{2+}, Co^{2+}, Mn^{2+}, Cu^{2+}, Se^{4+}, P^{3+}, As^{3+}, P^{5+}	$[X^{n+}Mo_6O_x]_m^{m(2x-36-n)-}$

[a] For the tungstate analog of the Co^{2+} compound it has been found that $m = 2$.

ably insoluble. Table 30-6 lists the principal types of heteropolymolybdates giving stoichiometric types, hetero atoms, and formulas of the heteropoly anions they contain. A great many of these have exact or similar heteropolytungstate analogs.

There are several systems of nomenclature for the heteropoly acids and salts, but the system recommended by the International Union of Pure and Applied Chemistry is to be preferred and will be used here. Table 30-7 gives some representative heteropolymolybdates and the names for them which are in accord with the IUPAC system, the rules of which should be evident from the table.

TABLE 30-7

Some Representative Heteropoly Salts and Their IUPAC Names

Formula	IUPAC names
$Na_3[P^{5+}Mo_{12}O_{40}]$	Sodium 12-molybdophosphate; sodium dodecamolybdophosphate
$H_3[P^{5+}Mo_{12}O_{40}]$	12-Molybdophosphoric acid; dodecamolybdophosphoric acid
$K_8[Co_2^{2+}W_{12}O_{42}]$	Dimeric potassium 6-tungstocobaltate; dimeric potassium hexatungstocobaltate(II)
$Na_8[Ce^{4+}Mo_{12}O_{42}]$	Sodium 12-molybdocerate(IV); sodium dodecamolybdocerate(IV)

Structures of Iso- and Heteropoly Anions. In all cases so far studied definitively by X-ray diffraction, the tungsten and molybdenum atoms lie at the centers of octahedra of oxygen atoms and the structures are built up of these octahedra by means of shared corners and shared edges (but not shared faces). In the structural diagrams we will use here, an MoO_6 or WO_6 octahedron will be represented by the sort of sketch shown in Figure 30-8a. It should be noted that in the complete structures of the poly anions the octahedra are frequently distorted.

The isopoly anions whose structures are definitely known from X-ray studies of crystals are the paramolybdate ion, $[Mo_7O_{24}]^{6-}$, and the octamolybdate ion, $[Mo_8O_{26}]^{4-}$, both of whose structures are shown in Figure 30-8b and 8c, the metatungstate ion $[W_{12}O_{40}]^{8-}$ whose structure is the same as that of the 12-tungsto and 12-molybdo hetero anions of type A (see Fig. 30-9) to be discussed shortly, and the paratungstate ion, whose structure is shown in Figure 30-8d.

Detailed X-ray structural studies have been made of the 12-molybdo hetero anions with P^{5+}, As^{5+}, Ti^{4+}, and Zr^{4+} and of the isomorphous 12-tungsto species containing the hetero atoms B^{3+}, Ge^{4+}, P^{5+}, As^{5+}, and Si^{5+}. All of these have the structure shown diagrammatically in Figure

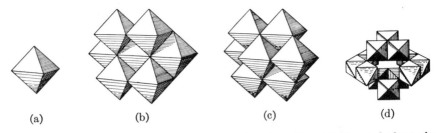

(a)   (b)   (c)   (d)

Fig. 30-8.   (a) The diagrammatic representation of MoO_6 and WO_6 octahedra to be used in showing structures of some isopoly and heteropoly anions. (b) The structure of the paramolybdate anion, $[Mo_7O_{24}]^{6-}$. (c) The structure of the octamolybdate anion, $[Mo_8O_{26}]^{4-}$ (note that one MoO_6 octahedron is completely hidden by the seven which are shown). (d) The structure of the paratungstate ion, $[W_{12}O_{46}]^{20-}$.

30-9. It may be thought of as consisting of four groups of three MoO_6 or WO_6 octahedra. In each group there is one oxygen atom common to all three octahedra. In the complete structure these groups are so oriented by sharing of oxygen atoms between groups that the four triply shared oxygen atoms are placed at the corners of a central tetrahedron. The hetero atom sits in the center of this tetrahedron in the heteropoly ions

Fig. 30-9.   The structure of the series A 12-molybdo and 12-tungsto heteropoly anions of general formula $[X^{n+}Mo_{12}O_{40}]^{(8-n)-}$.

and in the metatungstate ion there is no hetero atom. It will be noted that all of the hetero species occurring in the A series (Table 30-6) of 12-heteropoly anions are small enough to make a coordination number of four toward oxygen appropriate.

In the 12-hetero acids of type B, the hetero species are larger than those in the ones of type A, and it might be expected that their structures would be such as to have the hetero atoms in central octahedra of oxygen atoms. Their structures are not actually known, but it is noteworthy that the paratungstate structure (Fig. 30-8d) has just such a central octahedron.

The 9-molybdo heteropoly anions are built by packing MoO_6 octahedra so as to produce a central octahedron of oxygen atoms. The structure is shown in an exploded view in Figure 30-10. Closer inspection of this structure reveals that it is asymmetric and these anions should exist in enantiomorphic forms. No resolution has as yet been reported, however.

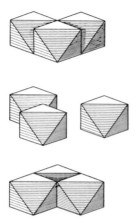

Fig. 30-10. An exploded view of the structure of the 9-molybdo heteropoly anion $[X^{n+}Mo_9O_{32}]^{(10-n)-}$, showing the nine MoO_6 octahedra. When the upper and lower sets of three are moved in so as to share some corners with the equatorial set, a central octahedron of oxygen atoms occupied by the hetero atom is created.

The structure of the $[TeMo_6O_{24}]^{6-}$ anion has been determined and it is shown in Figure 30-11. Six MoO_6 octahedra share edges in such a way as to create a ring with a central octahedron of oxygen atoms which is occupied by the tellurium atom. It is noteworthy that although the paramolybdate ion, $[Mo_7O_{24}]^{6-}$, might be formally regarded as a 6-molybdomolybdate ion, $[MoMo_6O_{24}]^{6-}$, it is structurally different in detail from the $[TeMo_6O_{24}]^{6-}$ ion.

It is considered probable that the various dimeric 9-molybdo and

Fig. 30-11. The structure of the $[TeMo_6O_{24}]^{6-}$ ion with the central TeO_6 octahedron lifted out to show the ring of six MoO_6 octahedra.

Fig. 30-12. The structure of the dimeric anion $[P_2W_{18}O_{62}]^{6-}$.

9-tungsto heteropoly anions, of general formula $[X_2Mo_{18}O_{62}]^{6-}$, have the same structure as that found for the $[P_2W_{18}O_{62}]^{6-}$ ion and shown in Figure 30-12. This structure can be thought of as consisting of two half units, each of which is derived from the series A 12-molybdo heteropoly anion structure (Fig. 30-9) by removal of three MoO_6 anions. It has been suggested that the 11-molybdo and 10-molybdo heteropoly anions may also be dimeric and consist of appropriate fragments of the 12-molybdo structure, but nothing is definitely known of their structures.

30-10. Halides and Oxyhalides

Both molybdenum and tungsten form compounds with all of the halogens, and among these halides both metals are represented in oxidation states from II to VI.

Fluorides. The known fluorides and their chief physical properties are shown in Table 30-8.

TABLE 30-8

Fluorides of Molybdenum and Tungsten

Formula	Type	Melting point, °C.	Boiling point, °C.
MoF_3	Yellowish solid, nonvolatile		
MoF_4	Green solid, nonvolatile		
MoF_5	Yellow solid	67	213
MoF_6	White solid	175	350
WF_4	Red-brown solid		
WF_6	Colorless liquid or gas	2.3	17

Direct fluorination of the metals yields in both cases the hexafluorides. They are colorless, diamagnetic substances which are quite volatile. They have octahedral molecular structures. The chemical properties of these hexafluorides are not known in great detail, but the following important reactions can be mentioned. They are readily hydrolyzed and must be handled in scrupulously dry vacuum lines. Although the dry gases do not attack glass, attack is rapid in presence of traces of moisture which generate traces of HF by hydrolysis. MoF_6 is rather easily reduced and attacks organic matter; WF_6 is less reactive in both these respects. WF_6 exhibits Lewis acidity as indicated by the reactions

$$WF_6 + 4NH_3 = WF_6 \cdot 4NH_3$$
$$WF_6 + 3Am = WF_6 \cdot 3Am$$
$$(Am = \text{pyridine or } CH_3NH_2)$$

The structures and hence the true coordination numbers of tungsten in these compounds are unknown. WF_6 also reacts with SO_3 to yield a compound of the composition $WF_4(SO_3F)_4$.

MoF_3 is obtained by treatment of MoF_5 with Mo at $\sim400°C$. It is a nonvolatile yellowish or brown solid in which the molybdenum atoms are surrounded by octahedra of fluorines similar to the trifluorides of V, Cr, Fe, Ru, and Ga.

The two other lower fluorides of molybdenum were prepared as follows. The treatment of molybdenum carbonyl with fluorine diluted in nitrogen at $-75°C$. gives a product of composition Mo_2F_9. The nature of this substance has not been investigated, but when it is heated to $150°C$. it yields the nonvolatile MoF_4 as a residue and the volatile MoF_5 condenses in cooler regions of the apparatus. It is also possible to obtain MoF_5 by direct reaction of MoF_6 with $Mo(CO)_6$,

$$5MoF_6 + Mo(CO)_6 = 6MoF_5 + 6CO$$

These lower fluorides of molybdenum have not as yet been well characterized structurally and chemically, but MoF_5 may be $MoF_4^+MoF_6^-$, which would explain its ready disproportionation at $165°C$.

The only lower fluoride of tungsten which has been described is WF_4. This is a nonvolatile, red-brown solid obtained by reduction of WF_6 with benzene at $110°C$.

Chlorides. An extensive group of these are known, namely,

—	$MoCl_5$	$MoCl_4$	$MoCl_3$	$MoCl_2$
WCl_6	WCl_5	WCl_4	—	WCl_2

Direct chlorination of the metals at elevated temperatures produces WCl_6 or $MoCl_5$. The hexachloride of molybdenum does not appear to exist.

WCl_6 occurs as blue-black crystals. It is moderately volatile (m.p. 275°C., b.p. 346°C.) and the vapor is monomeric, consisting of octahedral molecules. It is soluble in many organic solvents such as CS_2, CCl_4, alcohol, and ether. It is slightly soluble in cold water with which it slowly reacts, whereas warm water hydrolyzes it quickly to tungstic acid.

$MoCl_5$ occurs as dark greenish black crystals and is also moderately volatile (m.p. 194°C., b.p. 268°C). In the gaseous state it exists as monomers which probably have a trigonal bipyramid structure. In the crystal, however, dimers are formed by sharing of chlorine atoms so that each molybdenum is hexacoordinate. The structure is virtually identical with that of the $NbCl_5$ dimer which is shown in Figure 30-3. Crystalline $MoCl_5$ is paramagnetic, with a magnetic moment which indicates that there is only weak coupling of electron spins of the two molybdenum atoms in each dimer. $MoCl_5$ is soluble in a great variety of both polar and nonpolar organic solvents. It is hydrolyzed by water.

The lower chlorides of tungsten can all be prepared by reduction of WCl_6 in hydrogen under appropriate conditions of temperature, pressure, and reaction time. Mild conditions maximize the yield of WCl_5, which forms volatile black-green needles and a monomeric vapor. It does not seem to have been established whether or not crystalline WCl_5 is isomorphous with its molybdenum analog.

More drastic conditions in the reduction process lead to the formation of WCl_4 and WCl_2, but no WCl_3 appears to exist under conditions so far used. Use of very high temperature in the reduction reaction will lead to the production of metallic tungsten.

The lower chlorides of molybdenum are prepared in a variety of ways. $MoCl_3$ is obtained in good yield by reducing the pentachloride with hydrogen. The tetrachloride is obtained by treatment of the dichloride with chlorine in carbon tetrachloride solution in a sealed tube at 250°C. or by the action of Cl_2 on MoO_2 in refluxing hexachlorobutadiene. The dichloride is itself prepared by the action of phosgene ($COCl_2$) on molybdenum at red heat; it is a yellow powder.

Tungsten and molybdenum dichlorides are undoubtedly not simply chlorides of W^{II} and Mo^{II}. Although the exact structures of the anhydrous materials are unknown, there is indirect chemical and structural evidence that they are more complex. Thus, the molybdenum compound is insoluble in water and acids and shows little reducing power. The tungsten compound is attacked by water, however, liberating hydrogen, and it exhibits reducing power in other reactions. On treatment of "$MoCl_2$" with aqueous silver nitrate, it is found that only one-third of the chlorine is immediately available to form AgCl. Also, even after boiling "$MoCl_2$" with ^{36}Cl-labeled hydrochloric acid for 1.5 hours, only one-third of the chlorine has undergone exchange.

The molybdenum compound can be dissolved in aqueous base, and from these solutions it is possible to precipitate a series of compounds which all appear to contain the $[Mo_6Cl_8]^{4+}$ unit, namely, $[Mo_6Cl_8](OH)_4 \cdot 14H_2O$, $[Mo_6Cl_8]Br_4 \cdot 6H_2O$, $[Mo_6Cl_8]I_4 \cdot 6H_2O$, $[Mo_6Cl_8]Cl_4 \cdot 2C_5H_5N$, $(H_3O)_2$ $[Mo_6Cl_8]I_6 \cdot 6H_2O$, and $K_2[Mo_6Cl_8]Cl_6 \cdot 6H_2O$. An X-ray study of the first of these has shown that the $[Mo_6Cl_8]^{4+}$ group has a structure in which the molybdenum atoms lie at the apices of an octahedron with the chlorine atoms lying above the centers of the eight triangular faces, thus forming three-way bridges between the metal atoms, as shown in Figure 30-13. This structure is very reminiscent of the one for $[Ta_6Cl_{12}]^{2+}$ (page 775), and it appears that formation of such octahedral groups of metal atoms with halogen bridges between them may be a recurring feature for these metals in formally low oxidation states.

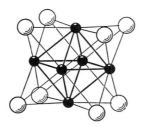

Fig. 30-13.   The structure of the $[Mo_6Cl_8]^{4+}$ group. (Reprinted with permission from L. Pauling, *The Nature of the Chemical Bond*, 3rd ed., Cornell University Press, Ithaca, N. Y., 1960, p. 440.)

Other Halides.   The bromides and iodides of tungsten and molybdenum are:

—	—	$MoBr_4$	$MoBr_3$	$MoBr_2$
WBr_6	WBr_5	WBr_4	—	WBr_2
—	—	MoI_4	MoI_3	MoI_2
—	—	—	—	WI_2

The bromides resemble the corresponding chlorides, although they have not been investigated so much. The iodides are of relatively little importance.

Oxyhalides.   Quite a number of these are known to exist. Those listed below are the definite, well-characterized ones.

WOF_4	WO_2F_2?	$WOCl_4$	WO_2Cl_2	$WOBr_4$	WO_2Br_2
$MoOF_4$	MoO_2F_2	—	MoO_2Cl_2	—	MoO_2Br_2

$$(MoO_2Cl_2 \cdot H_2O \stackrel{?}{=} MoO(OH)_2Cl_2)$$

The following general remarks may be made about the entire group. It will be noted that all of them contain the metals in the VI oxidation state. Just as there are no Mo^{VI} halides other than the fluoride, so the oxyhalides of Mo^{VI} are much less stable than those of W^{VI}. All of these oxyhalides are very volatile and behave as molecular compounds. They are all more or less rapidly hydrolyzed by water. The oxyhalides are quite often observed in preparations of the metal halides by direct reaction of the metals with the halogens unless the systems have been rigorously purged of oxygen. It is even necessary to pretreat the metal powders with hydrogen in order to eliminate traces of the oxyhalides formed by the action of the halogens on traces of metal oxides. Unless extremely pure metal halides are required, however, oxyhalide formation to a limited extent is not a serious problem since the oxyhalides are more volatile than the halides and can be pretty effectively removed by sublimation at lower temperatures.

$MoOF_4$ and WOF_4 can both be prepared by the same types of reaction,

$$\left.\begin{array}{l} M + O_2 + F_2 \\ MO_3 + F_2 \\ MOCl_4 + HF \end{array}\right\} \rightarrow MOF_4$$

$$(M = Mo \text{ or } W)$$

They are both colorless, volatile solids, not as reactive as the hexafluorides.

WO_2F_2 has been reported but there is some doubt of its actual existence. MoO_2F_2 can be obtained by the action of HF on MoO_2Cl_2; it is a white solid subliming at 270°C. at 1 atm.

The two tungsten oxychlorides are formed together when WO_3 is heated in carbon tetrachloride vapor, phosgene, or PCl_5. They are easily separated since $WOCl_4$ is much more volatile than WO_2Cl_2. On strong heating above 200°C. the following reaction occurs

$$2WO_2Cl_2 = WO_3 + WOCl_4$$

$WOCl_4$ forms scarlet crystals, a red monomeric vapor, and is in general highly reactive. It is violently hydrolyzed by water. WO_2Cl_2 occurs as yellow crystals and is not nearly so reactive as $WOCl_4$; it is hydrolyzed only slowly by cold water.

MoO_2Cl_2 is best made by the action of chlorine on heated, dry MoO_2. It is fairly volatile and dissolves with hydrolysis in water. An electron diffraction study of MoO_2Cl_2 vapor has shown the existence of tetrahedral molecules.

A substance of the formula $MoO_2Cl_2 \cdot H_2O$ is obtained when MoO_3 is treated with dry hydrogen chloride at 150–200°C. It is a pale yellow, very volatile compound soluble in various polar organic solvents. Its molecular structure is not known, but the formulation $MoO(OH)_2Cl_2$ seems reasonable.

The tungsten oxybromides are very similar in properties and reactivity to the oxychlorides.

30-11. Interstitial Compounds with Nonmetals

Both molybdenum and tungsten react at high temperatures with non-metals, especially boron, carbon, nitrogen, and silicon, to produce hard, refractory, interstitial compounds.

Among the well-characterized borides are those of the compositions M_2B, MB, MB_2, and M_2B_5 ($M = Mo$ or W). In all cases save the M_2B_5 compounds the corresponding Mo and W phases are isostructural. These borides are good examples of the various types of interstitial borides cited earlier (page 182). Thus the M_2B phases have close-packed arrays of metal atoms with isolated boron atoms in tetrahedral holes; the MB compounds exist in both high- and low-temperature polymorphs, but in both of these there are zigzag chains of boron atoms running through an array of metal atoms. In the MB_2 and M_2B_5 phases (which are generally encountered in nonstoichiometric condition) there are two-dimensional hexagonal nets of boron atoms penetrating the array of metal atoms.

The carbides and nitrides of a given metal are quite similar to one another, and both metals form the following well-studied phases: M_2C, M_2N, MC, and MN. All of them are interstitial. For the M_2C and M_2N phases there are two closely related structures which involve the C or N atoms occupying octahedral (or slightly distorted octahedral) holes in hexagonal or cubic close-packed arrays of metal atoms. In the MC and MN phases the metal atoms form cubic close-packed arrays and the C or N atoms occupy octahedral interstices.

Both metals form a series of isomorphous silicide phases, of which the best known ones are M_3Si, M_3Si_2, M_5Si_3, and MSi_2. The structures of the M_3Si and M_5Si_3 phases are based upon cubic and hexagonal arrays of metal atoms with silicon atoms in the interstices. The structure of the M_3Si_2 phases is not yet known. In the MSi_2 phases there are interpenetrating hexagonal nets of silicon atoms forming polyhedra which are square prisms with pyramidal ends. A metal atom is at the center of each of these polyhedra.

All of these interstitial compounds are of technological interest because they are hard, refractory, and chemically inert. Their uses, or potential uses, are in the fabrication of internal structural elements of kilns, gas turbines, jet engines, in sand-blast nozzles, cutting tools, etc.

All of these various interstitial compounds or phases can be prepared by direct reaction of the elements at high temperatures in atmospheres which are inert or reducing (H_2). The relative quantities of the constituents used and the temperature of reaction determine the phase formed. The nitrides can also be made by reaction of the heated metals with ammonia.

30-12. Complexes

As in all other phases of their chemistry, molybdenum and tungsten are sharply differentiated from chromium in the number and kinds of complexes they form. Whereas chromium forms an enormous number of kinetically inert, cationic complexes in the trivalent state, molybdenum and tungsten form relatively few complexes, which are practically all anionic, and the metals occur in these in oxidation states of III, IV, V, and

VI. It has been shown that molybdenum at least is capable of forming complexes in the II state with ligands of the highest π-bonding ability such as arsines or carbon monoxide. Those reported are the seven-coordinate compounds [Mo(diars)(CO)$_3$I$_2$] and [Mo(diars)$_2$(CO)$_2$I]$^+$I$^-$. Also, the interaction of Mo(CO)$_6$ with glacial acetic (and other carboxylic) acid produces yellow needles of the diacetate Mo(OCOCH$_3$)$_2$. This acetate is highly insoluble in other than donor solvents. Since it is very stable, subliming at over 300°C., it is presumably polymeric with bridging acetate groups and tetrahedrally coordinated Mo^{II}. However, these are unusual, and we turn now to the better-known complexes containing the metals in their higher oxidation states.

Molybdenum(III) and Tungsten (III) Complexes. Relatively recently the only known cationic complexes of these metals in higher oxidation states were reported. On treatment of K$_3$MoCl$_6$ in aqueous ethanol containing hydrochloric acid with 1,10-phenanthroline (o-phen), the compound [Mo(o-phen)$_3$]Cl$_3$ is obtained. The bromide and iodide salts of the [Mo(o-phen)$_3$]$^{3+}$ cation have also been prepared, and so also have analogous dipyridyl complexes, namely, [Mo(dipy)$_3$]X$_3$. The tungsten analogs have not been reported.

Molybdenum(III) forms complexes of the type [MoX$_6$]$^{3-}$ with several halogens and pseudohalogens. Electrolytic reduction of a solution of MoO$_3$ in concentrated hydrochloric acid gives a solution of Mo^{III} in the form of chloro complexes, of which [MoCl$_6$]$^{3-}$ and [MoCl$_5$(H$_2$O)]$^{2-}$ can be precipitated with the larger alkali metal cations, for example, K$^+$. The salts of these complex anions are red, fairly stable in dry air, but rapidly hydrolyzed and oxidized in the presence of water. They are strong reducing agents.

K$_3$MoCl$_6$ reacts with molten KHF$_2$ to produce brown, cubic K$_3$MoF$_6$. It reacts with an oxygen-free solution of potassium cyanide to give black crystalline K$_4$Mo(CN)$_7$·2H$_2$O, but in the presence of oxygen the molybdenum(IV) complex K$_4$Mo(CN)$_8$·2H$_2$O is obtained. It reacts with solutions of alkali metal thiocyanates even in the presence of oxygen to give salts of the general formula M$^I_3$[Mo(SCN)$_6$]·nH$_2$O. The ammonium salt of the [Mo(SCN)$_6$]$^{3-}$ ion can be prepared directly by electrolytic reduction of a solution of ammonium molybdate at a bright platinum cathode in presence of an excess of ammonium thiocyanate. There is infrared evidence that the thiocyanate groups are bound to molybdenum through sulfur in the [Mo(SCN)$_6$]$^{3-}$ ion.

Other complexes of Mo^{III} are the tris(acetylacetonate), an air-sensitive compound prepared by refluxing Mo(CO)$_6$ in acetylacetone, and a compound of the unusual formula $K_2Mo(CN)_5$, which appears to contain pentacoordinate Mo^{III}, since the infrared spectrum gives no indication that bridging cyanide ions are present.

It is somewhat surprising that W^{III}, in contrast to the behavior of Mo^{III}, forms practically no complexes, the only two known being polynuclear chloro complex anions. When K_2WO_4, dissolved in saturated aqueous hydrochloric acid, is reduced with stannous ion in presence of potassium ions, yellow-green $K_3[W_2Cl_9]$ or red $K_5[W_3Cl_{14}]$ precipitates, depending on the Cl^- concentration. There appears to be a chloride-ion-dependent equilibrium between the two ions, or others closely related, in solution. The $W_2Cl_9^-$ ion has the structure of two octahedra sharing a triangular face with chlorine atoms at each of the nine distinct apices. Thus three of the chlorine atoms are bridging. The magnetism of $K_3W_2Cl_9$ has been studied by two groups, one reporting it to be diamagnetic, the other stating that it was very weakly paramagnetic, with a susceptibility corresponding to a moment of only 0.46 B.M. per tungsten atom. From these results it is clear that there is considerable if not complete pairing of electron spins of adjacent tungsten atoms.

The magnetic and spectral properties of Mo^{III} complexes, to the extent that they are known, can be accounted for satisfactorily by ligand field theory. The octahedral complexes should have three unpaired electrons and the magnetic moments, like those of octahedral Cr^{III}, should be slightly below the spin-only value (3.86 B.M.) because of spin-orbit coupling. This is found to be so in all cases examined, the moments of Mo^{III} in such complexes as $[Mo(o\text{-phen})_3]^{3+}$, $[Mo(dipy)_3]^{3+}$, $[MoCl_6]^{3-}$, $[MoF_6]^{3-}$, and $[Mo(SCN)_6]^{3-}$ being in the range 3.7–3.85 B.M. In the spectrum of $[MoCl_6]^{3-}$ the $^4A_2 \rightarrow {}^4T_2$ and $^4A_2 \rightarrow {}^4T_1$ transitions have been observed, and from their energies the value of the ligand field parameter Δ is found to be 19,200 cm.$^{-1}$, while the Racah parameter B is found to be 435 cm.$^{-1}$. For $[CrCl_6]^{3-}$ the Δ value is only 13,600, which provides a good illustration of the generalization (page 595) that there is a general increase of $\sim30\%$ in Δ values on passing from analogous complexes of one transition series to those of the next heavier one. The B value is about 70% of that for the free Mo^{3+} ion; this degree of reduction in B is quite typical (see page 596).

The only nonoctahedral complex of Mo^{III} which has been studied magnetically is $K_4Mo(CN)_7 \cdot 2H_2O$, and this has a moment of 1.75 B.M., indicating the presence of just one unpaired electron. For either of the two formulations which have been proposed for the complex anion, that is, $[Mo(CN)_7]^{4-}$ or $[Mo(CN)_7(H_2O)]^{4-}$, the symmetry of the ligand field would be low. The presence of only a single unpaired electron could then be due to the presence of one or two d orbitals lying well below the others.

Molybdenum(IV) and Tungsten (IV) Complexes. These are not very numerous.

When a solution of K_2WO_4 in hydrochloric acid is treated with tin under certain definite conditions, W^{IV} is produced in solution and can be isolated as the dark green complex salt, $K_2[W(OH)Cl_5]$. It is interesting that, though paramagnetic, this compound has a magnetic moment of only 2.2 B.M., which is well below the spin-only value (2.83 B.M.) for two unpaired electrons. The reason for this is not known with certainty, but it may be caused either by antiferromagnetic interactions or by the effect of spin-orbit coupling in the octahedral t_{2g}^2 configuration, as discussed on page 763. Hexafluoromolybdates, for example, the dark brown Na_2MoF_6, can be obtained by reduction of MoF_6 with an excess of NaI; the hexafluoromolybdates(IV) are much more stable with respect to hydrolysis than are the Mo^V species.

A few diamagnetic, presumably octahedral oxycyanide complexes of the type $[MoO_2(CN)_4]^{4-}$ are known, but the most important complexes of Mo^{IV} and W^{IV} are the octacyanides, $[Mo(CN)_8]^{4-}$ and $[W(CN)_8]^{4-}$. The molybdenum one will form in solutions of Mo^{III} or Mo^V on treatment with a large excess of potassium cyanide. In the former case it appears, as noted earlier, that molecular oxygen must be present as the oxidizing agent; in the latter case the manner of reduction has not been established. Both $[Mo(CN)_8]^{4-}$ and $[W(CN)_8]^{4-}$ are remarkably stable species, thermally, toward hydrolysis, and toward acids and oxidizing agents. In addition to their occurrence in various salts, these complex ions also occur in the acids $H_4[W(CN)_8] \cdot 6H_2O$. They can be oxidized by very powerful oxidants, for example, Ce^{IV} or MnO_4^-, to the corresponding octacyano complexes of Mo^V and W^V.

The structure of the $[Mo(CN)_8]^{4-}$ ion has already been discussed and illustrated (page 525). The diamagnetism of this complex and its tungsten analog suggests that the distortion of the arrangement of the eight CN^- ions from that of a cube splits the d_{z^2} and $d_{x^2-y^2}$ orbitals sufficiently so that the two d electrons become paired in the one of lower energy. An investigation of the Raman spectrum of $[Mo(CN)_8]^{4-}$ has been reported to provide evidence that this complex has the configuration of a square antiprism rather than the dodecahedral structure (page 525) previously deduced from X-ray study. Whether there is an error in one study or the other or whether there is a change in configuration when the crystalline salt is dissolved in water remains to be determined.

Molybdenum(V) and Tungsten(V) Complexes. These are all anionic and contain oxygen, halogens, thiocyanate, or cyanide groups as ligands. The hexafluoromolybdate(V) and hexafluorotungstate(V) anions can be obtained as salts of the larger alkali metal cations (Na, K, Rb, Cs) by the general reaction shown in equation 30-1 in which IF_5 serves both as the fluorinating agent and the solvent.

$$W(Mo)(CO)_6 + M^II + IF_5 \rightarrow M^IW(Mo)F_6 + 6CO + \text{other unidentified products} \quad (30\text{-}1)$$

In all of these complexes there is considerable interionic electron spin coupling which makes them antiferromagnetic (Neél temperatures of the order of 100–150°K.). These couplings must take place by overlap of orbitals of the fluoride ions of adjacent $[MF_6]^-$ units in the crystals, that is, by a superexchange process similar in principle to that described for the halides and chalconides of some divalent metals of the first transition series (see page 593). Such an explanation of course requires the assumption of significant overlap of metal $d\pi$ (t_2) orbitals with fluoride ion $p\pi$ orbitals.

It is also possible to isolate K_3MoF_8 and K_3WF_8 from the above reaction system under certain conditions. It is not known whether these compounds contain octacoordinated metal ions or not.

A considerable number of oxyhalide complexes of the pentavalent metals have long been known. Representative ones are alkali metal salts with the general formulas $M^I_2[MoOCl_5]$, $M^I_2[MoOBr_5]$, $M^I[MoOBr_4]$, $M^I_2[MoO(SCN)_5]$, $M^I_2[WOCl_5]$, $M^I[WOCl_4]$, and $M^I[WOCl_4(H_2O)]$. They are all obtained by reducing aqueous solutions of Mo^{VI} and W^{VI} under appropriate conditions of temperature and concentration of alkali halides and acidity. All of them are magnetically normal, having moments of 1.5–1.8 B.M.

W^V also gives alkali metal salts of $[WO_2(C_2O_4)_2]^{3-}$ when solutions of alkali tungstates are reduced in presence of excess oxalate and high acidity.

As noted earlier, potassium permanganate oxidizes $M^I_4[W(CN)_8]$ to $M^I_3[W(CN)_8]$, which is also yellow. The corresponding free acid can also be isolated as $H_3[W(CN)_8] \cdot 6H_2O$. Similarly, $K_4[Mo(CN)_8] \cdot 2H_2O$ can be oxidized by Ce^{IV} to give $K_3[Mo(CN)_8]$.

Molybdenum(VI) and Tungsten(VI) Complexes. All of the complexes known with the metals in the VI oxidation state are anionic with fluorine and/or oxygen as the ligand atoms.

By reaction of $W(CO)_6$ with IF_5 in excess (using IF_5 as the reaction medium) and in presence of KI the compound K_2WF_8 is obtained. It has been shown that the unit cell of this compound is cubic, but the shape of the coordination polyhedron about the tungsten atom is not yet known. The compounds $CsWF_7$ and $RbWF_7$ have also been prepared. They, too, have cubic unit cells, but again the shape of the coordination polyhedron about the tungsten has not been established.

Complexes containing both oxide and fluoride ions as ligands are more numerous, and include the following types:

$[MoOF_5]^-$	and	$[WOF_5]^-$
$[MoO_2F_3]^-$		
$[MoO_2F_4]^{2-}$	and	$[WO_2F_4]^-$
$[MoO_3F_2]^{2-}$		
$[MoO_3F_3]^{3-}$	and	$[WO_3F_3]^{3-}$

Oxychloro complexes of the types $[MoO_2Cl_4]^{2-}$ and $[WO_2Cl_4]^{2-}$ are also known.

In addition, molybdenum(VI) occurs in some molybdenyl complexes. Thus when MoO_3 is refluxed for about 18 hours with acetylacetone (HAcAc), orange-yellow $MoO_2(AcAc)_2$ is obtained. On cooling a hot, saturated solution of MoO_3 in concentrated sulfuric acid molybdenyl sulfate, MoO_2SO_4, crystallizes out. By treating this compound with alkali metal sulfate solutions complex salts of the formulas $M^I_2[Mo_2O_6(SO_4)]$ and $M^I_2[MoO_4(SO_4)_3]$ have been obtained. Nothing is known of the structures of these substances, and no tungsten analogs appear to have been made.

TECHNETIUM AND RHENIUM

Technetium and rhenium resemble each other closely in chemistry and differ noticeably from manganese, although there are of course similarities in stoichiometries, for example, MnO_4^- and ReO_4^-, and in some complexes with π-bonding ligands. The most stable and characteristic oxidation state for manganese is the II state, and manganese generally gives high-spin complexes, forming low-spin compounds or complexes rather reluctantly. Like other metals of the second and third transition groups, technetium and rhenium in most of their compounds and complexes have low spin; also, the halides give only poorly defined and ill-characterized species in solution, and there is no evidence for any simple 2+ cationic species for either element—indeed there is no good evidence for simple cationic species at all, although green, readily oxidized solutions of Tc^{III} can be obtained by cathodic reduction of TcO_4^- in phosphate buffer and similar observations have been made for other anions for both Tc and Re. In general, the higher oxidation states are the most stable. For technetium the IV and VII states are the best known with the III, V, and VI difficult to prepare and poorly characterized and the II state known only in a few complexes; for rhenium the V and VI states are difficult to obtain, and the III, IV, and VII states are the commonest. Technetium and rhenium are quite similar in their chemistries to both molybdenum and platinum. Only in the carbonyls and their derivatives is there any close similarity to manganese.

There is very little cationic aqueous chemistry, and, as noted above, the constitution of cationic species in solution, other than a few complexes, is not known. The oxy anions TcO_4^- and ReO_4^- are well known in aqueous solution, however. Polarographic studies of the reduction of these ions in aqueous solution containing different anions have been made, but, although potential values can be associated with the observed reduction steps, the precise nature of the species present is obscure. Some oxidation-reduction potential data—of limited reliability—are as shown in Figure 30-14. The

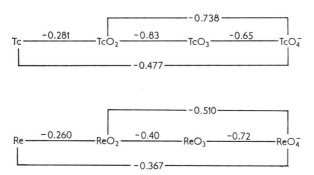

Fig. 30-14.   Oxidation-reduction potential data for technetium and rhenium.

oxidation states and stereochemistry of the elements are summarized in Table 30-9.

30-13. The Elements

Although its existence was predicted much earlier from the periodic table, rhenium was first detected by its X-ray spectrum only in 1925. Several prior attempts to isolate the element failed mainly because of its low abundance ($\sim 1 \times 10^{-9}\%$) in the earth's crust. The discoverers, Noddack and Tacke, later isolated about a gram of rhenium from molybdenite. Rhenium is now recovered on a fairly substantial scale from the flue dusts in the roasting of molybdenum sulfide ores and from residues in the smelting of some copper ores. The element is usually left in oxidized solution as perrhenate ion, ReO_4^-. After concentration, the perrhenate is precipitated by addition of potassium chloride as the sparingly soluble salt, $KReO_4$. The metal can be obtained by the reduction by hydrogen of this salt or of K_2ReCl_6, but is best obtained by thermal decomposition in hydrogen of

TABLE 30-9

Oxidation States and Stereochemistry of Technetium and Rhenium

Oxidation state	Coordination	Geometry	Examples
Tc^{-I}, Re^{-I}	5	?	$[Re(CO)_5]^-$
Tc^0, Re^0	6	Octahedral	$Tc_2(CO)_{10}$, $Re_2(CO)_{10}$
Tc^I, Re^I, d^6	4	?	$\pi\text{-}C_5H_5Re(CO)_2C_5H_5$, $\pi\text{-}C_5H_5Re(CO)_3$
	6	Octahedral	$Re(CO)_5Cl$, $K_5[Re(CN)_6]$, $Re(CO)_3py_2Cl$, $[(CH_3C_6H_4NC)_6Re]^+$
Tc^{II}, Re^{II}, d^5	4?	?	py_2ReI_2?
	6	Octahedral	$Re(diars)_2Cl_2$, $Tc(diars)_2Cl_2$
Tc^{III}, Re^{III}, d^4	3		$(\pi\text{-}C_5H_5)_2ReH$
	4^a	Tetrahedral(?)	$ReCl_4^-$, Re_2Cl_6, $(\pi\text{-}C_5H_5)_2ReH_2^+$
	5	Trigonal bipyramid(?)	$(Ph_3PO)_2ReCl_3$
	6	Octahedral	$Re(AcAc)_3$, $[Tc(diars)_2Cl_2]^+$, $[Re(diars)_2Cl_2]^+$
Tc^{IV}, Re^{IV}, d^3	4	?	ReF_4, $TcCl_4$
	6^a	Octahedral	K_2TcI_6, K_2ReCl_6, ReI_4py_2
Tc^V, Re^V, d^2	5	Trigonal bipyramid(?)	$ReCl_5$, ReF_5
	6	Octahedral	$ReOCl_3(PPh_3)_2$
	8	Dodecahedral(?)	$[Re(diars)_2Cl_4]^+$, $K_3[Re(CN)_8]$, $[Tc(diars)_2Cl_4]^+$
Tc^{VI}, Re^{VI}, d^1	6	Octahedral	ReO_3, ReF_6
	8	Dodecahedral(?)	$[Re(CN)_8]^{2-}$
Tc^{VII}, Re^{VII}, d^0	4^a	Tetrahedral	ReO_4^-, TcO_4^-, ReO_3Cl, Re_2O_7
	7	?	ReF_7
	9(?)	?	$[Re(CN)_8OH]^{2-}$

^{a} Most common states.

NH_4ReO_4. A variety of other methods of extraction and conversion to the metal have been reported.

The discoverers of rhenium also believed that they had detected element 43 to which they gave the name masurium. However, it is now known that all isotopes of this element are unstable toward β decay or electron capture and traces exist in nature only as fragments from the spontaneous fission of uranium. The element was named technetium by the discoverers of the first radioisotope—Perrier and Segré. Three isotopes have half-lives greater than 10^5 years, but the only one which has been obtained on a macro scale is ^{99}Tc (β^-, 2.12×10^5 years). Technetium is recovered from waste fission product solutions after removal of plutonium and uranium. It is recovered by precipitation of tetraphenylarsonium pertechnetate, $(Ph_4As)TcO_4$, using perchlorate ion as carrier. The precipitate is dissolved in alcohol and passed through an anion exchange resin in the chloride form; the TcO_4^- ion is absorbed while the soluble tetraphenylarsonium chloride is eluted and recovered. The TcO_4^- ion is eluted with $2N$ perchloric acid and is purified by distillation (as Tc_2O_7) from perchloric acid solution. Other extraction procedures, such as solvent extraction with methyl ethyl ketone, can be used. The metal is obtained by hydrogen reduction of ammonium pertechnetate or by electrolysis of NH_4TcO_4 in $2N$ sulfuric acid containing a trace of F^-.

The metals resemble platinum in appearance but are usually obtained as grey powders. Both crystallize in a hexagonal close-packed arrangement. They burn in oxygen on heating above 400°C. to give the oxides M_2O_7 which sublime away; in moist air the metals are slowly oxidized to the oxy acids. The latter are also obtained by dissolution of the metals in concentrated nitric acid or hot concentrated sulfuric acid. The metals are insoluble in hydrofluoric and hydrochloric acids but are conveniently dissolved by warm bromine water. Rhenium, but not technetium, is soluble in hydrogen peroxide; also, technetium is unattacked by chlorine gas, although rhenium is on heating.

At the present time rhenium is not widely used and its alloys suffer from their reactivity toward oxygen; with inert gas protection a very useful Pt–Re thermocouple can be made. The pertechnetate ion in very low concentrations has been shown to be a powerful corrosion inhibitor for steels, but there does not seem to be commercial utilization of this property.

30-14. Binary Compounds

Oxides. The known oxides are shown in Table 30-10. The most important are the *heptoxides* obtained by burning the metals. Both are

TABLE 30-10

Oxides of Rhenium and Technetium

Rhenium			Technetium		
Oxide	Color	Melting point, °C.	Oxide	Color	Melting point, °C.
$Re_2O_3 \cdot xH_2O$	Black				
ReO_2	Brown		TcO_2	Black	
ReO_3	Red		TcO_3	Purple	
Re_2O_7	Yellow	220	Tc_2O_7	Yellow	119.5

quite volatile, Tc_2O_7 melting at 119.5 and boiling at 311°C.; indeed, if acid solutions containing TcO_4^- are evaporated, the oxide is driven off, a fact which can be utilized to isolate and separate technetium. Rhenium is not lost from acid solutions on evaporation. The heptoxides readily dissolve in water giving acidic solutions, and Re_2O_7 is deliquescent. The oxides are not isomorphous and differ in other respects; for example, solid Tc_2O_7 conducts electricity just below its melting point, although the liquid is nonconducting—Re_2O_7 shows just the opposite behavior for reasons obscure.

The lower oxides can be obtained by either thermal decomposition of NH_4MO_4 or by heating $M_2O_7 + M$, for example,

$$Re + 3Re_2O_7 \overset{200°C.}{=} 7ReO_3$$

The hydrated dioxides, $MO_2 \cdot 2H_2O$, can be obtained by addition of base to M^{IV} solutions, for instance, of $ReCl_6^{2-}$, or, for Tc, by reduction of TcO_4^- in hydrochloric acid with zinc. For rhenium a hydrated sesquioxide, $Re_2O_3 \cdot xH_2O$ has been obtained by addition of base to Re_2Cl_6 solution in water; this oxide is readily oxidized by water to $ReO_2 \cdot xH_2O$.

Rhenium(VI) oxide has a structure which is also found in other trioxides, such as CrO_3 and WO_3. This structure is commonly called the ReO_3 structure and is shown in Figure 30-7.

Sulfides. The isomorphous sulfides TcS_2, ReS_2 and Tc_2S_7, Re_2S_7 are known. The black heptasulfides are obtained by saturation of 2–6N hydrochloric acid solution of TcO_4^- or ReO_4^- with hydrogen sulfide. The precipitation is sensitive to conditions and is often incomplete. The treatment of neutral solutions of the oxy anions with thioacetamide or sodium thiosulfate followed by acidification gives a better yield. Excess sulfur in the precipitates may be extracted with CS_2. The disulfides are obtained by heating the heptasulfides with sulfur in vacuum; they have a tendency to be nonstoichiometric.

Halides. The known halides of the elements are shown in Table 30-11. The binary halides of technetium so far known are $TcCl_4$, $TcCl_6$, and TcF_6. The first is obtained as paramagnetic red crystals by the action of carbon tetrachloride on Tc_2O_7 in a bomb; $TcCl_6$ is obtained on direct chlorination of the metal. TcF_6, a golden-yellow volatile solid, results from the fluorination of technetium at 400°C.; it is stable in nickel or dry pyrex vessels for an extended period of time. On hydrolysis, like ReF_6, it gives a black precipitate, presumably of hydrous TcO_2.

Rhenium forms several solid fluorides. The most common one, ReF_6, is obtained by direct interaction of the elements at 120°C.; it is a low melt-

TABLE 30-11

The Halides of Technetium and Rhenium

		$TcCl_4$ blood red		$TcCl_6$ green		
		ReF_4 pale blue, subl. > 300°C.	ReF_5 greenish yellow, m.p. 48°C.	TcF_6 golden yellow, m.p. 33°C.	ReF_7 pale yellow	
	Re_2Cl_6 dark red	$ReCl_4(??)$ red	$ReCl_5$ dark red-brown	ReF_6 pale yellow,		
	Re_2Br_6 red-brown	$ReBr_4$ dark red	$ReBr_5$ green	m.p. 18.7°C.		
$ReI(?)$ black	$(ReI_3)_n$ black	ReI_4 black		$ReCl_6$ green-brown, m.p. ~22°C.		

ing solid (18.8°C.) with a high vapor pressure at 25°C. Spectroscopic studies have shown that it is an octahedral molecule and the absorption spectrum of its d^1 system has been assigned. The compound is very sensitive to moisture and on hydrolysis gives ReO_2, $HReO_4$, and HF. The heptafluoride, ReF_7, is also obtained by direct interaction of the metal at 400°C. with fluorine under slight pressure. ReF_5 is obtained along with ReF_4 and oxyfluorides by the reduction of ReF_6 with metal carbonyls; its ready thermal decomposition and its magnetic properties suggest that it may be $ReF_4^+ReF_6^-$. The nonvolatile ReF_4 is best made by reduction of ReF_6 with hydrogen at 200°C.

On heating rhenium metal (freshly prepared by thermal decomposition of ammonium perrhenate in hydrogen) in oxygen-free chlorine, the hexachloride is obtained as a green vapor which condenses to a green-brown solid. If commercial rhenium metal powder is heated in chlorine at 500°C., the pentachloride, $ReCl_5$, is obtained as a dark red-brown vapor which condenses to a dark red-brown solid; chlorination at higher temperatures gives a mixture of $ReCl_5$ and $ReCl_6$. $ReCl_5$ is rapidly hydrolyzed by water or moist air. If it is heated in a nitrogen atmosphere, it loses chlorine and the almost nonvolatile trichloride, Re_2Cl_6, is obtained as dark red crystals. This halide is dimeric in acetic acid and is soluble in alcohol, acetone, and similar solvents giving red solutions. It is also soluble in water, but the chloride cannot be precipitated immediately by Ag^+ though on standing hydrolysis occurs to give hydrated ReO_2.

The other halides are of less importance. The tetrabromide and tetraiodide can be made by careful evaporation of solutions of $HReO_4$ in excess

HBr or HI. The iodide is unstable and on heating at 350°C. in a sealed tube gives ReI_3; at 110°C. in nitrogen, ReI is supposed to be formed, but this halide is not well characterized.

30-15. Oxy Acids and Oxyhalides

The formation of the pertechnetate and perrhenate ions is one of the most important aspects of the chemistry of technetium and rhenium. The aqueous acids or their salts are formed on oxidation of all technetium or rhenium compounds by nitric acid, hydrogen peroxide, or other strong oxidizing agents. Pure perrhenic acid has not been isolated, but a red crystalline product, claimed to be $HTcO_4$, has been obtained; both acids are strong acids in aqueous solution. The solubilities of the salts generally resemble those of the perchlorates. Thus the ammonium and potassium salts are sparingly soluble in water (e.g., $KTcO_4$, 120 g./liter at 20°C.), and highly insoluble precipitates, suitable for gravimetric determination, are given by tetraphenylarsonium chloride.

The TcO_4^- and ReO_4^- ions are both tetrahedral with Tc—O = 1.75 A. and Re—O = 1.83 A. Unlike MnO_4^-, both TcO_4^- and ReO_4^- are quite stable in alkaline solution. They are also much weaker oxidizing agents than MnO_4^-, but they are reduced by HCl, HBr, or HI. In acid solutions, the ions can be extracted into various organic solvents such as tributylphosphate, and cyclic amines will extract them from basic solution. Such extraction methods of purification suffer from difficulties due to reduction of the ions by organic material. The anions can be readily absorbed by anion exchange resins, from which they can be eluted by perchloric acid.

For rhenium, some less well-characterized oxy anions exist. Thus on fusing ReO_2 with NaOH, the sodium salt of the ion ReO_3^{2-} is obtained, and color changes occurring when rhenium metal is fused with KOH in air show that there are intermediate stages in the oxidation to the colorless ReO_4^- ion. In excess hydroxide perrhenate takes up oxygen on heating, and a greenish yellow salt, $Ba_3(ReO_5)_2$, has been isolated. The natures and structures of these oxy anions are not known.

There are a number of oxyhalides, all of which are solids, readily hydrolyzed by water. They are shown in Table 30-12.

Pertechnyl chloride, TcO_3Cl, is the only well-established technetium oxychloride. It is obtained by adding 12M hydrochloric acid to $KTcO_4$ in 18M sulfuric acid and extracting the product into chloroform from which it is removed by evaporation of the solvent.

There are several oxyfluorides of rhenium. The most important one, perrhenyl fluoride, ReO_3F, is obtained by the action of IF_5 on $KReO_4$. The

TABLE 30-12

Oxy halides of Rhenium and Technetium

V	VI	VII	
$ReOF_3$ black, nonvolatile	$ReOF_4$ blue, t.p. 107.8°C.	TcO_3F?	
	$ReOCl_4$ brown, m.p. 30°C.	TcO_3Cl colorless	
	$ReOBr_4$ blue, dec. >80°C.	ReO_3F yellow, m.p. 71°C.	$ReOF_5$ cream, t.p. 40.8°C.
		ReO_3Cl colorless liquid, b.p. 131°C.	ReO_2F_3 pale yellow, m.p. 90°C.
		ReO_3Br colorless, m.p. 39.5°C.	

fluorides $ReOF_5$ and ReO_2F_3 are formed when dry ReO_2 is heated with fluorine, whereas $ReOF_4$ and $ReOF_3$ are obtained among other products by the action of metal carbonyls on ReF_6. Perrhenyl chloride and bromide are made by the action of oxygen on the heated trihalides. The halides ReO_3F, ReO_3Cl, and MnO_3F have been studied by microwave and nuclear quadrupole spectroscopy. The molecules are symmetric tops and it was concluded that the tetrahedral σ bonds are *dsp* hybrids, the remaining d electrons being involved in metal-to-oxygen multiple bonding.

A substituted perrhenyl compound, $(CH_3)_3SiOReO_3$, has been made by the action of $(CH_3)_3SiCl$ on $AgReO_4$; other compounds of this type can probably be made similarly.

30-16. Complexes of Technetium and Rhenium

The chemistry of Tc in complexes has been barely studied and even that of Re is much less well known than that of neighboring elements. What is known, however, accords with the general behavior of second and third row elements in that there are large spin-orbit-coupling effects and low-spin complexes predominate. Complexes with the metals in oxidation states II–VII are known, whereas in the carbonyls, cyanides, nitriles, and hydrocarbon complexes, $-I$, 0, and I oxidation states are known. The number of cationic complexes is rather small. The chemistry of rhenium (and presumably technetium) includes several unusual features not well known or unknown elsewhere. First, there are some complexes of Re^{III} which are diamagnetic and possibly tetrahedral, although none of the structures have yet been unambiguously established. As noted earlier (page 569), tetrahedral fields are in general too weak to cause spin pairing, but one or more of these species, perhaps most likely $ReCl_4^-$, may constitute an exception to this generalization. Second, since the higher oxidation states are readily obtained, thereby freeing orbitals for bonding to ligands, high coordination numbers can exist. Thus eight-coordinate complexes, such as $K_3[Re(CN)_8]$ and $[Re(diars)_2Cl_4]ClO_4$ (diars = o-phenylenebis-dimethylarsine), are known, and there is some evidence that a nine-coordinate ion, $[Re(CN)_8OH]^{2-}$, may exist (see below).

Complex Halides. Both technetium and rhenium form a series of stable hexahalo complex anions, MX_6^{2-}. No fluorotechnates are known so far, although they doubtless can be made; the hexafluororhenate ion, ReF_6^{2-}, is an exceedingly stable ion in aqueous solution even when alkaline. The salts can be made in several ways, for example, by heating K_2ReBr_6 with MF or K_2ReI_6 with KHF_2, by reducing ReF_6 in liquid SO_2 with KI, or by heating $KReO_4$ with aqueous HF and KI. The salt K_2ReF_6 forms green octahedral crystals.

The most important and useful complexes are the hexachloro salts, which are obtained by reducing TcO_4^- or ReO_4^- with 8–13M hydrochloric acid, preferably with the addition of KI as reductant. The salts K_2TcCl_6 (yellow) and K_2ReCl_6 (yellow-green) form large octahedral isomorphous crystals. The solubilities of these and other salts are similar to those of the $PtCl_6^{2-}$ ion in that large unipositive ions give insoluble salts. In water, K_2ReCl_6 is hydrolyzed to give $ReO_2 \cdot xH_2O$. In the reduction of TcO_4^- or ReO_4^- by hydrochloric acid, the intermediate V oxidation state complexes can be isolated. These are of the type $K_4[Cl_5MOMCl_5]$ in which the M—O—M bonds are linear because of the multiple bonding with oxygen as in the rather similar ruthenium complex (page 826). The technetium compound forms beautiful red crystals.

The hexabromo complexes of Tc and Re are made by the action of HBr on the chloro complex, and the hexaiodo by heating the bromide with HI.

So far, only rhenium has been found to give the salts of composition M^IMX_4; $RbReCl_4$ and $CsReCl_4$ can be precipitated as red powders from strong hydrochloric acid solutions of Re_2Cl_6. Several oxyhalide complexes, some of which are binuclear, are also known.

Cyano Complexes. Although qualitative differences between Tc and Re chemistries appear to be few, one definite example is found in the complex cyanides. The action of KCN on a methanolic solution of K_2TcI_6 leads to a dark red product, $K_2[Tc(CN)_6]$, which is soluble in, but rapidly hydrolyzed by, water. By contrast, the addition of KCN to K_2ReI_6 in methanol produces the brown octacyanide, $K_3[Re(CN)_8]$, which is soluble in, and stable in, aqueous solution. This oxidation during complexing is a further example (cf. Co^{II}–Co^{III} complexes with amines) of the loss of an electron from a high-lying orbital. An eight-coordinate Re^{III} complex would have one electron in an antibonding orbital from which it would be readily lost.

If the octacyanide(V) is acidified in presence of air, it is first oxidized to the purple paramagnetic Re^{VI} species,

$$2[Re(CN)_8]^{3-} + \tfrac{1}{2}O_2 + 2H^+ = 2[Re(CN)_8]^{2-} + H_2O$$

However, further oxidation occurs rapidly to give a diamagnetic ion, salts of which can be isolated, which appears to be $[Re(CN)_8OH]^{2-}$. This complex would require the use of all nine s, p, and d orbitals and would be a unique case of this in a mononuclear ion, although the same involvement of all available orbitals has been postulated also for the ion $[Mo_6Cl_8]^{4+}$.

In addition to the above species, other cyanide complexes are known. Thus the addition of hydrazine hydrate to $KReO_4$ in KCN solution gives orange crystals of $K_3[ReO_2(CN)_4]$; the presence of Re=O bonds is shown by the presence in the infrared spectrum of a band at $\sim$900 cm.$^{-1}$. A dark green hexacyanide, $K_5[Re(CN)_6]$, has been prepared by the reduction of K_2ReCl_6 in KCN solution by potassium amalgam, and a similar complex, $K_5[Tc(CN)_6]$, is also known.

Complexes with Oxygen and Nitrogen Donor Ligands. Several complexes with oxygen ligands are known for Re, but, so far, not for Tc. The trisacetylacetonate, $Re(C_5H_7O_2)_3$, which is prepared by the action of acetylacetone on hydrated ReO_2 or Re_2O_3, is similar to other trivalent metal acetylacetonates; it is paramagnetic, but the moment is temperature dependent owing to spin-orbit coupling interactions. Some carboxylate complexes can be obtained by the direct interaction of the acid with Re_2Cl_6. Thus propionic acid gives orange needle crystals of a polymeric complex, $[(C_2H_5COO)_2ReCl]_n$. Complex oxalates are also known.

A variety of amine complexes have been prepared, although some of them are not well characterized. The majority are solids, either insoluble in water (and most other solvents) or hydrolyzed by it; the stoichiometry depends on the nature of the amine, but most of them appear to be at least dimeric with halogen bridges.

Complexes with Phosphine, Arsine, and Sulfur Ligands. The direct interaction of Re_2Cl_6 with various ligands gives purple crystals of complexes such as $[Ph_3PReCl_3]_2$ and $[Ph_3AsO]_2 \cdot ReCl_3$; these may be converted to hydrides by the action of $LiAlH_4$. The reduction of $HReO_4$ by HCl in presence of Ph_3P or Ph_3As gives yellowish green oxyhalide complexes of Re^V such as $(Ph_3P)_2ReOCl_3$. Chelating disulfides give species such as $[CH_3S(CH_2)_2SCH_3]ReCl_3$; dithiocarbamate complexes, such as $[C_2H_5NCS_2]ReCl_2$, have also been prepared. Using ditertiary arsines, complexes in oxidation states from II to V have been characterized for Re, and similar derivatives of Tc^{II} and Tc^{III} have been obtained. These diarsine complexes are the only well-established examples of the divalent state for Tc and Re. The preparative scheme used is as shown in equation 30-2. For both Tc^V and Re^V the diarsine complexes are eight coordinate.

$$HReO_4 \; + \; \text{(diars)} \; + \; HCl \xrightarrow[\text{C_2H_5OH}]{\text{H_3PO_2 in}} [Re^{III}(diars)_2Cl_2]^+ \qquad (30\text{-}2)$$

Complexes with Re—H Bonds. In 1937, Lundell and Knowles found that when acid perrhenate solutions are reduced with zinc amalgam in a Jones reductor, a reduced rhenium species was obtained which had a formal oxidation state of -1. They considered the reduced species to be the "rhenide" ion, Re^-, and it has been subsequently shown by polarographic reduction of ReO_4^- and also of TcO_4^- that an eight-electron reduction step is involved:

$$Re^{VII} + 8e = Re^{-I}$$

Until quite recently, it was believed that the rhenide ion as Re^- or $[Re(H_2O)_n]^-$ existed, and indeed several workers isolated what were thought to be solid rhenides by the reduction of concentrated aqueous potassium perrhenate by potassium in ethylenediamine. These solids were formulated as, for example, $K[Re(H_2O)_4]$. However, it has been shown that alkaline perrhenate solutions reduced by sodium amalgam, and also solutions of the solid rhenides, show the high-field nuclear magnetic resonance line characteristic of hydrogen atoms bound to transition metals. It was therefore clear that the rhenide ions were actually hydridic species. The precise nature of Lundell and Knowles's ion or of the crystalline salts is not finally settled, but recent work suggests that the latter may contain the ion $[ReH_8]^{2-}$ or $[Re_2H_{16}]^{4-}$.

White crystals of the salt of stoichiometry K_2ReH_8 can be isolated by a difficult and complex procedure from the products of the interaction of aqueous perrhenate with potassium in ethylenediamine, of Re_2O_7 with lithium aluminum hydride, or, in low yield, of aqueous perrhenate with sodium amalgam. This salt had been previously formulated as a rhenide and also as a hydride of stoichiometry $K[ReH_4](aq)$, but these earlier preparations were impure, probably containing carbonate. The crystals are sensitive to air and are decomposed by acid giving hydrogen and rhenium metal, but they are stable in alkaline solution for weeks. The infrared spectrum shows bands at ~ 1850 cm.$^{-1}$ which can be assigned as Re—H stretching frequencies. Since a mononuclear ion, $[ReH_8]^{2-}$, of Re^{VI} should be paramagnetic and the crystals as well as the solutions are apparently diamagnetic, it would appear that the ion may be binuclear with a metal–metal bond, that is, $[Re_2H_{16}]^{4-}$. However, this problem is not yet resolved.

The original "rhenide" solutions which are obtained in acid media cannot be obtained in concentrations high enough for nuclear magnetic resonance study. However, it seems quite likely that they are also hydridic ions, the apparent eight-electron reduction step then involving not only reduction of the metal atom but also transfer of hydrogen atoms from water to the metal. However, the nature of this species or its technetium analog is not known, and even the anionic nature is not established.

The formation of hydride complexes of metals with strong π-bonding ligands also has been discussed earlier (page 631), and rhenium complexes of this type, for example, $(C_6H_5)_3PReH_3$ and $HRe(CO)_5$, have been characterized. For rhenium, there is another important hydrido complex, the di-π-cyclopentadienylrhenium hydride, $(\pi\text{-}C_5H_5)_2ReH$. This compound was the first for which high-resolution nuclear magnetic resonance spectroscopy showed that the hydrogen atom bound to a transition metal has a very large chemical shift to high fields; the infrared spectrum of the compound also demonstrated for the first time that M—H stretching frequencies generally lie around 2000 cm.$^{-1}$. The compound was also of interest as the first indication that a transition metal complex could be protonated in acid solutions, the added proton being bound to the metal atom,

$$(\pi\text{-}C_5H_5)_2ReH + H^+ = (\pi\text{-}C_5H_5)_2ReH_2^+$$

The study of this hydride system and the related hydrides of Ta, Mo, and W has been of importance in demonstrating the existence of nonparallel rings in di-π-cyclopentadienyl "sandwich" compounds (page 649).

RUTHENIUM AND OSMIUM

30-17. The Platinum Metals

Ruthenium and osmium are the lightest members, respectively, of the six transition elements of the second and third series which are known collectively as the platinum metals.

The platinum metals are rare elements; platinum itself is the commonest with an abundance of about $10^{-6}\%$ whereas the others have abundances of the order of $10^{-7}\%$ of the earth's crust. The elements occur in nature, often as alloys such as osmiridium, which is one of the few sources of osmium. Although platinum-rich ores contain little osmium, the elements are usually associated not only with one another but also with other noble metals such as copper, silver, and gold. They occur in arsenide, sulfide, and other ores as well.

Since the relative concentrations of individual elements and associated elements differ widely, there are many different ways of extraction which we cannot attempt to consider in detail. One procedure however, may be treated for illustration. An important source is the nickel-copper sulfide of South Africa. Here the ore is physically concentrated by gravitation and flotation, after which it is smelted with lime, coke, and sand and bessemerized in a convertor. The resulting Ni–Cu sulfide "matte" is smelted with sodium sulfate to give a top layer of Cu_2S and Na_2S and a bottom layer of NiS. The latter is roasted to oxide, reduced with coal, and the metal cast into anodes. The copper layer is similarly converted to a copper anode. The anode slimes from electrolysis contain the platinum metals, silver, and gold. The refining of platinum metals, also varied and complicated, is highly developed and the metals can be obtained in purities of over 99.5%. Details of commercial procedures are by no means well publicized, although some accounts are available, for example, in Wichers, Gilchrist, and Swanger, *Trans. Am. Inst. Mining Met. Engrs.*, **76,** 702 (1928), and in the appropriate sections by Powell in Thorpe's *Dictionary of Applied Chemistry*, 4th ed., Longmans, London.

Some of the chemical steps in the separation of the elements depend on specific reactions, such as the following:

1. Os and Ru are unattacked by any acids up to the boiling point, whereas Pd is fairly readily soluble in nitric acid and the others are more or less readily soluble in aqua regia.

2. Os and Ru are attacked by alkaline oxidizing fusion, for example, with Na_2O_2 or $NaOH + NaClO_3$, and the melts dissolve in water to give osmates and ruthenates. Ruthenates are reduced to black, insoluble $RuO_2 \cdot xH_2O$ by aqueous alcohol, whereas osmium remains in solution as osmate(VI) which can be precipitated as the ammonium salt. The elements are purified by distillation of their tetroxides.

3. On reduction of the oxidized chloride solutions of the other elements with $FeSO_4$, gold is precipitated, lower oxidation states of Rh, Ir, and Pd are obtained, while $PtCl_6^{2-}$, which is the most stable chloro anion with respect also to hydrolysis, can be precipitated as the ammonium salt.

4. Rhodium and iridium can be precipitated as hydrated oxides by treatment of solutions of Rh^{IV} and Ir^{IV} with ClO_2^- or BrO_3^- in $NaHCO_3$ buffered solution.

5. A useful separation of platinum, probably not used commercially, is the ether or ethyl acetate extraction of the red species, of unknown constitution, obtained by reduction of H_2PtCl_6 with $SnCl_2$.

6. Sodium hexachlororhodate(III), either hydrated or anhydrous, is insoluble in ethanol and can be separated from the sodium salts of the hexachloro anions of palladium(IV), platinum(IV), and iridium(IV), all of which are readily soluble in ethanol.

The metals are obtained initially as sponge or powder by ignition of ammonium salts of the hexachloro anions. Essentially all complex compounds

TABLE 30-13

Oxidation States and Stereochemistry of Ruthenium and Osmium

Oxidation state	Coordination number	Geometry	Examples
$Ru^{-II}(?)$	4		$Ru(CO)_4{}^{2-}(?)$
Ru^0, Os^0	5	Trigonal bipyramid(?)	$Ru(CO)_5, Os(CO)_5$
Ru^{II}, Os^{II}, d^6	5	Trigonal bipyramid	$NORu(S_2CNEt_2)_2$
	6[a]	Octahedral	$[RuNOCl_5]^{2-}$, $[Ru (dipy)_3]^{2+}$, $[Ru(NH_3)_6]^{2+}$, $[Os(CN)_6]^{4-}$, $RuCl_2CO(PEtPh_2)_3$, $OsHCl(C_2H_4PEt_2)_2$
Ru^{III}, Os^{III}, d^5	6[a]	Octahedral	$[Ru(NH_3)_5Cl]^+$, $[RuCl_5H_2O]^{2-}$ $[Os (dipy)_3]^{3+}$, K_3RuF_6, $[OsCl_6]^{3-}$
Ru^{IV}, Os^{IV}, d^4	6[a,b]	Octahedral	$K_2OsCl_6, K_2RuCl_6, [Os (diars)_2X_2]^{2+}$,
	8	?	$[Os (en)_2(en-H)_2]^{2+}$
Ru^V, Os^V, d^3	5 in vapor(?)		RuF_5 (apparently polymerized in liquid)
	6	Octahedral	$KRuF_6, NaOsF_6$
Ru^{VI}, Os^{VI}, d^2	4	Tetrahedral	RuO_4^{2-}
	5	?	$OsOCl_4$
	6[b]	Octahedral	$RuF_6, OsF_6, [OsO_2Cl_4]^{2-}$, $[OsO_2(OH)_4]^{2-}, [OsNCl_5]^{2-}$
Ru^{VII}, d_1	4	Tetrahedral	RuO_4^-
$Ru^{VIII}, Os^{VIII}, d^0$	4	Tetrahedral	$RuO_4, OsO_4, [OsO_3N]^-$
	5	?	OsO_3F_2
	6	Octahedral	$[OsO_3F_3]^-, [OsO_4(OH)_2]^{2-}$

[a] Most common states for Ru.
[b] Most common states for Os.

and many binary compounds give the metal on heating. Above 200°C., however, in air or oxygen, osmium is oxidized to the volatile OsO_4.

The platinum metals are noble metals and not readily chemically attacked. Binary compounds such as halides, phosphides, sulfides, etc., can be obtained at elevated temperatures by direct interaction. There are few simple cationic species in aqueous solution, and most solution chemistry is one of complex ions.

For Ru and Os, which we consider first, the chemistries bear little relation to the chemistry of iron except in certain solid-state compounds and in complexes of π-bonding ligands such as CO or π-C_5H_5. The higher oxidation states VI and VIII are much more readily obtained than for iron. There are quite close analogies between the chemistries of Ru, Os, and Re, for example, in oxyhalides such as $MOCl_4$ and $[MO_2F_4]^{2-}$.

The oxidation states and stereochemistries of Ru and Os are given in Table 30-8.

30-18. The Elements

Ruthenium is a grey-white, brittle, and fairly hard metal (m.p. $\sim$2450°C.), and osmium (m.p. $\sim$2700°C.) is similar. Both are unaffected by any acids below $\sim$100°C., but are attacked by halogens on heating. Ruthenium and osmium alone among the platinum metals show a readiness to combine with oxygen, and above 200°C. osmium gives OsO_4. At dull red heat ruthenium gives RuO_2.

The elements are best dissolved, as noted above, by alkaline oxidizing fusion.

30-19. Lower Oxides

There are only two oxides of ruthenium, RuO_2 and RuO_4; the latter will be discussed together with its osmium analog and related oxy anions later. RuO_2 is a blue-black crystalline solid with the rutile structure. It is obtained by heating the sulfide, RuS_2, the trichloride, or the metal in oxygen at temperatures of 500–700°C. It is stable at red heat but loses oxygen when more strongly heated. There is evidence that it is seldom if ever obtained entirely pure, but rather is usually somewhat defective in oxygen with a corresponding amount of Ru^{III} in place of Ru^{IV}. It is not attacked by acids but is readily reduced by hydrogen at slightly elevated temperatures. A gaseous oxide, RuO_3, exists in oxygen at 800–1500°C.

Although one or more hydrous oxides of ruthenium may exist, none has been obtained pure. From solutions of some Ru^{III} compounds, for example, the chloride, alkali hydroxides precipitate a black solid which is difficult to wash free of alkali and which also readily undergoes air oxidation. It is probably mainly $Ru_2O_3 \cdot nH_2O$. Hydrous RuO_2 has also been shown to exist, but no exact composition has been established for it. It is obtained by reduction of RuO_4 or $M^I_2RuO_4$ and probably also by oxidation of $Ru_2O_3 \cdot nH_2O$.

Osmium also forms only two oxides, OsO_2 and OsO_4, although OsO_3 exists in oxygen at 800–1500°C. In this case the tetroxide is thermally more stable than the dioxide; thus OsO_4 is the normal product of heating osmium or one of its compounds in the air, and the dioxide is obtained only by less direct procedures. Further discussion of the tetroxide will be found in Section 30-23.

OsO_2 can be obtained in hydrous form, reported to be a definite dihydrate, by mild reduction of a solution of OsO_4, or by addition of hydroxide to a solution of K_2OsCl_6. It is difficult to obtain pure as it readily becomes colloidal and adsorbs foreign ions. Anhydrous OsO_2 can be obtained by drying the hydrate and by heating the metal in nitric oxide or in a stream of osmium tetroxide vapor. It is a dark solid having the rutile structure. Although its reactivity depends a good deal on the method of preparation, generally it is easily reduced by hydrogen and oxidized on heating in air and reacts with hydrochloric acid to give a solution containing chloro-osmates(IV).

30-20. Sulfides, Phosphides, Etc.

Both ruthenium and osmium form a series of chalconides—MS_2, MSe_2, and MTe_2—which are quite similar in most ways. Thus they can all be made by direct reaction of the elements; they all have the pyrite structure (page 415); and they are all dark colored, relatively unreactive substances attacked only by nitric acid or even aqua regia. The osmium compounds have been made only by direct combination of the elements at temperatures above 600°C. The selenide and telluride of ruthenium are also made only in this way, but RuS_2 can also be obtained in other ways such as by heating $RuCl_3$ in a stream of hydrogen sulfide or by passing H_2S into an aqueous solution of an Ru^{IV} compound.

Ruthenium and osmium also combine with phosphorus forming a number of different phases of which the following have been well established and studied structurally: Ru_2P, RuP, RuP_2, OsP_2. The first has the same structure as Co_2P_5, a complicated one of low symmetry which is the anti-$PbCl_2$ structure, RuP has the NiAs structure (page 414), and RuP_2 and OsP_2 have the marcasite structure (page 415). These phosphides are all dark, relatively inert chemically, and some have semimetallic properties. Arsenides have been reported but little studied.

30-21. Halides of Ruthenium and Osmium

Fluorides. Fluorides of these elements are known in the following oxidation states: Ru^{III}, Os^{IV}, Ru^V, Os^V, Ru^{VI}, and Os^{VI}. No fluorides of Os^{III} or Ru^{IV} have been reported, and the claim for OsF_8 which persisted in the literature for many years was shown in 1958 to be erroneous.

Brown RuF_3 is best obtained by reduction of RuF_5 with iodine:

$$5RuF_5 + I_2 = 2IF_5 + 5RuF_3$$

It is stable in moist air for some time but eventually turns red. A more reactive yellow form is said to result when RuF_5 is reduced with carbon monoxide. RuF_3 shows some variation in composition which is thought to be caused by the presence of small amounts of Ru in other valence states.

OsF_4 is a yellow solid obtained by the reaction of OsF_6 with $W(CO)_6$. Its further characterization has not been reported.

RuF_5 is the usual product of the direct fluorination of ruthenium or RuO_2, and it can also be prepared by treatment of ruthenium with BrF_3 at room temperature followed by heating of the BrF_3 adduct (uncertain stoichiometry) which is the initial product of the reaction. It also forms when RuF_6 is heated to $\sim 200°C$. or higher. RuF_5 is a green solid melting (107°C.) to a green liquid which boils ($\sim 270°C$.) to give a colorless vapor. Its molecular structure is not known. It is a very reactive substance, attacking glass if even traces of moisture are present, and it is rapidly hydrolyzed.

OsF_5 is obtained by decomposition of OsF_6 under irradiation by ultraviolet light or by reduction of OsF_6 with iodine dissolved in IF_5. It is a green solid which melts (70°C) to a green liquid. The liquid turns blue on heating and boils at 225°C. to give a colorless vapor. OsF_5 is also very reactive.

Ruthenium hexafluoride was first prepared only in 1961. Direct fluorination of the metal produces RuF_6 initially, but, since the reaction is quite exothermic and RuF_6 decomposes into RuF_5 and F_2 above $\sim 200°C$., the actual isolation of RuF_6 requires special techniques to trap it on a cold surface immediately after formation. The material so obtained is a dark brown solid (m.p. 54°C.) and is fairly volatile (vapor pressure equals 0.1 atm. at $\sim 18°C$.), though somewhat less so than the other hexafluorides. The molecule has been shown to have an octahedral structure. RuF_6 reacts instantly with water and oxygen and with borosilicate glass, but it can be handled in quartz and stored in prefluorinated nickel systems.

Osmium hexafluoride is prepared by the action of fluorine on osmium metal at 300°C. It exists as a yellow-green solid (m.p. 32.1°C.), a yellow liquid (b.p. 47°C.), and a colorless vapor. The molecule is octahedral. It is rather easily reduced by iodine and decomposes on irradiation with ultraviolet light to give OsF_5. It is rapidly hydrolyzed by water giving OsO_4, HF, and a complex fluoro anion, probably $[OsF_6]^-$.

Chlorides. The only dihalide of ruthenium or osmium is $OsCl_2$, which is in fact the only simple compound of divalent ruthenium or osmium. It is made by heating $OsCl_3$ in vacuum to about 500°C., whereupon it disproportionates

$$2OsCl_3 = OsCl_2 + OsCl_4$$

The $OsCl_4$ volatilizes away; the residue is purified by boiling with dilute hydrochloric acid and then with water. $OsCl_2$ is a very inert substance which has not been very thoroughly studied.

Both ruthenium and osmium form trichlorides, but these differ considerably in their properties and relative stabilities. $RuCl_3$, one of the most important compounds of ruthenium, can be prepared in many ways, of which the best are by the action of chlorine containing some carbon monoxide on the metal at 700–800°C., which yields the anhydrous compound, and by evaporating in a stream of hydrogen chloride gas a solution of RuO_4 in hydrochloric acid, which affords the hydrate, $RuCl_3 \cdot H_2O$. The anhydrous compound is practically insoluble in water; it exists as black, opaque leaflets and has a layer lattice structure. The anhydrous chloride decomposes with some sublimation on strong heating. The hydrate, on the other hand, is soluble in water, but from a fresh solution silver ion precipitates no chloride, thus indicating that the solute species are chloro complexes of Ru^{III}. These solutions are quite unstable; they hydrolyze, especially on warming, with precipitation of hydrous Ru^{III} oxide.

For osmium the trichloride is not so stable. Chlorination of the metal produces a mixture of $OsCl_3$ and $OsCl_4$, and the trichloride predominates only at lower temperatures (<500°C.) and with a limited supply of chlorine. It is best made by thermal decomposition of $(NH_4)_2[OsCl_6]$ in a stream of chlorine. It is a brown, hygroscopic powder which dissolves easily in water and alcohol. On heating it begins to sublime at ~350°C. and at 560–600°C. decomposes into volatile $OsCl_4$ and $OsCl_2$. In solution, however, $OsCl_3$ is more stable than $RuCl_3$. Aqueous and alcoholic solutions are stable even on boiling and resistant to mild reducing agents, although a hydrous oxide can be precipitated on boiling with alkalies or ammonia.

Both ruthenium and osmium form tetrachlorides which again differ quite a bit in their properties. Ru^{IV} chloride is known only in hydrated condition, $RuCl_4 \cdot 5H_2O$, and in the related hydroxychloride, $Ru(OH)Cl_3$. Both of these apparently occur as products of reduction or decomposition of RuO_4 in hydrochloric acid under various conditions. For the deliberate preparation of the hydrated chloride in the form of red, hygroscopic crystals, a solution of the complex oxychloride, $H_2RuO_2Cl_4$, in hydrochloric acid is heated with a stream of chlorine passing through it and then evaporated over P_2O_5. It must be assumed that the water functions as the reducing agent in this curious reaction. The hydroxychloride can be isolated by evaporating a solution of RuO_4 in hydrochloric acid to dryness. It, too, is a dark red solid, extremely soluble in water. Their colors suggest that one or both of these substances may be similar in nature (though containing H_2O in place of NH_3) to the ruthenium reds and hence much more complex than the simple formulas given would indicate.

Osmium tetrachloride is formed by the action of excess chlorine on the metal at 650–700°C. It forms a black crust which sublimes readily at these temperatures. Its chemistry is little known. It is insoluble in all common reagents except oxidizing acids such as nitric. It slowly reacts with water giving unidentified products except for the ultimate one, OsO_2.

Bromides and Iodides.   These are virtually unknown, the only ones which have been described being $RuBr_3$, RuI_3, and OsI_4. $RuBr_3$ has never been obtained in a completely pure state. It occurs as dark green, hygroscopic crystals which are best obtained by evaporating a solution of hydrous Ru^{III} oxide in hydrobromic acid. It dissolves in water to give an unstable solution which readily hydrolyzes and in hydrobromic acid and aqueous solutions of alkaline bromides, probably to give bromo complexes.

RuI_3 is obtained from reaction of $RuCl_3$ with potassium iodide or by reaction of hydriodic acid with hydrous Ru^{IV} oxide. It is a black solid, insoluble in all common solvents and rather easily oxidized with liberation of iodine.

OsI_4 can be obtained by evaporating a solution of hydrous OsO_2 in hydriodic acid as a violet-black solid, readily soluble in water. The solution is stable in the cold but evolves hydrogen iodide on warming.

30-22. Complexes of Ruthenium and Osmium

In this section we treat complexes of these elements in the lower oxidation states, II, III, IV, and V. Complexes in the higher states, VI and VII, all contain oxygen and are most conveniently discussed in relation to the other oxygen compounds of ruthenium and osmium in high oxidation states. These compounds are described in the next section.

Complexes of Ruthenium(II) and Osmium(II).   Although there are no simple compounds of Ru^{II} and none of Os^{II} with the exception of the chloride (page 817), these species are stabilized in various complexes. The complexes of the dipositive ions are thus all obtained by reduction of Ru^{III}, Os^{III}, or Os^{IV} in presence of the ligands, and often with the ligand in excess functioning as the reducing agent.

$RuCl_3$ reacts with 2,2'-dipyridyl either in the molten state at 250°C. or, more slowly, in aqueous or alcoholic solution, to yield $[Ru(dipy)_3]Cl_2$. The dipyridyl is oxidized to an unidentified product. By metathetical reactions an extensive series of salts of $[Ru(dipy)_3]^{2+}$ as well as the free base, $[Ru(dipy)_3](OH)_2$, may be obtained. The $[Ru(dipy)_3]^{2+}$, which lends an intense red color to all of its compounds, is extremely stable (the chloride is not decomposed by heating to 300°C., or boiling in concentrated hydrochloric acid or 50% potassium hydroxide) and, as the bromide salt, has been resolved into its optical antimers which do not racemize in cold aqueous solution and only slowly at 90°C.

The analogous Os^{II} complex, $[Os(dipy)_3]^{2+}$, has also been prepared by treatment of $K_2[OsCl_6]$ or $(NH_4)_2[OsBr_6]$ with excess dipyridyl at 270°C. These reactions also yield the complex cations $[Os(dipy)_2X_2]^+$. The racemic $[Os(dipy)_3]^{2+}$ has been resolved, and the enantiomorphs are quite stable. A most remarkable feature of the $[Os(dipy)_3]^{2+}$ ion is that it can be oxidized to $[Os(dipy)_3]^{3+}$, which can then be reduced to regenerate $[Os(dipy)_3]^{2+}$ without loss of optical activity.

Both Ru^{II} and Os^{II} form very stable hexacyano anions. The complexes are obtained in various ways such as

$$Ru + (NaOH\text{--}NaNO_3, \text{ fused}) \longrightarrow RuO_4^{2-} \xrightarrow[100°C.]{KCN/H_2O} K_4[Ru(CN)_6]$$

by evaporating $RuCl_3$ repeatedly on a steam bath with excess KCN until a colorless residue is obtained, or by evaporating K_2OsO_4 with KCN and igniting the residue. From the potassium salts obtained by these procedures many other salts can be made by metathesis and, for ruthenium, the free acid, $H_4[Ru(CN)_6]$, has been isolated.

Both Ru^{II} and Os^{II} form complexes of the type $[M(diars)_2X_2]$, where M is Ru or Os, diars is o-phenylenebisdimethylarsine, and X is a halide or thiocyanate ion. These complexes are obtained by treating Ru^{III} halides or $[Os^{IV}X_6]^{2-}$ in alcohol with excess of the diarsine, which functions as a reducing agent. The complexes are yellow, orange, or brown and are non-electrolytes.

Ru^{II} has also been reported to form a series of complexes containing ammonia and one of the sulfur-containing ligands, SO_2, HSO_3^-, or SO_3^{2-}, and perhaps also chloride ions. Typical ones are $[Ru(NH_3)_5SO_3]\cdot 2H_2O$, $[Ru(NH_3)_4SO_2Cl]Cl$, and $Na_4[Ru(NH_3)_2(SO_3)_2(SO_3H)_2]\cdot 6H_2O$. They are obtained by the action of sodium bisulfite on Ru^{III} ammine complexes.

All complexes of Ru^{II} and Os^{II} are octahedral, diamagnetic, and, excepting possibly the last-mentioned Ru^{II} ones, kinetically inert. These characteristics are all interrelated with the presence of a t_{2g}^6 electron configuration.

Ruthenium nitrosyl complexes can be most reasonably formulated as containing Ru^{II}, but since these constitute a unique and extensive group they are discussed separately below.

On treatment of $[Os(Et_2PhP)_3Cl_3]$ with a solution of potassium hydroxide in ethanol, a complicated reaction, which is not understood mechanistically, takes place to give $[Os^{II}HCl(CO)(Et_2PhP)_3]$, that is a complex containing the ligands H^-, Cl^-, CO, and Et_2PhP. The analogous ruthenium(II) complex, $[RuHCl(CO)(Ph_3P)_3]$, is also known. The reaction of complexes of the heavy metals containing halide ions and phosphines or arsines as ligands with alcohols in presence of base to give products containing H^-, CO, or both as ligands is fairly general, and further examples will be mentioned in subsequent sections on the other platinum metals. Mechanistic details on how the H^- and CO groups are derived from the alcoholic alkali solution are at present quite unknown.

Nitric Oxide Complexes of Ruthenium and Osmium. Nitric oxide complexes of various types are known for both elements, but the osmium ones are not especially stable or important. However, for ruthenium, nitric oxide complexes are very numerous—more than for any other element—and are a most important feature of ruthenium chemistry. The ruthenium nitric oxide species contain the group RuNO, and this group can occur in both anionic and cationic octahedral complexes in which it is remarkably stable, being able to persist through a variety of substitution and oxidation-reduction reactions. Ruthenium solutions or compounds which have at any time been treated with nitric acid can be suspected of containing nitric oxide bound to the metal. Indeed, commercial products such as the "tetrachloride" quite often contain bound NO and should be tested before use in other preparations. The presence of NO is conveniently shown by the infrared spectrum since all RuNO complexes have a strong band in the region 1845–1930 cm.$^{-1}$.

Almost all ligands can be associated with the RuNO group and some typical complexes are $K_2[RuNO(OH)(NO_2)_4]$, $K_2[RuNOCl_5]$, $K_2[RuNO(CN)_5]$, $[RuNO(NH_3)_4Cl]Cl_2$, and $RuNO[S_2CN(CH_3)_2]_2$. The complexes can be obtained in a variety of ways and the source of NO can be HNO_3, NO, NO_2, or NO_2^-. A few examples will illustrate the preparative methods. If RuO_4 in $\sim 8M$ HCl is evaporated with HNO_3, a purple solution is obtained from which the addition of ammonium chloride will precipitate the salt $(NH_4)_2[RuNOCl_5]$. If this salt is boiled with ammonia, it is converted to the golden-yellow salt $[RuNO(NH_3)_4Cl]Cl_2$. When commercial ruthenium "tetrachloride" in hydrochloric acid solution is heated with NO and NO_2, a plum-colored solution containing $RuNOCl_3$ is obtained. The addition of base to this solution gives a dark brown gelatinous precipitate of $RuNO$ $(OH)_3 \cdot H_2O$. When this hydroxide is boiled with $8M$ nitric acid and the solution evaporated, red crystals of the compound $[RuNO(NO_3)_3(H_2O)_2]$ $\cdot 2H_2O$ are obtained, but both cationic and anionic nitrato aquo species of general formula $[RuNO(NO_3)_y(OH)_{3-y}(H_2O)_2]$ can be obtained also, and in addition, polynuclear species can occur. With $NaNO_2$, on the other hand, $RuNOCl_3$ or $RuCl_3$ in HCl gives $Na_2[RuNO(NO_2)_4OH]$.

A particularly interesting complex is that obtained as an orange-brown precipitate by the reaction of NO on RuO_4 in carbon tetrachloride, in which nitrous oxide is formed simultaneously according to the equation

$$2RuO_4 + 8NO = Ru_2N_6O_{15} + N_2O$$

This brown precipitate has the stoichiometry $Ru_2N_6O_{15}$ and is soluble in organic solvents containing oxygen as well as in water. The infrared spectrum of the compound has only one NO stretching frequency, at 1976 cm.$^{-1}$, so that if two NO groups are present on each atom they must be *trans* to each other. The spectrum also contains bands characteristic of a bound nitrate which is confirmed by the oxidation of Fe^{2+} in presence of MoO_4^{2-} by the compound in aqueous solution. Although the structure is not completely certain, it is believed that it is that shown in Figure 30-15

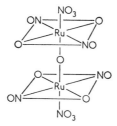

Fig. 30-15. The structure postulated for $Ru_2N_6O_{15}$ on the basis of infrared and chemical evidence.

where the two Ru^{IV} atoms are joined by a linear oxygen bridge as in the ion $[Cl_5RuORuCl_5]^{4-}$, to be discussed later. The formation of this oxo bridge as well as the production of N_2O in the reaction of RuO_4 with NO could arise from a reaction such as

$$Ru—ON + NO—Ru = Ru—O—Ru + N_2O$$

As noted above, the vast majority of ruthenium nitric oxide complexes are of the general type $RuNOL_5$ in which the metal atom is formally in the divalent state, if we postulate electron transfer from NO to the metal as Ru^{III} followed by donation from NO^+. For iron, very few such octahedral complexes are known except with cyanide as an associated ligand, and the different behavior of the two elements could be attributed in part to the relatively low stabilization energy of the $t_{2g}^3 e_g^2$ ion for ruthenium and the consequent readiness of Ru^{III} to accept an electron from NO giving Ru^{II} (t_{2g}^6); the larger size of Ru^{3+}, (~ 0.72) compared to Fe^{3+} (~ 0.64) would also favor better $d\pi-p\pi$ overlap for NO π-bonding. For osmium, nitric oxide complexes are rather scarce and they are less resistant than the ruthenium analogs, but here the difference may be due to the general low stability of divalent osmium complexes toward oxidation. It is also, presumably, the ease of oxidation of the $+1$ states that does not allow two nitric oxide groups to be bound to any of these elements in octahedral complexes. We may note finally that Russian X-ray studies have shown that, in $[RuNO(NH_3)_4OH]$ Cl_2, the NO and OH groups are *trans* and it is claimed that the Ru—N—O angle is 150°; nonlinear bonding of the NO group has been established only in two or three cases, and it is not known whether this is a general phenomenon.

Complexes of Ruthenium(III) and Osmium(III). The somewhat greater stability of the trivalent state for ruthenium compared with osmium is apparent in their complexes. Ru^{III} complexes are considerably more numerous than those of Os^{III}.

Ru^{III} ammines of several types are known. By the prolonged action of ammonia upon ruthenium trihalides, the colorless hexammines, $[Ru(NH_3)_6]X_3$, are obtained. These are very stable thermally and toward acids but are rather easily decomposed by alkalies to give various products most of which are unidentified but including the "ruthenium reds" which are discussed below. On prolonged boiling of the hexammines with acids, acido pentammines, $[Ru(NH_3)_5X]X_2$ (X may be Cl, Br, SO_4), are obtained. On treating the chloro pentammine with aqueous ammonia and then carefully acidifying, $[Ru(NH_3)_5(H_2O)]Cl_3$ can also be obtained. Tetraammines $[Ru(NH_3)_4X_2]X$, are also known and two forms, considered to be *cis* and *trans* isomers, have been obtained for the chloro compound. Two unstable triammines, $[Ru(NH_3)_3X_3]$ (X = Cl, Br) are also known.

Only a few osmium(III) ammine complexes have been described. There are the hexammines, $[Os(NH_3)_6]X_3$, obtained, among other products, by the action of liquid ammonia on hexabromoosmates(IV); a pentammine, $[Os(NH_3)_5Br]Br_2$; and various salts of the $[Os(dipy)_3]^{3+}$ ion, which is obtained by oxidation of $[Os(dipy)_3]^{2+}$, as noted earlier.

Ru^{IV} in perchlorate solution has been shown to be reduced to Ru^{III}, which is then complexed, by various compounds of the type $RHNC(S)NHNR_2$.

The complexes have not been isolated, but spectrophotometric studies of the solutions, which are variously colored, from red to blue, indicate that species such as 30-I are formed.

$$\left[\begin{array}{c} RN{=}C{-}S \\ \quad | \quad \quad \diagdown \\ N{-}N \diagup Ru \\ H \quad H_2 \end{array}\right]^{2+}$$

(30 - I)

Some hexahalo complexes of Ru^{III} and Os^{III} are known. No fluoro complexes of Os^{III} have yet been reported, but K_3RuF_6 can be prepared by treatment of $RuCl_3$ with molten KHF_2. It is a dark grey substance which is inert toward water but dissolves in dilute acids to give solutions in which the $[RuF_6]^{3-}$ ion apparently remains intact or is but little hydrolyzed. Ru^{III} occurs in quite a number of chloro complexes, some of which have less well-characterized bromo analogs, but no iodo complexes are known. The chloro complexes occur in the stoichiometric types $M^IRuCl_4 \cdot H_2O$, $M^I_2RuCl_5$, $M^I_2RuCl_5 \cdot H_2O$, $M^I_3RuCl_6$ and $M^I_4RuCl_7$. Although the hexachloro complexes (which, incidentally, have no bromo analogs) can probably be taken quite generally to contain the $[RuCl_6]^{3-}$ ion, the structures of the others have not been elucidated.

The only reported halo complexes of Os^{III} contain $[OsCl_6]^{3-}$ and $[OsBr_6]^{3-}$, and the latter is somewhat uncertain.

Because of the kinetic inertness of Ru^{III} complexes, it has been possible, using ion exchange resins, to separate and determine the total charge and anion/cation ratio of the lower chloro complexes of Ru^{III}. In this way it has been shown that the following well-defined species exist: $[Ru(H_2O)_6]^{3+}$, $[RuCl(H_2O)_5]^{2+}$, and the *cis* and *trans* isomers of $[RuCl_2(H_2O)_4]^+$. The number of coordinated water molecules was not measured, but the assumption of an octahedral coordination polyhedron seems reasonable. The visible and ultraviolet spectra of these species have been measured so that in future they may be identified spectroscopically.

Ru^{III} and Os^{III} form few complexes in which the donor atoms are oxygen. Both form trisacetylacetonates and a few similar complexes containing β-diketonate anions and complex oxalates of Ru^{III}, $M^I_3[Ru(Ox)_3]$, are known.

Both Ru^{III} and Os^{III} form rather stable complexes of the formulas $M^I_2Ru(NO_2)_5$ and $M^I_2Os(NO_2)_5$. These orange compounds are soluble in water and show no particular tendency to be hydrated. Their structures have not been investigated.

Arsine and phosphine complexes are also known. With *o*-phenylenebisdimethylarsine the complex cations $[Ru(diars)_2X_2]^+$ and $[Os(diars)_2X_2]^+$ can be obtained on oxidation of the analogous Ru^{II} and Os^{II} complexes described earlier. Reaction of certain phosphines with Ru^{IV} and Os^{IV} hexahalo complexes yields complexes of the type $[MX_3(R_3P)_3]$.

All known complexes of Ru^{III} and Os^{III} are of the low-spin type, having only one unpaired electron. In the approximation of exact octahedral symmetry of the ligand fields their electron configurations are t_{2g}^5. Study and interpretation of the spectra of these complexes has not been very conclusive. Transitions of the d–d type are rather difficult to observe because of strong charge-transfer bands appearing in the region where they would be expected. As noted in the introductory section of this chapter, the low-spin d^5 ions have normal magnetic behavior except when the quantity kT/λ becomes very small. Thus Ru^{III} complexes ($\lambda \approx 1.5 \times 10^3$ cm.$^{-1}$) have magnetic moments in the range 1.8–2.1 B.M. at room temperature, and even for the Os^{III} complexes, where λ is quite large ($\sim 5 \times 10^3$ cm.$^{-1}$), the moments are still practically "normal," that is, in the range 1.6–1.95 B.M.

Complexes of Ruthenium(IV) and Osmium(IV). Relatively few of these are known, and the most important ones are the halo complexes, particularly those of osmium.

Both Ru^{IV} and Os^{IV} can be obtained in hexafluoro complexes. The ruthenium complexes, K_2RuF_6 and Cs_2RuF_6, have been prepared by the action of water on the corresponding $M^IRu^VF_6$ compounds, and a barium salt by direct fluorination of a mixture of $RuCl_3$ and $BaCl_2$. The barium compound is blue and the others yellow or pink, depending on the color of the corresponding Ru^V complex (see below). These compounds decompose slowly in moist air and cold aqueous solutions precipitate hydrous Ru^{IV} oxide on standing. Warm or alkaline solutions decompose rapidly. On treatment with hydrochloric or hydrobromic acid, they are converted to the $[RuCl_6]^{2-}$ or $[RuBr_6]^{2-}$ ions. The hexafluoroosmate(IV) ion is obtained by treating the M^IOsF_6 salts with aqueous alkali, and from such solutions the K, Cs, Na, NH_3, and Ba salts have been isolated. They are cream or white and stable toward water and dilute acids.

The $[RuCl_6]^{2-}$ and $[RuBr_6]^{2-}$ ions are known but are not particularly stable. On fusing ruthenium with potassium chlorate and adding excess potassium chloride to the dissolved product, or by passing chlorine through solutions of Ru^{III} containing excess chloride ion, the potassium salt may be obtained and others may be obtained from it by metathetical reactions. The larger the cation the less soluble these salts are, which is a useful rule in preparing others. The salts are dark brown or purple, and the presence of octahedral $[RuCl_6]^{2-}$ ion is demonstrated by their isomorphism with corresponding Os, Ir, Pd, and Pt salts. In solution the $[RuCl_6]^{2-}$ ion is yellow, but the solutions fairly quickly decompose, turning black.

The corresponding black hexabromides are similar but even more easily hydrolyzed and hence of little importance.

The behavior of the Ru^{IV}–Cl system in aqueous solution of low chloride concentration is complicated—in regard to both kinetics and equilibrium—and not yet well understood. It appears less tractable than the Ru^{III} system. When chloride ions are added to a perchlorate solution containing Ru^{IV}, successive color changes take place, the sequence and persistence times being functions of the pH as well as of the Cl^- concentration. The sequence in solutions with $[Cl^-] > 0.1M$ and $[H^+] > 0.4M$ is

$$Ru^{IV}(\text{reddish}) \rightarrow \text{yellow(I)} \rightarrow \text{violet} \rightarrow \text{yellow(II)}$$

The yellow(I) stage is thought to contain several fairly labile and probably polynuclear species. The main species in the violet stage is thought to be $[Ru(H_2O)_2(OH)_2Cl_2]$ which is transformed by additional chloride ion to yellow anionic complexes, $[Ru(H_2O)(OH)_2Cl_3]^-$ and $[Ru(OH)_2Cl_4]^{2-}$. These suggestions are rather speculative, however.

The salts of $[OsCl_6]^{2-}$ and $[OsBr_6]^{2-}$ are among the most important of osmium complexes, being quite commonly used as starting materials in the preparation of others. The potassium salt of $[OsCl_6]^{2-}$ is prepared by heating osmium and potassium chloride in chlorine or by reducing OsO_4 with aqueous alcohol in presence of excess potassium chloride. Many other salts have been prepared from the potassium salt or from solutions which appear to contain the free acid. The latter are obtained on boiling solutions of $OsCl_4$ in hydrochloric acid until they turn brown and finally red. Clearly, $[OsCl_6]^{2-}$ is vastly more stable to hydrolysis than $[RuCl_6]^{2-}$. All of the salts are red to brown and give orange solutions.

Solutions of $H_2[OsBr_6]$ are obtained by boiling $OsCl_4$ in excess hydrobromic acid, and a variety of salts have been isolated. They are usually black and give dark purple solutions.

Some salts of the black and relatively unstable $[OsI_6]^{2-}$ have also been made, but they are not of much importance.

Hydroxyhalo complexes, $M^I_2[RuCl_5(OH)]$, $M^I_2[OsCl_5(OH)]$, and $M^I_2[OsBr_5(OH)]$ have also been reported. The first of these has been shown, however, to be $M^I_4[RuCl_5ORuCl_5] \cdot H_2O$ and this naturally raises a question, as yet unexplored, about the nature of the osmium complexes.

Ruthenium(IV) forms no authenticated cationic complexes and Os^{IV} forms only two types.

The Os^{III} diarsine complexes mentioned earlier resist oxidation by halogens, permanganate, or ceric ion, but using $15N$ nitric acid they can be converted to the $[Os(diars)_2X_2]^{2+}$ ions which have been iso.ated as the perchlorates. There are also some Os^{IV} complexes which evidently contain ethylenediamine molecules which have lost a proton (en-H) from the nitrogen, namely, $[Os(en-H)_2(en)]^{2+}$ and $[Os(en-H)(en)_2X_3]$. The latter are seemingly eight coordinated as is a similar complex of Os^V with en-H.

Of special interest is the compound $K_4[Ru_2Cl_{10}O]\cdot H_2O$, which was long formulated as $K_2[RuCl_5OH]$, on which basis its diamagnetism was difficult to explain. It is now known to contain a binuclear anion having the structure shown in Figure 30-16. Its diamagnetism can be understood using a

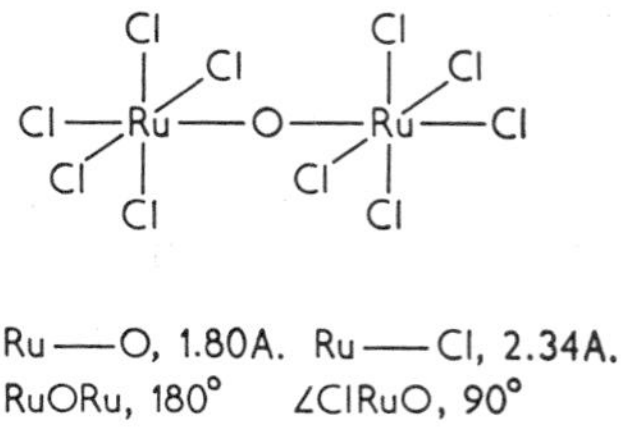

Ru —— O, 1.80A.   Ru —— Cl, 2.34A.
∠RuORu, 180°   ∠ClRuO, 90°

Fig. 30-16.   The structure of the $[Ru_2Cl_{10}O]^{4-}$ ion.

simple molecular orbital treatment of the Ru—O—Ru group. Assuming these three atoms to lie along the z axis of a coordinate system, and assuming further that the ligand field around each Ru^{IV} ion is essentially octahedral, the ruthenium(IV) ions will then each have a $d_{xy}{}^2d_{xz}d_{yz}$ configuration prior to interaction with the oxygen. By the interaction of the d_{zz} orbitals on each Ru^{IV} and the p_x orbital of oxygen, three three-center MO's, one bonding, one approximately nonbonding, and one antibonding, will be formed. The four electrons (one from each Ru^{IV} and two from oxygen) will occupy the lower two of these MO's. The same kind of interaction will occur in the Rud_{yz}—Op_y—Rud_{yz} set of orbitals, and thus all electron spins become paired.

Ruthenium Red.   A further characteristic of ruthenium complex ammine chemistry is the formation of highly colored red or brown species usually referred to as ruthenium reds. Thus, if commercial ruthenium "tetrachloride," which consists largely of polynuclear Ru^{IV} complexes, is treated with ammonia in air for several days, a red solution is obtained. Alternatively, if the "tetrachloride" is reduced by refluxing with ethanol and the resulting trichloride in hydrochloric acid is treated with ammonia and exposed to air at 90°C. with addition of more ammonia at intervals, again a red solution is obtained. Crystallization of the solutions gives the diamagnetic ruthenium red. The structure of the species appears to be that of a trinuclear ion with oxygen bridges (presumably linear) between the metal atoms, $[(NH_3)_5Ru-O-Ru(NH_3)_4-O-Ru(NH_3)_5]^{6+}$. This ion can be oxidized in acid solution by air, Fe^{3+}, or Ce^{4+} to a brown ion of the same constitution but with charge $+7$; the nitrate and the sulfate of the latter ion are paramagnetic with $\mu = 1.1$ B.M. It is quite likely that there are corresponding trinuclear chloro complexes, such as $[Ru_3O_2Cl_6(H_2O)_6]^0$, in the violet aqueous solutions of $RuCl_3$, since ruthenium red is produced from these by action of ammonia.

Ru^{IV} and Os^{IV} complexes all have octahedral or distorted octahedral structures and should thus have t_{2g}^4 electron configurations. As discussed on pages 763–764, this configuration is especially subject to anomalous magnetic behavior when the spin-orbit coupling constant of the metal ion becomes high as it is in Os^{IV}. The chief effect in this case is that the effective magnetic moment is brought far below the spin-only value (2.84 B.M.), typical values for Os^{IV} complexes at room temperature being in the range 1.2–1.7 B.M. As the temperature is lowered, μ_{eff} decreases as the square root of the absolute temperature. Ru^{IV} complexes have practically normal moments at room temperature (2.7–2.9 B.M.), but these also decrease with $T^{1/2}$ as the temperature is lowered.

Virtually nothing is known of the d–d transitions in Ru^{IV} and Os^{IV} complexes since the relevant absorption bands are severely masked by strong charge transfer bands.

Complexes of Ruthenium(V) and Osmium(V). This oxidation state is evidently an extremely unfavorable one for these elements, giving no simple compounds save the fluorides and practically no complexes either except for $[MF_6]^-$ species and one other.

The hexafluoro complexes can be prepared by various nonaqueous reactions of which the following are representative:

$$RuCl_3 + M^ICl + F_2 \xrightarrow{300°C.} M^I[RuF_6]$$
$$Ru + M^{II}Cl_2 + BrF_3 \longrightarrow M^{II}[RuF_6]_2$$
$$OsCl_4 + M^ICl + BrF_3 \longrightarrow M^I[OsF_6]$$

For several of them, X-ray studies have established that octahedral $[MF_6]^-$ ions are present. One curious feature of these compounds is that their colors vary with the method of preparation. For example, $KRuF_6$ samples prepared by high temperature fluorination are pale blue, whereas those from bromine trifluoride solution may be pale pink or cream. The colors are believed to be due to trace impurities.

The fluororuthenates(V) dissolve in water with evolution of oxygen undergoing reduction to $[RuF_6]^{2-}$ and also producing traces of RuO_4. The osmium salts dissolve in water without reaction, but when base is added oxygen is evolved and $[OsF_6]^{2-}$ is formed.

The $[MF_6]^-$ ions have t_{2g}^3 configurations with three unpaired electrons. Their magnetic moments are independent of temperature, averaging $\sim$3.7 B.M. for the $[RuF_6]^-$ salts and $\sim$3.2 B.M. for the $[OsF_6]^-$ salts. The differences from the spin-only moment (3.87 B.M.) may be due in part to certain second-order spin-orbit coupling effects but, since observed moments are perhaps lower than can be explained by this process alone, probably also to antiferromagnetic interactions.

A complex reported to have the formula $[Os(en-H)_3(en)I_2]\cdot 4H_2O$ (where en-H stands for an ethylenediamine anion obtained by removal of one amine hydrogen atom) is the only other Ru^V or Os^V complex for which there is any evidence. It has a magnetic moment of 1.78 B.M. and an apparent coordination number of 8. Such a singular compound should perhaps be more thoroughly investigated before complete reliance can be placed on the formula suggested.

30-23. Oxy Compounds of Ruthenium(VI), -(VII), and -(VIII) and of Osmium(VI) and -(VIII)

The highest oxidation states of ruthenium and osmium are best known in the tetroxides and oxy anions, and these species provide some of the more unusual as well as useful features of the chemistry. There is no evidence to date for the existence of Os^{VII} species. The main compounds or ions are shown in Table 30-14.

TABLE 30-14

Some Oxy Compounds and Ions
of Ruthenium and Osmium

VIII	VII	VI
RuO_4	RuO_4^{2-}	RuO_4^{2-}
		$RuO_2Cl_4^{2-}$
OsO_4		$[OsO_2(OH)_4]^{2-}$
OsO_3N^-		$[OsO_2X_4]^{2-}$ a
$OsO_4F_2^{2-}$		$[OsO_3X_2]^{2-}$ a

a X = Cl, CN, NO$_2$, etc.

The Tetroxides, RuO_4 and OsO_4. These are volatile crystalline solids; RuO_4 is yellow (m.p. 25°C., b.p. 100°C.), and OsO_4 is colorless (m.p. 40°C., b.p. 101°C.). They are both very poisonous substances with characteristic, penetrating, ozone-like odors. OsO_4 is a particular hazard, especially to the eyes, on account of its facile reduction by organic matter to a black oxide, a fact utilized in its employment in dilute aqueous solution as a biological stain.

Ruthenium tetroxide is obtained when acid solutions containing ruthenium are heated with powerful oxidizing agents such as HIO_4, MnO_4^-, Ce^{4+}, BrO_3^-, or Cl_2; the oxide can be distilled from the solutions or swept out by a gas stream. It may also be obtained by distillation from concentrated perchloric acid solutions or by acidification and oxidation of ruthenate(VI) solutions.

Osmium tetroxide can be obtained by burning osmium or by oxidation of osmium solutions with nitric acid (RuO_4 is *not* obtained by oxidation with nitric acid alone), persulfate in sulfuric acid, or similar agents.

Both compounds have been shown to have a tetrahedral structure. They have a band in the infrared at $\sim$900 cm.$^{-1}$ indicating multiple bonding, M=O. The oxides are extremely soluble in CCl_4 and can be extracted from aqueous solutions by it. RuO_4 is quite soluble, giving golden-yellow solutions, in dilute sulfuric acid; OsO_4 is sparingly soluble. The tetroxides are powerful oxidizing agents. Above $\sim$108°C., RuO_4 can explode, giving RuO_2 and O_2, and it is decomposed slowly by light; OsO_4 is more stable in both respects. OsO_4 finds limited use in organic chemistry since it can add to olefinic double bonds to give a *cis* ester which can be reduced to the *cis* dihydroxy compound by Na_2SO_4 (eq. 30-3). The oxide can be used catalytically for the same purpose in presence of H_2O_2 or ClO_3^-.

Both RuO_4 and OsO_4 are soluble in alkali hydroxide solution, but the behavior is quite different. RuO_4 is reduced by hydroxide first to perruthenate(VII), which in turn is further reduced to ruthenate(VI).

$$4RuO_4 + 4OH^- = 4RuO_4^- + 2H_2O + O_2$$
$$4RuO_4^- + 4OH^- = 4RuO_4^{2-} + 2H_2O + O_2$$

On the other hand, OsO_4 is soluble to give a yellow-brownish solution from which K or Cs salts, for example, $K_2[OsO_4(OH)_2]$, can be isolated. This difference between Ru and Os appears to be due to the ability of the $5d$ metal oxy anion to increase the coordination shell. Similar behavior occurs for ReO_4^-, which in concentrated alkali gives yellow *meso*-perrhenate

$$ReO_4^- + 2OH^- = ReO_4(OH)_2^{3-} = ReO_5^{3-} + H_2O$$

Ruthenates. There is a close similarity between Ru and Mn in the oxy anions, both MO_4^- and MO_4^{2-} being known.

The fusion of Ru or its compounds with alkali in presence of an oxidizing agent gives a green melt containing the *perruthenate* ion, RuO_4^-. Because of the high alkali concentration, on dissolution in water, an orange solution of the stable ruthenate is usually obtained. However, if RuO_4 is collected in ice-cold $1M$ KOH, black crystals of $KRuO_4$ can be obtained, which are quite stable when dry. Perruthenate solutions, which are a yellowish green, are reduced by hydroxyl ion, and kinetic studies suggest that unstable intermediates with coordinated OH^- are involved—this contrasts with the case of $3d$ metal oxy anions where there is no evidence for addition of OH^-. Since H_2O_2 is also formed in the reduction and RuO_4^- is incompletely reduced to RuO_4^{2-} by H_2O_2, a step such as

$$[RuO_4(OH)_2]^{2-} = RuO_4^{2-} + H_2O_2$$

is plausible.

The deep orange *ruthenate*(VI) ion, RuO_4^{2-}, is moderately stable in alkaline solution. It is paramagnetic with two unpaired electrons in contrast to osmate(VI) and has been shown to be tetrahedral. It may be noted that most ruthenium species in lower oxidation states are specifically oxidized to RuO_4^{2-} in alkaline solution by $KMnO_4$; hypochlorite gives a mixture of the RuO_4^- and RuO_4^{2-} ions. The RuO_4^- ion can be conveniently reduced to RuO_4^{2-} by iodide ion, although further reduction can occur with excess I^-.

Osmates. OsO_4 is moderately soluble in water and its absorption spectrum in the solution is the same as in hexane, indicating that it is still tetrahedral. However, in alkaline solution coordination of OH^- ion occurs and a yellow solution is formed

$$OsO_4 + 2OH^- = [OsO_4(OH)_2]^{2-}$$

This osmate ion can be isolated as salts such as $K_2[OsO_4(OH)_2]$. The reduction of such alkaline solutions by alcohol or other agents gives the osmate(VI) ion, which is pink in aqueous solutions but blue in methanol. Its salts, which are also obtained in the alkaline oxidative fusion of the metal, are often formulated $K_2OsO_4 \cdot 2H_2O$, but the ion in solution and in salts has been conclusively shown to be the octahedral $[OsO_2(OH)_4]^{2-}$ ion. Unlike the corresponding RuO_4^{2-} ion, it is diamagnetic; it is believed to have a *trans* configuration. The diamagnetism of the ion and of its substituted derivatives such as $OsO_2Cl_4^{2-}$ (and also of $RuO_2Cl_4^{2-}$) can be explained in terms of ligand field theory. If the z axis passes through the two oxide ligands and the x and y axes through OH, there will be a tetragonal splitting of the e_g level into two singlets, $d_{x^2-y^2}$, and d_{z^2}, whereas the t_{2g} level gives a singlet, d_{xy}, and a doublet, d_{xz}, d_{yz}. The oxide ligand will form an

$Os = O$ bond by π overlap mainly with d_{xz} and d_{yz} and will thus destabilize those orbitals, leaving a low-lying d_{xy} orbital which will be occupied by the two electrons, leading to diamagnetism.

Other Oxy Anions. When RuO_4 is treated with gaseous HCl and Cl_2, hygroscopic crystals of $H_2[RuO_2Cl_4]$ are produced, from which Rb and Cs salts can be obtained. The ion is instantly hydrolyzed by water

$$2Cs_2RuO_2Cl_4 + 2H_2O = RuO_4 + RuO_2 + 4CsCl + 4HCl$$

but there is evidence for other Ru^{VI} species in solution. If RuO_4 in dilute H_2SO_4 is reduced with $NaNO_2$, Na_2SO_3, or $FeSO_4$, green solutions are obtained. These contain Ru^{VI}, but the precise nature of the species is not known, although it is probably $[RuO_2(SO_4)_2]^{2-}$. The green ion can be formed by mixing freshly prepared Ru^{IV} solutions, which are an intense brown, with RuO_4 in dilute H_2SO_4

$$Ru^{IV} + Ru^{VIII} = 2Ru^{VI}$$

The green solutions decompose within a few hours to Ru^{IV} and, like all ruthenium species in the VI, VII, and VIII oxidation states, are reduced to Ru^{III} by excess iodide ion.

The addition of ammonia to $RuO_4{}^{2-}$ gives stable, colorless solutions which contain the ion $[RuO_2(OH)_2(NH_2)_2]^{2-}$. The osmate ion, $[OsO_2(OH)_4]^{2-}$, can undergo a variety of substitution reactions with various ions such as Cl^-, Br^-, CN^-, $C_2O_4{}^{2-}$, $NO_2{}^-$, etc., to give orange or red crystalline salts sometimes referred to as osmyl derivatives. They can also be obtained directly from OsO_4 with which, for example, aqueous KCN gives the salt $K_2[OsO_2(CN)_4]$. This particular ion is unaffected by hydrochloric or sulfuric acids, but the other oxy anions are not very stable in aqueous solutions, although they are considerably more stable than the ruthenyl salts mentioned above.

There are some less well-characterized derivatives of the type $[OsO_3X_2]^{2-}$, and the action of alkali fluorides on OsO_4 at low temperature gives red or brown salts of the ion $[OsO_4F_2]^{2-}$ which are soluble, but unstable, in water.

Nitrido Complexes of Osmium(VIII) and Osmium(VI). The osmiamate ion $[OsO_3N]^-$ was the first example to be prepared of complex ions in which nitrogen is bound to a transition metal by a multiple bond. Similar ions are now known, namely, $[MoO_3N]^{3-}$ and $[ReO_3N]^{2-}$.

When OsO_4 in KOH solution is treated with strong ammonia, the yellowish brown color of $[OsO_4(OH)_2]^{2-}$ changes to yellow and from the solution orange-yellow crystals of $K[OsO_3N]$ can be obtained. This ion has been shown to be distorted tetrahedral (C_{3v}). The infrared spectrum shows three main bands at 1023, 858, and 890 cm.$^{-1}$, the first of which is displaced on isotopic substitution with ^{15}N, which confirms the assignment as the Os—N stretching frequency; the high value suggests considerable Os—N multiple bond character, and we can formally write this Os≡N.

Although the osmiamate ion is stable in alkaline solution, it is readily reduced by HCl or HBr, and from the resulting red solutions red crystals of salts such as $K_2[Os^{VI}NCl_5]$ can be obtained. This nitridochloro anion is diamagnetic and presumably has two electrons in a low-lying d level (cf. the osmyl derivatives above). On further reduction with acidified stannous chloride, salts of the ion $[Os^{IV}NH_2Cl_5]^{2-}$ can be obtained.

The action of *tert*-butylamine on a petroleum solution of OsO_4 gives yellow crystals of $OsO_3NC(CH_3)_3$ which are soluble in organic solvents; this compound has an Os—N stretching frequency at 1184 cm.$^{-1}$. Some other amines act similarly.

The action of liquid ammonia on OsO_4 gives a black solid which is believed to contain Os=O, Os—NH$_2$—, Os—NH$_2$, and Os—NH$_3$ groupings.

Addition Compounds of RuO$_4$ and OsO$_4$.   The interaction of various donor ligands with both tetroxides has given black hygroscopic solids such as RuO_4PF_3, $(RuO_4)_2PF_3$, and $RuO_4(NO)_2$. The structures of these adducts are unknown.

Oxyhalides of Osmium.   The action of BrF_3 on OsO_4 in presence of KBr gives an orange crystalline solid, $KOsO_3F_3$, which is stable when dry but is hydrolyzed in water to OsO_4, HF, and F$^-$. If the reaction mixture is sublimed at 100°C. with an excess of OsO_4 present, or, if osmium metal is treated with a mixture of oxygen and fluorine, a volatile *oxyfluoride*, OsO_3F_2 (m.p. 170–172°C.), can be obtained as an orange solid.

The interaction of osmium with oxygen and chlorine at 400°C. gives brown needle crystals of what is believed to be $OsOCl_4$. If the solid is dissolved in concentrated hydrochloric acid and CsCl added to the deep green solution, a salt which may be of the ion $OsOCl_6^{2-}$ is obtained. Recrystallization of the latter from $2N$ HCl, in which it gives an orange solution, provides $Cs_2OsO_2Cl_2$ as a buff solid.

So far, attempts to prepare simple or complex oxyfluorides of ruthenium have failed.

RHODIUM AND IRIDIUM

Rhodium and iridium differ from all of the preceding heavy transition elements in forming no oxy anions or high valent oxides. Their chemistry centers mainly around the lower valence states III and IV. For rhodium, the III state is markedly preferred, whereas for iridium the IV state assumes some importance. Only iridium forms compounds in valence states higher than IV, and these are limited to the hexafluoride for the VI state and to complexes of general formula $M^I IrF_6$ for the V state.

Rhodium and iridium have a much greater tendency to form cationic complexes than do the heavy elements of the immediately preceding groups. Rhodium(III) forms a well-defined aquo ion and resembles Co^{III} rather closely in the extensive chemistry of its ammine complexes. Both elements form numerous anionic halo complexes, some of which are polynuclear.

The oxidation states and stereochemistry are summarized in Table 30-15.

TABLE 30-15

Oxidation States and Stereochemistries of Rhodium and Iridium

Oxidation state	Coordination number	Geometry	Examples
Rh^{-I}, Ir^{-I}	4	Tetrahedral(?)	$Rh(CO)_4^-$
	5?	?	$[Rh(NO_2)Cl]_4$(?)
Rh^0, Ir^0	?	?	$Rh_2(CO)_8$, $Ir(NH_3)_5$
Rh^I, Ir^I, d^8	4^a	Planar	$[Rh(CO)_2Cl]_2$, $C_8H_8RhCl(AsPh_3)$, $RhClCO(PEt_3)_2$
Rh^{II}, Ir^{II}, d^7	?	?	$[Rh_2I_2(CNPh)_8]^{2+}$
	5	?	$[Rh(dipy)_2Cl]^+$
Rh^{III}, Ir^{III}, d^6	$6^{a,b}$	Octahedral	$[Rh(H_2O)_6]^{3+}$, $RhCl_6^{3-}$, $IrH_3(PPh_3)_3$, $RhCl_3(PEt_3)_3$, $IrCl_6^{3-}$, $[Rh(diars)_2Cl_2]^+$, RhF_3, IrF_3 (ReO$_3$ type)
Rh^{IV}, Ir^{IV}, d^5	6^b	Octahedral	K_2RhF_6, $[Ir(C_2O_4)_3]^{2-}$, $IrCl_6^{2-}$ IrO_2 (rutile type)
Ir^V, d^4	6	Octahedral	$CsIrF_6$
Ir^{VI}, d^3	6	Octahedral	IrF_6

^a Most common states for Rh.

[a] Most common states for Rh.

[b] Most common states for Ir.

30-24. The Elements

These metals have quite high melting points—1966°C. for rhodium and 2454°C. for iridium—and both are silvery white in appearance. They differ in physical properties, however, rhodium being relatively soft and ductile, whereas iridium is hard and brittle.

Both metals are extremely resistant to attack by acids, neither one dissolving even in aqua regia when in the massive state. Very finely divided rhodium, known as rhodium black, can be dissolved in aqua regia, in hot concentrated sulfuric acid, and in hydrochloric acid in presence of atmospheric oxygen. Both metals dissolve in concentrated hydrochloric acid under pressure of oxygen or in presence of sodium chlorate in a sealed tube at temperatures of 125–150°C.

Both metals are attacked by chlorine at red heat giving the trichlorides.

30-25. Binary Compounds

Those of importance are the chalconides and the halides.

Oxides. Both metals react with oxygen at red heat, rhodium(III) oxide, Rh_2O_3, and iridium(IV) oxide, IrO_2, being the products. Both of these oxides are decomposed on heating to higher temperatures (over ~1100°C.) to regenerate metal and oxygen. However, in oxygen at 800–1500°C. rhodium will volatilize as the dioxide and iridium as the trioxide.

Rhodium(III) oxide may also be obtained conveniently by igniting rhodium(III) nitrate. It has the corundum (α-Al_2O_3) structure. The anhydrous oxide is insoluble in acids. Alkali hydroxides precipitate a hydrous form of Rh^{III} oxide, reported to have the definite stoichiometry $Rh_2O_3 \cdot 5H_2O$, which is soluble in acids and which yields the anhydrous oxide on heating. Rhodium(IV) oxide is distinctly less stable than Rh^{III} oxide. It is prepared only in wet ways, for example, by treatment of Rh^{III} solutions with powerful basic oxidizing agents, and by electrolysis of hexachlororhodate(III) solutions, and cannot be completely dehydrated without loss of oxygen to give Rh_2O_3.

Both Ir^{III} and Ir^{IV} oxides are of comparable stability, although the latter is formed in the presence of molecular oxygen or other relatively mild oxidizing agents. Hydrous Ir^{III} oxide is precipitated from Ir^{III} solutions by alkali hydroxides in an inert atmosphere; when there is free access of oxygen partial or complete oxidation to hydrous Ir^{IV} oxide takes place. This oxide is also obtained on addition of base to Ir^{IV} solutions. Neither of these hydrous oxides can be dried to afford the corresponding pure anhydrous oxide. In both cases some excess alkali is retained and in the case of $Ir_2O_3 \cdot nH_2O$ the water cannot be completely removed before evolution of oxygen begins. Impure dry Ir_2O_3 can be made by ignition of K_2IrCl_6 with sodium carbonate, when carbon dioxide and oxygen are evolved. The anhydrous IrO_2 made by heating the metal with oxygen is liable to contain some unreacted metal. IrO_2 has the rutile structure.

It is also possible to obtain in various ways, for example, by fusing the metal with sodium peroxide, a compound often called iridium trioxide. It is always obtained in an impure state, with a formula closer to $IrO_{2.7}$ than to IrO_3, and it is a very powerful oxidizing agent. There is, however, no definite evidence that it is an Ir^{VI} compound, and it has been suggested that it is a peroxide.

Sulfides, Selenides, Tellurides. There appear to be quite a number of chalconide phases formed by rhodium and iridium, but they have been little studied and are not of much importance. By direct reaction of the elements the following phases, stable at different temperatures and system composition, have been identified: Rh_9S_8, Rh_3S_4, Rh_2S_3, RH_2S_5, Rh_2Se_5, Rh_2Te_5, Ir_2S_3, IrS_2, Ir_3S_8, $IrS_3(?)$, Ir_2Se_3, $IrSe_2$, $IrSe_3$, $IrTe_2$, $IrTe_3$. It is probable that these phases are subject to nonstoichiometry as is common in other transition metal–chalconide phases (see page 414), and that the sulfide systems particularly contain chains of chalconide atoms, thus making the assignment of valences impossible in the absence of structural data, of which there are at present practically none. These chalconides are in general quite resistant to acids.

On passing hydrogen sulfide into solutions of Rh^{III} and Ir^{III}, brown or black precipitates are obtained. These are generally assumed to be hydrated forms of Rh_2S_3 and Ir_2S_3, but their exact compositions remain uncertain.

Compounds with the Group V Elements. Rhodium and iridium also form compounds with the group V elements which are somewhat similar to the chalconides but less completely characterized. The best known ones are phosphides of which Rh_2P and Ir_2P have been shown to have the antifluorite structure.

Fluorides. Both rhodium and iridium form tri- and tetrafluorides, and iridium also forms a hexafluoride.

Rhodium trifluoride is a red powder which is neither hygroscopic nor significantly attacked by water or aqueous acids or bases. It is prepared by treating rhodium metal or $RhCl_3$ with fluorine at $\sim$500–600°C. A small amount of RhF_4 is also formed but is volatile in the stream of F_2 at this temperature and moves toward cooler regions of the apparatus. RhF_3 can also be isolated in hydrated forms, $RhF_3 \cdot 6H_2O$ and $RhF_3 \cdot 9H_2O$, when rhodium(III) solutions are treated with soluble fluorides.

In addition to its formation as a by-product in the direct fluorination of rhodium or rhodium trichloride, blue RhF_4 can be obtained in better yield by treating $RhCl_3$ with bromine trifluoride. An adduct of RhF_4 with excess BrF_3 is first formed and must be heated to expel the BrF_3. The formation of such adducts occurs often in the preparation of heavier transition metal fluorides using BrF_3. In no case has the structure of one been determined and in quite a few instances the actual stoichiometry has not yet been established.

Direct fluorination of iridium at 250–300°C. produces the hexafluoride and small amounts of the tetrafluoride. The hexafluoride is a yellow solid melting at 44°C. to a dark yellow liquid which boils at 53°C. to give a bright yellow vapor. It has a molecular lattice—as do the other known hexafluorides of the heavy metals—which is in accord with its low melting and boiling points. It can be prepared and stored in a glass vacuum system provided the system has been baked thoroughly dry in vacuum and pre-treated with some of the hexafluoride. It is extremely reactive, fuming strongly in the air and being rapidly hydrolyzed and reduced by water to give hydrous iridium(IV) oxide, hydrogen fluoride, oxygen, and ozone. The tetrafluoride is a yellow solid which melts at 106°C. to a yellow oil which readily supercools. It can also be prepared by careful reduction of IrF_6 with iridium at $\sim$200°C. It is quite reactive, undergoing instant hydrolysis, and is also rather volatile which is unusual in comparison to the typically salt-like properties of other tetrafluorides of heavy metals.

Iridium trifluoride can be obtained only indirectly by reduction or decomposition of the higher fluorides. When IrF_6 in a stream of nitrogen is passed over the metal at 500°C., IrF_3 is obtained in a well-crystallized form but mixed with unreacted metal. Pyrolysis of IrF_4 at 400–450°C. affords poorly crystallized but pure IrF_3. IrF_3 is black and relatively inert to water.

Both rhodium and iridium trifluorides have structures which are distorted forms of the cubic ReO_3 structure (see page 780), each metal atom being surrounded by a slightly distorted octahedron of fluorine atoms.

Other Rhodium Halides. Rhodium(III) chloride occurs in several forms and also exhibits some interesting behavior in solution. Chlorine combines with the metal at 250°C. and above forming a red powder which is insoluble in water and acids. Its structure is unknown but is presumably polymeric. Dissolving the hydrous oxide of Rh^{III} in hydrochloric acid, followed by evaporating, yields dark red $RhCl_3 \cdot 4H_2O$, which is quite soluble in water. This hydrate loses all water on heating to 180°C. in a stream of hydrogen chloride, but on heating to temperatures above 300°C. it is rendered insoluble. The structure of this modification is also unknown.

There are apparently temperature-dependent equilibria between aquo ions and chloro complexes in solution. The hydrate dissolves to give a brown solution from which no chloride can be immediately precipitated by silver ion. On heating this solution, however, it turns yellow, and all of the chloride can be precipitated. Comparable behavior of the sulfate is described later.

The bromide and iodide of Rh^{III} have been little studied and are of no particular importance.

No rhodium(IV) halides other than the fluoride described earlier are known to exist.

Other Iridium Halides. Except for the tetrafluoride, the hexafluoride, and a somewhat uncertain tetrachloride, the known iridium halides are all of Ir^{III}.

$IrCl_3$ can be obtained in various ways, the easiest being by direct reaction of the metal with chlorine at $\sim 600°C$. It may be olive green, brown, or black, depending upon particle size, and is quite insoluble in water. Several hydrated forms of iridium(III) chloride are also known, one of which is evidently a hydroxy chloride, $IrCl_2(OH) \cdot nH_2O$, while others have the formulas $IrCl_3 \cdot nH_2O$. They are all dark green and water soluble.

Ir^{III} bromide and iodide are obtained as hydrates from solutions of hydrous Ir^{III} oxide in the appropriate hydrohalic acids. The anhydrous bromide and iodide can be obtained by dehydration of these.

There is some evidence that the iridium trihalides pass through definite dihalide and monohalide stages in the course of pyrolysis ultimately to give the metal and the halogen. These lower halides have not been characterized structurally or to any great extent chemically or physically. They are stated to be insoluble in water.

Iridium tetrachloride is, at the least, rather unstable and has apparently never been obtained pure. It is obtained in hydrated form by the action of chlorine or aqua regia on $(NH_4)_2[IrCl_6]$. It loses some water on heating but cannot be completely dehydrated before loss of chlorine sets in.

30-26. Salts of Oxy Acids

Very little is known of such compounds. Aside from a poorly characterized and perhaps doubtful sulfate of Ir^{IV}, only a few Rh^{III} and Ir^{III} salts have been described.

The best-known salt of this class is Rh^{III} sulfate which occurs in two forms (cf. $RhCl_3$). One of these is yellow and is usually obtained as the hydrate, $Rh_2(SO_4)_3 \cdot 14H_2O$, by dissolving hydrous Rh_2O_3 in cold sulfuric acid and evaporating the solution in vacuum at $0°C$. From fresh aqueous solutions of this compound, barium ion immediately precipitates all of the sulfate. It is therefore presumed that this sulfate contains $[Rh(H_2O)_6]^{3+}$ ions (see next section) and uncoordinated sulfate ions. A red form of the sulfate, which crystallizes as the hydrate $Rh_2(SO_4)_3 \cdot 6H_2O$, is obtained by evaporating a solution of the yellow sulfate to dryness at $100°C$. From a fresh solution of the red sulfate, barium ion precipitates no sulfate. It is therefore believed that in the red form all sulfate ions are coordinated to the Rh^{III} ion. Rh^{III} complexes are known to be kinetically inert.

A rhodium(III) perchlorate, $[Rh(H_2O)_6](ClO_4)_3$, is also known and its structure is discussed in the next section.

For iridium(III) only a sulfite, $Ir_2(SO_3)_3 \cdot 6H_2O$, which crystallizes from solutions of $Ir_2O_3 \cdot nH_2O$ in water saturated with SO_2, and a sulfate $Ir_2(SO_4)_3 \cdot nH_2O$, which is prepared by dissolving $Ir_2O_3 \cdot nH_2O$ in sulfuric acid with exclusion of oxygen, have been reported. They do not appear to have been characterized further.

30-27. Complexes of Rhodium and Iridium

Rhodium(III) Complexes. A very considerable number of these are known. All of them are octahedral and they are generally kinetically inert.

Rh^{III} is the only cation of the second or third transition series which has been shown to form a definite, well-defined, and reasonably stable aquo ion, $[Rh(H_2O)_6]^{3+}$. Hydrous rhodium(III) oxide dissolves in moderately strong acids to give yellow solutions which appear to contain the hexaquo ion. Although it is possible that, at low acidity, species such as $[Rh(OH)(H_2O)_5]^{2+}$ or $[Rh(OH)_2(H_2O)_4]^+$ might be present or, in hydrohalic acids, mixed halo aquo complexes might be present, it seems certain that, in concentrated nitric and perchloric acids, the hexaquo ion must be the only significant rhodium species. From the solution obtained by prolonged boiling of Rh^{III} chloride tetrahydrate with concentrated perchloric acid, $[Rh(H_2O)_6](ClO_4)_3$ can be crystallized. X-ray study has shown that it is isomorphous with $[Co(NH_3)_6](ClO_4)_3$, $[Cr(NH_3)_6](ClO_4)_3$, $[Co(NH_3)_5(H_2O)](ClO_4)_3$, and $[Cr(NH_3)_5(H_2O)](ClO_4)_3$. The hexaquorhodium ion is also known to occur in the rhodium alums, $M^IRh(SO_4)_2 \cdot 12H_2O$.

Rh^{III} forms a considerable number of cationic complexes which closely resemble those of Co^{III}. These include hexammines, such as $[Rh(NH_3)_6]X_3$, $[Rh(en)_3]X_3$, and $[Rh(dipy)_3]X_3$; pentammine acido complexes, $[Rh(NH_3)_5X]Y_2$; pentammine aquo complexes, $[Rh(NH_3)_5(H_2O)]X_3$; and some tetrammine diacido complexes, such as $[Rhpy_4Cl_2]X$ and $[Rh(dipy)_2Cl_2]X$. Neutral complexes of the types $[Rh(NH_3)_3X_3]$ and $[Rh(\beta\text{-diketonate})_3]$, which also have their Co^{III} analogs, are known.

The Rh^{III} ammines are prepared in various ways, but the usual starting materials are the hydrated chloride $RhCl_3 \cdot 4H_2O$ or a chlororhodate(III). These are treated with aqueous ammonia, ethylenediamine, etc.

Rh^{III} is conspicuously different from Co^{III} in its complex chemistry in forming a considerable number of anionic complexes. The $[Rh(CN)_6]^{3-}$ and $[Rh(NO_2)_6]^{3-}$ ions have their cobalt analogs, but the $[RhX_6]^{3-}$ and $[RhX_5(H_2O)]^{2-}$ (X = Cl, Br, and SCN) species, which are quite important in rhodium chemistry, have no Co^{III} analogs. In addition to these hexahalo complexes, which may safely be assumed to contain simple octahedral anions, other types of less obvious structure are known. Many of these are formed only with the very large cations obtainable by protonation of organic bases. They include a few anhydrous $M^I{}_2[RhX_5]$ compounds, some $M^I{}_4[RhX_7]$ compounds, and the binuclear ones, $M^I{}_3[Rh_2X_9]$, which are especially common where X is bromide. No structural data are available for any of these. The various halide complexes are generally prepared by dissolving hydrous Rh^{III} oxide or hydrated halide in the appropriate hydro-halic acid, adding the desired cation, and crystallizing the salt under appropriate conditions of temperature and concentration. The most important salts are those of the hexachlororhodate(III) ion, $RhCl_6{}^{3-}$, which forms characteristic rose red solutions; they can also be prepared by treating a heated mixture of rhodium metal and alkali chloride with chlorine, extracting the melt with water, and crystallizing.

It is noteworthy that, although the cationic and neutral complexes of Rh^{III} are, like their Co^{III} analogs, kinetically inert, most of the anionic complexes are labile. It has been suggested that these anionic complexes react by way of a rapid unimolecular dissociation step, whereas the neutral and cationic species can react only by undergoing slow bimolecular substitution.

Salts of the hexafluororhodate(III) ion are also known, but these, as is often the case, have no essential relation to the other halo complexes since they are made by nonaqueous processes and have no aqueous chemistry. For example, $K_3[RhF_6]$ is prepared by the fusion of $K_3[Rh(NO_2)_6]$ with KHF_2. It is a buff solid, inert toward cold water but soluble in dilute acid with decomposition of the $[RhF_6]^{3-}$ ion.

Rhodium(III) chloride reacts with phosphines and arsines in boiling alcohol to yield complexes of the type $[RhCl_3(R_3P)_3]$ or $[RhCl_3(R_3As)_3]$. These complexes undergo several interesting reactions. They can be reduced by hypophosphite or borohydride to give the hydride complexes, $[RhHCl_2(R_3P)_3]$, and the arsine analogs. Iridium similarly forms an entire series of such hydride complexes which are discussed below. The alkyl phosphine complexes are also reduced by boiling in alcoholic ethanol or in pure allyl alcohol to yield rhodium(I) complexes of the type $[RhCl(CO)(R_3P)_2]$. It has been shown that the CO is derived from the alcohol, but the reaction mechanism has not been further elucidated. Comparable reactions also occur with similar complexes of Os, Ru, and Pt, whereas iridium reacts differently, yielding $[IrH_2Cl(R_3P)_3]$.

Rhodium also forms a remarkable carbonyl fluoride, $[RhF_3(CO)_2]_2$, by the action of CO on RhF_3. Since the infrared indicates the absence of bridging CO groups, the presence of bridging fluorine atoms has been postulated. Because metal–CO bonds are ordinarily believed to require extensive donation of metal $d\pi$ electrons to antibonding π orbitals of CO, (cf. Section 27-1), the stability of bonds from a tripositive metal atom to CO seems surprising.

In their magnetic and spectral properties the Rh^{III} complexes are fairly simple. All of the complexes—and apparently all of the simple salts as well—of rhodium(III) are diamagnetic. This includes even the $[RhF_6]^{3-}$ ion, of which the cobalt analog constitutes the only example of a high-spin Co^{III}, Rh^{III}, or Ir^{III} ion in octahedral coordination. Thus the intrinsically high tendency of the octahedral d^6 configuration to adopt the low-spin t_{2g}^6 arrangement (see page 568), together with the relatively high ligand field strengths prevailing in these complexes of a tripositive second transition series ion, as well as the fact that all $4d^n$ and $5d^n$ configurations are more prone to spin pairing than their $3d^n$ analogs, is a combination of factors which evidently leaves no possibility of there being any high-spin octahedral complexes of Rh^{III}.

The visible spectra of Rh^{III} complexes have the same explanation as do those of Co^{III} complexes. As illustrated in Figure 30-17 for the

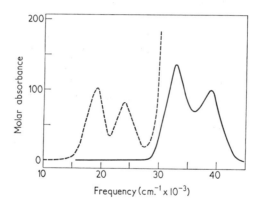

Fig. 30-17.   The visible spectra of the $[RhCl_6]^{3-}$ (– – – – –) and $[Rh(NH_3)_6]^{3+}$ (————) ions.

$[Rh(NH)_6]^{3+}$ and $[RhCl_6]^{3-}$ ions, there are in general two bands toward the blue end of the visible, which, together with any additional absorption in the blue due to charge-transfer transitions (see page 605), are responsible for the characteristic orange, red, yellow, or brown colors of rhodium(III) compounds. These bands are assigned as transitions from the $^1A_{1g}$ ground state to the $^1T_{1g}$ and $^1T_{2g}$ upper states just as shown in the energy level diagram for Co^{III} (page 730).

Rhodium(IV) Complexes.   The only types known are the complex flluorides and chlorides. The salts $M^I_2[RhF_6]$, where M^I may be Na, K,

Rb, or Cs, are prepared by the action of fluorine or bromine trifluoride upon a stoichiometric mixture of $RhCl_3$ and $M^I Cl$. They are yellow solids which are rapidly and completely hydrolyzed by water with concomitant reduction of the Rh^{IV} to Rh^{III}. They have magnetic moments of ~ 1.8 B.M. consistent with the presence of a t_{2g}^5 configuration. The dark green, insoluble Cs_2RhCl_6 is precipitated when Na_3RhCl_6 solutions are oxidized by ceric ion in presence of CsCl. The salt is stable when dry, but is unstable in water.

The oxidation of rhodium(III) sulfate solutions with sodium bismuthate produces red solutions which may contain the metal in the higher oxidation state, but the species present have not been identified.

Iridium(III) Complexes. These are on the whole very similar to those of Rh^{III}. The same general types of cationic, neutral, and anionic complexes are known for both Rh^{III} and Ir^{III}, and their chemical properties are not too different. Like those of Rh^{III}, the Ir^{III} complexes are kinetically inert when cationic but labile when anionic.

Iridium(III) forms the following series of hydride complexes: $[IrHCl_2(R_3P)_3]$, $[IrH_2Cl(R_3P)_3]$, and $[IrH_3(R_3P)_3]$, of which only the first has a known rhodium analog. This is the most extensive homologous series of hydride complexes so far reported, although the other platinum metals and rhenium are all capable of sustaining bonds to hydrogen in similar complexes. This particular series provides a very clear demonstration that, with a heavy metal atom in a nonlabile oxidation state, the hydride ion can behave very much like the classically recognized anionic ligands such as halide ions, CN^-, or SCN^-.

Iridium(IV) Complexes. Only a few cationic complexes are known, and these are generally unstable and of little importance. The important complexes of Ir^{IV} are the hexahalo ones, in which the halide may be fluoride, chloride, or bromide. A trisoxalato complex, $K_2[Ir(C_2O_4)_3] \cdot 4H_2O$, is also known and is shown to be kinetically inert by resolution into its optical isomers.

The $[IrF_6]^{2-}$ salts have been obtained only by indirect methods because fluorine or other strong fluorinating agents oxidize iridium to the V state. When $K[IrF_6]$ or $Cs[IrF_6]$ is treated with water, the iridium is reduced and the $[IrF_6]^{2-}$ ion, which is apparently kinetically inert to water, acids, and bases, is produced. The $[IrF_6]^{2-}$ salts of large uni- and divalent cations may then be precipitated or crystallized from the solutions. Several salts of $[IrF_6]^{2-}$ have also been made by nonaqueous processes.

Hexachloroiridates(IV) can be prepared in a dry way by chlorination of a mixture of iridium powder and an alkali metal chloride or in solution by adding the alkali metal chloride to a solution of hydrous Ir^{IV} oxide in hydrochloric acid. All of the salts of $[IrCl_6]^{2-}$ are dark red solids which form brownish red solutions fading to yellow on dilution. In general, solubility decreases with increasing cation size: thus $Na_2[IrCl_6]$ is extremely soluble in water, whereas the cesium salt and those of many large organic cations or complex cations (e.g., $[Co(NH_3)_6]^{3+}$) are only slightly soluble and easily isolated. The $[IrCl_6]^{2-}$ ion seems to be kinetically fairly inert; solutions are hydrolyzed only slowly, and in dilute hydrochloric acid the ion seems to be stable indefinitely.

Hexabromoiridates(IV) are isolated from solutions of hydrous Ir^{IV} oxide in hydrobromic acid. The salts are deep blue-black crystals or dark blue powders, and the solutions are bright blue. Their solubilities as a function of cation size show the same trend as do the hexachloro analogs. The $[IrBr_6]^{2-}$ is also kinetically inert, but differs from its fluoro and chloro analogs in that its slow decomposition in solution involves not only hydrolysis but also evolution of free halogen. Solutions in dilute hydrobromic acid to which a small quantity of bromine has been added are evidently stable indefinitely.

Octahedrally coordinated Ir^{IV} has a t_{2g}^{-5} configuration with one unpaired electron. Magnetic susceptibility measurements on hexachloroiridates(IV) have revealed effective magnetic moments in pure compounds of 1.6–1.7 B.M. Theory shows that the moment of the isolated $[IrCl_6]^{2-}$ ion should be 1.7–1.8 B.M., and, in fact, studies of the variation of susceptibility of $[IrCl_6]^{2-}$ as a function of its concentration in isomorphous, diamagnetic $[PtCl_6]^{2-}$ salts have shown quite clearly that antiferromagnetic interactions between $[IrCl_6]^{2-}$ ions, occurring by a superexchange mechanism across intervening chloride ions, cause the lowering from the theoretically expected value of the magnetic moment.

The spectra of the $[IrCl_6]^{2-}$ and $[IrBr_6]^{2-}$ ions have been studied. Their colors are due to the occurrence of moderately strong charge-transfer bands (molar absorbances of ~2500) in the visible region. Weak bands due to d–d transitions were not observed, and it may be that the orbital overlap in these complexes is sufficient to blur the distinction between these two types of band.

Iridium(V) Complexes. The only ones known are the fluoro complexes of the types $M^I[IrF_6]$ and $M^{II}[IrF_6]_2$. They are prepared by treating a stoichiometric mixture of $IrBr_3$ and M^ICl or $M^{II}Cl_2$ with bromine trifluoride. They are pink in color and paramagnetic, and they dissolve in water with evolution of oxygen and reduction of the iridium, giving the $[IrF_6]^{2-}$ ion. They contain slightly distorted $[IrF_6]^-$ octahedra and would thus be expected to have t_{2g}^4 electron configurations. They have magnetic moments which are ~1.25 B.M. at room temperature and variable with temperature. Despite the presence of two unpaired electrons, an isolated $[IrF_6]^-$ ion would be expected to have a moment of only this magnitude at room temperature (and a marked temperature dependence) because of strong spin-orbit coupling (see page 763) and in addition there may be antiferromagnetic coupling between $[IrF_6]^-$ units in the lattice.

30-28. Lower Valence States of Rhodium and Iridium

Very little is known of these in the case of iridium. For rhodium there has been little systematic study, but a fair body of somewhat scattered observations indicates that rhodium and probably also iridium are capable of forming a considerable number of compounds in the I and II oxidation states and that further investigations would be rewarding.

Carbonyl Halides. Rhodium forms carbonyl halides of the general formula $Rh(CO)_2X$. The chloride has been thoroughly studied. It is diamagnetic, and in solution it is dimeric and has a dipole moment of 1.65 Debye. These data, together with certain characteristics of the infrared spectrum, led to the postulation of a chlorine-bridged structure with planar coordination about each Rh^I and a small dihedral angle along the Cl—Cl line. Such a structure has been proved by X-ray study to occur in the solid compound as shown in Figure 30-18. The cause of the dihedral

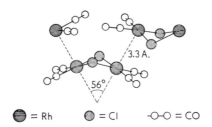

Fig. 30-18.   The structure of crystalline $[Rh(CO)_2Cl]_2$.

angle is not known, but a direct interaction between electrons in rhodium orbitals perpendicular to the planes of coordination has been discussed qualitatively. The carbonyl chloride or a corresponding bridged olefin complex such as that of norbornadiene, $[C_7H_8RhCl]_2$, can be cleaved by ligands such as amines and phosphines to planar Rh^I complexes as illustrated in equations 30-4 and 30-5.

Iridium is reported to form two series of carbonyl halides, $Ir(CO)_3X$ and $Ir(CO)_2X_2$, but little is known about their structures and chemical properties. Both iridium and rhodium chlorides, on refluxing with triphenylphosphine in diethylene glycol, give the *carbonyl* complexes, for example, $(Ph_3P)_2Rh^I(CO)Cl$. These square planar complexes add HCl, CH_3I, CCl_4 (as CCl_3 and Cl), and H_2, giving octahedral species.

$$+ \; 2py \longrightarrow 2[RhClpy(CO)_2] \qquad (30\text{--}4)$$

(*cis* or *trans*?)

$$+ \; 2Ph_3P \longrightarrow 2 \qquad (30\text{--}5)$$

= Chelating diolefin, norbornadiene

Isonitrile Complexes. These are known only for rhodium. Rh^I occurs in three major types: (*1*) those containing only isonitrile ligands, $[Rh(CNR)_4]X$; (*2*) those containing both isonitriles and phosphine or arsine ligands, $[Rh(CNR)_2(R_3P)_2]X$; and (*3*) the two compounds $[RhCl(CO)(CNC_7H_7O)_2]$ and $[RhBr(CO)(CNC_7H_7O)_2]$. As far as is known all of these compounds are diamagnetic and probably have square coordination since Rh^I is isoelectronic with Pd^{II}.

Rh^{II} also forms some isonitrile complexes which contain iodine and are binuclear but not structurally characterized. Representative ones are $[Rh_2I_2(CNC_6H_5)_8](ClO_4)_2$ and $[Rh_2I_3(CNC_6H_5)_7]I_3$.

Miscellaneous Complexes. A few other compounds of lower valent rhodium and iridium may be mentioned. Reduction of dipyridyl complexes of Rh^{III} using borohydrides, sodium amalgam, or zinc amalgam produces the following transformations:

$$[Rh(dipy)_3](ClO_4)_3 \rightarrow [Rh^I(dipy)_2]ClO_4 \cdot 3H_2O$$
$$[Rh(dipy)_2Cl_2](ClO_4) \rightarrow [Rh^{II}(dipy)_2Cl]_2(ClO_4)_2 \cdot 4H_2O$$

These dipyridyl complexes are certainly not hydrides, since no high-field resonance line can be detected, and are thus probably authentic Rh^I and Rh^{II} complexes. However, with the bis(ethylenediamine)dichlororhodium(III) ion, borohydride displaces chloride to give hydride species

$$[Rh(en)_2Cl_2]^+ + BH_4^- = [Rh(en)_2HCl]^+ + \tfrac{1}{2}B_2H_6$$

The treatment of K_3RhCl_6 with warm formic acid gives a green solution from which green crystals form; their nature is not well known.

Dimethylglyoxime, $HON{=}C(CH_3)C(CH_3){=}NOH$, abbreviated Dmg, reacts with rhodium trichloride in aqueous solution to give yellow crystals of the compound $H[Rh(Dmg)_2Cl_2]$, which is a strong monobasic acid. On reduction of this with hypophosphorus acid or a neutral solution of borohydride, dark red-brown solutions believed to contain Rh^{II} complexes, for example $[Rh(Dmg)_2Cl_2]^{2-}$, are obtained.

As noted earlier, there is some evidence that in the course of thermal decomposition of iridium(III) halides into the elements, mono and dihalides constitute intermediate stages. Divalent iridium has also been reported to occur in some complexes, including a cyanide, $K_4[Ir(CN)_6]$; some ammines, for example, $[Ir(NH_3)_4]Cl_2$; and some sulfito complexes, for example, $Na_6[Ir(SO_3)_4] \cdot 10H_2O$. These reports are in some cases quite old, and more complete characterization of the compounds would be desirable.

Rh^0 and Ir^0 occur in the carbonyls (page 612) and apparently also in a substance which approximates to the composition $Ir(NH_3)_5$. This yellow, diamagnetic substance, which decomposes into the metal and ammonia at about 90°C., is obtained by reducing a solution of bromopentammine-iridium(III) bromide in liquid ammonia with potassium.

PALLADIUM AND PLATINUM

Palladium and platinum are rather similar to each other (although, of course, many specific differences exist), but there are rather few similarities to nickel. A Pd^{2+} ion does appear capable of existence, although it is not of major importance in the chemistry of the element, but no simple Pt cation or aquo ion has been observed. As with nickel the II state is a common one, but with Pd and Pt the IV state is also important. In the complex chemistry there are some resemblances to nickel(II), and several series of isomorphous complexes, for example, the salts of $[M(CN)_4]^{2-}$, are known. Important differences include the lack of any simple carbonyls of Pd and Pt (some carbonyl halides are known), the fact that although planar nickel(II) complexes are kinetically labile, those of Pd^{II} are moderately inert and those of Pt^{II} very much so, and the fact that nickel(II) is commonly six coordinated whereas this is rare for Pd^{II} and Pt^{II}.

The oxidation states and stereochemistry of Pd and Pt compounds are summarized in Table 30-16.

30-29. The Elements

The metals are grey-white and lustrous. They are not particularly hard and are malleable and ductile. Palladium, with a melting point of 1555°C., is the most fusible of the platinum metals; platinum has a somewhat higher melting point, 1773°C.

Both are chemically inert, but there are specific differences between

TABLE 30-16

Oxidation States and Stereochemistry of Palladium and Platinum

Oxidation state	Coordination number	Geometry	Examples
Pd^0, Pt^0	?	?	$[Pd(NO)_2Cl_2]_n$, $Pt(NH_3)_5$, $Pten_2$
	4	Tetrahedral(?)	$Pt(Ph_2PCH_2CH_2PPh_2)_2$
Pd^{II}, Pt^{II}, d^8	4[a,b]	Planar	$[PdCl_2]_n$, $[Pd(NH_3)_4]Cl_2$, PdO, PtO, $PtCl_4^{2-}$, $HPtBr(PEt_3)_2$, $Pd(CN)_4]^{2-}$, PtS, $Pd(dmg)_2$,[c] $[(py)_2PdCl_2]_2$, PdS
	5	Trigonal bipyramidal	$[PtCl(triars)]^+$,[d] $[Pd(diars_2)Cl]^+$
	6	Octahedral	PdF_2(rutile type), $[PtNOCl_5]^{2-}$, $[PtNO(NH_3)_4Cl]^{2+}$, $[PdNO(NO_2)_4NO_3]^{2-}$
Pd^{III}, Pt^{III}, d^7	?	?	PdF_3, $PtCl_3$(?), PtI_3(?)
Pd^{IV}, Pt^{IV}, d^6	4	Tetrahedral	$PtCl_4$
	6[a,b]	Octahedral	$[Pt(en)_2Cl_2]^{2+}$, $PtCl_6^{2-}$, $[Pt(NH_3)_6]^{4+}$, $Me_3PtAcAc$, $[PtMe_3]_4$
Pt^V, d^5	?	?	PtF_5
Pt^{VI}, d^4	?	?	$PtOF_4$, PtO_3
	6	Octahedral	PtF_6
Pt^{VIII}(?), d^2	?	?	$PtF_8(CO)_2$

[a] Most common states for Pd.

[b] Most common states for Pt.

[c] Has planar N atoms with weak octahedral Pd—Pd bonds.

[d] triars = tris-(o-diphenylarsinophenyl)arsine.

them in this respect. Palladium is not attacked by mineral acids except nitric which does slowly dissolve it, even in the massive state, and especially in presence of oxygen and oxides of nitrogen. In the finely divided state palladium is slowly attacked by hydrochloric acid in the presence of oxygen. It is rather easily soluble in aqua regia. Platinum is considerably more resistant to acids and is not attacked by any single mineral acid. It does readily dissolve in aqua regia, however.

Both metals are rapidly attacked by fused alkali oxides and especially peroxides.

Both metals are attacked by fluorine at red heat and by chlorine.

It is of importance in the use of platinum for laboratory equipment that on heating it combines directly with elemental P, Si, Pb, As, Sb, S, Se, and some other metalloid elements. When compounds of these elements are heated in contact with platinum under reducing conditions, the platinum is also attacked.

Both palladium and platinum are capable of absorbing large volumes of hydrogen gas. Palladium at 80°C. will absorb up to 900 times its own volume at 1 atm. pressure, corresponding approximately to a composition of $PdH_{0.75}$. At higher temperatures the volumes absorbed at a given pressure become smaller. The absorption causes both the electrical conductivity and magnetic susceptibility to fall, and these and other observations lead to the general belief that there is a definite hydride phase. However, the limiting composition and structure of this phase have not been definitely established.

30-30. Binary Compounds

Binary compounds of palladium and platinum are relatively few in number and with a few exceptions neither common nor important.

Oxides. Palladium(II) oxide is the most stable oxide of palladium. It is obtained as a black powder on heating palladium powder in oxygen or as a yellow precipitate by the addition of dilute alkali to solutions of Pd^{II} salts. This gelatinous precipitate dries in air to a brown, less hydrated form and on heating to $\sim100°C$. it loses further water and turns black. It does not become completely anhydrous below temperatures at which loss of oxygen begins. The pressure of oxygen over PdO has been reported to reach 1 atm. at 875°C., the product of dissociation being the metal. Dry PdO is remarkably inert, being insoluble in all acids including aqua regia.

It has also been reported that hydrous Pd^{III} and Pd^{IV} oxides can be prepared, but they are ill characterized and uncertain.

Platinum(IV) oxide is the most stable oxide of platinum. It is obtained in a hydrated condition, as a red-brown precipitate, when a solution of Pt^{IV} chloride is boiled with sodium carbonate. In the hydrous state it is soluble in acids and in strong alkalies, but after heating to about 200°C. it becomes insoluble. It decomposes to metal and oxygen if heated much above 200°C. although PtO_2 can be volatilized in oxygen in the range 800–1500°C.

A very unstable hydrous Pt^{II} oxide is obtained on addition of dilute alkali to a solution of $[PtCl_4]^{2-}$. After it has been dried at 120–150°C. in a stream of CO_2 its composition approximates to $Pt(OH)_2$; at higher temperatures it decomposes to give Pt^{IV} oxide and metal. A hydrous Pt^{III} oxide has been claimed but its existence appears uncertain.

Chalconides. The palladium and platinum chalconide systems are, like those of other heavy transition metals, quite complicated, but, unlike most others, they have been quite systematically investigated. The following outline is designed to give an impression of the extent and complexity of which the heavy metal chalconide systems are capable.

The palladium phases shown in Table 30-17 have been definitely identified (except where a question mark indicates some uncertainty about the

TABLE 30-17

Palladium Chalconide Phases

With S	With Se	With Te
Pd_4S	Pd_4Se	Pd_4Te
$Pd_{14}S_5$	$Pd_{14}Se_5$	$Pd_3Te(?)$, $Pd_5Te_2(?)$, $Pd_2Te(?)$
$Pd_{11}S_5$	$Pd_{11}Se_{10}(?)$	
PdS	PdSe	PdTe
PdS_2	$PdSe_2$	$PdTe_2$

composition—but not the existence—of certain phases). The existence of these phases, some of which may occur in defect condition, has been deduced from phase diagrams and X-ray investigations. The X-ray studies have, in some cases, been carried far enough to provide information on the atomic arrangements. Thus the Pd_4X phases have a body centered cubic structure in which one-fifth of the atoms are chalconides in an ordered fashion. PdTe has the NiAs structure (page 414), and $PdTe_2$ has the same structure as all of the PtX_2 phases (see below). PdS_2 and $PdSe_2$ are isomorphous but different from $PdTe_2$; the atomic arrangement has not been determined.

The platinum chalconide phases shown in Table 30-18 have been defi-

TABLE 30-18

Platinum Chalconide Phases

With S	With Se	With Te
—	$Pt_{10}Se_8$	—
PtS	—	PtTe
PtS_2	$PtSe_2$	$PtTe_2$

nitely identified. Of these the atomic arrangements are known in several. PtS_2, $PtSe_2$, $PtTe_2$, and $PdTe_2$ are isomorphous and have the $Cd(OH)_2$ structure; thus each Pt (or Pd) atom is surrounded by an octahedron of chalconide atoms. PtS has a structure in which Pt has only four near sulfur atoms which surround it in a square array.

All of these palladium and platinum chalconides are dark, chemically relatively inert solids, some with semimetallic properties. They can all be obtained by direct combination of the elements at high temperatures; some can be obtained in other ways as well. Thus PtS and PtS_2 are obtained by passing hydrogen sulfide into solutions of $[PtCl_4]^{2-}$ and $[PtCl_6]^{2-}$ respectively, PdS by passing hydrogen sulfide into solutions of Pd^{II} salts or by heating $(NH_4)_2[PdCl_4]$ with sulfur, and PdS_2 by heating $PdCl_2$ with an excess of sulfur.

Phosphides, Arsenides, Bismuthides. Palladium and platinum also combine with the group V elements to form binary phases. These systems have not been as thoroughly studied as the chalconide ones which they resemble in many ways. The Pd–P system is evidently quite complex, at least four intermediate phases having been found between 0 and 25 atom % P. The phase Pd_3P has been found by X-ray study to have the cementite (Fe_3C) structure.

Among the platinum phases, structural work has shown that PtP_2, $PtAs_2$, $PrSb_2$, and one form of $PtBi_2$ are isostructural and have the pyrite structure (page 415). It appears that many of the platinum group metal phosphides generally show structural similarities to those of the iron group. Thus Ru_2P is isostructural with Co_2P, RuP with FeP and CoP, RuP_2, and OsP_2 with FeP_2, RhP_3 and PdP_3 with CoP_3 and NiP_3.

Salts of Oxy Acids. These are virtually unknown. None have ever been reported for platinum. Hydrous palladium(II) oxide dissolves in nitric and sulfuric acids, and from these solutions $Pd(NO_3)_2$ and $PdSO_4 \cdot 2H_2O$ are obtained as brown deliquescent crystals.

Halides. Palladium forms all four halides in the divalent state and also a trifluoride. Although a few halo complexes of Pd^{IV} are known, no simple Pd^{IV} halides have been prepared. Even using the rapid quenching technique which has permitted the isolation of RuF_6 (page 816) and RhF_6 (page 835) it has not been possible to prepare a hexafluoride of palladium, although PtF_6 (see below) is fairly stable.

The direct action of fluorine on palladium or Pd^{II} halides produces black Pd^{III}. It can also be obtained by the action of BrF_3 on $PdCl_2$:

$$PdCl_2 \xrightarrow{BrF_3} PdF_3 \cdot BrF_3 \xrightarrow{\Delta} PdF_3 + BrF_3$$

It is very hygroscopic and very reactive, being a strong oxidizing agent. The effective magnetic moment of Pd^{III} in this compound at room temperature has been reported to be 3.05 B.M. For a d^7 system, even with a large spin-orbit coupling constant, this moment, if genuine, might be taken to mean that the Pd^{III} ion is low spin, but there is also the possibility that this low effective moment is due to strong antiferromagnetic interactions between high-spin Pd^{III} ions. A low-spin Pd^{III} ion in an octahedral environment would have a $t_{2g}^6 e_g$ configuration, which would be prone to cause distortion of the octahedron according to the Jahn-Teller theorem (page 582). As noted earlier (page 584), in several ions of the first transition series the presence of an odd number of e_g electrons causes rather pronounced distortions, but the structure of PdF_3, although not known with complete certainty, appears to contain essentially PdF_6 octahedra. Evidently further magnetic and structural studies are needed to elucidate fully the nature of this compound.

Pd^{II} fluoride was reported by Berzelius to be formed as a brown precipitate on adding a solution of an alkali metal fluoride to a solution of a Pd^{II} salt. Not until the middle of this century was it shown that PdF_2 is, in fact, completely hydrolyzed by water and, hence, that the precipitate of Berzelius is actually hydrous PdO. PdF_2 can be obtained by reduction of PdF_3. With reducing agents such as I_2, H_2, SO_2, and Pd, the product is contaminated with palladium metal. Pure PdF_2, showing no X-ray diffraction lines attributable to the metal, has only been obtained relatively recently by reaction 30-6:

$$2PdF_3 + SeF_4 \xrightarrow{\text{reflux}} 2PdF_2 + SeF_6 \tag{30-6}$$

It is pale violet and has the rutile structure. It has an effective magnetic moment of 1.84 B.M. at room temperature, for which the most likely interpretation is that the Pd^{II} ions, which are in essentially regular octahedra of fluoride ions, have high-spin d^8 configurations with strong antiferromagnetic coupling between ions.

Palladous chloride, $PdCl_2$, is probably the most important simple compound of palladium. It is made by the action of chlorine on the metal at red heat and is obtained as red crystals or an orange-red powder which is hygroscopic and soluble in water. From the aqueous solution crystals of the dihydrate, $PdCl_2 \cdot 2H_2O$, are obtained. In the anhydrous substance, the structure involves infinite flat chains of the form 30-II. Palladium(II)

(30 – II)

chloride is quite soluble in hydrochloric acid or alkali metal chloride solutions owing to formation of $[PdCl_4]^{2-}$ ions. The chloride reacts with many ligands, L, such as amines, phosphines, sulfides, etc., to give complexes of the types L_2PdCl_2 and $[LPdCl_2]_2$.

Pd^{II} bromide and iodide are also known. $PdBr_2$ is made from the elements in presence of nitric acid; it is obtained as a brown mass, insoluble in water but soluble in hydrobromic acid. PdI_2 can be precipitated from solutions of Pd^{II} chloride on addition of iodide ions. It is dark red to black, very insoluble in water, but slightly soluble in excess potassium iodide to give a red solution which evidently contains $[PdI_4]^{2-}$ ions. $K_2[PdI_4]$ can be isolated from the solution. Neither $PdBr_2$ nor PdI_2 have been characterized structurally.

Pt^{II} halides are relatively less stable than those of Pd^{II}. No Pt^{II} fluoride is known. $PtCl_2$ can be made by heating the metal in chlorine at $500°C$. or by thermal decomposition of the tetrafluoride. It is a brownish green solid, insoluble in water but soluble in hydrochloric acid to give a solution containing $[PtCl_4]^{2-}$ ions. Many salts containing this ion are known. The brown dibromide and black diiodide are both formed by thermal decomposition of the tetrahalides, trihalides being possible intermediates (page 859). The dihalides have narrow thermal stability ranges and it is extremely difficult to obtain pure compounds. The iodide can also be obtained in the same way as PdI_2, namely, by treating a suspension of the chloride with a solution of potassium iodide.

Pt^{IV} forms salts with all of the halogens. The major product of the direct fluorination of platinum metal is PtF_4. It can also be prepared by fluorination of $PtCl_4$ and by treatment of platinum with bromine trifluoride followed by further heating to decompose a BrF_3 adduct of PtF_4 which is the initial product of the reaction. It is an orange solid, volatile in a stream of fluorine at high temperature, and violently hydrolyzed by water.

Pt^{IV} chloride is a red-brown crystalline substance which can be made by heating platinum with chlorine at $250–300°C$. or by heating platinum with arsenic trichloride and selenium tetrachloride in a sealed tube. It is also often prepared by heating chloroplatinic acid, $H_2PtCl_6 \cdot nH_2O$, to $300°C$. It is easily soluble in water and acetone, and from aqueous solutions it crystallizes in several hydrated forms, some of which probably contain mixed chloro–hydroxo complexes such as $[PtCl_4(OH)_2]^{2-}$.

$PtBr_4$ and PtI_4 are both brown-black powders only slightly soluble in water but moderately soluble in alcohol and ether. They decompose on heating to $\sim180°C$. into the halogen and the Pt^{II} halide.

Platinum also forms a hexafluoride, an oxyfluoride, $PtOF_4$, and a pentafluoride. PtF_6 is formed in small amounts in the fluorination of platinum metal. It is a dark red to black solid, somewhat volatile to give a brown vapor and melting at $56.7°C$. Its octahedral structure is established by X-ray study which shows it to be isostructural with OsF_6 and IrF_6. The pentafluoride is also formed by direct fluorination of the metal at temperatures of about $350°C$. It is a dark red solid which sublimes at $155°C$. and is vigorously hydrolyzed by water. In silica apparatus, fluorination of platinum sponge also produces $PtOF_4$, a deep red solid, m.p. 75–76°C., The oxygen is presumably derived from the silica.

30-31. Complexes of Palladium(II) and Platinum(II)

The characteristic shape of the complexes formed by Pd^{II} and Pt^{II} is square. However, there are indications that in solution and in some crystalline compounds there is an additional weak affinity for two more ligands. Thus, current views on the mechanism of substitution reactions of the type shown in equation 30-8 involve the assumption that there are two solvent

$$\left[L{-}Pt^{II}{-}X \atop \substack{L \\ L} \right]^{+} + Y^{-} = \left[L{-}Pt^{II}{-}Y \atop \substack{L \\ L} \right]^{+} + X^{-} \qquad (30\text{-}8)$$

molecules, S, weakly bound in the remaining (*trans*) positions of an octahedron about the Pd^{II} or Pt^{II} ion, which move in as the leaving group, X^-, moves out giving a five-coordinated intermediate, $[PtL_3S_2]^{2+}$, which then combines rapidly with the new group, Y^-. Similarly, in the recently discovered carbonylation reaction of Pd^{II} and Pt^{II} alkyl complexes, for example,

$$[Pt(Et_3P)_2ClCH_3] + CO = [Pt(Et_3P)_2Cl(COCH_3)]$$

the transition state is believed to be a five-coordinated species of the type 30-III. Only a few stable octahedral complexes of Pd^{II} and Pt^{II} are known,

$$\begin{array}{c} O \\ \| \\ C \\ | \quad PEt_3 \\ Cl{-}Pt{-}CH_3 \\ Et_3P \end{array}$$

(30 – III)

examples being the nitrosyl complexes, $[PtCl_5(NO)]^{2-}$, $[Pt(NH_3)_4Cl(NO)]^{2+}$, and $[Pd(NO_2)_4(NO_3)(NO)]^{2-}$, and the arsine complexes, $[Pt(diars)_2Br]ClO_4$ and $[Pt(triars)_2](ClO_4)_2$, where diars is *o*-phenylenebisdimethylarsine and triars is a similar tridentate arsine. Also, the dimethylglyoxime complex of Pd^{II}, $[Pd(Dmg)_2]$, like its nickel analog, has chains of metal atoms perpendicular to the molecular planes with metal–metal bonding; the Pt^{II} compound, however, has a different structure in which there is weak but definite interaction between each platinum atom and oxygen atoms of adjacent $Pt(Dmg)_2$ units in the crystal.

All Pd^{II} and Pt^{II} complexes are diamagnetic. As a general rule, Pd^{II}

complexes are somewhat less stable, in both the thermodynamic and kinetic senses, than their Pt^{II} analogs, but otherwise the two series of complexes are very similar. The kinetic inertness of the Pt^{II} (and also Pt^{IV}) complexes has allowed them to play a very important role in the development of coordination chemistry. Many studies of geometrical isomerism, and, more recently, kinetic studies such as those which led Russian workers (especially Chernaev) to discover the *trans* effect (page 552) have had a profound influence on our understanding of coordination compounds.

All of the possible types of mononuclear complexes, namely, $[ML_4]^{2+}$, $[ML_3X]^+$, *cis*- and *trans*-$[ML_2X_2]$, $[MLX_3]^-$, and $[MX_4]^{2-}$, where M represents Pd^{II} or Pt^{II}, L represents a neutral ligand, and X a uninegative acido group, are known as well as a number of internal salt type of bischelates with ligands such as β-diketones, dialkylglyoximes, salicylaldoximines, etc. As a general rule, Pd^{II} and Pt^{II} show a great preference for nitrogen (in aliphatic amines and in —NO_2), halogens, cyanide, and heavy donor atoms, such as phosphorus, arsenic, sulfur, and selenium, and relatively small affinity for oxygen and fluorine. The strong binding of the heavy atom donors is due in great measure to the formation of metal–ligand π bonds by overlap of filled $d\pi$ orbitals (d_{xz}, d_{xy}, and d_{yz}) on the metal with empty $d\pi$ orbitals in the valence shells of the heavy atoms. This π bonding has already been discussed and illustrated in connection with theories of the *trans* effect on page 553. Cyanide ions, nitro groups, and carbon monoxide are also bound in a manner involving π bonding which results in these cases from overlap of filled metal $d\pi$ orbitals with empty $p\pi$ antibonding molecular orbitals of these ligands.

A number of complexes are known of the general type $[ML_4][M'X_4]$, where M and M' may both be Pd or Pt, or M may be some other element such as Cu while M' is Pd or Pt, and L and X represent, respectively, a neutral ligand and a halide or pseudohalide ion. One of the best known examples in Magnus' green salt, $[Pt(NH_3)_4][PtCl_4]$. Others include $[Pd(NH_3)_4][Pd(SCN)_4]$, $[Pt(CH_3NH_2)_4][PtBr_4]$, and $[Cu(NH_3)_4][PtCl_4]$. They generally have the same structure as Magnus' green salt in which anions and cations are stacked up with parallel planes creating chains of metal atoms. It appears that whenever both M and M' are Pt^{II} the substance shows a green color (although the constituent cations are colorless or pale yellow and the anions red), and marked dichroism with high absorption of light polarized in the direction of the metal chains has been observed. This has been interpreted in terms of Pt—Pt bonding. If steric hindrance is too great, as in $[Pt(C_2H_5NH_2)_4][PtCl_4]$, a different structure is adopted and the compound has a pink color, which is merely the sum of the colors of its constituent ions. It has also been found that even when the compound has the Magnus' green structure, no anomalous color results unless both M and M' are Pt^{II}. Wolfram's red salt is a similar case; it has octahedral $[Pt(C_2H_5NH_2)_4Cl_2]^{2+}$ and planar $[Pt(C_2H_5NH_2)_4]^{2+}$ ions linked in chains through the chloride ion, together with four other chloride ions in the lattice.

Besides the mononuclear complexes there are a considerable number of bridged binuclear complexes of the type 30-IV where the bridge groups, X, are commonly halide ions, RS^- groups, or thiocyanate ions. Bridging thi-

(30-IV)　　　　　　(30-V)

ocyanate ions are coordinated by both sulfur and nitrogen as in 30-V. Such bridged binuclear complexes quite generally are subject to attack by other ligands whereby the bridges are split and two mononuclear species are formed, for example, as in equation 30-9. When Cl^- or Br^- are the bridges,

$$\begin{bmatrix} Bu_3P & Cl & Cl \\ & Pd & Pd \\ Cl & Cl & PBu_3 \end{bmatrix} + 2C_6H_5NH_2 = 2\begin{bmatrix} Bu_3P & Cl \\ & Pd \\ Cl & NH_2C_6H_5 \end{bmatrix} \qquad (30\text{-}9)$$

the equilibria generally lie toward the mononuclear complexes. It might be supposed that such bridge-splitting reactions should give the *trans* mononuclear complexes, but when amines are present in the binuclear complex a mixture of *cis* and *trans* products is obtained, presumably because of isomerization of the initially produced *trans* isomer.

Platinum(II) complexes can also be converted to Pt^{IV} complexes, with retention of configuration, by oxidation with reagents such as Cl_2, Br_2, or H_2O_2 as illustrated by equation 30-10.

$$(30\text{-}10)$$

Pt^{II} forms some novel hydride complexes. For example, on adding an aqueous solution of $K_2[PtCl_4]$ to a solution of triphenylphosphine in alcohol containing potassium hydroxide, reaction 30-11 occurs.

$$[PtCl_4]^{2-} + 2OH^- + 2C_2H_5OH + 4Ph_3P \rightarrow$$
$$[Pt(Ph_3P)_4H_2] + 2CH_3CHO + 4Cl^- + 2H_2O \qquad (30\text{-}11)$$

In benzene solution this compound loses triphenyl phosphine stepwise:

$$[Pt(Ph_3P)_4H_2] = [Pt(Ph_3P)_3H_2] + Ph_3P$$
$$[Pt(Ph_3P)_3H_2] = [Pt(Ph_3P)_2H_2] + Ph_3P$$

and tris- and bis(triphenylphosphine)dihydridoplatinum(II) can also be isolated. The compounds with three and four molecules of triphenylphosphine appear to be five- and six-coordinated Pt^{II} complexes, but their structures have not yet been fully established. Several other Pt^{II} hydrido complexes, for example, of the type $[Pt(PR_3)_2ClH]$, are also known.

A large number of aryl and alkyl complexes of the types $[ML_2R_2]$ and $[ML_2RX]$, where M is Pt or Pd, R is an alkyl or aryl group, X is a halide ion, and L is a neutral ligand of the strongly π-bonding type such as phosphine or arsine, are known. The Pd ones are less stable than those of Pt. Analogous Ni complexes are known only for certain special aryl groups.

Platinum and palladium are also outstanding in their ability to form complexes with alkenes and alkynes. The alkene complexes and those alkyne complexes in which μ bonds are believed to exist have been described (page 638). Platinum also forms some alkyne complexes in which the alkyne appears to fill two positions in the coordination shell, and it is believed that an opening of one of the π bonds may occur so that the alkyne–metal bonding can be represented as shown in 30-VI.

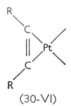

(30-VI)

30-32. Complexes of Palladium(IV) and Platinum(IV)

Pd^{IV} is somewhat more stable in complexes than in simple compounds. Nevertheless, only a few complexes of Pd^{IV} are known, and they are not very common or important. Those known are of two types: $M^I_2[PdX_6]$ (X = F⁻, Cl⁻, or Br⁻) and diammines of the type $PdAm_2X_4$ (X = Cl⁻ or Br⁻).

The hexahalo complexes are the more stable, those of chlorine and bromine being about equally easy to prepare and somewhat more stable than the fluoro one. X-ray study has shown that octahedral $[PdBr_6]^{2-}$ ions are present in $Rb_2[PdBr_6]$. The $[PdCl_6]^{2-}$ ion is formed when palladium is dissolved in aqua regia or on saturating a solution of Pd^{II} chloride with chlorine. The $[PdBr_6]^{2-}$ ion is formed when saturated solutions of $M^I_2PdBr_4$ salts are exposed to bromine vapor. Ammonium, potassium, rubidium, and cesium salts of both complex ions have been isolated. The $[PdCl_6]^{2-}$ salts are red, and the $[PdBr_6]^{2-}$ salts are black. They lose halogen on mild heating to leave the $M^I_2[PdX_4]$ salts. They react rapidly with concentrated aqueous ammonia evolving nitrogen, and they are decomposed by hot water to generate chlorine or bromine leaving the corresponding Pd^{II} complexes.

The three yellow $M^I_2[PdF_6]$ compounds, in which the alkali metal may be K, Rb, or Cs, can be prepared by the action of bromine trifluoride on the $M^I_2[PdCl_4]$ or $M^I_2[PdCl_6]$ compounds or by the action of elemental fluorine on the $M^I_2[PdCl_4]$ compounds. X-ray studies have demonstrated the presence of octahedral $[PdF_6]^{2-}$ ions in the crystals. The $[PdF_6]^{2-}$ ion is immediately hydrolyzed by water with precipitation of hydrous palladium oxide.

The diammine complexes, such as $Pdpy_2Cl_4$, which is obtained as a deep orange crystalline powder when $Pdpy_2Cl_2$ suspended in chloroform is treated with chlorine, are of marginal stability. They lose chlorine or bromine rapidly on standing in moist air. However, complexes such as $(NH_3)_2Pt(NO_2)_2Cl_2$ are stable.

In marked contrast to Pd^{IV}, platinum(IV) forms a vast number of very stable and kinetically inert complexes. As far as is known, Pt^{IV} complexes are invariably octahedral and, in fact, Pt^{IV} has such a pronounced tendency to be six coordinated that in some of its compounds quite unusual structures are adopted. Several interesting examples of this tendency of Pt^{IV} to be six coordinated even when very novel bonding must be used can be cited. The trimethylplatinum halides, $(CH_3)_3PtX$ (X = Cl, Br, I), and tetramethylplatinum, all have the tetrameric structure shown in Figure 11-6. In the halides, halogen atoms form three-way bridges while in the tetramethyl compound we have the unique situation of methyl groups functioning as three-way bridges, similar to their two-way bridging in dimethylberyllium and trimethylaluminum. In trimethylplatinum acetylacetonate, $[(CH_3)_3Pt(O_2C_5H_7)]_2$, long known to be a dimer in noncoordinating solvents, the structure is as shown in Figure 30-19. The acetylacetone functions as a tridentate ligand, the third donor atom, besides the two oxygen atoms which are normally the only donor atoms, being the middle carbon atom of the ring. The donor ability of this carbon atom can perhaps best be understood in terms of resonance structures of the chelate ring as shown in 30-VII. Ordinarily only 30-VIIa and 30-VIIb are considered, but 30-VIIc is also quite valid and must predominate in this platinum(IV) dimer.

In the monomeric compound, $(CH_3)_3Pt(dipy)(O_2C_5H_7)$, six rather than seven coordination is achieved by the formation of only one bond to the

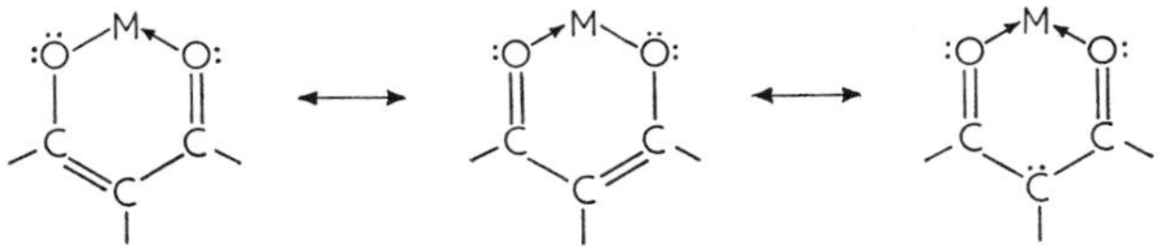

(30–VIIa)　　　　(30–VIIb)　　　　(30–VIIc)

acetylacetonate ion, but this, surprisingly, is to the carbon atom, as shown in Figure 30-20. The great strength of the Pt—C bond is shown by the fact that in the preparation of this compound from $[(CH_3)_3Pt(O_2C_5H_7)]_2$ by the action of dipyridyl, it is the Pt—O bonds rather than Pt—C which are broken.

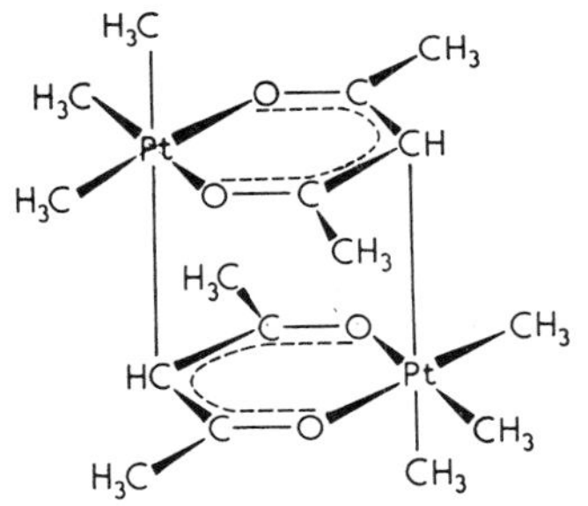

Fig. 30-19. The molecular structure of trimethylplatinum acetylacetonate dimer showing how the Pt^{IV} attains octahedral coordination.

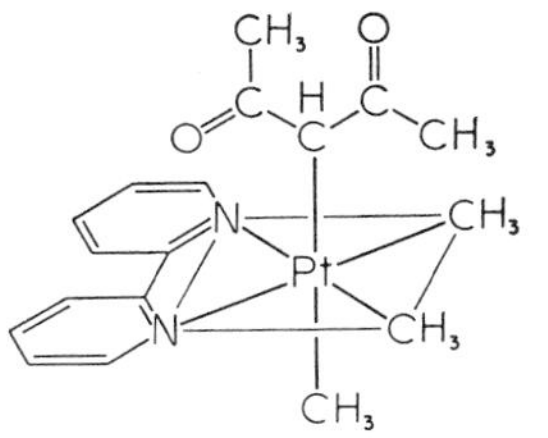

Fig. 30-20. Schematic representation of molecular structure of the dipyridyl adduct of trimethylplatinum(IV) acetylacetonate.

The most extensive and typical series of Pt^{IV} complexes are those which span the entire range from the hexammines, $[PtAm_6]X_4$, including all intermediates such as $[PtAm_4X_2]X_2$ and $M^I[PtAmX_5]$, to $M^I_2[PtX_6]$. Some of these have already been mentioned (page 516) as examples of the classical evidence which led Werner to assign the coordination number 6 to Pt^{IV}. The amines which occur in these complexes include ammonia, hydrazine, hydroxylamine, and ethylenediamine, and the acido groups include the halogens, thiocyanate, hydroxide, and the nitro group. Although not all of these groups are known to occur in all possible combinations in all types of compounds, it can be said that, with a few exceptions, they are generally interchangeable.

One notable exception is the fluoride ion, which occurs only in the $[PtF_6]^{2-}$ ion. Alkali metal salts of this ion are made by the action of fluorine or bromine trifluoride on the corresponding $M^I_2[PtCl_6]$ compound and in other ways. In contrast to the behavior of $[PdF_6]^{2-}$, the $[PtF_6]^{2-}$ ion is only slowly hydrolyzed by water.

The *trans* effect, which plays such an important role in determining the stereochemical course of reaction in the planar complexes of Pd^{II} and Pt^{II}, operates also for substitutions in octahedral Pt^{IV} complexes, and considerable advantage may often be taken of it in designing stereospecific syntheses. As we have mentioned before, many Pt^{IV} complexes can be obtained stereospecifically from appropriate Pt^{II} complexes by oxidative addition of Cl_2, Br_2, or H_2O_2.

A Pt^{IV} complex of interest is one which was originally believed to be a "cyclopropane–$PtCl_2$" complex, with the cyclopropane exhibiting some olefinic character in a manner never clearly specified. In 1960 evidence was presented to show that it is, in fact, a Pt^{IV} complex consisting of units shown in 30-VIII polymerized by chloride bridges. This then provides an

(30–VIII)   (30–IX)

explanation of its reaction with pyridine to yield the complex shown in 30-IX.

30-33. Valence States Other Than II and IV

In addition to the very common and important valence states II and IV, both palladium and platinum form some compounds in other valence states.

The hexa- and pentafluorides of platinum have already been mentioned. No compounds of palladium in higher oxidation states have been reported. A hydrous PtO_3 is also mentioned in the older literature but it is, at the very least, an extremely unstable substance.

In 1960 a most peculiar compound of the composition $PtF_8(CO)_2$, a pale yellow solid, volatile in vacuum at $\sim70°C.$, was reported to result by the action of carbon monoxide under pressure on PtF_4. It is extremely reactive, and the infrared shows no evidence of bridging carbonyl groups or of the presence of F_2CO. The structure of this substance is presently unknown.

The trifluoride of palladium has already been described. Aside from a few complexes which are reputed to contain Pd^{III} but which may, on the limited evidence available, contain Pd^{II} and Pd^{IV}, there are no other Pd^{III} compounds known.

Quite a number of Pt^{III} compounds have been reported, but again there appears to be no proof that they actually contain Pt^{III} rather than Pt^{II} and Pt^{IV}. The chief ones are the chloride, bromide, and iodide, all of which have been reported to form on equilibration of the di- or tetrahalide with halogen at an appropriate pressure and temperature. They are green to black solids very different in appearance from the pure di- or tetrahalides. If they are true trihalides, they should be paramagnetic, but no magnetic data appear to have been reported. A tricyanide of platinum has also been reported.

Several complexes having formulas consistent with the presence of Pt^{III} have been studied by X-rays, and the results show that there are no discrete units containing Pt^{III} present. Thus the compounds PtenBr$_3$ and Pt(NH$_3$)$_2$Br$_3$ can each be considered as built up of alternating square Pt^{II} complexes and octahedral Pt^{IV} complexes with *trans* Br$^-$ ions from the Pt^{IV} complexes serving as bridges, as shown in Figure 30-21. These substances

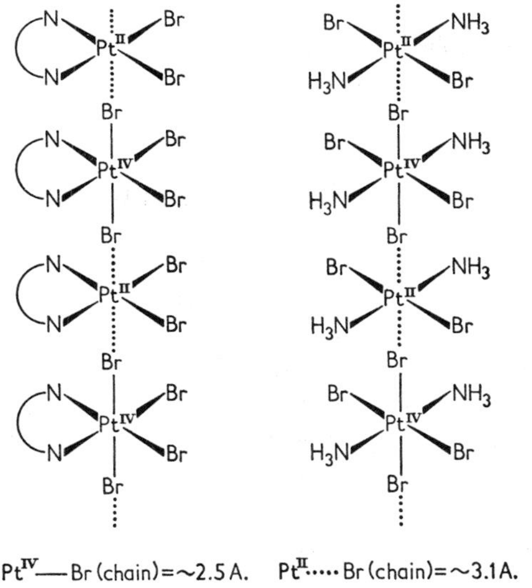

Pt^{IV}—Br (chain) = ~2.5 A. Pt^{II} ···· Br (chain) = ~3.1 A.

Fig. 30-21. Diagram showing the chains of alternating Pt^{II} and Pt^{IV} atoms with bridging bromide ions in PtenBr$_3$ and Pt(NH$_3$)$_2$Br$_3$.

have peculiar iridescent green colors, and examination under the polarizing microscope shows them to be markedly pleochroic with pronounced absorption of light polarized parallel with the $Pt^{II} \cdots Br$—Pt^{IV}—$Br \cdots Pt^{II} \cdots$ chains. Similarly, Pt(C$_2$H$_5$NH$_2$)$_4$Cl$_3 \cdot$2H$_2$O has been shown to exhibit marked pleochroism of a similar type, and a structure containing alternating $[Pt^{II}(C_2H_5NH_2)_4]^{2+}$ and $[Pt^{IV}(C_2H_5NH_2)_4Cl_2]^{2+}$, with the chlorine atoms in the latter serving as bridges, may be considered plausible. Several other compounds which seem likely to be similarly constituted are known. These compounds generally have a quite different appearance than either of the Pt^{II} and Pt^{IV} complexes which may be considered as their constituents. Thus in regard to the alleged simple Pt^{III} halides, appearance alone cannot be considered as evidence in favor of Pt^{III}.

Although there have been several reports of Pd^0 and Pt^0 complexes containing phosphines, phosphites, and isonitriles as ligands, it now appears that they are all hydrido complexes of Pd^{II} and Pt^{II}, the hydride ions having gone undetected in the earlier work. Some definite examples have been described (page 635). However, it seems that reduction of the bis(diphosphine) dichloride by borohydride in aqueous ethanol gives $Pt[Ph_2P(CH_2)_2PPh_2]_2$ as yellow plates. This compound is a nonelectrolyte of low dipole moment and shows no sign of Pt—H bonds spectroscopically or chemically. It is presumably tetrahedral.

A substance of approximate composition $Pt(NH_3)_4$ can be made by reducing tetrammineplatinum(II) dibromide with potassium in liquid ammonia. It is a yellow-white solid which readily decomposes to platinum and ammonia.

SILVER AND GOLD

Like copper, these elements have a single s electron outside a completed d shell, but in spite of the similarity in electronic structures and ionization potentials there are few resemblances between Ag, Au, and Cu, and there is no clear, simple explanation for many of the differences.

Apart from obviously similar stoichiometries of compounds in the same oxidation state (which do not always have the same structure) there are some similarities within the group—or at least between two of the three elements:

1. The metals all crystallize with the same face-centered cubic lattice.

2. Cu_2O and Ag_2O have the same body-centered cubic structure where the metal atom has two close oxygen neighbors and every oxygen is tetrahedrally surrounded by four metal atoms.

3. Although the stability constant sequence for halo complexes of many metals is F > Cl > Br > I, for Cu^I and Ag^I it is the reverse.

4. Cu^I and Ag^I (and to a lesser extent Au^I) form very much the same type of compounds. Thus the halides are polymeric and water insoluble; they form complex cyanides, $[M(CN)_2]^-$, and complexes with halides, phosphines, and other π-bonding ligands, such as $[Et_3AsMI]_4$ and K_2MCl_3.

5. Certain complexes of Cu^{II} and Ag^{II} are isomorphous, and Ag^{III}, Au^{III}, and Cu^{III} also give similar complexes, for example, $[M(ebg)_2]^{3+}$ (ebg = ethylenebiguanide, see page 866).

The only stable cationic species, apart from complex ions, is Ag^+. Gold(III) is invariably complexed in all solutions, usually as anionic species such as $[AuCl_3OH]^-$. The other oxidation states, Ag^{II}, Ag^{III}, and Au^I, are either unstable to water or exist only in insoluble compounds or complexed species. Intercomparisons of the oxidation potentials are of little utility, particularly since these strongly depend on the nature of the anion; some useful ones are, for silver:

$$Ag \xrightarrow{\ -0.799\ } Ag^+ \xrightarrow{\ -1.98\ } Ag^{2+}$$

$$Ag + 2CN^- \xrightarrow{\ 0.31\ } Ag(CN)_2^-$$

and for gold:

$$Au + 4Cl^- \xrightarrow{\ -1.00\ } AuCl_4^-$$

$$Au + 2CN^- \xrightarrow{\ 0.6\ } Au(CN)_2^-$$

The oxidation states and stereochemistry are summarized in Table 30-19.

TABLE 30-19

Oxidation States and Stereochemistry of Silver and Gold

Oxidation state	Coordination number	Geometry	Examples
Ag^I, d^{10}	2[a]	Linear	$[Ag(CN)_2]^-$, $[Ag(NH_3)_2]^+$, $AgSCN$
	3	Trigonal( )	$(Me_2NC_6H_4PEt_2)_2AgI$
	4[a]	Tetrahedral	$[Ag(SCN)_4]^{3-}$, $[AgIPR_3]_4$, $[Ag(PPh_3)_4]^+ClO_4^-$
	6	Octahedral	AgF, $AgCl$, $AgBr$ (NaCl structure)
Ag^{II}, d^9	4	Planar	$[Agpy_4]^{2+}$
Ag^{III}, d^8	4	Planar	AgF_4^-, $\frac{1}{2}$ of Ag atoms in AgO, $[Ag(ebg)_2]^{3+}$
	6	Octahedral( )	$[Ag(IO_6)_2]^{7-}$
Au^I, d^{10}	2[a]	Linear	$[Au(CN)_2]^-$, $Et_3P \cdot AuC \equiv C \cdot C_6H_5$; $(AuI)_n$
	4	Tetrahedral	$[Au(diars)_2]^+I^-$
Au^{III}, d^8	4[a]	Planar	$AuBr_4^-$, Au_2Cl_6, $[(C_2H_5)_2AuBr_2]_2$
	5	Trigonal bipyramidal	$[Au(diars)_2I]^{2+}$, $[Au(CN)_5]^{2-}(?)$
	6	Octahedral	$AuBr_6^{3-}$, $[Au(diars)_2I_2]^+$, $[Au(CN)_6]^{3-}(?)$, $KAuF_4$ (distorted)

[a] Most common states.

There is no proof of the existence of divalent gold compounds. For silver(I) particularly, the stereochemistry is sensitive to the nature of the ligand, and, although the dominant coordination number is 2, there are some types of ligand which give four coordination.

30-34. The Elements

The elements are widely distributed in nature in the free state and in sulfides and arsenides; silver also occurs as the chloride, AgCl. Silver is often recovered from the work-up of copper and lead ores. The elements are usually extracted by treatment with cyanide solutions in presence of air and are recovered from them by addition of zinc. They are purified by electrodeposition.

Silver is a white, lustrous, soft, and malleable metal (m.p. 961°C.) with the highest known electrical and thermal conductivity. It is chemically less reactive than copper, except toward sulfur and hydrogen sulfide, which rapidly blacken silver surfaces. The metal dissolves in oxidizing acids and in cyanide solutions in presence of oxygen or peroxide.

Gold is a soft, yellow metal (m.p. 1063°C.) with the highest ductility and malleability of any element. It is chemically unreactive and is not attacked by oxygen or sulfur. Halogens react readily with gold as do solutions which generate them such as aqua regia. Gold dissolves in cyanide solutions in presence of air or peroxide.

Since the chemistries of the compounds of these elements differ quite considerably, we treat them separately.

30-35. Silver Compounds

Argentous Compounds. The argentous (Ag^I) state is the normal and predominant oxidation state of silver. There is a well-defined, colorless argentous ion, Ag^+, in aqueous solution; there are several well-defined water-soluble salts, such as $AgNO_3$, $AgClO_3$ and $AgClO_4$, and a few rather sparingly soluble salts, such as Ag_2SO_4 and $AgOCOCH_3$.

Argentous Oxide. The addition of alkali hydroxide to Ag^+ solutions produces a dark brown precipitate which is difficult to free from alkali ions. It is strongly basic and its aqueous suspensions are alkaline

$$\tfrac{1}{2}Ag_2O(s) + \tfrac{1}{2}H_2O = Ag^+ + OH^- \qquad \log K_{so} = -7.42 \ (25°C., 3M \ NaClO_4)$$
$$\tfrac{1}{2}Ag_2O(s) + \tfrac{1}{2}H_2O = AgOH \qquad \log K = -5.75$$

and absorb carbon dioxide from the air to give argentous carbonate. The oxide decomposes thermally above ~160°C. and is readily reduced to the metal by hydrogen. Silver oxide is more soluble in strong alkaline solution than in water, and it has been shown that $Ag(OH)_2^-$ species are formed. The treatment of water-soluble halides with a suspension of silver oxide is a convenient way of preparing the hydroxides, since the silver halides are insoluble.

Argentous Sulfide. The action of hydrogen sulfide on argentous solutions gives black Ag_2S, which is the least soluble in water of all silver compounds (log $K_{SP} \approx -50$). The black coating often found on silver articles is the sulfide; the sulfide can be readily reduced by contact with aluminum in dilute sodium carbonate solution.

Argentous Halides. AgF is prepared by dissolving Ag_2O in aqueous hydrofluoric acid. On evaporation of the solution, crystals of the very water-soluble hydrate $AgF \cdot 2H_2O$ can be obtained, which can be dehydrated above 40°C.

The well-known water-insoluble compounds AgCl, AgBr, and AgI are precipitated by the addition of the appropriate halide ion to an Ag^+ solution. The color and insolubility increase Cl < Br < I. Silver chloride is appreciably soluble in concentrated nitric acid and also in concentrated solutions of hydrochloric acid and alkali chlorides where chloro complexes are formed. It also readily dissolves in ammonia, cyanide, and thiosulfate solutions to give complex ions. The solubility of AgCl in $AgNO_3$ solutions gives evidence for species such as Ag_2Cl^+ and Ag_3Cl^{2+} and confirms the conclusion that AgCl is a weak electrolyte. The bromide has similar solubility characteristics, but the iodide is only sparingly soluble in ammonia, although it readily dissolves in cyanide and thiosulfate solutions since the complexity constants are here greater than that for $[Ag(NH_3)_2]^+$.

Argentous Complexes. There are a great variety of silver complexes both in solution and in the solid state with π-bonding and non-π-bonding ligands. Oxygen is only feebly attached to silver, although the ion $[Ag(OH)_2]^-$ is known in strongly alkaline media. Since the most stable Ag^+ complexes have the linear structure, L—Ag—L, chelating ligands cannot form such simple ions and hence tend to give polynuclear complex ions. For monodentate ligands, the species AgL, AgL_2, AgL_3, and AgL_4 can exist, but the constants K_1 and K_2 are usually high whereas K_3 and K_4 are relatively small; hence the main species are usually of the linear AgL_2 type. The coordination number, however, is sensitive to the nature of the ligand and a variety of types can occur because of the possibilities of sp, sp^2, and sp^3 bonding of Ag^+. For ligands with $d\pi$ bonding potential, especially S, Se, P, and As ligands, the three- and four-coordinate species can predominate. Some complexity constants are given in Figure 30-22 and in Table 30-20.

The ligands are of three main types: (*1*) ligands with little or no $d\pi$-

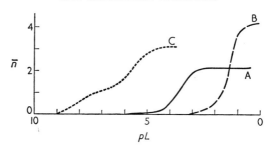

Fig. 30-22. Formation curves for Ag^+ complexes with three general classes of ligand L. A, Ligands with little or no π-bonding ability; B, ligands with intermediate π-bonding ability; C, ligands with marked π-bonding ability.

TABLE 30-20

Some Complex Constants for Ag^+

Ligand	K_1, liter mole^{-1}
Pyridine	110
Ethylamine	2340
Ammonia	1740
Chlorine	700
Bromine	1.4×10^4
Iodine	1.3×10^6
m-Ph$_2$PC$_6$H$_4$SO$_3^-$	1.4×10^8

bonding capacity, which show a marked inflection or a limiting value at $\bar{n} = 2$ in the complex constant curves (e.g., NH_3 gives only $[Ag(NH_3)_2]^+$ even in the highest concentrations of ammonia); (2) ligands having strong $d\pi$-bonding capacity which have a limit at $\bar{n} = 1$ or $\bar{n} = 3$ such as P, As, and I; and (3) ligands of intermediate $d\pi$-bonding capacity which show uniform formation up to $\bar{n} = 4$.

Acetylene and Olefin Complexes. The action of acetylene on Ag^+ solutions gives an initial yellow precipitate which subsequently becomes white. This reaction is reversible

$$C_2H_2 + 2Ag^+ = AgC\equiv CAg + 2H^+$$

With strong solutions of $AgNO_3$, precipitates of $C_2Ag_3NO_3$ are obtained; it is possible that here there is π bonding similar to that discussed for the cuprous acetylene complexes. Substituted acetylenes in presence of phosphine ligands can give complexes such as $[(C_2H_5)_3PAgC\equiv C\cdot C_6H_5]_2$ which undoubtedly involve π bonding between the silver atom and the triple bond.

Virtually all olefins, and also many aromatic compounds, give complexes with silver ion; these have been discussed previously (Chapter 28). Even where crystalline solids cannot be obtained, studies of the distribution of silver ion between aqueous and organic solvent phases allow equilibrium constants to be determined.

Argentic Compounds.   The argentic ion, Ag^{2+}, can exist in aqueous solution only as a transient species. Solutions in perchloric and nitric acids may be prepared by oxidation of Ag^I with ozone. Kinetic evidence suggests that this oxidation occurs by the following mechanism involving Ag^{III}:

$$Ag^+ + O_3 = AgO^+ + O_2$$
$$AgO^+ + Ag^+ + 2H^+ = 2Ag^{2+} + H_2O$$

Measurements of the $Ag^+ = Ag^{2+} + e$ electrode potential (25°C.) give -2.00 v. in $4M$ $HClO_4$ and -1.93 v. in $4M$ HNO_3, indicating that formation of nitrate complexes stabilizes Ag^{2+} (cf. Ce^{4+}). These potentials show that Ag^{2+} is a powerful oxidizing agent. It is believed that the catalytic effect of Ag^+ in various oxidations by persulfate is due to transient formation of Ag^{2+} and/or AgO^+.

Only two well-defined binary compounds are known, namely, the oxide, AgO, and the fluoride, AgF_2. Argentic oxide is best prepared by persulfate oxidation of Ag_2O in basic medium at $\sim90°C$. It can also be obtained by persulfate oxidation in neutral or HNO_3 media, whereby substances of compositions $Ag_{14}O_{16}SO_4$ or $Ag_7O_8NO_3$ are produced as black precipitates yielding AgO on boiling 2–3 hours in water. Black AgO is a semiconductor, stable to $\sim100°C.$, and it dissolves in acids evolving oxygen but giving some Ag^{2+} in solution. It is a powerful oxidizing agent. Since AgO is diamagnetic, it cannot in fact be Ag^{II} oxide. Chemical evidence rather definitely rules out the possibility of its being a peroxide, and the most likely formulation is therefore as $Ag^IAg^{III}O_2$. Neutron diffraction has shown this to be so since there are two types of silver atoms in the lattice, one with linear coordination to two oxygen atoms (Ag^I) and the other square planar with respect to oxygen (Ag^{III}). If AgF is heated with F_2 or other fluorinating agents, AgF_2, a dark brown crystalline solid, is obtained. This appears to be an authentic Ag^{II} compound. It is antiferromagnetic, having an effective moment at room temperature well below the spin-only value for one unpaired electron. It is both a strong oxidizing agent and a strong fluorinating agent.

Quite a number of Ag^{II} complexes are known. The cationic complexes $[Agpy_4]^{2+}$, $[Ag(dipy)_2]^{2+}$, and $[Ag(o\text{-phen})_2]^{2+}$ are obtained as crystalline persulfates, from which other salts of nonreducing anions, for example,

NO_3^-, ClO_3^-, ClO_4^-, and HSO_4^-, can be obtained metathetically or when Ag^+ is oxidized by persulfate in presence of the appropriate ligand. The salt $[Agpy_4]S_2O_8$ is isomorphous with its copper(II) analog which makes it seem certain that the $[Agpy_4]^{2+}$ ion is square planar. Similarly the bispicolinate complex (30-X) is isomorphous with its Cu^{II} analog which has

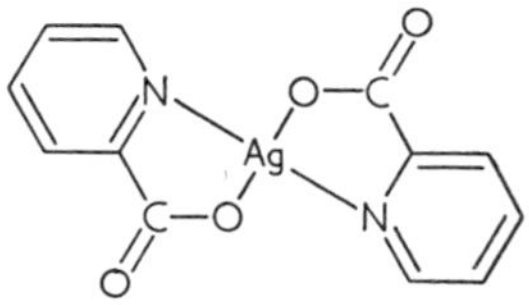

(30–X)

been shown to have a *trans*-planar structure. In all cases studied, Ag^{II} complexes have magnetic moments of 1.75–2.2 B.M. in accord with expectation for the d^9 configuration.

Tripositive Silver Compounds. Aside from the evidences for tripositive silver (Ag^{III}) mentioned in the preceding section, there is more definite information. Anodic oxidation of Ag^I in alkaline solutions gives a black oxide claimed to be impure Ag_2O_3. It is not readily purified, and its formulation as Ag_2O_3 is not conclusive, though supported by the most recent work.

When 1:1 mixtures of potassium or cesium halides with silver halides are heated in a stream of fluorine, yellow $KAgF_4$ and $CsAgF_4$ are obtained. They are diamagnetic and extremely sensitive to moisture. Periodato and tellurato salts, diamagnetic and yellow in color, are obtained by persulfate oxidation of Ag^+ in strongly basic solutions containing periodate or tellurate ions. Representative compounds are: $K_6H[Ag(IO_6)_2] \cdot 10H_2O$, $Na_6K[Ag(IO_6)_2] \cdot NaOH \cdot H_2O$, and $Na_6H_3[Ag(TeO_6)_2] \cdot 18H_2O$. These species are analogous to those of Cu^{III}. An Ag^{III} complex of remarkable stability is the one with ethylenedibiguanide (30-XI), which is obtained as

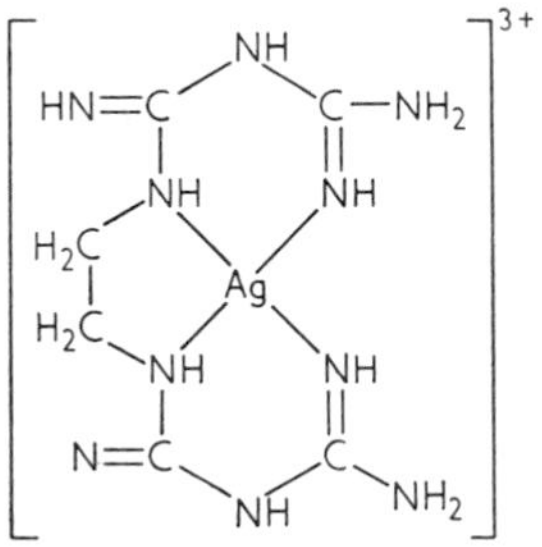

(30–XI)

the red sulfate when Ag_2SO_4 is treated with aqueous potassium persulfate in the presence of ethylenedibiguanidinium sulfate. The hydroxide, nitrate, and perchlorate have been prepared metathetically. These salts are diamagnetic and oxidize two equivalents of iodide ion per gram-atom of silver.

30-36. Gold Compounds

Aurous Compounds. The chemistry of gold is essentially a chemistry of complex compounds, and in this respect it resembles platinum. No simple gold cations exist in aqueous solution. The aurous ion, Au^+, like the cuprous ion, cannot exist except in vanishingly small concentrations, and even AuCl is decomposed by water to give gold and hydrolyzed gold(III) species. The aqueous chemistry of Au^I is thus mainly of complex *anions* such as $AuCl_4^-$ or $Au(CN)_2^-$. There is no evidence of any stable bivalent gold compounds at the present time, although it has been claimed that gold(I) dithiocarbamates when treated with the thiuram disulfide give gold(II) species in solution.

Aurous oxide has not been well characterized.

Thermal decomposition of auric chloride, Au_2Cl_6, at about 185°C., gives *aurous chloride* as a pale yellow powder. This compound is thermally unstable and is also decomposed by water, although it can be converted by alkali chlorides to the chloroaurates(I). The action of iodide ion on $Au^{III}Cl_4^-$ solutions precipitates *aurous iodide*, AuI, which is insoluble in water.

The addition of cyanide ion to auric solutions precipitates *aurous cyanide*, AuCN, which, like the iodide, has continuous zigzag chains through the crystal lattice.

There are several aurous complexes stable in aqueous solution, the most important ones being $Au(CN)_2^-$, $AuCl_2^-$, and the thiosulfate species. The cyanide complex is very stable ($K = 4 \times 10^{28}$) and is formed when AuCN is treated with excess cyanide or, more usually, when gold is treated with alkali cyanides in presence of air or hydrogen peroxide. Crystalline compounds such as $K[Au(CN)_2]$ can be obtained, and the free acid, $HAu(CN)_2$, is isolable by evaporation of its solutions. Numerous complexes of Au^I with substituted phosphine, arsine, and sulfide ligands as well as carbon monoxide can be obtained. Unlike the copper(I) and silver(I) complexes, which are polymeric with four-coordinated metal atoms, the gold(I) complexes are usually, though not invariably, monomeric. Thus the action of phosphorus trichloride or trialkyl phosphines on auric chloride in ether reduces the Au^{III} to give crystals of R_3PAuCl. Acetylene complexes such as $Et_3PAuC\equiv CPh$ are also monomeric.

Auric Compounds. Auric (Au^{III}) compounds are mostly complexes and are powerful oxidizing agents.

The addition of alkali hydroxide to $AuCl_4^-$ solutions gives a yellow-brown precipitate, $Au(OH)_3$, which can be dehydrated to brown Au_2O_3. The latter is unstable above $\sim$150°C., decomposing to give what is presumed to be a mixture of gold and aurous oxide. The hydroxide is weakly acidic and is soluble in alkalies to give anionic species of the type $[Au(OH)_4]^-$ or $[AuO_2]^-$(aq).

Gold is soluble in bromine trifluoride, and a crystalline salt, $AuBrF_6$, can be obtained. The latter decomposes at 180°C. leaving auric *fluoride*, AuF_3, as a crystalline solid, stable to $\sim$500°C., but decomposed at once by water. Fluoroaurates such as $KAuF_4$, in which Au appears to have distorted octahedral coordination, can also be made.

Auric chloride and *auric bromide* are obtained by direct interaction of the elements at about 200°C. They are both dimeric in the red crystals and in the vapor. The halides are soluble in water, in which they are partially hydrolyzed to species such as $[AuCl_3OH]^-$; on addition of excess halogen acid, the ions $AuCl_4^-$ and $AuBr_4^-$ are formed. Chloroauric acid, $HAuCl_4$, is the product obtained by dissolution of gold in aqua regia, and it can be obtained as yellow crystals, $HAuCl_4 \cdot 4H_2O$. Well-defined salts such as $KAuCl_4$ are formed. The anhydrous halides, as well as the acids, are soluble in organic donor solvents. Gold(III) in dilute aqueous acid solutions can be extracted with a high partition coefficient into ethyl acetate or diethyl ether as $[AuCl_3OH]^-$, which is presumably associated in an ion pair with an oxonium ion.

Although coordination numbers higher than 4 for gold(III) are rare, the tetrabromoaurate(III) ion reacts with bromide ion in nitrobenzene solution or in nitromethane, and some evidence for the ions $AuBr_6^{3-}$, $AuBr_5^{2-}$, and $Au_2Br_{10}^{4-}$ has been obtained. In alkaline cyanide solutions there is also evidence for coordination numbers of 5 and 6 since CN^- ion adds to $Au(CN)_4^-$.

Gold(III) salts of oxy anions are not very stable or important, but complex auric sulfates and nitrates, for example, $[Au(NO_3)_4]^-$, can be prepared. There are numerous four-coordinate complexes such as $[AuCl_2py_2]Cl$, $[Au(o\text{-phen})_2X_2]^+$, etc.

Important gold(III) complexes have been obtained using a chelating diarsine ligand from the interaction of sodium tetrachloroaurate(III) in presence of sodium iodide. The iodide $[Au(diars)_2I_2]I$ and other cations $[Au(diars)_2I]^{2+}$ and $[Au(diars)_2]^{3+}$ can be obtained. It is held that these are species with six, five, and four coordination for Au^{III} with octahedral, trigonal bipyramidal, and planar structures, respectively. The planar one is presumably dsp^2, whereas in the five-coordinate ion the $6p$ orbital, and in the six-coordinate ion the $6p6d$ hybrid orbitals, are being used for additional bonding.

Gold alkyls were among the first organometallic compounds of transition metals to be obtained. There are several types, but the dialkyls, R_2AuX ($X = Cl^-$, Br^-, CN^-, SO_4^{2-}, etc.), are stable and the most important. Of these the halides are dimeric in solution with halogen bridges, whereas the cyanides are tetrameric, presumably owing to the impossibility of forming cyanide bridges of the type given by bridging carbon monoxide groups. The cyanides are square planar with Au←N≡C—Au bridges. Phosphine gold(I) alkyls of the type R_3PAuR' are also known.

References

There are no recent encyclopedic books on the chemistry of these elements. For references to recent work the *Annual Reports of the Chemical Society*, London, should be consulted. Gmelin's *Handbuch der Anorganischen Chemie* is a source of information in the older literature and most of the works cited at the end of Chapter 29 are appropriate here also. A few recent review articles pertaining to specific aspects of the chemistry of these elements are:

Anders, E., *Ann. Rev. Nuclear Sci.* **9,** 203 (1959). A review of technetium (and astatine) chemistry.

Aronsson, *Arkiv. Kemi*, **16,** 379 (1961). Borides and silicides of transition elements.

McMillan, J. A., *Chem. Revs.*, **62,** 65 (1962). Higher oxidation states of silver.

Nyholm, R. S., *Quart. Revs.* (London), **3,** 321 (1949). Stereochemistry of group VIII elements.

Pascal, P., Nouveau traité de chimie minérale, Vol. 14, Masson, Paris, 1959.

Ramette, R., *J. Chem. Educ.*, **37,** 348 (1960). Solubility and equilibria of silver chloride.

Woolf, A. A., *Quart. Revs. (London)*, **15,** 372 (1962). An outline of rhenium chemistry.

Zacharaisen, H., and F. E. Beamish, *Talanta*, **4,** 44 (1960). Isolation of platinum metals from partially refined concentrates.

31

The Lanthanides; Scandium
and Yttrium

31-1. Introduction

The lanthanides—or lanthanons, as they are sometimes called—are strictly the fourteen elements (Table 31-1) following lanthanum in which

TABLE 31-1

Elements of the Lanthanide Series

Atomic number	Name	Symbol	Atomic number	Name	Symbol
58	Cerium	Ce	65	Terbium	Tb
59	Praseodymium	Pr	66	Dysprosium	Dy
60	Neodymium	Nd	67	Holmium	Ho
61	Promethium	Pm	68	Erbium	Er
62	Samarium	Sm	69	Thulium	Tm
63	Europium	Eu	70	Ytterbium	Yb
64	Gadolinium	Gd	71	Lutetium	Lu

the fourteen $4f$ electrons are being successively added to the lanthanum configuration. Since the term lanthanide is used to indicate that these elements form a closely allied group, for the chemistry of which lanthanum is the prototype, the term is often taken as including lanthanum itself and will be so used here.

The chemistry of these highly electropositive elements is largely ionic and is determined by the size of the M^{3+} ion. Since yttrium, which lies above lanthanum in transition group III and has a similar $+3$ ion with an inert-gas core, has both atomic and ionic radii lying between the corresponding values for terbium and dysprosium (a fact resulting from the lanthanide "contraction" to be discussed subsequently), this element is also considered here. It is generally found in nature along with the lanthanides and resembles terbium(III) and dysprosium(III) in its compounds.

The lighter element in group III, scandium, also has only the single oxidation state Sc^{III}; the scandium ion has a smaller radius, and thus does not fall within the range of the lanthanide ion radii, so that although scandium does show some similarities to the other elements discussed here, it is sufficiently different in many details to warrant separate treatment.

31-2. Occurrence

The lanthanide elements were originally known as the Rare Earth elements from their occurrence in oxide (or in old usage, earth) mixtures. They are not, however, particularly rare elements. Substantial deposits are located in Scandinavia, India, the Soviet Union, and the United States, with a wide occurrence in smaller deposits in many other places. Many minerals make up these deposits, one of the most important being *monazite*, which usually occurs as a heavy dark sand of variable composition. Monazite is essentially a lanthanide orthophosphate, but significant amounts of thorium (up to 30%) occur in most monazite sands. The distribution of the individual lanthanides in minerals is usually such that La, Ce, Pr, and Nd make up about 90%, with yttrium and the heavier elements together constituting the remainder. Monazite and other minerals carrying lanthanides in the +3 oxidation state are usually poor in europium which, because of its relatively strong tendency to give the +2 state, is often more concentrated in the calcium group minerals. The absolute abundances of the lanthanides in the lithosphere are relatively high. Thus even the least abundant, thulium, is as common as bismuth ($\sim 2 \times 10^{-5}$ wt. %) and more common than As, Cd, Hg, or Se, elements not usually considered rare.

31-3. Promethium

Promethium, $_{61}Pm$, does not occur in nature except in vanishingly small traces as a spontaneous fission fragment of uranium in uranium ores. As early as 1926, several groups of workers reported optical and X-ray evidence for the existence of element 61 in various lanthanide concentrates, and the names Illinium, Il, and Florentium, Fl, were proposed by workers at the Universities of Illinois and Florence.

From considerations of nuclear stability systematics it is now believed that all isotopes of element 61 must be unstable with respect to β^-, β^+, or electron capture decay and have quite short half-lives. Although tracer amounts had probably been made in cyclotron bombardments previously, it was only during World War II that Coryell and co-workers at Oak Ridge were able to isolate from fission products sufficient amounts of the isotope of mass 147 to allow conclusive identification. The element was given the name Promethium, Pm; ^{147}Pm is a β^- emitter of half-life 2–6 years and milligram quantities of the pink trivalent salts have been isolated. The longest-lived isotope, ^{145}Pm, has a half-life of only 30 years.

It is convenient to note at this point that the lanthanide elements contain several naturally occurring radioisotopes, viz., ^{176}Lu (β, γ, 4.6 $\times$ 10^{10} years), ^{138}La (K, β^-, $\sim$2 $\times$ 10^{11} years), ^{144}Nd (α, $\sim$5 $\times$ 10^{15} years), ^{147}Sm (α, 1.14 $\times$ 10^{11} years).

31-4. Electronic Structures; Oxidation States

In the general introduction to the discussion of transition elements (page 493), the position of the lanthanides in the periodic table was explained and the reasons for their occurrence in this position in terms of

TABLE 31-2

Outer Electronic Structures of Lanthanide Atoms and Ions[a,b]

Element	Atom	M^{2+}	M^{3+}	M^{4+}
La	$5d6s^2$	—	[Xe]	—
Ce	$4f^26s^2$	—	$4f$	[Xe]
Pr	$4f^36s^2$	—	$4f^2$	$4f$
Nd	$4f^46s^2$	$4f^4$	$4f^3$	$4f^2$
Pm	$4f^56s^2$	—	$4f^4$	—
Sm	$4f^66s^2$	$4f^6$	$4f^5$	—
Eu	$4f^76s^2$	$4f^7$	$4f^6$	—
Gd	$4f^75d6s^2$	—	$4f^7$	—
Tb	$4f^96s^2$	—	$4f^8$	$4f^7$
Dy	$4f^{10}6s^2$	—	$4f^9$	$4f^8$
Ho	$4f^{11}6s^2$	—	$4f^{10}$	—
Er	$4f^{12}6s^2$	—	$4f^{11}$	—
Tm	$4f^{13}6s^2$	$4f^{13}$	$4f^{12}$	—
Yb	$4f^{14}6s^2$	$4f^{14}$	$4f^{13}$	—
Lu	$4f^{14}5d6s^2$	—	$4f^{14}$	—

[a] Only the valence shell electrons, that is, those outside of the [Xe] shell, are given.
[b] A dash indicates that this oxidation state is not known in any isolable compounds.

their electronic structures given. The explicit electronic structures, not given previously, are shown in Table 31-2, along with the electronic configurations of the various known lanthanide ions. It should be remembered that not all of these electronic configurations are known with complete certainty owing to the great complexity of the electronic spectra of the atoms and ions and the attendant difficulty of analysis.

All of the lanthanides form M^{3+} ions and so do Sc and Y, which have the atomic structures $[Ar]3d4s^2$ and $[Kr]4d5s^2$, respectively. For several of the lanthanides other oxidation states occur although these are always less stable than the characteristic group valency. To a certain extent, the occurrence of the oxidation states $+2$ and $+4$ can be correlated with the electronic structures if we assume that there is a special stability associated with an empty, half-filled or filled f shell just as, to a lesser degree, the same phenomenon is seen in the regular transition series (notably, Mn^{2+}), in the ionization potentials of the first short period (cf. Fig. 7-1), etc. Thus Sc, Y, and La form only the M^{3+} ions since removal of three electrons leaves the inert-gas configuration. Lutetium and Gd form only the tripositive ions since the latter then have the stable $4f^{14}$ and $4f^7$ configurations, respectively. In all of these five cases, removal of *less* than three electrons under chemical conditions does not occur because the M^{2+} or M^+ ions would be so much larger than the M^{3+} ions that the energy saved in the ionization step would be less than the additional lattice or hydration energies of the salts of the small M^{3+} ions as compared with the lattice or hydration energies of the M^{2+} or M^+ ions.

The most stable di- and tetrapositive ions are formed by elements which can attain the f^0, f^7, and f^{14} configurations by so doing. Thus cerium and terbium attain the f^0 and f^7 configurations, respectively, by going to the IV oxidation state, whereas europium and ytterbium have the f^7 and f^{14} configurations, respectively, in the II oxidation state. These facts seem to support the view that "special stability" of the f^0, f^7 and f^{14} configurations is important in determining the existence of oxidation states other than III for the lanthanides. This argument becomes less convincing however when we note that samarium and thulium give M^{2+} species having f^6 and f^{13} configurations but no M^+ ions, whereas praseodymium and neodymium give M^{4+} ions with configurations f^1 and f^2 but no penta- or hexavalent species. Admittedly, the Sm^{II} and especially Tm^{II}, Pr^{IV}, and Nd^{IV} states are very unstable indeed, but the idea that stability is favored even by the mere *approach* to an f^0, f^7, or f^{14} configuration, even though such a configuration is not actually attained, is of dubious validity. The existence of Nd^{2+}, f^4, provides particularly cogent evidence for believing that although the special stability of f^0, f^7, f^{14} may be one factor, there are other thermo-dynamic and kinetic factors which are of equal or greater importance in determining the stability of oxidation states.

31-5. Magnetic and Spectral Properties

In several aspects, the magnetic and spectral behavior of the lanthanides is fundamentally different from that of the d-block transition elements. The basic reason for the differences lies in the fact that the electrons responsible for the magnetic and spectral properties of lanthanide ions are $4f$ electrons, and the $4f$ orbitals are very effectively shielded from interaction with external forces by the overlying $6s^2$ and $6p^6$ shells. Hence the states arising from the various $4f^n$ configurations are only slightly affected by the sur-

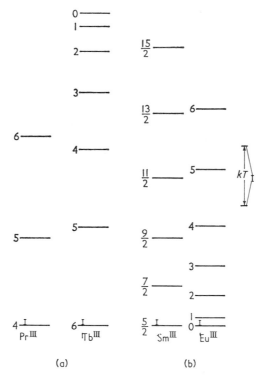

(a)   (b)

Fig. 31-1. J states for several trivalent lanthanides: (a) two of the several cases where the J states are widely separated compared to kT and (b) the two cases where the separations are of the same order as or less than kT.

roundings of the ions and remain practically invariant for a given ion in all of its compounds.

The states of the $4f^n$ configurations are all given, to a useful approximation, by the Russell-Saunders coupling scheme (Chapter 24, page 501). In addition, the spin-orbit coupling constants are quite large (order of 1000 cm.$^{-1}$). The result of all this is that, with only a few exceptions, the lanthanide ions have ground states with a single well-defined value of the total angular momentum, J, with the next lowest J state at energies many times kT (at ordinary temperatures equal to $\sim$200 cm.$^{-1}$) above and hence virtually unpopulated (Fig. 31-1a). Thus the susceptibilities and magnetic moments should be given straightforwardly by formulas considering only this one well-defined J state, and indeed such calculations give results which are, with only two exceptions, in excellent agreement with experimental values (Fig. 31-2). For Sm^{3+} and Eu^{3+}, it turns out that the first excited J

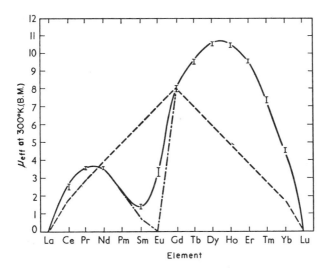

Fig. 31-2.   Measured and calculated effective magnetic moments (B.M.) of lanthanide M^{3+} ions at 300°K. I's are ranges of experimental values; ———— give values calculated for appropriate J ground states and allowing for the Sm and Eu anomalies; —·—·— gives values calculated without allowing for the Sm and Eu anomalies; – – – – – was calculated spin-only values.

state is sufficiently close to the ground state (Fig. 31-1b) that this state (and in the case of Eu^{3+} even the second and third excited states) is appreciably populated at ordinary temperatures. Since these excited states have higher J values than the ground state, the actual magnetic moments are higher than those calculated considering the ground states only. Calculations taking into account the population of excited states afford results in excellent agreement with experiment (Fig. 31-2).

It should be emphasized that magnetic behavior depending on J values is qualitatively different from that depending on S values—that is the "spin-only" behavior—which gives a fair approximation for many of the regular transition elements. Only for the f^0, f^7, and f^{14} cases, where there is no orbital angular momentum ($J = S$), do the two treatments give the same answer. For the lanthanides the external fields do not either appreciably split the free ion terms or quench the orbital angular momentum.

Because the f orbitals are so well shielded from the surroundings of the ions, the various states arising from the f^n configurations are split by external fields only to the extent of ~ 100 cm.$^{-1}$ (into $(2J + 1)$ or $(J + \frac{1}{2})$ sublevels, depending on whether J is integral or half-integral). Thus when electronic transitions, called f–f transitions, occur from one J state of an f^n configuration to another J state of this configuration, the absorption bands are extremely sharp. They are similar to those for free atoms and are quite unlike those for the d–d transitions. Virtually all of the absorption bands found in the visible and near-ultraviolet spectra of the lanthanide ions have this line-like character. There are, however, bands found in some cases which are quite broad; these may be assigned to transitions in which an f electron is excited to an outer d, s, or p orbital. Since these outer levels *are* very much broadened by external fields, the breadth of the absorption bands due to such transitions is attributable to the breadth of these upper states.

31-6. The Lanthanide Contraction

The lanthanide contraction has been alluded to previously in discussing the elements of the third transition series, since it has certain important effects on their properties. It consists of a significant and steady decrease in the size of the atoms and ions with increasing atomic number; that is, lanthanum has the greatest, and lutetium the smallest, radius (see Table 31-3). Note that the radius of La^{3+} is about 0.18 A. larger than that of Y^{3+}, so that if the fourteen lanthanide elements did not intervene we might have expected Hf^{4+} to have a radius ~ 0.2 A. greater than that of Zr^{4+}. Instead, the lanthanide contraction, amounting to 0.21 A., almost exactly wipes out this expected increase and results in almost identical radii for Hf^{4+} and Zr^{4+}, as noted previously.

The cause of the lanthanide contraction is the same as the cause of the less spectacular contractions which occur in the d-block transition series,

TABLE 31-3

Radii of Trivalent Lanthanide Ions, A.

Element	Radius	Δr	Element	Radius	Δr
Y	0.98		Gd	0.938	0.012
La	1.061		Tb	0.923	0.015
Ce	1.034	0.027	Dy	0.908	0.015
Pr	1.013	0.021	Ho	0.894	0.014
Nd	0.995	0.018	Er	0.881	0.013
Pm	0.979	0.016	Tm	0.869	0.012
Sm	0.964	0.015	Yb	0.858	0.011
Eu	0.950	0.014	Lu	0.848	0.010

namely, the imperfect shielding of one electron by another in the same subshell. As we proceed through the lanthanide series, the nuclear charge and the number of $4f$ electrons increases by one at each step. The shielding of one $4f$ electron by another is quite imperfect (much more so than with d electrons) owing to the shapes of the orbitals, so that at each increase the effective nuclear charge experienced by each $4f$ electron increases, thus causing a reduction in size of the entire $4f^n$ shell. The accumulation of these successive contractions is the total lanthanide contraction.

It should be noted also that the decrease, though steady, is not quite regular, the biggest decreases occurring with the first f electrons added; there also appears to be a larger decrease after f^7, that is between Tb and Gd. Some physical properties of lanthanide compounds sometimes show similar divergences from regularity as a consequence of the ionic size; thus for ion exchange elution there is a break in the regularity in the separations between Gd and Tb, and, in the extraction of lanthanides from strong nitric acid solutions by tributyl phosphate in carbon tetrachloride, there are changes in the distribution constants at Gd. A half-filled shell effect has also been noted from stabilities of lanthanide complexes of ethylenediaminetetraacetic acid.

31-7. The Metals

In recent years all of the metals have been obtained in a state of high purity. The lighter ones (La, Ce, Pr, Nd, Gd) are obtained by reduction of the trichlorides with calcium, at 1000°C. or more, whereas for the heavier ones (Tb, Dy, Ho, Er, Tm, and also Y) the trifluorides are used because the chlorides are too volatile. Eu, Sm, and Yb trichlorides are reduced only to the dihalides by calcium, but the metals can be prepared by reduction of the sesquioxides, M_2O_3, with lanthanum at high temperatures.

The metals are silvery white and very reactive. They tarnish readily in air and all burn easily to give the sesquioxides except cerium, which gives CeO_2. They combine rather easily between room temperature and about 250°C. with hydrogen to give stable MH_2 and MH_3 phases, which usually occur in a defect condition. The MH_2 phases have a fluorite structure and are thus salt-like, if not entirely ionic, hydrides rather than interstitial ones. These hydrides react readily with oxygen and water. The metals also react readily with carbon, nitrogen, silicon, phosphorus, sulfur, halogens, and other nonmetals at elevated temperatures. They all react directly with water, slowly in the cold, rapidly on heating, to liberate hydrogen. Their high oxidation potentials (Table 31-4) are in accord with their electropositive character.

TABLE 31-4

Oxidation Potentials of the Lanthanides
$(M = M^{3+}(aq) + 3e)$

Element	E^0, v.	Element	E^0, v.
La	2.52	Tb	2.39
Ce	2.48	(Y	2.37)
Pr	2.47	Dy	2.35
Nd	2.44	Ho	2.32
Pm	2.42	Er	2.30
Sm	2.41	Tm	2.28
Eu	2.41	Yb	2.27
Gd	2.40	Lu	2.25
		(Sc	1.88)

It is interesting that the atomic volumes, densities, and some other properties of the metals change smoothly except for Eu and Yb, and occasionally Sm and Tm. For example, Figure 31-3 shows a plot of atomic volumes and heats of vaporization. It is obvious that the deviations occur with just those lanthanides which have the greatest tendency to exist in the divalent state. Presumably these elements tend to donate only two electrons to the conduction bands of the metal, thus leaving larger cores and affording lower binding forces.

It may also be noted that europium and ytterbium metals dissolve in liquid ammonia at −78°C. to give characteristic blue solutions (cf. the alkalies and alkaline earths), but samarium is insoluble.

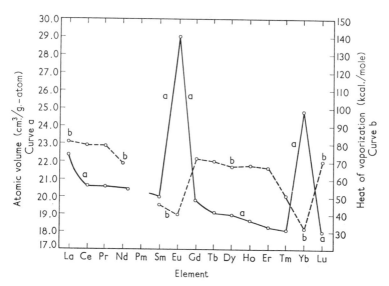

Fig. 31-3.   The atomic volumes (curve a) and heats of vaporization (curve b) of the lanthanide metals.

CHEMISTRY OF THE TRIVALENT LANTHANIDES AND YTTRIUM

31-8. General Chemistry

The trivalent state is the characteristic one for all of the lanthanides. They form *oxides*, M_2O_3, which resemble the Ca, Sr, Ba group oxides and absorb carbon dioxide and water from the air to form carbonates and hydroxides, respectively. The *hydroxides*, $M(OH)_3$, are definite compounds, having hexagonal structures, and not merely hydrous oxides. The basicity of the hydroxides decreases with increasing atomic number as would be expected because of the decrease in ionic radius. The hydroxides are precipitated from aqueous solutions by ammonia or dilute alkalies as gelatinous precipitates. They are not amphoteric.

Among the *halides*, the fluorides are of particular importance because of their insolubility. Addition of hydrofluoric acid or fluoride ions precipitates the fluorides from lanthanide ion solutions even $3M$ in nitric acid and is a characteristic test for lanthanide ions. The fluorides, particularly of the heavier lanthanides, are slightly soluble in excess HF owing to complex formation. They may be redissolved in $3N$ nitric acid saturated with boric acid which removes F^- as BF_4^-. The chlorides are soluble in water, from which they crystallize as hydrates. The anhydrous chlorides cannot easily be obtained from the hydrates because these lose hydrochloric acid on heating—to give the oxychlorides, $MOCl$—more readily than they lose water. (Scandium and cerium give Sc_2O_3 and CeO_2, respectively, however.) The anhydrous chlorides are best made by heating oxides (or oxalates, etc.) with ammonium chloride at about 300°C.

$$M_2O_3 + 6NH_4Cl = 2MCl_3 + 3H_2O + 6NH_3$$

The bromides and iodides are rather similar to the chlorides.

Lanthanide *salts of most oxy acids*—sulfates, nitrates, perchlorates, bromates, etc.—are known. They are generally soluble and crystallize as hydrates. The carbonates, phosphates, and oxalates are insoluble, and precipitation of the oxalates from dilute nitric acid solution is a quantitative and fairly specific separation procedure for the lanthanides; lanthanides can be determined gravimetrically in this way.

Double salts are very common, the most important ones being the double nitrates and double sulfates, such as $2M(NO_3)_3 \cdot 3Mg(NO_3)_2 \cdot 24H_2O$, $M(NO_3)_3 \cdot 2NH_4NO_3 \cdot 4H_2O$ and $M_2(SO_4)_3 \cdot 3Na_2SO_4 \cdot 12H_2O$. The solubilities of double sulfates of the latter type fall into two rough classes: the cerium group, La–Eu, and the yttrium group, Gd–Lu and Y. Those of the cerium group are only sparingly soluble in sodium sulfate, whereas those of the yttrium group are appreciably soluble. Thus a fairly rapid separation of the entire group of lanthanides into two main groups is possible. Various of the double nitrates were used in the past for further separations by fractional crystallization procedures.

The lanthanides form many well defined compounds with nonmetals and metalloids other than oxygen and halogens. The general preparation of all of these compounds is by direct combination of the elements at elevated temperatures. Among these are sulfides, M_2S_3 (not of europium, however), selenides, M_2Se_3, and oxysulfides, M_2O_2S. Nitrides, phosphides, arsenides, antimonides, and bismuthides, MN, MP, MAs, MSb, and MBi, crystallize in the $NaCl$ structure. Borides of the types MB_6 and MB_4 are well characterized as are the carbides, MC_2, and hydride phases MH_2 and MH_3. There are certain differences occasionally through the lanthanides; thus the carbide, M_3C, which has a c.c.p. type lattice except that it is deficient in carbon is found for the elements Sm–Lu, inclusive, but not for La, Ce, Pr or Nd.

The aqueous M^{3+} ions are slightly hydrolyzed according to

$$[M(H_2O)_n]^{3+} + H_2O = [M(H_2O)_{n-1}(OH)]^{2+} + H_3O^+$$

and the tendency to hydrolysis increases with increasing atomic number as would be expected from the contraction in radii.

The lanthanides form few complexes, and these are mostly with oxygen compounds. This is due in part to the unavailability of the f orbitals to form hybrid orbitals which might lead to covalent bond strength, and also to the fact that the lanthanide ions are rather large (radii 0.85–1.06) compared with those of the transition elements (e.g., Cr^{3+} and Fe^{3+} with radii of 0.60–0.65 A.), which lowers electrostatic forces of attraction. The only stable complexes which are at all common or important are those with chelate ligands. β-Diketones such as acetylacetone (31-I), dibenzoylmethane

(3I–I): $R_1 = R_2 = CH_3$
(3I–II): $R_1 = R_2 = C_6H_5$
(3I–III): $R_1 = CF_3$; $R_2 = $ (thienyl group)

(31-II), and thenoyltrifluoroacetone, TTA (31-III), form neutral complexes of type 31-IV, which are insoluble in water but soluble in organic solvents. The lanthanides can also be extracted from aqueous solution into organic solvents using certain complexing agents, such as tributyl phos-

(31 – IV)

phate in the presence of concentrated hydrochloric acid. Chelate ligands giving water-soluble complexes are polyfunctional organic acids and hydroxy acids such as tartaric, $HOOC(CHOH)_2COOH$, and citric, $HOOCCH_2$—$C(OH)(COOH)$—CH_2COOH, and various amino acids of the types $RN(CH_2COOH)_2$, $N(CH_2COOH)_3$, (NTA, nitrilotriacetic acid), and $(HOOCCH_2)_2NCH_2CH_2N(CH_2COOH)_2$ (EDTA).

Since the lanthanides are so highly electropositive, they have little or no tendency to form complexes with π-bonding ligands and none are known. Organo compounds similarly are not known with the exception of the thermally very stable but air-sensitive cyclopentadienides, $(C_5H_5)_3M$. The latter are ionic and have magnetic moments similar to the M^{3+} ions themselves; although they sublime in vacuum at $\sim 200°C$., presumably as molecules, their structures are not known.

31-9. Separation of the Lanthanides

Prior to the advent of ion exchange techniques, separation of the rare earths was an extraordinarily laborious task even on a small scale. For many years the only techniques used were fractional crystallization, most commonly of double sulfates, fractional precipitation, or fractional decomposition, but these were later supplemented by procedures involving the removal of cerium as Ce^{IV} and europium, samarium, and ytterbium in their divalent states. All such procedures, except in special cases (notably the removal of europium) have been rendered obsolete by ion exchange resin separations developed during 1941–46 and perfected for use on a large scale in the following decade. Although the chemistries of all the lanthanides in the III oxidation state are almost identical, there are of course slight quantitative differences, and these vary systematically from La through Lu (Y being placed approximately between Dy and Ho). The ion exchange separation is based upon the fact that the steady decrease in size and consequent decrease in basicity means that there is a steady increase with increasing atomic number in the binding of ligands. The first consequence of this is that the *hydrated* radii of the lanthanide(III) ions increase with increasing atomic number; since the binding of cations to the anionic sites of the exchange resin seems to involve electrostatic attraction of the hydrated cation by the negative site, it is found that the larger the hydrated radius of the ion, the less strongly it is bound. Thus this effect alone tends to give a separation of the lanthanide(III) ions when a solution containing several of them passes slowly through a column of a cation exchange resin, with the heavier members coming through first. This situation may be expressed using equilibria of the type

$$3H^+_R + M^{3+}(aq) = M^{3+}_R + 3H^+(aq) \qquad K = \frac{[H^+(aq)]^3}{[H^+_R]^3} \cdot \frac{[M^{3+}_R]}{[M^{3+}(aq)]}$$

where H^+_R and M^{3+}_R represent hydrogen ions and lanthanide ions bound to the resin, and the constants decrease with increasing atomic number of the lanthanide because $[M^{3+}_R]/[M^{3+}(aq)]$ decreases.

The separation obtainable because of differing preferences of the hydrated cations for the exchange resin can be significantly enhanced by the use of complexing agents, citric acid and citrates being commonly used in the laboratory as the aqueous eluting agents. Just as the smaller radius of the heavier of two lanthanide ions will cause it to have the larger hydrated radius and hence the smaller tendency to be held by the resin, its smaller radius will cause it to form stronger complexes thus positively enhancing its preference for the aqueous phase. Figure 31-4 shows the manner in

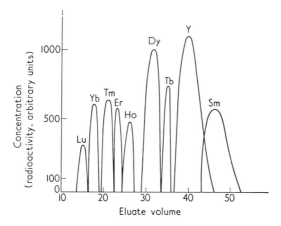

Fig. 31-4. A typical elution curve of lanthanide ions using buffered ammonium citrate solution as eluate. The eluate volume is given by number of sample tube from a rotary sample collector; the concentrations were measured by radioactive counting of tracers.

which the various lanthanides come off a cation exchange resin using an appropriately buffered citrate solution for elution. Further discussion of ion exchange procedures for both lanthanide and actinide elements appears on page 922.

Elaborate large-scale column techniques now allow the separation in a very pure state of kilogram quantities of the lanthanides, which are commercially available.

Although cerium(IV) nitrate (and other +4 nitrates such as those of Zr, Th, and Pu) is readily extracted from nitric acid solutions by tributyl phosphate dissolved in kerosene or other inert solvent and can thus be readily separated from the +3 lanthanide ions, the trivalent lanthanide nitrates can also be extracted under suitable conditions. Extractability under given conditions increases with increasing atomic number; it is higher in strong acid or high nitrate concentrations.

THE CHEMISTRY OF SCANDIUM

Scandium, with an electron configuration [Ar]$3d4s^2$, is a congener of aluminum, but is decidedly more basic in its properties; it is in many respects quite similar to yttrium and the lanthanides, although the distinctly smaller radius of the scandium(III) ion, $\sim$0.7 A., compared to a range of 0.85–1.06 for yttrium and the lanthanides) makes for some differences in chemistry. It is not a rare element, being as common as arsenic and twice as abundant as boron, but its chemistry is not on the whole well known. This is due partly to the absence of rich sources of the element and also to the difficulty (until recently) of obtaining it in a pure state. Scandium manifests only the III oxidation state in which it gives the oxide, Sc_2O_3, halides, ScX_3, and oxyhalides, $ScOX$, as well as numerous salts of oxy acids. The possibility of there being a dipositive oxidation state has been rather carefully examined and there is no evidence for its existence.

The scandium ion, being smaller, has a much greater tendency to hydrolysis than the lanthanide ions, and polymeric species of the type 31-V

$$\left[Sc(\underset{OH}{\overset{OH}{<}}>Sc)_n \right]^{(n+3)+}$$

(31-Ⅴ)

have been shown to arise with chain length increasing as pH increases. It is perhaps to be expected that, since it is closely related to both aluminum and the elements of the first transition series, scandium ion forms complexes far more readily than do the lanthanides.

Some significant differences between the chemistries of scandium and the trivalent lanthanides are the following:

1. Scandium forms a double sulfate $K_2SO_4 \cdot Sc_2(SO_4)_3 \cdot nH_2O$ which is very insoluble in K_2SO_4 solution. It can also be precipitated as potassium double fluoride, as ammonium double tartrate, or by disodium hydrogen phosphate,

2. In presence of thiocyanate ion, it gives a yellow thiocyanate, $Sc(NCS)_3$, which can be extracted into ether.

3. The thenoyltrifluoroacetone (TTA) complex of scandium may be extracted from aqueous solutions into excess TTA in a solvent such as benzene at pH's of 1.5–2.0, unlike the corresponding lanthanide complexes. Solvent extraction of the scandium oxine chelate by chloroform can also be made quantitative in one operation. Scandium acetylacetonate may be sublimed ($\sim$200°C.), whereas acetylacetonates of the lanthanides are pyrolyzed.

4. Scandium does not appear to form a definite hydroxide, but only

a hydrous oxide, $Sc_2O_3 \cdot nH_2O$, although a definite hydrated oxide containing OH is known, namely ScO(OH), which is similar in structure to AlO(OH). The "hydroxide" readily dissolves in concentrated NaOH and $Na_3[Sc(OH)_6] \cdot 2H_2O$ can be crystallized; this complex hydrolyzes at NaOH concentrations less than $8M$. Scandium oxide is more basic than aluminum oxide but less so than those of the lanthanides. If the oxide is heated with Li_2O or Na_2O, the readily hydrolyzed salts $Li(Na)ScO_2$ are formed.

Scandium resembles the lanthanides in many ways, of course, having, for instance, an insoluble oxalate, phosphate, carbonate, and fluoride. The fluoride, however, is readily soluble in excess HF or NH_4F and definite fluoro complexes, $ScF_6{}^{3-}$, exist. The chloride, $ScCl_3$, sublimes at a much lower temperature than the lanthanide chlorides, but is monomeric in the vapor and has no activity as a Friedel-Crafts catalyst (unlike volatile Al_2Cl_6).

THE IV OXIDATION STATE

31-10. Cerium(IV)

This is the only tetrapositive lanthanide species sufficiently stable to exist in aqueous solution as well as in solid compounds. The terms ceric and cerous are commonly used to designate the IV and III valence states of cerium. The only known binary, solid compounds of Ce^{IV} are the oxide, CeO_2, the hydrous oxide, $CeO_2 \cdot nH_2O$, and the fluoride, CeF_4. CeO_2, white when pure, is obtained by heating cerium metal, $Ce(OH)_3$, or any of several Ce^{III} salts of oxy acids such as the oxalate, carbonate, or nitrate in air or oxygen. It is a rather inert substance, not attacked by either strong acids or alkalies. It can, however, be dissolved by acids in the presence of reducing agents (H_2O_2, Sn^{2+}, etc.) giving then Ce^{III} solutions. Hydrous ceric oxide, $CeO_2 \cdot nH_2O$, is a yellow, gelatinous precipitate obtained on treating Ce^{IV} solutions with bases. It redissolves fairly easily in acids. CeF_4 is prepared by treating anhydrous $CeCl_3$ or CeF_3 with fluorine at room temperature; it is relatively inert to cold water and is reduced to CeF_3 by hydrogen at 200–300°C.

Ce^{IV} in solution is obtained by treatment of Ce^{III} solutions with very powerful oxidizing agents, for example, peroxydisulfate or bismuthate in nitric acid. The general aqueous chemistry of Ce^{IV} is similar to that of Zr, Hf, and, particularly, tetravalent actinides. Thus Ce^{IV} gives phosphates insoluble in $4N$ HNO_3 and iodates insoluble in $6N$ HNO_3, as well as an insoluble oxalate. The phosphate and iodate precipitations can be used to separate Ce^{IV} from the trivalent lanthanides. Ce^{IV} is also much more readily extracted into organic solvents by tributyl phosphate and similar extractants than are the M^{III} lanthanide ions.

The very highly charged Ce^{4+} ion has a pronounced tendency to hydrate, and the hydrated ion, $[Ce(H_2O)_n]^{4+}$, is a fairly strong acid. Thus, except at very low pH, hydrolysis and polymerization of ceric ion are considerable. It is probable that the $[Ce(H_2O)_n]^{4+}$ ion exists only in concentrated perchloric acid solution, since perchlorate ion has virtually no tendency to coordinate. In other acid media coordination of anions doubtless occurs. This affords an explanation of the dependence of the oxidation potential of Ce^{III} on the nature of the acid medium, as shown by the following figures:

$$Ce^{III} = Ce^{IV} + e \qquad E^0 = -1.28 \ (2M \ HCl), \ -1.44 \ (1M \ H_2SO_4),$$
$$-1.61 \ (1M \ HNO_3), \ -1.70 \ (1M \ HClO_4)$$

Cerium(IV) forms double salts readily, the best-known one being ceric ammonium nitrate, $Ce(NO_3)_4 \cdot 2NH_4NO_3$, which can be crystallized from nitric acid solutions. Although many complex cationic and anionic Ce^{IV} species are doubtless present in solution, few have been isolated. Whether complex anions are present in many double salts, for example, $Ce(NO_3)_6^{2-}$ in the one mentioned above, is uncertain. Although concentrated aqueous HCl is oxidized to Cl_2 by Ce^{IV}, the reaction of CeO_2 with HCl in dioxane gives orange needles of the dioxanate of hexachloroceric acid, $H_2CeCl_6 \cdot 4C_4H_8O_2$. The pyridinium salt is also known and is stable enough to be dried in vacuum at 120°C.

This pyridinium salt is used to prepare ceric alkoxides,

$$(C_5H_5NH)_2CeCl_6 + 4ROH + 6NH_3 = Ce(OR)_4 + 2C_5H_5N + 6NH_4Cl$$

The isopropoxide is a crystalline solid, subliming in vacuum at 170°C., but other alkoxides, prepared from the isopropyl compound by alcohol exchange, are nonvolatile and presumably polymerized by Ce—O(R)—Ce bridges.

31-11. Praseodymium(IV)

Praseodymium(IV) is known only in a few solid compounds. The Pr–O system has a very complex phase diagram. On heating praseodymium salts in air a black material having the approximate composition Pr_6O_{11} is obtained; this is believed to be $Pr_{32}O_{58}$ or $Pr_{32}O_{59}$ with some vacant oxygen sites like the intermediate oxides of Tb (Section 31-12) and derived from the $M_{32}O_{64}$ unit cell structure. PrO_2 can be obtained by heating finely divided $PrO_n (n < 2)$ with oxygen at 100 atm. at 500°C. for 8–12 hours. This oxide has a fluorite structure. Even using ozone, no Pr—O compound containing

Pr beyond the IV state has been obtained. PrF_4 is not obtained by fluorination of PrF_3, but in mixed systems Pr^{IV} can be obtained by fluorination. For example, the compounds $NaPrF_5$, Na_2PrF_6, K_2PrF_6, Rb_2PrF_6, and Cs_2PrF_6 are obtained when alkali fluorides, mixed in correct stoichiometric ratio with praseodymium salts, are treated with fluorine gas at 300–500°C. The tetravalence of Pr in these compounds has been firmly established by magnetic, spectral, and X-ray data.

Pr^{IV} is a very powerful oxidizing agent; a value of -2.9 v. has been estimated for the potential of the reaction

$$Pr^{III}(aq) = Pr^{IV}(aq) + e$$

This potential is such that Pr^{IV} would oxidize water itself so that its nonexistence in solution is not surprising. Pr_6O_{11} dissolves in acids to give aqueous Pr^{III} and to liberate oxygen, chlorine, etc., depending on the acid used.

31-12. Terbium(IV)

The chemistry of terbium(IV) appears to resemble that of Pr^{IV}, although it is rather less known. The Tb–O system is complex. When terbium or its common oxy acid salts are ignited under ordinary conditions, an oxide of approximately the composition Tb_4O_7 is obtained. Actually, this formula ($TbO_{1.75}$) is not the correct formula for the stable phase obtained, but is the nearest approach, using small whole numbers, to the true formula, which may be anywhere from $TbO_{1.71}$ to $TbO_{1.81}$ depending on details of ignition temperature, oxygen pressure, and rate of cooling. Thus nonstoichiometry is characteristic of this system. For the average formula Tb_4O_7, Tb^{III} and Tb^{IV} are present in equal amounts. TbO_2, with a fluorite structure, can be obtained by oxidation of Tb_2O_3 with atomic oxygen at 450°C. Colorless TbF_4, isostructural with CeF_4 and ThF_4, is obtained by reacting gaseous fluorine with TbF_3 at 300–400°C. Also, compounds of the type M_nTbF_{n+4}($M = K$, Rb, or Cs; $n \geqslant 2$) have been reported, but not yet fully described. No numerical estimate has been given for the Tb^{III}–Tb^{IV} potential, but it must be as negative as the potential for the Pr^{III}–Pr^{IV} couple, since dissolution of any oxide containing Tb^{IV} gives only Tb^{III} in solution and oxygen is evolved. TbF_4 is even less reactive than CeF_4 and does not react rapidly even with hot water.

31-13. Neodymium(IV) and Dysprosium(IV)

Although there are many reports in the literature of the preparation of higher oxides of these elements, supposedly containing Nd^{IV} and Dy^{IV}, recent studies leave little doubt that these claims are erroneous. Even treatment of Nd_2O_3 with atomic oxygen gave no Nd^{IV}-containing product. Only in the products of fluorination of mixtures of RbCl and CsCl with $NdCl_3$ and $DyCl_3$ is there fair evidence for the existence of Nd^{IV} and Dy^{IV}. Apparently such compounds as Cs_3NdF_7 and $CsDyF_7$ can be formed, at least partially, in this way.

THE II OXIDATION STATE

31-14. Europium(II)

Of the five divalent species given by the lanthanides, Eu^{II} is by far the most stable. This is reflected, for example, in the potential of the Eu^{II}–Eu^{III} couple, 0.43 v. Aqueous solutions of Eu^{II}, which are colorless, are obtained by treating Eu^{III} solutions with various reducing agents such as magnesium, aluminum, iron, or zinc, and the reduction may also be carried out electrolytically at a mercury cathode. The solid halides are usually made by reducing the solid trihalides with hydrogen or ammonia or by thermal decomposition,

$$EuI_3 \rightarrow EuI_2 + \tfrac{1}{2}I_2(g)$$

Other salts can be made by metathetical reactions with the halides.

A large number of compounds containing Eu^{II} are known, including the halides, the sulfate, phosphate, perchlorate, hydroxide, carbonate, oxide, sulfide, selenide, and telluride. The structures of many of these have been studied, and in most cases isomorphism with other M^{II} salts, especially Ba and Sr salts, is found. Eu^{II} ion has a crystallographic radius of about 1.10 A. (cf. Eu^{III} with $r = 0.95$ A.). The oxide, sulfide, selenide, and telluride have the rock salt structure as do many $M^{II}O$ compounds. $EuSO_4$ is isostructural with $BaSO_4$. $EuCl_2$ is isostructural with $PdCl_2$, as is $NdCl_2$ (see below); $EuBr_2$ is isostructural with $SrBr_2$, but EuI_2 is not isostructural with SrI_2 and its structure is not known in detail.

Eu^{II} in solution is a mild reducing agent, but otherwise similar in its chemistry to barium. The hydroxide is soluble in water, and the other lanthanides can be separated from Eu^{II} by precipitation of their hydroxides with carbonate-free ammonia; alternatively, europous sulfate can be precipitated and removed.

31-15. Samarium(II)

Sm^{II} is much less stable than Eu^{II} and less stable even than Yb^{II}. The most recent estimates of its oxidation potential give a value of about 1.55 v., which accords with its behavior as a very powerful reducing agent; indeed, aqueous solutions are not stable because water is reduced by Sm^{II}. Aqueous solutions containing blood-red Sm^{II} are prepared by treating aqueous Sm^{III} with alkali metal amalgams or electrolytically. The divalent halides are obtained by reduction of anhydrous Sm^{III} halides with hydrogen or ammonia at high temperatures. SmI_2 but not the other dihalides can be obtained by thermal decomposition of the Sm^{III} compound. Other compounds may be obtained by metathetical reactions of aqueous solutions of the halides. All compounds of Sm^{II} are thermodynamically unstable with respect to oxidation by water or oxygen but are stable indefinitely in an inert atmosphere.

A number of compounds of Sm^{II} are known including the halides, sulfate, chromate, phosphate, hydroxide, carbonate, and oxide, and the structures of some of these are known. The ionic radius of Sm^{II} is about 1.11 A. SmO has the rock salt structure. SmF_2 has the fluorite structure but readily dissolves SmF_3 and is thus difficult to obtain pure. $SmCl_2$ and $SmBr_2$ are isostructural with $SrCl_2$ and $SrBr_2$, while SmI_2 is isostructural with EuI_2 but not with SrI_2. $SmSO_4$ and $SmCO_3$ are isostructural with the corresponding barium compounds.

In their chemical as well as structural properties, Sm^{II} compounds resemble those of barium insofar as the strongly reducing character of Sm^{II} permits comparisons.

31-16. Ytterbium(II)

The green Yb^{II} ion is a powerful reducing agent and is rapidly oxidized by water in aqueous solution. Its oxidation potential appears to be about 1.15 v. according to the most recent estimates.

Yb^{II} is in general more stable than Sm^{II}, but distinctly less so than Eu^{II}. It has been prepared in aqueous solution mainly by electrolytic reduction of Yb^{III} at mercury or amalgamated lead cathodes or by electrolysis with a lithium amalgam.

Among the solid compounds known are the halides, sulfate, carbonate, oxide, sulfide, selenide, and telluride. Methods of preparation are analogous to those described above for corresponding Eu^{II} and Sm^{II} compounds. Solid Yb^{II} salts are stable in the absence of air and water. The oxide, selenide, and telluride have the NaCl structure and the carbonate is isostructural with $BaCO_3$. The sulfate has a structure like $CePO_4$. The fluoride has a fluorite structure, but, like EuF_2 and SmF_2, it dissolves the trifluoride extensively and pure YbF_2 has probably never been obtained. The structures of $YbCl_2$ and $YbBr_2$ are not known in detail; YbI_2 is isostructural with CdI_2. The ionic radius of Yb^{II} is about 0.93 A.

31-17. Thulium(II) and Neodymium(II)

These species are very unstable and of very rare occurrence. Definite evidence for their existence has been obtained only recently. Although there had been some inconclusive evidence for Tm^{II}, the preparation of the iodide, in 1959, by reduction of TmI_3 with Tm at 500–600°C. represents the only unequivocal evidence for the occurrence of Tm^{II}. The iodide has, like YbI_2, the CdI_2 structure. Tm^{II} is a very powerful reducing agent, reacting violently with water, and its oxidation potential is believed to be in excess of 1.5 v.

Nd^{II} was completely unknown, and, as noted in Section 31-4, unexpected until in 1959 the preparation of $NdCl_2$ and NdI_2, in each case by reduction of the trihalide with Nd, was reported. Actually, the dihalides do not exist at equilibrium at lower temperatures and are isolated by rapidly quenching a high temperature system. Like $SmCl_2$ and $EuCl_2$, $NdCl_2$ has a $PbCl_2$ structure; the structure of NdI_2 has not been determined, and no chemical properties of these halides have been reported. It may be assumed that they have powerful reducing properties.

References

Asprey, L. B., and B. B. Cunningham, "Unusual Oxidation States of Some Actinide and Lanthanide Elements," in F. A. Cotton, ed., *Progress in Inorganic Chemistry*, Vol. II, Interscience, New York–London, 1960, p. 267.

Spedding, F. H., and A. M. Daane, eds., *The Rare Earths*, Wiley, New York, 1961.

Vickery, R. C., *Chemistry of the Lanthanons*, Academic Press, New York, 1953. A general account of the elements.

———, *Chemistry of Yttrium and Scandium*, Pergamon Press, London, 1960.

Yost, D. M., H. Russell, and C. S. Garner, *The Rare Earth Elements and Their Compounds*, Wiley, New York, 1947. A classical book containing early references; still of value.

32

The Actinide Elements

32-1. Occurrence

The actinide elements, all of whose isotopes are radioactive, are listed in Table 32-1. The isotopes which can be obtained in macroscopic amounts are given in Table 32-2.

TABLE 32-1

The Actinide Elements: Electronic Structures and Ionic Radii[a]

Z	Symbol	Name	Electronic structure of valence shells	Radius M^{3+}, A.	Radius M^{4+}, A.
89	Ac	Actinium	$6d7s^2$	1.11	0.99
90	Th	Thorium	$6d^27s^2$		0.96
91	Pa	Protactinium	$5f^26d7s^2$ or $5f^16d^27s^2$		0.93
92	U	Uranium	$5f^36d7s^2$	1.03	0.93
93	Np	Neptunium	$5f^57s^2$	1.01	0.92
94	Pu	Plutonium	$5f^67s^2$	1.00	0.90
95	Am	Americium	$5f^77s^2$	0.99	0.89
96	Cm	Curium	$5f^76d7s^2$		0.88
97	Bk	Berkelium	$5f^86d7s^2$ or $5f^97s^2$		
98	Cf	Californium	$5f^{10}7s^2$		
99	Es	Einsteinium	$5f^{11}7s^2$		
100	Fm	Fermium	$5f^{12}7s^2$		
101	Md	Mendelevium	$5f^{13}7s^2$		
102	No	Nobelium	$5f^{14}7s^2$		
103	Lw	Lawrencium	$5f^{14}6d7s^2$		

[a] In the octahedral fluorides, MF_6, the M—F bond distance also decreases with increasing Z, namely, U—F, 1.994 A.; Np—F, 1.981 A.; Pu—F, 1.969 A.

TABLE 32-2

Actinide Isotopes Available in Macroscopic Amounts[a]

Isotope	Half-life	Source
^{227}Ac	22.0 yr.	Natural; ^{226}Ra$(n\gamma)^{227}$Ra $\xrightarrow[41.2 \text{ min.}]{\beta^-} {}^{227}$Ac
^{232}Th	1.39×10^{10} yr.	Natural; 100% abundance
^{231}Pa	34,300 yr.	Natural; 0.34 p.p.m. of U in uranium ores
^{235}U	7.13×10^8 yr.	Natural; 0.72% abundance
^{238}U	4.50×10^9 yr.	Natural; 99.274% abundance
^{237}Np	2.20×10^6 yr.	^{235}U$(n\gamma)^{236}$U$(n\gamma)^{237}$U $\xrightarrow[6.75 \text{ d.}]{\beta^-} {}^{237}$Np
^{239}Pu	24,360 yr.	^{238}U$(n\gamma)^{239}$U $\xrightarrow[23 \text{ min.}]{\beta^-} {}^{239}$Np $\xrightarrow[2.3 \text{ d.}]{\beta^-} {}^{239}$Pu
^{241}Am	458 yr.	^{239}Pu$(n\gamma)^{240}$Pu$(n\gamma)^{241}$Pu $\xrightarrow[13.2 \text{ yr.}]{\beta^-} {}^{241}$Am
^{242}Cm	162.5 d.	^{241}Am$(n\gamma)^{242m}$Am $\xrightarrow[160 \text{ hr.}]{\beta^-} {}^{242}$Cm
^{244}Cm	19 yr.	^{239}Pu$(4n\gamma)^{243}$Pu $\xrightarrow[5.0 \text{ hr.}]{\beta^-} {}^{243}Am(n\gamma)^{244}$Am $\xrightarrow[26 \text{ min.}]{\beta^-} {}^{244}$Cm

[a] Other long-lived isotopes of Pu, Am, Cm, Bk, Cf, and Es are known and in principle they could be obtained in macroscopic amounts.

The terrestrial occurrence of actinium, protactinum, uranium, and thorium is due to the long half-lives of the isotopes ^{235}U, ^{238}U, and ^{232}Th which are sufficiently long to have enabled the species to persist since genesis. They are the prime sources of actinium and protactinium (and also the other radioactive isotopes formed in the decay series), which are found in uranium and thorium ores. The half-lives of the most stable isotopes of the trans-uranium elements are such that any primordial amounts of these elements would have disappeared long ago. However, neptunium and plutonium have been isolated in trace quantities from uranium minerals in which they are formed continuously by neutron reactions such as

$$^{238}\text{U} \xrightarrow{n\gamma} {}^{239}\text{U} \xrightarrow{\beta^-} {}^{239}\text{Np} \xrightarrow{\beta^-} {}^{239}\text{Pu}$$

The neutrons arise from spontaneous fission of ^{235}U or from α,n reactions of light elements present in uranium minerals. In Congo uranium ore, the mass ratio ^{237}Np$/^{238}$U does not exceed 1.8×10^{-12}, whereas in Canada pitchblende the ratio ^{238}Pu$/^{238}$U is 7.1×10^{-12}.

Neptunium and plutonium were obtained in tracer amounts from bombardments of uranium by McMillan and Abelson and by Seaborg, McMillan, Kennedy, and Wahl, respectively, in 1940. Although both elements can be obtained in substantial quantities from the uranium fuel elements of nuclear reactors, only plutonium is recovered industrially. This is because ^{239}Pu undergoes fission like ^{235}U and is hence an important nuclear fuel.

Americium and curium have been obtained in macro amounts by Seaborg and his co-workers who have also shown that trace amounts of elements up to lawrencium, $Z = 103$, can be obtained by nuclear reactions of Pu Am, or Cm, isotopes with accelerated heavy ions.

The characterization of the transuranium elements has been one of the most stirring episodes in chemical history. The present detailed knowledge of the actinide elements as a whole—and indeed of many other elements such as those encountered as fission products or those used in nuclear technology—is primarily a result of the development of nuclear explosives and later of nuclear energy. The impact of these developments has also led further to revolutionary advances and progress in methods and techniques. Thus procedures such as ion exchange separations, solvent extraction, and handling of microgram quantities of material or of reactive or intensely radioactive substances, have been perfected in the nuclear energy programs.

32-2. Electronic Structures—Comparison with Lanthanides

The electronic structures of the neutral gaseous atoms are given in Table 32-1 from which it will be seen that there is still uncertainty in allocation in a few cases. In the actinide elements, the fourteen $5f$ electrons are added formally, though not necessarily actually, from thorium, $Z = 90$, onward, and the $5f$ shell is complete at element 103; element 104 should be hafnium-like in its properties.

Since f shells are being filled, the actinides have a close and instructive relation with the lanthanides. Thus actinium and lanthanum occupy corresponding positions as prototypes for the two series of elements. Although important similarities do exist between the actinides and lanthanides, very important differences also occur; both of these aspects will become apparent. The differences arise mainly from the relatively lower binding energies and less effective shielding by the outer electrons of the $5f$ as compared to the $4f$ electrons. In the elements preceding the lanthanides the $4f$ orbitals have relatively high energy and extend spatially outside the $5s$ and $5p$ shells, but over a small range of atomic numbers, at and after cerium, they become lower energy inner orbitals. As inner orbitals they are not accessible for bonding purposes, and the lanthanide elements have virtually no complexes or covalent compounds in which $4f$ orbitals are used.

For the 5f orbitals the change from outer to inner orbitals is similar to the 4f case. There is reason to believe that 5f electrons are not present in thorium or probably in protactinium, but for uranium and succeeding elements 5f electrons are present. A rough qualitative picture for the binding energies of the weakest bound 5f and 6d electrons is shown in Figure 32-1;

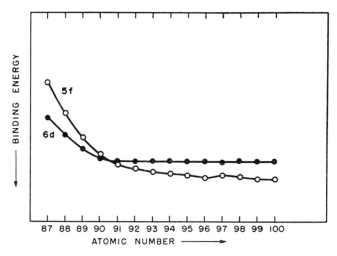

Fig. 32-1. Qualitative representation of electronic binding energies in the heaviest elements (J. J. Katz and G. T. Seaborg, *The Chemistry of the Actinide Elements*, Methuen, London, 1957, p. 465).

it appears from spectroscopic, chemical, and other data that the 5f level becomes progressively lower in energy compared to the 6d with increasing atomic number. The relative point of change is thus different in the two series and also the fall in energy and shrinkage in size are not so precipitous for the 5f orbitals compared to the 4f orbitals. The 5f orbitals thus have a greater spatial extension relative to the 6s and 6p orbitals than the 4f orbitals have relative to the 5s and 5p orbitals. The greater spacial extension of the 5f orbitals has been shown experimentally; the electron spin resonance spectrum of UF_3 in a CaF_2 lattice shows structure attributable to the interaction of fluorine nuclei with the electron spin of the U^{3+} ion. This implies a small overlap of 5f orbitals with fluorine and constitutes an f covalent contribution to the ionic bonding. With the neodymium ion a similar effect is *not* observed.

In the actinide series we therefore have a situation in which the energies of the 5f, 6d, 7s, and 7p orbitals are about comparable over a range of atomic numbers (especially U–Am), and, since the orbitals also overlap spacially, bonding can involve any or all of them. In the chemistries, this situation is indicated by the fact that the actinides are much more prone to complex formation than are the lanthanides where the bonding is almost exclusively ionic. Indeed the actinides can even form complexes with π-bonding ligands such as alkylphosphines, thioethers, and π-cyclopentadienyl as well as forming complexes with halide, sulfate, and other ions. The difference from lanthanide chemistry is usually attributed to contribution of covalent-hybrid bonding involving $5f$ electrons.

A further point is that since the energies of the $5f$, $6d$, $7s$, and $7p$ levels are comparable, the energies involved in an electron shifting from one to another, say $5f$ to $6d$, may lie *within* the range of chemical binding energies. Thus the electronic structure of the element in a given oxidation state may vary between compounds and in solution be dependent on the nature of the ligands. It is accordingly also often impossible to say *which* orbitals are being utilized in bonding or even to decide whether the bonding is covalent or ionic. The magnetic criterion which has often been found to be of utility for deciding hybridization schemes in the d transition elements is usually ambiguous for the actinides.

32-3. Oxidation States of the Actinide Elements

The known oxidation states are given in Table 32-3. The common and dominant oxidation state, as in the lanthanides, is $+3$, and the behavior of actinides and lanthanides in this state is very similar. For thorium and protactinium, the $+3$ state is unimportant, and for these elements the $+4$ and $+5$ oxidation states, respectively, predominate; accordingly thorium to some extent resembles hafnium and protactinium resembles tantalum, and there has been some rather pedantic argument as to whether or not they should be placed in groups IV and V.

From uranium onward there is a very closely related group, U, Np, Pu, and Am, in which the stability of the higher oxidation states falls. This fall is shown by the reduction potentials of the ions in solution and in simple compounds such as the halides, where the higher halides either do not exist, for example, $PuCl_5$, or require more vigorous conditions to prepare, for example, AmF_6.

All of the actinide elements form cationic species, the principal ions being M^{3+}, M^{4+}, MO_2^+, and MO_2^{2+} for the oxidation states $+3$ to $+6$, respectively. The general behavior of compounds or ions of different elements in the same oxidation state is the same, excepting differences in ease of oxidation or reduction. Most compounds of the same type are isomorphous. The oxygenated ions, MO_2^+ and MO_2^{2+}, are remarkably stable with respect to the strength of the M—O bond. Unlike other oxygenated ions, for example, VO_2^{2+}, they can persist through a variety of chemical changes, and they behave like cations whose properties are intermediate between those of M^+ or M^{2+} ions and those of ions of similar size but greater charge.

TABLE 32-3

Oxidation States of the Actinide Elements

Ac	Th	Pa	U	Np	Pu	Am	Cm	Bk	Cf	Es	Fm	Md
3[a]	3[b]	3	3	3	3	*3*	*3*	*3*	*3*	*3*	*3*	*3*
	4	4	4	4	*4*	4	4	4				
		5	5	*5*	5	5						
			6	6	6	6						

[a] Italic number signifies most stable state.
[b] Solid state only.

The possibility of several cationic species introduces complexity into the aqueous chemistries, particularly of U, Np, Pu, and Am. Thus for Pu, all four oxidation states can coexist in appreciable concentrations in a solution. The solution chemistries and the oxidation-reduction potentials are further complicated by the existence of *complex species* with ions other than perchlorate—cationic, neutral, and anionic species being known—by *hydrolysis*, even in solutions of low pH to give polymeric ions, and finally by *disproportionation* reactions which can occur in some cases and are particularly pH dependent.

Since extrapolation to infinite dilution is not possible for most of the actinide ions, owing to hydrolysis—for example, Pu^{4+} cannot exist in solution below $0.05M$ in acid—only approximate oxidation potentials can be given. The potentials are sensitive to the anions and other conditions. In Table 32-4 are given the potentials for $1M$ perchloric acid solutions, from which it can clearly be seen that the electropositive character of the metals increases with atomic number and the stability of the higher oxidation states falls off.

A comparison of the various actinide ions is given in Table 32-5.

32-4. Ionic Radii

The ionic radii are listed in Table 32-1 and are also shown together with the lanthanide radii in Figure 32-2. There is clearly an "actinide contraction" similar to that for the lanthanide ions and the trends are very

TABLE 32-4

Oxidation Potentials of the Actinides for $1M$ Perchloric Acid Solutions at 25°C.
(In volts; brackets [ ] indicate estimate)

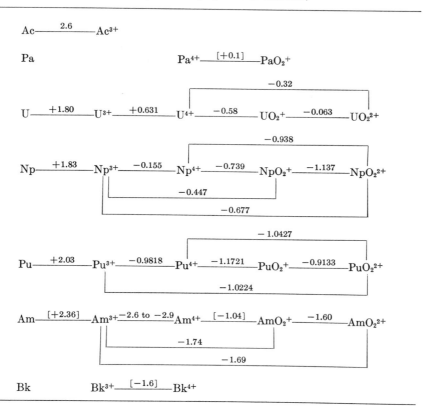

Notes:

1. Th = Th^{4+}, E = [1.90]; Pa + 2H$_2$O = PaO$_2^+$ + 4H$^+$, E = [1.0]
2. Couples involving oxygen transfer, for example, U^{4+} + 2H$_2$O → UO$_2^{2+}$ + 4H$^+$ + 2e, are *irreversible* and are of course hydrogen ion dependent. Couples such as PuO$_2^+$–PuO$_2^{2+}$ *are* reversible.

similar indeed. As would be expected, the chemistries of lanthanides and actinides in the M^{3+} and M^{4+} states are quite similar, and, if we compare an actinide and a lanthanide with the same radius for, say, M^{3+}, physical properties, such as thermochemical data for hydrolysis reactions, which depend closely on the ionic radius, are very similar. Actinide compounds in the same oxidation state have the same crystal structures differing only in the parameters. Despite the instability of Pa^{4+} and the nonexistence of

TABLE 32-5

The Actinide Ions[a] in Aqueous Solution

Ion	Color[b]	Preparation	Stability
U^{3+}	Red-brown	Na or Zn/Hg on UO_2^{2+}	Slowly oxidized by H_2O, rapidly by air to U^{4+}
Np^{3+}	Purplish	$H_2(Pt)$ or electrolytic	Stable in water; oxidized by air to Np^{4+}
Pu^{3+}	Blue-violet	SO_2, NH_2OH on higher states	Stable to water and air; easily oxidized to Pu^{4+}
Am^{3+}	Pink	I^-, SO_2, etc. on higher states	Stable; difficult to oxidize
U^{4+}	Green	Air or O_2 on U^{3+}	Stable; slowly oxidized by air to UO_2^{2+}
Np^{4+}	Yellow-green	SO_2 on NpO_2^+ in H_2SO_4	Stable; slowly oxidized by air to NpO_2^+
Pu^{4+}	Tan	SO_2 or NO_2^- on PuO_2^{2+}	Stable in $6M$ acid; disproportionates in low acid $\rightarrow Pu^{3+} + PuO_2^{2+}$
Am^{4+} [c]	Pink-red	$Am(OH)_4$ in $15M$ NH_4F	Stable in $15M$ NH_4F; reduced by I^-
Cm^{4+} [c]	Pale yellow	CmF_4 in $15M$ CsF	Stable only 1 hour at 25°C.
UO_2^+	?	Transient species	Stability greatest pH 2–4; disproportionates to U^{4+} and UO_2^{2+}
NpO_2^+	Green	Np^{4+} and hot HNO_3	Stable; disproportionates only in strong acid
PuO_2^+	?	Hydroxylamine on PuO_2^{2+}	Always disproportionates; most stable at low acidity
AmO_2^+	Pale yellow	Am^{3+} with OCl^-, cold $S_2O_8^{2-}$	Disproportionates in strong acid; reduced (2% per hour) by products of own α-radiation
UO_2^{2+}	Yellow	Oxidize U^{4+} with HNO_3, etc.	Very stable; difficult to reduce
NpO_2^{2+}	Pink	Oxidize lower states with Ce^{4+},	Stable; easily reduced
PuO_2^{2+}	Yellow-pink	MnO_4^-, O_3, BrO_3^-, etc.	Stable; fairly easy to reduce
AmO_2^{2+}	Rum		Reduced (4% per hour) by products from own α-radiation

[a] Ac^{3+}, Th^{4+}, Cm^{3+}, and ions of Pa are colorless.
[b] Depends on concentration and nature of ions.
[c] Presumably as fluoro anion.

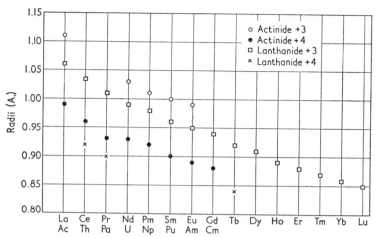

Fig. 32-2. Radii of actinide and lanthanide ions.

Am^{4+} and Cm^{4+} in solution, the dioxides MO_2 are stable owing to the high lattice energy of their fluorite lattice.

Although the lanthanide metals with the exception of Eu and Yb have also a steady decrease in the atomic volumes and metal radii, Pa, U, Np, and Pu metals have complicated structures which have no counterpart among the metals of the lanthanides. Americium is the first metal to show a similarity to the crystal structures of the lanthanide metals.

32-5. Absorption Spectra and Magnetic Properties

The absorption spectra of the actinide ions, like the lanthanide ions, consist of narrow bands in the visible, near-ultraviolet, and near-infrared regions which are less influenced by ligand fields than are the spectral bands of d transition metal ions. The bands, which are due to electronic transitions within the $5f^n$ levels, are generally about ten times as intense as the lanthanide bands. Spectra involving only one f electron are simple, consisting of only a single transition $^2F_{\frac{5}{2}}$–$^2F_{\frac{7}{2}}$; for the f^7 configuration (Cm^{3+}; cf. Gd^{3+}) the lowest excited state lies about 4 e.v. above the ground level so that these ions show only charge-transfer absorption in the ultraviolet.

The magnetic properties of the actinide ions are considerably more difficult to interpret than those of the lanthanide ions, and the situation is not yet fully understood. The experimental magnetic moments are usually lower than the values calculated using Russell-Saunders coupling, and this appears to be due both to ligand field effects similar to those operating in the d transition series and to inadequacy of this coupling scheme. It is now quite certain that $5f$ orbitals can participate to some extent in covalent bonding so that ligand effects are to be expected.

For the ions Pu^{3+} and Am^{3+}, the same phenomenon noted for Sm^{3+} and Eu^{3+} is found; since the multiplet levels are comparable to kT, anomalous temperature dependence of the susceptibilities is found.

32-6. Stereochemistry and Complexes

Although there is certainly some doubt concerning the extent of covalent bonding in actinide compounds, the angular distributions and relative strengths of various orbital combinations using f orbitals have been worked out theoretically in a manner similar to that for the familiar schemes in light elements. Examples are: sf, linear; sf^3, tetrahedral; sf^2d, square planar; d^2sf^3, octahedral. These hybridizations *could* be considered to hold in PuO_2^{2+}, $NpCl_4$, and UCl_6, for example. However, in view of the closeness in the energy levels of electrons in the valence shells, and the mutual overlap of orbitals of comparable size in these heavy atoms, several equally valid descriptions can be chosen in a particular case with little chance of being able to decide unequivocally between them. Any assignments of hybridization schemes in actinide compounds or complexes must hence be very tentative.

Except for ionic compounds such as the halides and oxides and rather volatile compounds like the hexafluorides, there is surprisingly little structural information on complex compounds even of uranium and thorium.

The hexafluorides are octahedral, and some complexes such as the acetylacetonates, $M^{III}(C_5H_7O_2)_3$, and donor complexes of halides, for example, $UCl_4 \cdot 2P(C_2H_5)_3$, are presumably octahedral also.

The $+4$ actinides show a strong tendency to form eight-coordinate complexes, but few structures have been determined. Thorium acetyl-

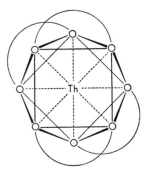

Fig. 32-3.   Square antiprism type of structure in thorium acetylacetonate.

acetonate, $Th(C_5H_7O_2)_4$, which is isomorphous with the uranium analog, has been shown to have a structure based on a square antiprism (Fig. 32-3) though slightly distorted. This structure is the one predicted on purely electrostatic grounds, and the volatility of the compound is no criterion of covalent bonding but is only a reflection of the almost spherical nature of the molecules and valence saturation of the outer atoms.

The MO_2 ions have been shown to be approximately linear, and for MO_2^{2+} the bond strengths as estimated from force constants decrease in the order $U > Np > Pu > Am$. Although uranyl and other similar ions as the halides or nitrates form a variety of complexes with other ions and donor molecules, few structures have been determined. It appears that four, five, or six ligand atoms can lie in the equatorial plane of the O—M—O group. A set of six ligand atoms, which may or may not be planar, depending on circumstances, appears to be the commonest. The structure of the anion in the complex salt $Na[UO_2(OCOCH_3)_3]$ is shown in Figure 32-4; the

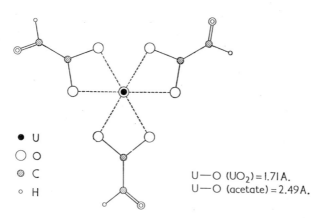

U—O $(UO_2) = 1.71$ A.
U—O (acetate) $= 2.49$ A.

Fig. 32-4. Structure of anion in $Na[UO_2(OCOCH_3)_3]$.

carboxyl groups are bidentate and equivalent. A similar structure (where the uranyl oxygens lie in the plane perpendicular to the paper) is found in the triethyl phosphate complex (32-I), where the phosphoryl oxygen of the phosphate and the nitrate group lie in the equatorial plane of the UO_2 group and in $[UO_2(NO_3)_2(H_2O)_2]\cdot 4H_2O$ where O—U—O is $173°$.

A vast amount of data exists on complex formation by the actinide ions, and generally the tendency to complex ion formation decreases in the direction controlled by factors of ionic size and charge, that is in the order $M^{4+} > MO_2^{2+} > M^{3+} > MO_2^+$.

For the complexing anions, the order of complexing power is as fol-

$$O$$
$$|$$
$$N$$
$$O \diagup \quad \diagdown O$$
$$\diagdown \diagup$$
$$(C_2H_5O)_3P\!-\!\!O\!-\!U\!-\!\!O\!-\!P(OC_2H_5)_3$$
$$\diagup \quad \diagdown$$
$$O \quad O$$
$$\diagdown \diagup$$
$$N$$
$$|$$
$$O$$

(32-I)

lows: unipositive ions: $F^- > NO_3^- > Cl^- > ClO_4^-$; bipositive ions: $CO_3^{2-} > C_2O_4^{2-} > SO_4^{2-}$. The formation of anionic complexes is of special importance in connection with ion exchange and solvent extraction behavior.

ACTINIUM

32-7. The Element and Its Compounds

Actinium was originally isolated from uranium minerals in which it occurs in trace amounts, but it is now made on a milligram scale by neutron capture in radium and β decay of ^{227}Ra (Table 32-2). The actinium $+3$ ion is separated from excess radium and isotopes of Th, Po, Bi, and Pb also formed by decay or in the bombardment, by ion exchange elution or by solvent extraction by thenoyltrifluoroacetone. Precipitation of AcF_3 from the solutions and reduction of the dry fluoride with lithium vapor at 1100–1275°C. or $AcCl_3$ with potassium vapor at 350°C. gives the silvery white metal (m.p. 1050°C.). The metal glows in the dark owing to its radioactivity. Like lanthanum, it is a very reactive metal and oxidizes in moist air; the intense radioactivity contributes to its reactivity.

The general chemistry of the Ac^{3+} ion in both solid compounds and in solution, where known, is very similar to that of lanthanum as would be expected from the similarity in position in the periodic table and in radii (Ac^{3+}, 1.10; La^{3+}, 1.06 A.) together with the inert-gas structure of the ion. Thus actinium is a true member of group III, the only difference from lanthanum being in the expected increased basicity. The increased basic character is shown by the stronger absorption of the hydrated ion on cation exchange resins, the poorer extraction of the ion from strong nitric acid solutions by tributyl phosphate, and by the hydrolysis of the trihalides with water vapor at ~1000°C. to the oxyhalides AcOX; the lanthanum halides are hydrolyzed to oxide by water vapor at 1000°C.

The crystal structures of actinium compounds where they have been studied, for example, in AcH_3, AcF_3, Ac_2S_3, and $AcOCl$, are the same as those of the analogous lanthanum compounds.

The study of even milligram amounts of actinium is rather difficult owing to the intense γ radiation of its decay products which rapidly build up in the pure material.

THORIUM

32-8. The Element

Thorium was discovered by Berzelius in 1828. It is widely distributed in nature and there are large deposits of the principal mineral, monazite, a complex phosphate containing uranium, cerium, and other lanthanides. The extraction of thorium from monazite is complicated, the main problem being the destruction of the resistant sand and the separation of thorium from cerium and phosphate. One method involves a digestion with sodium hydroxide; the insoluble hydroxides are removed and dissolved in hydrochloric acid. On adjusting the pH of the solution to 5.8, all of the thorium and uranium, together with about 3% of the lanthanides, are precipitated as hydroxides. The thorium is recovered by tributyl phosphate extraction from $>6M$ hydrochloric acid solution or by extraction with methylisobutyl or other ketone from nitric acid solutions in presence of excess of a salt such as aluminum nitrate as a "salting-out" agent.

The metal is made by calcium reduction of the tetrafluoride in presence of zinc chloride as a flux, by reduction of the oxide or tetrachloride by calcium, magnesium, or sodium, or by electrolysis of a fused mixture of ThF_4, KCN, and NaCl. Very pure metal can be made by thermal decomposition of the vapor of ThI_4 on an incandescent filament. The metal has a high melting point, 1750°C., and is quite electropositive in behavior, being comparable to the lanthanide metals in its chemical reactivity. Thus it tarnishes in air and is pyrophoric when finely divided; it is attacked by boiling water, by oxygen at 250°C., and by nitrogen at 800°C. Dilute hydrofluoric, nitric, and sulfuric acids and concentrated phosphoric and hydrochloric acids attack thorium only slowly, whereas strong nitric acid makes it passive. With hydrochloric acid, about 25% of the metal is converted to a black insoluble solid which is believed to be a mixture of oxide and hydride.

32-9. Binary Compounds of Thorium

Some typical thorium compounds are listed in Table 32-6.

TABLE 32-6

Some Thorium Compounds

Compound	Form	Melting point, °C.	Properties
ThO_2	White, crystalline; fluorite structure	3050	Stable, refractory; soluble in $HF + HNO_3$
ThN	Refractory solid	2500	Slowly hydrolyzed by water
ThS_2	Purple solid	1905	Metal-like; soluble in acids
$ThCl_4$	Tetragonal white crystals	770	Soluble in and hydrolyzed by H_2O; Lewis acid
$Th(NO_3)_4 \cdot 5H_2O$	White crystals, orthorhombic		Very soluble in H_2O, alcohols, ketones, ethers
$Th(IO_3)_4$	White crystalline solid		Precipitated from 50% HNO_3; very insoluble
$Th(C_5H_7O_2)_4$	White crystals	171	Sublimes in vacuum 160°C.
$Th(BH_4)_4$	White crystals	204	Sublimes in vacuum about 40°C.
$Th(C_2O_4)_2 \cdot 6H_2O$	White crystals		Precipitated from up to $2M$ HNO_3 solution

Oxide and Hydroxide. The only oxide, ThO_2, is obtained by ignition of oxy acid salts or of the hydroxide. The latter is insoluble in excess alkali hydroxides, although it is readily peptized by heating with Th^{4+} or Fe^{3+} ions or dilute acids; the colloid exists as fibers which are coiled into spheres in concentrated sols but which uncoil on dilution. The addition of hydrogen peroxide to Th^{4+} salts gives a highly insoluble white precipitate of variable composition which contains excess anions in addition to peroxide; the composition is approximately $Th(O_2)_{3.2}X_{0.5}{}^-O_{0.15}{}^{2-}$ but it is usually referred to as thorium peroxide.

Halides. The anhydrous halides may be prepared by dry reactions such as:

$$ThO_2 + 4HF(g) \xrightarrow{600°C.} ThF_4 + 2H_2O$$

$$ThO_2 + CCl_4 \xrightarrow{600°C.} ThCl_4 + CO_2$$

They are all white crystalline solids which, with the exception of ThF_4, can be sublimed in vacuum at 500–600°C. The hydrated tetrafluoride is precipitated by aqueous hydrofluoric acid from Th^{4+} solutions; it can be dehydrated by heating in an atmosphere of hydrogen fluoride. The other halides are soluble in acid and are partially hydrolyzed by water. They behave as Lewis acids and form complexes with ammonia, amines, ketones, alcohols, and donor molecules generally.

The *oxyhalides*, $ThOX_2$, can be obtained by hydrolysis of the halides with water vapor.

Other Binary Compounds. Various borides, sulfides, carbides, nitrides, etc., have been obtained by direct interaction of the elements at elevated temperatures. Like other actinide and lanthanide metals, thorium also reacts at elevated temperatures with hydrogen. Products with a range of compositions can be obtained, but two definite phases, ThH_2 and Th_4H_{15}, have been characterized.

32-10. Oxy Salts, Aqueous Solutions and Complexes of Thorium

Thorium salts of strong mineral acids usually have varying amounts of water of crystallization. The most common salt and the usual starting material for preparation of other thorium compounds is the nitrate, $Th(NO_3)_4 \cdot 5H_2O$. This salt is very soluble in water as well as in alcohols, ketones, ethers, and esters. Various agents give insoluble precipitates with thorium solutions, the most important being hydroxide, peroxide, fluoride, iodate, oxalate, and phosphate; the last four give precipitates even from strongly acid ($6M$) solutions and provide useful separations of thorium from elements other than those having $+3$ or $+4$ cations with similar properties.

The thorium, Th^{4+}, ion undergoes extensive hydrolysis in aqueous solution; the species formed are complex and dependent on the conditions of pH, nature of anions, concentration, etc. In perchlorate solutions below pH 3, the main ion appears to be $Th^{4+}(aq)$ in the concentration range 2.5×10^{-4} to 1.5×10^{-2} M. Polymeric species such as $Th[Th(OH)_3]_n^{n+4}$ where $n = 1, 2, 3$, etc. are formed in more concentrated solutions or at higher pH. The metal atoms are linked by hydroxy or oxo bridges. In crystals of the hydroxide, $Th(OH)_4$, or the compound $Th(OH)_2CrO_4 \cdot H_2O$, chain-like structures have been identified, the repeating unit being $Th(OH)_2^{2+}$; in solution, the polymers may have similar form (32-II) or may additionally be crosslinked.

(32-IIa)   (32-IIb)

The high charge on Th^{4+} makes it susceptible to complex formation, and in solutions with anions other than perchlorate, complexed species, which may additionally be partially hydrolyzed and polymeric, are formed. Equilibrium constants for reactions such as the following have been measured:

$$Th^{4+} + nCl^- = ThCl_n^{4-n}$$
$$Th^{4+} + NO_3^- = Th(NO_3)^{3+}$$
$$Th^{4+} + 2HSO_4^- = Th(HSO_4, SO_4)^+ + H^+$$

32-11. Lower Oxidation States of Thorium

There is no evidence for the existence of lower oxidation states in solution. The iodides ThI_2 and ThI_3 appear to exist, though some uncertainties in their characterization remain and poor X-ray patterns were obtained. The iodides are made by heating the metal with appropriate amounts of iodine at 555°C. in vacuum; ThI_2 is pyrophoric in air.

PROTACTINIUM

32-12. The Element

Protactinium as ^{231}Pa (α, 34,000 years) occurs in pitchblende, but even the richest ores contain only about 1 part Pa in 10^7. The isolation of protactinium from residues in the extraction of uranium from its minerals is difficult, as indeed is the study of protactinium chemistry generally, owing to the extreme tendency of the compounds to hydrolyze. In aqueous solution, polymeric ionic species and colloidal particles are formed, and these are carried on precipitates and adsorbed on vessels; in solutions other than those containing appreciable amounts of mineral acids or complexing agents or ions such as F^-, the difficulties are almost insuperable.

Protactinium can be recovered from solutions 2–8M in nitric or hydrochloric acids by extraction with tributyl phosphate, methyl isobutyl ketone, or other organic solvents. The protactinium can be stripped from the solvent by aqueous acid fluoride solutions; the addition to these solutions of Al^{3+} ion or boric acid, which form stronger complexes with fluoride ion than protactinium, then allows re-extraction and further purification of protactinium. Anion exchange procedures using mixtures of hydrofluoric and hydrochloric acids as eluants can also be used, since in these solutions anionic protactinium fluoro or chloro anions are formed. About 125 g. of protactinium have recently been isolated in a twelve-stage process from 60 tons of accumulated sludges of uranium extraction from Belgian Congo ore by the United Kingdom Atomic Energy Authority; previously only about 1 g. had ever been isolated. The metal, which is obtained by barium reduction of the tetrafluoride at 1400°C, is shiny and malleable, but tarnishes in air.

32-13. Protactinium Compounds

Only a few compounds have been characterized. The oxide system is complex and substances ranging in composition from PaO_2 to Pa_2O_5 can be obtained; the pentoxide, Pa_2O_5, is obtained by ignition of other compounds in air and is a white solid with a cubic lattice. The pentoxide is reduced by hydrogen at 1550°C. to the dioxide, PaO_2, a black solid insoluble in acids other than hydrofluoric.

Two fluorides are known; the tetrafluoride, PaF_4, is isostructural with ThF_4 and UF_4 and is a reddish, high-melting solid. It is formed by the action of hydrogen and hydrogen fluoride on the oxide at 600°C.; it readily hydrolyzes in air. The pentafluoride, PaF_5, is a very reactive compound which volatilizes in vacuum at 500°C.; it is made by treating Pa_2O_5 with BrF_3 at elevated temperatures. Although the product is believed to be PaF_5, the presence of oxyfluorides has not been disproved. Only one chloride, $PaCl_4$, is known; this is isostructural with $ThCl_4$ and UCl_4 and is a greenish yellow solid. It is formed by the action of hydrogen on the product—which may be $PaCl_5$—obtained through heating Pa_2O_5 in carbon tetrachloride at 300°C.

32-14. Aqueous Chemistry of Protactinium

The chemistry of Pa^V in solution is somewhat like that of niobium and tantalum, but protactinium is even less tractable because of hydrolysis. Simple cations do not exist under ordinary conditions, and indeed true solutions of protactinium do not even occur in nitric or hydrochloric acids of concentration below $3M$. Anionic complexes are formed by fluoride and citrate ions, but the nature of the species is not settled. Thiocyanate, sulfate, nitrate, and chloride also give complexes, and the data have been interpreted as showing the existence of ions such as $[PaO_2(NO_3)_4]^{3-}$ or $[PaOCl_6]^{3-}$. It is not yet established whether the protactinyl ion is PaO_2^+, like the other actinide ions, or PaO^{3+}, like the niobyl ion.

Lower oxidation states can be obtained in solution by the action of reducing agents such as titanous sulfate or zinc amalgam. The solutions are rapidly oxidized by air. The absorption spectrum of $PaCl_4$ dissolved in water is similar to that of the Ce^{3+} ion, providing some evidence for the presence of a single f electron in Pa^{IV}.

URANIUM

32-15. The Element

Uranium was discovered by Klaproth in 1789. Until the discovery of uranium fission by Hahn and Strassman in 1939, uranium had little commercial importance; its ores were sources of radium and small quantities were used for coloring glass and ceramics, but the bulk of the uranium was discarded. Uranium is now of critical importance as a nuclear fuel; its chemical importance lies in being the prototype for the succeeding three elements.

Uranium has three isotopes: ^{238}U ($99.2739 \pm 0.0007\%$), ^{235}U ($0.7204 \pm 0.0007\%$), and ^{234}U ($0.0057 \pm 0.0007\%$); ^{238}U is the parent of the $(4n + 2)$ radioactive decay series and ^{235}U the parent of the $(4n + 3)$ series, whereas ^{234}U is formed in the ^{238}U decay sequence. Uranium-235 is of great significance since it undergoes nuclear fission with neutrons, for example

$$^{235}_{92}U + n = {}^{140}_{56}Ba + {}^{92}_{36}Kr + 3n + \sim 200 \text{ m.e.v.}$$

In this process two main groups of fission products are obtained with the release of about 200 m.e.v. per fission (1 m.e.v. $= 10^6$ e.v.; 1 e.v. per atom $= 23.04$ kcal./mole) owing to the total mass difference between the fission product isotopes and $^{235}U + n$. In addition, since the process gives a distribution of fission fragments, about 2.5 neutrons per fission are liberated; these neutrons are very energetic and in pure ^{235}U can sustain a chain reaction leading to a nuclear explosion provided the mass of ^{235}U exceeds a certain critical value (a few kilograms). The fission neutrons can be slowed down or moderated by collisions with hydrogen, deuterium, or carbon atoms, and under these conditions a self-sustaining but controlled chain reaction can be set up using natural uranium in an appropriate reactor. In nuclear reactors where ^{235}U is consumed as fuel, the ^{238}U of natural uranium undergoes neutron capture reactions in the high neutron fluxes and plutonium, ^{239}Pu, is built up (Table 32-2).

The most important of the widely distributed sources of uranium is pitchblende, an oxide of variable composition approximating to UO_2. The methods of extraction of uranium are numerous and cannot be discussed here. The final stages of purification usually employ solvent extraction of uranyl nitrate from aqueous solutions. The metal, which must be extraordinarily pure for use in nuclear reactions and free from elements with high neutron-absorbing properties, for example, B or Cd, is obtained by reduction of the tetrafluoride with magnesium or calcium:

$$UF_4 + 2Mg = U + 2MgF_2$$

Other methods involve reduction of oxides or halides with electropositive metals or electrolysis of fused fluoride mixtures.

Uranium is the densest of metals (19.04 g./cm.³ at 25°C.) and has three crystalline modifications below its melting point of 1132°C. It forms a wide range of intermetallic compounds—U_6Mn, U_6Ni, USn_3, etc.—but, owing to the unique nature of its crystal structures, cannot form extensive ranges of solid solutions. Uranium is chemically reactive and combines directly with most elements in the periodic table. In air, the surface is rapidly converted to a yellow and subsequently a black nonprotective film. Powdered uranium is frequently pyrophoric. The reaction with water is complex; boiling water forms UO_2 and hydrogen, the latter reacting with the metal to form hydride, which causes disintegration. Uranium dissolves rapidly in hydrochloric acid (a black residue of U_3O_4 often remains) and nitric acid, but slowly in sulfuric, phosphoric, or hydrofluoric acid. It is unaffected by alkalies.

32-16. Uranium Compounds

The chemistry of uranium is varied and complex and has been intensively studied—indeed the chemistry is one of the best known of all metal chemistries. Accordingly we can discuss only some of the more important aspects; some representative compounds are given in Table 32-7.

Uranium Hydride. Uranium metal reacts rapidly with hydrogen at 250–300°C. to give a black powder, uranium hydride, UH_3. The reaction is reversible,

$$U + \tfrac{3}{2}H_2 = UH_3$$

the hydride decomposing at somewhat higher temperatures to give extremely reactive, finely divided metal. A study of the isostructural deuteride by X-ray and neutron diffraction shows that the deuterium atoms lie in a distorted tetrahedron equidistant from four uranium atoms; no U—U bonds appear to be present and the U—D distance is 2.32 A. The stoichiometric hydride, UH_3, can be obtained, but the stability of the product with a slight deficiency of hydrogen is greater.

The hydride is chemically very reactive and can inflame in air; it is often

TABLE 32-7

Some Representative Compounds of Uranium[a]

Compound	Form	Melting point, °C.	Properties
UO_2	Brown-black face-centered cubic crystals	2800	Soluble in nitric acid Chemically inert
UC	Black	2500	NaCl structure; hydrolyzed by acids
U_3Si_2	Metallic tetragonal crystals	1665	
$U(C_5H_7O_2)_4$	Green	175	Soluble in organic solvents, sublimes in vacuum
$U(OC_2H_5)_5$	Dark brown		Distillable liquid; readily hydrolyzed by H_2O
$(\pi\text{-}C_5H_5)_3UCl$	Red crystals	260	Air-sensitive; soluble in H_2O giving cation
$UO_2(NO_3)_26H_2O$	Yellow crystals		Soluble in water, ethers, alcohols, esters, etc.
UO_2Cl_2	Yellow solid	578	Soluble in water; forms hydrates
$NaUO_2(C_2H_3O_2)_3$	Pale yellow crystalline solid		Insoluble in sodium acetate

[a] The stoichiometries, structures, and properties of Np, Pu, and Am compounds, where they have been studied, are usually closely similar to those of the uranium analogs; the +3 and +4 compounds are also often similar to lanthanide compounds.

more suitable for the preparation of uranium compounds than is the massive metal. Some of its reactions are:

$$UH_3 + H_2O \xrightarrow{350°C.} UO_2$$

$$UH_3 + Cl_2 \xrightarrow{200°C.} UCl_4$$

$$UH_3 + H_2S \xrightarrow{450°C.} US_2$$

$$UH_3 + HF \xrightarrow{400°C.} UF_4$$

$$UH_3 + HCl \xrightarrow{250\text{-}300°C.} UCl_3$$

Uranium Oxides. The U–O system is one of the most complex oxide systems known, owing in part to the multiplicity of oxidation states of comparable stability. Deviations from stoichiometry are the rule rather than the exception. In the dioxide, UO_2, for example, about 10% excess oxygen atoms can be added before any notable structural changes are observable, and the UO_2 phase extends from UO_2 to $\sim UO_{2.25}$. The stoichiometric oxides are UO_2, brown-black; U_3O_8, greenish black; and UO_3, orange-yellow. Each of these oxides has several crystalline modifications of different thermal and thermodynamic stabilities and colors. The trioxide, UO_3, is obtained by decomposition at 350°C. of uranyl nitrate, or better, of ammonium diuranate (which is obtained by addition of aqueous ammonia to uranyl salt solutions).

$$(NH_4)_2U_2O_7 = 2UO_3 + H_2O + 2NH_3$$

The other oxides can be obtained by the reactions:

$$3UO_3 \overset{700°C.}{=} U_3O_8 + \tfrac{1}{2}O_2$$
$$UO_3 + CO \overset{350°C.}{=} UO_2 + CO_2$$

All the oxides readily dissolve in nitric acid to give UO_2^{2+} salts. The addition of hydrogen peroxide to uranyl solution gives a pale yellow precipitate, usually called the peroxide, of formula approximately $UO_4 \cdot 2H_2O$.

Uranium Halides. The principal halides are given in Table 32-8; they have been studied in great detail and their chemical, structural, and

TABLE 32-8

Uranium Halides

+3		+4				+5		+6	
UF_3	green	UF_4	green	U_2F_9	black	UF_5	white	UF_6	white
UCl_3	red	UCl_4	green	U_4F_{14}	black	UCl_5	red brown	UCl_6	black
UBr_3	red	UBr_4	brown			—		—	
UI_3	black	UI_4	black			—		—	

thermodynamic properties are well established. Uranium trifluoride is a high-melting, nonvolatile, crystalline solid resembling the lanthanum fluorides, and it is insoluble in water or dilute acids; the preparation is by the aluminum reduction of UF_4:

$$UF_4 + Al \overset{900°C.}{=} UF_3 + AlF$$

The hydrated tetrafluoride can be obtained by precipitation from U^{4+} solution, the anhydrous fluoride by reactions such as

$$UO_2 \xrightarrow[\text{500–600°C}]{C_2Cl_4F_2} UF_4$$

The nonvolatile solid is insoluble in water but is readily soluble in solutions of oxidizing agents. The hexafluoride, UF_6, is obtained by the action of fluorine on the lower fluorides; it forms colorless crystals subliming at

56.5°C. at 1 atm. with a vapor pressure at 25°C. of ~120 mm. It is the only readily accessible volatile uranium compound, and its physical properties have been intensively studied, primarily because it is used in the separation of uranium isotopes by gaseous diffusion in order to produce pure ^{235}U nuclear fuel. The structure has been shown to be octahedral in the gas and in the molecular crystals. UF_6 is a powerful fluorinating agent, and it is also hydrolyzed rapidly by water. The intermediate fluorides, UF_5, U_2F_9, and U_4F_{14}, are made by interaction of UF_6 and UF_4; they disproportionate quite readily. UF_5 is made by treating UF_4 with fluorine at ~100°; it has a polymeric chain structure. The fluoro complexes Na_3UF_7 and Na_3UF_8 are also known.

Uranium trichloride can be made only in anhydrous conditions, for example, by the action of hydrogen chloride on UH_3; the aqueous solutions obtained by reduction of acid solutions of UO_2^{2+} by zinc amalgam are readily reoxidized to U^{4+} by air. The most important chloride is UCl_4, which is best made by liquid phase chlorination of UO_3 by refluxing with hexachloropropene. The primary product is believed to be UCl_6 which thermally decomposes. UCl_4 is soluble in polar organic solvents and in water. The penta- and hexachlorides are both soluble in carbon tetrachloride; they are violently hydrolyzed by water. UCl_5 disproportionates on heating but can be isolated by chilling the gaseous products in the reaction scheme:

$$UCl_4 + \tfrac{1}{2}Cl_2 \xrightarrow{500°C.} UCl_5 \xrightarrow{120°C.} UCl_4 + UCl_6$$

The bromides and iodides are made by direct interaction; the tetraiodide is unstable.

Oxyhalides. Oxyhalides of the uranyl state are known. These stable compounds, UO_2X_2, are soluble in water. They are made by reactions such as

$$UCl_4 + O_2 \overset{350°C.}{=} UO_2Cl_2 + Cl_2$$

$$UO_3 + 2HF \overset{400°C.}{=} UO_2F_2 + H_2O$$

Other Binary Compounds. Direct interaction of uranium with B, C, Si, N, P, As, Sb, Se, S, Te, etc., leads to semimetallic compounds which are often nonstoichiometric, resembling the oxides. Some of them, for example, the silicides, are chemically inert, and the sulfides, notably US, can be used as refractories.

32-17. Aqueous Chemistry of Uranium

Uranium ions in aqueous solution can give very complex species because, in addition to the four oxidation states, complexing reactions with all ions other than ClO_4^- as well as hydrolytic reactions leading to polymeric ions occur under appropriate conditions. The formal potentials for $1M$ $HClO_4$ have been given in Table 32-4; in presence of other anions the values differ, thus the $U^{3+}-U^{4+}$ value for $1M$ $HClO_4$ is $+0.631$ v., but for $1M$ HCl it is $+0.640$ v. The simple ions and their properties are also listed in Table 32-5. Aqueous solutions of uranium salts have an acid reaction due to hydrolysis which increases in the order $U^{3+} < UO_2^{2+} < U^{4+}$. The uranyl and U^{4+} solutions have been particularly well studied. For UO_2^{2+}, polymeric species are undoubtedly formed, and their formation can account for the solubility of large amounts of UO_3 in UO_2^{2+} solutions; the polymers are believed to have double hydroxy bridges and to be of the type $UO_2[(OH)_2UO_2]_n^{2+}$. In water the main species resulting from the hydrolysis of UO_2^{2+} are $(UO_2)_2OH^{3+}$, $(UO_2)_2(OH)_2^{2+}$, and $(UO_2)_3(OH)_4^{2+}$. Although the U^{4+} ion can exist in considerable concentrations, mono as well as polynuclear species are formed, for example,

$$U^{4+} + H_2O = U(OH)^{3+} + H^+ \qquad K = 0.05 \ (\mu = 0.19 \text{ at } 25°C.)$$

The U^{4+} ion gives insoluble precipitates with F^-, PO_4^{3-}, and IO_3^- from acid solutions (cf. Th^{4+}).

The pentapositive uranium ion, UO_2^+, has a transistory existence under most conditions, although evidence for its occurrence can be obtained polarographically. It is also an intermediate in photochemical reduction reactions of uranyl ions in presence of sucrose and similar substances. The ion is most stable in the pH range 2.0–4.0 where the disproportionation reaction to give U^{4+} and UO_2^{2+} is negligibly slow, and millimolar solutions can be obtained by electrolytic reduction of UO_2^{2+} or by dissolving UCl_5.

Spectroscopic and other studies have shown that in aqueous solutions of UO_2^{2+} and U^{4+}, complex ions are often readily formed, for example,

$$U^{4+} + Cl^- = UCl^{3+} \qquad K = 1.21 \ (\mu = 2.0; 25°C.)$$
$$U^{4+} + 2HSO_4^- = U(SO_4)_2 + 2H^+ \qquad K = 7.4 \times 10^3 \ (\mu = 2.0; 25°C.)$$
$$UO_2^{2+} + Cl^- = UO_2Cl^+ \qquad K = 0.88 \ (\mu = 2.0; 25°C.)$$
$$UO_2^{2+} + 2SO_4^{2-} = UO_2(SO_4)_2^{2-} \qquad K = 7.1 \times 10^2 \ (\mu = 2.0; 25°C.)$$

Complex ions are also formed with citrate and anions of other organic acids, thiocyanate, dialkyl dithiocarbamates, and phosphates. The latter are important in view of the occurrence of uranium in phosphate minerals, and species such as $UO_2H_2PO_4^+$, $UO_2H_3PO_3^{2+}$, and at high concentrations anionic complexes are known.

32-18. Uranyl Salts

These are the only common uranium salts and the most important one is the nitrate which crystallizes with six, three, or two molecules of water, depending on whether it is obtained from dilute, strong, or fuming nitric acid. The most unusual and significant property of the nitrate is its solubility in numerous ethers, alcohols, ketones, and esters, when it distributes itself between the organic and an aqueous phase. The nitrate is also readily extracted from aqueous solutions, and this operation has become classical for the separation and purification of uranium since, with the exception of the other actinide MO_2^{2+} ions, few other metal nitrates have any extractability. A great deal of information is available, and phase diagrams for the $UO_2(NO_3)_2$–H_2O–solvent systems have been determined. The effect of added salts, for example, $Ca(NO_3)_2$ or NH_4NO_3, as "salting-out" agents is to increase substantially the extraction ratio to technically usable values. Studies of the organic phase have shown that $UO_2(NO_3)_2$ is accompanied into the solvents by $4H_2O$ molecules, but there is little or no ionization and the nitrate is undoubtedly coordinated in the equatorial plane of the UO_2 system. An important extractant for uranyl nitrate which does not require a salting-out agent for useful ratios is tributyl phosphate.

Other uranyl salts are given by organic acids, sulfate, halides, etc.; the water-soluble acetate in presence of excess sodium acetate in dilute acetic acid gives a crystalline precipitate of $NaUO_2(OCOCH_3)_3$.

NEPTUNIUM, PLUTONIUM, AND AMERICIUM

32-19. Isolation of the Elements

Although several isotopes of these elements are known, the most important long-lived ones that can be obtained in macroscopic amounts are given in Table 32-2. Both ^{237}Np and ^{239}Pu are found in the uranium fuel elements of nuclear reactions, but the amounts of neptunium are small and are normally not recovered in the extraction of plutonium, which is isolated on a kilogram scale. Americium is produced from intense neutron irradiations of pure plutonium. The problems involved in the extraction of these elements involve the recovery of the expensive starting material and the removal of hazardous fission products which are formed simultaneously in amounts comparable to the amounts of the synthetic elements themselves. Not only are the chemical problems themselves quite formidable, but the handling of highly radioactive solutions or solids (in the case of plutonium the exceedingly high toxicity is an additional hazard) has necessitated the development of remote control operations. For the large-scale extractions from fuel elements, detailed studies of the effects of radiation on structural and process materials have also been required. There are numerous procedures for the separation of Np, Pu, and Am, variously involving precipitation, solvent extraction, differential volatility of compounds and so on, and we can give only the briefest outline. The most important separation methods are based on the following chemistry.

1. Stabilities of oxidation states. The stabilities of the major ions involved are: UO_2^{2+}, NpO_2^{2+} > PuO_2^{2+} > AmO_2^{2+}; Am^{3+} > Pu^{3+} $\gg$ Np^{3+}, U^{4+}. It is thus possible (see also Table 32-5) by choice of suitable oxidizing or reducing agents to obtain a solution containing the elements in different oxidation states; they can then be separated by precipitation or solvent extraction. For example, Pu can be oxidized to PuO_2^{2+} while Am remains as Am^{3+}—the former could be removed by solvent extraction or the latter by precipitation of AmF_3.

2. Extractability into organic solvents. As noted previously, the MO_2^{2+} ions can be extracted from nitrate solutions into organic solvents. The M^{4+} ions can be extracted into tributyl phosphate in kerosene from $6M$ nitric acid solutions; the M^{3+} ions can be similarly extracted from 10–$16M$ nitric acid; and neighboring actinides can be separated by a choice of conditions.

3. Precipitation reactions. Only M^{3+} and M^{4+} give insoluble fluorides or phosphates from acid solutions; the higher oxidation states give either no precipitate or precipitation can be prevented by complex formation with sulfate of other ions.

4. Ion exchange procedures. Although ion exchange procedures, both cationic and anionic, can be used to separate the actinide ions, they are best suited for small amounts of material. Since they have found most use in the separation of the trans-americium elements, these procedures are discussed later.

The following examples are for the separation of plutonium from uranium; similar procedures using the same basic principles have been devised to separate Np and Am. The initial starting material in plutonium extraction is a solution of the uranium fuel element (plus its aluminum or other protective jacket) in nitric acid. The combination of oxidation-reduction cycles coupled with solvent extraction and/or precipitation methods remove the bulk of fission products (FP's); however, certain elements—notably ruthenium, which forms cationic, neutral, and anionic nitrosyl complexes—may require special elimination steps. The initial uranyl nitrate solution contains Pu^{4+} since nitric acid cannot effect the oxidation to Pu^V or Pu^{VI}.

1. Methyl isobutyl ketone (hexone) method. This is shown in Scheme 32-1.

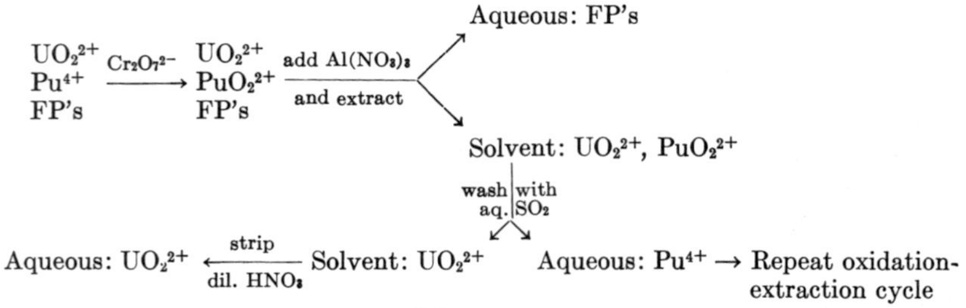

Aqueous: FP's

$$\begin{array}{c} UO_2^{2+} \\ Pu^{4+} \\ FP's \end{array} \xrightarrow{Cr_2O_7^{2-}} \begin{array}{c} UO_2^{2+} \\ PuO_2^{2+} \\ FP's \end{array} \xrightarrow[\text{and extract}]{\text{add Al(NO}_3)_3}$$

Solvent: UO_2^{2+}, PuO_2^{2+}

wash with
aq. SO_2

Aqueous: UO_2^{2+} $\xleftarrow[\text{dil. HNO}_3]{\text{strip}}$ Solvent: UO_2^{2+} Aqueous: Pu^{4+} → Repeat oxidation-
                                                                extraction cycle

Scheme 32-1

2. Tributyl phosphate method. The extraction coefficients from $6N$ nitric acid solutions are $Pu^{4+} > PuO_2^{2+}$; $Np^{4+} \gg Pu^{3+}$; $UO_2^{2+} > NpO_2^{+} > PuO_2^{2+}$; the M^{3+} have very low extraction coefficients in $6M$ acid, but from $12M$ hydrochloric acid or $16M$ nitric acid the extraction increases and the order is Np < Pu < Am < Cm < Bk.

Thus in the U–Pu separation, after addition of NO_2^{-} to adjust all of the plutonium to Pu^{4+}, we have Scheme 32-2.

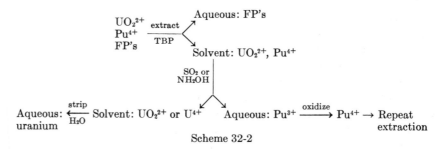

Aqueous: FP's

$$\begin{array}{c} UO_2^{2+} \\ Pu^{4+} \\ FP's \end{array} \xrightarrow[\text{TBP}]{\text{extract}}$$

Solvent: UO_2^{2+}, Pu^{4+}

SO_2 or
NH_2OH

Aqueous: $\xleftarrow[\text{H}_2\text{O}]{\text{strip}}$ Solvent: UO_2^{2+} or U^{4+} Aqueous: Pu^{3+} $\xrightarrow{\text{oxidize}} Pu^{4+}$ → Repeat
uranium   extraction

Scheme 32-2

3. Lanthanum fluoride cycle. This classical procedure was first developed by McMillan and Abelson for the isolation of neptunium, but it is applicable elsewhere and is of great utility. For the U–Pu separation again, we have Scheme 32-3. The cycle shown is repeated with progressively smaller amounts of lanthanum carrier and smaller volumes of solution until plutonium becomes the bulk phase. This fluoride cycle has also been used in combination with an initial precipitation step for Pu^{4+} using bismuth phosphate as a carrier.

32-20. The Elements and Binary Compounds

The metals of Np, Pu, and Am are prepared in the same way as uranium —by Ca or Ba reduction of the fluorides at $\sim 1200°C.$; they are silvery

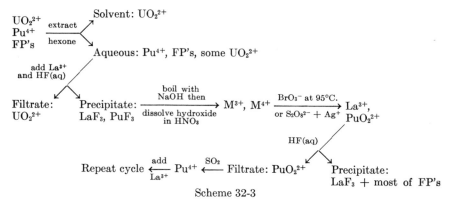

Scheme 32-3

metals and chemically very reactive. Plutonium metal has some unique properties; it has six allotropic forms below its melting point, each with different densities, coefficients of expansion, and resistivities and, most curiously, if the phase expands on heating the resistance decreases. Americium metal resembles the lanthanide metals much more than U, Np, or Pu and has physical properties quite different from them.

Oxides.   These are NpO_2, Np_3O_8, Pu_2O_3, PuO_2, Am_2O_3 and AmO_2. The important oxides of Np, Pu, and Am are the dioxides, which are obtained on heating the nitrates or hydroxides of any oxidation state in air; they are isostructural with UO_2. Ordinarily, PuO_2 is nonstoichiometric and may have different colors, but ignition at 1200°C. gives the stoichiometric oxide. For Pu, there is no higher oxide, but for Np, the oxide Np_3O_8, isomorphous with U_3O_8, can be obtained under specific conditions. Reduction of AmO_2 with hydrogen at 600°C. gives the reddish brown Am_2O_3, which is the first lanthanide-like sesquioxide in the actinide series.

All three oxide systems have various solid solutions and other non-stoichiometric complications.

Halides.   The halides are listed in Table 32-9.

The Np, Pu, and Am halides, which are isostructural with and chemically similar to those of uranium, clearly show the decrease in stability of compounds in the higher oxidation states, and this trend continues in the succeeding elements. The preparative methods used are also similar to those for uranium, for example,

$$NpO_2 + \tfrac{1}{2}H_2 + 3HF(g) \xrightarrow{500°C.} NpF_3 + 2H_2O$$

$$PuF_4 + F_2 \xrightarrow{500°C.} PuF_6$$

$$AmO_2 + 2CCl_4 \xrightarrow{800°C.} AmCl_3 + 2COCl_2 + \tfrac{1}{2}Cl_2$$

The fluorides, MF_3 and MF_4, can be precipitated from aqueous solutions

TABLE 32-9

Halides of Np, Pu, and Am

+3	+4	+6
NpF$_3$, purple-black	NpF$_4$, green	NpF$_6$, brown
PuF$_3$, purple	PuF$_4$, brown	PuF$_6$, red-brown
AmF$_3$, pink	AmF$_4$, tan	—
NpCl$_3$, white	NpCl$_4$, red-brown	
PuCl$_3$, emerald	—	
AmCl$_3$, pink	—	
NpBr$_3$, green	NpBr$_4$, red-brown	
PuBr$_3$, green	—	
AmBr$_3$, white	—	
NpI$_3$, brown	—	
PuI$_3$, brown	—	
AmI$_3$, yellow		

in hydrated form. The hexafluorides have been much studied since they are volatile; the melting points and stabilities decrease U > Np > Pu. PuF$_6$ contains two nonbonding $5f$ electrons and should be paramagnetic; however, like UF$_6$, where all the valence electrons are involved in bonding, it shows only a small temperature-independent paramagnetism. This observation has been explained by ligand field splitting of the f levels to give a lower-lying orbital which is doubly occupied.

Other Compounds. A substantial number of compounds, particularly of plutonium, are known, and most of them closely resemble their uranium analogs. The hydride systems of Np, Pu, and Am are more like those of thorium than that of uranium and are complex. Thus nonstoichiometry up to MH$_{2.7}$ is found in addition to stoichiometric hydrides such as PuH$_2$ and AmH$_2$.

32-21. Aqueous Chemistry of Neptunium, Plutonium, and Americium

The formal oxidation potentials have been given in Table 32-4 and the general stabilities of the ions in Table 32-5.

For Np, the potentials of the four oxidation states are separated, like those of uranium, but in this case the NpO$_2^+$ state is comparatively stable. With Pu, however, the potentials are not well separated and in 1M HClO$_4$ all four species can coexist in appreciable concentrations; PuO$_2^+$ becomes increasingly stable with decreasing acidity since the couples are strongly hydrogen ion dependent. The Am ions stable enough to exist in finite concentrations are Am^{3+}, AmO_2^+, and AmO_2^{2+}, and the Am^{3+} ion is the usual state since powerful oxidation is required to achieve the higher oxidation states. Alkaline solutions are more favorable for the stabilization of Am^{IV}, and for $1M$ basic solution the $Am(OH)_3$–$Am(OH)_4$ couple has a value of -0.5 v. (earlier estimates of $+0.4$ v. were wrong), nearly 2 v. more positive than the Am^{3+}–Am^{4+} couple in acid solution. Thus pink $Am(OH)_3$ can be readily converted to black $Am(OH)_4$ (or $AmO_2(aq)$) by the action of hypochlorite. This black hydroxide is also soluble in $15M$ ammonium fluoride solutions to give a fluoro anion of Am^{4+}.

As with uranium, the solution chemistry is complicated owing to hydrolysis and polynuclear ion formation, complex formation with anions other than perchlorate, and disproportionation reactions of some oxidation states. The tendency of ions to displace a proton from water increases with increasing charge and decreasing ion radius, so that the tendency to hydrolysis increases in the same order for each oxidation state, that is, $Am > Pu > Np > U$ and $M^{4+} > MO_2^{2+} > M^{3+} > MO_2^+$; simple ions such as NpO_2OH or $PuOH^{3+}$ are known in addition to polymeric species, which in the case of plutonium can have molecular weights up to 10^{10}.

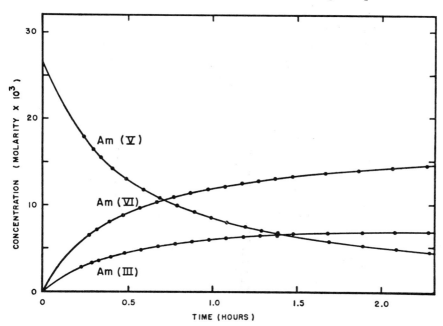

Fig. 32-5.   Disproportionation of AmO_2^+ in $6M$ perchloric acid at 25°C. (Reprinted with permission from J. S. Coleman, 138th Meeting, American Chemical Society, New York, Sept., 1960, Paper 62I.)

The complexing tendencies decrease in the same orders as the hydrolytic tendencies on the whole. The formation of complexes shifts the oxidation potentials, sometimes influencing the relative stabilities of oxidation states; thus the formation of sulfate complexes of Np^{4+} and NpO_2^{2+} is strong enough to cause disproportionation of NpO_2^+. The disproportionation reactions have been studied in some detail; Figures 32-5 and 32-6 illustrate some of the complexities involved.

The precipitation reactions of Np, Pu, and Am are similar to those of uranium in the corresponding oxidation states, for example, of $NaM^{VI}O_2(OCOCH_3)_3$ or MF_3, although differences occur owing to the

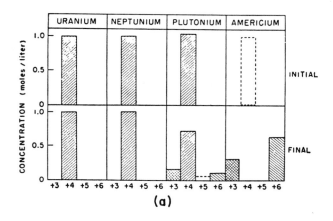

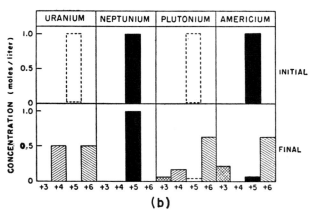

Fig. 32-6.   Disproportionation reactions of (a) tetra- and (b) pentapositive ions in $1M$ acid at 5°C. (Reprinted with permission from J. J. Katz and G. T. Seaborg, *The Chemistry of the Actinide Elements*, Methuen, London, 1957, p. 420.)

differing stabilities of the latter; thus Am^{3+} can be oxidized by ozone in rubidium carbonate to give the insoluble $Rb[Am^VO_2CO_3]$, which has no uranium analog.

THE TRANS-AMERICIUM ELEMENTS

32-22. General Remarks

The isotope ^{242}Cm was first isolated among the products of α-bombardment of ^{239}Pu, and its discovery actually preceded that of americium. Isotopes of the other elements were first identified in products from the first hydrogen bomb explosion or in cyclotron bombardments. Only curium has so far been obtained in macro amounts (Table 32-2), and all of the chemical information on Bk, Cf, etc., has been obtained on the tracer scale. Isotopes of sufficiently long life are now known for Bk, Cf, and Es so that in principle they could be isolated in macro amounts, although this possibility has not yet been realized; such macroscopic amounts would be intensely radioactive since even the longest-lived isotopes have fairly short half-lives. A few atoms of element 103, made by bombardment of Cf with B^{10} and B^{11} nuclei, have been recently identified by their α-particle energies; the isotope has a half-life of 8 seconds.

For these elements, the correspondence of the actinide and lanthanide series becomes most clearly revealed. The position of curium corresponds to that of gadolinium where the f shell is half-filled. For curium, the $+3$ oxidation state is the normal state in solution, although, unlike gadolinium, a solid tetrafluoride, CmF_4, has been obtained. Berkelium has $+3$ and $+4$ oxidation states, as would be expected from its position relative to terbium, but the $+4$ state of terbium does not exist in solution whereas for Bk it does.

The remaining elements, from Cf onward, have only the $+3$ state. The great similarity between the $+3$ ions of Am and the trans-americium elements has meant that the more conventional chemical operations successful for the separation of the previous actinide elements are inadequate, and most of the separations require the highly selective procedures of ion exchange discussed below; solvent extraction of the M^{3+} ions from $10-16M$ nitric acid by tributyl phosphate also gives reasonable separations.

32-23. Curium

Curium is isolated as macro amounts and the *metal* has been prepared on a microgram scale by reduction of CmF_3 with barium at $1275°C$. The metal is similar to the other actinides, but corrodes more rapidly, partially because of self-heating by radioactive decay.

A few solid curium compounds are known, for example, CmF_3, CmF_4, CmO_2. Where X-ray structural studies have been made—and these are difficult to achieve since amounts of the order of 0.5×10^{-6} g. must be used in order to avoid fogging of the film by radioactivity and destruction of the lattice by emitted particles—the compounds are isomorphous with other actinide compounds.

In view of the position of Cm in the actinide series, numerous experiments have been made to ascertain if Cm has only the $+3$ state in solution; no evidence for a lower state has been found. Concerning the $+4$ state, the potential of the Cm^{3+}–Cm^{4+} couple must be higher than that of Am^{3+}–Am^{4+}, which is -2.6 to -2.9 v., so that solutions of Cm^{4+} must be unstable. It has been found that if CmF_4, prepared by dry fluorination of CmF_3, is treated with $15M$ CsF at $0°C.$, a pale yellow solution is obtained which appears to contain Cm^{4+} as a fluoro complex. This solution exists for only an hour or so at $10°C.$; its spectrum resembles that of the isoelectronic Am^{3+} ion.

The solution reactions of Cm^{3+} closely resemble the lanthanide and actinide $+3$ ions, and the fluoride, oxalate, phosphate, iodate, and hydroxide are insoluble. There is some evidence for complexing in solution, although the complexes appear to be weaker than those of preceding elements.

The spectrum of CmF_3 closely resembles that of GdF_3 in the ultraviolet, and there is no long wavelength absorption (the ion is colorless); this supports the hypothesis that the ion has the $5f^7$ configuration, a view which is also confirmed by magnetic measurements on CmF_3 diluted in LaF_3.

32-24. Ion Exchange Separations

Ion exchange has been indispensable in the characterization of the transamericium elements and is also important for some of the preceding elements as well, particularly for tracer quantities of material. We have seen in the case of the lanthanides (Chapter 31) that the $+3$ ions can be eluted from a cation exchange column by various complexing agents, such as buffered citrate, lactate, or α-hydroxybutyrate solutions, and that the elution order follows the order of the hydrated ionic radii so that the lutetium is eluted first and lanthanum last. Using the actinide hypothesis and extrapolating from data obtained with the lighter actinides such as U^{3+}, Np^{3+}, and Pu^{3+}, it has been possible to predict quite precisely, *even to the exact drop*, where the heavier actinide ions should be eluted under prescribed conditions. Consummate use of these principles has allowed Seaborg and his collaborators to isolate and characterize the heavier actinides even when only a few *atoms* of the element have been present in the solution.

The main problems in this work have been two-fold: (*a*) the separation of the actinides as a group from the lanthanide ions (which are formed as fission fragments in the bombardments which product the actinides) and (*b*) the separation of the actinide elements from each other.

The first problem can be solved by the use of strong hydrochloric acid as an eluting agent; since the actinide ions form chloride complexes more easily, they are desorbed first from a cation exchange resin, thus effecting a *group* separation; conversely, the actinides are more strongly adsorbed on anion exchange resins. Although some of the actinide ions are themselves separated in the strong hydrochloric acid elutions on cationic columns, the resolution is not too satisfactory, particularly for Cf and Es.

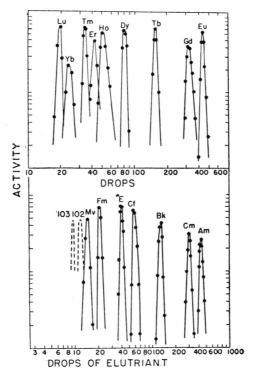

Fig. 32-7.   Elution of lanthanide +3 ions (upper) and actinide +3 ions (lower) from Dowex 50 cation exchange resin. Buffered ammonium α-hydroxylbutyrate was the eluant. The predicted positions of elements 102 and 103 (unobserved here) are shown by broken lines. (Reprinted with permission from J. J. Katz and G. T. Seaborg, *The Chemistry of the Actinide Elements*, Methuen, London, 1957, p. 435.)

A more effective group separation employs $10M$ LiCl as eluant for a moderately cross-linked, strongly basic anion exchange column operating at elevated temperatures up to $\sim 90°$C. In addition to affording a lanthanide-actinide separation, fractionation of the actinide elements into groups Pu, Am–Cm, Bk, and Cf–Es can be obtained. Except for unexplained reversals observed in the elution orders of Gd, Ho, Cm, and Es, the elution sequences proceed in the order of increasing Z, with La being the least strongly absorbed.

The actinide ions are effectively separated from each other by elution with citrate or similar eluants; some typical elution curves in which the relative positions of the corresponding lanthanides are also given are displayed in Figure 32-7. It will be noted that a very striking similarity occurs in the spacings of corresponding elements in the two series. There is a distinct break between Gd and Tb and between Cm and Bk, which can be attributed to the small change in ionic radius occasioned by the half-filling of the $4f$ and $5f$ shells, respectively. The elution order is not always as regular as that in Figure 32-7; with some complexing agents, for example, thiocyanate, complicated elution orders are found for the actinides. After the separation on ion exchange columns, the actinide ions are usually collected on an insoluble fluoride precipitate.

32-25. Chemical Properties of the Trans-Americium Elements

The chemical properties have been deduced from ion exchange behavior and from experiments with tracer quantities of material using other non-radioactive $+3$ ions as carriers.

Berkelium is the analog of Tb, and in addition to the $+3$ state could be expected to give a $+4$ ion. If Bk^{3+} solutions in nitric acid are oxidized with bromate or other powerful oxidant, the berkelium can be precipitated by phosphate, iodate, or phenylarsenate using Ce^{4+} or Zr^{4+} as carrier substance. By comparing the amounts of radioactive Ce^{4+} and Bk^{4+} carried by zirconium precipitates, it was concluded that the Bk^{3+}–Bk^{4+} couple lies within about 60 mv. of the Ce^{3+}–Ce^{4+} couple, so that the formal potential can be estimated to be about -1.62 v. In the $+4$ state, berkelium can be readily solvent extracted (cf. Ce^{4+}) by hexane solutions of bis(2-ethylhexyl) hydrogen phosphate or similar complexing agents.

There is no evidence that Cf exists in the $+4$ state in aqueous solution, but it behaves as a typical $+3$ ion, being coprecipitated with the fluoride, oxalate, or hydroxide of lanthanum; the ions of Es, Fm, and Md, insofar as they have been studied, also have only the $+3$ oxidation state.

We may finally note the origin of the names of the new synthetic elements. The names neptunium and plutonium follow uranium in being named after the planets; americium was named in honor of the Americas and corresponds to europium in the lanthanides; curium was named after the Curies since the corresponding lanthanide was named after the lanthanide pioneer Gadolin; berkelium, from Berkeley, is the homolog of terbium, which was named after Ytterby in Sweden where lanthanide ores were found; californium was named in honor of the university and state where the element was discovered; einsteinium and fermium were named after the great physicists Einstein and Fermi, nobelium after Nobel, lawrencium after Lawrence, originator of the cyclotron, and mendelevium in honor of the great Russian originator of the periodic table.

References

Asprey, L. B., and B. B. Cunningham, "Unusual Oxidation States of Some Actinide and Lanthanide Elements," in F. A. Cotton, ed., *Progress in Inorganic Chemistry*, Vol. II, Interscience, New York–London, 1960, p. 267.

Belle, J., ed., *Uranium Dioxide, Properties and Nuclear Applications*, Naval Reactors, Division of Reactor Development, U. S. Atomic Energy Commission (U. S. Govt. Printing Office, Washington, D. C.), 1961.

Comyns, A. E., *Chem. Revs.*, **60**, 115 (1960). A comprehensive review (584 references) of the coordination chemistry of the actinides.

Friedlander, G., and J. W. Kennedy, *Introduction to Nuclear Chemistry*, 2nd ed., Wiley, New York, 1955. Discussion of radioactivity and nuclear stability.

Grison, E., W. B. M. Lord, R. D. Fowler, eds., *Plutonium* **1960**, Cleaver-Hume Press, London, 1961.

Hindman, J. C., T. K. Keenan, B. B. Cunningham, and G. T. Seaborg, *J. Chem. Educ.*, **36**, 15 (1959). A symposium on the new elements and review articles on Np, Pu, Am, Cm, Bk, Cf, and the trans-californium elements.

Hodge, N., *Advances in Fluorine Chemistry*, Vol. II, Butterworths, London, 1961, p. 138. Fluorides of the actinide elements.

Katz, J. J., and G. T. Seaborg, *The Chemistry of the Actinide Elements*, Methuen, London, 1957. A lucidly written reference text containing most of the information on these elements.

Katz, J. J., and I. Sheft, in H. J. Emeléus and A. G. Sharpe, eds., *Advances in Inorganic Chemistry and Radiochemistry*, Vol. 2, Academic Press, New York, 1960, p. 195. Detailed account of the halides of the actinides with a collection of available physical data.

Makarov, E. S., *Crystal Chemistry of Simple Compounds of U, Th, Pu and Np*, (trans.), Consultants Bureau, New York, 1959.

Martin, F. S., and G. L. Miles, *Chemical Processing of Nuclear Fuels*, Butterworths, London, 1958. A short book with descriptions of the various procedures for isolating actinide elements from nuclear reactor fuels.

Roberts, L. E. J., *Quart. Revs. (London)*, **15**, 442 (1961). The actinide oxides.

Seaborg, G. T., and J. J. Katz, eds., *The Actinide Elements*, National Nuclear Energy Series, Vol. 14A, McGraw-Hill, New York, 1954. A detailed account of the actinide elements.

Appendix

A. ADDITIONAL DETAILS CONCERNING ATOMIC STRUCTURE

A-1. Bohr's Treatment of the Hydrogen Atom

Equation 1-1 can be derived easily using simple classical physics and the assumption that angular momentum can take only the values $\mathbf{h}/2\pi$, $2\mathbf{h}/2\pi$, $3\mathbf{h}/2\pi$, ..., $n\mathbf{h}/2\pi$. If one electron of mass m is moving in a circular path around a nucleus of atomic number Z, the centrifugal and centripetal forces on it must be equal. The centrifugal force is purely coulombic and is given by Ze^2/r^2, where e is the electronic charge, Ze is the nuclear charge, and r is the radius of the circular path. The centripetal force is equal to the mass, m, times the angular acceleration, v^2/r, where v is the linear velocity of the electron. Equating the centrifugal and centripetal forces and rearranging we get

$$\frac{Ze^2}{r^2} = \frac{mv^2}{r} \qquad \text{or} \qquad mvr = \frac{Ze^2}{v} \tag{A-1}$$

Now mvr is the classical angular momentum of the electron. Bohr *postulated* that this should be quantized in units of $\mathbf{h}/2\pi$, that is, that

$$mvr = n\frac{\mathbf{h}}{2\pi} \qquad n = 1, 2, 3, \ldots \tag{A-2}$$

which may be rearranged to read

$$v = \frac{n\mathbf{h}}{2\pi mr} \tag{A-3}$$

On substituting equations A-2 and A-3 into equation A-1, we obtain the following expression for the radii of the circular paths:

$$r = \frac{n^2}{Z}\frac{\mathbf{h}^2}{4\pi^2 me^2} = n^2\frac{a_0}{Z} \tag{A-4}$$

The quantity a_0 is the radius of the path of the electron in the hydrogen atom ($Z = 1$) in its ground state ($n = 1$), according to Bohr's theory. Its value, calculated from the known values of the fundamental constants which comprise it, is 0.5292 A. It is called the Bohr radius and is often used as a natural unit of length on the atomic scale.

In all of the above, there is a slight inaccuracy. We have implicitly assumed that the nucleus does not move and thus used the exact mass of the electron alone in expressions for force and momentum. Actually the nucleus and electron both rotate about a common point, the center of mass of the system. The above equations can be made exact by substituting for the mass of the electron, m, the *reduced mass*, μ, given by

$$\mu = m \left(\frac{M}{m + M} \right) \tag{A-5}$$

where M is the mass of the nucleus. Clearly, the greater the mass of the nucleus the more closely μ approaches m. Even for hydrogen, $m/\mu \sim 1.0005$.

The energy of the one-electron atom, as defined above, can be written classically as the sum of its kinetic and potential energies. The former is just $\mu v^2/2$, and the latter, the coulombic potential energy, $-Ze^2/r$ (negative since the two charges, $+Ze$ and $-e$, are of opposite sign).

$$E = \tfrac{1}{2}\mu v^2 - \frac{2e^2}{r} \tag{A-6}$$

If we now substitute for v and r the expressions given in A-3 and A-4, we obtain

$$E_n = \frac{2\pi^2\mu Z^2 e^4}{n^2 h^2}$$

from which equation 1-1 follows on setting $Z = 1$.

A-2. The Quantization of Light

Beginning around the turn of the century certain experiments were performed by physicists which led to the idea that in various physical systems the energy could not in fact have all of the values within the range allowed by the Newtonian laws, but only certain discrete values. A system restricted to such discrete energy values is said to be *quantized* and the theory describing quantized systems is called the quantum theory. The first instance in which it became necessary to assume quantization arbitrarily in order to calculate results in agreement with experimental observation was in interpreting the behavior of the so-called "black-body." This is defined as a body which does not reflect radiation but is a perfect absorber and hence also a perfect emitter. A small hole into a cavity is a physical approximation to the ideal black body. The presence of this small hole only slightly disturbs the equilibrium between the thermal energy of the inner walls of the box and the radiant energy in the box. At any given temperature the equilibrium distribution of radiant energy in the box as a function of frequency will have a definite form shown schematically in Figure A-1. At equilibrium the molecular dipole oscillators in the walls of the box are radiating energy of many frequencies into the cavity at the same rate at which they are absorbing radiation of those frequencies from the cavity. On the assumption that all values of energy for the oscillators and the radiation are permitted, Rayleigh and Jeans derived an expression for the distribution of radiation which is also shown in Figure A-1. It will be seen that at low frequencies it fits the experimental curve, but that it tends to infinity with increasing frequency, a fact so disturbing at the time that it was called the "ultraviolet catastrophe." Some time later, Max Planck showed that one could, by introducing one assumption into the Rayleigh-Jeans treatment, avoid the ultraviolet catastrophe and obtain a completely accurate description of black-body radiation. The necessary assumption was that only certain

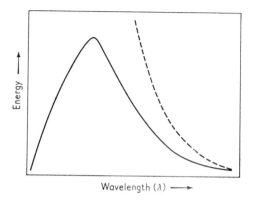

Fig. A-1. Distribution of energy as a function of wavelength in black body radiation: (——) experimental; (— — — —) Rayleigh-Jeans curve.

energies were permitted for the radiation and for the oscillators, namely, those energies, E, given by

$$E = \mathbf{h}\bar{\nu} \tag{A-7}$$

where $\bar{\nu}$ is the frequency of the radiation or the oscillator in oscillations per second and $\mathbf{h}$ is a constant, called *Planck's constant*. It was necessary to choose a value of 6.62×10^{-27} erg-seconds for $\mathbf{h}$. This *ad hoc* assumption that both radiation and mechanical oscillators are quantized had no justification in classical physics and had only the fact that it enabled one to obtain the correct answer to recommend it.

However, the notion of quantization, with exactly the same constant, $\mathbf{h}$, involved, was soon extended to other puzzling problems and its success required it to be entertained seriously, however much its disturbingly *ad hoc* nature might be deplored.

In 1905 Einstein proposed an explanation of the *photoelectric effect* which utilized the idea that radiant energy is quantized. The term photoelectric effect refers to the ejection of electrons from the surface of a body by radiation impinging on that surface. The experimental facts of the photoelectric effect may be briefly summarized with reference to Figure A-2.

Figure A-2a shows that no electrons are ejected at all until light of frequency at least equal to $\bar{\nu}_0$ is used, and that thereafter the maximum kinetic energy KE_{max} of the photoelectrons is a linear function of frequency. An equally important fact, exemplified in Fig. A-2b, is that for any frequency $\bar{\nu}$ greater than $\bar{\nu}_0$, the maximum kinetic energy of the photoelectrons is independent of the intensity of the light. The more intense the light, the *more* electrons are ejected, but none will have an energy greater than the kinetic energy characteristic of the frequency for the particular material. Einstein pointed out that these facts could be explained by the following equation

$$KE_{max} = \mathbf{h}\bar{\nu} - p \tag{A-8}$$

The energy, p, is called the work function of the surface and is the energy necessary merely to separate an electron from the surface with zero kinetic energy. Thus since the energy of radiation is $\mathbf{h}\bar{\nu}$, as soon as $\bar{\nu}$ becomes greater than $p/\mathbf{h}$ there is enough

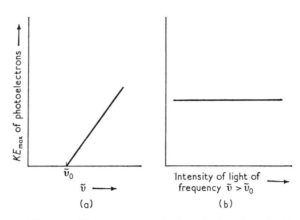

Fig. A-2.   Diagrams illustrating certain facts in the photoelectric effect.

energy available to detach an electron *and* impart some kinetic energy to it. The significance of the fact that $E_{\max}$ is independent of intensity is very considerable. It means that energy in the form of light is not continuously and uniformly distributed, but occurs in small packets, which Einstein called *quanta*. It must be assumed that light can only be produced or absorbed in whole quanta, and generally, only one quantum at a time if the above facts are to be accounted for. In 1916, Millikan made some beautiful experiments on the photoelectric effect in which he measured the slopes of the lines in plots like Figure A-2a, and could then calculate the value of h. His value was 6.62×10^{-27} erg-seconds, the same as found before in the other phenomena. This idea that light of frequency $\bar{\nu}$ is composed of indivisible quanta each of energy **h$\bar{\nu}$** is a very important result of old quantum theory which remains valid in later theories and should be clearly grasped.

This idea that light consists of discrete quanta recalls the Newtonian Corpuscular Theory of light which had been abandoned in favor of the wave theory for the very good reason that, on close observation, light behaves as if it were waves. Thus phenomena such as diffraction seemed inexplicable in the corpuscular theory but quite to be expected in the wave theory. In order to retain the wave theory with all its advantages along with the new idea of quanta which is also necessary for a description of all the properties of light, we must regard the amplitude of the wave as representing the density of discrete quanta at a point rather than as the envelope of a continuous distribution of radiant energy. Another way of stating the new interpretation of the wave form ascribed to the radiation is to say that the amplitude of the wave at any point represents the probability of photons being found at that point.

Einstein in 1907 showed that, if one assumes that the oscillatory motion of atoms and molecules in crystals is quantized according to equation A-7, an equation for the specific heat, C_v, of a solid can be derived which correctly predicts that C_v goes to zero at the absolute zero, whereas classical theory erroneously required a constant value of C_v equal to $3R$ at all temperatures. Later Debye improved the Einstein theory by considering the possible modes of vibration in detail, and, retaining the quantum condition, produced an equation which represents the actual specific heat of a solid extremely well at all temperatures.

Thus an understanding of all of these three phenomena—black body radiation, the photoelectric effect, and the specific heat of solids—require the idea of the quantization of light and of certain dynamic processes on the atomic scale.

A-3. Solution of the Wave Equation for the Hydrogen Atom

To solve equation 1-14, we may look for solutions of the general form

$$\psi = R(r)\Theta(\theta)\Phi(\varphi)$$

in which we write ψ, which is in general a function of all three coordinates, r, θ, and φ, as a product of $R(r)$, a function only of r, $\Theta(\theta)$, a function only of θ and $\Phi(\varphi)$, a function only of φ. If we substitute equation 1-16 into equation 1-14 and rearrange we get

$$\frac{1}{R}\frac{\partial}{\partial r}\left(r^2\frac{\partial R}{\partial r}\right) + \frac{8\pi^2\mu}{h^2}\left(E + \frac{e^2}{r}\right)r^2 = -\frac{1}{\Theta\sin\theta}\frac{d}{d\theta}\left(\sin\theta\frac{d\Theta}{d\theta}\right) - \frac{1}{\phi\sin^2\theta}\frac{d^2\Phi}{d\varphi^2} \quad \text{(A-9)}$$

Now the LHS of equation A-9 depends only on r whereas the RHS depends only on θ and φ. Consequently, in order for equation A-9 to hold for all values of r, θ, and φ, each side must separately equal a constant, λ. Thus we write, with a little rearrangement:

$$\frac{\sin\theta}{\Theta}\frac{d}{d\theta}\left(\sin\theta\frac{d\Theta}{d\theta}\right) + \lambda\sin^2\theta = -\frac{1}{\Phi}\frac{d^2\Phi}{d\varphi^2} \quad \text{(A-10)}$$

and

$$\frac{1}{r^2}\frac{d}{dr}\left(r^2\frac{dR}{dr}\right) + \left[\frac{8\pi^2\mu}{h^2}\left(E + \frac{e^2}{r}\right) - \frac{\lambda}{r^2}\right]R = 0 \quad \text{(A-11)}$$

Now inspection of equation A-10 shows that for the same reason we separated equation A-9 into equation A-10 and A-11, we can separate equation A-10 into equations A-12 and A-13:

$$\frac{\sin\theta}{\Theta}\frac{d}{d\theta}\left(\sin\theta\frac{d\Theta}{d\theta}\right) + \lambda\sin^2\theta = m^2 \quad \text{(A-12)}$$

$$\frac{d^2\phi}{d\varphi^2} = -m^2\Phi \quad \text{(A-13)}$$

where m is some constant. We now have three separate equations, A-11, A-12, and A-13, whose solutions will tell us how the form of the wave functions of the hydrogen atom depends on the coordinates r, θ, and φ, respectively.

We can begin by solving equation A-13. It is easily found that the only solutions which satisfy the requirements for good wave functions which we have discussed are

$$\Phi = (2\pi)^{-1/2}\exp(im\varphi) \quad \text{(A-14)}$$

in which m must be a positive or negative integer; m is therefore a quantum number. Now it is found that the solutions to equation A-12 are rather complicated when written out in their general form and we shall not give the general solution here. The most important point is that all of these solutions, that is, the various Θ's are functions of the quantum numbers l and m. l may take only positive integral values and m may take all integral values from $-l$ to $+l$ for any given value of l:

$$l = 0, 1, 2, 3, \ldots$$
$$m = l(l-1),\ (l-2),\ \ldots,\ 0,\ -1,\ \ldots,\ -l$$

Finally, when equation A-11 is solved in terms of l which is related to λ by the expression $\lambda = l(l+1)$, a set of radial wave functions is obtained. In so doing, we also solve equation A-11 for the energy of the system

$$E_n = -\frac{1}{n^2}\frac{2\pi^2\mu^2 e^4}{h^2} \tag{A-15}$$

where n is still another quantum number and may take all positive integral values from 1 to ∞. Furthermore, the possible values which l may have are related to the value of n so that

$$l = (n-1),\ (n-2),\ \ldots,\ 0$$

It will be noted that the energy of the hydrogen atom is found to depend only on the quantum number n, which is called the *principal quantum number*, and it is given by exactly the same expression as that derived by Bohr (eq. 1-1).

B. STUDY PROBLEMS FOR CHAPTERS 1 AND 2

B-1. Some Study Problems on Atomic Structure

1. Show that ψ_1 (eq. 1-15) is normalized.

2. Show by applying calculus that the maximum in Figure 1-5 lies at precisely a_0.

3. Insert ψ_1 into equation 1-14 and calculate the energy to show that it is the same as that obtained in the Bohr theory, namely, $(-2\pi^2 m e^4/h^2)$. The Bohr radius, a_0, is equal to $h^2/4\pi^2 m e^2$).

4. Make a list of all of the first 36 atoms which are paramagnetic in their ground states and give the number of unpaired spins in each.

5. The wavelengths of the first three lines in a certain series in the emission spectrum of hydrogen are 6562.8, 4861.4, 4340.5, and 4101.8 A. Identify the quantum number of the lower state, the quantum numbers of the upper states, and calculate the value of Rydberg's constant in units of cm.$^{-1}$.

6. Calculate the ionization potential of the F^{8+} ion from the ground state and the state $3d$.

7. Without consulting a periodic table, give the atomic numbers of the following: (a) the fourth inert gas, (b) the third alkali metal, (c) the third chalcogen, (d) the fourth halogen, (e) platinum, (f) atoms with maximum number of unpaired $3p$ and $4p$ electrons.

8. The following information can be given about the nitrogen atom: (a) electron configuration: $1s^2 2s^2 2p^3$; (b) number of unpaired electrons: 3; (c) the lowest energy configuration having two more unpaired electrons: $1s^2 2s 2p^3 3s$. Give the same information in the same form for boron, silicon, selenium, iron, etc. using no information other than the atomic number of the element (refer to Table 1-2).

B-2. Some Study Problems for Chapter 2

1. Evaluate the Madelung constant for a one-dimensional array of ions of alternating sign with a distance x between adjacent ions to five significant figures. Show that the

exact analytical expression for this Madelung constant is 2 ln 2. (Consult a handbook of chemistry and physics or other reference giving the sums of some commonly occurring infinite series.)

2. Show how the value of the critical radius ratio (4.55) for the zinc blende structure was obtained.

3. From the data in Table B-1 calculate two values for the electron affinity of chlorine and compare these values to that given in the literature (4.01 e.v.).

TABLE B-1

	NaCl	KCl[a]
ΔH_f, kcal./mole	−98.3	−104.4
ΔH_{sub} of metal, kcal.	25.9	19.8
I of metal, e.v.	5.14	4.34
Shortest interionic distance, A.	2.81	3.14
$\Delta H_{Cl_2}^{diss} = 57.8$ kcal./mole		

 [a] KCl has the NaCl structure.

4. Assuming that in $K^+[BF_4^-]$ the tetrahedral BF_4^- ion can be treated as a large, round monatomic anion, calculate the following: (a) the lattice energy of $K^+[BF_4]^-$; (b) the heat of formation of $BF_4^-(g)$; (c) the enthalpy of the reaction

$$BF_3(g) + F^-(g) = BF_4^-(g)$$

[KBF$_4$ has the NaCl structure, with the shortest cation to anion distance (K—B distance) equal to 3.63 A. Assume n in the Born repulsion term to be 9. ΔH_f° of KBF$_4$(s) = −424 kcal./mole. ΔH_f° of BF$_3$(g) = −268 kcal./mole. ΔH_{sub} of K = 19.8 kcal./mole. I of K = 4.34 e.v. $\Delta H_{F_2}^{diss}$ = 37.0 kcal./mole. A of F = 82 kcal./mole.]

5. Take the lattice energy of NaCl to be 7.94 e.v. The following interionic distances (A.) have been observed experimentally: Na—Cl in NaCl, 2.79; Mg—Cl in MgCl$_2$, 2.46; and Na—S in Na$_2$S, 2.88. If MgS is assumed to have the NaCl structure, what is the best estimate that can be made of its lattice energy using only the above data?

6. Using the mean value of the electron affinity of chlorine calculated in problem 3, calculate the lattice energy of CsCl in kcal./mole, using the Born-Haber cycle and the following data: ΔH_f(CsCl), −103.5 kcal./mole; ΔH_{sub}(Cs), 18.8 kcal./mole; I of Cs(g), 3.959 e.v.

7. Calculate the lattice energy of CsCl given that r(Cs—Cl) = 3.566 A. and that the Madelung constant for CsCl structure is 1.7627. Compare this with the result obtained in problem 6.

C. SOME ADDITIONAL DETAILS
CONCERNING COVALENT BONDS

C-1. The Construction of sp or Digonal Hybrids

They must be of the form $N(s + kp)$, where k must be ± 1 since the squares of the two contributions, $(1s)^2$ and $(kp)^2$, must be equal, and they must be orthogonal. It is easy to verify that the combinations $N(s + p)$ and $N'(s - p)$ are orthogonal:

$$\int N(s + p)N'(s - p)d\tau = NN' \int s^2 d\tau - NN' \int p^2 d\tau$$
$$= NN'(1 - 1) = 0$$

Finally it is easily shown that $N = N' = 1/\sqrt{2}$; for example,

$$\int [N(s + p)][N(s + p)]d\tau = N^2 \int s^2 d\tau + N^2 \int p^2 d\tau = 2N^2 = 1$$

Therefore
$$N = 1/\sqrt{2}$$

Thus normalized and orthogonal sp hybrid orbitals, also frequently called digonal hybrids, are:

$$\psi_1 = 1/\sqrt{2}(s + p)$$
$$\psi_2 = 1/\sqrt{2}(s - p)$$

It can easily be shown by plotting the angular wave functions that these two orbitals have their largest lobes directed in opposite directions along the axis of the original p orbital, as shown in Figure 3-6.

C-2. The Construction of sp² or Trigonal Hybrids

We can easily work out the expressions for these orbitals by invoking the requirements that they be equivalent, meaning that the proportion of s character to p character be the same in all of them, and that they be normalized. We shall see that in this particular case the orthogonality takes care of itself, but not all cases are as overdetermined as this one.

Let us choose to direct the first hybrid along the x axis (see Fig. 3-7), and make the coefficient of p_x $\sqrt{2}$ times that of s since the orbital must have twice as much p character as s character. This gives us

$$\psi_1 = N(s + \sqrt{2}p_x)$$

and the normalization factor is easily shown to have the value of $1/\sqrt{3}$. In order to work out the expressions for the other two orbitals to which s, p_x, and p_y will all contribute, we make use of the fact that orbitals behave like vectors in the sense that if an orbital makes a contribution χ in a certain direction it makes a contribution $\chi \cos \theta$ in a direction θ from the first. Thus, considering ψ_2 to be the orbital lying in the second quadrant (Fig. 3-7) and ψ_3 to be the one in the third quadrant, we proceed as follows. The contribution of the s orbital is isotropic and the three hybrid orbitals are all to have the same amount of s character. Moreover, by virtue of the vectorial properties of the atomic and hybrid orbitals, p_y and p_x must contribute to ψ_2 in the proportions cos 30°($\sqrt{3}/2$) and cos 120°($-1/2$) and to ψ_3 in the proportions $-\cos 30°(-\sqrt{3}/2)$ and cos 240°($-1/2$). Thus we can write

$$\psi_2 = (1/\sqrt{3})s + \alpha[(-1/2)p_x + (\sqrt{3}/2)p_y]$$
$$\psi_3 = (1/\sqrt{3})s + \beta[(-1/2)p_x - (\sqrt{3}/2)p_y]$$

It is now necessary to adjust α and β so that each of these orbitals is normalized. For α:

$$\int \psi_2\psi_2 d\tau = \tfrac{1}{3}\int ss d\tau + \tfrac{1}{4}\alpha^2 \int p_x p_x d\tau + \tfrac{3}{4}\alpha^2 \int p_z p_z d\tau$$
$$= \tfrac{1}{3} + \alpha^2 = 1$$

whence, α equals $\sqrt{2}/\sqrt{3}$. The same value is obtained for β and the final expressions for the three trigonal hybrid orbitals are therefore:

$$\psi_1 = (1/\sqrt{3})s + (\sqrt{2}/\sqrt{3})p_x$$
$$\psi_2 = (1/\sqrt{3})s - (1/\sqrt{6})p_x + (1/\sqrt{2})p_y$$
$$\psi_3 = (1/\sqrt{3})s - (1/\sqrt{6})p_x - (1/\sqrt{2})p_y$$

It is now easily shown that these orbitals are mutually orthogonal. For example:

$$\int \psi_1\psi_2 d\tau = \int [(1/\sqrt{3})s]^2 d\tau - \int [(\sqrt{2}/\sqrt{3})p_x][(1/\sqrt{6})p_x]d\tau$$
$$= 1/3 - 1/3 = 0$$

It is also easy to show that the ratio of p to s character is $2:1$ in ψ_2 and ψ_3 as well as in ψ_1:

$$\frac{(-1/\sqrt{6})^2 + (\pm 1/\sqrt{2})^2}{(1/\sqrt{3})^2} = \frac{1/6 + 1/2}{1/3} = \frac{2}{1}$$

C-3. Relative Energies of Simple Molecular Orbitals in the LCAO Approximation

When two hydrogen atoms interact, their 1s orbitals combine to form molecular orbitals. If the two 1s orbitals are ϕ_A and ϕ_B, these molecular orbitals will have the following forms according to LCAO theory:

$$\psi_b = (1/\sqrt{2})(\phi_A + \phi_B)$$
$$\psi_a = (1/\sqrt{2})(\phi_A - \phi_B)$$

Expressions for the energies of these MO's are easily derived as follows:

$$E \text{ of } \psi_a = \frac{\tfrac{1}{2}\int (\phi_A - \phi_B)H(\phi_A - \phi_B)d\tau}{\tfrac{1}{2}\int (\phi_A - \phi_B)(\phi_A - \phi_B)d\tau}$$
$$= \tfrac{1}{2}[\int \phi_A H\phi_A d\tau + \int \phi_B H\phi_B d\tau - 2\int \phi_A H\phi_B d\tau]$$
$$= \tfrac{1}{2}[E_A + E_B - 2E_{AB}]$$
$$= E_H - E_{AB}$$

Similarly

$$E \text{ of } \psi_b = E_H + E_{AB}$$

In the above derivation $E_A = E_B = E_H$ since each of these represents the energy of a hydrogen atom in its ground state. E_{AB} represents an additional energy due to the interaction. Since both E_H and E_{AB} are intrinsically negative quantities we see that the bonding MO, ψ_b is more stable than the 1s orbital of the hydrogen atom by E_{AB} whereas the antibonding MO, ψ_a, is less stable than the 1s orbital of hydrogen by E_{AB}. These conclusions are in agreement with our interpretation of the electron density distribution required by ψ_a and ψ_b, and are illustrated in an energy level diagram (Fig. 3-9).

D. MEASUREMENT OF MAGNETIC SUSCEPTIBILITIES BY THE GOUY METHOD

Figure D-1 shows a simple diagram of the Gouy apparatus.

The pole pieces (A) of the magnet are usually cylindrical (this is not essential, however), so that the magnetic field (B) is symmetrical about the axis of the magnet. It is strongest at the center where the bottom of the sample column is, and falls off rapidly in radial directions so that it is very small at the top of the sample column. The sample

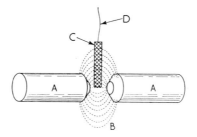

Fig. D-1.   Schematic diagram of the Gouy balance for measuring magnetic susceptibilities.

(C) is in the form of a cylindrical rod—either as a uniformly packed solid or a solution in a glass tube—and is suspended from a balance, not shown in Figure D-1. It can be shown that under these conditions there will be an apparent change in the mass of the sample when the field is turned on which is given by

$$\Delta m = \tfrac{1}{2}\kappa H^2 A$$

where H is the field strength at the center in Oersteds; κ is the volume susceptibility of the sample; and A is the cross-sectional area of the sample column. It is assumed that the field at the top of the sample is negligible, and the sample must be long enough to ensure that this is so. For a paramagnetic substance the mass will appear to increase when the field is applied and for a diamagnetic substance it will appear to decrease. Thus, knowing the field strength when the field is turned on—and this is ordinarily measured by measuring the change of mass for a substance of known κ—and knowing the cross-section of the sample, it is easy to determine κ.

Having ascertained the magnitude of κ, we convert this into χ_g, the susceptibility per gram, by dividing κ by the density, d, and we then convert χ_g to χ_M, the susceptibility per mole, by multiplying χ_g by the molecular weight,

$$\chi_M = M\chi_g = M\kappa/d$$

It is also customary to make a small correction to χ_M for the diamagnetic part of the susceptibility. This can usually be done with satisfactory accuracy using tables of the diamagnetic contributions of various atoms and structural units. From the value of χ_M^{corr} so obtained, we then calculate the magnetic moment of the particular paramagnetic ion or atom as described on pages 509–511 of the text.

E. EQUIVALENCE OF THE d_{z^2} AND $d_{x^2-y^2}$ ORBITALS IN AN OCTAHEDRAL FIELD

The equivalence of the d_{z^2} and $d_{x^2-y^2}$ orbitals in an octahedral field can be demonstrated in the following way.

The solutions to the wave equation for $l = 2$, that is, for a set of d orbitals, can be obtained as the following six functions:

$$\psi_1 \approx xy \qquad \psi_4 \approx x^2 - y^2$$
$$\psi_2 \approx yz \qquad \psi_5 \approx y^2 - z^2$$
$$\psi_3 \approx zx \qquad \psi_6 \approx z^2 - x^2$$

Only five such functions can be linearly independent, and the normal practice is to combine ψ_5 and ψ_6 to give the so-called "z^2" orbital:

$$"z^2" = (1/\sqrt{2})(\psi_6 - \psi_5) = (1/\sqrt{2})(2z^2 - x^2 - y^2)$$

Now in an octahedral field ψ_4, ψ_5, and ψ_6 are obviously all equivalent: $(y^2 - z^2)$ and $(z^2 - x^2)$ having forms analogous to that of $(x^2 - y^2)$, but differently oriented (Fig. E-1).

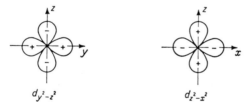

Fig. E-1.   Sketches of $d_{y^2-z^2}$ and $d_{z^2-x^2}$ orbitals which are usually combined to make the d_{z^2} orbital.

Since the $(y^2 - z^2)$ and $(z^2 - x^2)$ orbitals are equivalent to one another and to the $(x^2 - y^2)$ orbital, the normalized linear combination of $(y^2 - z^2)$ with $(z^2 - x^2)$ which we call the z^2 orbital must also be equivalent to the $(x^2 - y^2)$ orbital.

F. EXPERIMENTAL MEASUREMENT OF STABILITY CONSTANTS

There are a great many methods for experimental evaluation of equilibrium constants for the formation and transformation reactions of complexes in solution. We shall mention here just a few of the most common and important ones.

F-1. Leden's Method

This method is in principle always applicable, but it is used mainly for systems in which the ligand possesses no property such as acidity or basicity by means of which its concentration may be followed conveniently. It is then necessary to measure the activity of the metal ion as a function of varying ligand concentration. This can often be done with high sensitivity by measuring the potential, E, of the metal–metal ion electrode:

$$E = E^0 + (RT/nF) \ln [M^{n+}] \tag{F-1}$$

in which $[M^{n+}]$ represents the thermodynamic activity of the free metal ion, M^{n+}, and the collection of constants, $(RT \ln 10)/F$, has the value 59.16 mv. at 25°C. Thus equation F-1 may be written

$$E = E^0 + [(5.916 \times 10^{-2})/n] \log [M^{n+}]$$

The problem then is to relate the measured values of E and hence of $[M^{n+}]$ at various concentrations of ligand to the equilibrium constants for the system. Suppose we are dealing with a metal ion whose maximum coordination number for the ligand concerned is 4 (e.g., Cd^{2+}—CN^-). Then the total concentration of metal ion, C_M, free and in all of the possible complexes, is given by

$$C_M = [M] + [ML] + [ML_2] + [ML_3] + [ML_4] \tag{F-2}$$

The concentration of each complex may then be expressed in terms of the free ligand concentration, $[L]$, and the free metal ion concentration, $[M]$, using the over-all formation constants, β_i's (see Section 25-7). Thus:

$$\begin{aligned} C_M &= [M] + \beta_1[M][L] + \beta_2[M][L]^2 + \beta_3[M][L]^3 + \beta_4[M][L]^4 \\ &= [M]\{1 + \beta_1[L] + \beta_2[L]^2 + \beta_3[L]^3 + \beta_4[L]^4\} \end{aligned} \tag{F-3}$$

If the electromotive force measurements can be carried out on solutions in which the total metal concentration is only a very small fraction of the total ligand concentration, then the free ligand concentration, $[L]$, may be taken to good approximation as the same as the total ligand concentration. In the above example, then, e.m.f. measurements on each of four solutions containing different concentrations of ligand would provide sufficient data to define four simultaneous equations in the β_i's. Providing the data are obtained on solutions which differ sufficiently in their degrees of complex formation, these equations should be linearly independent and can be solved to give the β_i's. In practice an entire curve of E versus $[L]$ is obtained, and in this vastly overdetermined situation the constants can be evaluated quite accurately.

The chief drawback in this method is that relatively few metals form thermodynamically reversible electrodes.

An important variant on this method involves the use of a polarograph in place of the simple metal electrode.

F-2. Bjerrum's Method

This is a technique devised by J. Bjerrum to evaluate the formation constants for metal ammine complexes, and it takes specific advantage of our ability to follow the concentration of free ligand by following the pH with a glass electrode and potentiometer.

It can also be used, with trivial and obvious modifications, to determine the formation constants for complexes in which the ligands are anions of weak acids, and it has indeed been very widely used for this purpose, a good many organic ligands being of this weak acid anion type.

In a system having a certain total (i.e., both bound and unbound) ligand concentration, C_L, and a certain total metal ion concentration, C_M, the average number of ligands, $\bar{n}$, attached to each metal ion is given by equations F-4. These expressions show a direct

$$\bar{n} = \frac{\{C_L - [L]\}}{C_M} = \frac{\{[ML] + 2[ML_2] + 3[ML_3] + \ldots N[ML_N]\}}{\{[M] + [ML] + [ML_2] + [ML_3] + \ldots [ML_N]\}}$$

$$= \frac{\{\beta_1[L] + 2\beta_2[L]^2 + 3\beta_3[L]^3 + \ldots N\beta_N[L]^N\}}{\{1 + \beta_1[L] + \beta_2[L]^2 + \beta_3[L]^3 + \ldots \beta_N[L]^N\}}$$

$$= \frac{\sum\limits_{n=1}^{n=N} n[ML_n]}{\left\{ [M] + \sum\limits_{n=1}^{n=N} [ML_n] \right\}} \tag{F-4}$$

connection between the set of formation constants and the concentration of free ligand. Clearly if $\bar{n}$ and [L] are evaluated at N properly chosen points, a set of N linearly independent equations may be set up and solved for the values of the β_n's.

The experimental evaluation of $\bar{n}$ is in general not difficult. The usual practice is first to make accurate measurements of the acidity or basicity constant(s) of the ligand by titrating it alone. A second titration is then carried out in presence of the metal ion. At every point on the second titration curve it is possible to calculate [L] from the pH and the (known) total amount of ligand in all its forms (bound, free, and protonated) and thus $\bar{n}$ can be calculated at every point. Thus if the ligand is a weak base such as ammonia, the concentration of the free ligand, $[NH_3]$, is given by

$$[NH_3] = K_A[NH_4^+]/[H^+] \tag{F-5}$$

and the conservation equation,

$$C_T(\text{of } NH_3) = [NH_3] + [NH_4] + \sum\limits_{n=1}^{n=N} n[M(NH_3)_n] \tag{F-6}$$

If, as in Leden's method, $C_M \ll C_L$, the last term in equation F-6 can be neglected and simultaneous solution of equations F-5 and F-6 is straightforward.

From the values of $\bar{n}$ and [L], the formation constants are evaluated by solution of equation F-4. Methods for solving to obtain the constants are usually iterative, starting with estimated trial values, rather than analytic in nature, but they vary widely in detail, depending upon the relative magnitudes of the constants, the accuracy desired, and the preference of the individual. Digital computers have recently been used in complicated cases.

F-3. Other Methods

Any property of a system which can be (a) conveniently measured and (b) clearly related to the concentration of one of the species—the metal ion, the free ligand, or one of the complexes, ML_n—may be used to obtain data for the calculation of formation constants. A great number of properties have been used with varying degrees of success. A few of the techniques which seem to combine experimental practicality with a significant range of applicability will now be described very briefly.

Ion Exchange Equilibria. This method is especially useful in systems where some complexes are cationic and others anionic, for example in the system

$$Zn^{2+} + Cl^- \quad \text{to give} \quad ZnCl^+, ZnCl_2, ZnCl_3^-, ZnCl_4^{2-}$$

By using an anion exchange resin, the variation in the fraction of total zinc which is bound in anionic complexes can be measured as a function of changing total concentrations, C_{Zn} and C_{Cl}.

Solvent Extraction Equilibria. This method may be used in systems where only one species, usually the highest complex, is a neutral molecule which is soluble in organic media while all others are ions and hence insoluble in organic media. By measuring the fraction of total metal which is extracted into a water-immiscible organic layer (e.g., benzene, aliphatic hydrocarbon, carbon tetrachloride) as a function of total ligand concentration, the formation constant, β, of the extractable species may be directly obtained. Systems with β-diketonate ligands are well suited to study by this method. Thus the lower members of the Zr^{4+}–acetylacetone system, $[Zr(C_5H_7O)]^{3+}$, $[Zr(C_5H_7O_2)_2]^{2+}$, and $[Zr(C_5H_7O_2)_3]^+$ are not extractable, whereas $[Zr(C_5H_7O_2)_4]$ readily passes into the organic layer.

Spectrophotometric Methods. These are all based on the idea of following the concentration of a particular species by following the optical density in a spectral region where only that species absorbs significantly or where accurate corrections can be made for the absorption by other species. The method is widely applicable and the procedures for gathering and processing the data are legion.

The reader interested in details of the above methods or descriptions of still others is referred to the following works:

Bjerrum, J., *Metal Ammine Formation in Aqueous Solution*, P. Haase and Son, Copenhagen, 1941.

————, G. Schwartzenbach, and L. G. Sillén, eds., *Stability Constants*, Part I: *Organic Ligands*, Part II: *Inorganic Ligands*, The Chemical Society, London, 1957, 1958.

Martell, A. E., and M. Calvin, *Chemistry of the Metal Chelate Compounds*, Prentice-Hall, New York, 1952.

Rosotti, F. J. C., and H. Rosotti, *The Determination of Stability Constants*, McGraw-Hill, New York, 1961.

Sullivan, J. C., and J. C. Hindman, *J. Am. Chem. Soc.*, **74**, 6091 (1952).

General References and Supplementary Reading

More specialized references to aspects of the chemistries of the elements have been listed at the end of each chapter. Here are given some useful general sources of information in inorganic chemistry.

Reference Texts

There are several works in English which contain more detailed accounts of the chemistry of the elements than appear in this book, and they provide a useful first stage in the search for additional information.

Remy, H., *Treatise on Inorganic Chemistry* (translated by J. S. Anderson), Vols. I, II, Elsevier Publishing Co., New York, 1956. This book contains much detailed information on the elements and their compounds.

Sidgwick, N. V., *The Chemical Elements and Their Compounds*, Vols. I, II, Oxford University Press, 1950. This unique and personal book contains much useful and curious information and should be carefully read by all serious students.

Sneed, M. C., J. L. Maynard, and R. C. Brasted (with other contributors), *Comprehensive Inorganic Chemistry*, Van Nostrand, New York. A series of volumes on the elements, their compounds and some other selected topics which are useful sources of information but less exhaustive than those listed below.

Wells, A. F., *Structural Inorganic Chemistry*, 3rd ed., Clarendon Press, Oxford, 1962. The third edition of this well-known book is an exceedingly comprehensive source book for experimental methods of structural chemistry and detailed solid-state structures of oxides, sulfides, silicates, metals, and alloys, etc., as well as of compounds of a number of the elements. It can be strongly recommended as general reading for the student.

COMPREHENSIVE TREATISES

Gmelin's Handbuch der Anorganischen Chemie, Verlag Chemie, Weirheim. This series contains exhaustive treatments of all phases of inorganic and some physical chemistry. Some volumes are old, but supplementary volumes (which are still about ten years behind in literature coverage) are being issued regularly. The new volumes have subheadings in English.

Mellor's Comprehensive Treatise on Inorganic and Theoretical Chemistry, Longmans, Green, London, and Wiley, New York. Similar to Gmelin but less comprehensive. There are recent supplements.

Pascal, P., *Nouveau traité de chimie minérale*, Masson, Paris. Similar to Gmelin, though less comprehensive, but recent volumes are more up to date and critical.

Annual Reviews of Current Work

The *Annual Reports on the Progress of Chemistry* of the Chemical Society, London, provide a comprehensive review with multitudinous references to approximately the latest year's work.

Progress in Inorganic Chemistry, F. A. Cotton, ed., Interscience, New York, and *Advances in Inorganic Chemistry and Radiochemistry*, H. J. Emeléus and A. G. Sharpe, eds., Academic Press, New York, provide comprehensive reviews on selected topics in the field. Other reviews appear in *Quarterly Reviews (London)*, *Chemical Reviews*, and *Reviews of Pure and Applied Chemistry*.

More Specialized Text and Reference Books

Audrieth, L. F., and J. Kleinberg, *Non-Aqueous Solvents*: *Application as Media for Chemical Reactions*, Wiley, New York, 1953.

Bailar, J. C., ed., *The Chemistry of Coordination Compounds* (American Chemical Society Monograph, No. 131), Reinhold, New York, 1956.

Basolo, F., and R. G. Pearson, *Mechanism of Inorganic Reactions*, Wiley, New York, 1958. An excellent account and reference source for transition metal complex reactions.

Coates, G. E., *Organometallic Compounds*, 2nd ed., Methuen, London, 1960. Discusses the organo derivatives of the more metallic elements in a lucid and authoritative way.

Dekker, A. J., *Solid State Physics*, Prentice-Hall, Clifton, New Jersey, 1957. One of a number of similar books written in recent years presenting an introduction to the theory of the solid state in a manner which is of interest to inorganic chemists

Emeléus, H. J., and J. S. Anderson, *Modern Aspects of Inorganic Chemistry*, 3rd ed., Routledge and Kegan Paul, London, 1960. Contains articles on coordination compounds, nonmetallic chemistry, carbonyls, etc.

Inorganic Syntheses, Vols. 1–6, McGraw-Hill, New York. This series gives tested, detailed synthetic procedures for several hundred important inorganic compounds and also brief descriptions of their properties.

Latimer, W. M., *The Oxidation States of the Elements and Their Potentials in Aqueous Solution*, 2nd ed., Prentice-Hall, New York, 1952. Provides a detailed account of aqueous chemistry with particular reference to potentials, free energy changes, and entropies. The latter data are best obtained from the circulars of the National Bureau of Standards, Washington, D. C.

Lewis, J., and R. G. Wilkins, eds., *Modern Coordination Chemistry*, Interscience, New York–London, 1959. Contains authoritative reviews on several aspects of coordination chemistry.

Selwood, P. W., *Magnetochemistry*, 2nd ed., Interscience, New York–London, 1956. A general survey of magnetism and its measurement as well as applications in chemistry.

Wyckoff, R. W. G., *Crystal Structures*, Interscience, New York. An exhaustive compilation of crystal and molecular structures periodically supplemented to bring it up to date. Fully referenced.

Index

Some Useful Constants and Conversion Factors

Constants

AVOGADRO'S NUMBER ($C^{12} = 12.0000\ldots$), N_C, $= 6.0241 \times 10^{23}$ mole^{-1}

ICE POINT, absolute scale: $273.16 \pm 0.01°K$.

PLANCK'S CONSTANT, h, $= (6.6238 \pm 0.0002) \times 10^{-27}$ erg-sec.

GAS CONSTANT, R, $= 1.9872 \pm 0.0001$ defined cal. deg^{-1} mole^{-1}
$= 8.3144 \pm 0.0004$ abs. Joules deg^{-1} mole^{-1}

ELECTRON CHARGE, e, $= (4.8022 \pm 0.0001) \times 10^{-10}$ abs. e.s.u.

ELECTRON MASS, m, $= (9.1072 \pm 0.0003) \times 10^{-28}$ g.

PROTON MASS, M_p, $= (1.6722 \pm 0.0001) \times 10^{-24}$ g.

BOHR RADIUS, a_o, $= 0.529$ A.

CURIE-WEISS LAW: $\mu = 2.84\,[\chi_{mol}(T - \theta)]^{1/2}$

Conversion Factors

1 Angstrom $= 10^{-8}$ cm. $= 10^{-4}\,\mu$

1 Electron volt $= 8,066$ cm^{-1} $= 23.06$ kcal./mole

1 kcal./mole $= 349.5$ cm.$^{-1}$

RT ($T = 300°K$) $= 0.5962$ kcal./mole $= 208.4$ cm.$^{-1}$